THE
CHEMICAL ELEMENTS
AND THEIR COMPOUNDS

THE
CHEMICAL ELEMENTS
AND THEIR COMPOUNDS

BY

N. V. SIDGWICK

FELLOW OF LINCOLN COLLEGE
HON. STUDENT OF CHRIST CHURCH
FORMERLY PROFESSOR OF CHEMISTRY
IN THE UNIVERSITY OF OXFORD

VOLUME II

OXFORD
AT THE CLARENDON PRESS

Oxford University Press, Amen House, London E.C. 4

GLASGOW NEW YORK TORONTO MELBOURNE WELLINGTON
BOMBAY CALCUTTA MADRAS CAPE TOWN

Geoffrey Cumberlege, Publisher to the University

FIRST PUBLISHED 1950

Reprinted lithographically in Great Britain
at the UNIVERSITY PRESS, OXFORD, 1951, 1952

CONTENTS
VOLUME II

GROUP VI
INTRODUCTION

THIS group consists of the elements:

O	S	Se	Te	Po	(B)
	Cr	Mo	W	U	(A)

As usual among the later groups the difference between the subgroups is greater than in the preceding group; their resemblances are practically confined to the compounds in which the atoms have the group valency of 6, such as the sulphates and chromates; otherwise the subgroups are quite distinct from one another. The first two elements belong definitely to subgroup B rather than A.

Typical and B Elements

The radii of the neutral atoms and of the divalent anions A^{--} of these elements are as follows: for comparison those of the neutral atoms of the A subgroup (which of course give no simple anions) are added:

	O	S	Se	Te	Po^a
Rad. of atom	0·66	1·04	1·17	1·37	1·70
of ion A^{--}	1·32	1·74	1·91	2·11	..
	Cr	Mo	W	U	
Rad. of atom	1·25	1·36	1·37	1·49	

$$a = 1$$

The typical and B elements are all highly electronegative. They are the first elements we have dealt with which can form free monatomic anions; they all show the characteristic valency of 2, both in the simple ions and in their covalent compounds. This covalency is relatively seldom exceeded by oxygen, but with the other elements covalencies of 3, 4, and 6 are common. The metallic character is only slightly apparent even in the heaviest of these elements: the solid elements selenium, tellurium, and polonium occur in a metallic form, but the metallic properties of this form are feeble; they can form quadrivalent cations (with the first electron pair inert), and tellurium in particular gives a series of salts of this kind.

The most marked difference in the series[1a] is between oxygen and sulphur, and the least between sulphur and selenium: the properties of polonium, so far as they are known, are those to be expected from its position.

Of these elements oxygen will be discussed first, and then sulphur; selenium and tellurium are best discussed together.

[1] M. A. Rollier, S. B. Hendricks, and L. R. Maxwell, *J. Chem. Phys.* 1936, **4**, 648.

[1a] For a discussion of the changes in structure and in conductivity of the elements from oxygen to polonium, see A. von Hippel, ib. 1948, **16**, 372.

B

OXYGEN

MOST of the compounds of oxygen have been dealt with under the other elements they contain.

Oxygen is the most abundant of all the elements, and forms almost exactly half (49·4 per cent.) of the earth's crust by weight: of the atmosphere 20·8 per cent. by volume and 23·0 by weight. Its importance as the source of the energy of nearly all living matter is obvious: an adult man at rest consumes about 20 litres of oxygen (one ounce) per hour.

Oxygen has three natural isotopes, with atomic weights of 16, 17, and 18; none, except the commonest, ^{16}O, is abundant enough to be detected by the mass spectrograph; ^{17}O and ^{18}O were found spectroscopically by Giauque and Johnston in 1929.[2] The most probable proportions are[3] ^{16}O; ^{17}O; ^{18}O = 1; 1/2,500; 1/500.

The ^{18}O is much more difficult to concentrate than deuterium, though this is to some extent offset by its being 10 times as abundant. The electrolytic factor instead of being about 3 (as for H/D) is only 1·01: the electrolysis of 117 litres of water down to 1 c.c. only increased the proportion of ^{18}O by 10 per cent. The vapour pressure difference is also small, the ratio at 100° being $H_2^{16}O/H_2^{18}O$ 1·003 (HOH/HOD 1·025); the boiling-point of $H_2^{18}O$ is calculated to be 100·13° (HOD 100·76°), but a separation can be effected, though slowly, by its fractional distillation.[4-5] Other methods are the diffusion of oxygen gas (Herz), possibly the freezing out of water,[6] and a variety of reversible reactions in which the proportions of the isotopes are different on the two sides, for example:

$$2 H_2^{18}O + C^{16}O_2 = 2 H_2^{16}O + C^{18}O_2.$$

The calculated equilibrium ratio is 1·097, or the fractionation factor 1·047. This has been confirmed experimentally, and the reaction used for the enrichment of ^{18}O, but an enzyme derived from blood must be added to hasten the CO_2/H_2CO_3 equilibrium. Owing partly to the larger amount of the heavier isotope it was found possible to detect a difference in the proportions between atmospheric oxygen and natural water. This amounted to 6 parts per million in density for Lake Michigan water[7] and 8·6 p.p.m. at Washington[8]; the 1/500 of $H_2^{18}O$ normally present gives an increase in density of 222 p.p.m., so that this means that the proportion of ^{18}O is 3–4 per cent. greater in the air.

Exchange of Oxygen Isotopes

This is a new and important subject (for a general account see ref. [9]). The determination of the isotopic proportions is difficult, and the exchange

[2] W. F. Giauque and H. L. Johnston, *Nature*, 1929, **123**, 318, 831.

[3] B. F. Murphey, *Phys. Rev.* 1941, ii. **59**, 320.

[4] H. C. Urey and J. R. Huffman, *J. Ind. Eng. Chem.* 1937, **29**, 531.

[5] H. G. Thode, S. R. Smith, and F. O. Walkling, *Canad. J. Res.* 1944, **22**, B 127.

[6] R. V. Teis and K. P. Florenski, *C.R. Acad. Sci. U.R.S.S.* 1941, **32**, 199.

[7] M. Dole, *J. Chem. Phys.* 1936, **4**, 778.

[8] E. R. Smith and H. Matheson, *J. Res. Nat. Bur. Stand.* 1936, **17**, 625.

[9] O. Reitz, *Z. Elektrochem.* 1939, **45**, 100.

is not a question of yes or no; it has its own heat of activation, and the rate, like that of any other chemical reaction, is very sensitive to the conditions, and especially to the temperature. Some of the already numerous papers may be quoted under the oxygen compounds concerned. Water[12,31]; Metals:CaO[32]; Borates[28,33]; Carbon:CO_2[19,20,24,27]; Organic Compounds[13-18,21-3,25,35]; Saponification[23,36-7,26]; Silicates[33]; Nitrous oxide[33]; Nitrites[28]; Nitrates[28,33]; Phosphates[10,27,33-4]; Arsenates[27-8]; Sulphates[11,20,27-9,33-4]; Sulphites, etc.[28-9]; Selenates[28]; Chromates[28-9,33]; Halogen oxy-acids[28,33]; Manganese oxides[28-30].

Some of the conclusions reached with the organic compounds may be mentioned. In general the hydroxylic oxygen in the alcohols does not move,[16,21] but the carbonyl oxygen, especially in aldehydes, will do so.[13,15,21-2]

The behaviour of the carboxyl group is obscure[14-16,21,25]; the exchange is very slow with salts, but is catalysed by hydrogen ion; hence while it does not occur with acetic acid, it does so with chloracetic, and especially with trichloracetic. It has already been mentioned (IV. 527) that in the hydrolysis and esterification of esters the oxygen attached to the alkyl of the alcohol retains its place.

Physical Properties of Oxygen

Oxygen melts at $-218 \cdot 5°$ C. ($54 \cdot 7°$ K.), and boils at $-183°$; the Trouton constant is $18 \cdot 1$; the liquid and solid are pale blue. The solid is probably

[10] E. Blumenthal and J. B. M. Herbert, *Trans. Far. Soc.* 1937, **33**, 849.

[11] S. C. Datta, J. N. E. Day, and C. K. Ingold, *J.C.S.* 1937, 1968.

[12] N. Morita and T. Titani, *Bull. Chem. Soc. Japan*, 1937, **12**, 104.

[13] J. B. M. Herbert and I. Lauder, *Trans. Far. Soc.* 1938, **34**, 432.

[14] Id., ib. 1219.

[15] M. Koizumi and T. Titani, *Bull. Chem. Soc. Japan*, 1938, **13**, 463.

[16] Id., ib. 607.   [17] W. H. Mears, *J. Chem. Phys.* 1938, **6**, 205.

[18] M. Senkus and W. G. Brown, *J. Org. Chem.* 1937, **2**, 569.

[19] T. Titani, N. Morita, and K. Goto, *Bull. Chem. Soc. Japan*, 1938, **13**, 329.

[20] T. Titani and K. Goto, ib. 667.

[21] M. Cohn and H. C. Urey, *J.A.C.S.* 1938, **60**, 679.

[22] I. Roberts and H. C. Urey, ib. 880.

[23] W. H. Mears and H. Sobodka, ib. 1939, **61**, 880.

[24] G. A. Mills and H. C. Urey, ib. 534.

[25] I. Roberts and H. C. Urey, ib. 2580.   [26] Id., ib. 2584.

[27] T. Titani and K. Goto, *Bull. Chem. Soc. Japan*, 1939, **14**, 77.

[28] N. F. Hall and O. R. Alexander, *J.A.C.S.* 1940, **62**, 3455.

[29] G. A. Mills, ib. 2833.

[30] N. Morita, *Bull. Chem. Soc. Japan*, 1940, **15**, 1.   [31] Id., ib. 47.

[32] Id., ib. 71.

[33] E. R. S. Winter, M. Carlton, and H. A. V. Briscoe, *J.C.S.* 1940, 131.

[34] E. R. S. Winter and H. A. V. Briscoe, ib. 1942, 631.

[35] A. E. Brodsky, N. I. Dedussenko, I. A. Makolkin, and G. P. Miklukhin, *J. Chem. Phys.* 1943, **11**, 342.

[36] I. Roberts and H. C. Urey, *J.A.C.S.* 1938, **60**, 2391.

[37] M. Polanyi and A. L. Szabo, *Trans. Far. Soc.* 1934, **30**, 508.

trimorphic, with transition points at $-230 \cdot 6°$ and $-255 \cdot 6°$.[38-9] For the properties, and modes of formation and destruction of the negative gas ions O^- and O_2^-, see reference [40].

The *structure* of the O_2 molecule is peculiar, as can be seen from the fact that it is paramagnetic although it is an even molecule (the only other even molecule which owes its paramagnetism to oxygen is that of ozone). It has been shown[41] that instead of its having four shared electrons as a double bond the second two are unpaired (hence the paramagnetism). This $^3\Sigma$ state has $22 \cdot 4$ k.cals./mole less energy than the doubly linked $^1\Delta$ state: the heat of dissociation of O_2 is $118 \cdot 2$ k.cals., though that of the true $O{=}O$ link is only 96 k.cals.[42] This peculiar structure implies a kind of unsaturation, which accounts for the great chemical activity of molecular oxygen, and especially for the way in which whole O_2 molecules will often combine with readily oxidizable substances.

Atomic Oxygen

Molecular oxygen is dissociated by heat, the percentage of atomic oxygen present at equilibrium under 1 atm. pressure being 3×10^{-39} at $0°$ C., 1 per cent. at $2,300°$, and 96 per cent. at $4,730°$.[43-4] The same dissociation can be effected by an electric discharge (conveniently electrodeless), and as the atoms do not recombine at once, a gas containing 20 per cent. of atoms or more can be readily obtained.[45-6] Atomic oxygen is of course very reactive. At the ordinary temperature it will oxidize H_2S, CS_2 (with luminescence), HCl, HCN, and organic compounds in general.[50,52] At liquid-air temperatures[46-8,51] it combines largely with its own molecules to form ozone (which is not formed at the ordinary temperatures); with hydrogen it gives what seems to be a second form of hydrogen peroxide[49] (see p. 870); and in the same way with organic compounds it gives solid addition compounds (not isolated), which at about $-100°$ rearrange to give the usual oxidation products.

When oxygen combines readily in the cold with another substance, it usually does so by whole molecules of O_2; this process is known as autoxida-

[38] L. Vegard, *Nature*, 1935, **136**, 720.
[39] Id., *Z. Phys.* 1935, **98**, 1.
[40] D. R. Bates and H. S. W. Massey, *Phil. Trans.* 1943, **239**, 269.
[41] G. W. Wheland, *Trans. Far. Soc.* 1937, **33**, 1499.
[42] See further, L. Pauling, *Chemical Bond*, p. 253.
[43] H. L. Johnston and M. K. Walker, *J.A.C.S.* 1933, **55**, 187.
[44] G. v. Elbe and B. Lewis, ib. 507.
[45] E. Wrede, *Z. Phys.* 1929, **54**, 53.
[46] P. Harteck and U. Kopsch, *Z. Elektrochem.* 1930, **36**, 714.
[47] P. Harteck, *Trans. Far. Soc.* 1934, **30**, 134.
[48] P. W. Schlenk and H. Jablonowski, *Z. Elektrochem.* 1939, **45**, 650.
[49] K. H. Geib and P. Harteck, *Trans. Far. Soc.* 1934, **30**, 134.
[50] W. H. Rodebush and W. A. Nichols, *J.A.C.S.* 1930, **52**, 3864.
[51] P. Harteck and E. Roeder, *Z. physikal. Chem.* 1937, **178**, 389.
[52] P. Harteck and K. Stewart, ib. **181**, 183.

tion, and the product has been called a moloxide or holoxide: for example, with hexaphenyl-ethane:

$$\Phi_3C-C\Phi_3 + O_2 = \Phi_3C-O-O-C\Phi_3.$$

Often, too, if the autoxidizable substance is mixed with a second oxidizable but not autoxidizable substance, this latter is oxidized at the same time; and then the oxygen is nearly always equally shared between the two substances. This is usually, if not always, due to the primary formation by the autoxidizer of a moloxide, which is then reduced by the second (acceptor) substance. Thus indigo is not oxidized by elementary oxygen but benzaldehyde is: if the two are mixed, the indigo is oxidized at the same time as the aldehyde. Here it can be shown that the aldehyde is first converted to the per-acid $\Phi-C\underset{\textstyle O}{\overset{\textstyle O-O-H}{\big<}}$, which is then reduced by the indigo to ordinary benzoic acid.

Of the innumerable oxidations effected by oxygen the most important, and the most thoroughly investigated, is its combination with hydrogen. For this see references [53-7,57a].

OZONE, O_3

OZONE, the highly active allotropic modification of oxygen, is formed by a variety of methods, all of which involve the primary atomization of the oxygen, since it is the product of the combination of oxygen atoms with the diatomic oxygen molecule. As ozone is unstable, it must be formed at or chilled to the ordinary temperature, where its rate of change is slow; thus it is formed when oxygen is blown over a heated Nernst filament, and then chilled; it is also produced in many reactions in which oxygen is evolved at a low temperature, as in the decomposition of hydrogen peroxide, in the action of fluorine on water, in the thermal decomposition of periodic acid at 130° (but not in that of potassium perchlorate, because the temperature is too high), and in the electrolysis of fairly strong sulphuric acid.

Another series of methods of formation involves the action of the electric discharge or of ultra-violet light; the usual method is with the silent electric discharge; the action of light is very complicated, as one wavelength will atomize oxygen, and so produce ozone, while another will decompose the ozone.[58-9]

[53] C. N. Hinshelwood and A. T. Williamson, 'The Reaction between Hydrogen and Oxygen' (Oxford 1934).

[54] C. N. Hinshelwood, A. T. Williamson, and J. H. Wolfenden, *Nature*, 1934, **133**, 836; *Proc. Roy. Soc.* 1934, **147**, 48 (this confirms the previous conclusions by the use of deuterium).

[55] S. Kimata, N. Aomi, and R. Goto, *Rev. Phys.-Chem. Japan*, 1941, **15**, 42.

[56] G. v. Erbe and B. Lewis, *J. Chem. Phys.* 1942, **10**, 366.

[57] For a general account of the combination of oxygen and hydrogen, see Hinshelwood, Bakerian Lecture, *Proc. Roy. Soc.* 1946, **188**, 1.

[57a] A. H. Willbourn and C. N. Hinshelwood, ib., **185**, 353, 369, 376.

[58] A. Eucken and F. Patat, *Z. physikal. Chem.* 1936, B **33**, 459.

[59] W. H. Otto and W. H. Bennett, *J. Chem. Phys.* 1940, **8**, 899.

Ozone is found in nature, being formed by the action of sunlight on the oxygen in the upper layers of the earth's atmosphere. A careful examination by G. M. B. Dobson and others (in which the concentration of the ozone was determined from the absorption bands in the transmitted light), has shown that the height of this ozone layer is about 25 km.; the total amount is enough to form a layer about 3 mm.[61a] thick at atmospheric pressure on the surface of the earth (about 2 parts per million of the whole atmosphere). Near the earth's surface the concentration is much lower, and very difficult to determine. Paneth and Edgar[62-3] have, however, measured it by condensing the ozone on silica gel at $-180°$; they find that the air in London and Southport contains from 0·1 to 1·1 p.p.m. of ozone (from 1/20 to 1/2 of the concentration in the whole atmosphere).

The ozone molecule is triatomic, as was shown by Soret (1868), from the rate of diffusion of ozone in oxygen. For a discussion of the (remarkably large) force constants see reference[60]. For the conclusions from the infra-red spectra, which are not easy to reconcile with some of the other data, see Dennison.[61] It is paramagnetic. On cooling it forms a dark indigo-blue liquid and solid. Its melting- and boiling-points are as follows[64]:

	B. pt.	*M. pt.*	*Trouton*
Ozone	$-112·3°$	$-249·6°$ (23·5° K)	18·6
Oxygen	$-183°$	$-216·4°$ (56·7° K)	18·1

(Notice the effect of symmetry in raising the melting-point of the oxygen.) Below $-158°$ oxygen and ozone form two liquid layers, one of which at $-183°$ contains 30 per cent. of oxygen; no other element behaves in this way, though phosphorus can form a metastable system of solid red and liquid white phosphorus.

Ozone is endothermic[65-6]; the conversion of two molecules of ozone into three of oxygen evolves 68·0 k.cals.; hence the heat of formation of ozone from its atoms (H_a) is 144·3 k.cals. (see further below, under Structure). It follows by Nernst's theorem that at equilibrium even at 3,750° K. there is only 1 part of ozone in 40,000. Hence ozone is always unstable with respect to oxygen; the pure solid or liquid is highly explosive, and if the liquid mixture of oxygen and ozone is allowed to evaporate, the residue ultimately detonates.

Ozone is characterized by an extraordinarily intense absorption band— the most intense known for any gas—beginning about 2,900 A. The 3 mm. of ozone in the atmosphere absorb the light of this wave-length that falls

[60] D. M. Simpson, *Trans. Far. Soc.* 1945, **41**, 209.
[61] A. Adel and D. M. Dennison, *J. Chem. Phys.* 1946, **14**, 379.
[61a] J. Stair, *J. Res. Bur. Stand.* 1948, **40**, 9, finds 2·1 mm. in New Mexico.
[62] F. A. Paneth and J. L. Edgar, *Nature*, 1938, **142**, 112.
[63] J. L. Edgar and F. A. Paneth, *J.C.S.* 1941, **511**, 519.
[64] A. L. Spangenberg, *Z. physikal. Chem.* 1926, **119**, 419.
[65] S. Jahn, *Z. anorg. Chem.* 1908, **60**, 292, 337.
[66] A. Kailan and S. Jahn, ib. 1910, **68**, 250.

on the earth so completely that stellar spectra cannot be observed beyond this point. If the ozone were suddenly withdrawn, we should all be killed within a few minutes by the sun's ultra-violet light. H. N. Russell[67] says that a layer of ozone 'at its worst' (i.e. at the wave-length of maximum absorption) is as opaque as one of metal of the same mass per c.c., so that the 3 mm. layer in the upper atmosphere is as opaque to light of this wave-length as three sheets of gold leaf (thickness each 1/10,000 mm.).

The absorption spectrum of ozone shows that it is not a linear molecule and so it must either be a ring

$$ O\underset{O}{\diagdown\diagup}O \quad \text{or a bent chain} \quad O{=}\overset{+}{O}\diagdown_{\overset{-}{O}}. $$

The spectra indicate[68] that the angle is 122° and the O—O distance 1·29 A; electron diffraction gives[69] 127±3° and 1·26 A (theory O—O 1·32, O=O 1·10). This supports the second formula, which is like that of sulphur dioxide

$$ O{=}\overset{+}{S}\diagdown_{\overset{-}{O}} \;,\; \text{with resonance between the two forms} \quad O{=}\overset{+}{O}\diagdown_{\overset{-}{O}} \;\text{and}\; \overset{-}{O}{-}\overset{+}{O}\diagdown_{O}. $$

This agrees with the intense absorption band, which is found generally in molecules whose resonance forms differ in the position of an electric charge, as in rosaniline, the cyanine dyes, the meriquinoid compounds generally, and prussian blue. Sulphur dioxide has a similar though less intense band in the ultra-violet.

The energy relations are curious. As we have seen, H_a for ozone is 144·3 k.cals. For the O—O we may take the normal value of 34·9 k.cals.; for the O=O, since ozone is paramagnetic, we must use the value for molecular oxygen (118·2); but this would give $34·9+118·2 = 153·1$, and hence a negative resonance energy; even if we assume the O=O value to be less (on the analogy of nitrogen) because the central oxygen has only one unshared electron pair, and use the value

$$ (—O{=}O) = (O—O) \times \frac{(—N{=}N—)}{(\rangle N—N\langle)} = 34·9 \times \frac{60·8}{20·0} = 106·1, $$

we get for the theory $34·9+106·1 = 141·0$ k.cals., which gives a resonance energy of only 3·3 k.cals.

Ozone decomposes to oxygen very slowly at the ordinary temperature, but fairly quickly at 100°, and immediately at 300° (for details of this see Hinshelwood).[70,70a] The decomposition is greatly hastened by many catalysts, such as manganese dioxide, lead dioxide, and many metals, especially silver.[71] Ozone is a very powerful oxidizing agent, which com-

[67] H. N. Russell, *Nature*, 1935, **135**, 220.

[68] W. S. Benedict, *Phys. Rev.* 1933, ii. **43**, 580.

[69] W. Shand and R. A. Spurr, *J.A.C.S.* 1943, **65**, 179.

[70] *Chemical Change in Gaseous Systems*, ed. 3, 1933, pp. 80, 210.

[70a] G. R. Hill, *J.A.C.S.* 1948, **70**, 1306.

[71] L. I. Kashtanov, N. P. Ivanova, and V. P. Rishov, *J. Appl. Chem. Russ.* 1936, **9**, 2176: *B.C.A.* 1937, i. 315.

monly acts by reduction to diatomic oxygen; it will convert lead sulphide into sulphate, lead hydroxide $Pb(OH)_2$ into the dioxide, potassium iodide in solution into iodine and potassium hydroxide, etc. In contact with it silver becomes covered with a brown layer of oxide; mercury gives a highly characteristic reaction, a mere trace of ozone making it lose its mobility and adhere in a thin film to the containing vessel.

Organic compounds are readily oxidized by ozone; even hydrocarbons, of which the $>$C—H group is converted into —C—OH and the $>$CH$_2$ into $>$C=O.[72] It will oxidize thioethers to sulphoxides and sulphones.[73]

Its oxidation of formic acid has been shown[74] to be a chain-reaction, inhibited by chloride ion and by acetic acid.

A remarkable property of ozone is its addition to the double carbon link in unsaturated compounds (C. D. Harries, 1905).[75] This can be used to determine the position of the double link, as the ozonides hydrolyse with rupture of the carbon chain at this place. The addition usually takes place in indifferent solvents like chloroform, and the products, which were written by Harries as

are mostly green or colourless amorphous solids or oils, which are often explosive; they liberate iodine from potassium iodide, and react with water to give ketones (see also ref. [76]):

$$C\!=\!C \cdot O_3 + H_2O = \,>\!C\!=\!O + O\!=\!C\!< + H_2O_2.$$

Harries's formula with the otherwise almost unknown 3-oxygen chain is improbable, and Staudinger suggested another,

$$R_2C \underset{O}{\overset{O-O}{\diagdown\diagup}} CR_2;$$

this is equally compatible with the hydrolysis to two molecules of ketone $+H_2O_2$.

Recent work by Rieche *et al.*,[77] entirely supports Staudinger's view. Refractivity measurements indicate the presence of only one O—O link; the absorption spectra show a strong qualitative resemblance to those of the peroxides. It appears that the first step in the hydrolysis of these ozonides is the splitting of the ether link; thus Harries's 'formaldehyde peroxide' is shown to be $HO \cdot CH_2$—O—O—$CH_2 \cdot OH$. Stoll and Rouve[78] confirm these conclusions.

[72] J. R. Durland and H. Adkins, *J.A.C.S.* 1939, **61**, 429.
[73] H. Böhme and H. Fischer, *Ber.* 1942, **75**, 1310.
[74] H. Taube, *J.A.C.S.* 1941, **63**, 2453.
[75] C. D. Harries, *Ann.* 1905, **343**, 311.
[76] N. C. Cook and F. C. Whitmore, *J.A.C.S.* 1941, **63**, 3540.
[77] A. Rieche, R. Meister, and H. Sauthoff, *Ann.* 1942, **553**, 187.
[78] M. Stoll and A. Rouve, *Helv. Chim. Acta.* 1944, **27**, 950.

The simplest ozonide is the ethylene compound $C_2H_4O_3$.[79] It is an oil, boiling under 16 mm. at 20°, and becoming a glass at $-80°$; it is stable at 0°, but decomposes at the ordinary temperature (often with explosion) to formaldehyde and formic acid:

$$C_2H_4O_3 = CH_2O + CH_2O_2.$$

The propylene compound is similar.[80] Freezing-points in benzene indicate that most ozonides are mixtures of high polymers.

The heats of formation of the ozonides in the solid state or in solution are about 100 k.cals.[81]; their dipole moments are not more than 0·4 D greater than those of the unsaturated compounds from which they are derived.[82] Their Raman spectra contain lines, some of which resemble those of the carboxylic anhydrides, and others those of the peroxides.[83]

Tetratomic Oxygen, O_4

This has been said to exist, and has been called oxozone[84]; but no such compound can be isolated; Briner[85] ozonized oxygen by a variety of methods, and allowed the liquefied product to evaporate; but the tail fraction never gave any sign of the presence of any polymer other than O_3.

At the same time the behaviour of diatomic oxygen indicates the presence of O_4 molecules of a kind. These were discovered by G. N. Lewis[86] from the magnetic susceptibilities, and confirmed by the absorption spectra[87-8] (especially under 1,000 atm.). But the spectra show that the two O_2 groups cannot be linked by ordinary bonds; their heat of linkage is only 0·13 k.cal., and must be due to a kind of van der Waals force, which will be stronger than usual owing to the unpaired electron spins in the O_2 molecules[89]; they have no more oxidizing power than ordinary diatomic oxygen.

WATER

WATER is the typical associated liquid, as the following values show:

	$CH_3 \cdot O \cdot CH_3$	$CH_3 \cdot OH$	$H \cdot O \cdot H$
B. pt.	$-23°$ C.	$+66°$	100°
Crit. T.	127·1°	240°	374·2°[a]
Crit. P.	53 atm.	78·5 atm.	218 atm.

$$a = {}^{90}$$

[79] E. Briner and P. Schnorf, ib. 1929, **12**, 154.   [80] Id., ib. 181.

[81] E. Briner, K. Ryffel, and S. de Nemitz, ib. 1938, **21**, 357.

[82] E. Briner, D. Frank, and E. Perrottet, ib. 1312.

[83] E. Briner, S. de Nemitz, and E. Perrottet, ib. 762.

[84] C. D. Harries, *Ber.* 1912, **45**, 936.

[85] E. Briner and H. Biedermann, *Helv. Chim. Acta*, 1933, **16**, 207.

[86] *J.A.C.S.* 1924, **46**, 2027.

[87] W. Finkelnburg and W. Steiner, *Z. Phys.* 1932, **79**, 69.

[88] O. R. Wulf, *Proc. Nat. Acad. Sci.* 1928, **14**, 609.

[89] See Pauling, *Chemical Bond*, pp. 58, 253.

[90] E. Schröer, *Z. physikal. Chem.* 1927, **129**, 79.

Heat of fusion of ice 1·435 k.cals./mole (79·7 cals./g.).[91] Heat of evaporation 9·71 k.cals./mole; Trouton 26·0. The specific heat (per g.) is abnormally high, and almost exactly twice that of ice (0·502/−20°); the dielectric constant is 81 at 20°, one of the highest known.

The conductivity of the purest water was determined by Kohlrausch and Heydweiller[92]; they distilled the first 2 or 3 c.c. from about a litre of specially purified water, in a glass apparatus which had been aged for 10 years. They found the conductivity $0·043 \times 10^{-6}$, but they corrected this for its minute salt content by means of the temperature coefficient to 0·0384 (all at 18°). Using the mobilities of 318 for H^+ and 174 for OH^-, this gives $[H^+] = 0·78 \times 10^{-7}$, or $K_w = 0·608 \times 10^{-14}$ at 18°. Forty years later Harned,[93] by E.M.F. measurements, found at 18° the value $K_w = 0·58 \times 10^{-14}$.

Ice occurs in seven solid forms; these were first discovered by Tammann, but have lately been examined by Bridgman up to a pressure of 45,000 atm.[94] Excepting ordinary ice they can only exist under high pressure; thus ordinary ice (I) at −22·1° and 2,200 atm. goes over into ice (III), which expands on melting: at −37 and 2,240 atm. ice (III) goes over into ice (II).

Water vapour is measurably associated: the exact degree is uncertain, because the form of the van der Waals equation is the same (proportional to $1/v^2$) as that given by the law of mass action: but at 100° and under 1 atm. the association is somewhat less than 10 per cent. According to the osmotic properties water is H_2O in phenol (where it no doubt associates with the solvent) and H_4O_2 in ether and in *p*-toluidine.

The structure of the H_2O molecule has been examined by Mecke[95-7] by means of the absorption spectrum. (For infra-red see refs. [98-100]). The molecule is L-shaped (this is also required by the finite dipole moment): the angle is 105°, which supports Pauling's theoretical conclusion that the normal angle for a dicovalent octet is between 90° and 110°: in H_2O the angle is no doubt somewhat increased by the repulsion of the positive H atoms: the nuclear $O \cdots H$ distance is 0·95 A: the normal radius of singly linked oxygen is 0·66, so this gives 0·29 for the effective radius of the hydrogen, which is practically the normal value of 0·30 A. According to Mecke,[101] the rotation-oscillation spectrum of H_2O shows that it exists in ortho- and para- forms, like H_2.

[91] N. S. Osborne, *J. Res. Nat. Bur. Stand.* 1939, **23**, 643.
[92] F. Kohlrausch and A. Heydweiller, *Z. physikal. Chem.* 1894, **14**, 317.
[93] H. S. Harned and W. J. Hamer, *J.A.C.S.* 1933, **55**, 2194.
[94] P. W. Bridgman, *J. Chem. Phys.* 1937, **5**, 964.
[95] R. Mecke, *Z. Phys.* 1933, **81**, 313.   [96] W. Baumann and R. Mecke, ib. 445.
[97] K. Freudenberg and R. Mecke, ib. 465.
[98] H. M. Randall, D. M. Dennison, N. Ginsburg, and L. R. Weber, *Phys. Rev.* 1937, ii. **52**, 160 (μ 18–75).
[99] G. Bosschieter and J. Errera, *C.R.* 1937, **204**, 1719 (μ 2·7–3).
[100] J. J. Fox and A. E. Martin, *Proc. Roy. Soc.* 1940, **174**, 234 (μ 2·5–7·5).
[101] R. Mecke, *Naturwiss.* 1932, **20**, 657.

The structure of ice is discussed by Pauling.[102] The X-ray measurements[103-5] show the positions of the oxygen atoms, but not of course those of the hydrogens. Every oxygen atom is surrounded tetrahedrally by four other oxygens, all of them 2·76 A.U. away. Since each of these links involves two oxygen atoms, if each oxygen has four of them, the number of links will be twice the number of oxygens, or equal to the number of hydrogen atoms, so that there is one hydrogen for each link. Each may therefore be called a hydrogen bond, and the length is about normal for such a bond (O—H··O in $NaHCO_3$ and KH_2PO_4 2·5–2·6 A). But they are much longer than we should expect if the relation of the H to each O is the same as in hydroxyl; in water O—H is 0·95 A, so that O—H—O should be 1·90 A, whereas it is 2·76 A, 45 per cent. greater. This may mean either that the hydrogen is 1·38 A from each oxygen, or that it is as usual about 1 A from one, and is 1·76 from the other. Pauling[106] concludes that the second (unsymmetrical) alternative is true; the change in the vibration frequency of the hydrogen is too small for so large an increase,[107] and also the symmetrical structure is incompatible with the entropy of ice[108] and heavy ice[109] (for a further discussion of the hydrogen bond see I. 23–32). This unsymmetrical structure seems to mean that the bond is due rather to electrostatic attraction than to resonance.

The structure of liquid water has been discussed in a remarkable paper by Bernal and Fowler,[110] the first real attempt to discuss the physics of a liquid. They assume that the liquid has a sort of pseudo-crystalline structure, with three different crystalline states in proportions depending on the temperature; this is needed to explain the expansion of water below 4°. See further, Eucken[110a].

Two molecular species derived from water are free OH radicals, and oxonium cations.

Free hydroxyl radicals. At high temperatures, water vapour dissociates with the production of hydroxyl radicals, whose absorption spectra can be observed at 1,600°,[111] and even in the light of a carbon arc burning in ordinary moist air.[112] An electric discharge in water vapour produces the same effect. The hydroxyl radicals (as measured by the absorption spectrum) do not vanish as soon as the discharge stops, but persist for nearly a second.[114]

[102] *J.A.C.S.* 1935, **57**, 2680.   [103] D. M. Dennison, *Phys. Rev.* 1921, **17**, 20.

[104] W. H. Bragg, *Proc. Phys. Soc.* 1922, **34**, 98.

[105] W. H. Barnes, *Proc. Roy. Soc.* 1929, **125**, 670.

[106] *Chemical Bond*, pp. 301–6.

[107] P. C. Cross, J. Burnham, and P. A. Leighton, *J.A.C.S.* 1937, **59**, 1134.

[108] W. F. Gaiuque and M. Ashley, *Phys. Rev.* 1933, **43**, 81; W. F. Giauque and J. W. Stout, *J.A.C.S.* 1936, **58**, 1144.

[109] E. A. Long and J. D. Kemp, ib., 1829.

[110] J. D. Bernal and R. H. Fowler, *J. Chem. Phys.* 1933, **1**, 515.

[110a] A. Eucken, *Nachr. Ges. Wiss. Gött.* 1946, 38.

[111] K. F. Bonhoeffer and H. Reichardt, *Z. physikal. Chem.* 1928, **139**, 75.

[112] O. Oldenberg, *J. Chem. Phys.* 1934, **2**, 713.

Oxonium compounds. These are of the type

and correspond in structure to the ammonium salts, though they are less stable. The first clearly recognized example of 'quadrivalent' oxygen was the hydrochloride of methyl ether $(CH_3)_2O \cdot HCl$ discovered by Friedel in 1875: this boils at $-1°$, while of its components methyl ether boils at $-23\cdot6°$ and hydrogen chloride at $-85°$; it is partially but not wholly dissociated in the gaseous state. In 1899 Collie and Tickle showed that dimethyl pyrone

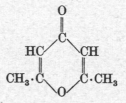

formed salts like a monacid base with a series of acids: more than forty of these salts are now known. Further developments were made by Baeyer and Villiger in 1901 and the following years.

The general analogy between $[H_3O]^+$ and $[H_4N]^+$ is obvious, but certain questions arise.

1. Friedel found[115] that $(CH_3)_2O \cdot HCl$ is not wholly dissociated in the vapour at $0°$, and later work[116-17] has confirmed this conclusion, which is very remarkable. An oxonium compound must be ionized; the structure

$$\underset{R}{\overset{R}{>}}O\underset{Cl}{\overset{H}{<}}$$

is impossible as it makes the oxygen exceed the octet limit, and a hydrogen bond $O—H \cdot \cdot Cl$ would be too weak to hold the parts together. But an ionized compound could not volatilize at $0°$; the external electric field of the ions must therefore be weakened in some way, perhaps by resonance between $(CH_3)_2O \; H—Cl$ and $(CH_3)_2O—H \; [Cl]$.

2. A second question is why the pyrone compounds of Collie and Tickle are so ready to form oxonium salts. They have two oxygen atoms, and the presence of both is necessary to produce the unusual stability of the salts, so they must both take part in the structure. This is explained by

[114] O. Oldenberg and F. F. Rieke, *J. Chem. Phys.* 1938, **6**, 439.

[115] C. Friedel, *Ber.* 1875, **8**, 77, 642.

[116] O. Maass and D. M. Morison, *Trans. Roy. Soc. Canada*, 1924, [iii]. 18, III. 49 (*J.C.S. Abstr.* 1925, ii. 500).

[117] J. Shidei, *Mem. Coll. Sci. Kyoto*, 1925, **9**, 97.

the production of an aromatic structure (with its various resonance forms)

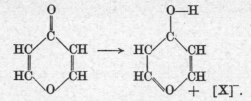

3. Three of the four forms of the oxonium ion

$$(1) \ [H_3O]^+ ; \ (2) \ [RH_2O]^+ ; \ (3) \ R_2HO]^+$$

(R = hydrocarbon radical) have long been known, being formed when an acid like hydrogen chloride is dissolved in water, alcohol, and ether respectively. The fourth type, $[R_3O]^+$, in which all three hydrogen atoms are replaced, has recently been discovered, and many of its salts isolated by Meerwein and his colleagues.[118] They showed that if the compound of boron tri-fluoride with ether $Et_2O{\rightarrow}BF_3$ is treated in ethereal solution with epichlorhydrin

$$\overset{O}{\overset{\diagup\diagdown}{CH_2-CH-CH_2Cl}}$$

a semi-solid mass is formed, of which the solid part is the triethyl oxonium salt $Et_3O[BF_4]$. It is very unstable, and melts at 92° with decomposition to $Et_2O{\rightarrow}BF_3$ and ethyl fluoride, from which also it can be made by heating them in a sealed tube. With sodium picrate this salt gives the picrate $Et_3O[C_6H_2(NO_2)_3O]$, m. pt. 58° with decomposition; attempts to make the iodide with potassium iodide failed. The borofluoride is a very powerful ethylating agent: with water it gives ethyl ether+alcohol, with phenol phenetol, etc. Epichlorhydrin will also act[119] in the same way on the etherates of antimony pentachloride, aluminium chloride, and ferric chloride, giving the salts (if $B = Et_3O$) $B[SbCl_6]$ (m. pt. 135–7°) $[B]AlCl_4$ and $[B]FeCl_4$. Their salt character is proved by their solubility in nitromethane and in sulphur dioxide, and their high conductivity in the latter solvent.

When $Et_3O[BF_4]$ is treated with sodium hydroxide it slowly decomposes, but by measuring the conductivity at intervals, and extrapolating back to zero time, it can be shown that $Et_3O[OH]$ is a base of the same high order of strength as $Me_4N[OH]$ or $Et_3S[OH]$.

By treating the borofluoride $Et_3O[BF_4]$ with other complex acids, a series of salts such as $[B]AuCl_4$ (m. pt. 92°), $[B]_2PtCl_6$ (decomposes 120°), $[B]_2SnCl_6$ (decomposes in the cold), and $[B]BiI_4$ were made. They are all similar; on heating they form $R_2O \cdot X + R \cdot hal$; they are remarkably powerful alkylating agents.

[118] H. Meerwein, G. Hinz, P. Hofmann, E. Kroning, and E. Pfeil, *J. prakt. Chem.* 1937, ii. **147**, 257; *B.C.A.* 37, ii. 46.

[119] H. Meerwein, H. Gold, E. Pfeil, G. Willfang, and E. Battenberg, *J. prakt. Chem.* 1939, ii, **154**, 83.

HYDROGEN PEROXIDE

THIS is the primary product of the action of oxygen on hydrogen: it is formed in small quantity when hydrogen burns in air,[119a] or when a mixture of hydrogen and oxygen is passed over palladium black. It is commonly made by the action of acids on sodium or barium peroxide, or recently often through peroxy-disulphuric acid by the electrolysis of acid sulphates in concentrated solution in presence of hydrofluoric acid or potassium ferrocyanide; it is concentrated by fractional distillation under reduced pressure.

Pure H_2O_2 is an oily liquid, freezing at $-1\cdot7°$ but very easily supercooling; b. pt. $69\cdot7°/28$ mm., extrapolated $144°/760$ mm. It has all the properties of a highly associated liquid, and physically resembles water very closely. It has an even higher dielectric constant of $89\cdot2$ at $0°$ (water $84\cdot4/0°$): a mixture of the two has a still higher dielectric constant, 120 in a 36 per cent. solution.[120] It is miscible with water in all proportions, but relatively slightly soluble in non-associated liquids.[121] It is an excellent ionizing solvent, in which salts are about as much dissociated as in water, though weak acids like acetic are very much less so.

The specific conductivity of pure H_2O_2 is, at $0°$, 2×10^{-6},[120] which implies a concentration of hydrogen ion 50 times as great as in pure water, and a dissociation constant of about 10^{-12}, since the true K for water is about 10^{-16}. This result is confirmed by the potentiometric titration with potassium hydroxide, which gives $1\cdot55\times10^{-12}$ at $20°$.[122] Hydrogen peroxide is thus definitely more acidic than water (compare carbonic acid, $k_1\ 3\times10^{-7}$ at $18°$, $k_2\ 5\times10^{-11}$; ortho-phosphoric acid $k_3\ 1\cdot2\times10^{-12}$).

It is endothermic and very unstable, readily breaking up according to the reaction

$$2\,H_2O_{2\,liq.}\ =\ 2\,H_2O_{\,liq.}\ +\ O_{2\,gas}\ +\ 46\cdot9\ \text{k.cals.}[125]$$

Assuming that H_2O_2 (b. pt. $144°$) has the same Trouton constant as water (a difference of 1 in this constant would only make a change of $0\cdot84$ k.cals.) the heat evolved if all the substances were gaseous would be $49\cdot3$ k.cals. The reaction really consists in the replacement of 2 O—O links by the double link in molecular oxygen, and so should evolve

$$118\cdot2\ -\ 2\ \times\ 34\cdot9\ =\ 48\cdot4\ \text{k.cals.;}$$

so the resonance energy seems to be much the same in hydrogen peroxide as in water. For this question, and the heat of the O—O link, see further, references [123-4].

In the complete absence of catalysts hydrogen peroxide remains for a

[119a] See A. C. G. Egerton and G. J. Minkoff, *Proc. Roy. Soc.* 1947, **191**, 145.
[120] A. C. Cuthbertson and O. Maass, *J.A.C.S.* 1930, **52**, 489.
[121] J. H. Walton and H. A. Lewis, ib. 1916, **38**, 633.
[122] V. A. Kargin, *Z. anorg. Chem.* 1929, **183**, 77.
[123] H. A. Skinner, *Trans. Far. Soc.* 1945, **41**, 645.
[124] G. Glockler and G. Mattack, *J. Chem. Phys.* 1946, **14**, 504.
[125] G. L. Matheson and O. Maass, *J.A.C.S.* 1929, **51**, 674.

long time unchanged, but its decomposition is promoted by a very large number of substances, such as alkalies, potassium iodide, finely divided platinum and palladium, and certain enzymes known as catalases. All finely divided and sharp-edged solids, even dust, promote the decomposition, and so the concentrated substances is commonly kept and sold in paraffin vessels. On the other hand, certain substances, even in small quantity, such as phosphoric and uric acids, are very effective in delaying the decomposition. 1 g. of uric acid will stabilize 30 litres of concentrated H_2O_2.[126]

Hydrogen peroxide can act both as an oxidizing and as a reducing agent. Its power of oxidation is most marked in alkaline solution: it can convert ferrous salts into ferric, sulphurous into sulphuric acid, hydrogen iodide into iodine, etc. Its reducing power is due to its removing oxygen atoms from other molecules in the form of diatomic oxygen. Thus silver oxide is reduced to silver, and potassium permanganate to a manganous salt; this reduction may often be due to the formation of an intermediate unstable oxidation product with an —O—O— group

$$H_2O_2 + A—O \longrightarrow H_2O + A—O—O;$$

with chromic acid a blue perchromic 'acid' is produced, which easily loses oxygen to give a chromic salt. (For the kinetics of the homogeneous decomposition of H_2O_2, catalysed by potassium bichromate, nitric acid, iodine, etc., see references [127-30]. For its reduction by zinc, cadmium, thallium, and lead amalgams see reference [131].)

Hydrogen peroxide shares with water the power of acting as a donor, and can replace water of crystallization in many salts.

There are two possible structures for H_2O_2

$$H—O—O—H \quad \text{and} \quad \overset{H\diagdown}{\underset{H\diagup}{}}O \to O.$$

By treatment in alkaline solution with dialkyl sulphate it can be converted into its dialkyl ethers, such as $(CH_3)_2O_2$, b. pt. 14°, and $(C_2H_5)_2O_2$, b. pt. 65° (both at 760 mm.). These compounds on reduction give alcohols, so that they have the structure Alk—O—O—Alk, and not $\overset{Alk\diagdown}{\underset{Alk\diagup}{}}O \to O$, which on reduction would give an ether. This does not, however, settle the structure of the hydrogen compound, which may well be tautomeric; the

[126] For an account of the physical and chemical properties of 90 per cent. aqueous hydrogen peroxide, see E. S. Shanley and F. P. Greenspan, *Ind. Eng. Chem.* 1947, **39**, 1536.

[127] N. I. Kobozev and E. E. Galbreich, *J. Phys.-Chem. Russ.* 1940, **14**, 1550.

[128] R. Livingston, *J. Phys. Chem.* 1943, **47**, 260.

[129] J. H. Walton, *Z. physikal. Chem.* 1904, **47**, 185.

[130] G. Bredig and M. v. Berneck, ib. 1899, **31**, 258.

[131] H. A. Liebhafsky, *J.A.C.S.* 1942, **64**, 852.

possible resonance formulae in the liquid could pass very easily into either
form:

On treatment with potassium iodide hydrogen peroxide liberates iodine,
and so does the half ether $C_2H_5 \cdot O_2H$, though less readily, but diethyl
peroxide does not. This agrees with the view that the oxidation of the
iodide is a reaction of the

$$\begin{array}{c} H \\ \end{array}\!\!\!>\!O\!\to\!O \text{ or } \begin{array}{c} Alk \\ \end{array}\!\!\!>\!O\!\to\!O$$

molecule. It should be noticed that if the O→O link has the same energy
as —O—O— (as is usually assumed) the two forms in the gaseous state
have as a first approximation the same energy, as both consist of two
H—O links and one O—O.

Penney and Sutherland[132-3] calculate that the H—O—O—H molecule
has no free rotation round the O—O link, and that the two $H\!\!\!\diagdown\!O$—O groups
are at right angles to one another. (They do not seem to have determined
the relative stability of the $\begin{array}{c} H \\ \end{array}\!\!\!>\!O\!\to\!O$ form.) Their conclusions are supported by the crystal structure of $CO(NH_2)_2, H_2O_2$[134]; in this the urea
molecules have the usual configuration, and the H_2O_2 that of Penney and
Sutherland, with the OH groups at an angle of 106°; the O—O distance is
1·46 A, which is exceptionally long (theory 1·32); the packing of the crystal
is effected by hydrogen bonds. The high dipole moment of hydrogen
peroxide also supports this view; it is 2·13 D in dioxane at 25°, and 2·06
in ether at 10°.[135]

If atomized hydrogen (see I. 15) at 0·5 mm. is allowed to act on
oxygen surrounded by liquid air, a colourless solid deposit is formed,
which has the composition H_2O_2, and seems to have the same absorption
spectrum as hydrogen peroxide.[136] On warming, this melts sharply at
—115°, evolving oxygen violently, and at the ordinary temperature a
liquid is left which contains up to 70 per cent. hydrogen peroxide. This
solid may well consist of the less stable of the two tautomeric forms,
which may melt at —115° and in so doing change with the loss of much of
its oxygen into the tautomeric mixture plus water (the 'natural' freezing-
point of hydrogen peroxide is —1·7°).

[132] W. G. Penney and G. B. B. M. Sutherland, *Trans. Far. Soc.* 1934, **30**, 898.
[133] Id., *J. Chem. Phys.* 1934, **2**, 492.
[134] C. S. Lu, E. W. Hughes, and P. A. Giguère, *J.A.C.S.* 1941, **63**, 1507.
[135] E. P. Linton and O. Maass, *Canad. J. Res.* 1932, **7**, 81.
[136] K. H. Geib and P. Harteck, *Ber.* 1932, **65**, 1551.

From hydrogen peroxide are derived a large number of compounds containing the O—O link: not only organic derivatives such as the alkyl and acyl peroxides, the percarboxylic acids like

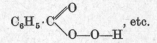

but also many inorganic derivatives, in which one or more oxygen atoms of a basic or acidic oxide, or an oxy-acid, are replaced by O—O groups. The binary inorganic compounds are commonly known as peroxides: this name should be confined to O—O compounds, but is often extended to include any metallic oxides with an unusually large amount of oxygen, such as PbO_2 and MnO_2. These two classes are as a rule easily distinguished. The oxide will dissolve in acids, and then if it contains a true O—O link, the solution will contain H_2O_2 (e.g. Na_2O_2, BaO_2). If it is not a true peroxide, but an oxide of an unstable high valency, this will often be reduced by the acid (as $MnO_2 + HCl \rightarrow MnCl_4 \rightarrow MnCl_2 + Cl_2$), but it does not give hydrogen peroxide.

True peroxides are those of the alkalies and alkaline earths, which are undoubtedly salts ($Na_2[O_2]$, $Ba[O_2]$, like $Na_2[O]$, and $Ba[O]$). (Per-hydroxides $M'[O_2H]$ also seem to occur[137].) This is shown by X-ray analysis which gives the O··O distance in SrO_2 and BaO_2 as 1·31[138] (theory for O—O 1·32). Metals which are less electro-positive, or in other words go over more readily into the covalent state, such as zinc, mercury, and nickel, give less certain or at any rate less stable peroxides.

Other compounds with the O—O link are numerous per-acids (or peroxy-acids), such as persulphuric, perboric, percarbonic, pertitanic, perchromic, etc. The elements of the A subgroups of Groups IV, V, and VI form these very readily, and they are most stable in the even groups, and in each group with the heaviest element.[139] X-ray analysis shows[140] that K_3CrO_8, K_3NbO_8, and K_3TaO_8 have the same lattices, with O—O 1·34 A.

A doubt whether some of these compounds are hydrated peracids, or normal acids with hydrogen peroxide of crystallization can often be settled by the 'Riesenfeld-Liebhafsky test'.[141] With potassium iodide in a phosphate-buffered solution at p_H 7·5–8·0 true peroxides, such as potassium persulphate $K_2S_2O_8$, give free iodine but no oxygen, while hydrogen peroxide itself, and salts which undoubtedly contain H_2O_2 of crystallization, give no iodine but liberate oxygen. When this test is positive—when it gives I_2—it is good evidence of a true O—O link not attached to two hydrogen atoms: when it fails (gives oxygen) we can deduce that the

[137] A. Aguzzi, *Gaz.* 1938, **68**, 816.

[138] J. D. Bernal, E. Djatlova, I. Karsanovski, S. Reichstein, and A. G. Ward, *Z. Krist.* 1936, **92**, 344.

[139] P. Melikov and L. Pissarjevsky, *Z. anorg. Chem.* 1899, **20**, 340.

[140] I. A. Wilson, *Arkiv. Kemi, Min. Geol.* 1942, **15** B, no. 5.

[141] R. Schwarz and F. Heinrich, *Z. anorg. Chem.* 1935, **223**, 387.

compound has liberated hydrogen peroxide in the solution, either because it was there as hydrogen peroxide of crystallization, or because the X—O—O—H group was so unstable as to react with the water to form X—O—H and H_2O_2.

By this test it can be shown that we have true peroxides (i.e. molecules with an O—O group attached to the central atom) in Caro's acid H_2SO_5, persulphuric acid $H_2S_2O_8$, percarbonic as in Na_2CO_4, pertitanic as in H_2TiO_4, H_2O, perzirconic H_2ZrO_4, H_2O, and perchromic (the blue) $R_2[Cr_2O_{12}]$. But the supposed per-compounds of silicon, germanium, and thorium seem to be only normal oxides with hydrogen peroxide of crystallization.

Organic Peroxides

Almost all classes of organic oxygen compounds can have an oxygen atom replaced by an —O_2— group. The simplest are the alkyl hydro-peroxides or per-alcohols Alk—O—O—H and the dialkyl peroxides Alk—O—O—Alk; these were first made by Baeyer and Villiger[142-3] by the action of alkaline hydrogen peroxide on alkyl sulphates.

Boiling-points [and Melting-points]

	$R \cdot O_2 H$	$R \cdot O_2 R$
R = CH_3	?	100°
$C_2H_5{}^a$	ca. 95°	65° [−78°]
C_3H_7	38°/30 mm.	51·3°/80 mm.
$(CH_3)_3C^b$	..	38°/18 mm. [−13·5°]

$$a = {}^{144}, b = {}^{145}$$

In general these two classes resemble the alcohols and ethers respectively. The per-alcohols decompose readily when concentrated, and are difficult to purify. The dialkyl peroxides are relatively stable, but explode on heating above their boiling-points.

In chemical behaviour (our knowledge is mainly of the ethyl compounds) the per-alcohols[148] are in most points, but not in all, intermediate between the alkyl peroxides and hydrogen peroxide. They are far less stable than the peroxides, which are almost as inactive as ether; the alkyl groups in Alk—O—O—Alk are not oxidized by permanganate or by chromic acid, and the O—O link is not reduced by sodium alone, and only very slowly by potassium iodide in presence of strong sulphuric acid; it is, however,

[142] A. v. Baeyer and V. Villiger, *Ber.* 1900, **33**, 3387.
[143] Id., ib. 1901, **34**, 738.
[144] E. J. Harris, *Proc. Roy. Soc.* 1939, **173**, 126.
[145] N. A. Milas and S. A. Harris, *J.A.C.S.* 1938, **60**, 2434.
[146] P. George and A. D. Walsh, *Trans. Far. Soc.* 1946, **42**, 94.
[147] N. A. Milas and D. M. Surgenor, *J.A.C.S.* 1946, **68**, 205.
[148] N. A. Milas and P. C. Panagiotakos, ib. 533.

reduced quantitatively by zinc and acetic acid with the production of ethyl alcohol, a proof that the structure is Et—O—O—Et and not

$$\begin{matrix} \text{Et} \\ \diagdown \\ \diagup \\ \text{Et} \end{matrix} \hspace{-6pt} \text{O} \rightarrow \text{O}.$$

But the vapour catches fire in air in contact with a thermometer at 250° (carbon disulphide does not do so below 300°), and if the liquid, in an atmosphere of carbon dioxide, is touched with a hot wire it vanishes, the main product being formaldehyde. The dialkyl peroxides have a faint smell like that of ethyl bromide, while ethyl per-alcohol smells like bleaching powder and acetaldehyde.

The per-alcohol $C_2H_5 \cdot O_2H$ is a weak acid about as strong as phenol, forming salts with alkalies and alkaline earths which are explosive and are decomposed by carbon dioxide. It differs markedly from hydrogen peroxide, having practically no reducing power, but only oxidizing. Chromic, molybdic, and titanic acids (which might either be reduced, e.g. to chromic salts, or oxidized to per-acids) have no action on it; acid permanganate is much more slowly decolorized by it (with evolution of oxygen) than by hydrogen peroxide. Silver oxide (which at once reduces hydrogen peroxide) has scarcely any action on the per-alcohol, while ordinary molecular silver, which has no action on hydrogen peroxide, decomposes the per-alcohol, sometimes explosively. On the other hand, it is a strong oxidizing agent; it oxidizes hydrogen iodide, with explosion in concentrated solution, and it can convert tertiary amines into amine oxides.

Tertiary butyl peroxide $(Me_3C)_2O_2$[145-7] is abnormally stable; unlike the other esters it can be made from the alcohol and hydrogen peroxide with a dehydrating agent ($MgSO_4$ and HPO_3); it will stand for months in the cold with 10 per cent. sodium hydroxide solution without change. For the kinetics of its decomposition in the gas at about 150° see reference [148a].

Egerton and his colleagues have shown[149-52] that in the oxidation of petrol by air, and in the 'knocking' of petrol engines under excessive compression, the alkyl peroxides and per-alcohols are probably starters of reaction chains. They find that diethyl peroxide is a strong 'pro-knock', and also that it greatly shortens the induction period of the slow oxidation of propane.

Numerous organic peroxides of other types are known, such as the per-anhydrides. Peracetic anhydride $CH_3 \cdot CO \cdot O_2 \cdot CO \cdot CH_3$ was made by Brodie in 1863 from acetic anhydride and barium peroxide; it melts at 30°, boils at 63°/21 mm., and is enormously explosive. Benzoyl peroxide $\Phi \cdot CO \cdot O_2 \cdot CO \cdot \Phi$ is used in organic chemistry as an oxidizing agent; for

[148a] J. H. Raley, F. F. Rust, and W. E. Vaughan, ib. 1948, **70**, 88.

[149] E. J. Harris and A. C. Egerton, *Nature*, 1938, **142**, 830.

[150] Id., *Proc. Roy. Soc.* 1938, **168**, 1.

[151] E. J. Harris, ib. 1939, **173**, 126; **175**, 254.

[152] E. C. Stathis and A. C. Egerton, *Trans. Far. Soc.* 1940, **36**, 606.

the kinetics of its decomposition see references [153-5]; for the kinetics of its thermal decomposition see references [156a-b].

The per-acids $RCO \cdot O_2H$ can be made by the hydrolysis of these per-anhydrides, or by the action of hydrogen peroxide on the ordinary acids in presence of sulphuric acid[156]; peracetic acid $CH_3 \cdot CO \cdot O_2H$ melts at $+0 \cdot 1°$ and explodes at 110°, which is taken to be its boiling-point.

[153] P. H. Hermans, *Rec. Trav.* 1935, **54**, 760.
[154] H. Erlenmeyer and W. Schoenauer, *Helv. Chim. Acta*, 1936, **19**, 338.
[155] J. D. Brown, *J.A.C.S.* 1940, **62**, 2657.
[156] J. d'Ans and W. Frey, *Ber.* 1912, **45**, 1845.
[156a] P. D. Bartlett and K. Nozaki, *J.A.C.S.* 1947, **69**, 2299.
[156b] B. Barnett and W. Vaughan, *J. Phys. Chem.* 1947, **51**, 926, 942.

SULPHUR
General

THE changes in properties to be expected when we go from oxygen to sulphur are these.

1. The covalency limit expands from 4 to 6 and that of the valency group from 8 electrons to 12, as in SF_6, to which oxygen forms no analogue.

2. It is improbable but not impossible that sulphur will show the inert pair of electrons. This is only just perceptible in arsenic (not in phosphorus) on the one side, and in chlorine on the other. In fact it is scarcely found with sulphur except in resonance forms. The mixed decet 2, 8, which can only occur when the two electrons are inert, is almost unknown; it would occur in compounds of the type SX_4 if wholly covalent, but SCl_4 exists only in the solid state, where it is probably a salt $[SCl_3]Cl$, while the supposed gaseous SF_4 does not seem to exist at all.

3. Sulphur, being in the second short period, should be much less ready to form multiple links than oxygen, as we found in silicon and phosphorus as compared with carbon and nitrogen. This no doubt explains the great instability of such molecules as S=S and S=O in comparison with O=O.

When we look at the observed facts, the most conspicuous differences between sulphur and oxygen are these.

1. Sulphur is more acidic; the first dissociation constant of water is 2×10^{-16}, and that of hydrogen sulphide $3 \cdot 31 \times 10^{-7}$; this is probably because H_2S is so much less associated than H_2O; otherwise we should have expected the larger anion to ionize less readily.

2. Sulphur has a much stronger tendency than oxygen to form long chains with itself. In its compounds no chains of more than two oxygen atoms are known, and even compounds with two linked oxygens, such as hydrogen peroxide and the organic peroxides, decompose very readily. With sulphur chains of two, three, and even more sulphur atoms (in the polysulphides) are readily formed and are stable: the most striking example is the remarkable stability of the S_8 molecule, under practically all conditions at temperatures below 800°. This is the exact reverse of the relations in Group IV, where carbon forms far more stable and longer chains than the second element silicon.

3. Sulphur has a much stronger tendency than oxygen to assume a valency greater than two, even where it retains the octet (as it almost always does). The comparison of the sulphonium and oxonium compounds illustrates this, and we have also such compounds as the sulphoxides, sulphones, and sulphates, to which oxygen offers no analogy. This difference, which is almost confined to the S—O compounds, may be due to the energy of the resonance between the S→O and S=O forms.

4. A curious difference is that hydrogen cannot form a link between two sulphur atoms (though it can link sulphur to other atoms such as nitrogen), and in consequence hydrogen sulphide and the mercaptans are entirely non-associated, though the donor power of the sulphur in these compounds is as great as that of oxygen in water and the alcohols.

According to Faessler[157-9] the position of the $K\alpha$ X-ray doublet for sulphur varies somewhat with the valency.

Elementary Sulphur

Sulphur occurs in the earth's crust to 500 parts per million (0·05 per cent.), in the free state (especially in Texas and in Sicily), as sulphates, and as sulphides. It has four natural isotopes:

Mass No.	.	. 32	33	34	36
Per cent.[a]	.	. 95·1	0·74	4·2	0·016

$$a = {}^{160}.$$

Stewart and Cohen,[161] by the exchange of sulphur dioxide with sodium hydrogen sulphite have got samples in which 25 per cent. of the sulphur was ^{34}S. But for the measurement of the exchange of sulphur atoms in compounds radioactive ^{35}S (half-life 88 days)[162] is always used; this is made by bombarding chlorine (carbon tetrachloride) with neutrons, or ordinary sulphur with deuterons.

In every state, gas, liquid, solid, elementary sulphur occurs in more than one modification, the whole constituting a confusing multitude of forms, whose relations are not yet fully understood.

Sulphur boils at 444·6° C. At all temperatures from 60°[163] up to about 800° its molecular weight in the vapour is S_8; this molecule is extraordinarily stable and widespread: it is the molecule of rhombic and monoclinic sulphur; it is the form in which sulphur occurs in all non-reacting solvents at all temperatures at which the molecular weight has been measured, and these measurements, which are mainly due to Beckmann,[164] extend to twenty-nine solvents, and to temperatures from —75° in S_2Cl_2 to 277° in anthraquinone. The structure of this S_8 molecule is given later.

Above 800° the vapour dissociates to S_2, with possibly[165-6] S_6 as an intermediate form; at 1,000° it is mainly S_2, and at 2,000° this is measurably broken up into single atoms. The heats of formation of the links from their atoms (H_a) are (A—A thermal[167]; A=A spectroscopic[168]):

	S	Se	Te
A—A	50·0	46·3	..
A=A	75·7	71·5	53·1 k.cals.
A=A/A—A	1·51	1·54	..

[157] A. Faessler, *Z. Phys.* 1931, **72**, 734.

[158] A. Faessler and M. Goehring, *Naturwiss.* 1943, **31**, 367.

[159] A. Faessler, *Z. Elektrochem.* 1944, **50**, 64.

[160] A. O. Nier, *Phys. Rev.* 1938, ii. **53**, 282.

[161] D. W. Stewart and K. Cohen, *J. Chem. Phys.* 1940, **8**, 904.

[162] M. D. Kamen, *Phys. Rev.* 1941, ii. **60**, 537.

[163] K. Neumann, *Z. physikal. Chem.* 1934, **171**, 399, 416.

[164] E. Beckmann, ib. 1909, **65**, 289; *Z. anorg. Chem.* 1909, **63**, 63; E. Beckmann and R. Hanslian, ib. 1913, **80**, 221.

[165] G. Preuner and W. Schupp, *Z. physikal. Chem.* 1909, **68**, 129.

[166] W. Klemm and H. Kilian, ib. 1941, B **49**, 279.

The values usually accepted (and quoted in the Introduction, pp. xxxi, xxxii) are S—S 63·8, S=S 103·4; Se—Se 57·6, Se=Se 92·5 k.cals.

In the solid state there are in addition to the crystalline rhombic and monoclinic forms, with a transition point of 96° (for the rate of change see ref.[169]), various other crystalline forms, all metastable with respect to the first two. There are also at least two amorphous forms, plastic sulphur, formed by chilling the liquid from 250° or above (see further, ref.[170]), and insoluble amorphous sulphur, which is formed from plastic sulphur on standing, and is contained in flowers of sulphur, as well as in other forms of the element.

This colloidal form is insoluble in carbon disulphide. If the insolubility is real and permanent, this must be the stable form as compared with the rhombic and the monoclinic; but it seems more likely that it is ultimately soluble in carbon disulphide, but for some reason dissolves very slowly.

At 200–250° liquid sulphur darkens and its viscosity enormously increases. At lower temperatures the molecules of liquid (as of dissolved) sulphur are no doubt S_8, but above 200° a new form must be produced, which is generally called $S\mu$. This has been identified with plastic sulphur and also with the insoluble colloidal form. Attempts, often regarded as conclusive, have been made to determine the proportion of $S\mu$ at various temperatures by chilling it, and after leaving it for some days in the cold to harden, grinding up and extracting with carbon disulphide. But Hammick has shown[175] that if the chilled mass is treated with carbon disulphide at once, nearly the whole dissolves, so that plastic sulphur appears to be soluble, and to produce the insoluble form on standing. The whole question of the relations of the liquid forms is very obscure.[171-2]

The structures of the three most definite forms, S_8, plastic sulphur, and S_2, have recently been determined. Warren and Burwell[173] showed by X-ray analysis of rhombic sulphur that the crystal cell contained 16 S_8 molecules, each forming an 8-ring, puckered in this way

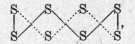

the distance between two neighbours being 2·12 A (theory for S—S 2·08), and the angle 105·4° (compare H_2O 105°). This has been confirmed by electron diffraction.[174-6] In the high-temperature S_2 molecule the S··S

[167] Bischowski and Rossini, *Thermochemistry*.
[168] P. Goldfinger, W. Jeunehomme, and B. Rosen, *Nature*, 1936, **138**, 205.
[169] P. G. Elias, N. H. Hartshorne, and J. E. D. James, *J.C.S.* 1940, 588.
[170] E. A. Fehnel, *J.A.C.S.* 1942, **64**, 3041.
[171] R. E. Powell and H. Eyring, ib. 1943, **65**, 648.
[172] N. S. Gingrich, *J. Chem. Phys.* 1940, 8, 29.
[173] B. E. Warren and J. T. Burwell, ib. 1935, **3**, 6.
[174] J. D. Howe and K. Lark-Horowitz, *Phys. Rev.* 1937, ii. **51**, 380.
[175] D. Ll. Hammick, W. R. Cousins, and E. J. Langford, *J.C.S.* 1928, 797.
[176] C. S. Lu and J. Donohue, *J.A.C.S.* 1944, **66**, 818.

distance was found from the band spectrum[177] to be 1·88 A, and by electron diffraction[178] to be at 800° 1·92±0·03 (theory for S=S 1·88).

Plastic sulphur was shown by K. H. Meyer[179] to have a simple fibre structure; it is amorphous, but like rubber it can be made crystalline by stretching: that is to say the sulphur chains, which seem to have the form

$$\text{S---S} \diagdown_{\text{S---S}} \diagup^{\text{S---S}} \diagdown_{\text{S---S}} \diagup^{\text{S}}$$

are normally tangled up with one another, but can be separated by pulling.

Chemical Behaviour of Elementary Sulphur

Sulphur is almost as ready to combine with other elements as oxygen, even in the solid state. It combines readily with hydrogen (for which its affinity is, as usual, less than that of oxygen, the lighter member of the group), it catches fire in oxygen below 260° (it only forms SO_2 unless catalysts are present), it combines in the cold with fluorine, chlorine, and bromine, though not with iodine: carbon reacts at high temperatures, silicon, phosphorus, arsenic, antimony, and bismuth at their melting-points: it does not combine with tellurium.

Nearly all metals combine with sulphur, and many of them in the cold. The combination takes place more easily, the earlier the group to which the metal belongs. Li, Na, K, Cu, Ag all react in the cold on contact with the solid (copper and silver have more affinity for sulphur than for oxygen): mercury does the same, even at $-180°$ according to Dewar. Be, Ca, Sr, do not react except with sulphur vapour at 400°: Mg, Zn, Cd, very slightly in the cold, but easily on heating: Al, In, Tl, and the IVth Group metals do not perceptibly react below a high temperature: still less readily the metals of the Vth to the VIIIth Groups, such as Cr, W, U, Fe, Co, Ni.

The only elements which are not known to combine directly with sulphur are iodine, nitrogen (except perhaps in the active state), tellurium, gold, platinum, and iridium.

HYDROGEN SULPHIDE, H_2S

SULPHUR forms three hydrides, H_2S, H_2S_2, and H_2S_3; the last two, having linked sulphur atoms, are considered later.

Hydrogen sulphide boils at $-60·4°$ and melts at $-85·5°$. The solid is trimorphic,[180-2] with transition points at $-146·9°$ and $-169·6°$, the latter being the point at which free rotation of the H_2S molecules begins. D_2S is dimorphic,[183] with a m. pt. 0·5° below that of H_2S. At $-78·6°$ the specific

[177] E. Olsson, *Nature*, 1936, **137**, 745.
[178] L. R. Maxwell, V. M. Mosley, and S. R. Hendricks, *Phys. Rev.* 1936, ii. **50, 41**.
[179] K. H. Meyer and Y. Go, *Helv. Chim. Acta.* 1934, **17**, 1081.
[180] W. F. Giauque and R. W. Blue, *J.A.C.S.* 1936, **58**, 831.
[181] K. Clusius and A. Frank, *Z. physikal. Chem.* 1936, B **34**, 420.
[182] A. Kruis and K. Clusius, *Phys. Z.* 1937, **38**, 510.
[183] Id., *Z. physikal. Chem.* 1937, B **38**, 156.

conductivity of liquid H_2S is $1 \cdot 2 \times 10^{-9}$, and its dielectric constant $8 \cdot 3$[184] (water $81/20°$).

It differs remarkably from water in having in every way the properties of an unassociated substance. This is shown, for example, by the boiling-points (see table); by the Trouton constant of $21 \cdot 0$ (water $26 \cdot 0$); by the low dielectric constant; by the low dipole moment (see below); and by the structure of the solid, which is[185] a close-packed assemblage of SH_2 molecules, very unlike the open structure of ice.

Boiling-points

				Diff.
H—O—H	$100°$ C.	H—S—H	$-60°$	$-160°$
CH_3—O—H	$66°$	CH_3—S—H	$+6°$	$-60°$
C_2H_5—O—H	$78°$	C_2H_5—S—H	$+36°$	$-42°$
C_2H_5—O—C_2H_5	$35°$	C_2H_5—S—C_2H_5	$92°$	$+57°$

This marked difference from the highly associated water is clearly due to the hydrogen bond being much weaker when between two sulphur atoms than when between two oxygens (see above, I. 32). It is accompanied by a marked difference in dipole moment.[186] The latest values are given in the table, which shows (1) the moment of the compound, (2) the moment of the X—H link, assuming the valency angle to be $105°$[187] in H_2S as it is in water, (3) the X$\cdots$H distance, (4) the charge, assuming it to be located on the hydrogen and the sulphur, and (5) the same, expressed as a fraction of the electronic charge.

XH_2	μ	μ(X—H)	Dist. X—H	dE	$\dfrac{dE}{E}$
OH_2	$1 \cdot 84$	$1 \cdot 51$	$0 \cdot 96$	$1 \cdot 59$	$0 \cdot 33$
SH_2	$0 \cdot 93$	$0 \cdot 76$	$1 \cdot 34$	$0 \cdot 57$	$0 \cdot 12$

These results scarcely support the view that the association of liquids like water is wholly due to the electrostatic attraction between the hydrogens and the central atom.

The general properties of hydrogen sulphide as a solvent are in agreement with its non-associated character. It is nearly four times as soluble in alcohol at $0°$ as in water, and it is miscible at $-80°$ with CCl_4, $SiCl_4$, and CS_2. It is practically a non-dissociating solvent for most salts, for which in general it is not a good solvent.[188] The liquid, especially in the dry and pure state, is relatively inactive.

[184] W. G. Bickford and J. A. Wilkinson, *Proc. Iowa Acad. Sci*, 1933, **40**, 89.

[185] L. Pauling, *J.A.C.S.* 1935, **57**, 2680.

[186] C. P. Smyth, ib. 1924, **46**, 2151.

[187] B. L. Crawford, and P. C. Cross, *J. Chem. Phys.* 1937, 5, 371, find from the intensities of the absorption band at 10,000 A that the H—S—H angle is $90°$, but this will only diminish (X—H) by about 10 per cent.

[188] W. Biltz and E. Keunecke, *Z. anorg. Chem.* 1925, **147**, 171.

The gas is about twice as soluble in water as carbon dioxide—about 0·4 per cent. by weight at 18° and 1 atm.

Hydrogen sulphide is a stronger acid than water, its first ionization constant being (in water) $3·3 \times 10^{-7}$,[189] whereas that of water (in itself) is 2×10^{-16}. This must be mainly due to the absence of association, which would diminish the ionization in water; otherwise the larger sulphur anion should go over into the covalent state more easily than the smaller oxygen.

As in all the last four groups (i.e. wherever hydrogen forms covalent links) the affinity for hydrogen falls off in the VIth Group from oxygen to sulphur: the heats of formation from the atoms in the gaseous state at 25° are:

$$O—H \text{ (half } H_2O) \; 110·2 \text{ k.cals.}: \; S—H \text{ (half } H_2S) \; 87·5$$

The difference is familiar from the way in which an H_2S solution deposits sulphur through oxidation when exposed to the air. For details of its oxidation see references [190-3]. When heated alone H_2S is decomposed above 400°. It forms a solid hydrate, probably $H_2S, 6H_2O$.[194]

Mercaptans (Thiols)

These, which are the mono-alkyl and aryl derivatives of hydrogen sulphide, also behave as normal non-associated liquids; this is indicated by their low boiling-points, almost the same as those of the isomeric thio-ethers, and also by the low Trouton constants. Thus we have:

Compound	M. pt.	B. pt.	Trouton constant
$CH_3 \cdot SH^a$	−123·0°	+6·0°	21·0
$C_2H_5 \cdot SH$	−147·3°	34·7°	22·4
n. $C_3H_7 \cdot SH$	−113·3°	68°	..
n. $Bu \cdot SH$	−115·9°	97°	..
$CH_3 \cdot OH$	..	67°	25·2
$C_2H_5 \cdot OH$	..	78°	27·1
$(CH_3)_2S$	..	36·2	21·3
$(C_2H_5)_2S$	..	91·6	20·7

$$a = {}^{194}$$

The same conclusion is supported by their other physical properties; thus unlike the alcohols they are only slightly soluble in water.

The mercaptans are much more acidic than the alcohols; the alkyl mercaptans are more like the phenols, and the aryl-mercaptans or thio-

[189] A. G. Epprecht, *Helv. Chim. Acta*, 1938, **21**, 205.
[190] B. Jakovleva and P. Schantarovitsch, *J. Phys.-Chem. Russ.* 1937, **9**, 112.
[191] N. M. Emanuel, ib. 1940, **14**, 863.
[192] N. Emanuel, *Acta Physicochem. U.R.S.S.* 1944, **19**, 360.
[193] Id., *J. Phys.-Chem. Russ.* 1945, **19**, 15.
[194] A. Korvezee and F. E. C. Scheffer, *Rec. Trav.* 1931, **50**, 256.
[195] H. Russell, D. W. Osborne, and D. M. Yost, *J.A.C.S.* 1942, **64**, 165.

phenols far more acidic than the corresponding phenols, phenyl-ortho-di-mercaptan $C_6H_4(SH)_2$ being nearly as strong an acid as acetic.[197] The mercaptans, like the phenols, dissolve in alkalies to form salts, which are considerably but by no means completely hydrolysed.

The polymethylene dimercaptans $HS(CH_2)_nSH$ are known[198] from $n = 2$ to $n = 12$; $CH_2(SH)_2$ could not be made. Their melting-points show a sharp alternation, those with n even being 20–40° higher than the next with n odd. The dibromides and glycols behave in the same way.

Though the alkaline derivatives of the mercaptans are no doubt true salts, those of the heavy metals are certainly as a rule covalent, especially those of mercury (see II. 320) and divalent lead; the latter, like the mercury compounds, have very low melting-points, for example,

$$(Et \cdot S)_2Pb \ 150°, \ (Bu \cdot S)_2Pb \ 80°,[199]$$

and are soluble in chloroform and benzene; these are almost the only covalent derivatives of divalent lead.

Like hydrogen sulphide the mercaptans are very easily oxidized; thus sulphuric acid, instead of forming alkyl thiosulphates $AlkHS_2O_3$ as $AlkHSO_4$ is formed from alcohol, oxidizes them to the di-sulphides. Stronger oxidizing agents convert them into sulphonic acids $Alk \cdot SO_3H$.

Thioethers

These resemble the O-ethers fairly closely in physical properties; they are immiscible with water, they are said to have no smell when pure, and they boil about 60° higher than their oxygen analogues; examples are:

	M. pt.	*B. pt.*	*Trouton*
Me_2S^a	−98·3°	37·3°	21·2
Et_2S^b	−102·1°	91·4°	21·7
$(C_6H_5)_2S^c$	Liquid	293°	..

$$a = {}^{207}, \ b = {}^{208}, \ c = {}^{209}$$

The barrier to rotation of the methyl group is found from the specific heat of the vapour to be 1·5 k.cals. in $CH_3 \cdot SH$[195] and 2·0 k.cals. in $(CH_3)_2S$.[207]

[197] G. Schwarzenbach, *Helv. Chim. Acta*, 1932, **15**, 1468.
[198] W. P. Hall and E. E. Reid, *J.A.C.S.* 1943, **65**, 1466.
[199] E. Wertheim, ib. 1929, **51**, 3661.
[200] W. Steinkopf, *Ver. Ges. d. Naturf.* 1912, ii. 220 (*J.C.S. Abstr.* 1912, i. 292).
[201] V. Schomaker and L. Pauling, *J.A.C.S.* 1939, **61**, 1769.
[202] G. W. Wheland, *Theory of Resonance*, 1944, p. 70.
[203] For more of these see *Richter*, ed. 12, ii. 3, p. 21.
[204] F. S. Fawcett and H. E. Rasmussen, *J.A.C.S.* 1945, **67**, 1705.
[205] F. S. Fawcett, ib. 1946, **68**, 1420.
[206] G. C. Johnson, ib. 1947, **69**, 150.
[207] D. W. Osborne, R. N. Doescher, and D. M. Yost, ib. 1942, **64**, 169.
[208] H. W. Thompson and J. W. Linnett, *Trans. Far. Soc.* 1935, **31**, 1743.
[209] Krause and v. Grosse, p. 661.

The valency angle of the sulphur in C—S—C has been measured only in the diaryl sulphides, where the aryl groups might be expected to increase it; it is little if at all larger than the tetrahedral angle (in H_2S it is much smaller, 105°). Thianthrene

has a moment of 1·50 D in carbon tetrachloride, so it must be non-planar with the S-angles less than 120°[210]; the dipole moments of their para-substitution compounds show that the valency angle in diphenyl sulphide is 113±3°,[212] but in diphenyl ether 128±4°[211]; finally, the crystal structure of the decamethylene ether of *p*-dihydroxy-phenyl sulphide $(HO \cdot C_6H_4)_2S$ gives the C—S—C angle as 112·4+1·5° and the C—S distance as 1·71 (theory 1·81).

Thiophene

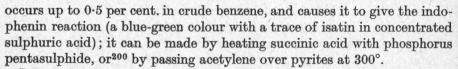

occurs up to 0·5 per cent. in crude benzene, and causes it to give the indophenin reaction (a blue-green colour with a trace of isatin in concentrated sulphuric acid); it can be made by heating succinic acid with phosphorus pentasulphide, or[200] by passing acetylene over pyrites at 300°.

It is a colourless liquid smelling like benzene, to which it has a remarkably close resemblance. Electron diffraction[201] shows the molecule to be planar, with the distances C—C 1·44, C=C 1·35, C—S 1·78 (theory C—C 1·54, C=C 1·33, C—S 1·81, C=S 1·61 A). The resonance energy as measured by the heat of combustion is 29 k.cals.[202] (benzene 41). In physical properties, and especially in boiling-points, thiophene and its derivatives closely resemble their benzene analogues, as the following values[203] show (the benzene values are added in brackets): thiophene[204] b. pt. 84·1° [80·5°]; 2-methyl thiophene 112·5°, 3-methyl thiophene 115·4°[205] [110·8°]; 2-chlorothiophene 130° [132°]; 2,5-dichlorothiophene 170° [172°]; 2-acetyl-thiophene[206] 213·9° [202°]; dithienyl 266° [254°]. Its chemical resemblances are equally close; it is as readily chlorinated as benzene, more easily sulphonated, and rather less easily nitrated. It can be removed from benzene through its more rapid reaction with sulphuric acid (V. Meyer) or with mercuric acetate (Dimroth). It reacts like benzene with diazoacetic ester.[203] Even the physiological action of drugs like cocain and atropine is little affected if their phenyl groups are replaced by thienyl.[203]

The sulphur in a thioether has a marked action on the behaviour of other atoms in the molecule. For example, the acidity of a phenol is enormously increased by the attachment of a sulphur atom to the benzene ring, as in

[210] G. M. Bennett and S. Glasstone, *J.C.S.* 1934, 128.
[211] L. E. Sutton and G. C. Hampson, *Trans. Far. Soc.* 1935, **31**, 945.
[212] R. Kohlhaas and A. Lütringhaus, *Ber.* 1939, **72**, 897.

para-$S(C_6H_4 \cdot OH)_2$.[213] Another effect which has become only too well known is on a chlorine atom attached to carbon. If one of the α-hydrogen atoms in diethyl sulphide is replaced by chlorine, as in the dichloride $(CH_3—CHCl—)_2S$, no special peculiarities are observed except that the chlorine is very easily replaced. But if the chlorine atoms are in the β-position, as in $(CH_2Cl—CH_2—)_2S$, two effects are produced; firstly, the chlorine atom becomes much more difficult to remove, and secondly, the substance acquires an intense physiological activity, especially the power of raising blisters in contact with the skin. It is of course the well-known mustard gas. The α-compound has no vesicating power. This distinction runs through all the chloro-thioethers, and the two properties always go together.

The thioethers, like the ethers, form a series of addition compounds, often with the same substances, the sulphur being on the whole perhaps as good a donor as the oxygen, though it is somewhat limited in its action. Comparison is difficult, because the additive powers of the sulphur compounds are for obvious reasons much less thoroughly investigated than those of their oxygen analogues. But so far as we know the mercaptans form very few addition compounds, only some three being described: $SbCl_3, EtSH$, and $TiCl_4$, 1 and 2 EtSH (the last two both red), so that they are very different from those of the alcohols. Presumably the same conditions which cause the hydrogen to ionize weaken the donor power of the sulphur.

The addition compounds of the thioethers are numerous. They include a remarkable group in which the acceptor atom is carbon. Ingold and Jessop[214] showed that fluorenyl-9-dimethyl-sulphonium bromide (I) when treated with potassium hydroxide loses hydrogen bromide to give a neutral product which is monomeric in benzene and must have the structure (II):

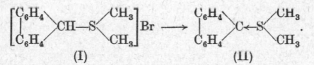

$$\qquad\qquad\text{(I)}\qquad\qquad\qquad\qquad\text{(II)}$$

This product is dimethyl-sulphonium-9-fluorenylidide; it is one of the rare cases where a carbon atom forms a co-ordinate link. The alternative structure with a double link

is impossible for various reasons, the simplest of which is that the compound reacts with dilute hydrobromic acid like a base, taking up the acid and regenerating a sulphonium salt (corresponding to I), the carbon atom, with the valency group 2, <u>6</u> behaving like the nitrogen atom of an amine, while the true $C\!=\!S$ group (as in carbon disulphide) does not do this;

[213] C. Lefèvre and C. Desgrez, *C.R.* 1935, **200**, 762.
[214] C. K. Ingold and J. A. Jessop, *J.C.S.* 1930, 713.

another reason is that the $\rangle$C=S$\langle$ structure would imply a valency group of 2, 8 (inert pair) for the sulphur atom.

In another small group of co-ordination compounds of the thioethers it is nitrogen that acts as acceptor. These are the *sulphylimines*, which are of the type

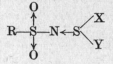

formed[215] by the action of 'chloramine-T' (the sodium salt of the sulphon-chloride) on a thioether. Their whole behaviour supports the —N$\leftarrow$S as against the —N=S structure. They have been resolved into stable antimers.[216-17]

Apart from these, the addition compounds of the thioethers are almost confined to a small group of elements in the periodic table,[218] which on the whole are those that form the most stable metallic sulphides.[219] These compounds are formed by the halides (and with silver by the nitrate) of the following elements:

Ni	Cu	Zn
Pd	Ag	Cd
Pt	Au	Hg

and otherwise only by those of Al, Ti, and Sn, the stannic halides, as usual, taking up two molecules of the sulphide; the disulphides Alk_2S_2 can replace the thioethers. Thus we have the following derivatives of dimethyl thioether CH_3—S—CH_3 (= A):

2 CuCl, A.	$TiCl_4$, Et_2S, and 2 Et_2S.
$ZnBr_2$, A.	$SnCl_4$, 2 A.
CdI_2, A.	$PdCl_2$, 2 A.
HgI_2, A.	$AgNO_3$, Et_2S_2.
	2 $AgNO_3$, $(CH_2$=CH$)_2$S.

Tschugaeff[220] showed that dithioethers of the type $R \cdot S \cdot (CH_2)_n S \cdot R$ can form such compounds unusually easily when $n = 2$, i.e. when a chelate 5-ring can be formed as in:

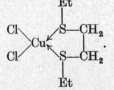

[215] F. G. Mann and W. J. Pope, *J.C.S.* 1922, **121**, 1052.
[216] S. G. Clarke, J. Kenyon, and H. Phillips, ib. 1927, 188.
[217] For further work on these compounds see L. A. Pink and G. E. Hilbert, *J.A.C.S.* 1946, **68**, 751.
[218] P. Pfeiffer, *Org. Molekülverbindungen*, ed. 2, 1927, p. 159.
[219] See G. T. Morgan and W. Ledbury, *J.C.S.* 1922, **121**, 2882.
[220] L. A. Tschugaeff, *Ber.* 1908, **41**, 2222.

Platinum and palladium form a very large number of addition compounds of this type. The thioamides also form many addition compounds similar to those of the thioethers.

A different type of addition products of the thioethers is that of the sulphonium compounds, $[R_3S]X$, corresponding to the oxonium salts $[R_3O]X$: they are described below, p. 890.

Metallic Sulphides

These are sometimes covalent and sometimes ionized. As a rule, apart from those of the alkalies and alkaline earths, they are characterized by great, and often extreme, insolubility. It is obvious that while the sulphides of the non-metals are usually very unlike the oxides, the metallic compounds of the two classes show a much greater similarity. So far as the latter are ionized, this is of course necessary.

Britzke and Kaputinsky[221] have shown that the affinities of the metals for sulphur at 1,000° in any given period fall regularly from the first Group to the seventh, and in any Group from the lightest element to the heaviest.

Many sulphides are remarkable for showing not only a metallic glance (i.e. a reflection of light as good as that of a metal, 30–70 per cent.), but also metallic conduction.[222-3] This is true of PbS, Fe_7S_8, FeS_2 (pyrites), ZnS, NiS.

The half derivatives, the hydrosulphides, are known only with the alkalies and alkaline earths. Their hydration is very odd: Li, 0; Na, 2 and 3; K, 1/2.[224]

Polysulphides

Corresponding to each series of sulphides already discussed is a series of polysulphides, containing in place of a single sulphur atom a group of two, three, or even more. The production of relatively stable compounds of this kind is highly characteristic of sulphur, and also raises interesting questions of structure, since a covalent compound say A_2S_3 might have any of the structures

$$A\text{—}S\text{—}S\text{—}S\text{—}A, \quad A\text{—}S\text{—}\underset{\displaystyle S}{\overset{\displaystyle}{S}}\text{—}A \quad \text{or} \quad A\text{—}\underset{\displaystyle S}{\overset{\displaystyle S}{S}}\text{—}A.$$

Like the sulphides, the polysulphides may be divided into the hydrogen compounds, the alkyl derivatives, and the metallic salts.

Hydrogen Polysulphides

If a strong solution of sodium polysulphide, made by dissolving flowers of sulphur in sodium sulphide solution, and preferably in the proportions

[221] E. F. Britzke and A. F. Kaputinsky, *Z. anorg. Chem.* 1933, **213**, 73.
[222] J. G. Königsberger, *Z. Elektrochem.* 1909, **15**, 97.
[223] For the theory see J. Weiss and J. G. Königsberger, *Phys. Z.* 1909, **10**, 956.
[224] See, however, A. Rule, *J.C.S.* 1911, **99**, 558.

Na_4S_5, is run into cooled hydrochloric acid, a yellow oil separates, which is mainly a solution of sulphur in a mixture of the only isolated polysulphides of hydrogen, H_2S_2 and H_2S_3. They are both unstable, and decompose into H_2S and sulphur so readily, especially in presence of traces of alkali, that the calcium chloride used to dry them, and the apparatus in which they are distilled, must be previously treated with gaseous hydrogen chloride.[225-7] The two sulphides are then isolated by fractional distillation at low pressures.

Hydrogen Disulphide, H_2S_2[227]

Colourless liquid, melting at $-89°$, and boiling under atmospheric pressure at $71°$.

It is miscible with CS_2, benzene, and ether: it is rapidly decomposed by water, alcohol, alkalies, and sulphuric acid, but can be dried with P_2O_5. It dissolves sulphur, but is not thereby converted into the trisulphide. It gives a normal molecular weight by the freezing-point in bromoform.[228] Electron diffraction[229] gives as the most probable structure

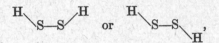

with the S—S distance $2 \cdot 05 \pm 0 \cdot 02$ A (theory $2 \cdot 08$); this agrees with the Raman spectrum,[230] which is just like that of H_2O_2. The dipole moment in benzene at $25°$ is $1 \cdot 17$ D,[231] which on the whole agrees with this structure assuming free rotation, though it is rather high.

Hydrogen Trisulphide, H_2S_3

Colourless or pale yellow oil, m. pt. $-52°$, b. pt. $50°/4$ mm. Molecular weight normal by freezing-point in benzene and in bromoform.

In general it is very like the disulphide. It is miscible with ether, benzene, and carbon disulphide. It seems to be rather more stable in the cold than the disulphide; like the latter it forms addition compounds with aldehydes and ketones, but they are less stable than those of H_2S_2.[232]

These two compounds are highly endothermic, are (according to Abegg, *Sulphur*, p. 275) weak acids, but stronger than hydrogen sulphide, and have a genuine resemblance to hydrogen peroxide, e.g. in their method of formation, in their sensitiveness to alkali, and in their power of forming

[225] I. Bloch and F. Höhn, *Ber.* 1908, **41**, 1971, 1975.

[226] R. Schenck and V. Falcke, ib. 2600 (these seem to be the latest references on the trisulphide).

[227] K. H. Butler and O. Maass, *J.A.C.S.* 1930, **52**, 2184 (disulphide).

[228] G. Bruni and A. Borgo, *Atti R.* 1909, [v] 18, i. 355.

[229] D. P. Stevenson and J. Y. Beach, *J.A.C.S.* 1938, **60**, 2872.

[230] F. Feher and M. Baudier, *Z. Elektrochem.* 1941, **47**, 844.

[231] C. P. Smyth, G. L. Lewis, A. J. Grossman, and F. B. Jennings, *J.A.C.S.* 1940, **62**, 1219.

[232] I. Bloch, F. Höhn, and G. Bugge, *J. pr. Chem.* 1910, [ii] **82**, 473, 486.

addition compounds, as well as in their spectra. The trisulphide very readily loses sulphur on heating to form the disulphide, suggesting that it is

$$\underset{\displaystyle S}{H—S—S—H} \;,$$

but the reverse reaction does not take place.

No hydride of sulphur beyond H_2S_3 can be isolated in the free state; but it is probable that hydrides with more sulphur occur (see p. 890), as their salts certainly do.

Organic Polysulphides[232a]

These are known with 2, 3, and 4 atoms of sulphur in the molecule (Alk_2S_2, Alk_2S_3, Alk_2S_4). In the *disulphides* the evidence is all in favour of a straight chain Alk—S—S—Alk. They are readily reduced to mercaptans: they are converted by alkali metals into the alkaline mercaptides, and the reaction with mercury

$$Alk_2S_2 + Hg \rightleftharpoons (Alk—S)_2Hg$$

is even reversible, so that we can hardly doubt that the two alkyls are attached to different sulphur atoms. This conclusion is also supported by the crystallographic evidence,[233] which gives the structure R—S—S—R for diphenyl and dibenzyl disulphides, as well as for the corresponding (and isomorphous) selenium compounds; and by the electron diffraction of dimethyl disulphide,[234] which indicates the structure CH_3—S—S—CH_3, with the distances S—S 2·02 and C—S 1·78 A (theory 2·08, 1·81) and the C—S—S angle $107\pm3°$. The dipole moments (e.g. 1·81 D for diphenyldisulphide)[235] agree with this, if we assume free rotation round the S—S line.[231]

With the *trisulphides* if the chain were branched as in

$$\underset{\displaystyle S}{Alk—S—S—Alk}$$

the dipole attraction of the co-ordinate link should cause an abnormal rise in the boiling-point as in the organic nitro-compounds. This, however, does not occur, as is shown by the boiling-points.

Me_2S	*Diff.*	Me_2S_2	*Diff.*	Me_2S_3
38°	78	116°	54	170°

The linear structure R—S—S—S—R, which this suggests, is supported

[232a] I. M. Dawson, A. McL. Mathieson, and J. M. Robertson, *J.C.S.* 1948, 322.
[233] L. Egartner, F. Halla, and R. Schacherl, *Z. physikal. Chem.* 1932, B **18**, 189.
[234] D. P. Stevenson and J. Y. Beach, *J.A.C.S.* 1938, **60**, 2872.
[235] E. Bergmann and M. Tchudnowsky, *Z. physikal. Chem.* 1932, B **17**, 107.

by the results of electron diffraction,[235a] which gives the distances C—S
1·78, S—S 2·04 A (theory 1·81, 2·08), and the angles C—S—S and S—S—S
both $104\pm5°$; and further by the X-ray evidence[232a] which indicates
unbranched sulphur chains up to S_5 in the bisulphonyl trisulphide

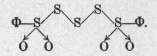

Aromatic sulphides with as many as 4 sulphur atoms, $Ar \cdot S_4 \cdot Ar$, are
known.[236] These are much less stable than the trisulphides, and readily
lose sulphur: for example, they are converted by mercury into the disulphides:

$$Ar \cdot S_4 \cdot Ar + Hg = Ar \cdot S_2 \cdot Ar + HgS + S.$$

This suggests that they may contain a branched chain of sulphur atoms.
Their boiling-points seem to be unknown.

Thioaldehydes and Thioketones

Of the numerous organic sulphur compounds, those which contain
oxygen or halogens (except carbon oxysulphide, below) are discussed
later, but the thioaldehydes and thioketones can be dealt with briefly here,
as well as carbon disulphide and its derivatives.

The thioaldehydes are remarkable for their strong tendency to polymerization, much stronger than that of their oxygen analogues. They are
scarcely known in the monomeric state; they polymerize at once, mainly to
cyclic tripolymers, such as trithioformaldehyde (Hofmann's trithiomethy-
lene, 1868)

$$CH_2 \underset{\diagdown S—CH_2}{\overset{\diagup S—CH_2}{\diagup}} S,$$

m. pt. 216°, which can be made from formaldehyde, sodium thiosulphate,
and hydrochloric acid; its ring structure has recently been established by
X-ray analysis.[237]

The aromatic thioaldehydes[238-9] and the thioketones polymerize with
the same ease. This much greater tendency to polymerization as compared
with the oxygen compounds is evidence that the strain of the double link
is much greater in C=S than in C=O, where it is very small.

Carbon Disulphide

This is formed (reversibly) when sulphur vapour is passed over red-hot
charcoal (Lampadius, 1796): it is practically insoluble in water, but
miscible with benzene, ether, or dry alcohol. It is endothermic (see below)

[235a] J. Donohue and V. Schomaker, *J. Chem. Phys.* 1948, **16**, 92.
[236] H. Lecher, *Ber.* 1925, **58**, 417.
[237] N. F. Moerman and E. H. Wiebenga, *Z. Krist.* 1937, **97**, 323.
[238] J. H. Wood and R. W. Bost, *J.A.C.S.* 1937, **59**, 1011.
[239] Id., ib. 1721.

and readily burns in air. It boils at $46\cdot2°$ and melts at $-111\cdot6°$. It catches fire in contact with a glass rod heated to $300°$; it is scarcely attacked by cold halogens, but is hydrolysed by alkalies in the cold, and by water at $400-500°$, giving carbon dioxide and hydrogen sulphide.

It has been shown[240] that there is no exchange between radioactive sulphur and CS_2 in a sealed tube at $100°$ in 68 hours; nor does such exchange occur with cysteine or thiourea.[241]

Carbon disulphide is evidence that a multiple link of sulphur to carbon is not impossible; but there must be resonance (as with carbon dioxide) between the three forms

$$S=C=S \qquad S\leftarrow C\lneqq S \qquad S\gneqq C\rightarrow S.$$

The heat of formation of CS_2 is -22 k.cals. (Bichowsky and Rossini), so that the heat of formation from the atoms (H_a) is 281 k.cals. per mole. The normal value for $C=S$ being 126, the resonance energy per CS_2 is $281-2\times126 = 29$ k.cals., practically the same as in CO_2.

Carbon Oxysulphide, $S=C=O$

This compound, discovered by A. Than in 1867, can be made by passing carbon monoxide and sulphur vapour through a red-hot tube, or by the action of water on carbon disulphide below $400°$. The rectilinear structure of the molecule has been denied,[242] but it was established by Eucken.[243-4] It melts at $-138\cdot8°$ and boils at $-50\cdot2°$; the heat of fusion is $1\cdot13$ k.cals./ mol. and that of evaporation $4\cdot432$, giving a Trouton constant of $19\cdot85$.[245]

The rate of hydrolysis of carbon oxysulphide in water, in alcohol, and in the gas have been examined by H. W. Thompson[246]; the last two reactions are much slower than would be expected from the heats of activation.

Carbon Monosulphide, CS

Indications of the formation of this compound from CS_2 under the electric discharge and in other ways were obtained by J. Dewar and H. O. Jones in 1910, and later by others.[247-8]

Kondrateev[249-50] claims to have made it in the gaseous form by the action of the electrical discharge on the vapour of carbon disulphide or a mixture of sulphur and paraffin vapour. It is detected by means of its absorption spectrum; it lives for about 10 minutes at room temperature, and 3 minutes at $100°$; the presence of oxygen does not affect its life.

[240] R. A. Cooley, D. M. Yost, and E. McMillan, *J.A.C.S.* 1939, **61**, 2970.
[241] J. L. Tuck, *J.C.S.* 1939, 1292.
[242] J. Wagner, *Z. physikal. Chem.* 1941, B **48**, 309.
[243] A. Eucken and K. Schäfer, ib. 1941, B **51**, 60, 126.
[244] A. Eucken and S. Aybar, ib. 1940, B **46**, 195.
[245] J. D. Kemp and W. F. Giauque, *J.A.C.S.* 1937, **59**, 79.
[246] H. W. Thompson, C. F. Kearton, and S. A. Lamb, *J.C.S.* 1935, 1033.
[247] A. Klemenc and E. Hayek, *Z. Elektrochem.* 1930, **36**, 722.
[248] K. Mayer and J. P. Wibaut, *Rec. Trav.* 1937, **56**, 359.
[249] V. Kondrateev and E. Magaziner, *J. Phys.-Chem. Russ.* 1940, **14**, 6.
[250] V. Kondrateev and A. Jakovleva, ib. 853.

Metallic Polysulphides

Numerous inorganic polysulphides are known, of the type $M_2'S_x$, or $M''S_x$, where x can have any value up to 5, and in exceptional cases up to 9 $((NH_4)_2S_9, 1/2\ H_2O)$. The hydrolysis of the alkaline polysulphides diminishes as the number of sulphur atoms increases. H. Mills and P. L. Robinson,[251] by treating dry $(NH_4)_2S_5$ with anhydrous formic acid, were able to isolate the acid H_2S_5 as a thin unstable yellow oil, which could not be distilled. For further work, see references [252-6].

It is clear that the ions S'', S_2'', S_3'', S_4'', S_5'' exist, of which S'' and S_4'' seem to be the most stable, and S_2'' and S_3'' the least.

Disulphides with a pyrites lattice have the sulphur atoms united in pairs, S—S forming a divalent group, so that in iron pyrites FeS_2 the metal is ferrous. The *trisulphide* BaS_3 has been shown by X-ray analysis[257] to have an anion of the structure S$\diagup$$\overset{S}{}$$\diagdown$S, with the S—S distance 2·15 A (theory 2·08) and the S—S—S angle 103°. The pentasulphide ion can scarcely be a 'perthiosulphate'

$$S \leftarrow \overset{\overset{\textstyle S}{\uparrow}}{\underset{\underset{\textstyle S}{\downarrow}}{S}} \rightarrow S,$$

since, if so, its salts would be those of a strong acid, whereas they are decomposed by formic acid, and they should readily be convertible into sulphates, whereas with lead oxide, for example, they give sulphides with separation of sulphur.

It has been shown[258] that the exchange between polysulphide ions and radioactive sulphide ions S^{--} is practically instantaneous and complete.

Sulphonium Compounds

Sulphur, like oxygen, is able to increase its valency by one by losing an electron, and so pass into a tricovalent cation $[R_3S]^+$, corresponding to the oxonium ion $[R_3O]^+$, but much more stable.

The sulphonium iodides are readily formed by the action of the alkyl iodides on the thioethers (for the kinetics of this reaction see refs. [259-60]), and readily return to these components on distillation. They can also be made by the action on a thioether of iodine or hydrogen iodide[261]:

$$2\ Alk_2S + HI\ =\ Alk_3SI + Alk\cdot SH$$
$$4\ Alk_2S +\ I_2\ =\ 2\ Alk_3SI + Alk_2S_2.$$

[251] *J.C.S.* 1928, 2326.

[252] T. G. Pearson and P. L. Robinson, ib. 1930, 1473 (Na salts).

[253] Id., ib. 1931, 413 (Li).   [254] Id., ib. 1304 (K).   [255] Id., ib. 1983 (Rb).

[256] P. L. Robinson and W. E. Scott, ib. 1931, 693 (Ca, Ba).

[257] W. S. Miller and A. J. King, *Z. Krist.* 1937, **94**, 439.

[258] H. H. Voge, *J.A.C.S.* 1939, **61**, 1032.

[259] J. K. Sirkin and I. T. Gladischev, *Acta phys. Chem. U.R.S.S.* 1935, **2**, 291.

[260] N. Hellström, *Z. physikal. Chem.* 1936, **177**, 337.

[261] G. Carrara, *Gaz.* 1892, **22**, 408.

They can also be prepared by treating alkyl halides with sulphur or metallic sulphides. This variety of methods of formation is a sign of their great stability. Bennett[262-3] has measured the rate of closure of the ring $Cl \cdot CH_2(CH_2)_n CH_2S \cdot Alk$ to form

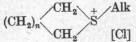

for rings of 5, 6, and 7 atoms ($n = 2, 3, 4$) and finds the relative rates of reaction to be

Size of ring	.	.	.	5	6	7
Rel. rate	.	.	.	5,700	75	1

The aromatic sulphonium compounds such as $[(C_6H_5)_3S]X$ (which of course cannot be made from the aryl halides) can be got, for example, from aromatic hydrocarbons and diaryl sulphoxides $Ar_2S \rightarrow O$ in presence of aluminium chloride.[264-5]

From these iodides a series of salts can be prepared. They are as a rule easily soluble in water, less in alcohol, and not in ether; there is no doubt about their salt character. With silver oxide the halides give the hydroxide $[R_3S]OH$, which is a strong base[266] and will dissolve aluminium with evolution of hydrogen.[267] It is a hygroscopic solid, which absorbs carbon dioxide from the air to give a carbonate.

The sulphonium compounds are the first by which the optical activity of sulphur derivatives was established. Pope and Peachey[268] resolved the camphor-sulphonate and the bromocamphor-sulphonate of methyl ethyl thetine

$$CH_3 \diagdown \;\;\;\;\; CH_2 \cdot COOH$$
$$\quad S$$
$$C_2H_5 \diagup \;\;\;\;\; [X]$$

and at the same time Smiles[269] resolved the compound

$$CH_3 \diagdown \;\;\;\;\; CH_2 \cdot CO \cdot C_6H_5$$
$$\quad S$$
$$C_2H_5 \diagup \;\;\;\;\; [X]$$

These results were of peculiar interest because it soon became obvious that these molecules only have three groups attached to the active centre, the fourth being a true ion. The discovery of the optically active sulphoxides

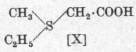

262 G. M. Bennett, F. Heathcoat, and A. N. Mosses, *J.C.S.* 1929, 2567.
263 G. M. Bennett and E. G. Turner, ib. 1938, 813.
264 E. Knoevenagel and J. Kenner, *Ber.* 1908, **41**, 3315.
265 C. Courtot and T. Y. Tung, *C.R.* 1933, **197**, 1227.
266 G. Bredig, *Z. physikal. Chem.* 1894, **13**, 302.
267 U. Alvisi, *Z. anorg. Chem.* 1897, **14**, 302, 308.
268 W. J. Pope and S. J. Peachey, *J.C.S.* 1900, **77**, 1072.
269 S. Smiles, ib. 1174.

(see later) made it certain that a 3-covalent sulphur atom could form an asymmetric molecule.

The sulphonium iodides, and even the hydroxides,[270] form addition compounds with methyl iodide, having one CH_3I for every sulphur atom.

The addition compounds of the thioethers with the halogens really belong to the class of sulphonium salts, as $[R_2SBr]Br$. They are soluble in water and almost completely hydrolysed to the sulphoxide R_2SO and hydrogen bromide. The same is true of the nitrate $[R_2SOH]NO_3$.

NITROGEN SULPHIDES

Several of these are known, as well as compounds containing in addition either hydrogen or halogens. Their structures are doubtful.

Nitrogen Sulphide, N_4S_4

This is formed by the action of sulphur on ammonia in the absence of water; the reaction

$$10\,S + 4\,NH_3 = N_4S_4 + 6\,H_2S$$

is reversible, and hence some sulphide-forming salt such as silver iodide must be added to remove the H_2S. In the same way it is produced by the action of ammonia on thionyl chloride $SOCl_2$ or sulphur chloride S_2Cl_2, the excess of hydrogen sulphide being in this case removed by interaction with the halide.

Nitrogen sulphide N_4S_4 forms golden yellow crystals, which turn red on heating: they melt at 178°, and can then be distilled, but the compound is endothermic and liable to explode, sometimes violently. It is moderately soluble in organic solvents. Its molecular weight is N_4S_4[271] by the melting-point in naphthalene and by the boiling-point in carbon disulphide. Its dipole moment in benzene solution at the ordinary temperature is 0·72 D.[272]

It is only slowly decomposed by water, which does not wet it. It is readily hydrolysed by alkali, the equation being[273-5a]:

$$S_4N_4 + 6\,NaOH + 3\,H_2O = Na_2S_2O_3 + 2\,Na_2SO_3 + 4\,NH_3.$$

N_4S_4 behaves in many ways as an unsaturated compound, and forms with halogens addition compounds such as

$N_4S_4Cl_4$	$N_4S_4Br_4$	$N_4S_4Br_6$
pale yellow	bronze	red

[270] See *Chem. Centr.* 1898, ii. 524.

[271] R. Schenck, *Ann.* 1896, **290**, 171.

[272] N. L. Phalnikar and B. V. Bhide, *Current Sci.* 1939, 8, 473.

[273] S. Wosnessensky, *J. Russ. Phys.-Chem. Ges.* 1927, **59**, 221; *Chem. Centr.* 1927, ii. 1680.

[274] A. Kurtenacker and E. Goldbuch, *Z. anorg. Chem.* 1927, **166**, 177.

[275] A. Meuwsen, *Ber.* 1929, **62**, 1959.

[275a] M. Goehring, *Chem. Ber.* 1947, **80**, 110.

It also reacts in water with lead iodide and with mercuric iodide to give respectively[276] PbN_2S_2,NH_3 and HgN_2S,NH_3.

It is quite clear that since decompositions and reductions always give ammonia or its derivatives, and never hydrazines or free nitrogen, the compound cannot have the nitrogen atoms linked to one another. Whether the sulphur atoms are linked is not so certain; Schenck has, however, shown[271] that secondary alkylamines convert all the sulphur in N_4S_4 into the thiodiamine $Alk_2N—S—NAlk_2$, which shows that the S—S links, if any, must be easily broken. The electron diffraction results[277] suggest a structure like that of realgar (V. 1774), a bisphenoid of S atoms with a square of 4 N atoms, the distances being N—S 1·62, S··S 2·09 (theory N—S 1·74, N=S 1·54, S—S 2·08); the nature of the links is uncertain. Meuwsen[275] has shown that the reduction product $(HNS)_x$, got by H. Wöbling[278] by treating N_4S_4 with $SnCl_2$, from its elevation of the boiling-point of acetone, must be $(HNS)_4$. This substance forms colourless crystals, stable to air and moisture, which on heating do not melt, but begin to change at 100°, and by 148° are completely decomposed, largely it would seem into ammonia and the original sulphide N_4S_4. It is scarcely soluble except in acetone, piperidine, and pyridine; it is only slowly attacked by acids or alkalies unless they are very concentrated. On treatment with concentrated alkali the whole of the nitrogen appears as ammonia, which is a further proof of the absence of N—N links.

The first question about this hydride is whether the hydrogen atoms are attached to nitrogen or to sulphur. Its resistance to fairly strong (even 3-normal) alkali makes the presence of N—H groups very improbable. On the other hand, it gives the Lecher test[279] for S—H, a deep yellow colour increasing on standing when it is treated with an alcoholic solution of ethyl nitrite. Stronger evidence of S—H groups is its giving with formaldehyde white crystals of $(NS \cdot CH_2OH)_4$. (The molecular weight was determined cryoscopically in benzene.) The analogy of many imino-compounds shows that if the hydrogen was on the nitrogen in $(HSN)_4$ it must give with formaldehyde $SN \cdot CH_2 \cdot NS$ or a polymer, just as diethyl-amine with formaldehyde gives $Et_2N \cdot CH_2 \cdot NEt_2$. If there are four S—H groups, and no N—N links, the only probable formula for $(HSN)_4$ would seem to be the following, which is that proposed by Meuwsen, except that co-ordinate links are written instead of double links:

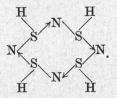

[276] O. Ruff and E. Geisel, *ib.* 1904, **37**, 1573.
[277] C. S. Lu and J. Donohue, *J.A.C.S.* 1944, **66**, 818.
[278] H. Wöbling, *Z. anorg. Chem.* 1908, **57**, 287.
[279] H. Lecher and W. Siefken, *Ber.* 1926, **59**, 2600.

An allied substance is $(SN \cdot Et)_4$, made by Stieglitz[280] from SCl_2 and $Et \cdot NH_2$, and found to have the right molecular weight; Meuwsen[281] has shown that this ethyl compound hydrolyses to give $Et \cdot NH_2$.

When N_4S_4 is heated with S_2Cl_2 in carbon tetrachloride it forms 'thio-trithiazyl chloride' $[N_3S_4]Cl$,[282-4] by the reaction

$$3 S_4N_4 + 2 S_2Cl_2 = 4 [N_3S_4]Cl.$$

With pure and dry materials a 90 per cent. yield can be got. This substance is undoubtedly a salt, and other salts can be made from it.

$[N_3S_4]Cl$ is a bright yellow powder, which is sternutatory. It is very stable in dry air, but explodes on heating. It is quite insoluble in many organic solvents (as CCl_4, CS_2, and ether) even on heating; others, such as chloroform, benzene, and acetone, decompose it.

This substance is only one of a series of similar derivatives which Meuwsen describes. Other sulphides of nitrogen are known, such as N_2S_5, formed when N_4S_4 is heated in solvents. It is a deep red oil, freezing at $+11°$ to a grey crystalline solid. It is rather less stable than N_4S_4.

Of the other S—N compounds the thiocyanic derivatives have already been dealt with under nitrogen (V. 674). The oxy-acids of sulphur, both the simple forms and their organic derivatives, yield amides, imides, etc. in the usual way. The amino-derivatives of sulphuric acid are of interest. All the three hydrogen atoms in ammonia can be successively replaced by SO_3 groups, giving the salts $M[H_2N \cdot SO_3]$, $M_2[HN(SO_3)_2]$, and $M_3[N(SO_3)_3]$. Some of these were discovered by Claus and Koch in 1869 and later examined by Divers and Haga in 1896. The crystal structure of the sulphamate $K[H_2N \cdot SO_3]$ has been determined by Brown and Cox,[285] who found that it has an almost tetrahedral anion with no hydrogen bridges between NH_2 groups; they get the distances S—O 1·44 (theory S—O 1·70, S=O 1·49) and N—S 1·57 (theory N—S 1·74, N=S 1·54 A.).

The salt $K_3[N(SO_3)_3]$ (potassium 'nitrilo-sulphite') is made[286] by heating potassium hydrogen sulphite with potassium nitrite. It is only slightly soluble in water, and is rapidly hydrolysed to the imido-disulphonate $K_2[HN(SO_3)_2]$, which then goes slowly to the sulphamate $K[H_2N \cdot SO_3]$.

SULPHUR AND OXYGEN

Six oxides of sulphur have been described, SO, S_2O_3, SO_2, SO_3, S_2O_7, and SO_4, of which S_2O_7 is doubtful.

Sulphur Monoxide S=O

This oxide, which has often been assumed to occur as an intermediate product in the formation of the oxy-acids of sulphur, was first detected

[280] F. Lengfeld and J. Stieglitz, *Ber.* 1895, **28**, 2742.

[281] A. Meuwsen, ib. 1931, **64**, 2301.

[282] E. A. Demarcay, *C.R.* 1880, **91**, 1066.

[283] A. Meuwsen, *Ber.* 1932, **65**, 1724.

[284] W. Muthmann and E. Seitter, ib. 1897, **30**, 627.

[285] C. J. Brown and E. G. Cox, *J.C.S.* 1940, 1.

[286] H. Sisler and L. F. Audrieth, *J.A.C.S.* 1938, **60**, 1947.

spectroscopically by Victor Henri,[287] but its preparation in quantity and the determination of its properties are almost wholly the work of Schenk and his pupils.[288-301]

Sulphur monoxide can be made by the action of the electric discharge on (1) sulphur dioxide, or (2) a mixture of the dioxide and sulphur, (3) by the regulated combustion of sulphur in oxygen, or (4) by the action of heat, or of certain metals, especially silver, on thionyl chloride $SOCl_2$. Method (1)[287-8,302] can give a good yield if it is used in an appropriate apparatus.[296] Method (2) gives at 150–200° almost pure SO; the thermal reaction of S on SO_2 gives very little, even at high temperatures.[303,306] By the third method $(S+O_2)$ at 10 mm. a mixture with 40 per cent. SO is said to be obtainable.[293] (4) Sulphur monoxide is also formed, but in very small quantity, by the action on thionyl chloride of metals which have a greater affinity for chlorine than for oxygen, especially silver; smaller yields are given by sodium, tin, and antimony; other metals reduce the chloride to chlorides of sulphur[292] (for the action of ammonia see ref. [300]). Heat alone will cause dissociation of $SOCl_2$ into SO and chlorine, as the spectra show.[297]

There are several reactions in which sulphur monoxide has been assumed to be formed but cannot in fact be detected; an example is the decomposition of hyposulphite and thiosulphate.[307] Another is the formation of pentathionate from H_2S+SO_2,[308] where Raschig assumed two reactions to occur:

$$H_2S + SO_2 = H_2O + S + SO;$$
$$5\ SO + H_2O = H_2S_5O_6.$$

It can, however, be shown that the reaction of sulphur monoxide with water is too slow to account for its observed absence from the gas; hence

[287] V. Henri and H. Wolff, *J. Phys. Radium*, 1929, [vi] 10, 81.

[288] P. W. Schenk, *Z. anorg. Chem.* 1933, 211, 150.

[289] H. Cordes and P. W. Schenk, *Z. Elektrochem.* 1933, 39, 594.

[290] E. Kondrateeva and V. Kondrateev, *J. phys. Chem. Russ.* 1944, 18, 102.

[291] H. Cordes and P. W. Schenk, *Z. anorg. Chem.* 1933, 214, 33.

[292] P. W. Schenk and H. Platz, ib. 215, 113.

[293] P. W. Schenk, ib. 1934, 220, 268.

[294] P. W. Schenk and H. Platz, ib. 1935, 222, 177.

[295] N. M. Emanuel, *Bull. Acad. Sci. U.R.S.S.* 1942, 36, 145.

[296] P. W. Schenk, *Z. anorg. Chem.* 1937, 233, 385.

[297] P. W. Schenk and H. Triebel, ib. 1936, 229, 305.

[298] P. W. Schenk, ib. 1941, 248, 297.

[299] Id., *Z. Elektrochem.* 1941, 47, 855. [300] Id., *Ber.* 1942, 75, 94.

[301] Id., *Z. physikal. Chem.* 1942, B 51, 113.

[302] V. Kondrateev and A. Jakovleva, *J. phys. Chem. Russ.* 1940, 14, 859.

[303] C. W. Montgomery and L. S. Kassel, *J. Chem. Phys.* 1934, 2, 417.

[304] H. Cordes, *Z. Phys.* 1937, 105, 251.

[305] E. Kondrateeva and V. Kondrateev, *J. phys. Chem. Russ.* 1940, 14, 1528.

[306] H. Zeise, *Z. physikal. Chem.* 1942, B 51, 120.

[307] O. v. Deines and G. Elstner, *Z. anorg. Chem.* 1930, 191, 340.

[308] F. Raschig, *Schwefel- und Stick-Stoffstudien*, p. 284.

the mechanism assumed by Foerster[309] and Hansen,[310] in which SO takes no part, is more probable. Again it was supposed[311] that SO is formed in the decomposition of the sesquioxide S_2O_3 (see below, p. 900), but the gas over the decomposing solid gave no trace of the spectrum of SO.

The very characteristic spectrum by which sulphur monoxide was first detected has been said[304] to be that of an unstable S_2 molecule, but this cannot be so, since it is only observed when oxygen is present.[301,305]

Properties of Sulphur Monoxide

These have a certain resemblance to those of a free radical like methyl. But the SO molecule has a much longer life; at pressures in the neighbourhood of 1 mm. and in well cleaned and dried vessels the gas persists for days in the cold with only slight decomposition.[291] After heating for 5 minutes to 100°, or 1 minute to 180° some still remains. But if it is concentrated, either by compressing the gas above a few mm., or by freezing it out with liquid air, it at once polymerizes irreversibly, giving an orange solid which has the composition of about S_2O,[296] and on heating to 100° gives off all its oxygen as SO and SO_2, leaving sulphur behind. There seem to be several polymerization products; a liquid polymer[298-9] has a molecular weight of 700–900 in CCl_4, and reacts with chlorine to give $SOCl_2$, so it must contain SO groups; it is probably a mixture of highly polymerized oxides.

Sulphur monoxide is not affected by dry oxygen [290] or sulphur dioxide,[291] but it is very sensitive to catalysts, especially traces of moisture, and it reacts at once with metallic mercury, iron, or copper. Its reaction with water has been examined with care.[294-5] It seems that the solid polymer at once gives thiosulphuric acid, whence it has been supposed to be the anhydride of this, $S{\leftarrow}S{\overset{\displaystyle O}{\underset{\displaystyle O}{<}}}$. When the gas (with nitrogen as carrier) is passed into water or alkali it gives sulphurous acid, H_2S, and (with alkali but not with water) thiosulphuric acid. With alcoholic potash, nothing is formed but sulphide and sulphite in the proportions required by the equation

$$3\ SO + H_2O = 2\ SO_2 + H_2S.$$

Soper has shown [312] that in sulphuric acid solution both nitrous and nitric acids are reduced irreversibly by sulphur monoxide to nitrogen.

The very peculiar properties of this substance are clearly due to the instability of the double bond with sulphur. The $S{=}O$ molecule is half-way between $O{=}O$, which is stable up to very high temperatures, and $S{=}S$, which below 800° C. goes over spontaneously into the singly linked (as we know from the distances) polymeric S_8. The observations of Schenk would

[309] F. Foerster and A. Hornig, *Z. anorg. Chem.* 1922, **125**, 86.

[310] C. J. Hansen, *Ber.* 1933, **66**, 1000.

[311] L. Wöhler and O. Wegwitz, *Z. anorg. Chem.* 1933, **213**, 129.

[312] C. J. Wilkins and F. G. Soper, *J.C.S.* 1939, 600.

seem to indicate that in the gas there is a reversible polymerization to a low, probably a double, polymer S_2O_2: this must be reversible, since there is no evidence that the gas is completely polymerized on standing at the ordinary temperature.[313] On the other hand, when the gas is frozen out, it is clear that an irreversible polymerization occurs.

Sulphur Dioxide

Sulphur dioxide is a colourless gas, melting at $-75.5°$ and boiling at $-10.02°$[314] (the values given by Faraday in 1845 were: m.pt. $-76.1°$, b.pt. $-10°$). The liquid is practically a non-conductor (specific conductivity at $0°$ between 1 and 0.5×10^{-7}, according to Walden and Centnerszwer (1902), Dutoit (1909), Franklin (1911), Bruner and Galecki (1913)). Other physical properties are given below, p. 898; they indicate, as does the relatively high boiling-point (compare SF_6, subliming point under 1 atm. $-64°$), that in the liquid there is considerable intermolecular attraction, but they give no sign of actual association.

The finite dipole moment (1.61 D) of the gaseous molecule shows that

it cannot be linear, but must have the structure $S{\Large\langle}^{O}_{O}$ suggested by

Langmuir in 1919,[315] and with resonance between the two states. This is confirmed by electron diffraction,[316] which gives the S—O distance as 1.43 A (theory S—O 1.70, S=O 1.49: the shortening is much greater here than in ozone, where we have (p. 861) O—O obs. 1.29, theory O—O 1.32, O=O 1.10); the angle is found to be $120 \pm 5°$, in good agreement with the value $121 \pm 5°$ derived from the spectrum and the entropy.

This structure is entirely in accordance with the intense absorption band in the ultra-violet (like that of ozone), and with the properties of the dioxide, which are those of a donor, as in the very similar nitro-group,

$$R—N{\Large\langle}^{O}_{O} \; ;$$

the S=O double link which is so unstable in the monoxide S=O is here stabilized by the resonance.[317]

Sulphur Dioxide as a Solvent

Liquid sulphur dioxide is an excellent solvent for a great variety of substances, as has been shown especially by Walden (see in particular P. Walden and M. Centnerszwer)[318-19] and recently by Jander and his

[313] P. W. Schenk, *Z. physikal. Chem.* 1942, B **52**, 295.

[314] W. F. Giauque and C. C. Stephenson, *J.A.C.S.* 1938, **60**, 1389.

[315] I. Langmuir, ib. 1919, **41**, 868.

[316] V. Schomaker and D. F. Stevenson, ib. 1940, **62**, 1270.

[317] G. M. Phillips, J. S. Hunter, and L. E. Sutton, *J.C.S.* 1945, 146.

[318] P. Walden and M. Centnerszwer, *Ber.* 1899, **32**, 2862; *Z. anorg. Chem.* 1902, **30**, 145.

[319] Id., *Z. physikal. Chem.* 1903, **42**, 432.

collaborators).[320-9] It will dissolve both organic and inorganic substances, and gives conducting solutions not only of salts and acids, but also of various covalent molecules such as chlorine, bromine, antimony penta-chloride, and acetyl chloride and bromide. With amines it forms (at least in solution) addition compounds such as $Et_3N{\rightarrow}SO_2$ (monomeric and slightly ionized in the SO_2 solution).[329a] Jander[320] gives a comparison of the physical properties of sulphur dioxide with those of ammonia and water; the most important of these (supplemented by values from Giauque and Stephenson[314]) are as follows:

	NH_3	H_2O	SO_2
Mol. wt.	17	18	64
Mol. vol./b. pt. . . .	25	19	44
M. pt.	$-77\cdot7°$	$0°$	$-75\cdot5°$
B. pt.	$-33\cdot4°$	$+100°$	$-10\cdot02°$
Crit. temp.	$132\cdot5°$	$374\cdot1°$	$157\cdot5°$
Ht. of evapn. . . .	5·60 k.cals.	9·65	5·96
Trouton	23·4	25·9	22·7
Sp. cond^y, Ohm^{-1} at m. pt. .	5×10^{-9}	60×10^{-9}	80×10^{-9}
Diel. const. . . .	$22/-34°$	$81/+18°$	$13\cdot5/+15°$
Dip. mom., gas . . .	1·48	1·84	1·61 D

Liquid SO_2 is partially miscible with water; at $22°$[330] 10 g. SO_2 will dissolve 2·3 g. water, and 100 g. water 49·1 g. SO_2; at $0°$ a crystalline solid SO_2,H_2O separates, which decomposes at $12°$ and may be

Liquid SO_2 is completely miscible with benzene,[334] but only partially with paraffins and some cyclic hydrocarbons, having the critical solution tem-peratures[331] (with normal paraffins) $C_5H_{12}+2°$; $C_{12}H_{26}$ $47°$; cyclohexane $12°$; hexahydromesitylene $30\cdot5°$.

Salts are as a rule less soluble in SO_2 than in water; thus the solubilities in g. per 100 g. solvent of the alkaline sulphites in SO_2 at $0°$, with the corresponding values for the hydroxides in water at $25°$, are:

in SO_2 at $0°$	Li_2SO_3	Na_2SO_3	K_2SO_3	Rb_2SO_3	Cs_2SO_3
	..	0·026	0·035	0·040	0·047

in H_2O at $25°$	LiOH	NaOH	KOH	RbOH	CsOH
	12·8	114·1	118	174·7	288

The order is the same for both (as it is for other weak acid salts in water). The solubilities of most salts are from 10^{-3} to 10^{-2} molar; exceptions are potassium bromide 2·81/100 at $0°$ (= 0·34 molar) and still more potassium

[320] G. Jander and K. Wickert, *Z. physikal. Chem.* 1936, **178**, 57.

[321] Id., *Ber.* 1937, **70**, 251.

[322] G. Jander and D. Ullmann, *Z. anorg. Chem.* 1937, **230**, 405.

[323] G. Jander, H. Knöll, and H. Immig, ib. 1937, **232**, 229.

[324] G. Jander and H. Ruppolt, *Z. physikal. Chem.* 1937, **179**, 43.

iodide (41·3 = 3·56 molar at 0°); iodides of the type MI are as a rule very soluble; molecular weight determinations by rise of boiling-point[329] showed that non-electrolytes, including the thionyl halides, are monomeric; electrolytes, especially thiocyanates, are more or less dissociated; binary electrolytes are shown by their conductivities to be much less dissociated than in water (the D.E.C. is only one-sixth) and to reach the limiting value of 2 for van't Hoff's i only at high dilution; the limiting mobilities are additive.

Many reactions can be carried out in sulphur dioxide solution. It is not exactly a reducing agent, as halogens can be recovered from it unchanged, and potassium iodide can be oxidized in it by ferric chloride with separation of iodine; aluminium sulphite is amphoteric in SO_2 as aluminium hydroxide is in water.

The exact nature of the ions in sulphur dioxide solution is by no means certain, and the relation between the conductivity and the degree of dissociation of the solute as measured by the freezing- and boiling-point is often complicated and obscure. It is, however, clear that the ionizing power depends, as it always does, not merely on the rather high dielectric constant (13·5 at 15°) of the liquid, but also on its power of solvating the ions: an exceptionally good ionizing solvent must always have an exceptional power of solvation.

This is confirmed by the large number of addition compounds of sulphur dioxide that have been isolated, both with salts[319,324,327,338-9] and with organic substances.[332-4,336,340-1] The triphenylmethyl halides, which are themselves colourless, give coloured and conducting solutions in SO_2, and with some of them, such as tri(diphenyl)methyl chloride, a solid compound, in this case $(\Phi \cdot C_6H_4)_3C \cdot Cl$, $4 SO_2$, is formed.[337] With salts the tendency to form solid solvates is greater the more soluble the salts (as with hydrates in water); most of the known solvates (see ref. [319]) are formed by the iodides, and a few by thiocyanates; they range in colour from yellow or brown to bright red, and in composition from $2 A$, SO_2 to A, $6 SO_2$. The

[325] G. Jander and H. Immig, *Z. anorg. Chem.* 1937, **233**, 295.
[326] G. Jander, *Naturwiss.* 1938, **26**, 779.
[327] G. Jander and H. Mesech, *Z. physikal. Chem.* 1938, **183**, 121.
[328] Id., ib. 255. [329] Id., ib. 277.
[329a] L. C. Bateman, E. D. Hughes, and C. K. Ingold, *J.C.S.* 1944, 243.
[330] K. Wickert, *Z. anorg. Chem.* 1938, **239**, 89.
[331] R. T. Leslie, *J. Res. Nat. Bur. Stand.* 1934, **13**, 589.
[332] A. E. Hill and T. B. Fitzgerald, *J.A.C.S.* 1935, **57**, 250.
[333] H. W. Foote and J. Fleischer, ib. 1934, **56**, 870.
[334] W. F. Seyer and E. G. King, ib. 1933, **55**, 3140.
[335] A. B. Burg, ib. 1943, **65**, 1629.
[336] N. F. Albertson and W. C. Fernelius, ib. 1687.
[337] W. Schlenk, T. Weickel, and A. Herzenstein, *Ann.* 1910, **372**, 10.
[338] F. Ephraim and J. Kornblum, *Ber.* 1916, **49**, 2007.
[339] F. Ephraim and C. Aellig, *Helv. Chim. Acta*, 1923, **6**, 37.
[340] F. J. Glavis, L. L. Ryden, and C. S. Marvel, *J.A.C.S.* 1937, **59**, 707.
[341] G. H. Locket, *J.C.S.* 1932, 1501.

organic solvates are mostly formed by amines[335] or by unsaturated or aromatic hydrocarbons, and a few also by ketones.

The reaction of hydrogen sulphide with sulphur dioxide to form sulphur[342] occurs very rapidly in water, alcohols, ketones, and amines, but very slowly in hydrocarbons and their halides, mercaptans, and thioethers; it seems to depend on the formation by the H_2S of an S—H··X bridge.

Sulphur Sesquioxide, S_2O_3

Powdered sulphur reacts with liquid sulphur trioxide with some violence to give a blue-green solid. This was supposed by its discoverer Stein[343] to be a solid solution of sulphur in the trioxide; but Weber[344] recognized that it was a new oxide of sulphur of the composition S_2O_3. This conclusion was confirmed by Vogel and Partington[345] and further by Wöhler and Wegwitz,[346] who, however, corrected some of Vogel and Partington's conclusions as to its reactions.

It is prepared by adding finely powdered pure dry sulphur to freshly distilled SO_3, which must be quite free from water (i.e. from H_2SO_4) so that it remains in the volatile form. The sesquioxide is then quite insoluble in the excess of SO_3, part of which can be poured off and the rest removed in a stream of CO_2 at 40°. In presence of sulphuric acid, however, it dissolves to form a greenish solution.

The sesquioxide is a blue-green solid, which decomposes by itself at the ordinary temperature, slowly at 15°, but more rapidly on warming, to give three products, elementary sulphur, SO_2 and SO_3. Schenk has shown[292] that in its dry decomposition sulphur monoxide is not formed, as it was thought to be. There is no solvent in which it dissolves without reaction. With sodium methylate, ethylate, or hydroxide it is decomposed to give (not, as was thought[345] the sulphoxylate Na_2SO_2, but) mixtures in varying proportions of free sulphur, and sodium sulphate, thiosulphate, and trithionate.

The non-volatility of the sesquioxide shows that it must be highly polymerized, but we have no evidence on which to base a structure.

Sulphur Trioxide, SO_3

Sulphur trioxide can be made in various ways; by the distillation of ferrous sulphate or of fuming sulphuric acid; by the action of light or an electric discharge on sulphur dioxide, or more often on a mixture of the dioxide and oxygen; the latter reaction can also be brought about by catalysts, especially platinum, as in the contact process for making sulphuric acid.

[342] N. F. Albertson and J. P. McReynolds, *J.A.C.S.* 1943, **65**, 1690.
[343] W. Stein, *J. prakt. Chem.* 1873, ii. **6**, 178.
[344] R. Weber, *Pogg. Ann.* 1875, **156**, 531.
[345] A. I. Vogel and J. R. Partington, *J.C.S.* 1925, **127**, 1514.
[346] L. Wöhler and O. Wegwitz, *Z. anorg. Chem.* 1933, **213**, 129.

The physical behaviour of sulphur trioxide is very complicated, and even now, after a great deal of investigation, is not fully understood.[355]

It is very volatile; its vapour is monomeric[349] and the dipole moment (as measured in the gas from 80° to 160° C.) is zero,[352] so that the molecule must be planar; this conclusion is supported by the Raman spectrum[354,357]; at lower temperatures the vapour seems to polymerize to some extent.[353] On cooling, the vapour condenses to a liquid which boils at 44·5° C. The heat of evaporation is 10·2 k.cals.[348,351-2], which makes the Trouton constant 32·1; at 16·8°[348-9,356] it freezes to large ice-like crystals, known as the α-form. Ordinarily the liquid soon deposits a felted mass of long feathery crystals (or apparent crystals), and ultimately goes over into this familiar form (the β-form) completely; this change, however, only occurs if the liquid contains a trace of water (or H_2SO_4): it can be prevented (certainly for weeks) by adding phosphorus pentoxide, or even by distilling the trioxide alone, when the acid is left behind. One molecule of water is able to polymerize at least several thousand molecules of SO_3.[348]

The liquid from which the α-form crystallizes, which is also produced slowly by heating the other forms, must itself be complex. It has the abnormally high coefficient of expansion with temperature of 1/448 per degree (more than half that of gas) which suggests an internal equilibrium much affected by temperature. This is confirmed by the parachor,[348,359] which rises from 100·3 at 19·0° to 111·3 at 78° (calculated for $O{=}S{\Large\langle}{}^{O}_{O}$

129·0). The enormous value (32·1) of the Trouton constant indicates high polymerization. The strongest evidence is the unique behaviour of the vapour pressure on freezing (Le Blanc,[349] Smits[350]). The results vary slightly, but Le Blanc's mean values were these. At 20° the vapour pressure of the liquid was 185 mm., and it fell in the usual way to 133·6 mm. at 13·9°; the liquid (m. pt. 16·7°) then froze, and the pressure rose quickly to 175·3 mm., and stayed there for 30 minutes. In another experiment it was 128·5 mm. at 13·9°; the liquid froze and its temperature rose to 16·7°; after cooling to 13·9° again the pressure was 149·1 mm. Smits got

[347] H. Giran, *C.R.* 1913, **157**, 221.

[348] A. Berthoud, *Helv. Chim. Acta*, 1922, **5**, 513.

[349] M. Le Blanc and C. Rühle, *Ber. Sächs. Akad. Wiss.* 1922, **74**, 106.

[350] A. Smits and P. Schoenmaker, *J.C.S.* 1924, **125**, 2554; 1926, 1108, 1603.

[351] R. Grau and W. A. Roth, *Z. anorg. Chem.* 1930, **188**, 173.

[352] A. Smits, N. F. Moerman, and J. C. Pathuis, *Z. physikal. Chem.* 1937, B **35**, 60.

[353] For the thermodynamic properties of the vapour see W. H. Stockmayer, G. M. Kavanagh, and H. S. Mickley, *J. Chem. Phys.* 1944, **12**, 408.

[354] H. Gerding, W. J. Nijveld, and G. J. Muller, *Z. physikal. Chem.* 1937, **B 35**, 193.

[355] P. Baumgarten (*Angew. Chem.* 1942, **55**, 115) has a lecture on SO_3.

[356] D. M. Lichty, *J.A.C.S.* 1912, **34**, 1440.

[357] H. Gerding and J. Lecomte, *Nature*, 1938, **142**, 718.

[358] H. H. Voge, *J.A.C.S.* 1939, **61**, 1032.

[359] A. N. Campbell and N. O. Smith, *Trans. Far. Soc.* 1937, **33**, 545.

the same effect from the side of the solid; its vapour pressure just below
the melting-point was always higher than that of the liquid just above
that point. The only possible explanation seems to be that the liquid
consists of (at least) two forms A and B, whose interconversion is slow,
the more volatile A having the lower freezing-point. The supercooled
liquid has a vapour pressure mainly due to A, but reduced by the solute B.
On freezing, it is chiefly B that separates, and the residual liquid, being A
with less B in it, has a higher vapour pressure. Smits's results would seem
to imply that the solid on complete solidification is a eutectic mixture.

The feathery β-form if warmed to any temperature above 29·7° is
converted in a few hours into an apparently clear liquid, but this mainly
consists of a doubly refracting jelly, from which more liquid can be
squeezed out by violent shaking, and which slowly diminishes on heating
to higher temperatures. This third or γ-form was discovered by Giran.[347]
If the α- with traces of H_2SO_4, or the β-form, is kept in a sealed tube at
temperatures below 29·7°, the ultimate product from the α- (as from the β-)
is the β-form. But at any temperature above 29·7° it is a mixture of the
liquid and the jelly, so that the β-form may be said to melt sharply at 29·7°
if it is given time enough (nearly all the changes of SO_3 seem to be slow).

Thus we have three solid forms, of which certainly the γ- and probably
the β- are colloidal and so mixtures of forms, while the liquid and perhaps
the solid α- must contain at least two modifications.

Little can be said of their structures. For a simple SO_3 molecule, such
as we probably[352,357] have in the vapour, three are possible:

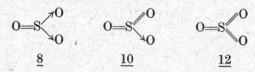

Valency Group   <u>8</u>   <u>10</u>   <u>12</u>

All these are permissible, and the actual state will be a resonance hybrid
of all three, the first two having resonance also between the double and the
single bonds. In the absence of evidence the structures of the various
polymers is unknown; the strong tendency to polymerize is a sign of the
instability of the S=O double link. There is a certain similarity, especially
in the physical nature of the polymers, between sulphur trioxide and
formaldehyde.

Sulphur trioxide is reasonably stable to heat, but is broken up into the
dioxide and oxygen on passing through a red-hot tube. Voge[358] has shown
by the use of radioactive sulphur that the trioxide and the dioxide begin
to exchange sulphur at about 300°, where presumably the trioxide begins
to dissociate.

Chemically sulphur trioxide is a powerful oxidizing agent, particularly
at high temperatures. It will oxidize hydrogen bromide, phosphorus, and
many metals, especially iron and zinc. It takes up water with great energy
(21·3 k.cals.), and a drop of water acts on the solid explosively. The
solution of sulphur trioxide in sulphuric acid is known as fuming sulphuric

acid or oleum (see below). The trioxide combines with hydrogen chloride to give chlorosulphonic acid HSO_3Cl. With organic compounds it readily forms sulphonic derivatives; with aromatic hydrocarbons, especially in presence of sulphuric acid, it gives mono- and poly-sulphonic acids. With alcohol it forms 'carbyl sulphate',[360] which is

$$CH_2-O-SO_2 \atop CH_2-\!-\!-SO_2 \Big\rangle O,$$

the anhydride of ethionic acid.

Sulphur Heptoxide, S_2O_7

This was first obtained by Berthelot[361] by the action of the electric discharge on a mixture of oxygen or ozone with sulphur di- or trioxide; its existence was later confirmed by Meyer, Bailleul, and Henkel.[362] It is a non-volatile white crystalline deposit, which on exposure to moist air soon explodes. The analyses varied from SO_3, $SO_4(S_2O_7)$ to SO_3, $2SO_4$ (S_3O_{11}); they think it is a mixture of SO_3 and SO_4, but it has since been shown (see below) that SO_4 evolves oxygen at $+3°$. The chemical individuality of S_2O_7 is thus doubtful. The method of formation (in which the effective reaction seems to be between the trioxide and ozone) and many of the reactions point to its having a peroxide —O—O— group; but otherwise its structure is unknown.

Sulphur Tetroxide, SO_4

This was made by Schwarz and Achenbach[363] by the same method as the heptoxide, but with excess of oxygen mixed with the SO_2 and SO_3, and a longer exposure to the discharge. It can also be made[364] as a 75 per cent. gaseous mixture with SO_3, by passing SO_2+O_2 through an ozonizer. It is[363] a white solid of the composition SO_4 and on heating melts at $+3°$, evolving oxygen and leaving a liquid of the composition S_2O_7; in water it is a powerful oxidizing agent, converting divalent to heptavalent manganese, and aniline to nitrobenzene. The aqueous solution slowly evolves oxygen, but gives no reactions for hydrogen peroxide, and so cannot contain the monoperacid (Caro's acid) H_2SO_5; hence the tetroxide is not the anhydride of this acid. According to Fichter and Maritz[364] if dissolved in alkali it gives the salt of the acid $H_2S_2O_8$. Except that it must contain a peroxide group —O—O— its structure is unknown.

[360] R. Hübner, *Ann.* 1884, **223**, 210.
[361] M. Berthelot, *Ann. Chim. Phys.* 1878, [5] **14**, 345; *C.R.* 1880, **90**, 269, 331; 1891, **112**, 1418.
[362] F. Meyer, G. Bailleul, and G. Henkel, *Ber.* 1922, **55**, 2923.
[363] R. Schwarz and H. Achenbach, *Z. anorg. Chem.* 1934, **219**, 271.
[364] F. Fichter and A. Maritz, *Helv. Chim. Acta*, 1939, **22**, 792.

OXY-ACIDS OF SULPHUR AND THEIR ORGANIC DERIVATIVES

THERE are at least twelve oxy-acids of sulphur, besides condensed forms like pyrosulphuric $H_2S_2O_7$. The simplest method of classification is to regard them as derived from three substances, (A) the compound $S(OH)_2$ (Sulphoxylic acid) and the products of its co-ordination with (B) one and (C) two oxygen atoms. We thus get

(A) 1. Sulphoxylic acid

(B) 2. Sulphurous acid

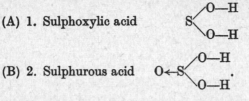

The condensation of these two gives us

3. Hydrosulphurous acid

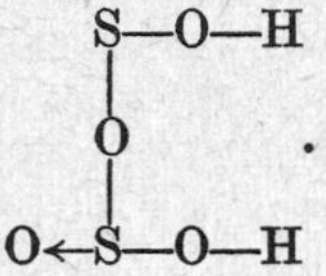

Sulphurous acid also forms

4. Thiosulphurous acid

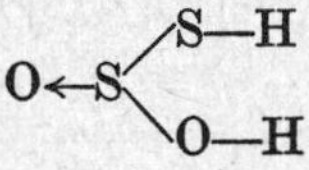

(C) 5. Sulphuric acid

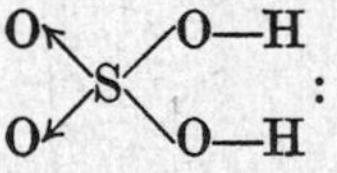

giving rise to

6. Thiosulphuric acid

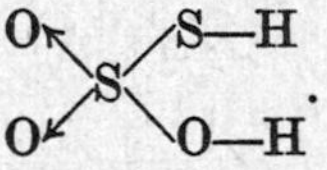

7, 8, 9, 10, and possibly 11: the thionic acids $H_2S_nO_6$, where $n = 2, 3, 4, 5$, and perhaps 6. These may be provisionally formulated as

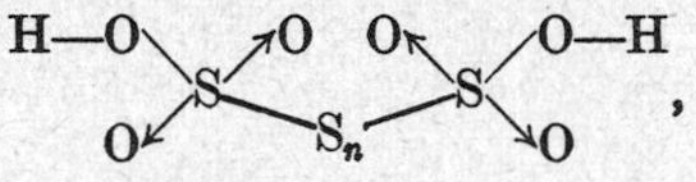

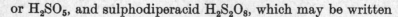

with $x = 0, 1, 2, 3$, and probably 4.

Finally, we have the two per-acids, with an O—O link,

(12) Caro's acid

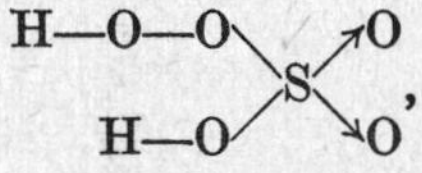

or H_2SO_5, and sulphodiperacid $H_2S_2O_8$, which may be written

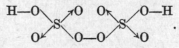

Sulphoxylic Acid, H—O—S—O—H

This might be expected to be a very stable molecule, but it is in fact very unstable, and is known only in the form of a single[365] salt, the cobaltous, together with a peculiar ester-salt and its esters.

The only known salt, cobaltous sulphoxylate Co[O—S—O], is made[366] by treating sodium hydrosulphite solution $Na_2S_2O_4$ with cobaltous acetate, and adding excess of ammonia, when the acid is broken up into a sulphite and sulphoxylate—the best proof of the structure of hydrosulphurous acid (see p. 907)—thus:

$$CoS_2O_4 + 2\,NH_4OH = CoSO_2 + H_2O + (NH_4)_2SO_3.$$

On saturating the solution with carbon dioxide a brown precipitate is formed, which is shown by determination of the cobalt, the sulphur, and the reducing power, to be cobalt sulphoxylate $CoSO_2$. Attempts to form the salts of other heavy metals failed. When Na_2S was added to the cobaltous solution, the cobalt was all precipitated as sulphide, but the resulting solution had no reducing power: it was shown to contain thiosulphate, obviously formed by the reaction

$$2\,Na_2SO_2 + H_2O = Na_2S_2O_3 + 2\,NaOH.$$

When the $CoSO_2$ solution is boiled it gives CoS, S, SO_2, and SO_3.

This salt cannot be the hydrosulphite of univalent cobalt $Co_2'S_2O_4$, since on treatment with concentrated acids it at once gives cobaltous salts without any evolution of hydrogen, and also when treated in solution with hydrochloric acid it at once gives a precipitate of cobalt sulphide CoS, whereas the mixture of $CoAc_2$ and $Na_2S_2O_4$ which has not been treated with ammonia (i.e. which is still the undecomposed hydrosulphite) gives with hydrochloric acid no cobalt sulphide but only a precipitate of free sulphur.

An aldehyde derivative, which is properly an ester-salt, is formed[368] by the action of formaldehyde and alkali on a hydrosulphite:

$$O{\Large\langle}\genfrac{}{}{0pt}{}{S\text{—}O\cdot Na}{SO\text{—}O\cdot Na} + O{\Large\langle}\genfrac{}{}{0pt}{}{H}{H} + \genfrac{}{}{0pt}{}{CH_2O}{CH_2O} = H_2C{\Large\langle}\genfrac{}{}{0pt}{}{OH}{O\cdot SO\cdot Na} + H_2C{\Large\langle}\genfrac{}{}{0pt}{}{OH}{O\cdot SO_2\cdot Na}$$

(giving oxymethyl sulphoxylate and oxymethyl sulphite). This sodium salt is known as Rongalite, and is used commercially in dyeing to reduce the dyes to their soluble leuco-compounds, which are then reoxidized on the fibre.

The sulphoxylic esters can be made[367] by the catalytic decomposition with sodium ethylate of the symmetrical esters of thiosulphurous acid

[365] The supposed alkaline sulphoxylates (I. A. Vogel and J. R. Partington, *J.C.* 1925, **127**, 1514) have been shown not to exist.
[366] R. Scholder and G. Denk, *Z. anorg. Chem.* 1935, **222**, 17.
[367] A. Meuwsen and H. Gebhardt, *Ber.* 1936, **69**, 937.
[368] K. Reinking, E. Dehnel, and H. Labhardt, ib. 1905, **38**, 1069.

(p. 912), such as Et—O—S—S—O—Et; the reaction presumably goes in two stages:

$$R—O—S—S—O—R \longrightarrow R—O—S—O—R$$
$$+ Na \cdot O—R \quad\quad + R—O—S \cdot Na \longrightarrow R—O \cdot Na + S.$$

This ethyl ester boils at 35°/32 mm., and at 117°/733 mm. It is a colourless liquid with an unpleasant smell, which is insoluble in water. It can be shown by analysis to contain two ethoxy-groups, which settles the structure. Also the only other at all probable structure, that of a sulphinate

was shown to be impossible by preparing that ester (p. 922) and proving that it was different: its boiling-point is nearly 30° higher (owing to the co-ordinate link), being 60°/13 mm., it is soluble in water (no doubt for the same reason) and it is stable to oxidizing agents.

Ethyl sulphoxylate is very easily oxidized, even by oxygen at the ordinary temperature in 30 hours; more rapidly by NO_2, $KMnO_4$, and SeO_2. None of these oxidizing agents—not even ozone—will convert it into ethyl sulphate: they all give ethyl sulphite, which none of them can oxidize to ethyl sulphate, though of course they all oxidize the SO_3'' ion readily to SO_4''.

On hydrolysis the ester is converted mainly into the thiosulphate, with some sulphide and sulphate: but no salts of sulphoxylic acid could be isolated, nor even an ester salt.

The structure of these compounds is clear, but their behaviour, and especially their instability and their extreme readiness to oxidize, are very remarkable.

Hydrosulphurous Acid*, $H_2S_2O_4$

The hydrosulphites are made by the reduction of sulphites, usually with zinc; they can also be made[369] by shaking sodium or potassium amalgam with dry sulphur dioxide. They are powerful reducing agents, and will convert, for example, cupric or mercuric salts into the metal with the formation of the sulphite. They are much used (especially the sodium salt) as reducing agents in the dyeing industry. In solution all the salts, and especially those of divalent metals like barium or lead,[381] are very unstable. In the air they oxidize to sulphites, and in its absence they soon decompose to form sulphites, thiosulphates, and free sulphur. This is due to two reactions, one going essentially in neutral or alkaline solution[371] and the other in acid solution, where thiosulphates cannot exist:

$$2\,Na_2S_2O_4 = Na_2S_2O_3 + Na_2S_2O_5 \text{ (pyrosulphite)}$$
$$2\,H_2S_2O_4 = 3\,SO_2 + S + 2\,H_2O.$$

* This name is better than the more obvious hyposulphurous acid (used e.g. by Abegg, *Sulphur*, 1927), as it avoids confusion with the old name for thiosulphates. (Dithionous acid is also used.)

[369] L. Rougeot, *C.R.* 1946, **222**, 1497.

Dry sodium hydrosulphite undergoes a remarkable reaction on heating.[370,375] At about 190° it suddenly evolves SO_2, and the residue has entirely lost its reducing power, being a mixture of sodium sulphite and thiosulphate. This reaction is strongly exothermic, evolving 10·35 k.cals. per $Na_2S_2O_4$.

The structure of this acid has been much disputed, but agreement seems to have been reached. There was for some time a doubt whether the formula was $H[SO_2]$ or $H_2[S_2O_4]$; the absence of acid salts seemed to support the former. But measurements of the freezing-points and conductivities of the salts showed[371-2] that the double formula must be accepted. The final proof was given by Klemm,[373] who showed that the sodium salt was diamagnetic. For $H_2S_2O_4$ the symmetrical structure[374]

$$\begin{array}{c} H\!-\!O\!-\!S\!\rightarrow\!O \\ | \\ H\!-\!O\!-\!S\!\rightarrow\!O \end{array},$$

that of a sort of disulphinic acid, though not impossible in itself, is incompatible with the behaviour of the acid; it does not explain the strong reducing power, which neither the sulphinic acids nor the S—S compounds possess, and further, if it were correct the salts should oxidize to dithionates $MO_3S\!-\!SO_3M$, whereas they never give dithionates, but on the contrary are readily oxidized either wet or dry to sulphites and pyrosulphites. This close relation to H_2SO_3 suggests the formula of a mixed 'anhydride' of sulphurous and sulphoxylic acids[376]

$$H\!-\!O\!-\!S\!-\!O\!-\!S\!\!\begin{array}{c} \nearrow O \\ \searrow O\!-\!H \end{array},$$

which is strongly supported by the fact[370] already mentioned above (p. 905), that hydrosulphurous acid can be hydrolysed in presence of cobalt salts into the sulphite and the sulphoxylate. The behaviour of the hydrosulphites is exactly what one would expect from such a 'mixed anhydride', though it is difficult to see why this mixed form should be, as it certainly is, more stable than the simple sulphoxylate.

Sulphurous Acid, H_2SO_3

Sulphur dioxide dissolves readily in water (some 10 per cent. by weight at 20° and 1 atm.), forming this acid; the hydration appears to be instantaneous,[377-9] unlike that of CO_2. The absorption spectrum suggests that the non-ionized part of the solute is partly in the non-hydrated form, as with NH_3. Sulphurous acid is a fairly strong acid; the apparent dissocia-

[370] R. Scholder and G. Dank, *Z. anorg. Chem.* 1935, **222**, 17, 41, 48.

[371] J. Meyer, ib. 1903, **34**, 43.   [372] K. Jellinek, ib. 1911, **70**, 93.

[373] L. Klemm, ib. 1937, **231**, 136.   [374] M. Bazlen, *Ber.* 1927, **60**, 1470.

[375] O. v. Deines and G. Elstner, *Z. anorg. Chem.* 1930, **191**, 340.

[376] H. T. Bucherer and A. Schwalbe, *Ber.* 1906, **39**, 2814.

[377] K. Schaefer, *Z. anorg. Chem.* 1918, **104**, 212.

[378] C. S. Garrett, *J.C.S.* 1915, **107**, 1324.

[379] R. Dietzel and S. Galanos, *Z. Elektrochem.* 1925, **31**, 466.

tion constants (i.e. on the assumption that all the unionized sulphur is present as H_2SO_3) are $K_1 = 0.013/25°$[380] and $K_2 = 1 \times 10^{-7}$.[381]   Thus the first dissociation constant is rather weaker than that of dichloracetic acid (0.05).

Sulphurous acid is a strong reducing agent; if it is heated with water in absence of air it oxidizes itself, forming sulphuric acid and free sulphur. In presence of air the solution is oxidized, gradually even in the cold, to sulphuric acid or a sulphate; this reaction is enormously retarded by the presence of small traces of certain organic substances such as isopropyl or benzyl alcohol,[382] owing, as is now clear, to the shortening of reaction chains.

A solution of sulphurous acid or a sulphite can effect a whole series of reductions, but it can also under some conditions act as an oxidizing agent, being reduced to elementary sulphur; its oxidizing is much weaker than its reducing power, but is strengthened by addition of excess of acid: it is able to oxidize ferrous salts to ferric, and mercurous to mercuric.[383-8]

Although free sulphurous acid cannot be isolated, any more than nitrous or carbonic, it is clearly H_2SO_3, and has two possible tautomeric (not resonance) formulae giving the same ion

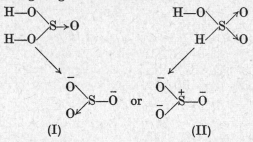

(I)   (II)

It has been shown by the X-ray examination of Na_2SO_3[389] that the SO_3 ion has a pyramidal structure (like the chlorate ion ClO_3'), as the above formula requires.

The two forms of the acid are, of course, inseparable, but they give rise to two isomeric series of esters (I) the symmetrical true sulphites, and (II) what should properly be called esters of alkyl-sulphonic acids:

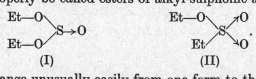

(I)   (II)

These esters change unusually easily from one form to the other.

[380] H. F. Johnstone and P. W. Leppla, *J.A.C.S.* 1934, **56**, 2233.
[381] I. M. Kolthoff, *Z. anorg. Chem.* 1919, **109**, 69.
[382] H. N. Alyea and H. L. Bäckström, *J.A.C.S.* 1929, **51**, 90.
[383] W. Wardlaw *et al.*, *J.C.S.* 1920, **117**, 1093, 1241.
[384] Id., ib. 1922, **121**, 1481.   [385] Id., ib. 1923, **123**, 969, 3417.
[386] S. R. Carter, *J.S.C.I.* 1926, **45**, 207.   [387] W. Wardlaw, ib. 210.
[388] S. R. Carter and F. James, *J.C.S.* 1924, **125**, 2231.
[389] W. H. Zachariasen and H. E. Buckley, *Phys. Rev.* 1931, **37**, 1295.

It was once thought that mixed salts, such as $NaKSO_3$, could occur in two isomeric forms, one with one metal attached to the sulphur, and the other with the other. This idea, which was not confirmed experimentally,[391] implies that the metal is covalently attached to the sulphur, which is intrinsically very improbable with an alkali metal, and has been disproved by showing that Na_2SO_3 has the conductivity to be expected of a normal 3-ionic salt.

Two series of salts are known, (1) the normal sulphites $M_2'SO_3$, $M''SO_3$; (2) the bisulphites $M'HSO_3$, which by loss of water are converted into the pyrosulphites $M_2'S_2O_5$.

The normal sulphites are as a rule rather insoluble salts, except those of the alkalies, which dissolve readily; the bisulphites, on the other hand, are usually soluble, especially those of the alkalies and the alkaline earths. Owing to the weakness of the second dissociation constant of sulphurous acid, the normal sulphites have an alkaline and the bisulphites a neutral reaction. The metabisulphite ion S_2O_5'' has been shown by X-ray examination[390] to have the structure

$$\begin{array}{c} \overline{O} \diagdown \qquad \diagup \overline{O} \\ \qquad S-S \rightarrow O. \\ O \diagup \qquad \diagdown O \end{array}$$

The sulphites are very reactive. In addition to being oxidizable to sulphates, they can be reduced by zinc to hydrosulphites, or further reduced, by treatment with carbon or metals at a high temperature, to sulphides. The solutions dissolve sulphur to form thiosulphates. The familiar bisulphite compound of acetaldehyde

$$\begin{array}{c} CH_3 \diagdown \qquad \diagup SO_3M \\ \qquad C \\ H \diagup \qquad \diagdown OH \end{array}$$

has been shown[392] to have a C—S link, since by treatment with ammonia and then nitrosyl chloride it can be converted into $CH_3 \cdot CHCl—SO_3H$, which is also obtainable from the trimer $(CH_3 \cdot CHS)_3$.

Complex Sulphites

Sulphurous acid forms a large number of complex salts,[393] containing as central atoms especially the metals

Mn	Fe	Co	Ni	Cu	Zn
	Ru	Rh	Pd	Ag	Cd
	Os	Ir	Pt	Au	Hg

as well as Be and Mg; these are the metals (with the addition of Fe, Ru, Os) which have been found (above, p. 884) to give complexes with the

[390] Wells, *S.I.C.* p. 305. [391] G. S. Fraps, *Am. Chem. J.* 1900, **23**, 202.
[392] R. L. Shriner and A. H. Land, *J. Org. Chem.* 1941, **6**, 888.
[393] For a summary, see Werner, *Neu. Ansch.* ed. 5 (Pfeiffer), p. 120.

thioethers. That some at least of these salts are true complexes has been proved experimentally. Thus Barth[394] showed that in the mercury salts, $M_2'[Hg(SO_3)_2]$ the mercury is not ionized, and is not precipitated by alkalies, phosphates, etc. It is a true complex acid, giving Na, K, Ag, Sr, and Ba salts. So, too, with the unusually soluble trisulphito - cobalt salt $Na_3[Co(SO_3)_3]$, $4 H_2O$; the cobalt migrates on electrolysis to the positive pole.[395]

There are four possible structures for these complex sulphito-anions:

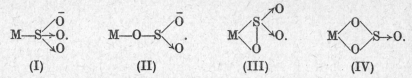

(I)	(II)	(III)	(IV)

(III) may be disregarded, since no chelate 3-ring ato-compounds are known, no doubt on account of the strain. It should be possible to decide between (I) or (II) and (IV), from the number of places occupied by the SO_3 in the complex. This number is usually 2, as is seen in such salts as $M_2[Pt(SO_3)_2]$, H_2O $(M = Na, NH_4)$ and $M_3'[M'''(SO_3)_3]$ $(M = Co, Rh, Ir)$, as well as mixed salts like $K_3[IrCl_4SO_3]$ and especially $[Co(en)_2SO_3]Cl$, which closely resembles the carbonato-compound. These may be taken to have structure IV; the fact that their central atoms are those which form thioether complexes must be due to some other cause than a M—S link. On the other hand, some ammine sulphito-complexes, especially of cobalt, are pentammines, in which the SO_3 can only occupy one place,[396] and must have the structure (I) or (II). The mercuric salts $M_2[Hg(SO_3)_2]$ are exceptional, and almost certainly have structure (I); the attachment of mercury is normally much stronger to sulphur than to oxygen, and with mercury (but with scarcely any other metal) a covalency of 2 with a shared quartet of electrons is especially stable.

Sulphurous Esters

The true esters of sulphurous acid,

must be distinguished from the isomeric alkyl-sulphonic esters, in which one alkyl group is attached directly to sulphur,

The true esters can be made by the action of alcohol on thionyl chloride

$$O \leftarrow S \begin{smallmatrix} Cl \\ \\ Cl \end{smallmatrix}$$

[394] K. Barth, *Z. physikal. Chem.* 1892, **9**, 176.
[395] G. Jantsch and K. Abresch, *Z. anorg. Chem.* 1929, **179**, 345.
[396] E. H. Riesenfeld, ib., 1924, **132**, 99.

or sulphur monochloride S_2Cl_2. They have the normal molecular weights in benzene solution by the freezing-point (for a full account of their properties see refs. [397-8]). Their boiling-points, with those of the isomeric sulphonic esters, and of the rather similarly constituted carbonates are:

Boiling-points

	R—O\\ R—O/ C=O	Diff.	R—O\\ R—O/ S→O	Diff.	R—O\\ R/ S ↗O ↘O
R = CH₃	90°	31·5°	121·5°	81·5°	203°
C₂H₅	127°	34°	161°	52·4°	213·4°
C₃H₇	168°	26°	194°	..	..

The marked rise in going from the sulphite to the isomeric sulphonate is no doubt due to the introduction of a second co-ordinate link with its large dipole moment. The rise from carbonate to sulphite is smaller, presumably because the carbonate is a resonance hybrid with the co-ordinated form

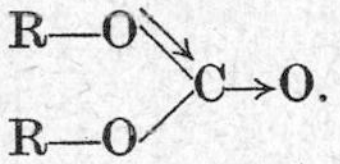

$$\begin{matrix} R—O \\ \diagdown \\ C{\to}O. \\ \diagup \\ R—O \end{matrix}$$

The sulphonic esters are rapidly saponified by alkalies to the salts of the alkyl-sulphonic acids $R \cdot SO_2 \cdot O[M]$, but the sulphites are only saponified very slowly, and then they give these same alkyl-sulphonic salts by an isomeric change:

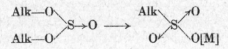

although the alkyl-sulphite salts

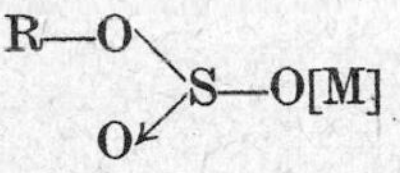

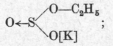

actually exist, and can be made by the action of sulphur dioxide on sodium alkylate.

This tautomeric change to the sulphonate can also be brought about with the true ethyl-alkali-sulphites, as

$$O{\leftarrow}S\begin{matrix} O—C_2H_5 \\ \\ O[K] \end{matrix};$$

these can be easily hydrolysed in the normal way to potassium sulphite (showing that the alkyl group is not directly attached to the sulphur) but they can also be converted (without hydrolysis) into the salts of the

[397] A. Rosenheim and W. Sarow, *Ber.* 1905, **38**, 1298.
[398] R. Levaillant, *Ann. Chim.* 1936, [xi] **6**, 459–581.

alkyl-sulphonic acid, by treatment in neutral solution with alkaline iodide, bromide, or thiocyanate, which can form complexes of the composition $(Alk—SO_2 \cdot OM)_4, KI$ (or NaBr, or NaCNS); these three salts will also combine with sulphur dioxide, the first giving $(SO_2)_4, KI$.[399]

Voss has shown[400-1] that the normal esters $(Alk \cdot O)_2 SO$ are good alkylating agents, converting carboxylic acids into their esters, and even alkylating the nitrogen in amino-acids.

Thiosulphurous Acid, H—O—S—S—O—H

This is known only in the form of esters: the salts decompose as soon as the esters are hydrolysed.[404] The esters are formed[402-6] by the action of dry sodium alkylate on sulphur monochloride S_2Cl_2 in ligroin solution. (A supposed second series of isomeric esters[403] does not exist.)[404-5] They have been shown to have the simple molecular weight in benzene solution:[403] the boiling-points are[403] $(CH_3 \cdot O \cdot S)_2$ 33°/15 mm., $(C_2H_5OS)_2$ 67°/16 mm. They can also be shown by the method of Vieböck[407] to contain two alkyloxy-groups in the molecule. This gives two possible formulae

$$R \cdot O—S—S—O—R \qquad\qquad \begin{matrix} R \cdot O \\ \\ R \cdot O \end{matrix} \Big\rangle S{\to}S$$

$$\text{(I)} \qquad\qquad\qquad\qquad \text{(II)}$$

between which it is difficult to decide. (They are isomeric with the known thio-esters of the sulphonic acids $R \cdot SO_2 \cdot S \cdot R$.) The stability to oxidation is remarkable: they are not oxidized by atmospheric oxygen or by selenium dioxide; this suggests that the S—S group has some unknown source of stability in these compounds. But they are rapidly hydrolysed by alkalies to give thiosulphates and free sulphur, probably by the two reactions

$$\text{ROS} \cdot \text{SOR} \longrightarrow \text{RO} \cdot \text{SK} + \text{RO} \cdot \text{S} \cdot \text{OH}$$
$$\longrightarrow \text{RO} \cdot \text{K} + \text{S} + \text{K}_2\text{S}_2\text{O}_3.$$

In presence of traces of dry sodium alkylate the esters undergo a very peculiar reaction

$$\begin{matrix} \text{RO} \cdot \text{S—S} \cdot \text{OR} \\ + \text{Na} \cdot \text{OR} \end{matrix} = \text{RO} \cdot \text{S[Na]} + \text{S(OR)}_2$$
$$\downarrow$$
$$\text{RO[Na]} + \text{S}$$

already mentioned under sulphoxylic acid, the alkylate being regenerated, and the ultimate products being free sulphur and the ester of sulphoxylic acid.[406]

[399] P. Walden and M. Centnerszwer, *Z. physikal. Chem.* 1903, **42**, 432.

[400] W. Voss and E. Blanke, *Ann.* 1931, **485**, 258.

[401] W. Voss and H. Vulkan, *Ber.* 1937, **70**, 388.

[402] F. Langfeld, ib. 1895; **28**, 449.   [403] A. Meuwsen, ib. 1935, **68**, 121.

[404] H. Stamm, ib. 673.   [405] A. Meuwsen, ib. 1936, **69**, 935.

[406] A. Meuwsen and H. Gebhardt, ib. 937.

[407] F. Vieböck and A. Schwappach, ib. 1930, **63**, 2818.

Sulphuric Acid, H_2SO_4

This is the most stable of all the oxy-compounds of sulphur. The following solid phases are formed by sulphur trioxide and water in various proportions (with melting-points):

$H_2SO_4, 3SO_3 + 4°$	$H_2SO_4 + 10°$ (b. pt. 320°)
$H_2SO_4, SO_3 + 36°$	$H_2SO_4, H_2O + 9°$
$3H_2SO_4, SO_3$?	$H_2SO_4, 2H_2O - 38·9°$
	$H_2SO_4, 4H_2O - 29°$

The so-called 100 per cent. sulphuric acid, though its melting-point comes, as it must, on the top of a curve (at $+10°$), is partly dissociated in the liquid state into SO_3 and perhaps the mono-hydrate. According to Domke and Bein[408] the presence of free SO_3 begins at about 98 per cent., which is where the acid begins to fume in air. The 100 per cent. acid has a definite electrical conductivity, and behaves like a fused salt rather than like an ordinary low melting covalent substance.

The properties of 'absolute' (i.e. 100 per cent.) sulphuric acid as a solvent have been investigated especially by Hantzsch.[409-11] It is a good solvent for many substances, but will not dissolve the halogens, halogen hydrides, phosphoric, or phosphorous acid, I_2O_5, CrO_3, TeO_2 (As_2O_3 and $HgCl_2$ only on heating), or aromatic and aliphatic hydrocarbons and their halides. The freezing-points and conductivities indicate that while some solutes give normal molecular weights, most of them are dissociated. Normal (undissociated) values are given by tellurium, oxalic, picric, and trichloracetic acids, methyl sulphate, phthalic anhydride, and many polynitrobenzenes. Abnormal (dissociated) molecular weights are found with boron trioxide: sulphates of the alkali metals, and of ammonium, thallous thallium, and barium: organic amines and amides, cyanic acid, water, alcohols and ethers, fatty esters, aldehydes, mono- and dicarboxylic acids. Apart from the sulphates, the conductivity must be due to the formation of oxonium salts, such as $[H_3O](SO_4H)$.

There are three possible structures for the monomeric H_2SO_4 molecule, which no doubt is really a resonance hybrid:

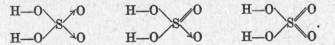

The properties agree far more closely with the first of these. There is no sign of its forming an 'ortho' acid H_4SO_5 or H_6SO_6, either in its salts or in its esters. In this it resembles selenic but strikingly differs from telluric acid, which appears to exist only in the form $Te(OH)_6$ (p. 983). This is

[408] J. Domke and W. Bein, *Z. anorg. Chem.* 1905, **43**, 125.

[409] A. Hantzsch, *Z. physikal. Chem.* 1908, **61**, 293.

[410] F. Bergius, ib. 1910, **72**, 338.

[411] See also G. Oddo and E. Scandaola, ib. 1908, **62**, 243; *Gaz.* 1909, **39**, ii. 1, 44; 1918, **48**, ii. 163; O. and A. Casalino, ib. 1917, **47**, ii. 200, 232; Oddo, ib. 1917, **48**, i. 17.

presumably due to the greater stability of the octet (as opposed to the duodecet) with the lighter element. This co-ordinated structure for sulphuric acid (its ion was actually the first molecule for which a co-ordinated structure was proposed (G. N. Lewis, 1916)), is also in accordance with all the evidence for the reluctance of sulphur to form double links. Evidence is accumulating that the $S \rightarrow O$ link has a good deal of $S=O$ character in it.

The SO_4 ion has been shown in an enormous number of X-ray examinations of sulphates to have the four O atoms at the points of an almost regular tetrahedron (slightly distorted by the attraction of the cation). The distance between the central atom and the oxygen is (in all AO_4 ions) much less than the single link requires, owing to the resonance with the doubly-linked forms. Pauling [412] gives the following values:

	Si—O in SiO_4^{---}	P—O in PO_4^{---}	S—O in SO_4^{--}	Cl—O in ClO_4^-
Observed . .	1·60	1·55	1·51	1·48
Radius sum . .	1·83	1·76	1·70	1·65
Difference . .	−0·23	−0·21	−0·19	−0·17

The mean shortening is 0·20 A; a double link $A=O$ would require a shortening of about 0·21 A, but the resonance shortening must of course be added (see further, p. 1039 below)

With radioactive sulphur it has been shown[413] that SO_4'' ions do not exchange sulphur with SO_3'' or S'' ions in 36 hours at 100°.

Both the free acid, as we all know, and also its salts, have a strong tendency to take up water. With the free acid this may be explained in two ways, probably both true, as due to the attachment by co-ordination of water to the oxygen of the anion, or to the hydration of the free hydrogen ion. Only an X-ray examination of the solid hydrates of the acid could prove the method of attachment; that the linkage is strong is shown both by the very low pressure of dilute solutions of water in the acid, and by the high melting-point of the monohydrate (+9°). The hydration of the SO_4 anion is shown by the frequency with which we find an odd number of molecules of water of crystallization in sulphates: e.g. the vitriols, $M''SO_4, 7 H_2O$ ($M'' = Mn''$, Co″, Ni, Zn, Fe″): copper sulphate, $CuSO_4$, 5·3·1 H_2O, with one molecule of water very difficult to remove, and cuprammonium sulphate, $[Cu(NH_3)_4]SO_4,H_2O$. It is at least probable that in all these salts one molecule of water is attached to the SO_4, leaving the usual 4 or 6 to hydrate the cation. In the particular cases of $CuSO_4$, 5 H_2O,[414] and $NiSO_4, 7H_2O$[415] this conclusion has been supported by X-ray evidence.

The 'simple' sulphates (those with the compositions of binary salts) have several peculiarities. The solubility in water tends (especially at

---

[412] *Chemical Bond*, p. 240.   [413] H. H. Voge, *J.A.C.S.* 1939, **61**, 1032.
[414] C. A. Beevers and H. Lipson, *Proc. Roy. Soc.* 1934, **146**, 570.
[415] C. A. Beevers and C. M. Schwartz, *Z. Krist.* 1935, **91**, 157.

higher temperatures) to fall as the temperature rises. This is a familiar property of anhydrous sodium sulphate; it is found with the sulphates of the following cations (the water of crystallization, if any, is appended in brackets): Li (1 H_2O: from 0° upwards); Na,Cu″ (3 H_2O: only above 140°); Zn (1); Cd (1); Y, La (9); Ce‴ (9, 8, 5, and 4); Yb (8); Th (4); U^{iv} (4); Mn″ (1), and Fe″ (1). It does not occur, so far as is known, with the sulphates of K, Rb, Cs, Ag′, Be, Mg, Ba, Tl′, Pb″, Co″, or Ni.

Again the sulphates, especially those with polyvalent cations, are very ready to form supersaturated solutions. Thus the solubility of anhydrous thorium sulphate (IV. 639) can be measured at 0°, though it is more than 44 times as soluble as the stable enneahydrate. Tetravalent uranium sulphate $U(SO_4)_2$ is similar, and so are the sulphates of trivalent vanadium, chromium, iron, and divalent titanium.

This is sometimes due to the presence of two different forms in solution, one of which must be complex. Thus the anhydrous forms of the last four sulphates will not dissolve in water or sulphuric acid (as the hydrated will), but only in boiling concentrated nitric acid. Again, trivalent rhodium sulphate $Rh_2(SO_4)_3$ (VIII. 1519) has a normal yellow form, and also a red form, from the solutions of which barium chloride does not precipitate the anion, nor potassium hydroxide the cation. The chromic salt is similar (VI. 1013).

The double sulphates form a large group of salts, whose structures are often very difficult to determine. The two most famous series are the alums, $M'M'''(SO_4)_2$, $12 H_2O$, and the double salts of vitriols, $M'_2M''(SO_4)_2$, $6 H_2O$ (Schönite series). The alums have already been discussed under aluminium (III. 427); the crystal structures show that they are not true complex salts at all, since six of the $12 H_2O$ molecules are grouped round the aluminium ion. A mixed alum, isomorphous with the true alums, has been obtained of the formula K_2BeF_4, $Al_2(SO_4)_3$, $24 H_2O$.[418]

The same is probably true of the vitriols, although our knowledge of their structures is less certain. Benrath[416-17] has obtained from solutions of mixed sulphates $M''SO_4 + M'_2SO_4$ the following series of double sulphates, all of the type $M''SO_4 \cdot M'_2SO_4$, $x H_2O$, with these values of x: Mg, Tl′; Zn, Tl′; Zn, NH_4 6; Cd, Rb 2, 6; Cd, K; Co, Na; Ni, Na 4.

At the same time it is clear that in some complexes the SO_4 group is covalently attached to the central atom. Werner pointed out that it sometimes occupies one co-ordination place, as in

$$A—O—S\substack{\nearrow O \\ \rightarrow O, \\ \searrow O}$$

and sometimes two, as in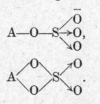

[416] A. Benrath, *Z. anorg. Chem.* 1931, **202**, 161.
[417] A. Benrath and C. Thönessen, ib. 1932, **203**, 405.
[418] W. R. C. Curjel, *Nature*, 1929, **123**, 206.

Only by this assumption can we reconcile the compositions of many complex salts with the established co-ordination numbers of the central atoms. For example, the sulphate group must occupy one place in $[(NH_3)_5CoSO_4]X$ and in the platinic salt $[(NH_3)_4PtBr(SO_4)]X$, and two in $[en_2Co(SO_4)]X$ and $[(NH_3)_4Pt(SO_4)]X_2$. The best evidence of complex 'sulphato' formation is when the SO_4 cannot be precipitated from the salt solution by barium chloride. This occurs, as we have seen, with the simple rhodium and chromium sulphates, with the chromisulphates, such as

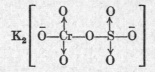

—dichromates in which one chromium is replaced by sulphur—and also with the double iridium salt $K_3[Ir(SO_4)_3]$, H_2O.

The acid sulphates $MHSO_4$ are converted on heating into the pyro-sulphates $M_2'S_2O_7$, which on further heating lose SO_3. The pyrosulphate obviously has a S—O—S link, and this seems to hydrolyse in water at once.

It is even possible to make a trisulphate $M_2S_3O_{10}$, corresponding to the trichromates $M_2Cr_3O_{10}$. Potassium sulphate reacts[419] with excess of sulphur trioxide at 50° to give $K_2S_3O_{10}$; the presence of traces of water (i.e. of bisulphate) seem to hasten this. The salt gives a characteristic X-ray pattern. It does not begin to lose sulphur trioxide till 150°; but it is at once decomposed by water to give potassium acid sulphate $KHSO_4$. A similar sodium salt $Na_2S_3O_{10}$ has been made.[420]

Alkyl Sulphates

	M. pt.	B. pt.
$(CH_3)_2SO_4$	−27°	188°
$(C_2H_5)_2SO_4$	−24·5°	208°

The alkyl sulphates are formed by the action of alcohol on sulphur trioxide, oleum, or chlorosulphonic acid, or by heating the half esters, such as ethyl hydrogen sulphate (from ethyl alcohol and sulphuric acid) to a high temperature.

These esters, especially methyl sulphate, are of great value in organic chemistry for the alkylation of hydroxylic groups by heating alone or in presence of alkali. Methyl sulphate was supposed to have a very poisonous effect on the lungs, but this can be avoided with care.

The cyclic esters of diatomic alcohols are of considerable interest.[421]

[419] P. Baumgarten and E. Thilo, *Ber.* 1938, **71**, 2596.
[420] E. Zintl and H. Roessler, ib. 1939, **72**, 191.
[421] W. Baker, *J.C.S.* 1931, 1765; W. Baker and F. B. Field, ib. 1932, 86.

Methylene sulphate can be made by the action of oleum on paraformaldehyde, and like methyl sulphate will form methylene esters either by its direction action on glycols, or with phenols by reaction in benzene in presence of solid potassium carbonate; in this way such compounds as

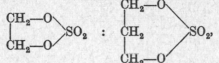 $(CH_2)_n$ ...CH$_2$ and $C_6H_5 \cdot O \cdot CH_2 \cdot O \cdot C_6H_5$ can be made.

The properties of methylene sulphate show that it can scarcely have the simple formula CH_2SO_4. Thus it melts without perceptible vapour pressure at 155°, while methyl sulphate melts at $-27°$ and boils under atmospheric pressure at 188°, only 33° higher than the melting-point of the methylene compound. In benzene solution it probably (the solubility is small) has the double formula. Ethylene and trimethylene sulphates, made from the glycol and methylene sulphate, have lower melting-points ($C_2H_4SO_4$ 90°; $C_3H_6SO_4$ 63°), and have the simple molecular weights in benzene by the freezing-point. They clearly have simple rings of 5 and 6 atoms respectively,

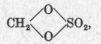

but the 4-ring required for the monomeric methylene compound

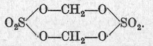

involves too much strain, and accordingly the double molecule is formed, with an 8-ring (not chelate)

For the same reasons of strain glyoxal sulphate $CH \cdot CH(SO_4)_2$, which is made by the action of oleum on acetylene tetrachloride $C_2H_2Cl_4$ in presence of mercury or copper salts and melts at 176–7°,[422] must have structure (I) with a 5-ring, and not (II) with a 4-ring:

$$O_2S \overset{O-CH-O}{\underset{O-CH-O}{\diagdown \diagup}} SO_2 \qquad O_2S \overset{O}{\underset{O}{\diagdown \diagup}} CH-CH \overset{O}{\underset{O}{\diagdown \diagup}} SO_2.$$

(I)   (II)

Thiosulphuric Acid, $H_2S_2O_3$

The free acid and the acid salts are unknown; they decompose as soon as they are formed. The neutral salts are made:

1. By the action of sulphur on a sulphite solution.
2. By the oxidation of H_2S or sulphides.

[422] P. Ruggli and E. Henzi, *Helv. Chim. Acta*, 1929, **12**, 364.

3. By the spontaneous decomposition of sodium hydrosulphite, along with the pyrosulphite:

$$2\,Na_2S_2O_4 \;=\; Na_2S_2O_3 + Na_2S_2O_5.$$

4. By the action of alkalies of polythionates.

The salts are numerous and commonly very stable. Those of the alkalies and alkaline earths are usually hydrated, but not those of NH_4, Pb, Ag, Tl'. Very soluble thiosulphates are those of the alkalies, Ca, Sr, (Ba only 1/480), Mg, Cd, Zn, Ni, Co, Fe", Mn". The thallous, silver, and lead salts are only slightly soluble and readily form double salts. The solutions are fairly stable in the cold and in absence of air; the alkaline solutions are readily oxidized by air to sulphates. On treatment with iodine they give tetrathionates:

$$2\,S_2O_3'' + I_2 \;=\; S_4O_6'' + 2\,I'.$$

In this familiar reaction, anhydrous $Na_2S_2O_3$ dried at 120° can be used as a primary analytical standard.[423] The best known of all the salts is, of course, that of sodium, $Na_2S_2O_3, 5\,H_2O$, which is the 'hypo' used in photography to fix the plate by dissolving out the unreduced silver halide.

The structure of the acid is clear: it is derived from sulphuric acid by replacing one oxygen by a sulphur

No other formulation would explain the stability, and strong confirmation has been obtained by the use of radioactive sulphur. This substance ^{35}S, made by bombarding the chlorine in carbon tetrachloride with neutrons (n, pr), has a half-life of about 80 days. It is dissolved,[424] along with some ordinary sulphur, in sulphite solution, and the silver salt $Ag_2S_2O_3$ precipitated from this with $AgNO_3$. On boiling, the salt breaks up into

$$Ag_2S + H_2SO_4,$$

and the whole of the activity is found in the silver sulphide. In the same way it was shown[425] that active S" ions exchange rapidly with half the sulphur in a thiosulphate solution.

Thiosulphates are decomposed by acids, giving amongst other products sulphur dioxide and free sulphur: the time lag before the turbidity due to colloidal sulphur begins to appear is probably due to the slow aggregation of the liberated sulphur into colloidal particles, since, if the solution is neutralized immediately after acidification, the thiosulphate is not reformed (Ephraim).

[423] H. M. Tomlinson and F. G. Ciapetta, *J. Ind. Eng. Chem.* [Anal.] 1941, **13**, 539.
[424] E. B. Andersen, *Z. physikal. Chem.* 1936, B **32**, 237.
[425] H. H. Voge, *J.A.C.S.* 1939, **61**, 1032.

The decomposition of thiosulphuric acid is a very complicated problem, but the main facts seem to be these.[426-9]

The S_2O_3 ion is relatively stable, and so does not decompose until the hydrogen ion concentration reaches about $2 \cdot 5 \times 10^{-5}$, and then the very unstable HS_2O_3' ion is formed, which decomposes thus:

$$HS_2O_3' = HSO_3' + S \text{ (quick)}.$$

This is the first main product: the second is pentathionic acid, which is formed less rapidly, by reaction

$$6\,H^+ + 5\,S_2O_3'' = 2\,S_5O_6'' + 3\,H_2O.$$

If concentrated HCl is used, H_2S and H_2S_2 are formed, presumably from the monatomic sulphur,[426] but no dithionate, and especially no sulphate. With less concentrated HCl, especially in presence of a little As_2O_3 as catalyst, the pentathionate is the main product.[427]

Complex Thiosulphates

Thiosulphuric acid forms a series of remarkably stable complex salts with a variety of heavy metals. Alkaline thiosulphate solutions will dissolve many insoluble salts of silver, lead, mercury, cuprous copper, etc. (and also the corresponding oxides, with the production of alkaline solutions); it is interesting that cupric salts form no such complexes, but are reduced to cuprous, which then form them.

This is obviously connected with the high affinity of many of these metals for sulphur. The radical, as in all the complexes formed by di-basic acids, can occupy either one or two co-ordination places in the complex:

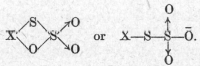

There is little doubt, for example, that the anion in $K_3[Bi(S_2O_3)_3]$ is trichelate (6-covalent); so, too, we must assume a ring structure in silver complexes $Na[AgS_2O_3]$ (2-covalent) and $Na_3[Ag(S_2O_3)_2]$ (4-covalent); but in $Na_2[Hg(S_2O_3)_2]$, on account of the strong tendency of mercury to assume a covalency of 2, together with its great affinity for sulphur, which enables it to dispense with the extra stability of the chelate ring, it is quite probable that the mercury is only 2-covalent, and no rings are formed.

In solution the mercury silver and aurous salts have a sweet taste, which with the silver salt is still perceptible in 1/320,000 solution.

[426] O. v. Deines, *Z. anorg. Chem.* 1928, **177**, 13.
[427] E. H. Riesenfeld and G. Sydow, ib. **175**, 49.
[428] J. Scheffer and F. Böhm, ib. 1929, **183**, 151.
[429] F. Prakke and E. Stiasny, *Rec. Trav.* 1933, **52**, 615.

The silver and gold salts are of peculiar interest. Bassett and Lemon[430] showed that in the system $Na_2S_2O_3$—$Ag_2S_2O_3$—H_2O at 25°, the following solid phases occur: $Na_3[Ag(S_2O_3)_2]$ 2 H_2O; $Na_5Ag_3(S_2O_3)_4$, 2 H_2O; $Na[AgS_2O_3]$, H_2O; and $NaAg_3(S_2O_3)_2$, H_2O. Some of them at least are undoubtedly complex salts, especially $Na[AgS_2O_3]$. The existence of this very stable and soluble salt explains the solubility of silver halides in sodium thiosulphate, and its use in photography. Its solution is precipitated by KI but not by NaCl, showing that the concentration of silver ions is so small that with the halide ions added it fails to reach the solubility product of silver chloride (10^{-10}) though it exceeds that of silver iodide (10^{-16}). The free acid $H[AgS_2O_3]$, H_2O is said[431] to be precipitated as an unstable white powder when nitric acid is added to the solution of the sodium salt.

The gold salt is made by dissolving auric (not aurous) chloride in $Na_2S_2O_3$. The auric chloride is reduced (like a cupric salt) to aurous by some of the thiosulphate, which is thereby oxidized to tetrathionate:

$$4\ Na_2S_2O_3 + AuCl_3 = Na_3Au(S_2O_3)_2 + Na_2S_4O_6 + 3\ NaCl.$$

The solution of this aurous complex $Na_3[Au(S_2O_3)_2]$ has a sweet taste: the gold is not reduced by ferrous sulphate or oxalic acid, and the salt is only slowly decomposed by hydrochloric acid or dilute sulphuric acid. Unlike the silver complex it is not even reduced in the human body.

From the corresponding barium salt H_2SO_4 liberates the free acid $H_3[Au(S_2O_3)_2]$, which, though it cannot be isolated, can be evaporated down to a syrup without decomposition. The electric conductivity, and the freezing-point data in water, agree with the sodium salt having 4 ions, so it must be a true complex salt.

Esters of Thiosulphuric Acid

Of these the only known derivatives seem to be the mono-alkyl ester-acids and their salts, in which the hydrocarbon radical is attached to sulphur. The alkyl compounds can be made[432] by the action of alkyl halide or dialkyl sulphate on sodium thiosulphate. The salts are fairly stable, but in acid solution the mercaptans are separated. The corresponding aryl compounds can be made[433] by the action of thiophenols on the so-called N-pyridinium sulphonic acids $C_5H_5\overset{+}{N}\cdot SO_2\cdot\overset{-}{O}$: the reaction occurs at once, with the formation of the pyridinium salt $C_6H_5S\cdot SO_2\cdot O$ [pyH]. These salts are stable in neutral solution; in acid solution they are very slowly hydrolysed to the thiophenol and sulphuric acid, but are quickly converted in alkaline solution into diphenyl disulphide and SO_2, with some phenyl sulphinic acid.[434-5]

[430] H. Bassett and J. T. Lemon, *J.C.S.* 1933, 1423.
[431] H. Baines, ib. 1929, 2763.   [432] Beilstein, i. 284, 328.
[433] P. Baumgarten, *Ber.* 1930, 63, 1330.
[434] H. Lecher, ib. 1925, 58, 410.   [435] A. Durnow, ib. 1939, 72, 568.

Organic Derivatives of Oxy-acids of Sulphur

The most important of these, with the oxides, acids, and halides from which they are derived are:

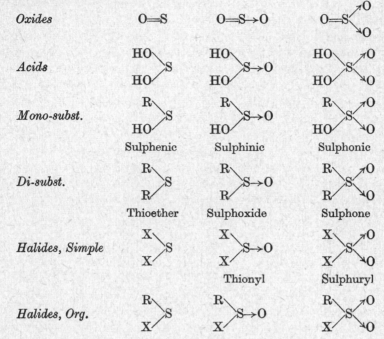

| Oxides | O=S | O=S→O | O=S(O)(O) |

| Acids | (HO)(HO)S | (HO)(HO)S→O | (HO)(HO)S(O)(O) |

| Mono-subst. | (R)(HO)S | (R)(HO)S→O | (R)(HO)S(O)(O) |
| | Sulphenic | Sulphinic | Sulphonic |

| Di-subst. | (R)(R)S | (R)(R)S→O | (R)(R)S(O)(O) |
| | Thioether | Sulphoxide | Sulphone |

| Halides, Simple | (X)(X)S | (X)(X)S→O | (X)(X)S(O)(O) |
| | | Thionyl | Sulphuryl |

| Halides, Org. | (R)(X)S | (R)(X)S→O | (R)(X)S(O)(O) |

The following list of the boiling-points of the diethyl compounds is of interest.

Et·Et·S 92°	Et·EtO·S 110°	EtO·EtO·S 119°	EtO·EtO·S→O 161°	EtO·EtO·S(O)(O) 208°
Et·Et·S→O 102°/17	Et·EtO·S→O 60°/18	EtO·EtO·S→O	Et·EtO·S(O)(O) 213·4°	
	Et·Et·S(O)(O) 248°			

Sulphenic Acids, R—S—OH

The free sulphenic acids are too unstable to be isolated, save in a few rare instances,[436] but their esters and halides (see below, p. 929) are to some extent known.

The ethyl ester Et·S·O·Et can be made[437] by shaking the thiocyanate Et·S·CNS (from ethyl mercaptan and thiocyanogen) with sodium ethylate at 0°. The diethyl ester is a colourless evil-smelling liquid, boiling at 108°/724 mm. It can be shown by the freezing-point to

[436] K. Fries, ib. 1912, **45**, 2970.
[437] A. Meuwsen and H. Gebhardt, ib. 1937, **70**, 792.

be monomeric in benzene, and by Vieböck's thiosulphate method[438] to contain one ethoxy-group in the molecule. It is a weaker reducing agent than the sulphoxylic ester $EtO \cdot S \cdot OEt$; it is not oxidized by air or by selenium dioxide, but ethyl hypochlorite $Et \cdot O \cdot Cl$ oxidizes it to the sulphinic ester $Et \cdot SO \cdot OEt$.

$$\text{Sulphinic Acids,} \qquad \begin{matrix} R \\ H—O \end{matrix} \Big\rangle S \to O$$

These are formed by reducing sulphonic chlorides with zinc, or by the action of a Grignard reagent on sulphur dioxide in ether.[439] The fact that they can be reduced to mercaptans shows that the alkyl or aryl group is attached directly to sulphur: they are in fact isomeric with the sulphoxylic ester-acids $Alk—O—S—O—H$. The free acids are unstable in air (being oxidized to the sulphonic acids) and in the absence of air they change rapidly at 100°, with the curious formation of the so-called 'thiosulphonate'[439]:

$$3\,R \cdot SO_2H = R \cdot SO_2 \cdot S \cdot R + R \cdot SO_3H + H_2O.$$

They react with thionyl chloride $SOCl_2$ to give their own acid chlorides, such as $Bu \cdot SO \cdot Cl$ (boiling-point 78°/12 mm.), which are hydrolysed by water much more violently than the sulphonic chlorides, and are slowly oxidized to these sulphonic chlorides by air; but unlike the free acids they are quite stable by themselves. For their sodium and magnesium salts see reference [440].

The esters of the sulphinic acids can be made[441] by the action of the Grignard reagent on the ester chlorides of sulphurous acid $\begin{matrix} Alk—O \\ Cl \end{matrix} \Big\rangle S \to O$, which themselves are made by treating the true alkyl sulphites with thionyl halides. The sulphinic esters are stable in air, and have rather high boiling-points, which perhaps is due to the dipole moments of the co-ordinate links not being relieved by resonance; thus:

$Et \cdot SO \cdot O \cdot Et$	Boiling-point	60°	at 18 mm.
$Bu \cdot SO \cdot O \cdot Et$	,,	91°	,, 13 mm.
$Bu \cdot SO \cdot O \cdot Bu$	,,	112°	,, 13 mm.

The sulphinic acids show the same curious tautomerism, due to the migration of a hydrogen atom from the hydroxyl to the sulphur, as occurs in the sulphites: their salts react with alkyl halides to give, not the sulphinic esters, but the isomeric sulphones:

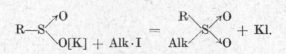

[438] F. Vieböck and A. Schwappach, *Ber.* 1930, **63**, 2818.
[439] J. v. Braun and K. Weissbach, ib 2836.
[440] P. Allen, *J. Org. Chem.* 1942, **7**, 23.
[441] P. Carré and D. Libermann, *C.R.* 1933, **197**, 1326; 1935, **200**, 2086.

Sulphonic Acids, $\begin{array}{c} R \\ \\ HO \end{array}\!\! S \!\!\begin{array}{c} O \\ \\ O \end{array}$

The sulphonic acids are isomeric with the half esters of sulphurous acid

$\begin{array}{c} RO \\ \\ HO \end{array}\!\! S \!\to\! O,$

and differ in having the hydrocarbon radical attached to sulphur directly and not through oxygen; this is proved by their being formed from the mercaptans by oxidation, and convertible into them by reduction. This linkage is much more stable than the link through oxygen, and accordingly the hydrocarbon radicals are much less easily split off from the sulphonic acids than from the sulphites.

The aliphatic sulphonic acids are made by oxidizing mercaptans or alkyl sulphides with concentrated nitric acid; by the action of alkyl halides on sodium or ammonium sulphite[442]; or by the oxidation of sulphinic acids

$\begin{array}{c} R \\ \\ H\!-\!O \end{array}\!\! S \!\to\! O.$

The aromatic sulphonic acids are formed directly by the action of concentrated sulphuric acid or oleum on the aromatic hydrocarbons: this is a characteristic aromatic property, and one of the signs that aromatic hydrogen is more easily replaced than aliphatic.

The sulphonation of benzene is a very peculiar reaction. It is only effected by strong acid, and when the acid has become diluted by the water produced to a certain extent, probably[443] about 85 per cent. acid (i.e. $[H_3O]SO_4H$), the sulphonation ceases.

To increase the yield it is necessary either to use oleum, or to remove the water formed in the reaction, for example, by blowing a rapid stream of benzene vapour through the hot liquid (Tyrer process).[444]

This is not a question of chemical equilibrium in a reversible reaction. The diluted acid does not hydrolyse the sulphonic acid back to benzene under the conditions of the sulphonation. Further, in presence of sulphuric acid, even at a dilution too great to cause any sulphonation at all, heavy water is able to replace the hydrogen atoms of benzene by deuterium.[445-6] Ingold[446] has found this the best method of preparing hexadeuterobenzene C_6D_6: ordinary pure benzene was shaken with a mixture of D_2O and D_2SO_4 in approximately equimolecular proportions (i.e. about 83 per cent. acid by weight): after four repetitions of this process with fresh acid the

[442] P. H. Latimer and R. W. Bost, *J. Org. Chem.* 1940, **5**, 24.

[443] C. K. Ingold, C. G. Raisin, and C. L. Wilson, *J.C.S.* 1936, 915.

[444] Similarly the sulphonation of phenol goes much more rapidly in acetic acid than in water, and seems to be due to the undissociated H_2SO_4 (E. Briner, J. W. Hoekstra, and B. Susz, *Helv. Chim. Acta*, 1935, **18**, 684.

[445] C. K. Ingold, C. G. Raisin, and C. L. Wilson, *Nature*, 1934, **134**, 734, 847.

[446] Id., *J.C.S.* 1936, 915.

C_6D_6 was about 99·8 per cent. He explains it by supposing the formation of an intermediate sort of compound

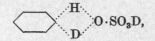

which can break up again to give either C_6H_6 or C_6H_5D.

Hinshelwood *et al.*[447-9] have shown that the rate of aromatic sulphonation in nitrobenzene by SO_3 is proportional to the square of the SO_3 concentration; the heats of activation are for chlorobenzene 7·72 and for nitrobenzene 11·40 k.cals.

The sulphonic acids (the aromatic are much better known than the aliphatic) are liquids or low-melting solids, which can be distilled in a high vacuum without decomposition; thus at 0·1 mm. benzene sulphonic acid boils at 171–2°, and *p*-toluene sulphonic acid at 185–7°.[454] They are usually very soluble in water, and are often separated from the excess of H_2SO_4 by the solubility of their calcium or barium salts. They are very stable, but can be converted into the usual acid derivatives (halides, esters, amides, etc.). The hydrolytic separation of the hydrocarbon radical from the sulphur occurs in two ways:

$$R \cdot SO_3H + H_2O \Bigg\langle \begin{array}{l} \nearrow R \cdot H + H_2SO_4 \\[2ex] \searrow R \cdot OH + H_2SO_3. \end{array}$$

In presence of alkalies the second reaction takes place (this is how phenol is made commercially): in acid solution, and usually at a rather high temperature, the first.

The relative stability of the C—S link in various aliphatic sulphonic acids has been examined[451] by determining the velocity of hydrolysis (exclusively to $R \cdot OH \cdot + K_2SO_3$) by concentrated potash at temperatures round 355° under pressure. The values of the velocity constant $\times 10^4$ at 355° are:

Me 1; Et 46; Pr 14, and a fall to Hexyl 7·1;

secondary alkyls decompose much quicker: isoPr 100; sec. Bu 88; phenyl 37·9. The C—S link in the mercaptans[452] varies in the same kind of way, but the change is about 1,000 times as quick.

Sulphonamides, $R \cdot SO_2 \cdot NH_2$[450]

The dipole moments of sulphanilamide and *p*-amino-phenyl-*p*-benzene sulphonamide[453] are 6·63 and 6·71 D, about 0·8 D more than those calculated

[447] D. R. Vicary and C. N. Hinshelwood, *J.C.S.* 1939, 1372.
[448] K. D. Wadsworth and C. N. Hinshelwood, ib. 1944, 469.
[449] E. Dresel and C. N. Hinshelwood, ib. 649.
[450] J. v. Braun and K. Weissbach, *Ber.* 1930, **63**, 2839.
[451] F. C. Wagner and E. E. Reid, *J.A.C.S.* 1931, **53**, 3407.
[452] E. C. Billheimer and E. E. Reid, ib. 1930, **52**, 4338.
[453] W. D. Kumler and I. F. Halverstadt, ib. 1941, 63, 2182.
[454] W. M. Rodionov, *Bull. Soc.* 1929, [iv] **45**, 109.

for the simple structures; this indicates some resonance with a zwitter-ion form

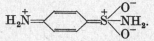

Sulphonic Esters

These are isomeric with the dialkyl sulphites. They have rather high boiling-points ($Et \cdot SO_2 \cdot O \cdot Et$ 213°), high dielectric constants, and are as good ionizing solvents as the dialkyl sulphates. These properties are to be expected from the presence of two co-ordinate links.

These esters can be used for alkylation.[454]

Thiosulphonic Acids, $R \cdot SO_2 \cdot SH$

The salts of these acids are got by the action of potassium sulphide on a sulphonic chloride, with the intermediate formation of a sulphinate:

$$R \cdot SO_2 \cdot Cl + K_2S = R \cdot SO_2K + KCl + S$$
$$R \cdot SO_2K + S = R \cdot SO_2 \cdot SK.$$

This salt reacts with alkyl iodide to form the ester $R \cdot SO_2 \cdot SR$, i.e.

The structure of this product is proved by the fact that it is identical with the oxidation product of the disulphide $R \cdot S$—$S \cdot R$. These esters are evil smelling, and high boiling, but volatile in steam.

Sulphoxides, $\underset{R'}{\overset{R}{\diagdown}} S \rightarrow O$

The sulphoxides are derived from sulphurous acid by replacing two hydroxyl groups by hydrocarbon radicals, the product of one such replacement being a sulphinic acid. They are made by oxidizing the corresponding sulphides, either with nitric acid or hydrogen peroxide,[457] or by the hydrolysis of their dibromides, or in other ways. The aromatic sulphoxides can also be made by the action of sulphur dioxide or thionyl chloride on aromatic hydrocarbons in presence of aluminium chloride.[455-6]

The sulphoxides are low-melting solids or oils, which boil at high temperatures and can only be distilled under greatly reduced pressure; for example, methyl sulphoxide $(CH_3)_2SO$ melts at 18·5°[459]; its vapour pressure is 0·600 mm. at 25° and 3·07 at 50°, giving an extrapolated boiling-point of 192° C.[459a]; ethyl sulphoxide $(C_2H_5)_2S \rightarrow O$ melts at 4–6°

[455] C. E. Colby and C. S. McLoughlin, *Ber.* 1887, **20**, 195.
[456] F. Loth and A. Michaelis, ib. 1894, **27**, 2547.
[457] R. Pummerer, ib. 1910, **43**, 1407.
[458] D. Ll. Hammick and R. B. Williams, *J.C.S.* 1938, 211.
[459] T. B. Douglas, *J.A.C.S.* 1946, **68**, 1072.   [459a] Id. ib. 1948, **70**, 2001.

and boils at 88–9° under 15 mm.[469]; diphenyl sulphoxide boils with some decomposition at 340° under 760 mm. (benzophenone at 307°). The dipole moment of dibutyl sulphoxide $Bu_2S{\rightarrow}O$ in benzene is 3·90 D,[458] while that of diphenyl sulphoxide is 4·00[460]; hence by Sutton's rule[461] the SO group should orient kationoid substituents to the meta positions. The sulphoxides are too unstable for this to be tested directly, but it is an indirect proof that an iodine atom in the para position to the SO is hydrolysed by alkalies under conditions that leave a meta iodine atom untouched, just as when the SO is replaced by an NO_2.

That the carbon atoms are attached to sulphur is proved by the formation of these compounds from and their reduction to the sulphides. The predominance of the co-ordinate link as in $R_2S{\rightarrow}O$ over the double link in $R_2S{=}O$ is shown by their behaviour, which is much more like that of an amine oxide $R_3N{\rightarrow}O$ than that of a ketone $R_2C{=}O$. Thus the alkyl sulphoxides at least are very soluble in water; they all show definite though weak basic properties. The product of the oxidation of a sulphide with concentrated nitric acid has the composition R_2SO,HNO_3, is soluble in water, and is converted into the sulphoxide by treatment with barium carbonate, and is obviously a salt $[R_2S{-}O{-}H]NO_3$. The same is true of the dibromides which are made by treating the sulphides with bromine: $(CH_3)_2SBr_2$ is a yellow solid which is completely hydrolysed by water to the sulphoxide and hydrobromic acid, and is clearly a sulphonium salt $[(CH_3)_2S{\cdot}Br]Br$. The unsymmetrical sulphoxides RR′SO such as *p*-aminophenyl tolyl sulphoxide, like the sulphinic esters $R{\cdot}SO{\cdot}OR$, can be resolved into their optical antimers.[462-3]

The asymmetry of the disulphoxides has been investigated by Bennett. If the three links of the sulphur do not lie in a plane, then a disulphoxide should give two isomeric forms, a cis and a trans: for example, the dithiane derivative according as the two oxygen

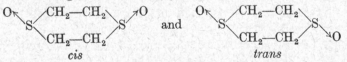

cis   and   trans

atoms are on the same or on opposite sides of the ring. Bennett and his collaborators have shown the existence of this isomerism in a series of different compounds.[464-71] Of special interest are the oxides of trimethylene trisulphide[467] the polymerization product of thioformaldehyde

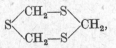

and the disulphoxides of thianthrene.[472]

[460] G. C. Hampson, R. H. Farmer, and L. E. Sutton, *Proc. Roy. Soc.* 1933, **143**, 147.

[461] L. E. Sutton, ib. 1931, **133**, 668.

[462] P. W. B. Harrison, J. Kenyon, and H. Phillips, *J.C.S.* 1926, 2079.

[463] J. Holloway, J. Kenyon, and H. Phillips, ib. 1928, 3000.

These active derivatives of 3-covalent sulphur racemise very slowly, often remaining unchanged for months in the cold; they seem to be as stereochemically stable as the carbon compounds, and more so than those of nitrogen. If we could assume a molecule $R_2S=O$ to have a plane of symmetry like $R_2C=O$, this stable activity would prove that it is not formed; indeed if $R_2S \rightarrow O$ is pyramidal and $R_2S=O$ planar, resonance is almost impossible. But we cannot assume this, since the sulphur has not an octet but a decet of electrons (2, 8). The arrangement of the co-valencies of such a decet with a double bond may well be unsymmetrical and nearly tetrahedral, so that the activity does not exclude it; it must, however, be relatively unstable, because, (1) a double link to sulphur always is so (as in $S=O$), and (2) the 'inert pair' with sulphur is very rare, and so no doubt is not a stable form.

$$\text{Sulphones,} \quad {R \atop R} \!\!\diagdown\!\! S \!\!\diagup\!\!\!\diagdown\!\! {O \atop O}$$

These are the results of replacing both OH groups in sulphuric acid by hydrocarbon radicals. They can be made by oxidizing the thioethers or the sulphoxides with fuming nitric acid or potassium permanganate, or by the action of alkyl halides on the sodium salts of sulphinic acids, which involves an intramolecular rearrangement:

$$R\!-\!S \!\!\diagup\!\!\!\diagdown\!\! {O \atop O[Na]} + Et\cdot I = {Et \atop R} \!\!\diagdown\!\! S \!\!\diagup\!\!\!\diagdown\!\! {O \atop O} + NaI.$$

In the aromatic series they are formed more readily, for example by the action of sulphur trioxide on the hydrocarbons (accordingly they are by-products in the manufacture of sulphonic acids); by heating the sulphonic acids with benzene and phosphorus pentoxide, or even alone; or by the action of sulphonic chlorides on the hydrocarbons in presence of aluminium chloride.

The sulphones are isomeric with the sulphinic esters $R \cdot SO \cdot OR$: that they have both hydrocarbon radicals attached to sulphur is almost the only possible explanation of the isomerism, and is further supported by their formation by the oxidation of thioethers, by their remarkable stability, and by the fact that with $AlCl_3$ the same sulphone is obtained from benzene sulphonic chloride and toluene as from toluene sulphonic chloride and benzene.

The sulphones are colourless solids of great stability, which distil at

[464] E. V. Bell and G. M. Bennett, ib. 1927, 1798.
[465] Id., ib. 1928, 86.   [466] Id., ib. 3189.   [467] Id., ib. 1929, 15.
[468] G. M. Bennett and E. V. Bell, ib. 1930, 1.
[469] G. M. Bennett and F. S. Statham, ib. 1931, 1684.
[470] Id., ib. 1690.
[471] G. M. Bennett, H. Baw, and P. Dearns, ib. 1934, 680.
[472] T. W. J. Taylor, ib. 1935, 625.

high temperatures without decomposition. The lower alkyl sulphones are very soluble in water, diethyl sulphone, for example, in 6·4 parts of water at 16°. Examples of the melting- and boiling-points are:

	M. pt.	B. pt.
Dimethyl sulphone $(CH_3)_2SO_2$	109°	238°
Diethyl sulphone $(C_2H_5)_2SO_2$	70°	248°
Diphenyl sulphone $(C_6H_5)_2SO_2$	76°	379°

Their great stability is shown by the fact that diphenyl sulphone not only boils undecomposed at 379°, but can be distilled unchanged at this temperature from zinc dust, and can be heated with yellow phosphorus to 250° without reaction. It is, however, converted by PCl_5 at 160° into chlorobenzene and benzene sulphonyl chloride. Substituted diphenyl sulphones can sometimes[473-4] break off one aryl group far more easily.

Aliphatic sulphones, on the other hand, react with potash to form the sulphonic acids and the unsaturated hydrocarbons: for example, diethyl sulphone gives ethylene and ethyl sulphonic acid.[475]

The bromine in $R \cdot SO_2 \cdot CH_2Br$ (where R = alkyl or aryl) is replaceable by hydrogen on treatment with the Grignard reagent or with $Na \cdot SEt$ or $Na \cdot OEt$ in alcohol.[476]

Certain aliphatic disulphones are of importance as drugs. These are the bodies formed by condensing ketones with mercaptans (e.g. in presence of HCl) and oxidizing the products to disulphones with permanganate or otherwise. Thus acetone and ethyl mercaptan give the disulphone which is sulphonal: the corresponding product

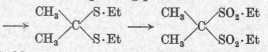

from methyl ethyl ketone is trional, and that from diethyl ketone tetronal. The hypnotic action of sulphonal was discovered by Kast in 1888.[477]

Oxy-halides of Sulphur

These may be classified as derivatives of the three types of oxy-acid,

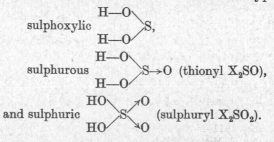

[473] L. A. Warren and S. Smiles, *J.C.S.* 1931, 2207.
[474] A. A. Levy, H. C. Rains, and S. Smiles, ib. 3264.
[475] G. W. Fenton and C. K. Ingold, ib. 1928, 3127.
[476] W. M. Ziegler and R. Connor, *J.A.C.S.* 1940, **62**, 2596.
[477] On these disulphones see further A. Récsei, *Ber.* 1927, **60**, 1420.

Either one hydroxyl may be replaced by halogen, in which case the product is still an acid, or both.

We also have the corresponding derivatives of the substituted organic acids, such as sulphonic.

Halogen Derivatives of Sulphoxylic Acid

The acid chloride is the rather unstable sulphur dichloride SCl_2 described below (p. 946). To this group belong also the aryl sulphur chlorides $Ar \cdot S \cdot Cl$ and the aryl dithiochlorides $Ar \cdot S \cdot S \cdot Cl$.

Aryl Sulphur Chlorides (Ar · S · Cl) and Bromides

These can be made[478-81] by the action of chlorine on mercaptans at a low temperature in CCl_4 solution, or on the disulphides:

$$\Phi \cdot S \cdot H + Cl_2 = \Phi \cdot S \cdot Cl + HCl$$
$$\Phi \cdot S \cdot S \cdot \Phi + Cl_2 = 2 \, \Phi \cdot S \cdot Cl.$$

Phenyl sulphur chloride $C_6H_5 \cdot S \cdot Cl$ is a red oil, boiling-point 149° at 12 mm.; its smell, colour, and absorption spectrum are very like those of sulphur dichloride SCl_2, which it also resembles in its reactions; for example, with ethylene it forms $C_6H_5 \cdot S \cdot CH_2 \cdot CH_2 \cdot Cl$, which has a vesicating action like that of mustard gas. By reduction with zinc or reaction with a thiophenol it is converted into a disulphide $\Phi \cdot S \cdot S \cdot \Phi$. It behaves as the acid chloride of the so-called phenyl-sulphenic acid $Ar \cdot S \cdot OH$; thus on treatment with aniline it gives the anilide $\Phi \cdot S \cdot NH\Phi$, and with sodium methylate the ester $\Phi \cdot S \cdot OCH_3$ (b. pt. 88°/4 mm.).

The corresponding bromide $\Phi \cdot S \cdot Br$ seems to exist, but is too unstable to isolate. Few aliphatic compounds of the R—S—Cl type are known[482]; but the tertiary alkyl compounds can be made[483-4] by the action of the halogens on the mercury mercaptides; for example,

$$(Me_3C \cdot S)_2Hg + 2 \, I_2 = 2 \, Me_3C \cdot S \cdot I + HgI_2.$$

The chloride and bromide are too unstable to be isolated. It is remarkable, since compounds with iodine attached to sulphur are almost unknown, that the corresponding iodide is more stable, though even this soon decomposes in the cold.

A curious compound of this type is perchloromethyl mercaptan Cl_3C—S—Cl, discovered by Rathke in 1873[485,487-8]; it is formed together

[478] H. Lecher and F. Holschneider, *Ber.* 1924, **57**, 755.

[479] H. Lecher, ib. 1925, **58**, 409.

[480] For literature of the earlier work see H. Lecher and M. Wittwer, ib. 1922, **55**, 1474.

[481] See also T. Zincke 1911–18, and especially *Ann.* 1918, **416**, 86.

[482] D. Vorländer and E. Mittag, *Ber.* 1919, **52**, 415.

[483] H. Rheinboldt and E. Motzkus, ib. 1939, 72, 657.

[484] H. Rheinboldt and F. Mott, ib. 668.

[485] B. Rathke, *Ann.* 1873, **167**, 195.

[486] H. Lecher and K. Simon, *Ber.* 1921, 54, 2249; 1922, 55, 2423.

[487] J. M. Conolly and G. M. Dyson, *J.C.S.* 1934, 822.

with sulphur chloride by the action of chlorine on carbon disulphide in presence of a trace of iodine; it is a yellow oil of very unpleasant smell which boils at 147°; it is hydrolysed to carbon dioxide, hydrochloric acid, and sulphur; it can be reduced to thiophosgene $S{=}CCl_2$, and oxidized by nitric acid to trichlormethyl sulphonyl chloride $Cl_3C \cdot SO_2 \cdot Cl$.

Aryl Dithiochlorides, $Ar \cdot S \cdot S \cdot Cl$

A compound of this series is *o*-nitrophenyl dithiochloride.[486] It is entirely covalent in behaviour, soluble in all organic solvents, gives non-conducting solutions in ethylene dichloride, and is hydrolysed by water. The chlorine has something of the mobility of a diazo-chlorine; it will couple with dimethyl aniline to give the disulphide

$$Ar{-}S{-}S{-}\!\!\left\langle\;\;\right\rangle\!\!{-}N(CH_3)_2.$$

DERIVATIVES OF SULPHUROUS ACID

These consist of the thionyl halides $SO(hal)_2$, and the halides of the sulphinic acids $R \cdot SO \cdot hal$. The molecular structure of the three thionyl halides has been determined by electron diffraction[489-91]; they are pyramidal, with the distances S—O 1·45, S—F 1·6, S—Cl 2·05, S—Br 2·27 (theory S—O 1·70, S—F 1·68, S—Cl 2·03, S—Br 2·18).

Thionyl Fluoride, $\begin{smallmatrix}F\\\\F\end{smallmatrix}\!\!\nearrow\!\!S{\rightarrow}O$

This can be made by the action of sulphur dioxide on zinc fluoride, or of thionyl chloride on a number of metallic fluorides, and on arsenic or antimony trifluoride.[492] It is a colourless gas, and smells like phosgene; it is soluble in ether and benzene. It is the stablest of the thionyl halides, whose stability falls off in the order $SOF_2 > SOCl_2 > SOBr_2$ (there is no SOI_2). It attacks glass at a red heat, but not an iron retort; it does not act on Si, Mg, Ni, Cu, Zn, or Hg up to 125°.[493] It is hydrolysed by water, but like many oxyfluorides, only very slowly.[494]

The fluorochloride SOFCl can be made[493] by treating $SOCl_2$ with antimony trifluoride and pentachloride; it changes in some months at the ordinary temperature into a mixture of the difluoride and the dichloride. The physical properties of these compounds are[493]:

	SOF_2	SOFCl	$SOCl_2$	$SOBr_2$
B. pt.	−43·8°	+12·2°	75·7°	42·5°/16 mm.
M. pt.	−110·0°	−139·5°	−99·5°	−49·5°
Trouton	22·6	20·7	21·4	..

[488] J. M. Conolly and G. M. Dyson, *J.C.S.* 1935, 679.

[489] D. P. Stevenson and R. A. Cooley, *J.A.C.S.* 1940, **62**, 2477.

[490] K. J. Palmer, ib. 1938, **60**, 2360.

[491] See D. M. Yost and H. Russell, *Syst. Inorg. Chem.*, p. 306.

[492] H. Moissan and P. Lebeau, *Ann. Chim. Phys.* 1902, [7] **26**, 145.

[493] H. S. Booth and F. C. Mericola, *J.A.C.S.* 1940, **62**, 640.

Thionyl Chloride, $\begin{smallmatrix} Cl \\ Cl \end{smallmatrix}\!\!>\!\!S\!\rightarrow\!O$

This can be made by the direct union of sulphur and chlorine monoxide, but it is usually prepared by the action of phosphorus pentachloride on sulphur dioxide or sodium sulphite. It can be freed from SO_2Cl_2 by heating it with sulphur (when this gives $SO_2 + S_2Cl_2$) and distilling.[495] It is a colourless liquid.[496] The dielectric constant is 9·05, and the dipole moment in benzene at 25° 1·58 D.[497] The vapour density is normal at 150°, and the molecular weight is normal in benzene. The electrical conductivity is 2×10^{-6} at 25° (Walden); it will dissolve the iodides of As, Sb, Sn, Hg, Co, and tetramethyl ammonium, to give coloured solutions of small conductivity. It is far less stable than the fluoride: it begins to dissociate near its boiling-point, and at 440° it is about two-thirds dissociated into $SO_2 + S_2Cl_2 + Cl_2$; accordingly its reactions are mainly those of $SO_2 + Cl_2$. It is readily hydrolysed by water.

Thionyl chloride reacts with ammonia in the gaseous phase to form thionylimide H—N=S=O, a gas condensing at −85° to a colourless liquid, which polymerizes at −70° to a yellow-brown insoluble solid looking like bakelite.[498]

The remarkable shortness of the S—O link (p. 930) suggests that there is a very large contribution of the $\begin{smallmatrix} Cl \\ Cl \end{smallmatrix}\!\!>\!\!S\!=\!O$ form to the resonance, and so is evidence that in this form the valencies of the sulphur decet (2, 8) are not planar but pyramidal.

Thionyl Bromide, $\begin{smallmatrix} Br \\ Br \end{smallmatrix}\!\!>\!\!S\!\rightarrow\!O$

This can be made by the action of hydrogen bromide on thionyl chloride; the yield at −80° is quantitative.[499]

It is a reddish liquid, less stable than the chloride, and decomposes below its boiling-point, though it can be distilled under reduced pressure. Its chemical behaviour is just like that of the chloride. Like many other possible S—I compounds thionyl iodide SOI_2 does not seem to exist.

HALOGEN-SULPHUROUS ACIDS

Fluorosulphinic acid $\begin{smallmatrix} HO \\ F \end{smallmatrix}\!\!>\!\!S\!\rightarrow\!O$ and its chlorine analogue $\begin{smallmatrix} HO \\ Cl \end{smallmatrix}\!\!>\!\!S\!\rightarrow\!O$ are unknown, and all attempts to prepare their esters have failed.

[494] O. Ruff and C. Thiel, *Ber.* 1905, **38**, 549.
[495] D. L. Cottle, *J.A.C.S.* 1946, **68**, 1380.
[496] W. C. Schumb and C. H. Hamblet, ib. 1935, **57**, 260.
[497] J. W. Smith, *Proc. Roy. Soc.* 1932, **138**, 154.
[498] P. W. Schenk, *Ber.* 1942, **75**, 94.
[499] F. Govaert and M. Hansen, *Natuurwet. Tijds.* 1938, **20**, 77.

HALOGEN DERIVATIVES OF SULPHURIC ACID

Of sulphuric acid both the mono- and the di- derivatives are known, the first being the halogen sulphonic acids HSO_3hal (below, pp. 933, 936) and the second the sulphuryl halides, $SO_2(hal)_2$.

Sulphuryl Fluoride, SO_2F_2

This is formed by burning fluorine in SO_2; it can also be made more conveniently by heating barium fluorosulphonate[500]:

$$Ba(SO_3F)_2 = BaSO_4 + SO_2F_2.$$

It is a gas, boiling at $-52°$ and melting at $-120°$. Its vapour density is normal.

It is surprisingly inert—almost as inert as sulphur hexafluoride. Water dissolves about a tenth of its volume of the gas at 9°, but it has no action on it even if the two are heated together in a sealed tube at 150°. It is not affected by heating either alone or with oxygen up to the softening point of glass (*ca.* 500°): or by sulphur or hydrogen chloride below a red heat: or by phosphorus or arsenic below their boiling-points, or by sodium below its melting-point. It is attacked by hydrogen on heating, and slowly combines with ammonia in the cold. It is only slowly absorbed by potash, with the production of potassium fluoride, fluorosulphonate, and sulphate; this is practically the only reaction in which sulphuryl fluoride behaves as a sulphuryl compound.[500]

The inertness is no doubt partly due to the thermodynamic stability of S—F, as is shown in HSO_3F, and we know from the behaviour of its organic compounds that the group $> XF_2$ is more stable than $> XF$ (VII. 1125); but it must also have a very high heat of activation, which is characteristic of atoms exerting their maximum covalency, and suggests the structure

the low boiling-point ($-52°$: SO_2Cl_2 boils at $+69°$) also supports this. The greater reactivity of SO_2Cl_2 may be due to the chlorine being much more prone to 'back-co-ordination', and so favouring forms like

The mixed halide SO_2FCl has been made[501] by heating sulphuryl chloride with antimony tri-fluoride and pentachloride under pressure; b. pt. $+7\cdot1°$, m. pt. $-124\cdot7°$, Trouton constant 22·6.

[500] W. Traube, J. Hoerenz, and F. Wunderlich, *Ber.* 1919, **52**, 1272.
[501] H. S. Booth and C. V. Herrmann, *J.A.C.S.* 1936, **58**, 63.

Fluorosulphonic Acid, $\mathrm{H-O}\diagdown\overset{\diagup O}{\underset{\diagdown O}{S}}$

This acid,[502-10] which boils at 162·6°, is reasonably reactive, and in general resembles chlorsulphonic acid HSO_3Cl, so that no doubt it has mainly the structure given above. It reacts much less readily than chlorosulphonic acid, but this difference is fully accounted for by its much greater thermodynamic stability. It is stable by itself up to 900°, but it is remarkable that in the presence of sulphur it is completely decomposed even at its boiling-point (163°) into SO_3 and HF.[503] It is incompletely and reversibly hydrolysed by water[506-7]; a mixture of 12 moles each of H_2SO_4 and HF, and 20 moles H_2O have at equilibrium 1 mole of HSO_3F (determined by precipitation as the nitron salt). The effect of the water can be to a considerable extent neutralized by the addition of strong acids, such as $HClO_4$ or HNO_3 or benzene sulphonic, apparently because the water is removed by hydrating them.[510] Also the hydrolysis of the acid by water in the cold is a slow reaction: with one mole of HSO_3F per litre the half change takes 2 days. The anhydrous acid does not attack glass even when hot, and can be prepared[509] by distilling a mixture of KHF_2 and oleum from a Jena glass flask up to 250°.

The salts of this acid are correspondingly stable; they are only slowly hydrolysed even by warm water (and even in presence of acid), and can be recrystallized from it.[504] With ammonia they form sulphamates $M[SO_3NH_2]$.[511] These salts are remarkable in other ways too. They are very similar[505-6] in solubility and crystallographic properties to the salts of ClO_4', MnO_4', PO_2F_2', and BF_4, often forming mixed crystals with them. Thus HSO_3F forms a stable diazonium salt (as does HBF_4), and like HBF_4 and $HClO_4$ it forms a nitrosyl salt $[NO]SO_3F$, which is produced, along with $[NO]HSO_4$, when NO is passed into the acid. $CsSO_3F$ has a crystal lattice of the scheelite $(CaWO_4)$[512] type.

Esters of Fluorosulphonic Acid, $RO \cdot SO_2F$

These also are remarkable. The alkyl esters are made[509] by two rather unusual methods. The first is by the reaction of the acid with an ether, for example, by passing dimethyl ether into the acid. The reaction

$$Alk_2O + 2\,HSO_3F = 2\,Alk \cdot O \cdot SO_2 \cdot F + H_2O,$$

[502] W. Traube, J. Hoerenz, and F. Wunderlich, *Ber.* 1919, **52**, 1272.
[503] O. Ruff and H. J. Braun, ib. 1914, **47**, 646; O. Ruff, ib. 656.
[504] W. Traube and E. Reubke, ib. 1921, **54**, 1618.
[505] E. Wilke Dörfurt and G. Balz, ib. 1927, **60**, 115; *Z. anorg. Chem.* 1927, **159**, 197.
[506] W. Lange, *Ber.* 1927, **60**, 962.
[507] W. Lange and E. Müller, ib. 1930, **63**, 2653.
[508] E. Wilke Dörfurt, G. Balz, and A. Weinhardt, *Z. anorg. Chem.* 1930, **185**, 417.
[509] J. Meyer and G. Schramm, ib. 1932, **206**, 24.
[510] W. Lange, ib. 1933, **215**, 321.
[511] W. Traube and E. Brehmer, *Ber.* 1919, **52**, 1284.
[512] H. Seifert, *Z. Krist.* 1942, **104**, 385.

goes quite easily in the cold, but the yield is not very good, owing to the occurrence of by-reactions. For making the ethyl ester a better method is to pass ethylene into the acid.

The esters are volatile liquids, the methyl ester $CH_3O \cdot SO_2 \cdot F$ boiling at 92°, and the ethyl at 114°. They have a very unpleasant smell, and are lachrymators. They are immiscible with water but are soon hydrolysed by it; they etch glass, and are decomposed by strong acids. The methyl ester converts phenol into anisol.

The aryl esters are made in an entirely different way.[507] The diazonium salts of many complex halides decompose on heating to give the aryl halide, nitrogen, and the inorganic halide: for example,

$$Ar \cdot N_2[BF_4] = Ar \cdot F + N_2 + BF_3.$$

The salts of HPF_6, H_2SnCl_6, and H_2PtCl_6 behave in the same way. The diazonium fluorosulphonates are stable salts, which decompose somewhere near 100° quite quietly, but the result of this decomposition is found to be merely the elimination of nitrogen and the formation of the aryl ester of fluorosulphonic acid:

$$Ar \cdot N_2[SO_3F] = Ar \cdot SO_3F + N_2.$$

(The perchlorates under these conditions explode violently, possibly with the intermediate production of an unstable aryl perchlorate.) The phenyl ester boils at 180°/760 mm., and its vapour density is normal (HSO_3F like HF must from its high boiling-point be associated); it seems to be more stable than the alkyl esters, but this may be due only to its smaller solubility; it is not acted on by dilute acids, but is slowly hydrolysed to sulphuric acid by alkalies; it does not attack glass; it is volatile without decomposition in steam.

Alkyl and Aryl Sulphonyl Fluorides

These compounds, $R \cdot SO_2 \cdot F$, also differ from the corresponding chlorides in being much less reactive.[513-16]

The aryl sulphonyl fluorides can be made[513] by the action of fluorosulphonic acid on the aromatic hydrocarbons, on their sodium sulphonates, or on their sulphonic chlorides. A better method available in the aliphatic[515] as well as in the aromatic[514] series is to boil the sulphonic chloride with a saturated aqueous solution of a soluble metallic fluoride, such as potassium fluoride. This needs the presence of water; toluene sulphonic chloride gave no reaction when boiled with dry zinc fluoride for 5 days, but on adding water or steam the conversion was complete in an hour.

These are volatile compounds, for example:

$CH_3 \cdot SO_2F$	b. pt. 124°	$C_6H_5 \cdot SO_2F$	b. pt. 207°
$C_2H_5 \cdot SO_2F$	,, 135°	o-tol $\cdot SO_2F$	,, 224°
cy. Hexyl $\cdot SO_2F$	,, 218°		

[513] W. Steinkopf, *J. prakt Chem.* 1927, ii. **117**, 1.
[514] W. Davies and J. H. Dick, *J.C.S.* 1931, 2104.   [515] Id., ib. 1932, 483.
[516] Id., ib. 2042.

They have no unpleasant smell, but smell rather like the alkyl or aryl halides. They are far less reactive than the corresponding chlorides; they can be boiled with water or steam-distilled without hydrolysis; they only react slowly with amines or with boiling water: they do not react with pyridine in the cold, as the chlorides do, nor do they lose SO_2 when treated with $AlCl_3$. The aryl compounds share this inactivity, but it can be greatly modified by certain substituents in the ring.[516]

Sulphuryl Chloride, $\begin{matrix} Cl \\ Cl \end{matrix} > S < \begin{matrix} O \\ O \end{matrix}$

This is formed by the direct combination of sulphur dioxide and chlorine, which occurs at the ordinary temperature, but very slowly except in the presence of certain catalysts. In the cold, equilibrium in the reaction

$$SO_2 + Cl_2 \rightleftharpoons SO_2Cl_2$$

is almost wholly on the right-hand side, but even at 100° there is something like 90 per cent. dissociation.

A great variety of catalysts have been used to promote this reaction; nearly all are organic substances, including under that name active carbon.[517] Camphor is the commonest, but ethylene, acetic acid, ketones, and aldehydes have been used.[518] According to Durrans[519] saturated hydrocarbons and acids are useless, but limonene, pentene, esters, and ketones are active. Little or nothing is known of the way in which these substances act, but camphor forms a liquid containing a large percentage of sulphur dioxide.

Sulphuryl chloride is a colourless liquid, melting at −46° and boiling at 69·3°. Its vapour density is normal up to 130° (this does not represent the true equilibrium, at which it is largely dissociated), and so is its molecular weight as determined cryoscopically in benzene. The Trouton constant is 20·7. Electron diffraction[520] shows that the molecule is tetrahedral, with the distances S—O 1·43, S—Cl 1·99 A, and the angles O—S—O 120°, Cl—S—Cl 111°, Cl—S—O 106·5° (see SOX_2, p. 930).

Sulphuryl chloride dissolves many substances, such as SO_2, I_2, Br_2, $FeCl_3$, iodides of Rb, Hg, Cd, As, Sn, and the substituted ammoniums. Solutions of SO_2 and of I_2 have no measurable conductivity; those of salts have a low conductivity, except the tertiary and quaternary ammonium salts, which conduct well.

Sulphuryl chloride is hydrolysed very slowly by water. It reacts on heating with metallic oxides to give the chlorides and sulphates in various proportions,[518] and the vapour converts metallic sulphides into their chlorides.[521] In organic chemistry sulphuryl chloride is an active chlorinating

[517] H. Danneel, *Z. angew. Chem.* 1926, **39**, 1553.
[518] H. Danneel and W. Hesse, *Z. anorg. Chem.* 1933, **212**, 214.
[519] T. H. Durrans, *J. Soc. Chem. Ind.* 1926, **45**, 347.
[520] Yost and Russell, *Syst. Inorg. Chem.* 308.
[521] H. Danneel and F. Schlottmann, *Z. anorg. Chem.* 1933, **212**, 225.

agent either when heated or in presence of aluminium chloride, but not by itself in the cold.

Sulphuryl Chlorofluoride, $\begin{matrix} Cl \\ F \end{matrix} \diagdown S \diagup \begin{matrix} O \\ O \end{matrix}$

This has been made[522] from sulphuryl chloride by fluorination with antimony trifluoride and antimony pentachloride, best at 300° and under 4 atm.

SO_2ClF is a gas with the normal density, melting at $-124\cdot7°$ and boiling at $+7\cdot1°$. The Trouton constant is $22\cdot6$.

The gas is hydrolysed at once by water, and absorbed rapidly by an alkaline solution; it has a pungent smell like SO_2Cl_2, but does not fume in air.

Sulphuryl bromide and iodide do not seem to exist.

Chlorosulphonic Acid, $\begin{matrix} H{-}O \\ Cl \end{matrix} \diagdown S \diagup \begin{matrix} O \\ O \end{matrix}$

This is formed by the combination of hydrogen chloride and sulphur trioxide: by the action of phosphorus pentachloride on oleum, or more usually by treating oleum with hydrogen chloride. It is much less stable than the fluorine compound; it dissociates readily, and in consequence it is difficult to purify and its physical constants are not very certain. It boils at 151° (lower than fluorosulphonic acid) and melts at $-80°$; the boiling-points of these halides are compared in the table:

	SOX_2	SO_2X_2	HSO_3X	HX	CH_3X
X = F	$- 30°$	$- 52°$	$+162\cdot6°$	$+ 19\cdot5°$	$-78°$
X = Cl	$+ 79°$	$+ 69°$	$+151°$	$- 83°$	$-24°$
Diff.	$+109°$	$+121°$	$- 11°$	$-102\cdot5°$	$+54°$

The heat of evaporation at the boiling-point is $12\cdot86$ k.cals.[523]; this gives the enormous Trouton constant of $30\cdot4$, due probably to the large dissociation at the boiling-point. Solutions in chlorosulphonic acid have a very small conductivity (Walden).

The acid is violently—almost explosively—decomposed by water; its salts are almost impossible to prepare, but an ammonium salt $[NH_4]SO_3Cl$ has been made. It is an energetic chlorinating and (for hydrocarbons) sulphonating agent.

Its esters have been prepared[524]; they can be made from SO_2Cl_2, and are lachrymators. The boiling-points are: *n*-Bu 76–77°/13 mm.; *n*-Am. 75–75°/4 mm.

[522] H. S. Booth and C. V. Herrmann, *J.A.C.S.* 1936, **58**, 63.
[523] J. Ogier, *C.R.* 1883, **96**, 16, 646, 647.
[524] R. Levaillant, ib. 1933, **197**, 335, 648.

Sulphonyl Chlorides, $\underset{Cl}{\overset{R}{>}}S\underset{\searrow O}{\overset{\nearrow O}{}}$

These are formed by the action of phosphorus pentachloride on the salts of the sulphonic acids (aliphatic, Beilstein, iv. 5; aromatic, ib. xi. 34–6). They are colourless liquids or solids, which boil usually undecomposed at rather high temperatures: for example:

	B. pt.	M. pt.
$CH_3 \cdot SO_2Cl$	161·5°/730 mm.	..
$C_2H_5 \cdot SO_2Cl$	177·5°/760 mm.	..
$C_6H_5 \cdot SO_2 \cdot Cl$	252°/760 mm.	14·5°

Their dipole moments (in benzene or dioxane) are very high.[525]

R	$R \cdot SO_2Cl$	$R \cdot SO_2NH_2$
Phenyl	4·54	4·75 D
p-tolyl	5·01	5·02

They are readily hydrolysed by hot water, but only slowly by cold, and can be purified by washing with water. This is partly due to their very slight solubility in water.

These compounds, especially the aromatic, are important reagents in organic chemistry. They are readily reduced, first to the sulphinic acids and then to the mercaptans or thiophenols. They have the usual properties of acid chlorides of giving esters, amides, and anhydrides.

Sulphonyl Bromides, $\underset{Br}{\overset{R}{>}}S\underset{\searrow O}{\overset{\nearrow O}{}}$

These have long been known.[526] For example, $C_2H_5 \cdot SO_2 \cdot Br$, b. pt. 80°/13 mm.[527] and $n\text{-Bu} \cdot SO_2Br$, b. pt. 102°/11 mm.

It is interesting, in view of the marked way in which the affinity of sulphur for a halogen always falls off with a rise of the atomic weight of the halogen, to see that these bromides are much less stable than the corresponding chlorides (not to mention the fluorides). In particular they are readily reduced on heating by a mixture of PBr_5 and PBr_3, or even in some case by PBr_5 alone (or $PBr_3 + Br_2$) to the disulphides:

$$2 R \cdot SO_2Br + 5 PBr_3 = PBr_5 + 4 POBr_3 + R \cdot S \cdot S \cdot R.$$

This reaction occurs both with the aryl[528] and with the alkyl[529] derivatives. It does not occur with the chlorides, nor if the bromides are heated with

[525] E. N. Gurganova, *Acta phys. Chem. U.R.S.S.* 1941, **14**, 154.
[526] R. Otto, *Ann.* 1867, **142**, 98.
[527] E. Cherbuliez and O. Schnauder, *Helv. Chim. Acta*, 1923, **6**, 249.
[528] A. H. Kohlhase, *J.A.C.S.* 1932, **54**, 2441.
[529] W. H. Hunter and B. E. Sorenson, ib. 3364, 3368.

phosphorus trichloride. This is the more remarkable since the reaction should be more exothermic with chlorine than with bromine.[528]

PERACIDS OF SULPHUR

Of these acids, which contain the peroxide link —O—O—, there are two, persulphuric acid $H_2S_2O_8$ and sulphomonoperacid H_2SO_5, also known as 'Caro's acid'.

$$Persulphuric\ Acid,\ H_2S_2O_8 = \begin{array}{l} O{-}SO_2{-}OH \\ | \\ O{-}SO_2{-}OH \end{array}$$

This acid, of which S_2O_7, if it really exists (see p. 903), is presumably the anhydride, is made by the electrolysis of sulphuric acid, or by treating hydrogen peroxide with chlorosulphonic acid. The electrolysis needs special precautions, because $H_2S_2O_8$ hydrolyses to the monoperacid H_2SO_5.

Persulphuric acid is a crystalline solid, which melts at 65° with decomposition; in the pure dry state it keeps better than H_2SO_5, but it always has a smell of ozone. It is very hygroscopic, and is hydrolysed by water (see below). It reacts with organic compounds more violently than H_2SO_5; it explodes with alcohol or ether, and carbonizes paraffins slowly.

It was shown by H. Palme[530] that in 5 to 10 times normal sulphuric acid, $H_2S_2O_8$ decomposes through the following stages:

(1) $H_2S_2O_8 \longrightarrow H_2SO_5 + H_2SO_4$

(2) $H_2SO_5 \longrightarrow H_2SO_4 + H_2O_2$

(3) $H_2O_2 \longrightarrow O_2$

The salts are best prepared by the oxidation of sulphates, but they can also be made by the action of fluorine on an aqueous solution of $KHSO_4$.[531] The persulphates are comparatively insoluble, there being a marked rise in solubility in the order $K < Rb < Cs < Tl$; which would normally indicate a weak acid. The acid is of course a powerful oxidizing agent.

The conductivities and the freezing-points of solutions of its salts in water[532] indicate that the alkaline salts break up into three ions—i.e. that the formula of the acid is $H_2S_2O_8$ and not HSO_4. The formation (see below) of H_2SO_5 from chlorosulphonic acid and hydrogen peroxide, and its further conversion by more HSO_3Cl into $H_2S_2O_8$, as well as the course of hydrolysis of $H_2S_2O_8$ given above, all support this doubled structure, and suggest the formula

$$\begin{array}{l} O{-}SO_2{-}OH \\ | \\ O{-}SO_2{-}OH \end{array}.$$

This conclusion has been confirmed and made more precise by the work of Mooney and Zachariasen,[533] who showed that in the ammonium and

[530] *Z. anorg. Chem.* 1920, **112**, 97.

[531] F. Fichter and K. Humpert, *Helv. Chim. Acta*, 1923, **6**, 640.

[532] For references see Abegg, p. 498.

[533] R. C. L. Mooney and W. H. Zachariasen, *Phys. Rev.* 1933, [ii] **44**, 327.

caesium persulphates the S_2O_8 ion is made up of two tetrahedral SO_4 groups joined to one another through two oxygen atoms, the O—O link passing through a centre of symmetry. The distance from each S to each of its four neighbouring O atoms is 1·50 A, and that between the two linked O atoms is 1·31 A (theory S—O 1·70, S=O 1·49; O—O 1·32, O=O 1·10). The angle at each of these linking oxygens in the group

was found to be 128°.

Sulphomonoperacid (Caro's Acid), H_2SO_5

This can be made by the electrolysis of sulphuric acid, or the action of sulphuric acid on a persulphate, or of hydrogen peroxide on sulphuric acid or chlorosulphonic acid. The solid acid has been made[534-5] by treating chlorosulphonic acid with the theoretical quantity of 100 per cent. hydrogen peroxide.

It forms large hygroscopic crystals melting at 45°, which keep for weeks if they are pure. It does not attack pure paraffins, and is soluble in alcohol, ether, acetic anhydride, acetonitrile, and acetic acid[536]; but it explodes when mixed with aniline, benzene, phenol, etc.

Its first dissociation constant is very large and the second very small; the freezing-point in water gives a molecular weight of 55, whereas half of $H_2SO_5 = 57$. It titrates as a mono-basic acid with soda, but as dibasic with baryta, because this latter hydrolyses it to sulphuric acid[537-8] (possibly owing to the insolubility of barium sulphate). In water it is slowly hydrolysed to sulphuric acid and hydrogen peroxide. High concentration of H_2SO_4 hastens this, but in presence of phosphoric acid, or of 8 per cent. H_2SO_4, it is fairly stable. The acid solutions are more stable than those of persulphuric acid, but the neutral and alkaline are less stable.

Potassium iodide liberates iodine at once with H_2SO_5, even in great dilution, though it forms it only slowly with persulphuric acid, and scarcely at all with hydrogen peroxide.

A mixture of sulphomonoperacid and potassium permanganate is an extraordinarily strong oxidizing agent; it is decolorized by benzene at once,[539] and converts aniline into nitrosobenzene, and phenyl iodide into iodosobenzene.[540]

The formula H_2SO_5 was proposed by Baeyer, and is supported by the production of the acid by the hydrolysis of $H_2S_2O_8$; it was established by

[534] J. d'Ans and W. Friederich, *Ber.* 1910, **43**, 1880.
[535] Id., *Z. anorg. Chem.* 1912, **73**, 325.
[536] G. Toennies, *J.A.C.S.* 1937, **59**, 552.
[537] H. Ahrle, *J. prakt. Chem.* 1909, [2] **79**, 129.
[538] Id., *Z. angew. Chem.* 1909, **22**, 1713.
[539] A. v. Baeyer and V. Villiger, *Ber.* 1900, **33**, 2488.
[540] Id., ib. 124.

Willstätter and Hauenstein,[541] who showed that salts of sulphomonoperacid with benzoyl or benzene-sulphonyl chloride give salts of the composition $M \cdot Ac \cdot SO_5$ ($Ac = ArCO$ or $Ar \cdot SO_2$). If the acid was $H_2S_2O_9$, since it takes up 1 acyl to every S, it should give $Ac_2S_2O_9$, which would not be an acid at all, and so could not give a salt.

The salts of H_2SO_5 have not yet been obtained in the pure state.

With the formula H_2SO_5, and a peroxide link, the acid must be (in the ionized state)

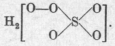

THIONIC ACIDS

These acids have the general formula $H_2S_nO_6$, where $n = 2, 3, 4, 5,$ and 6. The names trithionic and tetrathionic were invented by Berzelius.

The structures of these acids cannot be certainly known until they have been confirmed by the X-ray analysis of the crystals. This has so far only been done for the first two, of which the ions have been shown to be

Dithionic[542]   Trithionic[543]

The dithionic anion has the sulphur atoms tetrahedral and the trigonal axis along S—S; S—S is 2·08, S—O 1·50 (theory S—S 2·08; S—O 1·70, S=O 1·49).

It is usually assumed (for reasons given later) that the remaining acids are formed from trithionic by the co-ordination of one, two, or three sulphur atoms to the central sulphur, the ions being

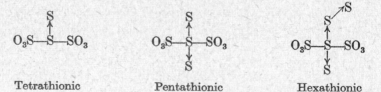

Tetrathionic   Pentathionic   Hexathionic

Dithionic Acid, $H_2S_2O_6$

This acid in many ways stands apart from the rest.[544] The fact that it is formed by the oxidation of sulphur dioxide, while the other thionic acids are formed by its reduction, though true, is a mere stoichiometric

[541] R. Willstätter and E. Hauenstein, *Ber.* 1909, **42**, 1849.
[542] W. H. Barnes and A. V. Wendling, *Z. Krist.* 1938, **99**, 153.
[543] W. H. Zachariasen, ib. 1934, **89**, 529.
[544] See E. H. Riesenfeld and G. W. Feld, *Z. anorg. Chem.* 1921, **119**, 225.

necessity, since the successive stages of polymerization of sulphurous acid would give:

$$2\,H_2SO_3 \;=\; H_4S_2O_6 \;=\; H_2O + H_2S_2O_5$$

$$3\,H_2SO_3 \;=\; H_6S_3O_9 \;=\; 2\,H_2O + H_2S_3O_7$$

$$4\,H_2SO_3 \;=\; H_8S_4O_{12} \;=\; 3\,H_2O + H_2S_4O_9$$

$$5\,H_2SO_3 \;=\; H_{10}S_5O_{15} \;=\; 4\,H_2O + H_2S_5O_{11}$$

$$6\,H_2SO_3 \;=\; H_{12}S_6O_{18} \;=\; 5\,H_2O + H_2S_6O_{13}.$$

A much stronger argument is that the higher acids can be made by treatment with alkali to lose sulphur until finally they are reduced to trithionic acid, but the loss will go no further; it is indeed possible to make trithionic acid lose sulphur by treatment with potassium cyanide, but then the product is not dithionic acid but sulphurous and sulphuric. Again, unlike the higher thionic acids dithionic acid is unaffected by strong oxidizing agents, even by concentrated nitric acid in the cold; nor will it take up sulphur to form the higher thionic acids.

These differences support the formulae suggested above; we may assume that any co-ordinated sulphur atoms can be removed from a thionic acid in this way, or can be added on by the action of colloidal sulphur, but that all these reagents leave the —S—S— and —S—S—S— chains intact.

Dithionic acid is made by the oxidation of sulphurous acid, being formed by the combination of two HSO_3 groups. Hence the oxidizing agent must not react too quickly, or it will convert the H_2SO_3 into H_2SO_4. The agents usually employed are therefore especially solid substances, which act only on the surface, and so give a low concentration of oxidizing agent: such are MnO_2 (most often used, especially in the finely divided or precipitated state), ferric hydroxide, or cobaltic hydroxide $Co(OH)_3$; Caro's acid can also be used, since it forms H_2O_2 slowly: but H_2O_2 itself, or barium peroxide, oxidize it straight to sulphuric acid.

It is prepared by the oxidation of H_2SO_3 with finely ground MnO_2. From the solution baryta precipitates all the oxy-acids of sulphur present except the dithionate, which can thus be separated. The free acid, obtained from the barium salt by precipitation with sulphuric acid, can be concentrated *in vacuo* to sp. gr. 1·347, but then begins to decompose into SO_2 and H_2SO_4.

No acid salts have been obtained, and so Kolbe thought that the acid was HSO_3; but Ostwald showed from the conductivity that the sodium salt is tri-ionic in water, and the freezing-points of the solutions confirm this.

The acid is slowly oxidized by air; zinc or sodium amalgam reduce it to H_2SO_3.

The salts are all soluble in water, like the nitrates and chlorates. The alkaline and alkaline earth salts are stable in water up to the boiling-point, but the others decompose to give SO_2 and sulphates. In the dry state this change occurs reversibly at a definite temperature depending on the metal.[545]

For the (unexplained) values of the X-ray absorption edges with the dithionates see reference [546].

Trithionic Acid, $H_2S_3O_6$

This is formed by the action of sulphur dioxide, or of hydrogen peroxide, on a thiosulphate:

$$3 SO_2 + 2 K_2S_2O_3 = 2 K_2S_3O_6 + S.$$

At the same time the free sulphur is partly taken up, with the formation of tetra- and pentathionate. Whether the tri- or the tetra-thionate separates is merely a matter of solubilities: for example, if it is aniline thiosulphate which is used, the tetrathionate separates out.[547-8] The salt can also be made by shaking strong aqueous potassium hydrogen sulphite solution with a solution of sulphur dichloride in light petroleum below 0°.[549]

The free acid is known only in aqueous solution.

Tetrathionic Acid, $H_2S_4O_6$

This is made, as has already been described under trithionic acid, by the action of sulphur dioxide on a thiosulphate. It is also made by the action of iodine on a thiosulphate:

$$2 Na_2S_2O_3 + I_2 = Na_2S_4O_6 + 2 NaI,$$

or by treating a saturated aqueous solution of sulphur dioxide below 0° with a solution of sulphur dichloride in light petroleum.[549]

The free acid is only known in solution. The salts are all soluble in water, but the solutions on evaporation usually decompose into a trithionate and free sulphur. On the other hand they combine with nascent (though not with ordinary) sulphur to form pentathionates.

The crystal structure of potassium tetrathionate seems to be very complicated.[550]

Pentathionic Acid, $H_2S_5O_6$

This can be made by the action of freshly separated sulphur on a tetrathionate, but it is usually obtained from 'Wackenroder's solution', of which it is a main constituent. This solution is made by passing H_2S at 0° into water saturated with SO_2, as long as it is taken up. The solution[551] is very complex, and contains much free sulphur; but if it is treated with potash and allowed to evaporate, a mixture of potassium tetra- and pentathionate separates.

[545] G. Tammann and W. Boehme, *Z. anorg. Chem.* 1932, **204**, 143.
[546] R. E. Winger and D. M. Yost, *Proc. Nat. Acad. Sci.* 1929, **15**, 462.
[547] E. Josephy and E. H. Riesenfeld, *Ber.* 1927, **60**, 252.
[548] F. Foerster and K. Centner, *Z. anorg. Chem.* 1926, **157**, 45.
[549] H. Stamm and M. Goehring, ib. 1942, **250**, 226.
[550] G. Tunell, H. E. Merwin, and C. J. Ksanda, *Amer. J. Sci.* 1938, [v] 35, A, 361.
[551] H. Debus, *J.C.S.* 1888, **53**, 278–357.

A solution of the salt decomposes on standing to give the tetrathionate and free sulphur.

Hexathionic Acid, $H_2S_6O_6$

Salts of this acid can be made by the action of concentrated hydrochloric acid on a thiosulphate, in presence of a trace either of arsenious oxide[552,554-5] or of potassium nitrite.[553] The formation in presence of nitrite is obscure; an intermediate green compound is formed which then loses its colour with evolution of nitric oxide. The salts are stable when dry, but in solution they slowly decompose to give pentathionate and free sulphur; in 6 weeks in this way one atom of sulphur had separated from every 2 S_6O_6''.[555] In alkaline solution the decomposition is quicker.

Alkaline sulphites convert hexathionates, as they do penta- and tetra-, to trithionates.[556]

SULPHUR AND THE HALOGENS

THE reactions of the different halogens with sulphur are usually so different that it is better to treat them separately.

SULPHUR AND FLUORINE

Five compounds of these elements have been described, (1) S_2F_2, (2) SF_2, (3) SF_4, (4) SF_6, (5) S_2F_{10}. Of these the last two are quite certain and the first nearly so; the second is doubtful and the third almost certainly wrong.

Sulphur Hexafluoride

This remarkable substance was discovered in 1900 by Moissan,[557-8] who made it from its elements; for later work see references [559-62].

It is a gas which melts at $-50 \cdot 7°$ C., and sublimes under one atmosphere at $-63 \cdot 8°$: the critical temperature is $+54°$.[563] The solid is dimorphic with a transition point at $94 \cdot 3°$ K, a melting point at $222 \cdot 5°$ K ($50 \cdot 7°$ C.), a heat of transition 0·384 and of fusion 1·201 k.cals./mole.[564] It has a normal vapour density, and is very slightly soluble in water and rather more in alcohol. It is surprisingly stable, behaving more like nitrogen

[552] A. Kurtenacker and A. Czernotzky, *Z. anorg. Chem.* 1928, **174**, 179.

[553] E. Weitz and F. Achterberg, *Ber.* 1928, **61**, 399.

[554] J. R. Partington and A. F. Tipler, *J.C.S.* 1929, 1382.

[555] A. Kurtenacker and K. Matejka, *Z. anorg. Chem.* 1936, **229**, 19.

[556] For further work on the thionic acids, and especially on their reactions with sulphurous and with thiosulphuric acid, see H. Stamm, O. Seipold, and M. Goehring, ib. 1941, **247**, 277.

[557] H. Moissan and P. Lebeau, *C.R.* 1900, **130**, 865, 984.

[558] Id., *Ann. Chim. Phys.* 1902, [7] **26**, 145.

[559] W. C. Schumb and E. L. Gamble, *J.A.C.S.* 1930, **52**, 4302.

[560] D. M. Yost and W. H. Claussen, ib. 1933, **55**, 888.

[561] O. Redlich, T. Kurz, and P. Rosenfeld, *J. Chem. Phys.* 1934, **2**, 619.

[562] D. M. Yost, C. C. Steffens, and S. T. Gross, ib. 311.

[563] E. B. R. Prideaux, *J.C.S.* 1906, **89**, 316.

[564] A. Eucken and E. Schröder, *Z. physikal. Chem.* 1938, B **41**, 307.

than a halide of sulphur. It can be heated in glass up to the softening point of the latter without change, and without attacking the glass. It is not absorbed by fused potash or fused lead chromate: it is unaffected below a red heat by fluorine, chlorine, iodine, oxygen, hydrogen, boron, silicon, carbon, copper, magnesium, hydrogen chloride, or ammonia. Sodium melted in it retains its bright surface until it begins to boil, when combination takes place. Phosphorus and arsenic can be distilled in it unchanged. It is only slowly decomposed even by a powerful electric discharge, either alone or when mixed with oxygen or hydrogen. Super-heated vapour of sulphur or selenium decomposes it, forming apparently lower fluorides, which at once attack the glass.

When it was first discovered, its composition and its properties were equally unexpected: but it is now clear that each of the 6 valency electrons is shared with a different fluorine, and that the stability is due to the valency group being of the maximum permissible size, and wholly shared. This conclusion is much strengthened by the fact that SeF_6 (where the covalency maximum is still 6) shows a similar stability, whereas TeF_6, though similar in physical properties, is hydrolysed by water, since the covalency maximum has now expanded to 8. Yost and Claussen[560] have fully confirmed these conclusions, in two ways: they have re-examined the differences in reactivity between SeF_6 and TeF_6, and confirmed and extended them, and by a careful determination of the thermodynamic properties they have shown that thermodynamically SF_6 should be com-pletely hydrolysed by water at 25°, so that its inertness is due to the magnitude of the heat of activation.

Sulphur Decafluoride, S_2F_{10}

This was discovered by Denbigh and Whytlaw-Gray[565] on fractionating the product of the action of fluorine on sulphur. It is a liquid boiling at $29 \pm 1°$, and melting at $-92°$. The Trouton constant is 23·0, and the parachor 236 ± 4. Like SF_6 it is chemically inactive, and obviously for the same reason, having the same 6-covalent sulphur atom, F_5S—SF_5.

[*Sulphur Tetrafluoride*]

This compound, which would indicate the presence of the inert pair in sulphur, was described by Fischer and Jaenckner in 1929[566]: but as this 'preliminary communication' has not been followed by another one, and no subsequent worker has obtained the compound, it presumably does not exist.

Sulphur Difluoride, S_2F_2 [*and* ? SF_2]

It is clear that there is a lower fluoride of sulphur, which is far more active and is absorbed by potash. This was found by Moissan, by Whytlaw-Gray (who says it boils at $-90°$), and others, among the products of the

[565] K. G. Denbigh and R. Whytlaw-Gray, *J.C.S.* 1934, 1346.
[566] J. Fischer and W. Jaenckner, *Z. angew. Chem.* 1929, **42**, 810.

action of fluorine on sulphur. It was also made by Centnerszwer and Strenk,[567-8] by the action of sulphur on silver or mercurous fluoride, but later Strenk[569] says that it attacks glass, and so the earlier work cannot be trusted. Trautz and Ehrmann[570] find that the substance readily decomposes to give sulphur and a fluoride SF_2, and that it is not possible to get either of these compounds pure. These conclusions have been confirmed by Dubnikoff and Zorin,[570a] who make the S_2F_2 by the action of excess of sulphur on silver fluoride at 200°, and find that at higher temperatures it decomposes to $S + SF_2$. It seems quite probable that the lower fluorides have these two formulae, like the chlorides S_2Cl_2 and SCl_2: there is no doubt that some lower fluoride exists, and that it is very reactive.

SULPHUR AND CHLORINE

Sulphur and chlorine can be mixed in the liquid state in all proportions, and the number of compounds which they form is large, and not quite certain. SCl_4, SCl_2, S_2Cl_2, S_3Cl_2, and S_4Cl_2 have all been described: of these the first three certainly exist, and one at least of the last two. Aten[571] has shown from the pressure and composition of the vapour given off by mixtures of the two elements, that there is a definite compound S_2Cl_2 which at its boiling-point (138°: m. pt. −80°) is only slightly dissociated in the vapour, and another compound SCl_2 which is only slowly formed from S_2Cl_2 and chlorine; it melts at about the same temperature as S_2Cl_2, and boils at +59°, but with very considerable dissociation.

Sulphur 'monochloride' S_2Cl_2 behaves as a non-associated covalent liquid. Its molecular weight is S_2Cl_2 according to the vapour density, and by the freezing-point in acetic acid, benzene, etc.: by the boiling-point in phosgene, ethyl chloride, sulphur dioxide, and even in liquid chlorine, since it combines with it to SCl_2 only slowly. It has a dielectric constant of 4·9 at 22°, a dipole moment of 1·60 D,[579] and is a non-conductor.

The exchange of radioactive sulphur with the monochloride is very slow in the cold, but measurable at 100° C.[572]

S_2Cl_2 is decomposed by water to give sulphur, H_2S, sulphite, thio-sulphate, and in acid (not in alkaline) solution much polythionic acids, especially the penta.[573-6]

[567] M. Centnerszwer and C. Strenk, *Ber.* 1923, **56**, 2249.
[568] Id., ib. 1925, **58**, 914.
[569] C. Strenk, *Latvij Univ. Raksti*, 1930, **1**, 233; *B.C.A.* 1930, 1538.
[570] M. Trautz and K. Ehrmann, *J. prakt, Chem.* 1935, [ii] **142**, 79.
[570a] M. Dubnikoff and N. I. Zorin, *J. Gen. Chem. U.S.S.R.* 1947, **17**, 185.
[571] A. H. W. Aten, *Z. physikal. Chem.* 1906, **54**, 55.
[572] R. A. Cooley and D. M. Yost, *J.A.C.S.* 1940, **62**, 2474.
[573] M. Goehring and H. Stamm, *Z. anorg. Chem.* 1942, **250**, 56.
[574] H. Böhme and E. Schneider, *Ber.* 1943, **76**, 483.
[575] H. Stamm and M. Goehring, ib. 737.
[576] M. Goehring, ib. 742.   [577] A. H. Spong, *J.C.S.* 1934, 490.
[578] G. Giacomello, *Atti R.* 1935, [vi] **21**, 36.
[579] K. J. Palmer, *J.A.C.S.* 1938, **60**, 2360.

There are two possible structures, Cl—S—S—Cl and

$$\begin{matrix} Cl \\ \searrow \\ \nearrow \\ Cl \end{matrix} S \rightarrow S,$$

and the substance may be tautomeric.[577-8] Electron diffraction[579] indicates in the vapour only the Cl—S—S—Cl form, with S—S 2·05, S—Cl 1·99 A, (theory 2·08, 2·03), and the Cl—S—S angle 103°.

Sulphur dichloride, SCl_2. This can be made by adding chlorine to S_2Cl_2 and distilling. It is a garnet red liquid, b. pt. +59°, melting over a long range from −80° to −60°: cryoscopic measurements in benzene, *p*-xylene, acetic acid, and ethylene dibromide all gave molecular weights from 103 to 110 ($SCl_2 = 103$); but $2 SCl_2$ will give the same molecular weight as $S_2Cl_2+Cl_2$. Beckman, however, showed that the substance gave the same molecular weight by the boiling-point in S_2Cl_2 and by the freezing-point in Cl_2. Electron diffraction shows[580] that the S—Cl distance is 2·00 A (theory S—Cl 2·03), and the Cl—S—Cl angle 103±3°; the dipole moment is 2·0 D. The reaction by which it is formed: $S_2Cl_2+Cl_2 = 2 SCl_2$ is slow at the ordinary temperature, but it is much hastened by iodine trichloride, or by stannic chloride. The products of its hydrolysis are very like those from S_2Cl_2.[573]

Supposed tri- and tetra-S-dichlorides, S_3Cl_2 *and* S_4Cl_2

The freezing-points of systems lying between S_2Cl_2 and sulphur suggest[581] that S_3Cl_2 and S_4Cl_2 are formed; it seems clear that at least one of these compounds is genuine.[582-3]

The one remaining chloride of sulphur is the *tetrachloride*, SCl_4. This can be obtained[584] as a yellow solid, which melts at about −30° to a red liquid, which at once begins to evolve chlorine. It is completely dissociated into SCl_2 and chlorine at the ordinary temperature.

This compound is of peculiar interest. All the other chlorides can be simply formulated, and their structures, though uncertain, are obviously possible. SCl_4, if it is a covalent compound, analogous to the tetrachlorides of silicon or tin, must have the valency group 2, 8, that is, it must show the inert pair of electrons, which is otherwise almost unknown with sulphur.

It is therefore important that all the evidence is against the existence of SCl_4 in anything but the solid state. The liquid formed on fusing it has all the properties (including the colour) of a mixture in equimolecular proportions of SCl_2 and Cl_2. This has been clearly established by Lowry.[585-6]

[580] D. P. Stevenson and J. Y. Beach, *J.A.C.S.* 1938, **60**, 2872.
[581] O. Ruff and H. Golla, *Z. anorg. Chem.* 1924, **138**, 33.
[582] T. M. Lowry *et al.*, *J.C.S.* 1927, 746; 1929, 1421; 1930, 782, 1005; 1931, 323.
[583] D.Ll. Hammick and M. Zvegintzov, ib. 1928, 1785.
[584] O. Ruff, *Ber.* 1904, **37**, 4513.
[585] T. M. Lowry and G. Jessup, *J.C.S.* 1930, 1005.
[586] T. M. Lowry, *Z. Elektrochem.* 1930, **36**, 733.

He has also shown that while the other chlorides of sulphur have a higher dielectric constant in the liquid than in the solid state (like polar covalent molecules in general), the dielectric constant of a solution of sulphur in chlorine of the composition SCl_4 rises from 3 to about 6 on freezing, which must mean that a new and highly polar solid form of SCl_4 is produced. Its high dielectric constant is that of a salt, and so it must be $[SCl_3]Cl$— trichlorosulphonium chloride; it behaves like ammonium chloride, which can only exist in the solid state. Hence the valency group of the sulphur has the sulphonium form of 2, 6, and so this compound is no evidence for the occurrence of the inert pair in sulphur.

This seems to be the only halide of sulphur which is capable of forming addition compounds. Such are $SbCl_5$, SCl_4 (stable in an atmosphere of chlorine, where it melts and sublimes about 125°: $SbCl_5$ forms no compound with SCl_2); $TlCl_4$, SCl_4 (soluble in CS_2, ligroin, etc.); $SnCl_4$, $2 SCl_4$; $FeCl_3$, SCl_4; $AlCl_3$, SCl_4; $2 ICl_3$, SCl_4 (soluble in ligroin, $CHCl_3$, CCl_4, etc.); $2 AsF_3$, SCl_4. These compounds are all, except the last two, characteristic of a donor molecule. Some of them could be complex salts of the SCl_3 cation, as $[SCl_3](SbCl_6)$; but the low melting-points (this compound melts at 125°) and the solubility in non-associated liquids suggest that some at least are covalent molecules such as $Cl_4S \rightarrow SbCl_5$. This gives the sulphur a decet of shared electrons, as in PF_5, with no 'inert pair'.

SULPHUR AND BROMINE

Only one compound of these elements has been prepared, S_2Br_2; it is made by heating bromine with excess of sulphur in a sealed tube, and distilling under very low pressure.[587] It is a garnet-red liquid, boiling at 57° under 0·22 mm., and at atmospheric pressure probably about 200°, but with much dissociation. The molecular weight is S_2Br_2 in bromine, and cryoscopically in $POCl_3$. It is slowly decomposed by water, giving sulphur, SO_2, and HBr. It has been shown[587-8] that more highly brominated compounds do not exist.

SULPHUR AND IODINE

A variety of solid phases have been examined, but there is no evidence that any of them are anything more than solid solutions of iodine in sulphur. The solubility of sulphur or of iodine in chloroform or in carbon disulphide is practically unaffected by the presence of the other element.[589]

The regularity and the extent to which the affinity for a halogen falls off with the increase of the atomic number of the halogen, is far greater with sulphur than with any other element.

[587] O. Ruff and G. Winterfeld, *Ber.* 1903, **36**, 2437.
[588] W. Finkelstein, *Z. physikal. Chem.* 1923, **105**, 10.
[589] A. Jakovkin and P. A. Archangelski, *Z. anorg. Chem.* 1936, **226**, 350.

SELENIUM AND TELLURIUM

THE frequency of these elements in the earth's crust is:

	Sulphur	*Selenium*	*Tellurium*	*Polonium*
G./ton	500	0·6	0·01	$1·4 \times 10^{-11}$

Selenium and tellurium are usually found in small quantities in the sulphide ores of heavy metals; they seldom occur as pure compounds, especially selenium. They are commonly obtained from the flue dust formed on roasting sulphide ores, or from the lead-chamber mud of the sulphuric acid manufactures.

In properties selenium lies much nearer to sulphur than to tellurium; for example, the tendency of selenium to form cations Se^{++++} is very small, and selenic acid is H_2SeO_4, like sulphuric H_2SO_4, whereas telluric is $(HO)_6Te$.

The most important theoretical differences between selenium and tellurium are:

(1) that the covalency limit for selenium is 6 and for tellurium 8, and

(2) that the inertness of the first valency pair of electrons is much more marked in tellurium than in selenium. In sulphur, there is practically no sign of it, any more than in phosphorus; but as usual it is more marked in the later groups—more evident in tellurium than in antimony, and more in selenium than in arsenic, where it is barely perceptible.

Elementary Selenium

This element like sulphur occurs in several allotropic forms. There probably[590] are, as with sulphur, at least two molecular species in the liquid (though this does not show the same anomalous changes of colour and viscosity with temperature[591] as sulphur) and three if not four solid forms.

The molecular weight in the vapour is that of Se_2 at 900° and above,[592-3] but falls to Se at 2,000°[594]; at 200° (the b. pt. is 685°) it is $Se_{6·03}$.[595] Electron diffraction[596] indicates that in Se_2 the Se—Se distance is 2·19 (theory Se—Se 2·34, Se=Se 2·14), and that the large molecule present at low temperatures has a puckered ring,[597] though the results agree better with a 6-ring than with an 8-ring; but the size of the molecule is Se_8 in

[590] See G. Briegleb, *Naturwiss.* 1929, **17**, 51; *Z. physikal. Chem.* 1929, **144**, 321, 340.

[591] S. Dobinski and J. Weselowski, *Bull. Acad. Polonaise*, 1937, A. 7.

[592] H. Biltz, *Z. physikal. Chem.* 1896, **19**, 385.

[593] E. C. Szarvasy, *Ber.* 1897, **30**, 1244, 1343.

[594] H. v. Wartenberg, *Z. anorg. Chem.* 1908, **56**, 320.

[595] K. Neumann and E. Lichtenberg, *Z. physikal. Chem.* 1939, **184**, 89.

[596] L. R. Maxwell and V. H. Mosley, *Phys. Rev.* 1940, ii. **57**, 21.

[597] J. D. Howe and K. Lark-Horovitz. ib. 1937, ii. **51**, 380.

solution in carbon disulphide and in liquid sulphur[598] and also, according to X-ray analysis,[599] in the red monoclinic form of the element.

The heats of linkage of the atoms in elementary sulphur, selenium, and tellurium[600-1] are given above, p. 876.

In colour the vapour of selenium comes between sulphur and chlorine. The liquid is brownish-red; it boils at 685°[603]; its heat of evaporation is 32·77 k.cals. per Se$_8$ mol.[595] (Trouton 34·3); the heat of fusion is 12·45 k.cals.

The solid forms are of two kinds, one red, bulky, and transparent, and the other grey, opaque, dense, and semi-metallic; there are probably two forms of each kind. There is also an amorphous form[604] which becomes elastic, like plastic sulphur, at 70°; on cooling it solidifies, but becomes plastic again at 72°.

The red forms are commonly those first produced; they are got by cooling molten selenium; they separate from the ruby-red solution in carbon disulphide, and on the reduction of selenium compounds such as the dioxide. One at least of these red forms is monoclinic, and is red by transmitted and blue by reflected light; it has a density of 4·42, a dielectric constant of 7·39 at 3°, and melts at 144°. It is metastable, and goes over into the grey form. X-ray examination has shown that there are two forms of red selenium.[595,605]

Grey selenium also occurs in two forms A and B, of which B is the stable form, and is ordinary grey selenium. It melts at 220·2°, has a density of 4·82 (9 per cent. greater than the red form), and is isomorphous with tellurium. Its solubility in carbon disulphide is 2 mg. in 100 c.c. at the ordinary temperature. The A form is slightly more soluble (3·2 mg.) and is metastable, going over slowly to the B. Its metallic character is almost confined to its appearance: its electrical conductivity in the cold is only 2×10^{-6}.

The effect of light in increasing the conductivity of selenium is well known and is made use of technically. This is a property of the grey form: the conductivity increases up to something like a thousand times on exposure to light: the most effective wave-length is 7,000 A. The phenomenon is very obscure: the resistance of this form varies even in the dark with the E.M.F., the time, and the history of the specimen. The change is probably due to the shifting of electrons, as with silver iodide or zinc sulphate.[606-13]

[598] C. R. Platzmann, *Bull. Chem. Soc. Japan*, 1930, **5**, 79.
[599] F. Halla, F. X. Bosch, and E. Mehl, *Z. physikal. Chem.* 1931, **B 11**, 455.
[600] P. Goldfinger, W. Jeunehomme, and B. Rosen, *Nature*, 1936, **138**, 205.
[601] H. v. Wartenberg, *Z. anorg. Chem.* 1907, **56**, 320.
[603] M. de Selincourt, *Proc. Phys. Soc.* 1940, **52**, 348.
[604] K. H. Meyer and J. F. Sievers, *Naturwiss.* 1937, **25**, 171.
[605] H. P. Klug, *Z. Krist.* 1934, **88**, 128.
[606] R. Marc, *Die physikalische Eigenschaften des Selens, Leipsig*, 1907.
[607] A. H. Pfund, *Phys. Z.* 1909, **10**, 340.
[608] C. Ries, ib. 1911, **12**, 480, 522.

The molecular weight found for selenium in various solvents is very variable, owing no doubt to its tendency to form compounds: the natural solubility of the stable grey form is small, judging by its high melting-point, and solvents like the selenium halides, the sulphur halides, etc., give low values (Se_1—Se_2) which are probably due to combination with the first two, and the formation of solid solutions with the last. But the Se_8 molecule is clearly very stable, as it is with sulphur, and this molecule weight has been found in carbon disulphide, in diphenyl, in molten sulphur, and in yellow phosphorus.[615]

A remarkable use of elementary selenium is in organic chemistry, for the dehydrogenation of hydroaromatic to aromatic compounds,[616-17] which is of great importance in elucidating the structure of natural products: they are heated for some hours with selenium to temperatures of 250–350°, and SeH_2 is evolved. Sulphur reacts in the same way, but more violently, and may enter the organic molecule, or even break it down altogether.

Elementary Tellurium

Of solid tellurium there are only two certain forms, one amorphous, and, like most amorphous substances, variable in properties, and the other, the ordinary form, crystalline and isomorphous with grey selenium B. This is a silver-white substance with a metallic glance. Beyond this, however, it has little of the metal about it. Its electrical conductivity is very small, being at 500° about 1 per cent. of that of cold mercury[618]: at the ordinary temperature the number of free electrons cannot be more than 1 to every 10^6 atoms of tellurium. Even this minute conductivity may be due to impurities, to which the conductivity is extraordinarily sensitive[619]: 0·2 per cent. of antimony or bismuth increases it 100 times, and the presence of less than 0·01 per cent. of either of these elements would account for the whole conductivity of 'pure' tellurium.

Light causes a small increase in the conductivity.

'Metallic' tellurium melts at 449·8°[620] to a dark liquid which boils at 1,390° C. The heat of evaporation obtained from the vapour pressures at

[609] C. Ries, *Ann. D. Phys.* 1911, [4] **36**, 1055.

[610] L. Amaduzzi, *Phys. Z.* 1912, **13**, 165.

[611] P. J. Nicholson, ib. 1913, **14**, 1211.

[612] B. Gudden and R. Pohl, ib. 1921, **22**, 529.

[613] W. Späth, *Z. Phys.* 1921, **8**, 165.

[615] For this last see E. Beckmann and H. Pfeiffer, *Z. physikal. Chem.* 1897, **22**, 615.

[616] O. Diels and A. Karstens, *Ber.* 1927, **60**, 2323; for the limitations of the reaction see G. R. Clemo and H. G. Dickenson, *J.C.S.* 1935, 735.

[617] Id., ib. 1937, 255; R. L. Barker and G. R. Clemo, ib. 1940, 1277.

[618] C. A. Kraus and E. W. Johnson, *J. Phys. Chem.* 1928, **32**, 1281.

[619] C. H. Cartwright and M. Haberfeld-Schwarz, *Nature*, 1934, **134**, 287; *Proc. Roy. Soc.* 1935, **148**, 648.

[620] F. C. Kracek, *J.A.C.S.* 1941, **63**, 1989.

lower temperatures 480–671° [621] is 22·0 k.cals., which gives the remarkable Trouton constant of $22,000/1663 = 13·2$.

In the vapour the molecular weight is that of Te_2 from 1,400 to 1,800°, with perhaps a small tendency to further association at lower temperatures. The Te—Te distance is found by electron diffraction[622-3] to be 2·59 and from the spectrum[624] to be 2·61 A (theory Te—Te 2·74, Te=Te 2·54).

Tellurium is insoluble in benzene and in all solvents that do not react with it, so that its molecular weight at the ordinary temperature cannot be determined, and we do not know whether the peculiar M_8 molecule of sulphur and selenium occurs with tellurium as well. It burns in air, and combines with the halogens, but not with sulphur or selenium. Its compounds are nearly always colourless, except the polytellurides, which are deep red.

Tellurium is one of the very few elements which undoubtedly form both monatomic anions and monatomic cations. Te^{--} and Te^{++++} are both colourless, and both very readily go over into the covalent form, Te^{--} giving the polytellurides, and Te^{++++} readily forming complexes, especially those with a co-ordination number of 6, such as K_2TeCl_6. Te^{--} thus resembles O^{--} or S^{--}, while Te^{++++} (in which, of course, the first electron pair is inert) is more like quadrivalent platinum.

If two tellurium electrodes are immersed in potassium hydroxide solution, and a current passed, tellurium is dissolved from each electrode and transported to the other, the anode giving Te^{++++} and the cathode Te^{--}. Polonium behaves in the same way.[625] If either electrode is replaced by platinum, tellurium is deposited on it.

The solution potential of these elements in decinormal potassium hydroxide is[626] S 0·53; Se 0·804; Te 1·07 v., so that tellurium may be called the 'noblest metalloid'.[627-8]

Hydrides

The hydrides of all the five elements of this series, O, S, Se, Te, Po are known, the last only slightly. Since they are all two places before an inert gas in the table, the hydrides MH_2 are all volatile. A comparison of the properties of the first four is interesting.

	H_2O	H_2S	H_2Se	H_2Te
M. pt. . . .	0°	−85·5°	−66°[d]	−51·2°[f]
B. pt. . . .	100°	−60·4°	−41·5°	+ 2°
Diss. const. k . .	$1·3+10^{-16}$	1×10^{-7}	$1·3 \times 10^{-4e}$	$2·3 \times 10^{-3c}$
k rel. . . .	$1·3+10^{-9}$	1	1,300	23,000
Ht. of fusion[b] . .	1·44	0·4	1·57	0·97 k.cals.
Ht. of evap.[b] . .	10·57	4·5	4·71	4·58
Trouton const.[b] . .	28·3	21·1	20·4	16·7
Ht. of formn. from atoms[a] . . .	220·7	175·0	146·3	124·6

$a = $ [629], $b = $ [630], $c = $ [631], $d = $ [632], $e = $ [633], $f = $ [634]

Hydrogen selenide H_2Se is made by the action of acids on metallic selenides, especially aluminium selenide, or by heating elementary selenium with a high boiling paraffin motor oil to $380°$.[635] It is colourless in all states; it has a very offensive smell, and is far more poisonous than H_2S. From the infra-red spectrum[636-7] the Se—H distance is $1·6$ A (theory $1·47$), and H—Se angle rather more than $90°$. Solid H_2Se is trimorphic.[638] Water dissolves about 3 times its volume of the gas at $0°$.[639] It forms a solid hydrate (H_2Se, xH_2O) with a dissociation tension of 432 mm. at $2°$, and 11 atm. at $30°$, above which temperature it apparently melts.

Chemically hydrogen selenide is very unstable, and it decomposes slowly at the ordinary temperature, and rapidly above $300°$, even in absence of air, especially in presence of elementary selenium. For its oxidation by gaseous oxygen see reference[639a].

Hydrogen telluride H_2Te is made like the selenide by the action of acids on metallic tellurides, especially that of aluminium Al_2Te_3, and must be purified by freezing out. Its vapour density is normal. It forms a pale yellow liquid and a colourless solid; it is even more offensive in smell than the selenide, and at least as poisonous.

It is the least stable of the four gases, the affinity for hydrogen always falling as the atomic weight increases. It decomposes alone and in the cold unless it is quite dry; like H_2Se if it is pure and dry it is not decomposed by light. It is fairly soluble in water, but the solution soon begins to deposit tellurium.

There is some evidence for a hydride H_2Se_2[640]; the gas evolved when aluminium and hydrochloric acid are added to aqueous selenious acid gives with lead acetate a black precipitate of $PbSe_2$, and so may contain H_2Se_2 (this is a very delicate test for selenium, and will detect it in wheat ash). Otherwise more complex hydrides of selenium and tellurium, corre-

[621] J. J. Doolan and J. R. Partington, *Trans. Far. Soc.* 1924, **20**, 342.

[622] L. R. Maxwell and V. M. Mosley, *Phys. Rev.* 1937, ii. **51**, 684.

[623] Id., ib. 1940, ii. **57**, 21.

[624] M. L. Huggins, *J. Chem. Phys.* 1937, **5**, 201.

[625] M. Le Blanc, *Z. Elektrochem.* 1906, **12**, 649.

[626] E. Müller and R. Novakovski, ib. 1905, **11**, 931.

[627] D. Reichinstein, *Z. physikal. Chem.* 1921, **97**, 257.

[628] R. T. Glauser, *Z. angew. Chem.* 1921, **34**, 154.

[629] Bichowski and Rossini, *Thermochemistry*, New York, 1936.

[630] N. O. Stein, *J.C.S.* 1931, 2134.

[631] M. de Hlasko, *Extr. Bull. Akad. Pol.* 1919, [A] 73.

[632] Id., ib. 1921, [A] 18.

[633] H. Hagisawa, *Bull. Inst. Phys. Chem. Res. Japan*, 1941, **20**, 384.

[634] P. L. Robinson and W. E. Scott, *J.C.S.* 1932, 972.

[635] C. Green and W. E. Bradt, *Proc. Indiana Acad. Sci.* 1934, **43**, 116.

[636] W. C. Sears, D. M. Cameron, and H. H. Nielsen, *Phys. Rev.* 1938, ii. **53**, 330.

[637] Id., *J. Chem. Phys.* 1939, **7**, 994.

[638] A. Kruis and K. Clusius, *Z. physikal. Chem.* 1937, B **38**, 156.

[639] A. J. McAmis and W. A. Felsing, *J.A.C.S.* 1925, **47**, 2633.

[639a] D. J. G. Ives and R. W. Pittman, *J.C.S.* 1948, 766.

[640] J. P. Nielsen, S. Maeser, and D. S. Jennings, *J.A.C.S.* 1939, **61**, 440.

sponding to H_2O_2 or H_2S_2, do not seem to be known.[641] Organic derivatives of these types are known.

Metallic Selenides and Tellurides

The metallic selenides are very like the sulphides. Those of the alkalies[642-3] are soluble in water, and colourless when pure; they all have fluorite lattices except Rb_2Se and Cs_2Se; in solution they are soon oxidized by air with the separation of selenium. The hydrogen selenides $MSeH$[644] can be made in alcohol; they all have NaCl lattices except CsSeH, which has a CsCl lattice; they are decomposed by air and water. Polyselenides up to M_2Se_5 can be made,[645-7] for example, by acting on the metal with a solution of selenium in liquid ammonia.[648]

The alkaline earth selenides are similar; BeSe, ZnSe, and HgSe have zinc blende, and CdSe a wurtzite lattice.[649]

The tellurides are on the whole similar, but even less stable. The alkaline tellurides are soluble in water and give colourless solutions when pure, but these are very readily oxidized to polytellurides; hence these tellurides are strong reducing agents, and will, for example, reduce a tellurite to metallic tellurium. The behaviour of fused mixtures of sodium telluride and tellurium has been examined by Kraus.[650] He showed that the liquid if it contained but little sodium telluride conducted electricity like a metal, but if it contained much, like a salt. The solid phases isolated were Na_2Te, Na_2Te_2, and Na_2Te_6, this last having a congruent melting-point of 436°.

Polytellurides are only known of the alkalies, and mostly only in solution. They are dark red, and, as we have seen, very sensitive to atmospheric oxygen.

ALKYL AND ARYL COMPOUNDS

A LARGE number of dialkyl and diaryl selenides are known, as well as a series of cyclic compounds of the polymethylene-selenide type. They differ markedly from the ethers, and to a less extent from the thioethers, in having a definitely unsaturated behaviour. While the ethers are very inactive and stable substances, the thioethers can react with alkyl halides to form stable sulphonium salts: the analogous oxonium salts cannot as a rule be formed, unless one of the radicals attached to the oxygen is a hydrogen, and then of course they readily dissociate. The selenoethers have the same power of going over into selenonium salts of the type

[641] For attempts to prepare these selenides, see E. Müller, *Ber.* 1903, **36**, 4262.
[642] A. Bergmann, *Z. anorg. Chem.* 1937, **231**, 269.
[643] W. Klemm, H. Sodomann, and P. Langmesser, ib. 1939, **241**, 281.
[644] W. Teichert and W. Klemm, ib. 1939, **243**, 86.
[645] E. Müller and R. Novakovski, *Ber.* 1905, **38**, 3779.
[646] Id., *Z. Elektrochem.* 1905, **11**, 931.
[647] M. Le Blanc, ib. 813.
[648] F. W. Bergstrom, *J.A.C.S.* 1926, **48**, 146, 2319.
[649] W. H. Zachariasen, *Z. physikal. Chem.* 1926, **124**, 436.
[650] C. A. Kraus and S. W. Glass, *J. phys. Chem.* 1929, **33**, 984, 999.

$R_3Se[X]$, but in addition, they can take up oxygen in presence of oxidizing agents, or halogens, to form such compounds as Alk_2SeO or Alk_2SeCl_2. In these the valency group of the Se is $6+4 = 10_4 = 2, \underline{8}$; in other words it has an inert pair, which is possible for selenium (and also for tellurium) but scarcely for sulphur.

The boiling-points of a series of alkyl derivatives are given below:

X =	O	S	Se	Te
$CH_3 \cdot XH$	65°	$+7 \cdot 6°$	12°	57°
$Et \cdot XH$	78·5°	34·7°	53·5°	90°
$Pr \cdot XH$	97·2°	68°	84°	121°
$(CH_3)_2X$	−24°	36·2°	58°	82°
Et_2X	34·5°	91·6°	108°	137·5°
Pr_2X	91°	142°	159°	..
$C_6H_5 \cdot XH$	183°	169°	183·6°	..

The effect of association in the alcohols is obvious: apart from this the average difference is $(S)-(O) = 55°$; $(Se)-(S) = 15°$; $(Te)-(Se) = 30-40°$: thus the general conclusion that the resemblance is closer between sulphur and selenium than between selenium and tellurium is borne out here too. (The atomic weight differences are Se—S 46·9, Te—Se 48·6.)

Selenomercaptans, $R \cdot Se \cdot H$

These compounds[651] are very like the mercaptans in their general behaviour, but are far more readily oxidized, and must be made (from the alkyl halide and sodium selenide solution: or by distilling $Alk \cdot SO_4H$ with alkaline MSeH: or from the Grignard reagents and elementary selenium) in an atmosphere of hydrogen. The telluromercaptans are still less stable.

The selenomercaptans have a most repulsive smell (far worse than that of the selenoethers) and soon infect not only the laboratory but the whole neighbourhood as well. They are not miscible with water (the boiling-points show that like the mercaptans they are not associated), but they dissolve in aqueous alkali, and themselves dissolve mercuric oxide.

The aromatic analogues $Ar \cdot Se \cdot H$ are got by the reduction of the diselenides Ar_2Se_2, or the seleninic $Ar \cdot SeO_2H$ or selenonic $Ar \cdot SeO_3H$ acids by sodium and alcohol. They are very like the alkyl compounds[652]; they dissolve very slightly in water, easily in ether and chloroform, and are rapidly oxidized by air to the diselenides $Ar \cdot Se \cdot Se \cdot Ar$. This oxidation occurs particularly easily in the presence of ortho- or para-nitro-groups; they then are at once oxidized by air to the diselenides,[653] like their sulphur analogues.[654-5]

[651] L. Tschugaeff, *Ber.* 1909, **42**, 49.
[652] F. Krafft and R. E. Lyons, ib. 1894, **27**, 1763.
[653] D. G. Foster and S. F. Brown, *J.A.C.S.* 1928, **50**, 1182.
[654] H. Lecher and K. Simon, *Ber.* 1922, **55**, 2426.
[655] K. Brand and A. Wirsing, ib. 1913, **46**, 822.

Dialkyl Selenides, Alk_2Se

These can be made (like the sulphur compounds) from alkaline selenides and alkyl sulphuric acid (S. C. Löwig, 1836), and in other ways; for example, the reaction

$$SeBr_4 + 3 Ar_2Hg = Ar_2Se + Ar \cdot Br + 3 Ar \cdot Hg \cdot Br$$

goes almost quantitatively.[656] The C—Se—C angle in dimethyl selenide is found by Raman and infra-red spectra to be $99 \cdot 3°$.[657] The following dipole moments have been found[658] in benzene at $25°$: $(p\text{-tol})_2Se$ $1 \cdot 81$; $(p\text{-Cl} \cdot C_6H_4)_2Se$ $0 \cdot 77$ D.

They are unassociated liquids: their smell is offensive, but not as bad as that of the selenomercaptans. They are not so extremely sensitive to oxidation, since they have no hydrogen on the selenium, but still they behave definitely as unsaturated compounds. They readily add on halogen to form the dihalide $Alk_2Se(hal)_2$ and are converted by oxidizing agents such as dichromate or permanganate to the selenoxides Alk_2SeO, or by nitric acid to a salt of the selenoxide $Alk_2Se \cdot OH[NO_3]$, which can be converted by hydrochloric acid into the dichloride. They cannot be oxidized to the selenonic acids $Alk \cdot SeO_3H$ (corresponding to the sulphonic acids, which are the product of the oxidation of mercaptans): these acids are indeed little known.

Diaryl selenides are easily got by the action of selenium on mercury aryls: sulphur and tellurium act in the same way. They can also be made by heating the diaryl sulphones with selenium[659]

$$\Phi_2SO_2 + Se = \Phi_2Se + SO_2.$$

Unsymmetrical selenides can be made from the diaryl selenides and the Grignard reagent, or from mercury diaryl and aryl selenium bromide $Ar \cdot Se \cdot Br$.[660] They are as unsaturated as the alkyl compounds. They are oxidized, for example, by dichromate in acetic acid, to the selenoxides, and are converted by bromine into the dibromides, such as Φ_2SeBr_2, which is a yellow or red crystalline substance, forming mixed crystals with Φ_2TeBr_2. It is to be noticed that whereas diphenyl sulphide is at once brominated by Br_2 in the cold, Φ_2Se, which also reacts with bromine at once, is not brominated but converted into the dibromide Φ_2SeBr_2, on which excess of bromine has scarcely any action.[659]

The diaryl selenides are, however, stable enough to be nitrated without rupture, the NO_2 groups going to the meta position [661-2] ($\Phi \cdot Se \cdot CN$ nitrates wholly in the ortho- and para-positions).[663]

[656] H. M. Leicester, *J.A.C.S.* 1938, **60**, 619.
[657] P. Donzelot, *C.R.* 1936, **203**, 1069.
[658] M. T. Rogers and T. W. Campbell, *J.A.C.S.* 1947, **69**, 2039.
[659] F. Krafft and W. Vorster, *Ber.* 1893, **26**, 2813.
[660] T. W. Campbell and J. D. McCullough, *J.A.C.S.* 1945, **67**, 1965.
[661] C. K. Banks and C. S. Hamilton, ib. 1939, **61**, 2306.
[662] D. G. Foster, ib. 1941, **63**, 1361.
[663] F. Challenger and D. I. James, *J.C.S.* 1936, 1609.

Cyclic Selenoethers

These compounds, which may also be called polymethylene selenides, have the general formula $(CH_2)_n$ Se: the C_3, C_4, C_5, and C_6 have been made by Morgan and Burstall[664-7] by the action of alkaline selenide in aqueous solution on the requisite polymethylene bromide in the absence of air. In general they resemble the dialkyl selenides: they readily form dihalides, from which the selenoxides can be prepared; these latter are almost neutral[665] or even slightly acid [664] in character. They are all volatile liquids, and it is interesting to compare their boiling-points with those of the corresponding compounds of other elements of this series:

Boiling-points of Cyclic Ethers

Type X =	O	S	Se	Te
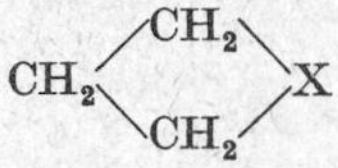 $CH_2\underset{CH_2}{\overset{CH_2}{\diagup\diagdown}}X$	50°	94°	118°	..
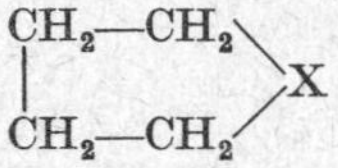 $\underset{CH_2-CH_2}{\overset{CH_2-CH_2}{\diagup}}\diagdown X$	57°	118°	135°	166°/760 mm.
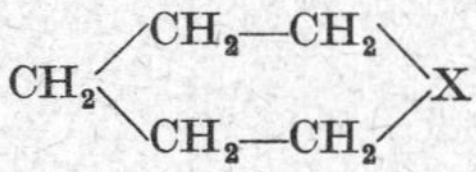 $CH_2\underset{CH_2-CH_2}{\overset{CH_2-CH_2}{\diagup\diagdown}}X$	81°	142°	158°	82°/12 mm.
$CH_2\underset{CH_2-CH_2}{\overset{CH_2-CH\diagdown CH_3}{\diagup\diagdown}}X$	..	..	170°	..
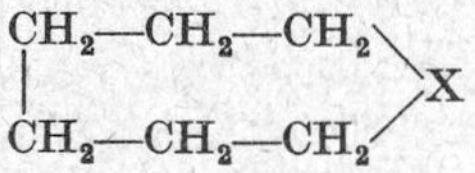 $\underset{CH_2-CH_2-CH_2}{\overset{CH_2-CH_2-CH_2}{\diagup}}\diagdown X$	..	..	190°	..

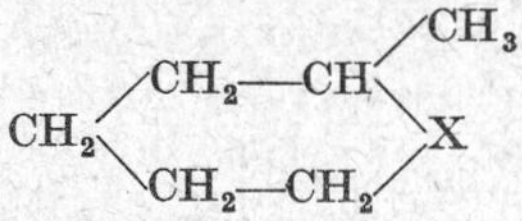

Thiophene type

	O	S	Se	Te
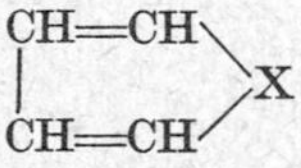 $\underset{CH=CH}{\overset{CH=CH}{\diagup}}\diagdown X$	32°	87°	110°	..

The two extreme members of the series, the trimethylene and the hexamethylene[668] compounds (i.e. the 4-ring and the 7-ring) have pecu-

[664] G. T. Morgan and F. H. Burstall, *J.C.S.* 1929, 1096 (C_4Se).
[665] Id., ib. 2197 (C_5Se).   [666] Id., ib. 1930, 1497 (C_3Se).
[667] Id., ib. 1931, 173 (C_6Se).
[668] Morgan (Pres. Address, *J.C.S.* 1935, 564) has been able to get a small yield of the compound with a C_{18}Se ring, $(CH_2)_{18}$ Se, though in the formation most of the material polymerizes. Other compounds with rings of the dithian type, as

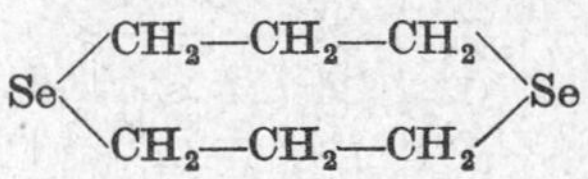

$$Se\underset{CH_2-CH_2-CH_2}{\overset{CH_2-CH_2-CH_2}{\diagup\diagdown}}Se$$

have also been made.

liarities. With both of them the yield is small, the reaction leading mainly to polymerization; the structures of these polymers are not understood.

Spiro compounds with Se—C rings can also be made[669]; thus

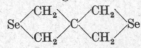

m. pt. 67°, is got from potassium selenide and tetrabromopenterythritol $C(CH_2Br)_4$.

Selenophene

Dimethyl selenophene

was prepared in 1885[670] by the action of phosphorus pentaselenide on acetonyl acetone; but the mother substance was first made in 1928 by Briscoe and his co-workers,[671-4] by the action of selenium vapour on acetylene at about 400°; bauxite (Al_2O_3) can be used as a catalyst.*

Selenophene

$$\begin{array}{c} CH=CH \\ | \quad\quad\; \rangle Se \\ CH=CH \end{array}$$

boils at 108° and has a normal vapour density. It has a dipole moment of 0·78 D in benzene and 0·77 D in hexane.[675] Like thiophene it is in many ways very stable: it is unaffected by boiling with water, alkalies, or hydrochloric acid, or by heating with methyl iodide in a sealed tube for 24 hours at 160° (no selenonium compound is formed), and it is not oxidized by permanganate. But nitric or sulphuric acid decomposes it completely. Halogens, if they are very dilute, will replace the hydrogen, but otherwise they form tetra- and hexahalides, in which first one halogen adds on to every carbon, and then two more to the selenium.[676]

Selenophthene

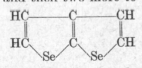

is stated to have been made[676-7] in a cis and two trans forms, the first a liquid of dipole moment 1·52, and the others (a) m. pt. 51°, dip. mom. 0: (b) m. pt. 124°, dip. mom. 1·07.

* McMahon and Pearson[674] have tried to make tellurophane in this way, and believe they obtained some, though they could not isolate it.

669 H. J. Backer and H. J. Winter, *Rec. Trav.* 1937, **56**, 492, 691.

670 C. Paal, *Ber.* 1885, **18**, 2255.

671 H. V. A. Briscoe and J. B. Peel, *J.C.S.* 1928, 1741.

672 H. V. A. Briscoe, J. B. Peel, and P. L. Robinson, ib. 2628.

673 H. V. A. Briscoe, J. B. Peel, and G. W. Young, ib. 1929, 2589.

674 F. A. McMahon, T. G. Pearson, and P. L. Robinson, ib. 1933, 1644.

675 B. Tamamushi, H. Akiyama, and S. Umezawa, *Bull. Chem. Soc. Japan*, 1939, **14**, 310.

676 H. Suginome and S. Umezawa, ib. 1936, **11**, 157.

Selenanthrene

The X-ray analysis of this compound indicates a fold of 127° round the Se—Se line, with the C—Se distance 1·96 (theory 1·94) and the angle at Se (i.e. C—Se—C) 96°.[678] [Compare thianthrene, p. 882.]

Selenonium Compounds, $R_3Se[X]$

These compounds[679-80] are formed with great readiness by the action of alkyl halides on the selenoethers (including the cyclic ethers, but not the unsaturated selenophene). The halides are definite salts $R_3Se[hal]$, usually soluble in water but not in ether, and with silver oxide they give the strongly basic hydroxides $R_3Se[OH]$ (the di-hydroxides of the selenoxides R_2SeO are scarcely if at all basic).

The p-hydroxy-aryl compounds can be made[681] by the action of phenols on selenium oxychloride $SeOCl_2$.[682] The so-called selenitines, in which one radical is that of a carboxylic acid, such as CH_2—COOH, were used by Pope and Neville[683] to obtain optically active selenium compounds. They resolved the compound

$$\underset{CH_3}{\overset{\Phi}{>}}Se\underset{[Br]}{\overset{CH_2—COOH}{<}}$$

through the bromo-camphor-sulphonate, and showed that the product gave an active chloroplatinate, although the double mercuric iodide was inactive.[684]

Another way of making the aryl selenonium salts is by the action of aluminium chloride on a mixture of the diaryl selenium dichloride $Ar_2Se(hal)_2$ and benzene.[685] They seem to be weak salts (the hydroxide is a stronger electrolyte than the iodide) and dissolve in water and also in chloroform, in the latter perhaps in a polymerized or colloidal form, like the substituted ammonium salts. On heating they break up into the aryl halide and the selenoether $Ar_3Se[I] = Ar_2Se+ArI$. It is remarkable that if the chloride Ar_3SeCl is recrystallized from ethylene dibromide, it is converted quantitatively into the bromide Ar_3SeBr.

All attempts to prepare a compound Alk_4Se or Ar_4Se have failed.

[677] B. Tamamushi, H. Akiyama, and S. Umezawa, *Bull. Chem. Soc. Japan*, 1939, **14**, 318.   [678] R. G. Wood and G. Williams, *Nature*, 1942, **150**, 321.

[679] L. C. Jackson, *Ann.* 1875, **179**, 1.

[680] L. v. Pieverling, ib. 1877, **185**, 331.

[681] G. T. Morgan and F. H. Burstall, *J.C.S.* 1928, 3260.

[682] For the positions taken up by substituents in aryl selenonium compounds see J. W. Baker and W. G. Moffitt, ib. 1930, 1722.

[683] W. J. Pope and A. Neville, ib. 1902, **81**, 1552.

[684] This has been confirmed by M. P. Balfe and H. Phillips, ib. 1933, 127.

[685] H. M. Leicester and F. W. Bergstrom, *J.A.C.S.* 1929, **51**, 3587; 1931, **53**, 4428.

Di- and Tri-selenides

Dialkyl and diaryl di- and tri-selenides R_2Se_2 and R_2Se_3 can be pre-pared. They are more or less volatile liquids[686,686a] (for example, Me_2Se_2, b. pt. 156°; Et_2Se_2, b. pt. 186°; Et_2Se_3, b. pt. 100°/26 mm.; Φ_2Se_2, m. pt. 63·5°, b. pt. 203°/11 mm.) which presumably, like their sulphur analogues, have unbranched chains R—Se—Se—R and R—Se—Se—Se—R. This has been proved by X-ray analysis[687] for

$$\Phi \cdot Se \cdot Se \cdot \Phi \quad \text{and} \quad \Phi \cdot CH_2 \cdot Se \cdot Se \cdot CH_2 \cdot \Phi,$$

which are isomorphous with the corresponding sulphur compounds. The following dipole moments have been found[658] in benzene at 25°: $(\Phi \cdot Se—)_2$ 1·67 D; $(p\text{-tol} \cdot Se—)_2$ 2·29; $(\Phi \cdot CH_2 \cdot Se—)_2$ 1·54; $(p\text{-Br} \cdot C_2H_4Se—)_2$ 0·70. The diselenides are readily formed from alkyl sulphuric acids and the alkaline diselenides M_2Se_2 or by reducing the monohalides $R \cdot Se \cdot hal$ with zinc dust.[688] With these halides there is often[689] an equilibrium between the monohalide on one side and the trihalide and the diselenide on the other

$$3\ Ar \cdot Se \cdot Cl \rightleftharpoons Ar \cdot Se \cdot Cl_3 + Ar \cdot Se—Se \cdot Ar,$$

where the equilibrium varies with the nature of the aryl radical, and is sometimes very far over on the right-hand side.

Morgan and Burstall[690] have prepared the cyclic diselenide

$$\begin{array}{c} CH_2—CH_2—Se \\ | \qquad\qquad | \\ CH_2—CH_2—Se \end{array},$$

and showed that on heating this eliminates selenium to give the tetra-methylene selenide

$$\begin{array}{c} CH_2—CH_2 \\ | \qquad\quad \diagdown \\ \qquad\qquad\ Se. \\ | \qquad\quad \diagup \\ CH_2—CH_2 \end{array}$$

They also[691] showed that a diselenide could be made in an unexpected way by heating the 6–7-fold polymer of

$$CH_2\diagup\!\!\!\begin{array}{c}CH_2\\ \\ CH_2\end{array}\!\!\!\diagdown Se,$$

which gives propylene $CH_3 \cdot CH{=}CH_2$ and the diselenide

$$CH_2\diagup\!\!\!\begin{array}{c}CH_2—Se\\ \\ CH_2—Se\end{array}\!\!\!\diagdown|\ .$$

[686] H. J. Backer and W. van Dam, *Rec. Trav.* 1935, **54**, 531.
[686a] G. G. Stoner and R. W. Williams, *J.A.C.S.* 1948, **70**, 1113.
[687] L. Egartner, F. Halla, and R. Schacherl, *Z. physikal. Chem.* 1932, B **18**, 189.
[688] O. Behaghel and H. Seibert, *Ber.* 1932, **65**, 812.
[689] O. Behaghel and W. Müller, ib. 1935, **68**, 1540.
[690] *J.C.S.* 1929, 1096.
[691] Ib. 1930, 1497.

Triselenides

These are formed[692] by the action of selenium on dialkyl selenides, or of selenium oxychloride $SeOCl_2$ on selenomercaptans. It is also possible to make compounds in which any or all of the three selenium atoms are replaced by sulphur: boiling-points:

Et_2S_3	Et_2SeS_2	Et_2Se_2S	Et_2Se_3
84–5°/15 mm.	94°/26 mm.	98°/26 mm.	100°/26 mm.

Alkyl and Aryl Selenium Halides

These can be of four types: (1) the selenonium halides already described; (2) the monohalides $R \cdot Se \cdot hal$; (3) the dihalides $R_2Se(hal)_2$; (4) the trihalides $R \cdot Se(hal)_3$. Their formulae, valency groups, and the products (stable or not) of their hydrolysis are:

$R_3Se[hal]$	2, <u>6</u>	$R_3Se[OH]$ (Strong base)
$R \cdot Se \cdot hal$	4, <u>4</u>	$R \cdot Se \cdot OH$ (Selenenic acid)[697]
$R_2Se(hal)_2$	(2), <u>8</u>	$R_2Se(OH)_2 {\rightarrow} R_2SeO$
$R \cdot Se(hal)_3$	(2), <u>8</u>	$R \cdot Se(OH)_3 {\rightarrow} R \cdot SeO \cdot OH$ (Seleninic acid).

The selenonium compounds are always ionized; the last two types have some tendency to give monovalent cations, with the valency pair no longer inert (valency octet); and all the last three types are readily hydrolysed by water.

Mono-[693–700] and Tri-[693–9] halides

The monohalides were discovered by Zincke.[701] They are much more stable than their sulphur analogues, and so can all be isolated. They are best made by the action of bromine on the selenocyanides in ether or CCl_4. This gives

$$Ar \cdot Se \cdot CN + Br_2 = Ar \cdot Se \cdot Br + Br \cdot CN;$$

but if excess of bromine is used, the tribromide is formed.[693] The monohalides can also be made[702] by the action of $AlCl_3$ on selenium dioxide in an aromatic hydrocarbon as solvent, for example, $C_6H_5 \cdot Se \cdot Cl$ in benzene. They are hydrolysed by water.

The fluorides[703] are all less stable to heat than the corresponding chlorides or bromides. They are very soluble in water, and all seem to behave like salts.

The monobromides are readily reduced by zinc dust to the diselenides

[692] G. R. Levi and A. Baroni, *Atti R. Linc.* 1929, [vi] **9**, 1019.
[693] O. Behagel and H. Seibert, *Ber.* 1932, **65**, 812.
[694] Id., ib. 1933, **66**, 708.　　　　　　　　　　　　　[695] Id., ib. 922.
[696] O. Behagel and W. Müller, ib. 1934, **67**, 105.
[697] Id., ib. 1935, **68**, 1540.　　　　　　　　　　　　[698] Id., ib. 2164.
[699] D. G. Foster, *J.A.C.S.* 1933, **55**, 822.
[700] Id., *Rec. Trav.* 1934, **53**, 405.
[701] T. Zincke, *Ber.* 1911, **44**, 769.
[702] R. E. Lyons and W. E. Bradt, ib. 1927, **60**, 60.
[703] H. J. Emeléus and H. G. Heal, *J.C.S.* 1946, 1126.

Ar·Se·Se·Ar[704]; when treated with water or alkalies they go into the diselenides and the seleninic acid Ar·SeO·OH ('disproportionation').[693,697,700]

The trihalides[693] are, of course, the halides of the seleninic acids Ar·SeO·OH (corresponding to the sulphinic), into which they are converted by alkali. But they readily lose Br_2 even *in vacuo* over P_2O_5 and potash, returning to the monobromides. C_6H_5·Se·Br_3 forms scarlet crystals, melting at 105°. The trichlorides also exist; they lose halogen less easily than the bromides (only on fusion), but they are much more easily hydrolysed to the seleninic acid Ar·SeO·OH.

All these trihalides are much more stable than the corresponding sulphur compounds.

Dialkyl and Diaryl Dihalides, $R_2Se(hal)_2$

These are formed with great ease by the direct addition of chlorine or bromine to the selenoether (with diphenyl sulphide bromine would give $(Br·C_6H_4)_2S$). An X-ray examination shows[705-6] that the diphenyl compounds have a trigonal bipyramidal structure (the normal structure for AB_5), with the halogen atoms at the poles, and the phenyl groups at two of the three positions on the equator. In the bromide[705] the angles are C—Se—C $110\pm10°$, Br—Se—Br $180\pm3°$, and the distances Se—C 1·91, Se—Br 2·52 (theory 1·94, 2·31); with the chloride[706] Cl—Se—Cl— is $180\pm5°$ and Se—Cl 2·30 (theory 2·16). The compounds dissociate in carbon tetrachloride to some extent (the iodide in N/10 solution about 6 per cent.) into $\Phi_2Se + Hal_2$.[707-8]

The dihalides are to some extent soluble in and hydrolysed by water. They seem to be more stable when derived from the diaryl selenides than from alkyl-aryl selenides. Thus[709] ΦCH_3SeBr_2 (yellow needles melting at 115° with decomposition) is converted quantitatively in 10 minutes at 120° into Φ·SeBr and methyl bromide. With silver oxide the halogen atoms of the dihalides are replaced by hydroxyls, but the product $ArMeSe(OH)_2$ cannot be isolated, as it begins at once to lose water to form the selenoxide ArMeSeO.

Selenoxides, R_2SeO

These are formally similar to the sulphoxides R_2SO, but differ from them in many (though not in all) respects. They are no doubt resonance hybrids of the formulae

$$\begin{matrix} R\diagdown \\ \diagup \\ R \end{matrix} Se{\rightarrow}O: \text{ val. Gp. 2, } \underline{6} \quad \text{and} \quad \begin{matrix} R\diagdown \\ \diagup \\ R \end{matrix} Se{=}O: (2)\ \underline{8}.$$

---

[704] The sulphur analogue Ar·S·Cl reacts in the same way, but even more vigorously (H. Lecher, *Ber.* 1924, **57**, 758).

[705] J. D. McCullough and G. Hamburger, *J.A.C.S.* 1941, **63**, 803.

[706] Id., ib. 1942, **64**, 508.   [707] Id., ib. 2672.

[708] J. D. McCullough and B. A. Eckerson, ib. 1945, **67**, 707.

[709] O. K. Edwards, W. R. Gaythwaite, J. Kenyon, and H. Phillips, *J.C.S.* 1928, 2293.

They can be made[710] by oxidizing the selenides with dichromate or permanganate or nitric acid, or by the action of potassium hydroxide on the dibromides. For example, diphenyl selenoxide Φ_2SeO melts at 113–14°. At 230° *in vacuo* it breaks up into the selenide and oxygen; with concentrated nitric acid it forms a salt $R_2Se(OH)NO_3$; excess of concentrated hydrochloric acid converts it into the dichloride Φ_2SeCl_2. The selenoxides are fairly soluble in hot water. They absorb moisture from the air up to about the composition $R_3Se(OH)_2$, and lose it again in a desiccator.

The sulphoxides are readily oxidized further to the sulphones, R_2SO_2, a very stable and rather inactive group of substances, but no such oxidation is normally possible for the selenoxides. Compounds of the composition of selenones R_2SeO_2 can be made, but their methods of preparation and their properties are quite different from those of the sulphones (see pp. 963–4). On the other hand the selenium in a selenoxide has a strong tendency to form an easily decomposed addition compound with nitric

acid, which may be written R_2SeO,HNO_3, but presumably is $R_2Se\begin{matrix} \diagup OH \\ [NO_3] \end{matrix}$.

This is a common tendency of quadrivalent selenium. Thus benzene seleninic acid forms[711] the compound $C_6H_5SeO_2H,HNO_3$: benzyl[712] and methyl and ethyl seleninic acids[713] behave in the same way. The same compounds R_2SeO,HNO_3 are formed[714] when the selenoethers are oxidized with nitric acid. This nitric acid compound (known as the 'hydronitrate') cannot be further oxidized. Selenium seems to have a much smaller tendency than sulphur to go over to the hexavalent selenonic form.

Phillips and Kenyon[715-17] have tried to resolve the bromo-camphor sulphonates of the unsymmetrical selenoxides as they did those of the sulphoxides; but though the salts were prepared they could not be resolved.

As the selenoxides are not (normally) oxidized further to the selenones, so too[715] if a seleninic acid $Ar \cdot SeO \cdot OH$ is recrystallized from fairly strong nitric acid, instead of being converted into the selenonic acid, as a sulphinic acid would be converted into a sulphonic, it merely separates as the hydronitrate; again, while ethyl iodide reacts with silver sulphite to give the unsymmetrical sulphonate $Et \cdot SO_2 \cdot OEt$, with silver selenite it forms the symmetrical selenite $(EtO)_2SeO$.[718] These are all examples of the reluctance which selenium shows (as compared with sulphur) to go into the hexavalent state.

[710] F. Krafft and W. Vorster, *Ber.* 1893, **26**, 2821.
[711] M. Stoecker and F. Krafft, ib. 1909, **39**, 2200.
[712] C. L. Jackson, *Ann.* 1875, **179**, 13.
[713] E. H. Shaw and E. E. Reid, *J.A.C.S.* 1926, **48**, 520.
[714] D. G. Foster and S. F. Brown, ib., 1928, **50**, 1182.
[715] W. R. Gaythwaite, J. Kenyon, and H. Phillips, *J.C.S.* 1928, 2280.
[716] Id., ib. 2287.
[717] O. K. Edwards, W. R. Gaythwaite, J. Kenyon, and H. Phillips, ib. 2293.
[718] C. A. Michaelis and B. Landmann, *Ann.* 1887, **241**, 150.

Phenyl-aminophenyl selenoxide

$$\begin{array}{c} H_2N \cdot C_6H_4 \\ \diagdown \\ C_6H_5 \diagup \end{array} SeO$$

if it is heated above its melting-point (147°) suddenly evolves oxygen, leaving the phenyl aminophenyl selenide,[716] very unlike the sulphur compound $H_2N \cdot C_6H_4(CH_3)SO$, which is stable up to a high temperature.

Selenoxides with alkyl groups attached to the selenium undergo a different reaction on heating, which occurs so readily that they are difficult to make; they then decompose with elimination of an aldehyde:

$$\begin{array}{c} R' \\ \diagdown \\ RCH_2 \diagup \end{array} SeO = R'SeH + R \cdot CHO.$$

Alkyl sulphoxides do the same; for example, dibenzyl sulphoxide on heating gives off benzaldehyde.[719-20] The selenitine

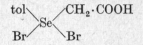

does not lose its two Br atoms on heating, but is converted into

$$tol \cdot SeBr + Br \cdot CH_2 \cdot COOH.$$

Many selenoxides cannot be isolated, as the dihydroxides, formed from alkalies and the dibromides, begin to decompose before all their water has been removed.

Selenones, R_2SeO_2

The selenoxides, unlike the sulphoxides, are highly resistant to further oxidation. There are, however, two groups of compounds known of the composition of selenones. The behaviour of the first, comprising only Φ_2SeO_2, is in many ways different from that of a sulphone, but it may not have a different structure.

Diphenyl selenone Φ_2SeO_2[721] cannot be made by the oxidation of the selenoxide in acid solution, either by nitric acid or by dichromate, but in alkaline solution, or in water, on treatment with permanganate the selenoxide is converted into a colourless crystalline compound $(C_6H_5)_2SeO_2$, melting at 155° and boiling under 9·5 mm. pressure at 270° with slight decomposition. If it is heated in a test tube it explodes feebly, and at 300–400° it decomposes quietly into diphenyl selenide and oxygen, whereas diphenyl sulphone is stable up to a red heat.

When the selenone is heated with sulphur it is reduced to the selenide with formation of sulphur dioxide; selenium has the same effect on diphenyl sulphone. The selenone, like selenic acid H_2SeO_4, but unlike

[719] E. Fromm and O. Achert, *Ber.* 1909, **36**, 534.
[720] R. Pommerer, ib. 1909, **42**, 2282; 1910, **43**, 1404.
[721] F. Krafft and R. E. Lyons, ib. 1896, **29**, 424.

diphenyl sulphone, reacts with hydrochloric acid even in the cold to form the dichloride and liberate chlorine. But while the selenoxide reacts with potassium iodide to liberate iodine at once, the selenone only does so slowly.

There is a marked resemblance between diphenyl selenoxide Φ_2SeO and iodosobenzene $\Phi \cdot IO$: both are definitely basic, easily obtained from the dichloride, easily lose oxygen, liberate iodine from potassium iodide; and a similar parallel may be instituted between the selenone Φ_2SeO_2 and iodoxybenzene $\Phi \cdot IO_2$, which are both of them more stable, neutral, explosive, and only slowly reduced.

A second group of selenones has been obtained by Backer[722] by a remarkable method, the direct addition, in cold chloroform solution, of selenium dioxide SeO_2 to an alkyl butadiene (butadiene itself will not react); for example, from 2-methyl butadiene he obtains the selenone

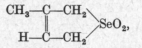

m. pt. 67° with some decomposition. It is scarcely soluble in benzene, but easily in water and in chloroform; it is stable when pure and dry, but when it is wet, or in aqueous solution, it readily decomposes, especially in light, with separation of selenium.

It is very difficult with our present knowledge to say what the structure of these selenones is, or why they are so seldom formed. For the possible peroxide structure there is no real evidence. It will be noticed that the two kinds of selenones have the selenium attached either to a benzene nucleus or to an unsaturated ring.

ORGANIC COMPOUNDS OF TELLURIUM

Tellurium and selenium resemble one another more in their organic compounds than elsewhere.

Telluromercaptans, $R \cdot Te \cdot H$

These are difficult to make, but have been prepared[723] by the action of hydrogen telluride on alkyl halides in an alcoholic solution of sodium alkylate; boiling-points at 760 mm. are:

Me·TeH	Et·TeH	n-Pr·TeH	n-Bu·TeH
57°	90°	121°	151°

Dialkyl Tellurides

These can be made from barium alkyl-sulphate and potassium telluride[724]; by the reduction of the dihalide Alk_2TeI_2; by passing ether or

[722] H. J. Backer and J. Strating, *Rec. Trav.* 1934, **53**, 1113.
[723] A. Baroni, *Atti R.* 1938, [vi] 27, 238.
[724] F. Wöhler and J. Dean, *Ann.* 1855, **93**, 233.

alcohol vapour over Al_2Te_3 at high temperatures:[725] or best from tellurium dihalides and the Grignard reagents. They are colourless liquids with a very repulsive smell.

$(CH_3)_2Te$ is formed by the action of moulds on a sugar solution containing H_2TeO_3.[726]

The boiling-points of some of these tellurides have already been given (p. 954): they have an unsaturated character like the selenides, but perhaps not quite so strong. They add on Cl_2 and Br_2, and are oxidized (slowly even by atmospheric air) to the telluroxides Alk_2TeO, or with nitric acid to the 'hydronitrates' Alk_2TeO,HNO_3. They form complexes with mercuric halides in acetone solution, such as $Me_2Te, HgBr_2$, m. pt. 160–1°.[731]

Diaryl Tellurides

These were first prepared by Krafft and his collaborators[727-30] by the action of tellurium on mercury diaryls. An example is diphenyl telluride $(C_6H_5)_2Te$, b. pt. 182° at 16·5 mm.

A more convenient mode of preparation is by the action of the Grignard reagent on tellurium dihalide.[732]

Cyclic Tellurides

These are similar to the selenides, and made in the same way. Examples are: the 'tellurohydrocarbon'

$$CH_2\begin{array}{c} CH_2-CH_2 \\ \diagdown \\ CH_2-CH_2 \end{array}Te,$$

b. pt. 82–3° at 12 mm.,[733-5] and the 5-ring

$$\begin{array}{c} CH_2-CH_2 \\ | \qquad\qquad Te, \\ CH_2-CH_2 \end{array}$$

b. pt. 166°/760 mm. made[735] from tellurium and tetramethylene dibromide, which gives the dibromide, which is then reduced with sulphite. See further references [736-7].

[725] G. Natta, *Brit. Chem. Abstr.* 1926, 1023.
[726] M. L. Bird and F. Challenger, *J.C.S.* 1939, 163.
[727] F. Krafft and R. E. Lyons, *Ber.* 1894, **27**, 1769.
[728] F. Zeiser, ib. 1895, **28**, 1670.
[729] O. Steiner, ib. 1901, **34**, 570.
[730] See also K. Lederer, *C.R.* 1910, **151**, 611; *Ber.* 1911, **44**, 2287; 1913, **46**, 1358, 1810.
[731] F. Carr and T. G. Pearson, *J.C.S.* 1938, 282.
[732] K. Lederer, *Ber.* 1915, **48**, 1345.
[733] G. T. Morgan and H. Burgess, *J.C.S.* 1928, 321.
[734] F. L. Gilbert and T. M. Lowry, ib. 2658.
[735] G. T. Morgan and F. H. Burstall, *J.C.S.* 1931, 180.
[736] C. Courtot and M. G. Bastiani, *C.R.* 1936, **203**, 197.
[737] W. V. Farrar and J. M. Gulland, *J.C.S.* 1945, 11.

Telluronium Compounds, $R_3Te[X]$

These can be made by the action of tellurium tetrachloride on zinc alkyls, or better from the alkyl iodides and dialkyl tellurides.[738] They are salts, like the selenonium compounds; their melting-points are low, e.g.:

		Et_3TeCl	—Br	—I
M. pt.	.	174°	162°	92°

They are insoluble in ether, but very soluble in alcohol and in water. Their curious formation by the rearrangement of the dialkyl tellurium di-iodides is described below (p. 967).

Whereas Φ_2S and Φ_2Se do not add on methyl iodide or only with difficulty, Ar_2Te does so very readily, but it adds ethyl and other alkyl iodides with difficulty. But the pure $[Ar_3Te]X$ can be made from the action of the Grignard reagent on Ar_2TeX_2 or $TeCl_4$. Diphenyl benzyl telluronium bromide $\Phi_2(\Phi \cdot CH_2)Te[Br]$,[739] melts at 90°; it is very easily soluble in chloroform, though only slightly in water.

Diphenyl methyl telluronium iodide $\Phi_2(CH_3)TeI$, obtained[740] from diphenyl telluride and methyl iodide, gives with silver oxide the base $\Phi_2CH_3Te[OH]$, which smells like piperidine, and is a moderately strong base, expelling ammonia from solutions of its salts, but forming a carbonate only in solution. The Ar_3TeOH base is similar.

Lederer's phenyl *p*-tolyl methyl telluronium iodide $\Phi(tol)(CH_3)Te[I]$, was resolved[741] through the bromo-camphor sulphonate and the camphor sulphonate. The active cation racemizes very rapidly, with a half-life of only a few minutes; but it was possible to show that the iodide prepared from the extreme fraction had an initial optical activity which vanished in a few minutes.

Ditellurides

These are less stable than their selenium analogues, and only one ditelluride (and no tritelluride) is known. This is the diphenyl compound $\Phi \cdot Te \cdot Te \cdot \Phi$,[742] formed as a by-product in the action of phenyl magnesium bromide on tellurium dibromide; blood-red crystals melting at 53°; sodium in alcohol reduces it to the telluromercaptan $\Phi \cdot Te \cdot H$, and nitric acid oxidizes it to $\Phi \cdot TeO \cdot NO_3$.

Aryl Monohalides, $R \cdot Te \cdot hal$

These are very little known, but they seem to resemble the selenium compounds quite closely.

[738] A. Marquardt and C. A. U. Michaelis, *Ber.* 1888, **21**, 2043.
[739] K. Lederer, ib. 1915, **48**, 1345.
[740] Id., *Ann.* 1913, **399**, 262, 267.
[741] T. M. Lowry and F. L. Gilbert, *J.C.S.* 1929, 2867.
[742] K. Lederer, *Ber.* 1915, **48**, 1345.

Dialkyl Tellurium Dihalides

These are formed as in the selenium series by the direct combination of the telluroethers with chlorine or bromine. Diphenyl tellurium dibromide Φ_2TeBr_2[743] is isomorphous with its selenium analogue.

Dimethyl tellurium di-iodide was formerly thought to establish the plane structure of 4-covalent tellurium. Vernon[744] showed that it can be obtained in two different forms. The original α-iodide, made by the action of tellurium on methyl iodide, yields in solution a hydroxide, from which it can be re-formed by the addition of hydrogen iodide. But if this hydroxide is heated, it is converted into an isomer, which with hydriodic acid gives a new (β) iodide. The isomeric bromides and chlorides were also prepared. The molecular weights of both forms of all three halides were found in solution to correspond to the simple formula $(CH_3)_2Te(hal)_2$. It was assumed that $(CH_3)_2TeI_2$ could occur in two structures, which like the forms of the 4-covalent platinous compounds of Werner, must be the cis and trans. Lowry[745] showed that the ethyl compounds behaved in the same way.

Then Drew[746] showed that while the α-series of halides of Vernon have the simple molecular weight, and are covalent compounds as he had supposed, the β-series are not isomers but polymers: they have twice the molecular weight $(Me_4Te_2X_4)$, though this difference does not appear in the molecular weight determinations, since they are highly ionized. Hence the occurrence of the two forms cannot be regarded as evidence for the steric disposition of the groups. Drew further showed that when the α-base is converted into the β-base there is a migration of a methyl group from one Te to another: and of an oxygen atom in the opposite direction:

$$2 \begin{array}{c} CH_3 \\ \diagdown \\ CH_3 \diagup \end{array} Te{\rightarrow}O = [(CH_3)_3Te]\left[CH_3Te{\begin{array}{c} \diagup O \\ \diagdown \\ O \end{array}} \right].$$

If the β-base is treated with an equivalent of hydriodic acid the colourless trimethyl telluronium iodide crystallizes out, and then on evaporation a colourless substance $CH_3 \cdot TeO \cdot O \cdot TeO \cdot CH_3$ separates, which is the anhydride of $CH_3 \cdot TeO \cdot OH$ (methyl tellurinic acid). With more hydriodic acid this gives the chocolate tri-iodide CH_3TeI_3, which if it is mixed with the telluronium iodide $(CH_3)_3TeI$, gives Vernon's black β-iodide, which thus must be $[(CH_3)_3Te][CH_3TeI_4]$. Finally if the β-iodide is treated with potassium iodide a colourless precipitate of the telluronium salt $(CH_3)_3Te[I]$ separates, and the red filtrate on evaporation gives the potassium salt of the anion $K[CH_3 \cdot TeI_4]$—a rather unusual form, since the tellurium is 5-covalent.

[743] G. Pellini, *Ber.* 1901, **34**, 3807; *Gaz.* 1902, **32**, i. 131.

[744] R. H. Vernon, *J.C.S.* 1920, **117**, 86, 889; I. E. Knaggs and R. H. Vernon, ib. 1921, **119**, 105; Vernon, ib. 687.

[745] T. M. Lowry, R. R. Goldstein, and F. L. Gilbert, ib. 1928, 307; Lowry and Gilbert, ib. 1997, 3179.

[746] H. D. K. Drew, ib. 1929, 560.

Thus we have so far no evidence of the positions in the molecule

$$\begin{array}{c} CH_3 \diagdown \diagup I \\ Te \\ CH_3 \diagup \diagdown I \end{array} ;$$

the tetrahedral structure of $R_3Te[X]$, with an octet, has no bearing on it, as here the Te has the decet 2, 8, and we should expect the structure to be that of a trigonal bipyramid with one position unoccupied, as has actually been established by X-ray analysis for the selenium analogue Φ_2SeCl_2 (p. 961).

The suggestion that the Te—I links in this compound are singlets seems incompatible with the diamagnetism of the compounds $(CH_3)_2TeX_2$, where $X = Cl$, Br, I, or NO_3.[747]

The aryl dihalides are as easily made as the alkyl; Ar_2Te will take up halogen in ether.[748-9] The dipole moments of the compounds Ar_2AX_2, where $A = S$, Se, Te have been measured[750] in benzene; the values obtained are:

$(\Phi \cdot CH_2)_2SI_2$	Φ_2SeCl_2	Φ_2SeBr_2	$(p\text{-tol})_2TeCl_2$
4·4	3·21	3·40	2·98

$(p\text{-tol})_2TeBr_2$	$[(p\text{-tol})_2TeCl]_2O$	$TeCl_4$
3·21	6·1	2·57 D

The dipole moments though large are not large enough for real salts of the type $[R_2AX]X$, which should have moments of about 10 D.

Trihalides, $R \cdot Te(hal)_3$

The acid $CH_3 \cdot TeO_2H$, obtained from Vernon's β-base, forms a yellow tribromide and a chocolate tri-iodide.[746] They are soluble in acetone and in ether to give red solutions; they are hydrolysed by boiling water to the colourless acid and halogen hydride, but on cooling these recombine and the trihalide crystallizes out. They decompose above 100°. The corresponding 'acids' $R \cdot TeO_2H$, the tellurinic acids, are described below (p. 983).

The aryl di- and tri-halides can also be made by the action of tellurium tetrachloride or the so-called 'basic chloride', which probably contains oxychloride, on aromatic compounds with powerful *o, p*-directing substituents, such as hydroxyl[751] or amino groups.[752] Thus when the addition compound $2 Me_2N \cdot C_6H_5, TeCl_4$ is boiled with water, the tellurium enters the para position on the ring, giving $(Me_2N \cdot C_6H_4)_2TeCl_2$. This consists of yellow plates soluble in benzene, which turn blue at 181° and at 188-9° melt to a purple liquid.

[747] S. S. Bhatnagar and T. K. Lahiri, *Z. Phys.* 1933, **84**, 671.

[748] Krause and v. Grosse, p. 683.

[749] K. Lederer, *Ber.* 1916, **49**, 1082, 1615.

[750] K. A. Jensen, *Z. anorg. Chem.* 1943, **250**, 245.

[751] G. T. Morgan and H. Burgess, *J.C.S.* 1929, 2214; G. T. Morgan and F. H. Burstall, ib. 1930, 2599.

[752] G. T. Morgan and H. Burgess, ib. 1929, 1103.

Cresols react in the same way, taking up Te in the *o* or *p* positions, and giving all three types of compounds $Ar_3Te[Cl]$, Ar_2TeCl_2, and $Ar \cdot TeCl_3$.

Telluroxides, R_2TeO

The dialkyl or diaryl tellurides are readily oxidized by atmospheric air or by nitric acid. The first give the telluroxide directly, the second its addition product with nitric acid, or 'hydronitrate', which probably has the structure $R_2TeOH[NO_3]$; this is converted by concentrated hydrochloric acid into the dichloride R_2TeCl_2, which with silver oxide gives the water-soluble alkaline base R_2TeO. According to Wöhler[753] Et_2TeO is a thick alkaline oil which is very unstable, and forms a series of salts (soluble in water) with HNO_3 or one half of H_2SO_4.

Morgan's cyclic tellurohydrocarbon dibromides are converted in the same way by alkalies into telluroxides, which can also be made by the aerial oxidation of the tellurohydrocarbons themselves[735]; these oxides are very like the selenoxides: they are soluble in water and alcohol, and they regenerate the dichlorides with hydrochloric acid.

The aryl compounds are similar. Di-phenyl telluroxide Φ_2TeO and its derivatives Φ_2TeX_2 (where $X = Cl$, Br, etc.) have been made.[754] The oxides are easily soluble in benzene or chloroform, but only slightly in alcohol or water; from the latter they crystallize as the dihydrates, which gradually lose water in the air, and return to the oxide. With strong acids they give salts or ionizable compounds, such as Ar_2TeCl_2 or $Ar_2Te(NO_3)_2$.

The tendency of the diaryl tellurides to oxidize is so strong that if diphenyl telluride is dissolved in ether, and the solution poured on to concentrated hydrochloric acid and air blown through the liquid, it is converted into the dichloride.

The structure of the telluroxides must be the same as that of the selenoxides (p. 962), whatever that may be.

Tellurones, R_2TeO_2

$(CH_3)_2TeO_2$ can be made by the prolonged action of excess of H_2O_2 on Me_2Te (the first product is Me_2TeO); it is a white powder insoluble in all solvents.[755] In the same way from cyclotelluropentane $C_5H_{10}Te$ a white amorphous powder of the composition $C_5H_{10}TeO_2,H_2O$ is obtained.[756] It is insoluble; it explodes on rapid heating; it darkens at 195°; it liberates chlorine from hydrochloric acid, decolorizes permanganate solution, and decomposes violently on treatment with concentrated nitric or sulphuric acid.

These are obviously highly polymerized in comparison with the sulphones and selenones: but little more is known about them.

[753] *Ann.* 1852, **84**, 80.   [754] K. Lederer, *Ann.* 1912, **391**, 332.
[755] Krause and v. Grosse, p. 675.
[756] G. T. Morgan and H. Burgess, *J.C.S.* 1928, 327.

SELENIUM OXIDES AND OXY-ACIDS

[*Selenium Monoxide.* Although sulphur monoxide occurs, and probably tellurium monoxide (see below, p. 980), all attempts to prepare selenium monoxide have failed.][757]

Selenium Dioxide, SeO_2

This is the only certain oxide of selenium. It is formed by the direct oxidation of the element, which burns in air with a blue flame; the oxidation is catalysed by traces of nitrogen peroxide, and hindered by alkalies.

Selenium dioxide forms colourless crystals, which sublime under 1 atmosphere at 315°, and melt under pressure at 340°.[758] The liquid is orange-yellow and the vapour yellow-green; this change of colour is reversible (it becomes colourless again on solidifying) and is not due to any loss of oxygen.[759] TeO_2 behaves in the same way. The vapour density is normal from 360° to 500°.[760] X-ray examination of solid SeO_2 shows that it consists of chains

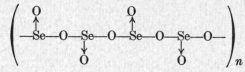

with Se—O 1·79 in the chain, and 1·73 outside[761] it (theory Se—O 1·83, Se=O 1·65).

Selenium dioxide gives a yellow solution in concentrated sulphuric or selenic acid,[759] but no analogue of dithionic acid is formed. It absorbs moisture from the air, and is converted into selenious acid H_2SeO_3. It is easily reduced: thus with sulphur it gives SO_2 and free selenium, showing that the affinity of selenium for oxygen is weaker than that of sulphur. This ready reduction makes selenium dioxide a valuable oxidizing agent in organic chemistry (see below). With halogen acids SeO_2 forms compounds some of which are certainly oxy-halides, while others may be hydrated halides.

The use of selenium dioxide as an oxidizing agent in organic chemistry is due to H. L. Riley[762-6]: see also references [767-82]. He showed that ketones and aldehydes containing the —CH_2—CO group, when warmed with the dioxide, readily reduce it to elementary selenium, with the conversion of

[757] P. W. Schenk, *Z. anorg. Chem.* 1937, **233**, 401.
[758] J. Meyer and J. Jannek, ib. 1913, **83**, 57; *Ber.* 1913, **46**, 2876.
[759] J. Meyer and M. Langner, ib. 1927, **60**, 285.
[760] D. M. Yost and J. B. Hatcher, *J.A.C.S.* 1932, **54**, 151.
[761] J. D. McCullough, ib. 1937, **59**, 789.
[762] H. L. Riley, J. F. Morley, and N. A. C. Friend, *J.C.S.* 1932, 1875.
[763] H. L. Riley and N. A. C. Friend, ib. 2342.
[764] S. Astin, A. C. C. Newman, and H. L. Riley, ib. 1933, 391.
[765] S. Astin and H. L. Riley, ib. 1934, 844.
[766] S. Astin, L. de V. Moulds, and H. L. Riley, ib. 1935, 901.

the group into —CO—CO—; thus acetone gives methyl glyoxal $CH_3 \cdot CO \cdot CHO$. The yields are good, and the SeO_2 is easily regenerated by filtering off the selenium, oxidizing it back to SeO_2 with nitric acid, and subliming. Ketones without an adjacent CH_2 group, such as benzophenone, are much less readily oxidized. Ethylene and propylene react[783] in the same way to give glyoxal $CHO \cdot CHO$ and methyl glyoxal; malonic ester gives mesoxalic ester $EtO \cdot CO \cdot CO \cdot CO \cdot OEt$, and tartaric ester the keto-hydroxy-succinate $EtO \cdot CO \cdot CO \cdot CHOH \cdot CO \cdot OEt$.

This curious tendency—which extends to many more complicated organic compounds—to oxidize an active methylene or similar group to carbonyl but no further, even when the product is an aldehyde—is very remarkable, and almost suggests that the ketone formed is protected from further oxidation by forming a complex with the dioxide, though of this there is no evidence.[766] It is singular that precisely the same peculiarity is observed with the A element of Group VI which is in the same period as selenium, namely chromium: dichromates, and chromyl chloride (as in the Étard reaction) have a strong tendency to oxidize CH_2 groups to the ketone or aldehyde, and no further.

Selenium Trioxide, SeO_3

Selenium occupies an anomalous position in the series S—Se—Te like that of bromine in the series Cl—Br—I; it has less tendency than either of the other members of the series to form compounds with several oxygen atoms: thus selenium gives no (or practically no) trioxide, though we have SO_3 and TeO_3, as we have $HClO_4$ and HIO_4, but no $HBrO_4$. Selenium trioxide cannot be made by heating selenic acid H_2SeO_4, or by treating it with P_2O_5 (which give the trioxide of S and Te): what is formed is the

[767] R. Truchet, *C.R.* 1933, **196**, 706, 1613.

[768] R. K. Callow and O. Rosenheim, *J.C.S.* 1933, 387.

[769] C. H. Fisher, *J.A.C.S.* 1934, **56**, 2056.

[770] W. C. Evans, J. M. Ridgion, and J. L. Simonsen, *J.C.S.* 1934, 137.

[771] K. F. Armstrong and R. Robinson, ib. 1650.

[772] J. J. Potovski and B. P. Lugovkin, *Ber.* 1935, **68**, 852.

[773] W. Borsche and H. Hartmann, ib. 1940, **73**, 839.

[774] The SeO_2 becomes less efficient on keeping: H. Kaplan, *J.A.C.S.* 1941, **63**, 2654.

[775] J. Vène, *C.R.* 1943, **216**, 772.

[776] A. Guillemonat, ib. 1938, **206**, 1126.

[777] Id., *Ann. Chim.* 1939, [xi] **11**, 143–211.

[778] N. N. Melnikov and M. S. Rokitskaja, *J. Gen. Chem. Russ.* 1938, **8**, 1369; 1939, **9**, 1158, 1808.

[779] Id., ib. 1937, **7**, 1532.

[780] I. J. Postovski, B. P. Lugovkin, and G. F. Mandrik, ib. 37.

[781] N. N. Melnikov and M. S. Rokitskaja, ib. 1944, **14**, 1054, 1059; 1945, **15**, 657.

[782] J. A. Arbusov, N. D. Zelinski, and N. I. Schulkin, *Bull. Acad. Sci. U.R.S.S.* 1945, 163.

[783] Selenium dioxide also acts as a catalyst in the oxidation of olefines by hydrogen peroxide: see P. Seguin, *C.R.* 1943, **216**, 667.

dioxide SeO_2 and oxygen; and if selenium is oxidized with ozone it only goes as far as the dioxide.

The claim[784] that the trioxide can be made by passing ozone through a solution of selenium in the oxychloride $SeOCl_2$ has not been confirmed.[785]

It was, however, found by Rheinboldt[786] that the trioxide is formed when a high-frequency glow discharge takes place in dry oxygen in presence of selenium; a white sublimate is produced, which turns deep green when it comes in contact with selenium, perhaps from the formation of a compound Se_2O_3, like the green $SeSO_3$ or the blue S_2O_3. This sublimate is very hygroscopic, and hisses with water, and the solution on treatment with alkali gives a mixture of selenite and selenate, with about 40 per cent. of the latter. This work has been confirmed by Olsen and Meloche.[787]

Selenious Acid, H_2SeO_3

This is made by the wet oxidation of the element, or by the action of water on the dioxide, which dissolves (unlike TeO_2) and crystallizes out as the acid. An examination of the solid–liquid system SeO_2, water[788] showed that the only solid phases are SeO_2, H_2SeO_3, and ice; unlike SO_2, SeO_2 forms no hydrates other than H_2SeO_3.

Selenious acid H_2SeO_3 is a colourless[789] crystalline substance, which is hygroscopic, and dissolves very readily in water; at the cryohydric point, $-23°$, the solution contains 57 per cent. SeO_2. The crystals easily lose water in dry air, and go over into the dioxide.

Selenious acid is rather a weak acid, the first dissociation constant K_1 being about 4×10^{-3} (about a quarter of the strength of sulphurous acid, for which $K_1 = 1·7 \times 10^{-2}$), and the second about 10^{-8}.[790-1] The solution is very easily reduced, for example by sulphur dioxide: in strongly acid solution the product is free selenium, but in a less acid solution in presence of heavy metal salts their selenides may be produced: thus with copper sulphate cuprous selenide Cu_2Se is formed.[792]

The salts are not very well known; they all decompose on heating, often to selenides. The alkaline[793] salts have an alkaline reaction; the

---

[784] R. R. le G. Worsley and H. B. Baker, *J.C.S.* 1923, **123**, 2870.

[785] J. Meyer and A. Pawletta, *Ber.* 1927, **60**, 985; G. F. Hoffmann and V. Lenher, *J.A.C.S.* 1929, **51**, 3177; G. B. L. Smith and C. L. Mehltretter, ib. 1931, **53**, 3562.

[786] H. Rheinboldt, A. Hessel, and K. Schwenzer, *Ber.* 1930, **63**, 1865.

[787] E. N. Kramer and V. W. Meloche, *J.A.C.S.* 1934, **56**, 1081; E. Olsen and V. W. Meloche, ib. 1936, **58**, 2511, 2514.

[788] W. Manchot and K. Ortner, *Z. anorg. Chem.* 1922, **120**, 300.

[789] Its solution in water is sometimes red, but this is due to an impurity (perhaps free selenium) which can be removed by animal charcoal: J. Janickis, ib. 1932, **205**, 49.

[790] E. Blanc, *J. Chim. Phys.* 1920, **18**, 28; E. B. R. Prideaux and J. S. Willcox, *J.C.S.* 1925, **127**, 1543.

[791] H. Hagisawa, *Bull. Inst. Phys.-Chem. Res. Japan*, 1939, **18**, 648.

[792] L. M. Clark, *J.C.S.* 1928, 2388.

[793] J. Janickis, *Z. anorg. Chem.* 1932, **205**, 49; J. Janickis and A. Gutmanaite, ib. 1936, **227**, 1.

potassium salt is much more soluble than the sodium, as is usual for the salts of a weak acid. Selenious acid is remarkable for its tendency to form acid salts, giving not only the usual acid salts $MHSeO_3$, but also a 'tetra-selenite' $MH_3(SeO_3)_2$ where $M = Na$, K, or NH_4. It also has a strong tendency to form complex salts; according to Riley[794] the 'selenito' salts tend to have the SeO_3 group attached only by one oxygen, as in $[Co(SeO_3)(NH_3)_5]Cl$. This, however, may be peculiar to those salts in which the SeO_3 complex is part of the cation. For barium selenites see reference [795].

Selenious Esters

The sulphurous esters occur in two isomeric forms, a symmetrical $OS(OR)_2$ and an unsymmetrical (sulphonate) $R \cdot SO_2 \cdot OR$, but the sele-nious[796] can only be prepared directly in one form, the symmetrical, although the unsymmetrical (selenonic) acid can be made in other ways (see below, p. 977). A careful study of these compounds[797] has shown that whether they are made from selenium oxychloride $SeOCl_2$ and sodium alkylate, or from silver selenite and alkyl iodide, the same product is obtained, as judged by boiling-point, density, and refractive index. These esters are all rapidly and completely saponified by water, which is good evidence that both the alkyls are attached to oxygen and not to selenium. The boiling-points are: Me_2 60°/15 mm.; Et_2 83°/15 mm.; Pr_2 110°/15 mm. Phenyl magnesium bromide, which distinguishes the two isomeric sulphite esters by converting the unsymmetrical $R \cdot SO_2 \cdot OR$ into the sulphone $\Phi SO_2 \cdot R$ and the symmetrical $OS(OR)_2$ into the sulphoxide Φ_2SO, reduces the selenites to selenium. A very unstable ester-acid $EtO \cdot SeO \cdot OH$ can be made and also its chloride $EtO \cdot SeO \cdot Cl$, b. pt. 175°.

Selenious Acid Halides.

Selenium dioxide has the power of absorbing gaseous hydrogen halides to form solid and liquid addition products; these on heating lose water and hydrogen halide, and are ultimately converted either into the acid halides $SeO(hal)_2$ or into the tetrahalides. The structures of the com-pounds containing hydrogen are obscure; often they may equally well be regarded as hydrogen halide addition products of the dioxide, or as hydrates of the acid halide or of the tetrahalide.

Fluorides

Dry SeO_2 absorbs hydrogen fluoride gas very readily, giving a colourless mobile fuming liquid, which attacks glass slightly. On distillation a product is left which has a composition very near to $SeO_2 5HF$.[798] The acid fluoride $SeOF_2$ can be made[799] from the chloride by heating it with

[794] H. L. Riley, *J.C.S.* 1928, 2985.

[795] J. L. Neal and C. R. McCrosky, *J.A.C.S.* 1938, **60**, 911.

[796] C. A. Michaelis and B. Landmann, *Ann.* 1887, **241**, 150.

[797] W. Strecker and W. Daniel, ib. 1928, **462**, 186.

[798] E. B. R. Prideaux and J. O. N. Millott, *J.C.S.* 1926, 167.

[799] E. B. R. Prideaux and C. B. Cox, ib. 1927, 928; 1928, 739.

silver fluoride at 140°. It is a colourless fuming liquid, b. pt. 124°, m. pt. $+4\cdot6°$, which attacks glass, silica, and elementary silicon violently, giving SeO_2.

Chlorides

These are similar to the fluorides. Selenium dioxide absorbs hydrogen chloride gas readily, the amount depending on the temperature. The results[800] are compatible with the formation of two addition compounds, (1) SeO_2, 4 HCl, a yellow solid stable at 0°, and (2) SeO_2, 2 HCl, a yellow liquid capable of dissolving HCl, stable up to 170°, and then distilling with some decomposition. If hydrogen chloride is passed over the dioxide at 30°, the product has the exact composition of SeO_2, 2 HCl.

The oxychloride $SeOCl_2$ can be made[801] from $SeO_2 + SeCl_4$, or by the action of a little water on the tetrachloride, or most conveniently[800] by treating SeO_2, 2 HCl with P_2O_5 and distilling. It is an almost colourless liquid, boiling at 177°, and melting at $+8\cdot5°$; its electrical conductivity is low (about 10^{-6}),[801-2] but its dielectric constant is high: $51\cdot0$ for the liquid at 10°, and $16\cdot8$ for the solid at 0°.[803] It is obviously covalent in the liquid state, being miscible with CCl_4, chloroform, carbon disulphide, and benzene, though not with paraffins. It is hydrolysed by water to $HCl + SeO_2$. It forms a variety of co-ordination products, for example with stannic chloride, and with unsaturated hydrocarbons.[804]

Bromides

Hydrobromic acid combines with selenium dioxide, though not quite so readily as hydrogen chloride, $SeO_2, 2 HBr$ being formed at 107° (instead of 30°); more is taken up at lower temperatures.[805] The oxybromide $SeOBr_2$ can be made from the chloride $SeOCl_2$ and sodium bromide, or by the action of bromine on a mixture of SeO_2 and Se.[806] It melts at $41\cdot6°$, and boils at about 220° with some decomposition. It resembles the chloride very closely, but is less stable.

Seleninic Acids, $R \cdot SeO_2H$

These, which are selenious acid with one hydroxyl replaced by R, are the analogues of the sulphinic acids, and can be made by the oxidation of the diselenides with nitric acid.[807-12]

[800] T. W. Parker and P. L. Robinson, *J.C.S.* 1928, 2853; 1931, 1314.
[801] V. Lenher, *J.A.C.S.* 1921, **43**, 29; 1922, **44**, 1664.
[802] A. P. Julien, ib. 1925, **47**, 1799.
[803] J. E. Wildish, ib. 1920, **42**, 2607.
[804] A. Müller, *Chem. Ztg.* 1919, **43**, 843.
[805] T. W. Parker and P. L. Robinson, *J.C.S.* 1931, 1314.
[806] V. Lenher, *J.A.C.S.* 1922, **44**, 1664.
[807] Wöhler and Dean, *Ann.* 1856, **97**, 6.
[808] R. Rathke, ib. 1869, **152**, 216.
[809] F. Krafft and R. E. Lyons, *Ber.* 1896, **29**, 424.
[810] M. Stoecker and F. Krafft, ib. 1906, **39**, 2197.
[811] H. J. Backer and W. van Dam, *Rec. Trav.* 1935, **54**, 531.
[812] W. H. Porritt, *J.C.S.* 1927, 27.

It is remarkable that whereas nitric acid will oxidize sulphur in a disulphide to the sulphonic acid $R \cdot SO_3H$, it will only take Se in a diselenide as far as the seleninic acid $R \cdot SeO_2H$, just as it only oxidizes selenium to selenious acid, but sulphur to sulphuric: chlorine, however, which oxidizes selenium to selenic acid, correspondingly oxidizes the selenides or di-selenides to the selenonic acids $R \cdot SeO_3H$. The seleninic acids can also be made[812] by the action of hydrogen peroxide on an aryl seleno-glycollic acid $Ar \cdot Se \cdot CH_2 \cdot COOH$, formed by condensing the aryl selenomercaptan $Ar \cdot Se \cdot H$ with chloracetic acid.

The alkyl seleninic acids are hygroscopic, and they are all soluble in water. They are even weaker than the carboxylic acids,[811] but they form salts, such as $CH_3 \cdot SeO \cdot ONa$, $4\,H_2O$, and ΦSeO_2Ag, from which other salts such as the barium and cupric salts (the last explosive) can be prepared. The acid cannot be got by treating the silver salt with H_2S, as this reduces it to Se,[810] but the silver can be removed with HCl, and the filtrate on evaporation leaves white crystals of $\Phi \cdot Se(OH)_3$, m. pt. 122°, which at 130° loses water and goes over to the acid $\Phi \cdot SeO_2H$, m. pt. 170°. Like the sulphinic acids this is reduced by zinc dust to the mercaptan $\Phi \cdot Se \cdot H$.

This 'acid' is amphoteric, and has definite basic properties, forming addition products with a whole series of strong acids, such as $Ar \cdot SeO_2H$, HNO_3 and $CH_3 \cdot SeO_2H, HCl$, which should no doubt be written $[Ar \cdot Se(OH)_2]NO_3$ and $[CH_3Se(OH)_2]Cl$. The nitrate is explosive.

This amphoteric character is shared by the selenonic acids (p. 978), and is possessed even more strongly by the tellurium analogues.

Selenic Acid, H_2SeO_4

This is made by the vigorous oxidation of selenium or the dioxide, usually with chloric acid or fused potassium nitrate; nitric acid is not powerful enough. The best method of preparation,[813] giving over 90 per cent. yield, is to oxidize selenium to SeO_2 with nitric acid, and then heat this with chloric acid (from barium chlorate and H_2SO_4) not above 170°, and finally *in vacuo*. Solutions of selenic acid must not be heated above 210°, or in the presence of chlorides above 170°, or they will lose oxygen.

Selenic acid H_2SeO_4, m. pt. 57–8°, is isomorphous with sulphuric acid, which it resembles very closely in many ways. It is a strong acid, about twice as strong as sulphuric (at $p_H 3$ K is $2 \cdot 6 \times 10^{-2}$ for this, and $1 \cdot 3 \times 10^{-2}$ for H_2SO_4).[815] Like sulphuric acid it forms two hydrates H_2SeO_4, H_2O and $H_2SeO_4, 4\,H_2O$; that corresponding to $H_2SO_4, 2\,H_2O$ has not been found. The melting-points are:

H_2SeO_4	. . .	$+57\text{–}8°$	H_2SO_4 . . .	$+10 \cdot 4°$
H_2SeO_4, H_2O	. .	$+26°$	H_2SO_4, H_2O . .	$+ 8 \cdot 5°$
..		..	$H_2SO_4, 2\,H_2O$ . .	$-38°$
$H_2SeO_4, 4\,H_2O$.	.	$-51 \cdot 7°$	$H_2SO_4, 4\,H_2O$ . .	$-29°$

[813] J. Meyer and H. Moldenhauer, *Z. anorg. Chem.* 1921, **116**, 193.

[814] For the comparison of sulphur and selenium see J. Meyer, ib. **118**, 1.

[815] A. L. Agafonova and J. V. Chodakov, *C.R. Acad. Sci. U.R.S.S.* 1943, **40**, 350.

In general,[814] while selenium and tellurium are very similar to one another in their quadrivalent compounds, much more than they are to sulphur, in the -ic acids the resemblance is between selenium and sulphur, and tellurium is very different. Sulphur and selenium both form crystalline acids H_2XO_4, which melt easily to thick oily (highly associated) liquids; they form similar hydrates; they both have a strong affinity for water; they readily form condensed acids both with one another and with other elements of the series, such as $H_2S_2O_7$, H_2SSeO_7, H_2SeCrO_7, and $H_2Se_2O_7$[816]; the salts of the same base are usually isomorphous and have similar solubilities; the two acids can usually replace one another in complexes. In all these points tellurium behaves quite differently: H_2TeO_4 does not exist at all, and telluric acid is H_6TeO_6.

The chief difference between selenic and sulphuric acid is that the former is the less stable, and more easily loses oxygen. Sulphuric acid can be heated to 300° without decomposition, whereas selenic acid begins to decompose in presence of chlorides below 200°. Sulphurous acid is oxidized by atmospheric air to sulphuric; but selenious acid can only be made to take up more oxygen by a powerful oxidizing agent. So, too, concentrated sulphuric acid has no action on hydrochloric acid hot or cold, though it oxidizes hydrobromic acid when hot and hydriodic when cold. But even dilute selenic acid will oxidize hydriodic acid quantitatively, so that the reaction can be used for its analysis, and will oxidize hydrobromic acid fairly easily; while concentrated selenic acid will oxidize hydrochloric, so that a mixture of the two concentrated acids behaves like aqua regia and dissolves gold and platinum. In the same way while the sulphuric esters are very stable, the selenic esters (see below) are liable to explode on heating, like nitric esters, owing to internal oxidation and reduction. Again the hydrazine salt[817] is colourless when pure, but soon goes pink from the separation of selenium. If it is touched with a hot rod it explodes loudly, giving off a red aerosol of selenium, which only settles slowly.

So, too, selenic acid is very readily reduced by reagents which will not attack sulphuric acid under the same conditions: as, for example, by zinc dust acting on the dilute acid.

The salts of selenic acid—the selenates—resemble the sulphates very closely. They are mostly isomorphous with the corresponding sulphates, chromates, and manganates. They form alums and vitriols. The solubilities of the selenates generally lie very near to those of the sulphates, but are rather larger: for example, $BaSO_4$ 2·6 mg. per litre; $BaSeO_4$ 82·5 mg. per litre at the ordinary temperature. The resemblances are often surprisingly close: thus,[819] calcium selenate forms a hemi-hydrate which behaves like plaster of Paris: Na_2SeO_4, 10 H_2O effloresces in air like Glauber's salt; at 31·8° (sodium sulphate at 32·4°) it goes over to the

[816] J. Meyer and V. Stateczny, *Z. anorg. Chem.* 1922, **122**, 1.

[817] J. Meyer and W. Aulich, *Ber.* 1928, **61**, 1839.

[819] Id., *Z. anorg. Chem.* 1928, **172**, 321.

anhydrous salt, of which the solubility diminishes with rise of temperature; like the sulphate it forms a metastable heptahydrate.

Again, both acids form nitrosyl $[NO]^+$ salts. The selenate[820] $[NO]HSeO_4$ is not formed from SeO_2 and nitric acid, as the sulphur compound is from SO_2 and nitric acid, but by the action of liquid nitrogen trioxide on the anhydrous selenic acid. It forms colourless crystals, decomposed by water with evolution of oxides of nitrogen, soluble without decomposition in sulphuric acid or alcohol, and melting at 80° with decomposition; in all these points it closely resembles the sulphur compound.

The same resemblance holds with the double salts[819] and also with the true complex salts.[821] Thus Meyer has made a long series of complex chromi- and cobaltiselenates, and shows that they always resemble the corresponding sulphates very closely.[821]

Selenic Esters, R_2SeO_4

Selenic acid reacts with alcohols[822] to give alkyl selenic acids, such as $EtO \cdot SeO_2 \cdot OH$, of which salts can be made. The acid and its salts are very unstable: the salts are isomorphous with the alkyl sulphates.

The dialkyl esters can be made[822-4] from the alkyl halide and silver selenate; the methyl ester can also be got from selenic acid and diazomethane. The esters can be distilled *in vacuo* without decomposition (b. pts. Me_2 100°/15 mm.; Et_2 105°/12 mm.; Pr_2 135°/25 mm.), but under ordinary pressure they decompose explosively (though not so violently as the alkyl nitrates) at about 150°, giving various products including free selenium and aldehydes.

Selenonic Acids, $R \cdot SeO_3H$

These acids cannot be made on the analogy of the sulphonic acids by oxidizing the selenomercaptans with nitric acid: or by the action of silver selenate on alkyl halides: or by heating phenyl hydrogen selenate: or by treating selenic acid with phenol. The alkyl selenonic acids were first made[825] by oxidizing with $KMnO_4$ the seleninic acids $Alk \cdot SeO \cdot OH$ made from the selenides Alk_2Se and H_2O_2, with elimination of one alkyl.

The aromatic selenonic acids can be made (like the sulphonic acids) by heating the hydrocarbon with H_2SeO_4: e.g. from benzene at 110°; or by the action of chlorine (the oxidizing agent always used for the preparation of derivatives of selenium trioxide) on the diselenides.[810] Thus if diphenyl diselenide $\Phi \cdot Se \cdot Se \cdot \Phi$ is suspended in water and treated with chlorine at 50° and then with excess of silver oxide, silver benzene selenonate $\Phi \cdot SeO_3Ag$ separates on evaporation; from this other salts can be made;

[820] J. Meyer and W. Wagner, *Ber.* 1922, **55**, 690.
[821] J. Meyer, *Z. anorg. Chem.* 1921, **118**, 1.
[822] J. Meyer and W. Wagner, *Ber.* 1922, **55**, 1216.
[823] W. Strecker and W. Daniel, *Ann.* 1928, **462**, 186.
[824] J. Meyer and W. Hinke, *Z. anorg. Chem.* 1932, **204**, 29.
[825] M. L. Bird and F. Challenger, *J.C.S.* 1942, 570.

the silver salt is explosive. The free acid can be got by treating the silver salt with H_2S: it is remarkable that while H_2S reduces the seleninic acids it does not reduce the selenonic (compare the relative reducibility of chloric and perchloric acids).

Phenyl selenonic (benzene selenonic) acid forms white crystals, which melt at 142°, and explode at 180°; it forms a hydrate. Heated alone it explodes feebly, giving diphenyl selenide, diphenyl diselenide, and free selenium. Cold concentrated hydrochloric acid reduces it, as it does selenic acid.

Selenonic acids can sometimes be made directly by a very peculiar reaction.[826] If selenic acid is heated with acetic anhydride in para- or ortho-xylene (in other hydrocarbons the reaction does not occur below temperatures at which the selenic acid is reduced) it reacts to form the selenonic acid $(Me_2C_6H_3)SeO_3H$. These acids (m. pts. ortho 108–110°; para 95–6°: the name refers to the relative positions of the methyl groups: the substitution is, of course, o, p) are very like the sulphonic acids; their salts are also very like the sulphonates.

Like the seleninic and also the telluronic acids (but unlike the sulphonic) the selenonic acids can act as bases and add on strong mineral acids. This power is more marked with tellurium.

Mixed Oxides

Sulphur, selenium, and tellurium all dissolve in sulphuric acid, sulphur trioxide, and selenic acid, to give coloured solutions. On standing there is often a reaction, for example with the separation of selenium or its dioxide, but the primary product seems to have the added element directly attached to the sulphur or selenium of the solvent, and not to its oxygen; for example, if sulphur is dissolved in selenic acid it is reprecipitated on immediate dilution, but on standing it is converted into SO_2: selenium dissolved in this acid is also reprecipitated on dilution, but on standing is converted into SeO_2. The colour of the compound depends on the dissolved element rather than on the dissolving acid or oxide; thus we have (SeO_3 is written for H_2SeO_4):

Blue	$S \cdot SO_3$	$S \cdot SeO_3$
Green	$Se \cdot SO_3$	$Se \cdot SeO_3$
Red	$Te \cdot SO_3$	$Te \cdot SeO_3$

These compounds have not all been isolated. $Se \cdot SO_3$,[827] from a solution of selenium in sulphuric acid or sulphur trioxide, forms green crystals, stable (unlike S_2O_3) to warming: it gives a green solution.

Various other mixed oxides or their hydrates are known. The melting-point curve of $H_2SeO_4 + SO_3$[828] shows maxima for H_2SeO_4,SO_3, melting-point $+6 \cdot 6°$ (salts known), and for $H_2SeO_4,2SO_3$, melting-point $+20°$.

[826] R. Anschütz, J. Kallen, and K. Riepenkröger, *Ber.* 1919, **52**, 1860.

[827] E. Moles, *J. Chim. Phys.* 1915, **13**, 207.

[828] J. Meyer and V. Stateczny, *Z. anorg. Chem.* 1922, **122**, 1.

Another mixed compound, of which also salts are known, is H_2SeO_4, CrO_3,[828] which melts at 200° to a green liquid.

Mixed Acids

The only very definite one seems to be selenosulphuric acid H_2SSeO_3,[829] the salts of which are got from a polyselenide and a bisulphite. On addition of acid Se is precipitated: there is probably an equilibrium

$$SeSO_3^{--} + H^+ \rightleftharpoons HSO_3^- + Se,$$

which is driven to the right by excess of acid.

The salts are isomorphous with the thiosulphates, but rather less stable; iodine liberates Se, but forms no dithionate. The formation of selenosulphates may explain why traces of selenium greatly promote the decomposition of sulphite to $SO_4'' + S$.[829]

Carbon Selenides

Carbon oxyselenide $O{=}C{=}Se$: Pearson and Robinson[830-1] showed that if dry carbon monoxide is passed over selenium at a low red heat, the issuing gas contains about 4 per cent. of this, which can be frozen out with liquid air. It is monomeric in the vapour, melts at $-122 \cdot 2°$, boils at $-20°/760$ mm.: critical temperature $+121°$. It is colourless and evil smelling. It is stable in the cold but easily decomposed to CO+Se on heating.

Carbon sulphoselenide CSSe can be made[832] by passing an arc between a selenium anode and a carbon cathode under CS_2, or more easily[833] by passing CS_2 vapour over ferrous selenide at 650°; the yield is very small; the CSSe is isolated by fractional distillation. It is a yellow liquid boiling at 84° and melting at $-85°$; the vapour density is normal, and so is the molecular weight determined cryoscopically in benzene and in bromoform. Unlike the disulphide it is a strong lachrymator, and has a very offensive smell. It is stable in the dark, but decomposes in the light; it is reduced by zinc and HCl to H_2S and H_2Se.

Carbon diselenide was obtained in traces by Rathke in 1869 from $P_2Se_5 + CCl_4$ at a red heat, and by Bartal in 1906 by passing CCl_4 over red hot cadmium selenide. A better yield was obtained[834] when a mixture of H_2Se and CCl_4 vapour was passed through a tube at 500° and the best by[834a] the action of methylene chloride vapour on selenium at 550–600°. It is a yellow liquid boiling at 124°/760 mm., and melting at $-45 \cdot 5°$; Trouton constant $22 \cdot 8$. It will not burn in air, and slowly decomposes on

[829] F. Foerster, F. Lange, O. Drossbach, and W. Seidel, ib. 1923, **128**, 289.

[830] T. G. Pearson and P. L. Robinson, *J.C.S.* 1932, 652.

[831] R. H. Purcell and F. D. Zahoorbux, ib. 1937, 1029.

[832] A. Stock and E. Willfroth, *Ber.* 1914, **47**, 144.

[833] H. A. V. Briscoe, J. B. Peel, and P. L. Robinson, *J.C.S.* 1929, **56**, 1048.

[834] H. G. Grimm and H. Metzger, *Ber.* 1936, **69**, 1356.

[834a] D. J. G. Ives, R. W. Pittman, and W. Wardlaw, *J.C.S.* 1947, 1080.

standing in light. It readily polymerizes in various complicated ways, especially in contact with ammonia. It forms a selenoxanthogenate CSe(SeK)OEt with alcoholic potash.

An attempt[834] to make CTe_2 in this way gave no result, although CSTe has been made.[835]

Seleno-ketones, $R_2C = Se$ *or* $[R_2C = Se]_2$

Thioketones are little known, and seleno- and telluroketones were quite unknown till in 1927 Lyons and Bradt[836], by treating a cooled mixture of ketone and concentrated hydrochloric acid with hydrogen selenide (on the analogy of the thioketones[837]), got the seleno-ketones $Me_2C = Se$, $MeEtC = Se$, $Et_2C = Se$. They were all heavy volatile red oils with a very unpleasant smell and were all shown by the freezing-point in benzene to be dimeric $(R_2CSe)_2$. $(Me_2CSe)_2$ boils at about $220-30°/760$ mm. and $94-7°/6-10$ mm. Acetophenone gives a similar compound, also dimeric, also red, but non-volatile in steam.

TELLURIUM OXIDES AND OXY-ACIDS

TELLURIUM certainly forms two, and probably three oxides.

Tellurium Monoxide, TeO

This compound is not quite certain. Divers and Shimosé[838] found that above 180° the mixed oxide $TeSO_3$ gives off SO_2 and leaves TeO. This was disputed,[839] but has been confirmed by Partington and Doolan,[840] who found that if $TeSO_3$ is heated until no more loss occurs, it turns black, and has nearly the right percentage of Te for TeO. The product is a black amorphous powder, which is stable in air in the cold. On heating *in vacuo* it is converted into a mixture of Te and TeO_2, and in moist air it is oxidized to TeO_2. Concentrated sulphuric acid dissolves it to a red solution, from which tellurium separates on standing.

Tellurium Dioxide, TeO_2

This is the stablest oxide, and is formed when tellurium is burnt in air or oxygen. It is a colourless crystalline substance, and is dimorphic, separating from water in octahedra, and from the fused substance in rhombic or monoclinic needles. It melts at $452·0°$,[841] and as with SeO_2 the colourless solid turns into a dark-yellow liquid. This can be distilled at a bright red heat, apparently without any decomposition.

Tellurium dioxide is almost insoluble in water: at the ordinary tempera-

[835] A. Stock and P. Praetorius, *Ber.* 1914, **47**, 131.

[836] R. E. Lyons and W. E. Bradt, ib. 1927, **60**, 824.

[837] E. Fromm and E. Baumann, ib. 1889, **22**, 1035, 2592.

[838] E. Divers and M. Shimosé, *J. pr. Chem.* 1881 [ii] **24**, 218; *Ber.* 1883, **16**, 1004.

[839] A. Damiens, *C.R.* 1924, **179**, 829.

[840] J. J. Doolan and J. R. Partington, *J.C.S.* 1924, **125**, 1402.

[841] A. Simek and B. Stehlik, *Coll. Czech. Chem. Comm.* 1930, **2**, 304.

ture 7 mg. dissolve in 1 litre,[842] presumably as a tellurous acid H_2TeO_3, though the solution is scarcely acidic. It is soluble in concentrated H_2SO_4, in concentrated hydrochloric acid, and to some extent in nitric acid, forming apparently a sulphate, a chloride, and a nitrate. It can be used like SeO_2 (but less effectively) for organic oxidations.[844]

Alkaline hydroxides (but not ammonia) dissolve it to form tellurites M_2TeO_3; alkaline carbonates react only on boiling, so that tellurous acid appears to be weaker than carbonic.

Tellurous acid can be oxidized to the tellurate by fusion with potassium nitrate, giving K_2TeO_4. But at high temperatures it is a strong oxidizing agent, being readily reduced to tellurium, and it has been suggested for use in organic combustions.

Tellurium dioxide is amphoteric, and like selenium dioxide forms a series of addition compounds with strong acids. With hydrochloric acid[843] it forms at $-10°$ TeO_2, 3 HCl, which easily loses HCl to give TeO_2, 2 HCl: this is stable up to $90°$, and then loses HCl and H_2O, forming perhaps an oxychloride. The solution of TeO_2 in HCl can be shown by E.M.F. measurements with a reversible tellurium electrode[845] to contain tellurium cations Te^{4+}. Their concentration is proportional to the fourth power of the hydrogen ion concentration, which is compatible with the reaction

$$H_2TeO_3 + 4 H^+ = Te^{4+} + 3 H_2O.$$

The concentration of Te^{4+} in a saturated solution of H_2TeO_3 is found to be 6×10^{-19}, which means that there are 360 individual ions per c.c.

The normal sulphate $Te(SO_4)_2$ is by no means well established; but 2 TeO_2, SO_3 can be made from TeO_2 and concentrated H_2SO_4, and forms 6-sided prisms.[846] When strongly heated, it melts, loses SO_3, and leaves TeO_2: it is violently hydrolysed by water. A white compound 2 TeO_2, TeO_3 has been prepared.[847]

With concentrated nitric acid[848] fairly stable crystals of 2 TeO_2, HNO_3 are formed.

On treatment with 70 per cent. $HClO_4$ a crystalline compound 2 TeO_2, $HClO_4$, is obtained,[849] which can be dried at $300°$, but is at once hydrolysed by water.

Tellurium Trioxide, TeO_3

This substance is obtained by heating telluric acid, H_6TeO_6. The last traces of water are very hard to remove. At a low red heat it breaks up

[842] D. Klein and J. Morel, *C.R.* 1884, **99**, 540, 567; 1886, **100**, 1140; *Bull. Soc. Chem.* 1885, [2] **43**, 204; *Ann. Chim. Phys.* 1885, [6] **5**, 81.

[843] A. Ditte, *C.R.* 1876, **83**, 446.

[844] C. H. Fisher and A. Eisner, *J. Org. Chem.* 1941, **6**, 169.

[845] J. Kasarnowsky, *Z. physikal. Chem.* 1924, **109**, 287.

[846] B. Brauner, *J.C.S.* 1889, 55, 382; K. Vrba, *Z. Krist.* 1891, **19**, 1.

[847] R. Metzner, *C.R.* 1897, **124**, 32.

[848] P. Köthner, *Ann.* 1901, **319**, 15.

[849] F. Fichter and M. Schmid, *Z. anorg. Chem.* 1916, **98**, 141.

into oxygen and the dioxide. It is not attacked by cold water, cold HCl, hot HNO_3, or moderately concentrated potassium hydroxide; it dissolves in water on prolonged heating to give the acid H_6TeO_6, and in solutions of alkaline hydroxides and carbonates; its general behaviour is very like that of ignited ferric or stannic oxide, but it is a strong oxidizing agent.[850] Hot concentrated HCl converts it into $Cl_2+TeO_2+TeCl_4$: boiling with concentrated potassium hydroxide converts it into the tellurate. On prolonged heating it changes into a second form which is grey, denser (6·21 instead of 5·075), insoluble in concentrated acids and alkalies, and generally much less reactive.[850a]

Tellurous Acid, H_2TeO_3

In the series of dioxides SO_2, SeO_2, TeO_2, the volatility falls (b. pts. $-10°$, $315°$, *ca.* $500°$) owi. g presumably to increasing auto-complex formation, and at the same time the tendency to hydrate, and also the acidity of the acids H_2XO_3, diminish, although the acidities of the hydrides go in the opposite direction:

First dissociation constants, and ratio $K_{H_2XO_3}/K_{H_2X}$.

				Ratio
H_2SO_3	$1·7 \times 10^{-2}$	H_2S	1×10^{-7}	170,000
H_2SeO_3	4×10^{-3}	H_2Se	$1·9 \times 10^{-4}$	21
H_2TeO_3	$0·6 \times 10^{-5}$	H_2Te	$2·3 \times 10^{-3}$	0·0026

The compound H_2TeO_3 has never really been isolated. When the potassium salt is treated with nitric acid, white flocks separate, but they have no definite formula; they dissolve easily in water to give an acid solution, but on warming above 40° TeO_2 separates out.

Salts are known not only of tellurous acid H_2TeO_3, but also of condensed acids such as $H_2Te_2O_5$, and even up to $H_2Te_6O_{13}$. In alkaline solution all these tend to be oxidized by air to the tellurate; in acid solution, on the other hand, they are very readily reduced to tellurium, for example, by SO_2, H_2NOH, tin, zinc, copper, mercury, etc., as well as by many organic substances.[851] The normal alkaline tellurites M_2TeO_3 are colourless and easily soluble in water, but the solutions decompose easily, and absorb carbon dioxide from the air. The acid salts $MHTeO_3$ are converted by water into $M_2TeO_3+TeO_2$.

The ease of oxidation diminishes as the complexity increases: atmospheric air will oxidize M_2TeO_3 at 450°, but it has no action on $M_2Te_4O_9$.[852]

No tellurous esters are known.

[850] E. Montignie, *Z. anorg. Chem.* 1943, **252**, 111.
[850a] Id., *Bull. Soc.* 1947, 564.
[851] e.g. by oxalic acid in light: A. Benrath, *Z. wiss. Phot.* 1915, **14**, 218.
[852] V. Lenher and E. Wolesensky, *J.A.C.S.* 1913, **35**, 718.

Tellurinic Acids, $R \cdot Te \diagup^O_{\diagdown OH}$

These are the analogues of the sulphinic and seleninic* acids. Phenyl (or benzene) tellurinic acid $\Phi \cdot Te \diagup^O_{\diagdown OH}$ was made by Lederer[853]; he converted diphenyl telluride $\Phi \cdot Te \cdot Te \cdot \Phi$ by oxidation with nitric acid into the nitrate $\Phi \cdot Te \diagup^O_{[NO_3]}$: the replacement of the sulphur of a sulphinic acid by tellurium makes the compound amphoteric; this nitrate when treated with alkali gives the phenyl tellurinic acid, a white powder of m. pt. 211°, which is soluble in alkalies and in acids, but not in the ordinary organic solvents.

Tellurium Oxyhalides

These are very uncertain. From solutions of the dioxide in halogen acids, various solids have been obtained, but none which correspond to the simple oxyhalides. For the fluorides see Prideaux,[854] and for the chlorides and bromides Parker and Robinson.[855]

Telluric Acid

While selenic acid has a great resemblance to sulphuric, telluric acid is quite different. It has a strong tendency to polymerize or condense, and as the molecular weight increases the solubility gets less and less, and the solutions tend to become colloidal; in fact the general behaviour of telluric acid is not unlike that of stannic acid.

But among these various forms of the acid the simple form H_2TeO_4 does not occur, though its salts are known. The normal or ortho acid, with one Te atom in the molecule, is H_6TeO_6, or $Te(OH)_6$ (isoelectronic with the stannate ion $[Sn(OH)_6]^{--}$). This ortho acid is made by oxidizing tellurium or its dioxide[856] with chromic acid in nitric acid[857]; on cooling the solution H_6TeO_6 crystallizes out.

There are at least two definite forms of the acid, ordinary or ortho-telluric acid H_6TeO_6, and allotelluric or poly-meta-telluric acid, of the formula $(H_2TeO_4)_n$, where n is about 11. Very possibly there are other intermediate condensed forms as well; but the simple form H_2TeO_4 does not exist.

* For these see p. 974 and reference [809].

[853] K. Lederer, *Ber*. 1915, **48**, 1345.
[854] E. B. R. Prideaux and J. O'N. Millott, *J.C.S.* 1929, 2703.
[855] T. W. Parker and P. L. Robinson, ib. 1928, 2853; 1931, 1314.
[856] L. Staudenmaier, *Z. anorg. Chem.* 1895, **10**, 189; J. Meyer and H. Moldenhauer, ib. 1921, **119**, 132.
[857] J. Meyer and W. Franke, ib. 1930, **193**, 191.

Ortho-telluric acid H_6TeO_6 is the most stable form. It has been shown by X-ray analysis[858] that the 6 OH groups are arranged octahedrally. Salts of this form are known, such as the silver salt Ag_6TeO_6,[859] and an ester $Te(OCH_3)_6$ (below). In the alkaline salts the hydrogen is only partially replaced, as in $M_4H_2TeO_6$ or $M_2H_4TeO_6$. In general the alkaline tellurates are not isomorphous with the sulphates and selenates, but there are exceptions; K_2TeO_4, K_2SeO_4, and K_2SO_4 have been shown by X-ray analysis to have the same structure,[860] and the acid salts $RbHSO_4$, $RbHSeO_4$, and $RbHTeO_4$ give mixed crystals with one another.[861]

H_6TeO_6 appears to be dimorphic. On heating it gradually loses water, and it is possible to stop when the composition is that of H_2TeO_4, but there is no indication that this is an individual. Further heating converts it into TeO_3 and then into tellurium dioxide and oxygen. The acid crystallizes from cold water as H_6TeO_6, $4 H_2O$, and loses its $4 H_2O$ at $10°$; its solubility in water is about $34/18°$.[862] The solution is colourless and has a metallic taste. In cold water telluric acid behaves as a normal electrolyte: its molecular weight is almost exactly that required for 1 Te atom per molecule.[863] On heating the acid polymerizes and the solution becomes colloidal; on cooling it returns again to its previous state. The same is true of the alkaline tellurates such as $Na_2H_4TeO_6$, whose solutions (at least on heating) are optically inhomogeneous; they have been called 'half colloids'.[864]

Ortho-telluric acid is a very weak acid, with

$$K_1 = 6 \times 10^{-7}, \quad K_2 = 4 \times 10^{-11}.^{[865]}$$

It cannot be titrated as it is not much stronger than hydrogen sulphide (1×10^{-7}), but like boric acid it gives strongly acid complexes with glycerol, which can be titrated with phenol-phthalein.[866]

The ester $Te(OCH_3)_6$ is made by the action of diazomethane on telluric acid in absolute alcohol[867]; it forms white crystals melting at $86-7°$ to a turbid liquid. It is readily saponified by water, acids, or alkalies.

Ortho-telluric acid is distinctly more easily reduced than its sulphur or selenium analogues, and often (for example, by SO_2, zinc, iron, or hydrazine) to tellurium.

[858] L. Pauling, *J.A.C.S.* 1933, **55**, 1898; see also L. Passerini and M. A. Rollier, *Atti R. Linc.* 1935, [vi] **21**, 364.

[859] See E. Montignie, *Bull. Soc. Chem.* 1935, [v] **2**, 864.

[860] M. Patry, *C.R.* 1936, **202**, 1516.

[861] G. Pellini, *Atti R. Linc.* 1909, [v] **18**, ii. 279; *Gaz.* 1910, **40**, i. 380; ii. 37.

[862] F. Mylius, *Ber.* 1901, **34**, 2219.

[863] A. Gutbier, ib. 2724; *Z. anorg. Chem.* 1904, **40**, 260; **42**, 174.

[864] A. Rosenheim and G. Jander, *Koll. Z.* 1918, **22**, 23.

[865] E. Blanc, *J. Chim. Phys.* 1920, **18**, 28.

[866] See A. Hantzsch, *Z. Elektrochem.* 1918, **24**, 201.

[867] G. Pellini, *Gaz.* 1916, **46**, ii. 247.

Allo-telluric Acid

Mylius[862] found that the ortho-acid if heated in a sealed tube to 140° melts to a colourless syrupy mass, which is miscible with water. In solution its conductivity is 3 or 4 times as great as that of the ortho-acid, but on standing this falls, and if the solution is concentrated the ortho-acid crystallizes out. Freezing-points indicate that polymerization has occurred and this allo-acid is presumably a polymerization or condensation product of the ordinary acid. Mylius's work has been repeated and confirmed by Pascal and Patry.[868-72] The product of heating the ortho-acid is a mixture, but owes its peculiar properties to a polymerized acid $(H_2TeO_4)_n$, of which esters can be obtained by refluxing with alcohol.[871] Patry concludes that this is the only telluric acid other than the ortho, and thinks that $n = 11 \pm 1$. It is clear that in water this goes over to the ortho-acid, the two being in equilibrium, and the polymer being favoured by rise of temperature and by increase of concentration.

Carbon Sulphotelluride, $S{=}C{=}Te$

This has been made by Stock[873] by passing an arc between an electrode of carbon and one of mixed carbon and tellurium under carbon disulphide at 0°. The product contains up to 5 per cent. CSTe with up to 1 per cent. carbon subsulphide C_3S_2; the latter is removed by fractional distillation below 0° and by combination with β-naphthylamine. Carbon sulphotelluride has a melting-point of $-54°$ and an extrapolated boiling-point of about $+110°$; it is yellow-red, and melts to a bright red liquid which soon decomposes; it smells of garlic. It is monomeric by the freezing-point in benzene and the boiling-point in CS_2. It is very unstable; it is decomposed by light and must be prepared in the dark; it soon decomposes at the ordinary temperature, evolving carbon disulphide and apparently leaving a mixture of carbon and tellurium.

Telluroketones, $R_2C{=}Te$

These were made[874] by the same method as the selenoketones (p. 980), by passing hydrogen telluride into a 1:1 mixture of the ketone and concentrated hydrochloric acid at 20–5°. The products are clearly of quite a different type from the selenoketones; they are all more volatile (b. pts. Me_2CTe 55–8°/10–13 mm.; MeEtCTe 63–6°/9–10 mm.; Et_2CTe 69–72°/8–11 mm.); they are all found by the freezing-points to be monomeric in benzene, and they have a different smell, which is choking, but not unpleasant.

[868] P. Pascal and M. Patry, *C.R.* 1935, **200**, 708.
[869] M. Patry, ib. 1597.
[870] Id., ib. 1936, **202**, 64.
[871] Id., ib. 2088.
[872] Id., *Bull. Soc. Chim.* 1936, [v] **3**, 845.
[873] A. Stock and P. Praetorius, *Ber.* 1914, **47**, 131.
[874] R. E. Lyons and E. D. Scudder, ib. 1931, **64**, 530.

SELENIUM AND THE HALOGENS

THERE are four possible types of these, with the formulae (M = Se or Te):
$M_2(hal)_2$; $M(hal)_2$; $M(hal)_4$; $M(hal)_6$.

SELENIUM AND FLUORINE

Here there are two definite known compounds, SeF_4 and SeF_6: there are no indications of Se_2F_2 or SeF_2.

Selenium tetrafluoride was formerly confused with the oxyfluoride $SeOF_2$ (p. 973). SeF_4 was obtained by Prideaux[875] by the action of silver fluoride on selenium tetrachloride. It boils at 93°, melts at −13·2°, and has a density of 2·77. It is colourless and is converted by silicon in the cold into silicon tetrafluoride and selenium.

Selenium Hexafluoride

This was discovered in 1906 by Prideaux[876] and further investigated by Yost and Claussen[877] and Henkel and Klemm.[878] In the table[877] H_a is the heat of formation of the gaseous molecule from its atoms.

| Sbst. | H_a | Heat of | | M. pt. | Subl. pt. |
		Subl.	Fusion		
SF_6	428·5	5·64	1·39	−50·8°	−63·8
SeF_6	407·2	6·60	(2·01)	−34·6°	−46·6
TeF_6	470·2	6·74	(1·90)	−37·8°	−38·9

The heats of formation from the atoms (H_a) are calculated from the heats of atomization: F 31·75; S 66·3; Se 61; Te 55. They give for the heat of formation of the links:

$$\begin{array}{ccc} S\text{---}F & Se\text{---}F & Te\text{---}F \\ 71\cdot5 & 67\cdot2 & 78\cdot4 \text{ k.cals.} \end{array}$$

SeF_6 has the same kind of extreme stability as SF_6; it does not attack glass and is not absorbed or changed by water. Yost and Claussen[877] have shown that SeF_6 reacts with ammonia slowly at 200° and much more rapidly at 330°, to give nitrogen, selenium, and hydrofluoric acid. This agrees with the calculated heat of reaction:

$$2\,NH_3(g) + SeF_6(g) = N_2(g) + Se(s) + 6\,HF(g) + 116\cdot0 \text{ k.cals.}$$

Hence the chemical inertness of these hexafluorides is not due to the lack of a thermodynamic tendency to react.

The evidence that SeF_6 and SF_6 are covalently saturated and TeF_6 is not, will be discussed under TeF_6 (p. 990).

[875] E. B. R. Prideaux, *J.C.S.* 1928, 1603.
[876] Id., ib. 1906, **89**, 316.
[877] D. M. Yost and W. H. Claussen, *J.A.C.S.* 1933, **55**, 885.
[878] P. Henkel and W. Klemm, *Z. anorg. Chem.* 1935, **222**, 65.

SELENIUM AND CHLORINE

Three compounds of these elements probably occur in one state of aggregation or another, Se_2Cl_2, $SeCl_2$, and $SeCl_4$.

Diselenium Dichloride, Se_2Cl_2

This substance, often called selenium monochloride, can be made[879] from its elements, by the action of selenium on its tetrachloride, by reducing $SeCl_4$ with PCl_3 (giving PCl_5), or by dissolving selenium in oleum and passing gaseous hydrogen chloride into the hot solution. It is a brownish-yellow oily liquid, smelling like S_2Cl_2. Its molecular weight in ethylene dibromide is that of Se_2Cl_2.[880] It is heavier than water and is slowly decomposed by it to give selenious acid, hydrochloric acid, and free selenium. Unlike S_2Cl_2 it will not distil without fairly complete decomposition.

It can be distilled[881] in a high vacuum, being condensed with solid CO_2: the distillate is nearly pure, but some selenium remains behind, and obviously the vapour is dissociated.

Se_2Cl_2 is miscible with benzene. Its dipole moment in the solution is 2·1 D.[882] This suggests that there is some

present. When warm it is a good solvent for selenium, which separates on cooling in the grey form, which is insoluble in carbon disulphide. It behaves as an unsaturated compound: with chlorine it gives the tetrachloride, with bromine the compound $SeClBr_3$: with phenyl magnesium bromide it gives diphenyl diselenide $\Phi \cdot Se \cdot Se \cdot \Phi$, which reacts with excess of bromine to give the tetrabromide $C_6H_5 \cdot SeBr_2 \cdot SeBr_2 \cdot C_6H_5$. It reacts with ethylene like S_2Cl_2 to give 'selenium mustard gas' $Se(CH_2 \cdot CH_2Cl)_2$.[883] $SSeCl_2$, b. pt. 68°/20 mm. can be made[884] by heating sulphur and Se_2Cl_2 in a sealed tube at 200°.

Selenium Dichloride, $SeCl_2$

The solid–liquid curve[880] of the system Se—Cl gives no evidence of the existence of $SeCl_2$, which probably does not occur in the liquid or the solid state; but it has been shown[886-7] that the vapour of selenium tetrachloride

[879] F. Krafft and O. Steiner, *Ber.* 1901, **34**, 560; F. H. Heath and W. F. Semon, *J. Ind. Eng. Chem.* 1920, **12**, 1100. For a good summary of its properties see V. Lenher and C. H. Kao, *J.A.C.S.* 1926, **48**, 1550.

[880] E. Beckmann, *Z. physikal. Chem.* 1910, **70**, 1.

[881] A. Voigt and W. Biltz, *Z. anorg. Chem.* 1924, **133**, 294.

[882] C. P. Smyth, G. L. Lewis, A. J. Grossmann, and F. B. Jennings, *J.A.C.S.* 1940, **62**, 1219.

[883] C. E. Boord and F. F. Cope, ib. 1922, **44**, 395.

[884] A. Baroni, *Atti R.* 1937, [vi] **25**, 719; **26**, 456.

[886] J. H. Simons, *J.A.C.S.* 1930, **52**, 3483.

[887] D. M. Yost and E. C. Kircher, ib. 4680.

has half the expected molecular weight, and, from the effect of excess of chlorine on the vapour pressure,[887] that the vapour must consist of $SeCl_2 + Cl_2$. Also, if Se_2Cl_2 is heated, Se is left behind, so that probably here too the vapour contains $SeCl_2$. The vapour density of $SeCl_2$ is constant from 190° to 600°,[886-7] which is evidence that in the vapour state $SeCl_2$ is very stable, as we might expect it to be. But in the liquid or solid state it seems to go over to Se_2Cl_2 or $SeCl_4$ or both.

Selenium Tetrachloride, SeCl₄

This is formed by the action of excess of chlorine on selenium, or of PCl_5 on SeO_2, or better by chlorinating selenium under carbon tetrachloride.[888] It is even formed by the action of concentrated HCl on SeO_2.[889]

Selenium tetrachloride forms colourless crystals which sublime on heating. There has been much dispute about the density of the vapour; but recent work[886-7] agrees in showing that the vapour has, from 190° to 600° at least, just half the density of $SeCl_4$, and (above) that it consists of $SeCl_2 + Cl_2$, and not of $Se_2Cl_2 + 3 Cl_2$. $SeCl_4$ melts under pressure at $305 \pm 3°$ to a red liquid, and it sublimes with a vapour pressure of one atmosphere at 196°. As with SCl_4, there is no evidence that it occurs in anything but the solid state.

$SeCl_4$ is quite insoluble in CS_2, but it can be recrystallized from $POCl_3$; it decomposes when it is dissolved in sulphur, and it is decomposed by water, first to $SeOCl_2$ and then to selenious acid H_2SeO_3. It reacts with the Grignard reagent to give Ar_2SeCl_2,[890] or with benzene in presence of aluminium chloride to give Φ_2Se, Φ_2Se_2, and $\Phi_3Se[Cl]$.[891]

It forms addition compounds such as $SeCl_4, AuCl_3$[892] and $SeCl_4, SbCl_5$.[893] Yost shows [886] from the vapour pressures that the heat of reaction is

$$SeCl_4(s) = SeCl_2(g) + Cl_2(g) - 35 \cdot 58 \text{ k.cals.}$$

Hence, if we adopt Julius Thomsen's value of 46·16 k.cals. for the heat of formation of H_f of $SeCl_4(s)$, we have for the H_f of $SeCl_2$

$$Se(s) + Cl_2(g) = SeCl_2(g) - 10 \cdot 58.$$

SELENIUM AND BROMINE

The volatility and vapour density of mixtures of selenium and bromine[894] show that the only selenium compound in the vapour is $SeBr_2$, which in the vapour is stable from 250° to 500° at least, but on condensation gives as liquid or solid only bromine, Se_2Br_2, and $SeBr_4$. It is especially marked

[888] V. Lenher, *J.A.C.S.* 1920, **42**, 2498.

[889] J. Meyer, *Z. anal. Chem.* 1914, **53**, 145.

[890] W. Strecker and A. Willing, *Ber.* 1915, **48**, 196.

[891] W. E. Bradt and J. F. Green, *J. Org. Chem.* 1937, **1**, 540.

[892] L. Lindet, *C.R.* 1885, **101**, 1492.

[893] Weber, *Pogg. Ann.* 1865, **125**, 78.

[894] D. M. Yost and J. B. Hatcher, *J.A.C.S.* 1931, **53**, 2549.

that a mixture in the proportions of 2 Br to 1 Se if vaporized gives practically no sign of the band spectrum of bromine, but when it is cooled, as soon as the vapour begins to condense, the bromine bands appear.

The descriptions of Se_2Br_2 thus apply only to the liquid, and those of $SeBr_4$ only to the solid.

Se_2Br_2

It is a very deep red liquid, less stable than the chloride Se_2Cl_2. It is slowly decomposed by water or alkalies to give HBr, selenious acid, and free selenium. It dissolves undecomposed in CS_2.

$SeBr_4$

This is less stable than Se_2Br_2; it easily loses bromine, and at 70–80° is wholly converted into $Se_2Br_2+Br_2$. It forms yellow crystals and sublimes as a mixture of Se_2Br_2 and $SeBr_4$. It gives a clear solution in water, being hydrolysed to H_2SeO_3+HBr. With SO_3 it forms a compound $SeBr_4$, $2\,SO_3$ (m. pt. 75°), which on heating evolves bromine and SO_2, and gives a yellow sublimate of the composition $SeOBr_2,SO_3$.

SELENIUM AND IODINE

The supposed compounds of these elements do not appear to be isolable; the two elements give a simple eutectic curve.[895]

The molecular weight of Se as found by the freezing-point in iodine is Se_2.[896]

It has, however, been found[897] that light that has passed through two separate solutions of selenium and iodine in carbon disulphide has an absorption band at 4,200–4,500 A, which is absent when the two solutions are mixed. Also while selenium is not measurably soluble in carbon disulphide, it dissolves in presence of iodine, the ratio I_2/Se being $40 \cdot 0 \pm 0 \cdot 1$. Thus there is evidence of combination, though no compounds can be isolated.

SELENIUM COMPLEX HALIDES

These are all selenites of the type $M_2Se(hal)_6$, with the valency group 2, $\underline{12}$; the anions have been shown to be octahedral; they are formed by chlorine and bromine, but neither by fluorine nor by iodine.

Hexachloroselenites, M_2SeCl_6

Though the corresponding tellurium compounds M_2TeCl_6 are known, and also the bromoselenites, the chloroselenites have only been obtained

[895] G. Pellini and S. Pedrina, *Atti R. Linc.* 1908, [5] 17, ii. 78; E. Beckmann and R. Hanslian, *Z. anorg. Chem.* 1913, 80, 221; E. Beckmann, *Berl. Akad. Ber.* 1913, 886; E. Beckmann, E. Grünthal, and O. Faust, *Z. anorg. Chem.* 1913, 84, 97; E. Montignie, *Bull. Soc. Chim.* 1937, [v] 4, 132.

[896] F. Olivari, *Atti R. Linc.* 1908, [5] 17, ii. 389; 1909, [5] 18, i. 465; ii. 94, 264. E. Beckmann and O. Faust (*Z. anorg. Chem.* 1913, 84, 103) and R. Wright (*J.C.S.* 1915, 107, 1527) agree.

[897] J. D. McCullough, *J.A.C.S.* 1939, 61, 3401.

recently, chiefly, it would seem, owing to their great solubility. Petzold[898] has now made the salts of potassium, ammonium, and a series of alkyl-ammoniums. $SeCl_4$ is dissolved in concentrated HCl (no doubt as H_2SeCl_6, though this cannot be isolated), the alkaline chloride, also dissolved in concentrated hydrochloric acid, is added, and the solution cooled to $0°$. The salts (which are all anhydrous) crystallize out. They are very hygroscopic and are quickly decomposed by moisture.

Hexabromoselenites, M_2SeBr_6

These are made in the same way, by the combination of $SeBr_4$ with HBr or alkaline bromides; here, however, the free acid can be obtained, as dark red crystals from hydrobromic acid.[899-900]

The salts[901] are dark red; they give clear (but hydrolysed) solutions in water. The potassium salt is very unstable in air, easily losing bromine; the ammonium salt is much more stable.[900] The potassium salt is said[902] to be isomorphous with the tellurium analogue, and the ammonium salt $(NH_4)_2SeBr_6$ with the corresponding Pb, Pt, and Sn salts. This presumably implies that the anion in M_2SeBr_6 is octahedral in spite of the central atom having a valency group of 14 (2, <u>12</u>, with the inert pair), instead of 12 as in the Sn and Pt compounds.

TELLURIUM AND THE HALOGENS

THE compounds of tellurium with the halogens are on the whole very similar to those of selenium.

TELLURIUM AND FLUORINE

The only fluoride definitely isolated is the hexafluoride, although it is fairly certain that lower fluorides exist.

Tellurium hexafluoride is formed[903] by the action of fluorine on tellurium. For its physical constants see above, p. 986. It has an unpleasant smell, like a mixture of ozone and hydrogen telluride[903] (SF_6 has no smell: nothing seems to be said about SeF_6). It is slowly absorbed by water, with complete hydrolysis to telluric acid H_6TeO_6.[903] Also,[877] while SeF_6 does not react with selenium below the melting-point of glass, TeF_6 reacts with tellurium below $200°$, giving a white solid which is perhaps TeF_2.

The inactivity of SeF_6 as compared with TeF_6 is important as evidence that the covalency maximum of selenium is 6, while that of tellurium is higher. As we have seen (p. 986), the inactivity of SeF_6 is not due to any exceptional thermodynamic stability, and can only be explained by an

[898] W. Petzold, *Z. anorg. Chem.* 1932, **209**, 267.

[899] A. Gutbier and W. Grünewald, *J. pr. Chem.* 1911, [2] **85**, 321.

[900] J. Meyer and V. Wurm, *Z. anorg. Chem.* 1930, **190**, 90.

[901] W. Muthmann and J. Schäfer, *Ber.* 1893, **26**, 1008; J. F. Norris, *J.A.C.S.* 1898, **20**, 490; V. Lenher, ib. 555; A. Gutbier and F. Engeroff, *Z. anorg. Chem.* 1914, **89**, 307.

[902] E. Carozzi, *Gaz.* 1924, **54**, 556.

[903] E. B. R. Prideaux, *J.C.S.* 1906, **89**, 322.

abnormally great heat of activation, which in turn must be due to the covalent saturation of the central atom. This conclusion is further supported by the length of the covalent links in these hexafluorides, which have been measured by Brockway and Wall.[904] As they showed in the tetrachlorides of Si, Ge, and Sn, the occurrence of resonance is indicated by a shortening of the observed links, as compared with the lengths calculated from other compounds in which resonance cannot take place; and resonance is only possible if we can have as a constituent structure one with a double link between the halogen and the central atom, and this requires that the central atom should not already be covalently saturated. With the hexafluorides we have no means of calculating what the normal length of this link should be; we only know the radii of the 2-covalent S, Se, and Te atoms, which must certainly be somewhat larger. So we should expect all the distances to be rather short, but those where there was resonance (i.e. the link in TeF_6) should be shorter still. The observed facts bear this out, whether we consider the absolute or the percentage difference:

Length of X–F in A.U.

	SF_6	SeF_6	TeF_6
Calculated . . .	1·68	1·81	2·01
Observed	1·58	1·70	1·84
Difference . . .	−0·10	−0·11	−0·17
Difference per cent. . .	−6·0	−6·1	−8·5

It is clear that other compounds of tellurium and fluorine exist, but none have been isolated. These elements have been found (Moissan, Prideaux) to give solid products of doubtful composition. Yost and Claussen[877] on fractionating TeF_6 got about 1·3 c.c. of a liquid boiling at about $+60°$, which was not pure, but which gave a molecular weight from the vapour density of about 340 ($TeF_6 = 241·5$), so that it must have more than one Te atom in the molecule.

Whytlaw-Gray[905] finds that if TeF_6 is heated in a tube of Al_2O_3 to $200°$, the tube is not attacked, but the TeF_6 is completely absorbed, and fine white needles of the composition TeF_4 remain; these are rapidly hydrolysed by water, or even by exposure to ordinary air. Metzner[906] obtained from the action of concentrated hydrofluoric acid solution on tellurium, crystals of $HTeF_5, 5 H_2O$, from which salts can be got; a similar compound $TeF_4, 4 H_2O$ has been described.[907]

TELLURIUM AND CHLORINE

Two compounds have been described, $TeCl_2$ and $TeCl_4$.

[904] L. O. Brockway and F. T. Wall, *J.A.C.S.* 1934, **56**, 2373.
[905] G. A. R. Hartley, T. H. Henry, and R. Whytlaw-Gray, *Nature*, 1938, **142**, 952.
[906] R. Metzner, *Ann. Chim. Phys.* 1898, [7] **15**, 203.
[907] A. Högbom, *Bull. Soc. Chim.* 1881, [2] **35**, 60.

Tellurium Dichloride, $TeCl_2$

A black substance of this composition is formed by the action of chlorine on tellurium in the right proportions, or by heating $TeCl_4$ with Te.[908] It appears to be amorphous, melts at 175°, and boils at 324°. See further reference [909]. After distillation this always contains a slight excess of tellurium[910] (compare SCl_2).

The vapour obtained from this solid has a characteristic spectrum; its density corresponds to $TeCl_2$. The liquid formed on fusion has the fairly high conductivity of 0·042 at 206°.[910] The solid is fairly reactive, the tellurium easily going over into the quadrivalent state; for example, water converts it into H_2TeO_3+Te, oxygen into TeO_2+TeCl_4. It attracts water from the air and is soluble in ether. It is decomposed by acids and alkalies with the separation of tellurium.

Tellurium Tetrachloride, $TeCl_4$

This is readily formed from its elements, or by the action of tellurium on other chlorides such as S_2Cl_2 or $AsCl_3$. It forms[911] white crystals, melting at 225° and boiling at 390°. It gives an orange-red vapour, whose density up to 500° (where dissociation sets in) corresponds to $TeCl_4$. The heat of evaporation is 18·4 k.cals., which gives the very high Trouton Constant of 27·8. The parachor is 267·8 from 238° to 322°. The electrical conductivity is that of a salt; it is 0·1145 at 236° and 0·203 at 316°.[910]

In spite of the high conductivity it has the solubility of a covalent compound, being soluble in benzene and toluene, as well as in methyl and ethyl alcohol, but not in ether. Electron diffraction of the vapour[912] indicates a trigonal bipyramid with one equatorial place empty, as is to be expected with a valency decet (2, 8); Te—Cl 2·33 A (theory 2·36), angle Cl—Te—Cl 93±3°.

Its chemical properties are unlike those of the volatile chlorides of sulphur and selenium, and more like those of, say, $SbCl_3$. It has not a very strong affinity for water; cold water dissolves it and precipitates TeO_2; hot water (which does not dissolve TeO_2) gives a clear solution. Hydrochloric acid dissolves it to form the same solution as is got from TeO_2 and HCl, containing H_2TeO_3, TeO_2, $HTeCl_5$, H_2TeCl_6, and possibly an oxychloride.

$TeCl_4$ reacts with many organic compounds, especially those containing carbonyl groups,[913] and also with dimethylaniline,[914] forming first an addition compound $(Me_2N\Phi)_2,TeCl_4$, and then the diaryl dichloride $(Me_2N\cdot C_6H_4)_2TeCl_2$. It forms a number of addition products such as

[908] C. A. A. Michaelis, *Ber.* 1887, **20**, 1780, 2488.

[909] A. Damiens, *Ann. Chim.* 1923, [9] **19**, 44, 179.

[910] A. Voigt and W. Biltz, *Z. anorg. Chem.* 1924, **133**, 297.

[911] J. H. Simons, *J.A.C.S.* 1930, **52**, 3488.

[912] D. P. Stevenson and V. Schomaker, ib. 1940, **62**, 1267.

[913] G. T. Morgan and H. D. K. Drew, *J.C.S.* 1924, **125**, 731, 754, 760.

[914] G. T. Morgan and H. Burgess, ib. 1929, 1103.

$TeCl_4 \cdot 2\ AlCl_3$, $TeCl_4$, $2\ Et_2O$, $TeCl_4$, 3, and $6\ NH_3$[915]: and also a curious compound $TeCl_4, SO_3$, which is yellow and melts at 180°. Another is $TeCl_4$, $2\ SO_3$.

TELLURIUM AND BROMINE

Two compounds have been described, and probably exist, $TeBr_2$ and $TeBr_4$.

Tellurium Dibromide, $TeBr_2$

This is very like $TeCl_2$. It forms blackish-green crystals, m. pt. 210°, b. pt. 339°, giving a violet vapour. Measurements of the vapour density[916] show that the molecule is $TeBr_2$ up to 750°; it cannot be a mixture of $Te_2Br_2 + Br_2$ since it gives no bromine absorption bands. It is hydrolysed by water in the same way as $TeCl_2$, to $H_2TeO_3 + HBr + Te$.

$TeBr_2$ has been shown by electron diffraction[917] to have a Br—Te—Br angle of $98 \pm 3°$; the Te—Br distance is 2·51 A (theory 2·51).

Tellurium Tetrabromide

This again is made from its elements. Dark yellow or red crystals, m. pt. $380 \pm 6°$, b. pt. 414–27° with dissociation. At 432° the vapour is more than 90 per cent. dissociated into $TeBr_2 + Br_2$; at 600° this dissociation is practically complete; the $TeBr_2$ does not itself break up to $Te + Br_2$ below 1,000°.[916]

$TeBr_4$ gives a clear solution in a little water and, on cooling, red crystals, apparently a hydrate, separate. Much water precipitates TeO_2, which is soluble in HBr.

It forms[918] an addition compound with aniline $(H_2N \cdot C_6H_5)_2, TeBr_4$.

TELLURIUM AND IODINE

The two elements mix in the liquid state in all proportions, but the only certain compound is TeI_4. The only maximum in the solid–liquid Te—I curve[919] is at TeI_4, m. pt. 259°, in a sealed tube: black crystals which begin to volatilize and dissociate at any temperature above 100°. Insoluble in CCl_4, CS_2, ether, chloroform, acetic acid; slightly soluble in acetone and ethyl and amyl alcohols. This is the only binary compound of iodine with sulphur, selenium, or tellurium that has been isolated.

COMPLEX TELLURIUM HALIDES

Complex fluorides seem to be unknown, but the other halogens give complex acids and salts, which are always derived from the tetrahalide, and are of two types $M[Te(hal)_5]$ and $M_2[Te(hal)_6]$. The first kind, which is unusual, occurs as the free acid with all three halogens: $HTeCl_5$, $5\ H_2O$,

[915] W. Strecker and W. Ebert, *Ber.* 1925, **58**, 2527.
[916] D. M. Yost and J. B. Hatcher, *J.A.C.S.* 1932, **54**, 151.
[917] M. T. Rogers and R. A. Spurr, ib. 1947, **69**, 2102.
[918] A. Lowy and R. F. Dunbrook, ib. 1922, **44**, 614.
[919] F. M. Jaeger and J. B. Menke, *Z. anorg. Chem.* 1912, **77**, 320.

yellow needles: $HTeBr_5$, 5 H_2O, orange crystals, m. pt. 20°: $HTeI_5$, 8 H_2O,[920] black, m. pt. 55°. They are all unstable, and readily lose halogen acid in the air; only the chloride seems to be known to give salts. The presence in the chloride and the bromide of an odd number of water molecules suggests that one at least is part of the anion, which has probably the 6-covalent form $[Te(hal)_5, H_2O]^-$.

The more usual type $M_2Te(hal)_6$ has not been obtained at all as the free acid, but is well known in a series of salts, chlorides, bromides, and iodides.[921-2] Of the alkaline salts the hexachlorides are yellow, the hexabromides orange to scarlet, and the hexaiodides black. They dissolve without decomposition in a small quantity of water, but with more water they are hydrolysed, with the precipitation of TeO_2. Hence they must be recrystallized from the halogen acid.

The alkaline hexachloro- and hexabromo-tellurites, like the selenites, are isomorphous with the other salts M_2XBr_6, where X = Se, Pb, Pt, Sn, and also with M_2SiF_6: so that they must have an octahedral arrangement with a valency group of 14 (2, 12).

Halides of Sulphur, Selenium, and Tellurium: summary

[v. = vapour; l. = liquid; s. = solid.]

Type	F	Cl	Br	I
M_2X_2	S_2F_2 ? ? Se:no Te:no	S_2Cl_2 stable Se_2Cl_2 l. Te:no	S_2Br_2 Se_2Br_2 l. Te:no	S:no Se:no Te:no
MX_2	SF_2 ? ? Se:no Te:no	SCl_2 less stable $SeCl_2$ v. only $TeCl_2$ v., ? s.	S:no $SeBr_2$ v. only $TeBr_2$ s., l., v.	S:no Se:no Te:no
MX_4	S:no $SeF_4 + 93°$ TeF_4 ? ?	SCl_4 s. $-40°$ $SeCl_4$ s. only $TeCl_4$, s., l., v.	S:no $SeBr_4$ s. only $TeBr_4$ s., l.	S:no Se:no TeI_4 s.
MX_6	SF_6 SeF_6 TeF_6	S:no Se:no Te:no	S:no Se:no Te:no	S:no Se:no Te:no

[920] R. Metzner, *C.R.* 1897, **124**, 1448.
[921] H. L. Wheeler, *Z. anorg. Chem.* 1893, **3**, 428.
[922] A. Gutbier and F. Flury, *J. pr. Chem.* 1911, **83**, 145.

POLONIUM

POLONIUM was discovered in bismuth from pitchblende by the Curies in 1898, being the first element to be discovered by means of its radioactivity. It was separated by W. Marckwald in 1902[923] as a deposit formed on a bismuth plate when immersed in a solution of the chloride. Recent methods of concentration[924-6] follow the original plan, and usually end with separating the element by immersing a plate of silver (or sometimes gold or nickel) in the solution.

Polonium is a product of the decay of radium, and is identical with radium F. Its half-life is 138·7 days.[927] It is therefore present in old specimens of radium compounds to the extent of 1/5,000 of the radium: 1 gramme of polonium is contained in 25,000 tons of pitchblende, or in 7·5 kg. of radium more than 30 years old. It is now often got from old radon bulbs from hospitals, usually by electrolysis onto nickel or platinum. Other isotopes of No. 84 with their half-life periods are AcA (0·0015″), ThA (0·14″), RaA (3·05 min.), AcC′ (0·005″), ThC′ (10⁻¹¹ sec.), and RaC′ (10⁻⁶ sec.). Hevesy[928] has tried to find an inactive isotope in tellurium and bismuth minerals by adding a trace of polonium and concentrating this, when any inactive 84 should have been concentrated with it; but none was found, though 1 part in 10^{11} of the mineral could have been detected. Similar fruitless searches for inactive isotopes of radioactive elements have been made, by Aston for emanation 86, by Hahn and Donath for radium 88, and by Hevesy for actinium 89; but since bismuth 83 has both inactive and active isotopes there seemed to be more hope of finding an inactive 84.

Metallic polonium was obtained[929] by volatilization from nickel onto a thin collodion film; about 10⁻⁷ g. was got as a layer some 100 A thick. This gave a good X-ray pattern like that of tellurium, each Po having 4 nearest neighbours about 3·40 A away: so that the radius of Po is 1·70 A.

The chemistry of polonium is of great interest, as it is the heaviest member of the sulphur subgroup, but our knowledge of it is naturally small, and much of the evidence needs careful scrutiny.

On the whole its chemical properties seem to be those which we should expect from its position. It resembles tellurium (it was at one time called radio-tellurium) and also to some extent its neighbour bismuth. We should expect that the inert pair would be more marked in polonium than in tellurium, and accordingly that polonium would have more the character of a quadrivalent metal. This is so: hexavalency is very rare, and the

[923] *Ber.* 1902, **35**, 2285.

[924] I. Curie and F. Joliot, *J. Chim. Phys.* 1931, **28**, 201; L. R. Hafstad, *J. Franklin Inst.* 1936, **221**, 191; M. Haissinsky, *J. Chim. Phys.* 1936, **33**, 97.

[925] M. A. Rollier, *Gaz.* 1936, **66**, 797.

[926] D. M. Ziv, *C.R. Acad. Sci. U.R.S.S.* 1939, **25**, 743.

[927] A. Sanielevici, *J. Phys. Radium*, 1935, [vii] **6**, 73. M. A. da Silva (*C.R.* 1927, **184**, 197) gives 140·2 days.

[928] G. v. Hevesy and A. Guenther, *Z. anorg. Chem.* 1930, **194**, 162.

[929] M. A. Rollier, S. B. Hendricks, and L. R. Maxwell, *J. Chem. Phys.* 1936, **4**, 648.

usual valency is 4, which is well marked. The resemblance to bismuth is certain, but is much less than that to tellurium. The hexavalency is indicated by its forming solid solutions with the tellurate $K_2TeO_4, 3\,H_2O$.[930] The similarity to tellurium is shown by the value of the discharge potential, the easy reduction of the chloride, the large hydrolysis of the chloride and nitrate, the precipitation of the sulphide from acid solution, and the existence of a volatile hydride. Differences from tellurium are that the salts in acid solution are less easily reduced, that the hydroxide is insoluble in ammonia, and that the sulphide is insoluble in solutions of alkaline sulphides. The position of the element in relation to tellurium and bismuth is shown by the fact[928] that if alkali is added to an acid solution containing Te, Bi, and Po, the bismuth precipitates first as hydroxide, then the polonium, and last, just before the solution becomes neutral, the tellurium; if still more alkali is added, the tellurium goes first into solution, then the polonium, and lastly the bismuth.

Elementary polonium is volatile at about 1,000°; when it is made by reduction (e.g. of the chloride with zinc) in solution, it can separate in the colloidal state[931]; this is a general characteristic of polonium and its compounds.

It forms a volatile hydride, which was discovered by Paneth, and which no doubt has the formula PoH_2. This can be made by dissolving magnesium in a hydrochloric acid solution of polonium.[932] The maximum yield is 0·1 per cent. It can be separated from the hydrogen by condensation in liquid air. It is very unstable even at $-180°$; at the ordinary temperature, when mixed with the large excess of hydrogen which comes off with it, its time of half (chemical) decay is about 5 minutes.

The methods used for investigating the chemical properties of polonium are either electrochemical, or they consist in finding whether its compounds (identifiable only through their radioactivity) crystallize or dissolve with those of other elements.[933-42]

The electrochemical behaviour of polonium is complicated. It was shown by Paneth[943] that like tellurium it is a true 'Zwitterelement', in that it can be electrolytically deposited on, or dissolved off, both the anode and the cathode. It certainly occurs in three different states. In

[930] A. G. Samartzeva, *C.R. Acad. Sci. U.R.S.S.* 1941, **33**, 498.

[931] W. Marckwald, *Ber.* 1903, **36**, 2662.

[932] F. Paneth, ib. 1918, **51**, 1704; *Z. Elektrochem.* 1919, **24**, 298; 1920, **26**, 452; F. Paneth and A. Johannsen, *Ber.* 1922, **55**, 2622.

[933] M. Guillot, *C.R.* 1930, **190**, 127.   [934] Id., ib. 590.

[935] I. Curie and M. Lecoin, ib. 1931, **192**, 1453.

[936] M. Guillot, *J. Chim. Phys.* 1931, **28**, 14.   [937] Id., ib. 92.

[938] M. Haissinsky, *C.R.* 1932, **195**, 131.

[939] Id., *J. Chim. Phys.* 1933, **30**, 27.

[940] O. Erbacher and H. Käding, *Z. physikal. Chem.* 1933, **165**, 427.

[941] M. Servigne, *C.R.* 1933, **196**, 264.

[942] V. G. Chlopin and A. G. Smartseva, *C.R. Acad. Sci. U.R.S.S.* 1934, **4**, 433.

[943] *Z. Elektrochem.* 1925, **31**, 572.

non-reducing media[939] it is present as the simple cation Po^{4+}, as we should expect; this ion has the inert pair, and so should be more stable than with tellurium. Then in reducing solutions there is present a cation of lower valency, probably 2; if so it is suggested by Joliot[944] that the ion is the 'polonyl' ion $[O{=}Po]^{++}$, which seems very probable in view of the commonness of these 'yl' ions among the heavier B elements. The third state of the polonium is as the divalent anion, probably that of polonious acid H_2PoO_3, or perhaps sometimes the simple anion of the polonides, Po^{--}.

With the chemical evidence, there is the difficulty that the polonium compounds can never be obtained in quantity, and so they cannot be analysed. The assumption that if a polonium salt will come down with the same salt of another metal, the polonium must have the same valency as the other metal is not always true. There are many cases[940] where two compounds precipitate together without being of the same valency type: thus ThB(Pb) separates with silver chromate[945] and with alkaline sulphates,[946] and lead with alkaline halides.[947] One characteristic of the polonium compounds, which is unusual among radioactive elements though it is to be expected here, is that so many of them are not ionized.

As we should expect, polonium forms a polonide like a telluride, and Na_2Po forms mixed crystals with Na_2Te; in the same way it forms di-covalent derivatives (like telluro-ethers) such as the dibenzyl compound $Po(CH_2 \cdot C_6H_5)_2$, which crystallizes with its Te analogue.

It also forms an interesting non-ionized dithiocarbamate, obtained from the sodium salt $[Na](S \cdot CS \cdot NR_2)$.[933,937] This separates along with the dithiocarbamates of heavy metals such as Bi^{iii}, Co^{iii}, or Ni^{ii}, and can be recrystallized with them from chloroform.

Polonium hydroxide dissolves in acetyl-acetone to give a product soluble in benzene, obviously the covalent acetylacetonate. If this is recrystallized along with a mixture of the acetylacetonates of thorium and aluminium ThA_4 and AlA_3, the activity goes with the thorium and not with the aluminium,[941] so that we may presume that the polonium is quadri- and not trivalent.

Polonium may also form a carbonyl, as the metal is found to be more volatile in CO than in nitrogen[935,948]; the only carbonyl with an inert gas number of electrons would, however, be $Po{\leftarrow}C{\equiv}O$.

[944] F. Joliot, *C.R.* 1929, **189**, 986.
[945] R. Mumbrauer, *Z. physikal. Chem.* 1933, **163**, 142.
[946] O. Hahn, *Naturwiss.* 1926, **14**, 1197.
[947] H. Käding, *Z. physikal. Chem.* 1932, **162**, 174.
[948] M. Lecoin, *J. Chim. Phys.* 1931, **28**, 411.

SUBGROUP VI A

GENERAL

THIS subgroup consists of chromium, molybdenum, tungsten, and uranium, to which the 'uranide' elements, neptunium, plutonium, americium, and curium (which might be assigned to any Group from III to VI) must now be added. Some of their properties are:

	Cr	Mo	W	U
Abundance in g./ton . .	200	15	69	4
Radius of atom . .	1·25	1·36	1·37	1·49 A
M. pt.	1,800°	2,622°	3,380°	1,150°
B. pt.	2,660°	5,690°[a]	4,830°	

$$a = {}^{949}.$$

Since this is the sixth group, the resemblance of the A compounds to those of the B (sulphur) subgroup should be confined to the hexavalent derivatives, such as the chromates and molybdates, which should resemble the sulphates and selenates, as in fact they do. As we descend the series from chromium to molybdenum we should expect that (1) the lower valencies would become less stable, and (2) in any given valency the tendency to ionize would become less. This is the opposite to the behaviour in the B subgroup, and also to the simple covalency rules, which require that as the cation gets larger its tendency to ionize should increase. The general effect of both tendencies (1) and (2) is that as the atomic weight rises, these A elements ionize far less, and so become less metallic in character, whereas, as we have seen, in the B subgroups they become more metallic with rise of atomic weight.

We should also expect that especially in the oxy-compounds with the group valency (as in the acids H_2XO_4) there would be an increasing formation of condensed and ultimately colloidal acids: this happens in the B subgroups too, but to a less extent.

The actual facts bear out these expectations on the whole, especially in the series Cr—Mo—W, where we find, as usual, that molybdenum comes much nearer to tungsten than to chromium; but uranium in many respects does not fall into the series; in some ways it is more like chromium than like molybdenum or tungsten, and in others it is unlike any other member of the subgroup.

The valency of 6 is the highest for all these elements; it is also the stablest for molybdenum and tungsten, but for chromium it is the tri-valency that is the most stable, while with uranium there is a special valency of 4, which is nearly as stable as 6. This behaviour of chromium

[949] H. A. Jones, I. Langmuir, and G. M. Mackay, *Phys. Rev.* 1927, ii. **30**, 201. van Liempt in 1920 estimated it at 3,560°.

is noticeable: a certain instability in the higher valencies is characteristic of the period to which chromium belongs, and is shown by vanadium, arsenic, selenium, and bromine. Thus chromium alone of the elements of Group VI (except oxygen, which being in the first period cannot do so) forms no hexahalide, not even a hexafluoride.

In the oxy-acids H_2XO_4 these elements all show a stronger tendency than those of VI B to condense: even with chromium this occurs readily, not only to the dichromates $M_2Cr_2O_7$, but also to the tri- and even to the tetrachromates $M_2Cr_4O_{13}$. The molybdates and tungstates go much further, forming the highly condensed polyacids and hetero-poly-acids: in the latter we have one residue of another acid, such as boric or phosphoric, associated usually with 6, 9, or 12 units of a second acid, and this second acid is always molybdic or tungstic. With uranium the tendency is much smaller, but even the uranates are most frequently of the type $M_2U_2O_7$, corresponding to the dichromates, or the pyrosulphates.

The acidity of the H_2XO_4 acids falls off rapidly in the order

$$Cr > Mo > W > U:$$

H_2UO_4, or $UO_2(OH)_2$, is amphoteric, but is a very weak acid and quite a strong base, giving the stable uranyl salts $[UO_2]X_2$.

The increasing instability of the lower states of valency with rise of atomic weight is shown by the table below, in which single brackets indicate that the state rarely occurs, and double brackets that it is doubtful whether it occurs at all, while the more stable forms are underlined.

Cr	VI	(V)	((IV))	<u>III</u>	II
Mo	<u>VI</u>	V	IV	III	(II)
W	<u>VI</u>	V	IV	(III)	(II)
U	<u>VI</u>	V	<u>IV</u>	III	(II)

The second tendency, the decrease in ionization in any particular valency with increase of atomic weight, is equally clearly shown; chromium is fully ionized in the tri- and divalent states: molybdenum and tungsten never form simple cations at all, and uranium does so only in the tetravalent state which is quite peculiar.

Of the lower hydroxides, $U(OH)_4$ is only basic: $Cr(OH)_3$ is amphoteric but mainly basic; and it is particularly to be noticed, as being opposed to expectation (2) above (i.e. that ionization diminishes as atomic number increases), that while CrO_2Cl_2 is obviously covalent (b. pt. 116·7°) UO_2Cl_2 is as obviously a salt.

Chromium is remarkable for its enormous power in the trivalent state of forming complexes, which are practically all 6-fold, and the majority (as with cobalt and platinum) linked through nitrogen; in this it is equalled by a few elements, such as cobalt and platinum, but exceeded by none. Molybdenum and tungsten also form complexes, but nearly all of these are derived from their hexavalent derivatives.

CHROMIUM

SOME of the peculiarities of this element remain to be noticed. There is a remarkable absence of compounds with a higher covalency than 4: they seem to be confined to the complex derivatives of trivalent chromium, which have a covalency of 6, and a few compounds in which the chromium is joined to carbon, the carbonyl $Cr(CO)_6$, and perhaps some of the very peculiar chromium phenyl compounds. This absence of the higher valencies is common in the first long period.

Again hexavalent chromium like selenium has the power of oxidizing organic compounds to aldehydes, and no further, as in the Étard reaction.

In general the valencies exhibited by chromium are: VI, which is very stable; V, fairly certain, but unstable and rare; IV, probably non-existent unless in the chromium phenyl compounds which seem to break all valency rules; III, the most stable of all; II, quite definite but very unstable; (I, very improbable) 0 in the carbonyl compound $Cr(CO)_6$, since all the linking electrons here are provided by the CO groups.

Chromium was discovered by Vauquelin in 1797.[950] Its chief ore is chrome iron-stone, FeO, Cr_2O_3. It sometimes replaces aluminium in minerals, as in the spinels $M''[M'''O_2]_2$: Peruvian emerald is beryl coloured by chromium, which replaces aluminium.

Metallic Chromium

This can be obtained as an alloy with iron by reducing chrome iron-stone with carbon. To get the pure metal it must be reduced by Goldschmidt's thermite process with aluminium

$$Cr_2O_3 + 2 Al = Al_2O_3 + 2 Cr + 109 \text{ k.cals.}$$

An alternative method much used nowadays is the electrolytic. Chromium is dimorphic. A hexagonal form can be made by electrolysis of chromic acid solutions; the Cr—Cr distance is $2 \cdot 72$ A (theory $2 \cdot 50$); at $800°$ it reverts to the cubic form.[951-2] It is a hard metal[953] of a brilliant white colour with a tinge of blue: m. pt. $1,800°$, b. pt. *ca.* $2,660°$. It is chemically very resistant; it is stable in air in the cold; on heating it combines with the halogens, sulphur, carbon, nitrogen, silicon, boron, and various metals. It is soluble in dilute hydrochloric or sulphuric acid, but in nitric acid shows passivity in a more remarkable degree than any other metal.

In the active state the potential of Cr in contact with a solution of Cr″ is $-0 \cdot 56$ volt, so that it comes between zinc and iron, and will precipitate many metals, such as copper, zinc, and nickel from solutions of their salts. In the extreme passive state its potential is $+1 \cdot 2$ volts. Also while active chromium dissolves as the chromous ion Cr^{++}, passive does so as the

[950] *Ann. Chim.* 1798, [i] **25**, 21, 194; 1809, [i] **70**, 70.

[951] A. J. Bradley and E. F. Ollard, *Nature*, 1926, **117**, 122.

[952] L. Wright, H. Hurst, and J. Riley, *Trans. Far. Soc.* 1935, **31**, 1253.

[953] If chromium powder is degassed at $1,300°$ it becomes ductile when heated: W. Kroll, *Z. anorg. Chem.* 1935, **226**, 23.

chromate ion CrO_4^{--}. A result of this passivity is the curious periodic fluctuations of the rate of evolution of hydrogen from chromium dissolving in acids[954]; the period, which is of the order of 5 minutes, depends on the acid and on the catalysts present. The most probable explanation of the passivity is the formation of a superficial layer of oxygen.

Metallic chromium is used (1) for making chromium steels, which are very hard, and are used especially for ball bearings; the amount of carbon in them must be very small, and so the chromium is usually made by the thermite process. (2) Of recent years chromium has been much used as a protective layer on metal fittings. The difficulty that the hydrogen evolved at the high voltage required gets between the chromium layer and the metal on which it is being deposited and makes the chromium tend to split off, has been largely overcome by using for the electrolysis a solution of a chromic salt containing also a chromate, which is reduced by the hydrogen and so absorbs it.[955]

Chromium and Hydrogen

Chromium prepared electrolytically can contain a considerable amount of hydrogen, apparently as a supersaturated solution; at 60° most of it is suddenly and irreversibly given off. The hydrogen does not change the form of the metallic lattice, but it enlarges it (Hüttig, 1925). Claims[956] that a definite hydride can be obtained have not been confirmed.

Chromium and Carbon

Chromium Carbide

Various carbides of chromium of different composition have been prepared[957]; the most definite appears to be Cr_3C_2.[958] In this each carbon atom has 6 chromium atoms 2·02 to 2·07 A away (theory for Cr—C 2·02) at the points of a trigonal prism. The carbon is 1·665 A from its neighbouring carbon atoms on each side (theory for C—C 1·54), so that the carbons form a continuous slightly stretched chain. Cr_7C_3 and Cr_4C have also been made; for the stabilities and heats of formation of the carbides see reference [959].

Chromium Phenyl Compounds

Hein and his collaborators have described[960] a remarkable series of compounds with 3, 4, and 5 phenyl groups attached to the chromium.

[954] W. Ostwald, *Z. physikal. Chem.* 1900, **35**, 33, 204; E. Brauer, ib. 1901, **38**, 441.
[955] See, for example, I. Stscherbakov and O. Essin, *Z. Elektrochem.* 1927, **33**, 245; E. Liebreich, ib. 1928, **34**, 41.
[956] T. Weichselfelder and B. Thiede, *Ann.* 1926, **447**, 64.
[957] O. Ruff and T. Foehr, *Z. anorg. Chem.* 1918, **104**, 27.
[958] A. F. Wells, *S.I.C.* 456.
[959] K. K. Kelley, F. S. Boericke, G. E. Moore, E. H. Huffman, and W. M. Bangert, *U.S. Bur. Mines Techn. Paper*, 662, 1944.
[960] (i) F. Hein, *Ber.* 1919, **52**, 195; (ii) Id., ib. 1921, **54**, 1905; (iii) ib. 2708; (iv) ib. 2727; (v) F. Hein and O. Schwartzkopff, ib. 1924, **57**, 8; (vi) F. Hein and E. W. Eissner, ib. 1926, **59**, 362; (vii) F. Hein, J. Reschke, and F. Pintus, ib. 1927, **60**,

They find that certain chromium halides react with phenyl magnesium bromide to give halides of the bases Φ_3CrOH, Φ_4CrOH, and Φ_5CrOH—i.e. with tetra-, penta-, and hexavalent chromium; these hydroxides and a variety of their salts are described.

The evidence for many of their conclusions is not strong. In particular it is curious that the hydroxides and many of their salts have the same colour, that of a dichromate, in spite of the apparent changes of valency.

This difficulty is emphasized by the only independent examination of these compounds that has been published, that of Klemm and Neuber[961]; they measured the paramagnetism of ten compounds which according to Hein have 5, 4, and 3 phenyl groups on the chromium, whose existence and composition they confirmed; these are all found to have within 5 per cent. a moment of 1·73 Bohr magnetons, and so presumably contain pentavalent chromium. The structures which Klemm and Neuber suggest on this basis are not very satisfactory, but the facts are at present too uncertain for a detailed discussion.

Hein[962] has acknowledged Klemm and Neuber's paper, but has so far thrown no further light on the subject.

Chromium and Nitrogen

Above 800° chromium absorbs nitrogen up to about 14 per cent. (Cr_2N); the curves[963-4] are very like those of palladium and hydrogen, and indicate the separation of a solid phase CrN, which is a violet-black powder with no metallic glance.

Another nitride Cr_3N has been described,[965] as a green amorphous powder very resistant to acids. See also reference [966].

Chromium and Phosphorus

A phase rule and X-ray examination of the system chromium+phosphorus from the chromium end up to CrP indicates[967] that only two compounds are formed, Cr_3P, isomorphous with Fe_3P, and CrP, which is isomorphous with MnP, and has very nearly a nickel arsenide lattice.

679; (viii) Id., ib. 749; (ix) F. Hein and F. Pintus, ib. 2388; (x) F. Hein, O. Schwartzkopff, K. Hoyer, K. Klar, E. W. Eissner, and W. Clauss, ib. 1928, **61**, 730; (xi) F. Hein and E. Markert, ib. 2255; (xii) F. Hein, O. Schwartzkopff, K. Hoyer, K. Klar, E. W. Eissner, W. Clauss, and W. Just, ib. 1929, **62**, 1151; (xiii) F. Hein, *J. prakt. Chem.* 1931, [ii] **132**, 59; (xiv) F. Hein and W. Retter, *Z. physikal. Chem.* 1931, **156**, 81.

[961] W. Klemm and A. Neuber, *Z. anorg. Chem.* 1936, **227**, 261.

[962] F. Hein, ib. 272.

[963] G. Valensi, *J. Chim. Phys.* 1929, **26**, 152, 202.

[964] G. Tammann, *Z. anorg. Chem.* 1930, **188**, 396.

[965] H. ter Meulen, *Rec. Trav.* 1938, **57**, 591.

[966] L. Duparc, P. Wenger, and W. Schussele, *Helv. Chim. Acta*, 1930, **13**, 917.

[967] H. Nowotny and E. Henglein, *Z. anorg. Chem.* 1938, **239**, 14.

HEXAVALENT CHROMIUM

THIS is the most stable valency of chromium next to that of 3, and occurs in the chromic and polychromic acids, in the trioxide, and in some (not binary) halogen derivatives.

The chromates are important commercially for various purposes; they are made by oxidizing chrome iron-stone with air in the presence of alkali, some lime being added to keep the mass porous.

Chromium Trioxide

A strong solution of potassium dichromate (or the much more soluble sodium salt) is treated with excess of strong sulphuric acid, and the trioxide, which is only slightly soluble in the concentrated acid, crystallizes out; it is then washed free from sulphuric acid by means of nitric acid, which must not contain any oxides of nitrogen, as they would reduce the CrO_3; the HNO_3 can then be removed by warming. If necessary, the CrO_3 can be recrystallized from a small quantity of water.

Chromium trioxide forms bright red needles, which melt at 197°, and a little above that temperature begin to emit red vapours. At higher temperatures the trioxide loses oxygen (even the aqueous solution is said[968] to evolve oxygen on boiling), and is converted into various mixtures or compounds of CrO_3 and Cr_2O_3: thus at 500° the product has the composition $2 CrO_3, Cr_2O_3$; it is difficult by heat alone to reduce the oxygen content down to that of Cr_2O_3.

Chromium trioxide is excessively soluble in water; at the ('record') cryohydric point of $-155°$ the solution contains 60·5 per cent. CrO_3.[969]

Chromium trioxide is a violent oxidizing agent, especially for organic substances, being reduced to the green Cr_2O_3; but it can be boiled with acetic acid without change. It reacts with sulphur trioxide to give chromic oxide Cr_2O_3 and oxygen; for the kinetics of this, see reference [970].

Chromyl Fluoride, CrO_2F_2

This is formed in small yield when a mixture of calcium fluoride and lead chromate is treated with sulphuric, or better with fluorosulphonic acid. Efforts to purify it[971] failed until lately, when v. Wartenberg[972] showed that it is a brown gas condensing to a brown solid (v.p. 24 mm. at 0°), which slowly changes to a white solid not volatile below 200°, and apparently a polymer. The absorption spectrum of the gas is remarkably like that of chromyl chloride CrO_2Cl_2.[973]

[968] N. D. Birjukov, *J. Gen. Chem. Russ.* 1940, **10**, 942.
[969] E. H. Büchner and A. Prins, *Z. physikal. Chem.* 1913, **81**, 113.
[970] H. C. S. Snethlage, *Rec. Trav.* 1936, **55**, 712.
[971] O. Ruff and H. J. Braun, *Ber.* 1914, **47**, 658.
[972] H. v. Wartenberg, *Z. anorg. Chem.* 1941, **247**, 135.
[973] K. H. Hellwege, *Z. Phys.* 1941, **117**, 596.

Chromyl Chloride, CrO_2Cl_2

This can be made by the action of gaseous hydrogen chloride on dry CrO_3, or better by acting with concentrated H_2SO_4 on a mixture of dichromate and chloride.

Chromyl chloride is deep-red as solid, liquid, and vapour. It melts at $-96.5°$, and boils at $116.7°$; the molecular weight in the vapour is normal; in solution[974] it is normal in $POCl_3$ and slightly associated in acetic acid.

It is fairly stable in the dark, but in the light, or if heated, it decomposes, giving various complicated products. It is miscible with CCl_4, CS_2, and chloroform. It oxidizes organic compounds, often violently, but if it is diluted with CS_2 or chloroform it does so quietly, and in such solutions it forms with homologues of benzene addition-compounds of unknown structure which, when treated with water, break up into chromic salts and the aldehyde or ketone (Étard reaction); for example, benzaldehyde is formed from toluene; compare the action of SeO_2 in producing aldehydes.

All attempts to make chromyl bromide or iodide have failed, obviously because the oxidizing power of the Cr^{vi} is too great. Chromyl chloride can therefore be used as a test for chlorine: if the halogen compound (which must be free from fluorine) is heated with dichromate and strong sulphuric acid, and the vapour collected in alkali, then, if any chlorine is present, chromium will be found to have come over.

Chromic Acid

Chromic acid cannot be isolated, but is readily obtained in solution. This solution certainly contains the ions CrO_4'', $HCrO_4'$, and Cr_2O_7'', but we have no means of determining their amounts. Even the change of colour which obviously accompanies the change of the first kind of ion into the other two, is of little use. The absorption curves of the chromate and dichromate are very nearly the same, except that the absorption of the dichromate is rather more intense.[975] Endredy[976] finds that conductivity, molecular volume, and absorption all support the view that in an aqueous solution of the trioxide or a dichromate there is an equilibrium between Cr_2O_7'' ions with a mobility of $62-3/20°$, and $HCrO_4'$ ions, mobility $49.5/20°$; Vigdorov and Taratzujan[977] confirm this.

Chromates

All the metallic chromates except those of the alkalies and the lighter alkaline earths are insoluble in water. These are some solubilities of normal chromates (g./100 g. water):

	Na	K	Cs	Mg	Ca	Sr	Ba
Sol^y	76.6	62.9	41	72	2.3	0.123	0.00035
At °C.	20°	20°	30°	18°	19°	15°	18°

[974] E. Moles and L. Gomez, *Z. physikal. Chem.* 1912, **80**, 513; 1915, **90**, 594.
[975] E. Viterbi and G. Krauss, *Gaz.* 1927, **57**, 690.
[976] E. Endredy, *Ung. Akad. Wiss.* 1936, **54**, 459.
[977] S. Vigdorov and S. Taratzujan, *J. Appl. Chem. Russ.* 1938, **11**, 719.

Na_2CrO_4, K_2CrO_4, Cs_2CrO_4 are all exactly isomorphous with K_2SO_4 and Cs_2SO_4.[978] The sodium and potassium chromates and sulphates form a limited range of solid solutions.[979] The hexa- and deca-hydrates of Na_2CrO_4 form mixed crystals with the corresponding sulphates.[980]

Sodium chromate forms at least three hydrates:

$$10\,H_2O \overset{20°}{\rightleftharpoons} 6\,H_2O \overset{26°}{\rightleftharpoons} 4\,H_2O \overset{63°}{\rightleftharpoons} \text{Anhydr.}$$

Lead chromate is trimorphic.[981]

Dichromates and Polychromates

Salts are known containing not only two but three and even four CrO_3 groups to two equivalents of metal, but only the dichromates $M_2Cr_2O_7$ are of any great importance.

The absorption in the visible of solid potassium dichromate at 20° K. has been found[982] to give 20 sharp lines and 30 diffuse.

The solubilities of the sodium and potassium dichromates differ greatly: they are at 20°, Na 180, K 12·7. $Na_2Cr_2O_7$ gives only a dihydrate, and the cryohydric point is −48°.[983] Potassium dichromate is 20 times as soluble in water at 100° as at 0°. The dichromates of other elements are mostly (unlike the chromates) very soluble in water, for example, those of Mg, Ca, Sr, and Ba: the silver salt $Ag_2Cr_2O_7$ is one of the least soluble. In a solution of a chromate or a dichromate there is equilibrium between the CrO_4 and Cr_2O_7 ions, and so if $BaCl_2$ is added to a neutral dichromate solution, $BaCrO_4$ crystallizes out.

The chromates and dichromates are much used technically, as oxidizing agents in organic chemistry, in tanning, and in hardening gelatine for photographic reproduction.

Halochromates

Fluorochromic acid $HCrO_3F$ is not known in the free state, but its salts can be prepared by boiling a dichromate solution with excess of HF. If this boiling is really necessary, there must be a true chemical change taking place, confirming that the fluorochromate is a true complex and not merely a double salt.

The crystal structures of $KCrO_3F$ and $CsCrO_3F$ are[984] of the scheelite ($CaWO_4$) type, with tetrahedral anions. The salts (like the chlorochromates) are very readily hydrolysed by water, and accordingly they attack glass.

[978] J. J. Millar, *Z. Krist.* 1936, **94**, 131; 1938, **99**, 32.

[979] S. Z. Makarov and I. G. Drushinin, *Bull. Akad. Sci. U.R.S.S.* 1937, 1921.

[980] W. E. Cadbury, W. B. Meldrum, and W. W. Lucasse, *J.A.C.S.* 1941, **63**, 2262.

[981] H. Wagner, R. Haug, and M. Zipfel, *Z. anorg. Chem.* 1932, **208**, 249.

[982] J. Teltow, *Z. physikal. Chem.* 1939, B **43**, 375.

[983] W. H. Hartford, *J.A.C.S.* 1941, **63**, 1473.

[984] J. A. A. Ketelaar and F. E. Wegerif, *Rec. Trav.* 1938, **57**, 1269; 1939, **58**, 948.

Chlorochromates

Here again, the free acid is unknown (like H_2CrO_4 itself). The chloro-chromates, and perhaps the bromo- and iodochromates, are obtained by boiling a dichromate solution with the halogen acid. Potassium chloro-chromate $KCrO_3Cl$ is an orange salt, looking extraordinarily like azo-benzene ($KCrO_3F$ is ruby-red). The bromo-compound $KCrO_3Br$ is said to be dark brown and the iodo-compound $KCrO_3I$ garnet-red: it is difficult, however, to believe that the Cr^{vi} could coexist with the iodide group.

The chlorochromates are hydrolysed by water, but they can be recrystal-lized from dilute hydrochloric acid.

Perchromic Compounds

Many oxidized compounds react with hydrogen peroxide to replace oxygen atoms by O_2 groups. Among these the chromate derivatives are remarkable, especially for their brilliant colours. They are now realized to be of two kinds, binary peroxides, and perchromic acids or salts. The more important types are four, the first and last being peroxides, and the other two salts.

1. Acidic solutions of chromates on treatment with hydrogen peroxide give blue CrO_5 (formerly thought to be $HCrO_5$), which is soluble in, and stabilized by, ether. The blue solid formed when chromium trioxide is treated with a solution of hydrogen peroxide in methyl ether at $-80°$ (supposed[985] to be the acid H_2CrO_5, $2 H_2O$) is really[986] $(CH_3)_2O, CrO_5$; it explodes at $-30°$. CrO_5 also combines with pyridine and other organic bases to give co-ordination compounds, such as py, CrO_5, which is insoluble in water but soluble in organic solvents, and is monomeric in benzene, nitrobenzene, and bromoform.[987-8] With alkalies it forms no salt at all, but is at once decomposed. By its reactions with dilute acids, with silver nitrate, and with permanganate, Schwarz and Giese[987] showed from the amount of 'available oxygen' that the parent compound must be CrO_5 and not $HCrO_5$. The number of O_2 groups present in these compounds is found from their power of reducing permanganate with evolution of oxygen, which is quantitative in presence of a trace of molybdate[987-8]; there are two O_2 groups in CrO_5. The pyridine complex has a paramagnetic moment,[989] but so small ($160-330 \times 10^{-6}$ c.g.s. units: theory for one unpaired electron 1300) that we may assume that it is due to chromic impurities, and that the pure compound is diamagnetic, with hexavalent chromium, the formulae being such as

[985] E. H. Riesenfeld and W. Mau, *Ber.* 1914, **47**, 548.

[986] R. Schwarz and G. Elstner, ib. 1936, **69**, 575.

[987] R. Schwarz and H. Giese, ib. 1932, **65**, 871.

[988] Id., ib. 1933, **66**, 310.

[989] W. Klemm and H. Werth, *Z. anorg. Chem.* 1933, **216**, 127.

The peroxide CrO_2 group is often written $Cr\!\!<^O_O$, but this is improbable on account of the strain: it should be formulated as $Cr{\rightarrow}O{\rightarrow}O$ or $Cr{=}O{\rightarrow}O$.

2. $MCrO_6$. If the ethereal solution of CrO_5 is treated with alkaline hydrogen peroxide in alcohol, or if 30 per cent. hydrogen peroxide and a potassium salt are added to ice-cold ammonium dichromate, blue salts of the composition $KCrO_6, H_2O$ are obtained; the extra oxygen cannot be present as H_2O_2 of crystallization, since an anhydrous thallous salt $TlCrO_6$ can be made, which has a similar behaviour.[988] The compound has 2·5 O_2 groups per Cr, and is diamagnetic[989]; hence the chromium must be hexavalent and the molecule dimeric, as in

$$M_2\left[\begin{array}{c} \overset{O_2}{\underset{O_2}{\uparrow\downarrow}}\qquad\overset{O_2}{\underset{O_2}{\uparrow\downarrow}}\\ O\!-\!Cr\!-\!O\!-\!O\!-\!Cr\!-\!O \end{array}\right]^{--}.$$

3. M_3CrO_8, which is red, is formed by the action on a chromate of a more strongly alkaline H_2O_2 solution than is needed to make the previous salt $M_2Cr_2O_{12}$.[989,991-2] The blue salts are more easily formed and decomposed than the red. This red salt has 3·5 O_2 groups per Cr, which need not mean that it is dimeric: it could have the structure

$$K_3\left[\begin{array}{c} O_2 \diagdown \quad \diagup O_2 \\ \quad\; Cr \\ O_2 \diagup \quad \diagdown O_2 \end{array}\right]$$

with pentavalent chromium. The conductivities and freezing-points of aqueous solutions of the ammonium salt support the monomeric formula.[993]

One would think that the pentavalent state, which is rare and so presumably unstable with chromium, could not possibly exist in conjunction with so powerful an oxidizing group as —O—O—. There are, however, two arguments in its favour, the paramagnetism and the crystal structure. The red salt K_3CrO_8 (the monomeric formulae are used for simplicity) has been shown[989,994] to have the paramagnetic moment required for pentavalent chromium; the peroxide groups will not affect the moment, since $[Zn(NH_3)_6]MoO_8$ is diamagnetic, as is required for hexavalent molybdenum.

Again, the red M_3CrO_8 salts are isomorphous with the pervanadates,[988] and they have the same crystal lattice as the perniobates and pertantalates

[990] E. H. Riesenfeld, H. E. Wohlers, W. A. Kutsch, and H. Ohl, *Ber.* 1905, **38**, 1885, 3578; Riesenfeld, ib. 4068; 1908, **41**, 2826, 3536, 3941.

[991] E. H. Riesenfeld, *Z. anorg. Chem.* 1912, **74**, 48.

[992] E. Spitalsky, *Ber.* 1910, **43**, 3187.

[993] E. H. Riesenfeld, ib. 1908, **41**, 3941.

[994] B. T. Tjabbes, *Z. anorg. Chem.* 1933, **210**, 385.

(M_3AO_8)[995] (with O—O 1·34, theory 1·32). These Group V peracids have only one pentavalent atom in the molecule, and so we should infer that the same must be true of the perchromates.

The peroxide CrO_5 is known to be monomeric in its pyridine compound, which can be written

$$py \rightarrow Cr \underset{O \rightarrow O}{\overset{O}{\underset{\displaystyle O \rightarrow O}{\Big\langle}}}$$

or in other ways, with the chromium hexavalent.

4. A fourth type of compound is formed when the mixture used for preparing $(NH_4)_3CrO_8$ (3) is heated and then cooled; brown CrO_4, 3 NH_3 separates out. This gives a brown solution in water which liberates hydrogen peroxide with acids, and with potassium cyanide gives a brown compound CrO_4, 3 KCN.[990] These complexes can be formulated with hexavalent chromium as

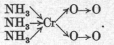

Bhatnagar, however, finds[996] that the former complex has the paramagnetic moment of two unpaired electrons, and so concludes that the chromium is tetravalent, as in

$$\begin{matrix} NH_3 \\ NH_3 \\ NH_3 \end{matrix} \!\! \Big\rangle Cr \underset{O \rightarrow O}{\overset{O \rightarrow O}{\Big\langle}} .$$

PENTAVALENT CHROMIUM

As we have seen, pentavalent chromium compounds occur probably among the chromium phenyl compounds of Hein (p. 1001), and possibly among the perchromates just described. Apart from these they have only been isolated in one or two types of compounds.

The fluoride CrF_5 has been obtained[997] as a red fairly volatile solid, which is instantly hydrolysed by water to compounds of hexavalent and trivalent chromium.

A small number of pentavalent chromium complexes have been prepared by Weinland.[998-9] Chromium trioxide is reduced by very concentrated hydrochloric acid at 0°, and complexes derived from Cr^VOCl_3 are formed. They are of the types $M_2[CrOCl_5]$, where M = K, Rb, Cs, NH_4: the Cs salt forms mixed crystals with the niobium salt $Cs_2[NbOCl_5]$. They are garnet-red in colour. Another series $M[CrOCl_4]$ (M = pyridine,

[995] I. A. Wilson, *Arkiv. Kemi, Min. Geol.* 1942, **15** B, no. 5.

[996] S. S. Bhatnagar, B. Prakash, and A. Hamid, *J.C.S.* 1938, 1428.

[997] H. v. Wartenberg, *Z. anorg. Chem.* 1941, **247**, 135.

[998] R. F. Weinland and W. Fridrich, *Ber.* 1905, **38**, 3784.

[999] R. F. Weinland and M. Fiederer, ib. 1906, **39**, 4042; 1907, **40**, 2090.

quinoline, H), which are orange-yellow, were obtained in a similar way by Meyer and Best in acetic acid.[1000]

Recently Wagner has shown[1001] that the kinetics of the oxidation of ferrous salts by chromic acid support the view of Luther[1002] that there is an intermediate pentavalent state of chromium. He also finds that chromic acid liberates no iodine from potassium iodide in presence of sodium bicarbonate, but does so if the chromic acid is engaged in oxidizing oxalic acid in presence of potassium iodide. There must therefore be some intermediate product in this oxidation which can oxidize hydriodic acid. Tests for hydrogen peroxide and percarbonates gave negative results.

TETRAVALENT CHROMIUM

THIS is a very unusual valency for chromium. v. Wartenberg has prepared the tetrafluoride CrF_4, which is a brown amorphous solid of v.p. 3 mm./220°, giving a blue vapour with a characteristic spectrum; it is at once hydrolysed by water to Cr^{iii} and Cr^{vi}.[1003-4] He has also shown[1005] that a gaseous tetrachloride $CrCl_4$ is formed when the trichloride and chlorine react at 600–700°, and can be condensed out by rapid cooling with solid CO_2; it begins to decompose to $CrCl_3$ at $-80°$.

Manchot has shown[1006] that if dry chromic hydroxide $Cr(OH)_3$ is heated in oxygen to 300–400°, oxygen is absorbed and a black powder is left, which, on the not quite certain assumption that the residue on ignition has the composition Cr_2O_3, analyses nearly for CrO_2. It is, however, quite possible that this is a basic chromate such as CrO_3, Cr_2O_3. There is also the possibility that tetravalent chromium may occur among the chromium phenyl compounds.

TRIVALENT CHROMIUM

THIS is the stablest form of the element. It exists as the trivalent cation, which is characterized by its strong tendency to form 6-covalent complexes by co-ordination; the simple ion in water is undoubtedly co-ordinated with the solvent as $[Cr(OH_2)_6]^{+++}$, which is violet in colour, as are the normal salts of the type $[Cr(OH_2)_6]X_3$, where the anion may be F, Cl, Br, I, ClO_3, BrO_3, SO_4, S_2O_5, NO_3, PO_4, etc.; but there are other salts, and some with the anions mentioned above, which occur in an isomeric green form, in which the acid radical is not wholly ionized.[1007]

Apart from this tendency to co-ordination, which is as marked as in any other known element and extends to all kinds of addenda, but is

[1000] R. J. Meyer and H. Best, *Z. anorg. Chem.* 1899, **22**, 192.

[1001] C. Wagner and W. Preiss, ib. 1928, **168**, 265; C. Wagner, ib. 279.

[1002] R. Luther and N. Schiloff, *Z. physikal. Chem.* 1903, **46**, 777; R. Luther and T. F. Rutter, *Z. anorg. Chem.* 1907, **54**, 1.

[1003] H. v. Wartenberg, *Z. anorg. Chem.* 1941, **247**, 135.

[1004] Id., ib. 1942, **249**, 100.   [1005] Id., ib. **250**, 122.

[1006] W. Manchot and R. Kraus, *Ber.* 1906, **39**, 3512.

[1007] For a complete list to that date, see P. Pfeiffer, *Z. anorg. Chem.* 1908, **58**, 317.

especially strong with nitrogen compounds, particularly amines, the chromic salts show a strong resemblance to those of aluminium, and also to the trivalent states of vanadium and titanium, and above all to trivalent cobalt, though this has three more electrons. They form alums, and are considerably hydrolysed in solution. Chromium sesquioxide Cr_2O_3 is isomorphous with corundum Al_2O_3, and can replace Al_2O_3 in the spinels: this is largely because the Cr''' ion (radius 0·65) is little smaller than the Al''' ion (0·83 A). Like practically all the compounds of chromium the trivalent are strongly coloured, Cr_2O_3 dark green, Cr_2S_3 black, $CrCl_3$ red-violet.

The chromic salts are widely used as mordants, like the ferric and aluminium salts.

Chromium Sesquioxide, Cr_2O_3

This is a green insoluble crystalline substance, isomorphous with corundum, which can be made by reducing chromates (for example with SO_2), by heating dichromates with sodium chloride, or by heating ammonium dichromate alone. When it is made by heating the hydroxide $Cr(OH)_3$ it is observed that as the last traces of water go off, the solid suddenly glows; the X-ray diagram shows (Böhm) that this is due to the heat evolved (23 k.cals. per Cr_2O_3) when the lattice of the sesquioxide is formed from the amorphous material.

Cr_2O_3 is much used as a pigment. Various mixed oxides, such as $2\,CrO, Cr_2O_3$ are known, and can be made by the electrolysis of mixtures of chromous and chromic salts (Bunsen).

Chromic Hydroxide, $Cr(OH)_3$

This is made by precipitating a chromic solution with alkali. The green precipitate has no definite composition, and is no doubt colloidal: on standing it becomes less soluble in acids. Various different forms have been described,[1008] but their individuality is very doubtful.

The hydroxide is amphoteric; it forms salts with acids which are highly hydrolysed in water, and also salts with alkalies, the chromites, which are likewise highly hydrolysed.

The salts with acids are described later. The chromites can be got in two ways, either by fusion of the oxides, when they are crystalline, or by the solution of $Cr(OH)_3$ in aqueous alkali: the solubility of the hydroxide in the alkaline solution is then evidence that an alkaline salt is formed, but the solids which separate are usually gelatinous and colloidal. Solid phases of definite composition can, however, be got,[1009] such as $Na_3[Cr(OH)_6]$ and the corresponding Sr and Ba salts, and $Na_5[Cr(OH)_8], 4\,H_2O$.

If the aqueous solution is concentrated, the salts though no doubt

[1008] G. Jander and W. Scheele, *Z. anorg. Chem.* 1932, **206**, 241; A. Hantzsch and E. Torke, ib. **209**, 60.

[1009] See R. Scholder and R. Pätsch, ib. 1934, **220**, 411; T. Meyer and G. F. Hüttig, *Z. Elektrochem.* 1935, **41**, 429.

hydrolysed are stable, but on dilution with alkali a colloidal mass separates, and on dilution with water the hydroxide $Cr(OH)_3$ is precipitated.

Chromic Sulphide, Cr_2S_3

This can be made by various high temperature reactions, but not as a rule (see, however, ref. [1010]) from aqueous solution; thus it is formed by the action of hydrogen sulphide on the hydroxide or chloride, or of sulphur on the oxide chloride or metal. It is green or black according to the state of division; it is paramagnetic[1011]; it burns in the air to the oxide or basic sulphate, but is very resistant to acids in the cold, being attacked only by nitric acid and aqua regia.

Chromic Fluoride, CrF_3

The anhydrous compound can be made from the sesquioxide and HF, or by passing HCl gas over a mixture of Cr_2O_3 and CaF_2 at a red heat: it is a green solid of very high melting-point, which sublimes at about 1,200°. It is isomorphous with AlF_3.[1012]

Chromic fluoride is remarkable for forming 5 (perhaps 6) violet or green hydrates. Werner[1013] has prepared 4, with 9, 6, 7/2 (in two forms), and 3 molecules of water to which he assigns formulae as follows.

(1) 6 aq.: $[Cr(OH_2)_6]F_3$: this is a violet salt, only slightly soluble in water, made by the action of KF on the violet nitrate; its formula is established by its giving the corresponding sulphate with H_2SO_4. On standing in moist air or in contact with its solution it takes up more water to form (2) CrF_3, 9 H_2O, probably $[Cr(OH_2)_6](F \cdot OH_2)_3$: (it is doubtful whether the F^- anion can really be hydrated) this loses its extra 3 H_2O very easily.

(3) CrF_3, 3 $H_2O = [Cr(OH_2)_6](CrF_6)$, a green salt, made by heating the hexahydrate (1) for a long time with water; its constitution is shown by the fact that it is formed from $[Cr(OH_2)_6]Cl_3 + (NH_4)_3[CrF_6]$: it is thus obtained first as the (4) 7/2 hydrate, really $[Cr(OH_2)_6](CrF_6)H_2O$, the last H_2O being easily removed. The second isomeric hepta-hydrate $(CrF_3)_2$, 7 H_2O was made by Poulenc[1014] by precipitating a solution of CrF_3 with alcohol. This is also green, but quite different from the first isomer. It may be written $[CrF_3(OH_2)_3]_2$, H_2O. It is easily soluble in water, but the solution gives no reaction for fluorine ions; it behaves as an acid, and has an acid reaction like the hydrate of platinic chloride.

Chromic Chloride, $CrCl_3$

This can be made in the anhydrous state by passing chlorine at a high temperature over the metal, or over chromic oxide+carbon. It forms

[1010] S. M. Veller, *Ukraine Chem. J.* 1936, **11**, 23.

[1011] E. Wedekind and C. Horst, *Ber.* 1915, **48**, 105.

[1012] For the heats of formation of the solid trihalides see H. v. Wartenberg, *Z. anorg. Chem.* 1942, **249**, 100.

[1013] A. Werner and N. Costachescu, *Ber.* 1908, **41**, 4242.

[1014] C. Poulenc, *C.R.* 1893, **116**, 253.

reddish-violet ('peach blossom') leaflets, which sublime at a red heat in chlorine, and, if heated alone, break up partly into chlorine and chromous chloride. If heated in air it gives the sesquioxide Cr_2O_3.

Anhydrous chromic chloride is quite insoluble in cold water, alcohol, acetone, or ether. But in presence of a trace of chromous chloride it dissolves readily in water, a soluble hydrated salt crystallizing out. This peculiar phenomenon occurs not only in water but also in alcohol, acetone, and ether.* One part of $CrCl_2$ will make 40,000 parts of $CrCl_3$ dissolve. Other substances of a reducing character, such as $SnCl_2$, $FeCl_2$, $CuCl$, and H_2SO_3, produce the same result, though less effectively; the effectiveness bears no relation to the electrode potential.[1015]

The hydrated chlorides, like the fluorides, are of various types; they can have none of the chlorine atoms ionized, or 1, or 2, or all 3. In presence of a trace of $CrCl_2$ the trichloride dissolves readily in water (evolving 21·3 k.cals. per $CrCl_3$), and a dark green hexahydrate with a sweet taste crystallizes out: if a fresh solution of this hexahydrate is treated with silver nitrate, only a third of the chlorine is precipitated, so that it must be $[(Cr(OH_2)_4Cl_2]Cl, 2 H_2O$.

A second pale green hydrate was obtained from this by Bjerrum,[1016] from which silver nitrate precipitates two-thirds of the chlorine, indicating the formula $[Cr(OH_2)_5Cl]Cl_2, H_2O$. Bjerrum supported this by showing that the two chlorine ions could be replaced by other anions, giving, for example, the salt $[Cr(OH_2)_5Cl](PtCl_6), 5 H_2O$.

If the first-mentioned dark green salt is boiled in water for some time, and then cooled to 0° and saturated with hydrogen chloride, a third salt, a grey-blue isomer, separates out. All the chlorine in this is precipitated by silver nitrate, and so it must be $[Cr(OH_2)_6]Cl_3$; this is the easiest of the isomers to prepare: it is precipitated if the solution of any chromic salt is saturated with HCl at zero. Its structure is supported by the X-ray examination of the crystals, which shows[1017] that the 6 H_2O groups are arranged octahedrally round the chromium. It has been found[1019] that at 25° fresh solutions of violet chromic chloride have lower, and those of green chromic chloride higher, vapour pressures than after standing; chromic sulphate behaves in the same way.

In solution the three ions of these forms attain equilibrium in time, but in the cold take months to do so. The blue form is favoured by low temperatures, and, as we should expect, by high dilutions.

Finally, a non-ionized hydrate of $CrCl_3$ was obtained by Recoura[1018] of the formula $[Cr(OH_2)_3Cl_3]$: this gives a stable brown solution in ether;

---

* The behaviour of ether is quite peculiar, and is discussed later, p. 1023.

1015 K. Drucker, *Z. physikal. Chem.* 1901, **36**, 173.
1016 *Ber.* 1906, **39**, 1597; *Z. physikal. Chem.* 1907, **59**, 581.
1017 K. R. Andress and C. Carpenter, *Z. Krist.* 1934, **87**, 446.
1018 A. Recoura, *C.R.* 1933, **196**, 1853.
1019 N. O. Smith, *J.A.C.S.* 1947, **69**, 91.

in alcohol it only reacts slowly with silver nitrate, and in presence of water it at once forms the dark green hexahydrate $[Cr(OH_2)_4Cl_2]Cl, 2 H_2O$.

Chromic Bromide, $CrBr_3$

This is very similar to the chloride, and forms similar isomeric hydrates, a green $[Cr(OH_2)_4Br_2]Br, 2 H_2O$ and a violet $[Cr(OH_2)_6]Br_3$.

Chromic Iodide

A violet hydrate $CrI_3, 9 H_2O$ is known. It has been shown by Hein[1020] that anhydrous chromic iodide is almost impossible to make, and that chromous iodide CrI_2 has often been mistaken for it. Chromium only reacts with iodine as a rule at high temperatures, and then the reaction does not go beyond CrI_2. By treating pyrophoric chromium (obtained by evaporating the mercury from chromium amalgam) with iodine at lower temperatures, or by treating CrI_2 with iodine at 300°, it is possible to get a product containing 90 per cent. of CrI_3: this is a loose black powder.

Chromic Nitrate

A hydrate $Cr(NO_3)_3, 9 H_2O$ is described, as well as lower hydrates. The solution is said to be blue by reflected, and red by transmitted light.

Chromic Sulphates

Anhydrous chromic sulphate $Cr_2(SO_4)_3$ is of peach-blossom colour, and, like the chloride, is insoluble in water except in presence of a chromous salt. It forms a series of hydrates, apparently of three types, a violet salt, a green crystalline salt, and a green amorphous salt. These three classes have been shown[1021] to be distinct: (1) the violet salts occur with 18, 9, 3, and 0 H_2O; (2) the green crystalline salt can have 6 or 0 H_2O; (3) the green amorphous salt forms no definite hydrates, and its water content is zeolitic. The structures are obscure: a fresh solution of (3) gives no precipitate with barium chloride for some time: (1) the violet salt precipitates all the SO_4 at once: (2) the first green salt is said only to give the precipitate slowly, but in fact the reaction goes fairly easily.

Chromic Chlorate and Perchlorate

The chlorate $Cr(ClO_3)_3$ has been made but is very unstable.

The perchlorate $Cr(ClO_4)_3, 6 H_2O$ forms blue-green crystals, excessively soluble in water; 9- and 10-hydrates have also been prepared.[1022]

The iodate $Cr(IO_3)_3$ is also known.

Salts of Organic Acids

Various complex forms of these are mentioned later.

A normal *formate* $Cr(HCOO)_3, 6 H_2O$, grey-green, is known, and a similar

[1020] F. Hein and I. Wintner-Hölder, *Z. anorg. Chem.* 1931, **202**, 81.

[1021] F. Krauss, H. Querengässer, and P. Weyer, ib. 1929, **179**, 413.

[1022] V. Biber and I. Neiman, *J. Gen. Chem. Russ.* 1940, **10**, 723.

acetate. The formate group is much less easily oxidized in this green compound than in an ordinary formate (Reihlen).[1080]

The usual form of the *oxalate* is hydrated, amorphous, very soluble, and blue; but a red crystalline form can be got. This also is excessively soluble in water and alcohol (a sign that it is complex), and from its aqueous solution sodium carbonate precipitates no Cr''' and silver nitrate no oxalate.

CHROMIC COMPLEXES

THE trivalent chromium ion has an enormous power of forming 6-covalent complexes; in this it is at least equal to either of the other two great complex-forming ions, trivalent cobalt and tetravalent platinum. The resemblance to cobalt is remarkably close: it extends not only to the co-ordination number of 6 and the valency of 3, but also in many compounds to the colour as well; this is peculiarly remarkable, because the atomic numbers of these two elements differ not by two but by three, which would certainly not lead us to expect a similarity.

While the most numerous and perhaps the most stable of these complexes are those in which the chromium is attached to nitrogen, there are a whole series of others, especially with oxygen links, such as the aquo-compounds, and various kinds of ato-derivatives, particularly the sulphato, carbonato, and oxalato compounds.

These complexes almost always have a co-ordination number of 6, but lower values sometimes occur among the ammines; higher are impossible by the covalency rule.

The compounds are all remarkable for their various and striking colours; investigations of the absorption spectra have shown certain relations between the groups present and the positions of the bands[1023]; the changes caused by the replacement of a neutral molecule by an ion, or an NH_3 by an H_2O, are fairly regular.

Chromicyanides

Chromium, like iron and cobalt, forms hexacyanide anions in both the divalent and the trivalent state. The chromicyanides $M_3[Cr(CN)_6]$ are much less stable than their ferric analogues.[1024] The salts are yellow both as solids and in solution, with an absorption spectrum quite different from that of the other chromic complexes; the free acid is quite different again, being blood-red.

This free acid $H_3Cr(CN)_6$ is only known in solution, and even there is very unstable. If a suspension of lead or silver chromicyanide is treated with hydrogen sulphide a blood-red solution is formed, which at once begins to precipitate chromic cyanide $Cr(CN)_3$ and to evolve prussic acid, and will not re-form chromicyanides with bases.[1025-6]

[1023] R. I. Colmar and F. W. Schwartz, *J.A.C.S.* 1932, **54**, 3204; C. H. Johnson and A. Mead, *Nature*, 1933, **131**, 399; G. Joos and K. Schnetzler, *J. physikal. Chem.* 1933, B **20**, 1; A. Mead, *Trans. Far. Soc.* 1934, **30**, 1052.

[1024] H. Grossmann, *Z. anorg. Chem.* 1903, **37**, 439.

[1025] Kaiser, *Ann.* 1864, spl. **3**, 163.   [1026] Röhlcke, *Diss. Berlin*, 1896.

Potassium chromicyanide $K_3Cr(CN)_6$ can be made by treating a solution of chromic hydroxide in acetic acid with potassium cyanide,[1027-8] or from the cyanide and chromous acetate in presence of air.[1029] The conductivities of the solution show it to be the salt of a tribasic acid.[1030] The solution is rapidly decomposed by acids, which at once turn it red, but excess of alkali acts on it only after prolonged boiling. It is not poisonous. Other salts of chromicyanic acids[1026] are of the type $M_3[Cr(CN)_6]$, x H_2O; NH_4, 0; Li, 5; Na, 5 or 8; K, 0; also of the type $M_3''[Cr(CN)_6]_2$ are $Ba_3[Cr(CN)_6]_2$, 20 H_2O, soluble in water and stable; and the zinc salt $Zn_3[Cr(CN)_6]_2$, 10 H_2O, an unstable yellowish white powder.

For a series of complicated heavy-metal chromicyanides see Reihlen and Kraut.[1031]

Hume and Stone [1032] find that the magnetic moments of the chromi- (as of the chromo-) cyanides are those required for an octahedral 6-covalent complex.

Thiocyanate Complexes

The formation of these chromic complexes has long been known (see, for example, Rosenheim[1033]). They were investigated in great detail by Bjerrum.[1034-5] He showed that a chromic salt reacts in solution with an alkaline thiocyanate slowly (in some days at 50°), giving all the possible compounds from $[Cr(SCN)(OH_2)_5]X_2$ through $[Cr(SCN)_3(OH_2)_3]°$ to $M_3[Cr(SCN)_6]$ in proportions depending on the concentrations. All but the first two of these can be extracted from the acid solution with ether; these two, $[Cr(SCN)(OH_2)_5]X_2$ and $[Cr(SCN)_2(OH_2)_4]X$, could not be isolated, but were shown to be present in the solution. The rest were all isolated, the acids as salts, often of pyridine or quinoline. Bjerrum was able to determine many of the velocities of formation and decomposition and especially the equilibrium constants for all the 6 ions $[Cr(SCN)_x(OH_2)_{6-x}]$.

$[Cr(SCN)_3(OH_2)_3]°$, the 'simple' chromic thiocyanate, separates from water in violet crystals, which are difficult to purify.[1033] It gives a red solution in water, which at first shows none of the reactions of the ions, and by the freezing-point is scarcely ionized at all, but on standing the compound ionizes and the solution turns green. In acid solution the compound is stable, but it is broken up by alkalies at once. The partition coefficient with ether at 15° is about 4 in favour of the ether.[1034]

The hexathiocyanato-salts of the alkalies, of ammonium, and of most of the divalent metals are soluble in water, the silver and lead salts insoluble. As with the simple thiocyanate the fresh solutions are red; they

[1027] O. T. Christensen, *J. prakt. Chem.* 1885, [2] **31**, 163.
[1028] F. v. Dyke-Cruser and E. H. Miller, *J.A.C.S.* 1906, **28**, 1132.
[1029] H. Moissan, *Ann. Chim. Phys.* 1882, [v] **25**, 401.
[1030] P. Walden, *Z. phys. Chem.* 1888, **2**, 49.
[1031] H. Reihlen and F. Kraut, *Ann.* 1930, **478**, 219.
[1032] D. N. Hume and H. W. Stone, *J.A.C.S.* 1941, **63**, 1200.
[1033] A. Rosenheim and R. Cohn, *Z. anorg. Chem.* 1901, **27**, 293.
[1034] N. Bjerrum, ib. 1921, **118**, 131.

give no reactions for chromic or thiocyanate ions, and the van 't Hoff i by the freezing-point is nearly 3. On standing, however (in a few days in the cold[1036]), the solution turns green, the conductivity increases, the freezing-point falls, and the solution gives the reactions of the simple ions. The rates and equilibria of the dissociations have been examined by Bjerrum.[1034-5]

Many of the lower chromic ammines contain thiocyanato-groups in the complex.[1037]

Nitrogen Complexes: Ammines

These form the largest group of chromic complexes; they closely resemble the ammines of trivalent cobalt, and of trivalent ruthenium.[1038] The co-ordination number—the number of atoms covalently linked to the chromium—is practically always 6; some of the hexammines can be made to take up more ammonia in the solid state, but this is much less firmly held.[1039] The electrovalency ranges from $+3$ in the hexammines $[Cr(NH_3)_6]X_3$ through zero in $Cr(NH_3)_3X_3$ to -1 in $M[Cr(NH_3)_2Br_4]$ and -3 in the halides $M_3[CrX_6]$. In the ammines all possible types have been realized except the last, $M_2[Cr(NH_3)X_5]$ (though the mono-aquo-compounds $M_2[Cr(OH_2)X_5]$ are known). A variety of amine bases may be used, ammonia, alkylamines, pyridine, urea (only one NH_2 here reacting with the Cr), as well as diamines, of which the best-known is ethylene-diamine ('en') $NH_2CH_2CH_2NH_2$.[1040] The replacement of successive hydrogen atoms in ammonia weakens the attachment, but this is more than counter-balanced by the extra stability due to the ring-formation in the diamines, as it is to a considerable extent by the aromatic character of the (tertiary) nitrogen in pyridine. Of the non-nitrogenous neutral molecules in the ammine complexes the most important is water. The acyl groups are very various, including OH^- (hydroxo-salts), halogens, NO_2^-, NO_3^-, as well as a number of anions of oxy-acids, usually dibasic as in SO_4^{--} and especially the oxalato-group $C_2O_4^{--}$. (Some of these series of salts have been given trivial names which are still in use: for example, $[CrAm_6]X_3$ luteo; $[CrAm_5(OH_2)]X_3$ roseo; $M_2[CrAm_5X]$ purpureo; $M_2[CrAm_5NO_2]$ xantho; the rhodo- and erythro-salts are of a more complicated Cr_2 type.)

The hexammine (luteo-) salts can be made from anhydrous chromic chloride and liquid ammonia, or by the action of ammonia and air on a chromous solution. They are yellow or orange[1041-2]; they do not seem to lose ammonia reversibly.[1043] Many salts both of simple and of complex

[1035] N. Bjerrum, *Z. anorg. Chem.* **119**, 39, 54, 179.

[1036] A. Cioci, ib. 1899, **19**, 314.

[1037] G. Scagliarini and G. Tartarini, *Gaz.* 1923, **53**, 139, 617.

[1038] K. Gleu, W. Cuntze, and K. Rehm, *Z. anorg. Chem.* 1938, **237**, 89.

[1039] F. Ephraim and W. Ritter, *Helv. Chim. Acta*, 1928, **11**, 848.

[1040] See C. L. Rollinson and J. C. Bailar, *J.A.C.S.* 1943, **65**, 250; 1944, **66**, 641.

[1041] For the colours of the chromammines see R. I. Colmar and F. W. Schwartz, ib. 1932, **54**, 3204; G. Joos and K. Schnetzler, *Z. physikal. Chem.* 1933, B **20**, 1.

[1042] For the changes in absorption spectra when NH_3 and H_2O are replaced by ND_3 and D_2O, see B. Duhm, *Z. physikal. Chem.* 1937, B **38**, 359.

[1043] F. Ephraim and S. Millmann, *Ber.* 1917, **50**, 529.

acids are known, the latter often being insoluble in water. The free base $[Cr(NH_3)_6](OH)_3$, made by treating the trichloride with silver oxide, has a strong alkaline reaction; it separates from water on addition of alcohol and ether as a yellow solid.

The corresponding 'en' complexes are also known[1044-5]; conductivity measurements confirm their great stability.

The aquo-pentammines $[Cr(NH_3)_5(OH_2)]X_3$ can be made from the hexammines by heating with water.[1046-9] They are yellow solids, less stable than the hexammines, and particularly sensitive to light.[1050-1]

The diaquo-salts are similar. The 'en' derivatives are of special interest here from their stereochemical relations [1052-4] (see below). The triaquo-[1055] and tetraquo-salts[1056-7] are similar. These last can be made[1058-9] by oxidizing the diammine $NH_4[Cr(NH_3)_2(SCN)_4]$ in presence of hydrobromic acid to $[Cr(NH_3)_2Br_2(OH_2)_2]Br$; the bromine in the complex is then hydrolysed by ammonia to OH in $[Cr(NH_3)_2(OH_2)_3(OH)_2]Br$, which is converted by acids into salts of the tetraquo-complex $[Cr(NH_3)_2(OH_2)_4]X_3$. These are reddish-violet salts, easily soluble (unlike the dihydroxo-compounds) in water.

When the complex has one NH_3 replaced by an acyl group it becomes divalent, as in $[Cr(NH_3)_5X]X_2$ (purpureo series). The acyl groups in the complex are reversibly hydrolysed by water to the aquo-pentammines at various rates[1062-3] (chlorine much more rapidly than iodine), with an increase of conductivity. The ethylamine compounds such as $[Cr(NH_2Et)_5Cl]X_2$ are very similar but less stable, and are slowly hydrolysed by cold water.[1064-5] The nitrato-base $[Cr(NH_3)_5NO_3]X_2$ is known.[1066]

[1044] P. Pfeiffer, *Z. anorg. Chem.* 1900, **24**, 279.

[1045] Id., ib. 1902, **29**, 107.

[1046] The stability relations of the various solid hexammines, aquo-pentammines, etc., in contact with one another and the solution have been examined by A. Benrath and H. Steinrath, ib. 1929, **177**, 292; 1930, **194**, 351.

[1047] S. M. Jörgensen, *J. prakt. Chem.* 1882, [2] **25**, 398.

[1048] A. Werner, *Ann.* 1914, **405**, 212.

[1049] S. Loria, *Ann. Phys.* 1912, [4] **38**, 889.

[1050] For the conductivities of these salts and their relations to the hydroxo (OH) compounds see H. J. S. King, *J.C.S.* 1925, **127**, 2100.

[1051] For their crystal structures (exactly like those of their cobalt analogues) see O. Hassel and G. B. Naess, *Z. anorg. Chem.* 1928, **174**, 24.

[1052] P. Pfeiffer, *Ber.* 1907, **40**, 3126.

[1053] Id., *Z. anorg. Chem.* 1907, **56**, 261.

[1054] Id., ib. 1908, **58**, 228.   [1055] A. Werner, *Ber.* 1906, **39**, 2656.

[1056] A. Werner and A. J. Klien, ib. 1902, **35**, 277.

[1057] P. Pfeiffer, *Z. anorg. Chem.* 1902, **31**, 401.

[1058] A. Werner and J. V. Dubsky, *Ber.* 1907, **40**, 4085.

[1059] J. V. Dubsky, *J. prakt. Chem.* 1914, [2] **90**, 61.

[1060] E. H. Riesenfeld and F. Seemann, *Ber.* 1909, **42**, 4222.

[1061] F. Frowein, *Z. anorg. Chem.* 1920, **110**, 107.

[1062] A. Werner and A. Miolati, *Z. physikal. Chem.* 1894, **14**, 506.

[1063] H. Freundlich and H. Pape, ib. 1914, **86**, 458.

[1064] H. Mandal, *Ber.* 1915, **48**, 2055.   [1065] Id., ib. 1916, **49**, 1307.

[1066] A. Werner and J. v. Halban, ib. 1906, **39**, 2668.

The hydroxo-compounds $[Cr(NH_3)_4(OH)(OH_2)]X_2$ can be made from the diaquo by treatment with pyridine; they have a neutral reaction, but are converted by acids back into the diaquo-salts.[1052,1059]

The salts of the monovalent base $[Cr(NH_3)_4X_2]X$ have various possibilities of isomerism; the two X groups may be attached to adjacent (*cis*) or opposite (*trans*) corners of the octahedron (X—Cr—X = 90° or 180°). The configuration is determined by finding whether a divalent radical (usually the oxalato-) can take the place of the two acyl groups; if it can, they must be a *cis*. With the *di-en* compounds of the type $[Cr(en)_2X_2]X$ there is a further possibility of optical isomerism in the *cis* (but not in the *trans*) series:

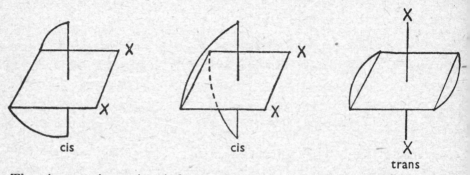

cis   cis

trans

The *cis–trans* isomerism is known in many series; the isomers ordinarily differ in colour and are interconvertible; whether the *cis* or the *trans* is the more stable depends on the nature of the groups in the complex.[1053,1067] Of the asymmetric compounds, Werner resolved $[Cr(en)_2Cl_2]X$ in 1911[1068] and the trichelate oxalato-salt $K_3[Cr(C_2O_4)_3]$ in 1912.[1069]

With three kinds of groups in the complex, as in $[Cr(NH_3)_3(OH_2)Cl_2]X$ a third series of isomers becomes possible, and has been isolated in some cases.[1060-1]

Fluorine compounds are unusually common among these complexes, especially those with pyridine; all three types $[CrF_2py_4]X$, $[CrF_3py_3]°$, and $[CrF_3py_2(OH_2)]°$ are known.[1070] The salts of the first series can be made by the action of pyridine on hydrated chromic fluoride.[1070-1]

The triacyl compounds CrX_3Am_3 must of course be non-ionized, and they behave as such. CrF_3py_3, also made from the hydrated fluoride and pyridine,[1070] is soluble in water, and the solution has practically no conductivity, and gives no precipitate with polyvalent anions like PO_4 or $PtCl_6$. The chlorides $CrCl_3Am_3$, which can be made in a similar way,[1044,1072-3] and also by heating the chloropentammine chloride in hydrochloric acid at 270°,[1074] is insoluble in water but dissolves in chloroform; its undis-

[1067] See Table in Abegg, p. 246.   [1068] A. Werner, *Ber.* 1911, **44**, 3132.
[1069] Id., ib. 1912, **45**, 3061.
[1070] N. Costachescu, *Chem. Centr.* 1912, i. 1970.
[1071] Id., ib. 1914, i. 2141.   [1072] P. Pfeiffer, *Ber.* 1900, **33**, 2686.
[1073] Id., *Z. anorg. Chem.* 1907, **55**, 97.
[1074] H. I. Schlesinger and R. K. Worner, *J.A.C.S.* 1929, **51**, 3520.

sociated character is further shown by its being precipitated unchanged by water from its solution in concentrated nitric acid.[1073]

The monovalent anions $[CrAm_2X_4]^-$ occur in such salts as

$$NH_4[Cr(SCN)_4(NH_3)_2], H_2O$$

(Reinecke's salt),[1075] which is red and fairly soluble in water, and the oxalato-salt $NH_4[Cr(C_2O_4)_2(NH_3)_2]$.[1076]

In addition there are numerous binuclear (Cr_2) complexes, such as the diol salts $[Cr_2Am_8(OH)_2]X_4$, which presumably have the two hydroxyl groups acting as bridges,[1059] as in

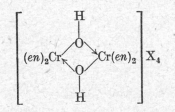

The remarkable monols occur in a normal $[Cr_2Am_{10}(OH)]X_5$ and a basic series $[Cr_2Am_{10}O]X_4$; each of these occurs in two isomeric series, known as the rhodo- and the erythro-salts. The explanation of the isomerism given by Werner (ascribing it to 'valency isomerism') is now seen to be meaningless; but Jensen has shown[1077] that it must be due to the link between the chromium atoms being an OH group in the rhodo- and an NH_2 in the erythro-series: thus

	Normal	Basic
Rhodo-salts . .	$\overset{H}{\overset{\vert}{[Am_5Cr-O-Am_5]}}X_5$	$[Am_5Cr-O-CrAm_5]X_4$
Erythro-salts . .	$\underset{\downarrow}{\overset{OH_2}{[Am_4Cr-NH_2-CrAm_5]}}X_5$	$\overset{OH}{\overset{\vert}{[Am_4Cr-NH_2-CrAm_5]}}X_4$

Oxygen Complexes

These again are numerous; they are formed by the usual three kinds of addenda, neutral molecules like water or alcohol, monovalent chelate groups like those of the β-diketones, and divalent acid radicals as in the oxalato and other 'ato' complexes; this third class is the most numerous. Examples of the complexes formed with water have been given above in the aquo-ammines; the extreme form $[Cr(OH_2)_6]^{+++}$ is the hydrated ion which occurs in solutions of all simple chromic salts, and in many of their

[1075] O. T. Christensen, *J. prakt. Chem.* 1892, [2] **45**, 213, 356.
[1076] A. Werner, *Ann.* 1914, **406**, 261.
[1077] K. A. Jensen, *Z. anorg. Chem.* 1937, **232**, 257.

crystals as well. Alcohol can behave like water, as in the compound $CrCl_3$, 3 EtOH.[1078]

Chromic acetylacetonate (CrA_3) can be made by heating chromic

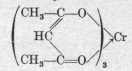

hydroxide with acetylacetone; it is a reddish-violet solid, and is remarkably stable; it melts at 214° and boils undecomposed at 340°, giving a green vapour[1079]; unlike, for example, the ferric compound it is unaffected by phenyl hydrazine.[1080]

The more numerous 'ato' complexes are formed both by monovalent and by divalent radicals. In the lower ammines we find nitrito $O—N=O$ and nitrato $O—NO_2$ groups in the complexes. Various double formates are known; most of these have 2 or 3 Cr atoms in the molecule,[1081] but there is a normal salt $Na_3[Cr(O \cdot CO \cdot H)_6]$, 4·5 H_2O, which only gives a precipitate with ammonia after a time.[1082]

With acetic acid there is a great variety of complicated types, mainly with three chromium atoms, as in $[Cr_3(O \cdot CO \cdot CH_3)_6(OH)_2]X$,[1081,1083] and the derived forms with $(OH)(OH_2)]X_2$ and $(OH_2)_2]X_3$.[1084-6]

The chelate derivatives of dibasic acids are more numerous. The complexity of at least some of the double sulphates (including chromic sulphate itself, but not the alums) is clear. A more important group is that of the oxalates. The 'simple' oxalate $Cr_2(C_2O_4)_3$, xH_2O must be complex as it is so soluble in water (p. 1014).[1087-8] Of the double oxalates there are two main types. One is the trichelate $M_3[Cr(C_2O_4)_3]$, which was resolved by Werner in 1912[1089]; these are blue salts, whose solutions give no reactions for chromium or oxalate; the soluble calcium salt $Ca_3[Cr(C_2O_4)_3]_2$ aq. is stable in solution in the cold, but on boiling calcium oxalate is precipitated. The dioxalato salts $M[Cr(C_2O_4)_2(OH_2)_2]$[1090-1] are red; their structures allow of their existing in two inactive forms, *cis* and *trans*, of which the latter are resolvable, and Werner showed[1076] that these two series occur.

[1078] I. Koppel, *Z. anorg. Chem.* 1901, **28**, 461.

[1079] G. Urbain and A. Debierne, *C.R.* 1899, **129**, 302.

[1080] H. Reihlen *et al., Ber.* 1925, **58**, 12.

[1081] A. Werner, ib. 1908, **41**, 3447.

[1082] H. S. Fry, *J.A.C.S.* 1911, **33**, 697.

[1083] R. F. Weinland and P. Dinkelacker, *Ber.* 1909, **42**, 2997.

[1084] R. F. Weinland, ib. 1908, **41**, 3236.

[1085] E. Späth, *Mon.* 1912, **33**, 235.

[1086] R. F. Weinland and H. Reihlen, *Z. anorg. Chem.* 1913, **82**, 426.

[1087] W. Lapraik, *J. prakt. Chem.* 1893, [2] **47**, 305.

[1088] A. Rosenheim, *Z. anorg. Chem.* 1896, **11**, 196, 225.

[1089] A. Werner, *Ber.* 1912, **45**, 3061.

[1090] A. Rosenheim and R. Cohn, *Z. anorg. Chem.* 1901, **28**, 337.

[1091] J. Meisenheimer, *Ann.* 1924, **438**, 217.

The racemization of the chromioxalates has been shown[1092-4] to be a first-order reaction, with a half-life (for the trichelate salt) of 59 minutes in a 0·08-normal solution at 18°. Since this reaction was shown not to be catalysed by oxalate ions, it would seem that it cannot involve the separation of oxalate ions from the complex. This has been conclusively established by Long.[1095] Oxalate made with radioactive carbon ^{11}C was mixed with the oxalato-compound at 35°, where the time of half-change in water is 24 minutes; samples removed after 12·5 and after 25 minutes showed that no isotopic exchange had occurred.

It has been shown[1096] that at 18° the chromioxalate racemizes 20 times as fast as the cobaltioxalate.

Catechol complexes $\left(\text{cat} = \text{⟨benzene ring⟩}{-O-\atop-O-}\right)$ have been made by Weinland.[1097] They prepared a series of compounds $M_3[Cr(cat)_3]$ ($M = Li$, K, NH_4, $\frac{1}{2}Mg$, $\frac{1}{2}Ca$, etc.), mostly hydrated. They are green and give green solutions, which on dilution turn red reversibly, presumably through hydrolysis to the dichelate $M[Cr(cat)_2(OH_2)_2]$.

Sulphur Complexes

Chromic sulphide Cr_2S_3 (p. 1011) will combine with metallic sulphides to form 'thiochromites' $MCrS_2$ or $M_2Cr_2S_4$. These cannot be made by dissolving the chromic sulphide in an alkaline sulphide solution, but only by heating a chromic compound with a metallic oxide or carbonate in presence of sulphur and in absence of air.[1098-9] Thus we have $NaCrS_2$, a brick-red powder, stable when dry, but oxidized by air and water to a thiosulphate. If this is boiled with the solution of a heavy metal salt, the corresponding thiochromite is produced, such as $AgCrS_2$, $Cu(CrS_2)_2$, or $Fe(CrS_2)_2$.[1098,1100] These are black insoluble substances, unaffected by hydrochloric acid but oxidized by nitric acid. Similar selenochromites are known.[1099,1101-2]

Complex Halides

Apart from one or two fluorides M_3CrF_6, these all seem to be of the type M_2CrX_5, H_2O, the water being no doubt in the complex. Chlorides of the types $MCrCl_4$ and M_3CrCl_6 have been described, but not recently.

[1092] C. H. Johnson, *Trans. Far. Soc.* 1935, **31**, 1612.
[1093] C. H. Johnson and A. Mead, ib. 1621.
[1094] N. W. Beese and C. H. Johnson, ib. 1632.
[1095] F. A. Long, *J.A.C.S.* 1939, **61**, 570.
[1096] E. Bushra and C. H. Johnson, *J.C.S.* 1939, 1937.
[1097] R. Weinland and E. Walter, *Z. anorg. Chem.* 1923, **126**, 141.
[1098] R. Schneider, *J. prakt. Chem.* 1897, [2] **56**, 401; 1898, **57**, 208.
[1099] J. Milbauer, *Z. anorg. Chem.* 1904, **42**, 442.
[1100] M. Gröger, *Mon.* 1881, **2**, 266.
[1101] P. B. Sarkar and S. N. Bhattacharya, *J. Ind. Chem. Soc.* 1930, **7**, 765.
[1102] P. C. Raychoudhury, ib. 1940, **17**, 623; 1941, **18**, 97, 277.

The hexafluoride $(NH_4)_3[CrF_6]$ can be made[1103-4] by heating a chromic salt with ammonium fluoride; it is green, and easily soluble in water.

The second type $M_2[CrX_5(OH_2)]$ occurs with fluorine, chlorine and bromine, and often in two series, one red or violet and the other green. The fluorides[1105-6] $M_2[CrF_5(OH_2)]$ are green. The chlorides separate in violet hygroscopic crystals[1107-8] unless the solutions are very concentrated, when a green salt separates which may contain 8 H_2O (Rb[1109]) or 4 H_2O (Cs[1110]); the green salts go over readily to the red forms. The bromides, such as $Rb_2[CrBr_5(OH_2)]$ are similar; their red aqueous solutions soon turn green. No iodides have been described.

DIVALENT CHROMIUM

THE chromous ion Cr^{++} is the first product of the solution of metallic chromium in acids, but it is very easily oxidized to the chromic ion Cr^{+++}, and all work on chromous compounds must be carried out in complete absence of air. Chromous compounds can also be made by the reduction (for example, electrolytically) of chromic, and the halides can be made by the combination of the elements in the proper proportions.

In solution, and in many hydrated salts, the chromous ion is bright blue. Its chemical behaviour is very like that of the ferrous ion: the same reagents precipitate both: with both, the hydroxide is precipitated by ammonia, but not in the presence of ammonium salts: chromous solutions like ferrous absorb nitric oxide, though the chromous, instead of forming a compound with it like the ferrous, reduce it, in neutral solution to ammonia, and in acid solution to hydroxylamine. But there is a marked difference between the two, in that the tendency to pass from the di- to the trivalent state is far stronger with chromium than with iron. The discharge potential, that is, the E.M.F. with a hydrogen electrode of a platinum plate in a solution containing normal chromous and normal chromic ion, is -0.4 volts, while the corresponding value for iron is $+0.75$ volts. As a result a chromous salt should be just able to decompose water with evolution of hydrogen, and in fact this does occur under the catalytic influence of platinum; without a catalyst there is no evolution of hydrogen from water unless the solution is fairly acid. But its reducing power is very strong. In solution it removes oxygen from air, and it is often used to remove the last trace from a gas; the relative amounts of oxygen left in nitrogen after passing various reagents are: quinone hyposulphite or $CuCl$—NH_3 260; pyrogallate 390; $CrCl_2$ 1; so that it is by far the most efficient.[1111] As

[1103] G. Fabris, *Gaz.* 1890, **20**, 582.

[1104] H. v. Helmolt, *Z. anorg. Chem.* 1898, **3**, 125.

[1105] O. T. Christensen, *J. prakt. Chem.* 1887, [2] **35**, 161.

[1106] A. de Schulten, *C.R.* 1911, **152**, 1107, 1261.

[1107] G. Neumann, *Ann.* 1888, **244**, 336.

[1108] A. Werner and A. Gubser, *Ber.* 1901, **34**, 1579.

[1109] Id., ib. 1906, **39**, 1823.

[1110] R. F. Weinland and A. Koch, *Z. anorg. Chem.* 1904, **39**, 296.

[1111] H. W. Stone, *J.A.C.S.* 1936, **58**, 2591.

occurs with strong reducing agents the oxygen is thereby activated (autoxidation); thus chromous chloride in alcohol is oxidized by air and at the same time the alcohol is oxidized to aldehyde: in presence of an arsenite, while a chromous salt takes up oxygen to become chromic, an equal amount of oxygen goes to oxidize the arsenite to arsenate. Chromous salts reduce mercuric salts to mercurous, cupric to cuprous, while they separate platinum, gold, and even tin from solutions of their salts.

Chromous Oxide, CrO

This is formed by oxidizing chromium in its amalgam by air: when heated in air it burns to the sesquioxide. Unlike the sesquioxide, if it is heated to a high temperature in hydrogen it is reduced to the metal.

Chromous Hydroxide, $Cr(OH)_2$

This is so readily oxidized that it is not certain if it has ever been prepared. When treated with alkalies, chromous chloride solutions give a yellow precipitate, which is rapidly converted by the water, with evolution of hydrogen, into the oxide Cr_3O_4.

Chromous Fluoride

This can be made by the action of hydrofluoric acid on red-hot chromium, or on chromous chloride in the cold. It is a green solid which melts at 1,100°, and is not volatile at 1,300°. It is only slightly soluble in water and insoluble in alcohol.[1112]

Chromous Chloride

Chromous chloride can be made by the action of hydrochloric acid on chromium at a white heat, or of hydrogen on chromic chloride at a red heat. It is a white substance[1113] which is easily fusible but only slightly volatile (the lowest temperature at which Nilson and Petterson got its vapour density was 1,300°); in the vapour state it is very largely Cr_2Cl_4 even above 1,500°. It dissolves readily in water (evolving 18·6 k.cals. per $CrCl_2$) to give a blue solution from which various hydrates can be obtained, namely:

$$6 \text{ aq.} \rightleftharpoons 4 \text{ aq.A} \rightleftharpoons 4 \text{ aq.B} \rightleftharpoons 3 \text{ aq.} \rightleftharpoons 2 \text{ aq.} \rightleftharpoons \text{anhydr.}$$

	ca.+10°	50°			
		Dark ⎱	Pale ⎱	Pale ⎱	
Blue	Blue	Green ⎰	Blue ⎰	Green ⎰	White.

All these except the green 4 aq.B behave in solution as normal strong electrolytes, but this form has a much lower conductivity, gives a green solution, and is obviously complex.

The behaviour of anhydrous chromous chloride with ether is very

---

[1112] C. Poulenc, *C.R.* 1893, **116**, 253.
[1113] For its magnetic properties see R. H. Weber, *Ann. Phys.* 1911, **36**, 624.

remarkable.[1114] Chromic chloride will not dissolve in ether unless it is mixed with chromous. If the mixed solid is treated with ether in the absence of air and moisture, it is found that the ether takes up practically only the chromous chloride. The solution, although it contains Cr and Cl in the ratio 1:2, has no reducing properties at all: it does not reduce Fehling's solution, nor ammoniacal silver, nor iodine, nor methylene blue, nor indigo; with hydrochloric acid and palladium there is no evolution of hydrogen, and the solution does not decolorize permanganate as chromous chloride does. It is in fact clear that the solution contains trivalent and not divalent chromium, and it gives all the usual chromic complexes. These are all derived from a compound $CrCl_2(OEt)$: for example,

$$(NH_3)_3CrCl_2(OEt);$$

and it seems certain that the chromous chloride must react with the ether to form this ethylate; but no one knows what happens to the rest of the ether molecule, which ought to give butane. The ethereal solution is a non-conductor of electricity. Chromous bromide and iodide behave in the same way. For the ether we can substitute dioxane or benzyl ethyl ether, but not a partly aromatic ether such as anisol or phenetol. This may, however, only mean that these last-mentioned ethers need a higher temperature for reaction than the product will stand.

Chromous chloride $CrCl_2$ has been used as a reducing agent in organic chemistry,[1115] especially for reducing iminochlorides to aldehydes, for example:

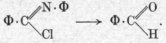

Chromous Bromide

This is a white solid which turns yellow on melting, and is easily soluble in water; it is only known in the anhydrous state and in solution. It forms a stable co-ordination compound with hydrazine of the formula $CrBr_2, 2N_2H_4$ (Traube).

Chromous Iodide

According to Hein[1116-17] this is dark red or red-brown, and melts at 790–5°; the colour cannot be due to free iodine, since it is not removed by shaking with mercury.[1117] At high temperatures it is much more stable than chromic iodide, and even as low as 300° the conversion by iodine into the tri-iodide is not complete. Above 800° chromous iodide is to some extent reduced by hydrogen to the metal, but attempts to prove the existence of a univalent CrI have all failed; there appears to be nothing between CrI_2 and $Cr+I_2$.[1117]

[1114] F. Hein, H. Farl, and H. Bär, *Ber.* 1930, **63**, 1418.
[1115] J. v. Braun and W. Randolph, ib. 1934, **67**, 269, 1735.
[1116] F. Hein and I. Wintner-Hölder, *Z. anorg. Chem.* 1931, **202**, 81.
[1117] F. Hein and G. Bähr, ib. 1943, **251**, 241.

Chromous Sulphate

This can be prepared[1118] by reducing chromic sulphate electrolytically with a platinum cathode in an atmosphere of hydrogen; it is precipitated by alcohol as $CrSO_4$, $5 H_2O$, and this is stable in dry air. The anhydrous salt is unknown, but a second blue hydrate $CrSO_4$, $7 H_2O$ has been made, which is isomorphous with the ferrous sulphate. It also forms double sulphates corresponding to the vitriols. The aqueous solution evolves hydrogen in presence of a platinum catalyst, or of hydrochloric acid.

Chromous Formate

This is a red salt, giving a blue solution in water.

Chromous Acetate

This also is red, and is only slightly soluble in water, so that it is a good source for making other chromous compounds; it must be prepared and used in an atmosphere of hydrogen or nitrogen.

Chromous Oxalate, CrOx, H_2O

This is a yellow powder looking like ferrous oxalate, which is very slightly soluble in water, and is relatively stable even when moist, and only slightly oxidized by air (Moissan).

CHROMOUS COMPLEXES

THE chromous compounds form a series of complexes, though much fewer than the chromic, owing to the smaller charge (compare cobaltous and cobaltic).

The *chromocyanide* $K_4[Cr(CN)_6]$ (Descamps, 1882) is a dark-blue solid giving a red solution in water. In acid solution it rapidly changes to the chromicyanide $K_3[Cr(CN)_6]$, but in neutral solution (in absence of air) it is quite stable.[1032] It has the paramagnetic moment required for an octahedral complex.[1032]

Various ammines are known[1119-20] including the very stable $CrCl_2$, $6 NH_3$, and compounds with hydrazine[1121] and dipyridyl.[1121,1123] The ease of oxidation of the chromous atom in these ammines varies greatly, depending on the stability both of the chromous complex and of the chromic complex into which it can pass. The ammines proper are usually stable in the air when dry,[1120-1] but if ammonia and ammonium chloride[1124] or ethylene diamine[1125] are added, hydrogen is evolved and a chromic complex formed. Pyridine complexes are oxidized by air even when wet.[1122]

[1118] A. Asmanow, *Z. anorg. Chem.* 1927, **160**, 209.
[1119] F. Ephraim and C. Zapata, *Helv. Chim. Acta*, 1934, **17**, 287.
[1120] H. I. Schlesinger and E. S. Hammond, *J.A.C.S.* 1933, **55**, 3971.
[1121] W. Traube and W. Passarge, *Ber.* 1913, **46**, 1505.
[1122] W. Traube, E. Burmeister, and R. Stahn, *Z. anorg. Chem.* 1925, **147**, 50.
[1123] G. A. Barbieri and A. Tettamanzi, *Atti R.*, 1932, **15**, 877.
[1124] A. Asmanow, *Z. anorg. Chem.* 1927, **160**, 209.
[1125] J. H. Balthis and J. C. Bailar, *J.A.C.S.* 1936, **58**, 1474.

Complexes of dipyridyl, such as $[Cr(dipy)_3]Br_2, 6 H_2O$, are only slowly oxidized by air.

Double sulphates $M_2Cr(SO_4)_2, 6 H_2O$ are formed by chromous sulphate as a vitriol (K salt Moissan, 1882: NH_4 salt[1126]). Carbonato-compounds such as $Na_2Cr(CO_3)_2$, 10 and 1 H_2O, and $K_2Cr(CO_3)_2$, 15 H_2O (Baugé, 1896) are yellow solids, and as they give brown solutions in water must be complex. No double oxalates are known (Abegg, 1921). A brownish-red double formate $NH_4Cr(HCO_2)_3$ and a double malonate

$$Na_2Cr(CO_2 \cdot CH_2 \cdot CO_2)_2, 4 H_2O$$

must be largely dissociated in water as the solutions are blue.[1127]

The double fluorides $KCrF_3$ (pale blue) and $NH_4CrF_3, 2 H_2O$ (blue) give blue solutions in water,[1122] and so are no doubt largely broken up.

Chromium Carbonyl, $Cr(CO)_6$

This can be made[1128] by the action of carbon monoxide on chromic chloride at the moment when it is being reduced by the Grignard reagent. A solution of ethyl magnesium bromide $Et \cdot Mg \cdot Br$ in ether is dropped into a cooled suspension of $CrCl_3$ in ether in presence of carbon monoxide, the product is decomposed by dilute H_2SO_4, and the ethereal layer, which contains the carbonyl, is separated and distilled. The carbonyl $Cr(CO)_6$ remains as a white powder, which can be purified by sublimation at 160°. The yield is about 24 per cent., but it can be raised to 60 per cent. by increasing the pressure of the carbon monoxide to 50 atm.[1130]

Hieber[1129] points out that the conditions of this reaction are exactly those which Hein found necessary for the production of the chromium phenyls, even to the extent that the reaction goes only with covalent and not with ionized chromium derivatives; and he suggests that the first stage is that a phenyl group becomes attached to the Cr, and that this is then replaced by a CO, which will in fact sometimes react farther with the phenyls to produce ketones, etc. Hieber and Romberg[1129] show that this method of Job's can also be used with advantage for the preparation of the molybdenum and tungsten carbonyls (which can also be made in other ways that are not available for chromium) and they redetermine the physical properties of the three carbonyls as follows:

	$Cr(CO)_6$	$Mo(CO)_6$	$W(CO)_6$
B. pt. extrap. . .	145·7°	156·3°	175·0°
Ht. of Subln. . .	17·2	16·3	17·7
(k.cals./mol.)			

[1126] C. Laurent, *C.R.* 1900, **131**, 111.

[1127] W. Traube and A. Goodson, *Ber.* 1916, **49**, 1679.

[1128] A. Job and A. Cassal, *C.R.* 1926, **183**, 392; *Bull. Soc. Chim.* 1927, [iv] **41**, 814, 1041.

[1129] W. Hieber and E. Romberg, *Z. anorg. Chem.* 1935, **221**, 321.

[1130] B. B. Owen, J. English, H. G. Cassidy, and C. V. Dundon, *J.A.C.S.* 1947, **69**, 1723.

All three carbonyls have been shown by X-ray analysis [1131] and by electron diffraction[1132] to be octahedral.

The chromium compound is colourless, and melts at 149°. It can be recrystallized from benzene, ether, chloroform, or CCl_4. The carbonyls of this subgroup are remarkably stable, as compared with those of either iron or nickel, and among them the chromium compound is the stablest, perhaps because it alone is covalently saturated. Its vapour does not decompose below 120°, and it is not attacked by concentrated HCl or H_2SO_4, or by bromine, which decomposes molybdenum carbonyl.

In these compounds the carbonyl groups can be replaced by other donors, especially pyridine and o-phenanthroline.[1133] But here again the great stability of the hexacarbonyls, and especially of the chromium compound, can be seen. Thus pyridine attacks nickel carbonyl, and expels carbon monoxide from it, at the ordinary temperature: it does not attack molybdenum carbonyl below 116°, nor chromium carbonyl below 140°. The main products of its action are with chromium $Cr(CO)_4py_2$ and $Cr(CO)_3py_3$ and with molybdenum $Mo(CO)_3py_3$.

These compounds have the normal behaviour of carbonyls (see IV. 547). They contain the groups $M{\leftarrow}C{\equiv}O$, and the E.A.N. of the central metallic atom (of which the valency strictly speaking is zero, since all the linking electrons are provided by the CO) is that of an inert gas. Every CO group contributes 2 to this number, and accordingly the simple (monometallic) carbonyls will be formed only by elements with even atomic numbers. Thus in the first long period we have

$$28 \text{ Ni} : \text{Ni(CO)}_4 \text{ E.A.N.} - 28 + 2 \times 4 - 36.$$
$$26 \text{ Fe} : \text{Fe(CO)}_5 : 26 + 2 \times 5 = 36.$$
$$24 \text{ Cr} : \text{Cr(CO)}_6 : 24 + 2 \times 6 = 36.$$

The positions of Mo and W (54 and 86) are obviously similar.

[1131] W. Rüdorff and U. Hofmann, *Z. physikal. Chem.* 1935, B **28, 351**.

[1132] L. O. Brockway, R. V. G. Ewens, and M. W. Lister, *Trans. Far. Soc.* 1938, **34**, 1350.

[1133] W. Hieber and F. Mühlbauer, *Z. anorg. Chem.* 1935, **221, 337**.

THESE two elements show very marked differences from chromium, in the same direction as in the earlier A subgroups, for example, between Ti and Zr—Hf, or V and Nb—Ta, but much more intense. On the other hand, the differences between the two elements themselves are quite small.

In chromium there is a sharp distinction between the hexavalent compounds, which are covalent and acidic, and the di- and trivalent which are definitely ionized, and in which the element is clearly metallic or basic; the intermediate valencies of V and IV either do not occur at all, or only very rarely.

The properties of hexavalent molybdenum and tungsten are very like those of hexavalent chromium, except that the tendency to polymerization and condensation of the oxy-acids has increased enormously, even more than in the previous subgroups. All the lower valencies down to 2 are represented, but none of them, not even the lowest, give simple ions corresponding to Cr^{++} and Cr^{+++}. The elements in these lower valencies are largely non-ionized (the usual effect of increasing atomic number in A subgroups) and when they form salts with acids these are not simple salts, but when not complex are partly oxides, the so-called 'yl' compounds, such as $Mo^{iv}O(SO_4)$. The result is that while the chromium compounds fall into two sharply distinguished classes, the covalent derivatives of the hexavalent acidic chromium and the basic and ionized tri- and divalent salts, we find among the molybdenum and tungsten compounds no such sudden contrast of properties: as we go from one of the five different valencies to the next, there is a smaller and much more gradual change.

The differences between molybdenum and tungsten are all small, and will be noted as we come to them. The most marked is an exemplification of the general rule that in A subgroups the lower valencies become less stable as the atomic number rises. So here, in the trivalent state molybdenum has a trihalide and oxyhalides as well as complexes, while tungsten has the complexes alone: and in the divalent state the peculiar complex X_6hal_{12} which forms this group with both elements, is much more stable with molybdenum than with tungsten.

Molybdenum

Molybdenum was discovered by Scheele in 1778, in molybdenite MoS_2, which is its most important ore. The metal is obtained from this by roasting it to oxide, and then reducing this, either with carbon, or with aluminium (when calcium fluoride is added as a flux, and also to moderate the reaction), or electrolytically. It has also been suggested[1134] that the metal should be made by the action of heat on the carbonyl $Mo(CO)_6$.

The proportion of molybdenum in igneous rocks[1135] is $1·5 \times 10^{-5}$ (15 g. to the ton), being less than that of tungsten (70 g./ton) and much less than that of chromium (about 330 g./ton).

[1134] For refs. see list of patents quoted by Gmelin, *Molybdenum*, p. 36.
[1135] G. v. Hevesy and R. Hobbie, *Z. anorg. Chem.* 1933, **212**, 134.

Tungsten

This was discovered by Scheele and also by Bergmann in 1781. The chief ores are Wolframite, a tungstate of iron and manganese $(Fe,Mn)WO_4$, and Scheelite or Tungstein $CaWO_4$. The name tungsten is derived from the Swedish tungsten $=$ heavy stone (the density of $CaWO_4$ is 6·06); the other name is from Wolfrahm or spuma lupi, because the ore interferes with the smelting of tin, and was imagined to eat it up.

Tungsten is of great commercial importance; the amount of ore containing 60 per cent. WO_3 which was produced in the world in 1927 was 9,500 tons, of which 7,700 came from Asia (mainly China and Burma), 1,145 from America (mainly California and Colorado), and 500 from Europe (mainly Portugal). In its metallurgy the wolframite is first converted into the alkaline tungstate; this is then turned into WO_3, and the oxide reduced with carbon, or, if it is wanted in the pure state, with hydrogen.

Metallic Molybdenum

Owing to its high melting-point of 2,622° molybdenum is usually obtained as a black powder, but if it is compressed and heated electrically nearly to its melting-point it forms a coherent mass of a brilliant silver-white colour. The boiling-point is found by extrapolation from the vapour-pressure curve to be 3,560° (van Liempt, 1920) or 4,510° (Zwikker,[1136] 1927). Its specific conductivity at 0° is about one-third of that of silver.

Molybdenum is one of those metals (like chromium and also tungsten) which according to its previous treatment can behave either as a noble (inactive) metal or as an ignoble or active metal.[1137] The difference is very large; the potential to the normal hydrogen electrode of the extreme passive form is $+0.66$ volts, and of the most highly active -0.74 volts.

The metal is fairly stable at the ordinary temperature; it is attacked by fluorine in the cold, by chlorine and bromine when it is heated, but by iodine not at all. Dilute acids, and concentrated HCl, have very little action: fairly concentrated HNO_3 will dissolve it, if it is not strong enough to make it assume the passive state. The metal is practically insoluble in alkaline solutions, and very nearly so in fused alkali; but fused potassium nitrate dissolves it at once.

Metallic molybdenum is used for a variety of special steels, as the addition of a small amount of it greatly increases the hardness. For the filaments of incandescent lamps it is much less used than tungsten, as it is more volatile; but it is used in these lamps to hold the filament, since (unlike tungsten) it can be fused into glass.

[1136] C. Zwikker, *Physica*, 1927, **7**, 71. He gives the values of a series of physical properties of the element between 900° and 1,100° C.

[1137] E. Becker and H. Hilberg, *Z. Elektrochem.* 1925, **31**, 33; W. Muthmann and F. Fraunberger, *Ber. Bayr. Akad.* 1904, **34**, 201.

Metallic Tungsten

The fused metal is a brilliant white; it melts at 3,400°, and its boiling-point is calculated by Langmuir[1138] to be 6,700°; it is among the least fusible and least volatile of metals. It is stable in air at the ordinary temperature, but on heating it is oxidized by air to WO_3 and by steam to WO_2. Nitrogen has no action on it below 1,500°, but above that temperature forms a nitride: fluorine acts on it in the cold and chlorine at 250–300°, giving in absence of air the hexachloride WCl_6, and in presence of air the oxychloride or the trioxide.

Tungsten is very stable to acids, largely because it easily becomes passive; compact tungsten is only superficially acted on even by concentrated nitric acid or aqua regia. A fused mixture of sodium hydroxide and nitrate, however, dissolves it rapidly.

Tungsten can be made to assume the passive state by CrO_3, $FeCl_3$, HNO_3, HCl, H_2SO_4, etc. The highest passive potential to the hydrogen electrode is $+0.88$ volts, and the lowest in the active state is -0.70 volts.[1139]

Extreme Electrode Potentials to Hydrogen Electrode

	Cr	Mo	W
Active	−0·56	−0·74	−0·70 v.
Passive	+1·2	+0·66	+0·88
Difference	1·76	1·40	1·58 v.

Applications of Metallic Tungsten

Tungsten is a constituent of various special hard steels, in particular (usually along with chromium) of high-speed tool steels.

It is now the sole metal used for incandescent-lamp filaments, on account of its high melting-point and its low volatility. Its efficiency as a source of light is about 4 times as great as that of the old carbon filament, about one-fourth of that of a neon lamp, and about one-sixteenth of ideal perfection. For this use the tungsten must be specially pure, and so is made by reducing WO_3 with hydrogen. It is thus obtained as a powder, and the problem was to discover a way in which it could be converted into fine wires of sufficient strength. This is done in two ways. In the first the powder is compressed, and the rods so formed are submitted alternately to high temperature and to vigorous hammering, until finally the metal ceases to be brittle, and can be drawn into wires of 0·01 mm. diameter. A second and even better method is to convert the wire into a single crystal: for this purpose the powder is mixed with about 2 per cent. of thorium oxide (which has a great effect, though we do not know why) and an adhesive such as gum, and forced through a fine orifice under pressure so as to form a thin wire. This wire is then made to pass through a short spiral of tungsten wire heated to 2,200–2,400°, at the rate of about

[1138] H. A. Jones, I. Langmuir, and G. M. J. Mackay, *Phys. Rev.* 1927, ii. **30**, 201.
[1139] W. Muthmann and F. Fraunberger, *Ber. Bayr. Akad.* 1904, **34**, 214.

3 metres per hour (about 1 mm. per second); the crystals start in the hot zone, and the wire is moved at the rate at which they grow: in this way single crystals several metres long can be obtained. They have the advantage that they do not become brittle on repeated heating and cooling—i.e. on long use—which the drawn wires do, presumably owing to recrystallization.

The reason for the effectiveness of the ThO_2 is unknown. It is found that the addition to tungsten of between 0 and 2·5 per cent., or more than 4 per cent. of ThO_2 diminishes the tendency to crystal formation, but that between these two concentrations this tendency increases and passes through a sharp maximum.

Tungsten and the Inert Gases

The compound of tungsten and helium which Boomer considered that he had prepared has already been discussed under helium (0. 9).

With argon it was shown by Langmuir[1140-1] that the electron emission of a heated tungsten wire was the same in argon at 0·07–55 mm. as *in vacuo*; hence under these circumstances no compound with argon can be formed.

Molybdenum and Hydrogen

No hydride is known. Even the powdered metal takes up very little hydrogen, and loses it all again at 300°.[1142]

Tungsten and Hydrogen

Like molybdenum, tungsten absorbs only a minute amount of hydrogen at any temperature up to 1,500°, and no compound seems to be formed.

Molybdenum and Carbon

The metal can be made to take up carbon either by heating it with carbon in an atmosphere of CO_2, or by heating a molybdenum wire in CO. Though there are evidently compounds formed, their nature is very obscure, and solid solutions are also produced.[1143] Two probable compounds are Mo_2C and MoC: they seem to be very similar; the first forms white crystals melting at 2,960±50°; it is slowly attacked by water, and also by oxidizing acids. The second is said to melt at 2,965±50°.

Tungsten and Carbon

Its behaviour appears to be similar to that of molybdenum, but the compounds are much better known. The C—W diagram[1144] contains two compounds, W_2C and WC, with a limited formation of solid solutions.

[1140] I. Langmuir, *Phys. Z.* 1914, **15**, 522.
[1141] J. F. Congdon, *Phil. Mag.* 1924, [6] **47**, 458.
[1142] L. Hamburger, *Chem. Weekblad*, 1916, **13**, 11.
[1143] A. Westgren and C. Phragmen, *Z. anorg. Chem.* 1926, **156**, 27.
[1144] See Gmelin, *Tungsten*, p. 188.

WC melts at 2,770° C., and has an electrical conductivity at the ordinary temperature about 40 per cent. of that of tungsten: at 2·5° Abs. it is superconducting. Its crystal structure has been worked out.[1145] Its heat of formation from graphite and the metal is 4 k.cals./mole (exothermic).[1146]

W_2C. This has been said to be not a compound but only a solid solution, but Becker has shown[1147] that the crystal structure points to a true compound. M. pt. 2,780°: (within 10° of WC) electrical conductivity 7 per cent. of that of tungsten at the ordinary temperature. It is very resistant to chemical attack, and in general behaves like tungsten itself. But unlike both tungsten and the other carbide WC it is strongly attacked by chlorine at 400°, giving WCl_6 and graphite.

Molybdenum and Nitrogen

Molybdenum does not absorb nitrogen below 1,000°, but if it is heated in nitrogen at 1,000° and 1 atm., and allowed to cool in it, a new phase of nitride separates, as X-ray diagrams show.[1148] If the powdered metal is heated with ammonia this is decomposed, and the nitrogen is absorbed. Nothing is known of the chemistry of the products, but an X-ray examination shows that at least three compounds are formed,[1149] of which one is MoN, with the same crystal structure as WC, and another Mo_2N.

Tungsten and Nitrogen

Nitrogen has no action on tungsten until a temperature is reached (about 2,000°) at which the metal begins to evaporate, and combination then takes place with the formation of one or perhaps two compounds.

WN_2 is certain: it is formed as a brown deposit on the walls when a tungsten wire is strongly heated in nitrogen.[1150] Water readily converts it into ammonia and a tungstate. Its crystal structure has been measured.[1151]

W_2N_3 has also been described as being formed from WCl_6 and NH_3, but it has not been confirmed.

Hexavalent Molybdenum and Tungsten

This is the group valency, and so it is here that we expect the closest resemblance to sulphur and the B elements. This we find in the acids of the class of H_2XO_4 and its derivatives. But the increased tendency of the XO_4 group to polymerize and condense, which is always greater in

[1145] K. Becker, *Z. Phys.* 1928, **51**, 484; A. Westgren and G. Phragmen, *Z. anorg. Chem.* 1926, **156**, 27. They find the distances W—C 2·22; W—W 2·86; C—C 2·86 A.

[1146] L. D. McGraw, H. Seltz, and P. E. Snyder, *J.A.C.S.* 1947, **69**, 329.

[1147] K. Becker, *Z. Elektrochem.* 1928, **34**, 640. He finds the distances W—C 2·15; W—W 2·78; C—C 2·99 A. But Westgren and Phragmen (loc. cit. above) do not agree.

[1148] A. Sieverts and G. Zapf, *Z. anorg. Chem.* 1936, **229**, 61.

[1149] G. Hägg, *Z. physikal Chem.* 1930, B **7**, 339.

[1150] I. Langmuir, *J.A.C.S.* 1913, **35**, 932; *Z. anorg. Chem.* 1914, **85**, 261.

[1151] G. Hägg, *Z. physikal. Chem.* 1929, B **6**, 221; 1931, B **12**, 33.

A elements than in B, is very marked here, where most of the salts are derived from highly complex acids: there is practically no difference in this respect between molybdenum and tungsten.

With the oxyhalides, which all these elements form, it will be noticed that those of molybdenum and tungsten are more stable than those of either chromium or selenium (and in V A : V < Nb < Ta).

With the halides themselves we have peculiar relations. Chromium forms no hexahalides. Molybdenum gives a hexafluoride, and no more. Tungsten gives a hexafluoride, and also a hexachloride and hexabromide, the latter the only compound of its type known at all. Uranium gives a hexafluoride, and a hexachloride. The reason for these differences is quite unknown; it cannot be steric, because the sizes of the molybdenum and tungsten atoms are practically the same, the radii being Mo 1·36 and W 1·37 A and U 1·49 A.

The hexavalent state is the most stable both for molybdenum and for tungsten, in marked contrast to chromium, where, as usual in a lighter element, a lower valency, that of 3, is more stable. It is commonly said that the hexavalent state is more stable with tungsten than with molybdenum; this may quite possibly be true, but the evidence usually given for it is the existence of WCl_6 and WBr_6, and the absence of the corresponding molybdenum compounds. This, however, is only evidence for the stability of the 6-covalent state: in chromium we saw that the 6-covalent state was so unstable that no compounds of this type are known, though the 6-valent state was shown to be very stable by the behaviour of chromic acid and chromyl chloride, in which the chromium is hexavalent, though not hexacovalent.

Molybdenum Hexafluoride

This can be made from its elements.[1152] It is a white crystalline substance, melting at 17·5° and boiling at 35°. The heat of fusion in 1·94 k.cals., and that of evaporation 6·36, giving a Trouton constant of 20·6.

It is immediately hydrolysed by moisture: in this it resembles TeF_6 but differs from SeF_6, the maximum covalency for molybdenum as for tellurium being 8 (Mo gives quite stable 8-fold complexes) while that for Se is 6, so that MoF_6 like TeF_6 is co-ordinately unsaturated, and capable of further co-ordination and reaction.

Otherwise molybdenum hexafluoride is quite stable; it is not affected by dry air, chlorine, or sulphur dioxide.

It forms double oxy-fluorides (p. 1044).

Tungsten Hexafluoride

Our knowledge of this compound also is mainly due to Ruff.[1153-6] It can be made (1) in 30 per cent. yield by the action of HF on WCl_6 in the

[1152] O. Ruff and F. Eisner, *Ber.* 1907, **40**, 2928; O. Ruff and E. Ascher, *Z. anorg. Chem.* 1931, **196**, 419.
[1153] O. Ruff and F. Eisner, *Ber.* 1905, **38**, 747.

cold.[1154] Better methods of preparation are, (2) by the action of arsenic trifluoride on WCl_6 in the cold, or (3) by the action of antimony trifluoride on the hexachloride, according to the equation

$$WCl_6 + 3\,SbF_3 = WF_6 + 3\,SbFCl_2.$$

But the easiest method of preparation, if elementary fluorine is available, is its direct action on the metal.

Tungsten hexafluoride melts at $2 \cdot 5°$ under a vapour pressure of 375 mm., and boils at $19 \cdot 5°$ ($15°$ below MoF_6); its vapour density is normal. It is very reactive; it fumes in air and attacks practically all metals except gold and platinum. In every way it behaves just like the molybdenum compound. It forms complex oxy-fluorides (see p. 1044). It is remarkable for giving coloured solutions in many aromatic or oxygenated organic solvents, such as benzene, acetone, and ether, owing presumably to co-ordination. With benzene at low temperatures a white solid, probably WF_6,C_6H_6 separates.[1156a]

Tungsten Hexachloride

This and UCl_6 are the only known compounds XCl_6. WCl_6 is made by the action of chlorine on freshly reduced tungsten at a low red heat in the complete absence of oxygen,[1157] or by that of chlorine, sulphur chloride, PCl_5, etc., on tungsten trioxide or trisulphide.

Electron diffraction shows that it is a regular octahedron with the W—Cl distance $2 \cdot 26$[1160] (theory $2 \cdot 36$). Crystal structure measurements show that the molecule has the same form in the solid.[1158] It forms dark violet or steel-blue crystals melting at $275°$ and boiling at $347°$[1159]; the contrast to the colourless hexafluoride boiling $328°$ lower, is remarkable; but as regards the boiling-point it may be pointed out that this means an average rise of $55°$ for each replacement of F by Cl, and the corresponding value for the methyl compounds is $-24°-(-78°) = 54°$, and for the ethyl $+13°-(-32°) = 45°$. The change of colour is more remarkable: it is possible that it is something like the effect produced by several bromine or still more iodine atoms attached to the same atom, as in iodoform: but if so it is curious that no such effect is noticed in the hexachloro- or even the octachloro-anions of complex salts.

The vapour is slightly dissociated even at the boiling-point, the vapour density (to $H_2 = 1$) being $190 \cdot 9$ at $350°$, and $168 \cdot 8$ at $440°$: theory for WCl_6 $198 \cdot 4$. The liquid is practically a non-conductor: conductivity 2×10^{-6} at $280°$.

[1154] O. Ruff, F. Eisner, and W. Heller, *Z. anorg. Chem.* 1907, **52**, 256.

[1155] O. Ruff and F. Ascher, ib. 1931, **196**, 413.

[1156] P. Henkel and W. Klemm, ib. 1935, **222**, 67.

[1156a] H. F. Priest and W. C. Schumb, *J.A.C.S.* 1948, **70**, 2291.

[1157] For recent details see A. J. Cooper and W. Wardlaw, *J.C.S.* 1932, 636.

[1158] J. A. A. Ketelaar and G. W. van Oosterhout, *Rec. Trav.* 1943, **62**, 197.

[1159] Id. and P. B. Braun, ib. 597.

[1160] R. V. G. Ewens and M. W. Lister, *Trans. Far. Soc.* 1938, **34**, 1358.

The compound is easily soluble in CS_2, ether, chloroform, and CCl_4, giving red-violet solutions. It is only slowly attacked by air, and by water only above 60°; it is very readily converted into the oxychlorides.

Tungsten Hexabromide

This compound so far as it is known closely resembles the hexachloride. It can be made by passing bromine vapour in nitrogen over warmed tungsten,[1161] and sublimed as blue-black needles fuming in the air. It decomposes even on gentle heating, so that the vapour density is unknown. Water converts it into the blue oxide, but aqueous ammonia gives a colourless solution presumably of the tungstate.

It seems[1162] that mixed hexahalides WCl_xBr_{6-x} occur.

Molybdenum Oxyfluorides[1163]

There are two of these with hexavalent molybdenum, $MoOF_4$ and MoO_2F_2.

$MoOF_4$ is best made by the action of HF on $MoOCl_4$.[1164] It forms colourless crystals, m. pt. 97°, b. pt. *ca.* 180°. It is very hygroscopic and deliquescent, and turns blue in contact with air owing to its reduction by the dust. It gives a colourless solution in water, which on evaporation leaves the trioxide MoO_3 behind.

MoO_2F_2. This is made in the same way[1164] from HF and MoO_2Cl_2. It is colourless, stable to water, giving a colourless solution in $AsCl_3$ and in $SiCl_4$, but insoluble in toluene and practically in ether.

Tungsten Oxyfluoride

Only WOF_4 is known for certain. It is made from HF and the chloride $WOCl_4$, or by the action of lead fluoride on the trioxide WO_3. It melts at 110°, and boils at 185°.[1165] It forms white crystals, insoluble in CCl_4, slightly soluble in CS_2 and benzene, and easily in chloroform. It is very hygroscopic, and when exposed to moisture soon begins to deposit yellow tungstic acid H_2WO_4. It attacks metals when warm, turning blue in the process.

The other oxyfluoride WO_2F_2 has never been isolated but may be present, mixed with some WOF_4, when this last is treated with a little water.[1165] When PbF_2 is heated with even a large excess of WO_3 no WO_2F_2 can be isolated, so that evidently if it is formed in this reaction it is wholly converted at a red heat into $WO_3 + WOF_4$.

[1161] H. A. Schaffer and E. F. Smith, *J.A.C.S.* 1896, **18**, 1098.

[1162] E. Defacqz, *C.R.* 1899, **129**, 516; *Ann. Chim. Phys.* 1901, [7] **22**, 250.

[1163] For earlier references to the (mostly old) work on the oxyhalides of hexavalent molybdenum and tungsten, see Gmelin, ed. 8, *Molybdenum*, p. 151, etc.; *Tungsten*, p. 157, etc.

[1164] O. Ruff and F. Eisner, *Ber.* 1907, **40**, 2931.

[1165] O. Ruff, F. Eisner, and W. Heller, *Z. anorg. Chem.* 1907, **52**, 256.

Molybdenum Oxychloride

While WOF_4 is certain, and WO_2F_2 doubtful, the reverse is the case with the oxychlorides of molybdenum: there only MoO_2Cl_2, is certain.

$MoOCl_4$ is supposed to be the product of the action of chlorine on partially reduced MoO_2 (this is the material used for making $MoOF_4$), but it is likely that this is really a mixture of $MoCl_5$ and MoO_2Cl_2.[1166]

MoO_2Cl_2 is formed by passing chlorine over hot dry molybdenum dioxide.[1167] The reaction begins at 500°, and is rapid at 700°.[1168] The compound is fairly volatile, and melts only under pressure. It is easily soluble in and hydrolysed by water. A variety of more complicated halides with 2 and 3 atoms of molybdenum in the molecule have been described.

A possible hydrate MoO_2Cl_2, H_2O, which should perhaps be written $MoO_3, 2 HCl$, is made by heating MoO_3 to 150–200° in dry hydrogen chloride gas.[1169] It sublimes easily, and as it is easily made is a convenient substance to use as a starting-point for the preparation of other molybdenum compounds. It forms white or pale yellow crystals, easily soluble in water, alcohol, ether, and acetone; the aqueous solution on evaporation leaves MoO_3; in ether and acetone the molecular weight is nearly normal, but in alcohol there is some dissociation.

The structure of this substance is uncertain; $H_2[MoO_3Cl_2]$ seems an improbable formula because (1) the substance does not behave as an acid, and no salts of it are known, and (2) if it were a strong acid it would need some water to hydrate the hydrogen ions. The formula $O=Mo(OH)_2Cl_2$ seems on the whole the most likely, especially if the substance is really not dissociated in ether and acetone.

Tungsten Oxychlorides

One difference between molybdenum and tungsten is that the latter can take up more chlorine and bromine atoms than the former, and this difference persists in the oxychlorides. Just as we have WCl_6 and WBr_6, but no corresponding molybdenum compounds, so we have $WOCl_4$ and $WOBr_4$, while $MoOCl_4$ is doubtful and $MoOBr_4$ quite unknown.

The two oxychlorides $WOCl_4$ and WO_2Cl_2 are always formed together,[1170] and can be separated by means of the greater volatility of the former; but whenever the mixture is distilled, there is a certain loss of the dichloride through its disproportionation:

$$2 WO_2Cl_2 = WO_3 + WOCl_4.$$

[1166] See I. Nordenskjöld, *Ber.* 1901, **34**, 1575.
[1167] O. Ruff and F. Eisner, ib. 1907, **40**, 2933.
[1168] W. Kangro and R. Jahn, *Z. anorg. Chem.* 1933, **210**, 327.
[1169] See A. Werner, ib. 1895, **9**, 407; A. Vandenberghe, ib. **10**, 52.
[1170] According to A. V. Komandin and D. N. Tarasenkov (*J. Gen. Chem. Russ.* 1940, **10**, 1333) a stream of $3 N_2 + 2 Cl_2$ passed over WO_2 for 1 hour at 540° gives mainly WO_2Cl_2 but some $WOCl_4$; the reaction $2 WO_2Cl_2 \rightleftharpoons WOCl_4 + WO_3$ (reversible) begins at 240°.

WOCl$_4$ is formed[1171-3] by the action of oxygen or moisture on WCl$_6$; by passing moist chlorine over tungsten; or from WO$_3$ by treatment with PCl$_5$, with CCl$_4$, or with WCl$_6$ vapour. It melts at 209° and boils at 233°. Its heat of fusion is said to be 1·44 k.cals. and that of evaporation 16·84 k.cals.[1174] If this last figure is correct, the Trouton constant has the enormous value of 33·2. The vapour density is nevertheless normal at 350° and at 440°. The substance is practically a non-conductor of electricity.

It reacts violently with water to give WO$_3$.

WO$_2$Cl$_2$.[1175-7] Yellow crystals, melting at 265° and volatile on further heating: stable in moist air and only slowly hydrolysed by water.

Tungsten Oxybromides

WOBr$_4$. Made by the action of bromine on a mixture of WO$_3$ and carbon, or of WO$_2$ and tungsten. It is very like the chloride: brownish-black crystals, m. pt. 277°, b. pt. 327°. It is very hygroscopic and decomposes easily in air.

WO$_2$Br$_2$. Made in the same way as WO$_2$Cl$_2$, for example by passing a mixture of air and bromine vapour over red-hot tungsten. It is a red or yellow substance, infusible, and less volatile than WOBr$_4$. If it is rapidly heated it is converted into WO$_3$+WOBr$_4$. It is only slowly acted on by cold water.

Molybdenum Trioxide, MoO$_3$

This is the stablest oxide of molybdenum, and so is the final product of the ignition of the element or its oxides or sulphides, or other compounds, in air, or of their oxidation by nitric acid. It is a white powder, which turns yellow on heating, and melts at 795° to a dark yellow liquid: the colour disappears again on cooling. It has a perceptible vapour pressure even below its melting-point (0·30 mm. at 700°), and boils at 1,155°. The crystal structure has been examined by Wooster[1178]: the oxygen atoms form distorted octahedra round the Mo atoms.

MoO$_3$ is insoluble in water, but soluble in alkaline solutions, including ammonia and alkaline carbonates, to form molybdates, such as M$_2$[MoO$_4$]: it can scarcely be called an anhydride of molybdic acid since it will not form it with water.

Hydrogen reduces it at temperatures between 300° and 470° to MoO$_2$, and above 500° to the metal.

[1171] E. F. Smith and V. Oberholzer, *Z. anorg. Chem.* 1894, **5**, 65.

[1172] E. F. Smith and H. Fleck, *J.A.C.S.* 1899, **21**, 1008.

[1173] K. Lindner and A. Köhler, *Ber.* 1922, **55**, 1461.

[1174] W. Reinders and J. A. M. van Liempt, *Rec. Trav.* 1931, **50**, 997.

[1175] O. Ruff, F. Eisner, and W. Heller, *Z. anorg. Chem.* 1907, **52**, 267.

[1176] C. Friedheim, W. H. Henderson, and A. Pinagel, ib. 1905, **45**, 397.

[1177] G. Jander and D. Mojert, ib. 1928, **175**, 272.

[1178] N. Wooster, *Z. Krist.* 1931, **80**, 504. The distances are: Mo—O 1·90 to 2·34; O—O 2·75 to 3·75 Å.

Tungsten Trioxide, WO_3

This resembles MoO_3 in that it is the final product of heating tungsten and its compounds in the air. It is a lemon-yellow powder, orange when hot, and melting at $1,473°$ to a green liquid[1179]; its boiling-point is above $1,750°$. Its crystal structure resembles that of MoO_3.[1180-1] It is completely volatile in chlorine at $500°$, presumably being converted into the oxychloride. It is quite insoluble in water, but dissolves in alkaline solutions to give tungstates. Hydrogen reduces it according to the temperature to the blue W_4O_{11}, WO_2, or metallic tungsten. A solution of chlorine in CCl_4 in a sealed tube at $200°$ converts it into $WOCl_4$, and at $280°$ into WCl_6. It is insoluble in concentrated H_2SO_4 or HNO_3, or dilute HCl: it is almost unattacked by HF.

Molybdenum Trisulphide, MoS_3

This can be made from a molybdate solution by saturating it with H_2S, which converts the salt into the thiomolybdate $M_2[MoS_4]$: from this HCl precipitates the trisulphide MoS_3 as a dark brown solid, which easily goes over (like As_2S_3) into a colloidal form. On heating it changes irreversibly into MoS_2 and sulphur.[1182] It is soluble in alkalies, and especially in alkaline sulphides, including $(NH_4)_2S$, with which it reforms the thiomolybdates.

A persulphide MoS_4 can be made by the action of H_2S in excess on a molybdate solution: it is a brown powder like the trisulphide.

A triselenide $MoSe_3$ is also known: in general it may be said that the S in the thio-derivatives of Mo (or W) can be replaced by Se but not by Te.

Tungsten Trisulphide, WS_3

This is made in the same way by the action of HCl on a solution of a thiotungstate M_2WS_4. It is a black powder slightly soluble in cold water, and more in hot. It very readily goes over into a colloidal form, even on washing with water. If it is heated in the absence of air it is converted into WS_2, and in presence of air into WO_3.

A similar selenide is known.[1183]

It is obvious that the trisulphides of the two elements, like the trioxides, are extremely similar.

Molybdic Acid and the Molybdates

Molybdic acid—and the same is true of tungstic acid—has an enormous power of condensation* and polymerization, not only with itself, but with a variety of other acids.

* Condensation means the combination of two or more molecules with loss of water: polymerization the same, but without loss of water; with many of these complex acids the formation can be described by either term, according to whether we regard the acid as made up from the simple acid or its anhydride the trioxide.

[1179] F. M. Jaeger and H. C. Germs, *Z. anorg. Chem.* 1921, **119**, 149.

[1180] H. Bräkken, *Z. Krist.* 1931, 78, 487. Each W is surrounded octahedrally by 6 Os: W—O $= 1·86$ to $1·91$ A.

Molybdic Acid

The free acid $H_2[MoO_4],H_2O$ forms yellow crystals, which separate slowly from a solution of a molybdate in concentrated HNO_3: the yellow deposit often seen in bottles of ammonium molybdate solution for analytical purposes consists of this acid.[1184] On gentle warming, even in contact with the solution, it is converted into the anhydrous acid H_2MoO_4, fine white needles occurring in two modifications which look alike, but differ in many properties especially in the ease with which they lose water.[1185]

Molybdic acid dissolves in water up to about 1 g. in the litre at 18°. The aqueous solution reddens litmus and seems to be fairly strongly acid, but determinations of the dissociation constant vary very much, probably from the substance going over to the colloidal state.*

The acid is, of course, reduced under various conditions to various lower valencies.[1186]

Like boric acid molybdic acid combines, probably to form ring-compounds, with sugars, as is shown by its effect on their rotatory power.[1187]

Molybdates

Simple molybdates of the type M_2MoO_4 are known, but the tendency to condensation is so great that they only separate from solutions containing a large excess of alkali; most known molybdates are polymolybdates, even the familiar ammonium molybdate. In Ag_2MoO_4 the Mo—O distance was found by Donohue and Shand[1191] to be 1·83, 0·17 A less than would be expected; they quote these similar instances (among others) of a shortening of the A—O distance in AO_4 ions: AsO_4 0·10, VO_4 0·22, IO_4 0·15: see above, p. 914. Jander[1188] using the rate of diffusion as a measure of the molecular weight (not a very certain method) claims to have shown that with diminishing alkalinity of the solution the molybdate ions pass through separate stages with 1, 3, 6, 12, and 24 Mo atoms in the molecule.

The total number of known molybdates (even excluding for the present those which contain other acids as well) is very large, and examples are

---

* There is a danger that these acids when precipitated carry down with them some of the precipitating acid.

[1181] For the system $WO^3 + W$ see O. Glemser and H. Sauer, *Z. anorg. Chem.* 1943, **252**, 144.

[1182] W. Biltz and A. Köcher, *Z. anorg. Chem.* 1941, **248**, 172.

[1183] L. Moser and K. Atynski, *Mon.* 1925, **45**, 241.

[1184] According to V. Auger (*C.R.* 1938, **206**, 913) this deposit usually contains NH_3, and owes its yellow colour to traces of silicomolybdate from the glass. He finds, however (ib. **207**, 1213), that there is a brownish-yellow labile form of H_2MoO_4.

[1185] A. Rosenheim and I. Davidsohn, *Z. anorg. Chem.* 1903, **37**, 316.

[1186] W. F. Jakob and W. Koslowski, *Rocz. Chem.* 1929, **9**, 667; G. Canneri, *Gaz.* 1930, **60**, 113; P. Krumholz, *Z. anorg. Chem.* 1933, **212**, 97.

[1187] G. Tanret, *C.R.* 1921, **172**, 1363; E. Darmois and J. Martin, ib. 1930, **190**, 294; Z. Soubarev-Chatelain, ib. 1935, **200**, 1942.

[1188] G. Jander and A. Winkel, *Z. physikal. Chem.* 1930, **149**, 97; G. Jander, K. F. Jahr, and W. Heukeshoven, *Z. anorg. Chem.* 1930, **194**, 383.

known containing, to every two monovalent M atoms, 1, 2, $2\frac{1}{3}$, 3, 4, 6, 8, 10, and 16 MoO_3 groups in the molecule. Various classifications have been proposed, but none of these are of much value unless we have the corresponding X-ray data.[1189] The simpler molybdates have been examined in detail by Hoermann[1190] together with the corresponding tungstates. He shows that double molybdates, and also double tungstates with two different alkali metals, are common, but that double molybdate-tungstates are rare. The alkalies Li, Na, and K nearly always give salts with 1, 2, 3, and 4 MoO_3 (for example, $Na_2Mo_4O_{13}$): the melting-points of the simple anhydrous salts $R_2[MoO_4]$ are Li 705°; Na 687°; K 926°. The paramolybdates have been definitely shown to be $M_6[Mo(Mo_6O_{24})]$, 4 H_2O[1192]; the paratungstates are similar (see p. 1041).

Tungstic Acid

Free tungstic acid occurs in two forms, a yellow, which is precipitated on addition of acid to a hot solution of a normal or para-tungstate, and a white one, which is precipitated in the cold.

1. The yellow form has the composition H_2WO_4, is crystalline, and is almost insoluble in water, its solubility being at the ordinary temperature about 1.5×10^{-5} equivalents (3·75 mg.) per litre.[1193] It is soluble in HF, and slightly soluble in concentrated HCl.

2. The white form, which is precipitated in the cold if enough HCl is added to the tungstate solution, is white or pale yellow, and very voluminous: its composition approaches H_2WO_4,H_2O. This has been shown to be really crystalline.[1194] It is soluble in water, and is said to give the solution an acid reaction, but this is largely due to the release of adsorbed mineral acid. It has a strong tendency to pass into a colloidal state. It is unstable, and with concentrated acid, or even with water, especially if it is warmed, it goes over into the yellow form.

Tungstates

The salts of tungstic acid, like those of molybdic, have very variable proportions of acid and base.[1195] We can distinguish three kinds:

1. Normal tungstates M_2WO_4.
2. Metatungstates commonly written $M_2W_4O_{13},xH_2O$, but more correctly $M_6[H_2W_{12}O_{40}],xH_2O$ (see below).

[1189] See A. Rosenheim and J. Felix, ib. 1913, **79**, 297; G. Jander et al., ib. 1930, **194**, 383; Gmelin, *Molybdenum*, pp. 114–29.

[1190] F. Hoermann, Z. anorg. Chem. 1928, **177**, 145.

[1191] J. Donohue and W. Shand, J.A.C.S. 1947, **69**, 222.

[1192] J. H. Sturdivant, J.A.C.S. 1937, **59**, 630.

[1193] A. J. Rabinovitsch and V. A. Kargin, Z. physikal. Chem. 1931, **152**, 26.

[1194] H. C. Burger, Z. anorg. Chem. 1922, **121**, 241.

[1195] For further information on tungstates and suggestions of possible structures, see the following: G. Jander and W. Heukeshoven, Z. anorg. Chem. 1930, **187**, 60; A. M. Morley, J.C.S. 1930, 1987; K. F. Jahr and H. Witzmann, Z. anorg. Chem. 1932, **208**, 145; R. H. Vallance and E. C. K. Pritchett, J.C.S. 1934, 1586.

3. Para-tungstates, with still more complicated formulae, formerly written $5 M_2O, 12 WO_3, xH_2O$, but more correctly $3 M_2O, 7 WO_3, xH_2O$.

The separation of the alkaline tungstates, both from water and from the fused melt, has been examined by Hoermann.[1190] They vary in composition from M_2O, WO_3 to $M_2O, 4 WO_3$. The melting-points of the simple tungstates M_2WO_4 are: Li 742°, Na 700°, K 921°. Of the ordinary sodium salt, $Na_2WO_4, 2 H_2O$, from which most of the compounds of tungsten are derived, 73 g. will dissolve in 100 g. water at 21°.

The meta series are very different from the other two; for example, they do not precipitate the free acid with hydrochloric acid, as (1) and (3) do, since metatungstic acid is soluble in water.

It has been pointed out[1196] that the metatungstates have the structure of a hetero-poly-acid, with the hetero-group replaced (in the formula, but not necessarily in a stereochemical sense) by H_2, to judge by the following examples of isomorphism:

$$K_6[H_2W_{12}O_{40}], 18 H_2O \qquad K_4[SiW_{12}O_{40}], 18 H_2O$$
$$Ba_3[H_2W_{12}O_{40}] 27 H_2O \qquad Ba_{2.5}[BW_{12}O_{40}], 27 H_2O$$
$$H_6[H_2W_{12}O_{40}], 24 H_2O \qquad H_3[PW_{12}O_{40}], 24 H_2O$$

Again, the pentahydrates of $H_5BW_{12}O_{40}, H_4SiW_{12}O_{40}$ and of metatungstic acid $H_6[H_2W_{12}O_{40}]$ are all isomorphous with $H_3PW_{12}O_{40}, 5 H_2O$, the structure of which is known. All these acids give similar Cs_3 salts in spite of their different basicities, so that the packing is of primary importance. The correctness of this view has been definitely established by the X-ray examination of metatungstates by Signer and Gross[1205] and Santos,[1206] which has shown that they have the structure of a 12 Mo heteropolyacid but with the central 'hetero' group left out.

The para-tungstates (like the para-molybdates) have been written both as $5 M_2O, 12 WO_3, xH_2O$ and as $3 M_2O, 7 WO_3, yH_2O$, which can scarcely be distinguished analytically unless M is heavy. The latter composition is supported by the analysis of a triethanolamine paramolybdate derivative,[1197] and established by Sturdivant's X-ray measurement of the cell

[1196] H. Copaux, *Ann. Chim. Phys.* 1909, [8] **17**, 245; 1912, **26**, 22; see also A. Rosenheim and F. Kohn, *Z. anorg. Chem.* 1911, **69**, 247; A. Rosenheim, ib. 1912, **75**, 141.

[1197] F. Garelli and A. Tettamanzi, *Atti Acad. Sci. Torino*, 1935, **70**, 382 (*Chem. Abstr.* 1935, 7864).

[1198] Gmelin, *Handbuch*, 'Molybdenum' (1935), pp. 312–93; 'Wolfram' (1933), pp. 324–96.

[1199] L. Pauling, *J.A.C.S.* 1929, **51**, 1010.

[1200] G. Canneri, *Gaz.* 1926, **56**, 642, 871.   [1201] L. Fernandes, ib. 655.

[1202] G. Jander, D. Mojert, and T. Aden, *Z. anorg. Chem.* 1929, **180**, 129.

[1203] A. Rosenheim, J. E. Koch, and N. Siao, ib. 1930, **193**, 47; Rosenheim and A. Wolff, ib. 64.

[1204] J. F. Keggin, *Nature*, 1933, **131**, 908; *Proc. Roy. Soc.* 1934, **144**, 75.

[1205] R. Signer and H. Gross, *Helv. Chim. Acta*, 1934, **17**, 1076.

[1206] J. A. Santos, *Proc. Roy. Soc.* 1935, **150**, 309.

dimensions and density of the ammonium salt $(NH_4)_6[Mo(Mo_6O_{24})]$, $4 H_2O$, with a central molybdenum atom.[1192]

Hetero-poly-acids

The discovery of this enormous group of compounds was due to Marignac, who in 1861 found that silicic acid will dissolve in tungstic acid to give crystalline compounds. Hetero-poly-acids in the widest sense are complicated structures, in which two or more kinds of highly oxidized acid residues take part. For practical purposes we can distinguish two classes of these: (1) those in which the two kinds of radicals are represented to more or less the same extent, and are relatively few in the molecule, as in the salt $K_2O, I_2O_5, 2 MoO_3, H_2O$; these are produced by an enormous number of oxyacids; (2) those in which a large number—usually 6, 9, or 12—residues of one kind, which is almost always either molybdic or tungstic acid, are combined with a single residue of another acid, which may be any one of a large number of oxyacids including those of B, Si, Ge, Ti, Zr, Th, P, V, As, and Mn. It is this second class which is generally understood by hetero-poly-acids, and it is with these that we are mainly concerned. The most frequent have one residue of boric, phosphoric, arsenic, or silicic acid, combined with 6, 9, or 12 WO_3 or MoO_3—sometimes 8, but never more than 12; when the single residue is that of telluric or periodic acid the number is usually 6. They are practically always hydrated, usually with large numbers of water molecules, which, however, are perfectly definite: thus one has 29 H_2O, which can be shown not to be 28 or 30. The reasons for these numbers are, of course, steric. Some of the more important papers on the hetero-poly-acids are quoted below.[1198-1207]

It may be mentioned that reference [1199] is a classification of hetero-poly-acids in general and a suggested assignment of structures to the various types, on theoretical principles; [1204] is an X-ray study of the 12-phospho-tungstates; and [1205] and [1206] are X-ray studies of the 12-silico- and 12-boro-tungstates, and of metatungstic acid.

The structures assigned to these compounds in a great deal of the earlier work are very speculative. The theoretical ideas of Pauling[1199] were of fundamental importance: in particular he showed that the various acid residues must all be united through oxygen atoms; see further.[1210] The fact is that these molecules are too complicated for it to be possible to assign structures to them until we have the X-ray evidence. This has, however, now been provided[1204-6] for several acids, which are nearly all tungstic, but it is obvious that the molybdates are built on the same lines. As an example of the complications involved, it may be mentioned that

[1207] G. Jander, *Z. physikal. Chem.* 1940, **187**, 149. He gives a general review of the hetero-poly-acids, and also discusses their dialysis co-efficients.

[1208] For a description of the structures with diagrams, see Wells, *S.I.C.*, pp. 341–2.

[1209] J. S. Anderson, *Nature*, 1937, **140**, 850.

[1210] E. H. Riesenfeld and M. Tobiank, *Z. anorg. Chem.* 1935, **221**, 287.

Keggin[1204] worked out the structures of the two hydrates of 12-phospho-tungstic acid, $H_3PW_{12}O_{40}$, 5 and 29 H_2O (see further refs. [1211-12]). These give us the clue to the general lines on which all these hetero-poly-acids are built up. It is clear that the unique radical—say the PO_4 in a phospho-tungstate—occupies the centre, the P atom being surrounded tetrahedrally by 4 oxygen atoms. On the 6 edges of this tetrahedron are then disposed in some way the 6, 9, or 12 MoO_3 or WO_3 groups.[1208]

As to the rest of the structures we may consider (1) the 12-acids, and (2) the 6-acids.

In the 12-acids the unique atom—say the phosphorus in a phospho-tungstate—occupies the centre, being surrounded tetrahedrally by 4 oxygen atoms. Each of these is attached to 3 tungsten atoms which form a W_3O_{10} group. In each of the four W_3O_{10} groups every W atom is surrounded by 6 oxygen atoms, (1) the oxygen atom of the PO_4 group, (2) an oxygen atom not otherwise linked, (3) two oxygen atoms shared with another tungsten atom in the same W_3O_{10} group, and (4) two oxygen atoms shared with tungsten atoms from two of the other W_3O_{10} groups, to form a closed network (these last atoms are barred (Ø) in the diagram). The whole 12 tungsten atoms of the group occupy the corners of a cubo-octahedron.

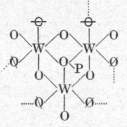

The 6-acids are derived from central atoms which have a characteristic co-ordination of 6, such as iodine and tellurium, for example, in $M_5[I(M_6O_{24})]$ (compare the paramolybdates and paratungstates, e.g. $M_6[Mo(Mo_6O_{24})]$). Anderson[1209] suggests that the octahedral WO_6 groups share edges to form a ring, the central cavity holding the nuclear hetero-atom by means of 6 inwardly directed (and octahedrally arranged) oxygen atoms.

For the heteropoly acids with intermediate numbers of molybdenum or tungsten atoms (8, $8\frac{1}{2}$,... up to 11) per central hetero-atom, Pauling suggests that the ion is binuclear, the molybdenum or tungsten groups forming a correspondingly larger polyhedron, capable of holding both XO_4 groups.

Thiomolybdates

The oxygen atoms in the molybdates can be replaced successively by sulphur, and the whole series of individual compounds from M_2MoO_4 to M_2MoS_4 are known.[1213] Even a perthiomolybdic acid H_2MoS_5, correspond-

[1211] A. J. Bradley and J. W. Illingworth, *Proc. Roy. Soc.* 1936, **157**, 113.
[1212] O. Kraus, *Z. Krist.* 1939, **100**, 394.
[1213] J. W. Retgers, *Z. physikal. Chem.* 1892, **10**, 548.

ing to permolybdic acid and obviously from its behaviour having a —S—S— linking, has been prepared.[1214]

Thiotungstates

All the possible members of the series are known, $M_2[WO_3S]$, $M_2[WO_2S_2]$, $M_2[WOS_3]$, and $M_2[WS_4]$; the last one on treatment with acids precipitates WS_3. The position is exactly the same as with molybdenum.

Corresponding selenium compounds, as

$$(NH_4)_2[WO_2Se_2] \quad \text{and} \quad (NH_4)_2[WSe_4]$$

are known.[1215]

Fluoromolybdates

A whole series of compounds in which one or more of the oxygens in molybdic acid are replaced by fluorine were elucidated by Werner.[1216] They are of the five types below:

$$M_2\left[Mo^{vi}\begin{matrix}O_3\\F_2\end{matrix}\right] \quad M_2\left[Mo^{v}\begin{matrix}O_2\\F_3\end{matrix}\right] \quad M_2\left[Mo^{vi}\begin{matrix}O_2\\F_4\end{matrix}\right] \quad M_3\left[Mo^{iv}\begin{matrix}O_3\\F\end{matrix}\right] \quad M_3\left[Mo^{vi}\begin{matrix}O_2\\F_5\end{matrix}\right]$$

$$\text{(I)} \qquad\qquad \text{(II)} \qquad\qquad \text{(III)} \qquad\qquad \text{(IV)} \qquad\qquad \text{(V)}$$

Examples of these salts are: type I, NH_4; type II, NH_4, K, Tl′; type III, NH_4, Na, K, Tl′, Cd, Zn, Ni, Co″, Cu″; type IV, NH_4; type V, NH_4.

Their isomorphous relations with other complexes illustrate the dependence of the crystal structure on ionic type and size rather than on the nature and valency of the central atom. Isomorphism has been established in the following groups (see Gmelin, Mo, p. 153).

(1) *Rhombic* (NH_4, Tl′)   (2) *Monoclinic*   (3) *Monoclinic*

$M_2[Mo^{vi}O_2F_4]$	$K_2[Mo^{vi}O_2F_4], H_2O$	$Cu[Mo^{vi}O_2F_4], 4\ H_2O$
$M_2[W^{vi}O_2F_4]$	$K_2[W^{vi}O_2F_4], H_2O$	$Cu[W^{vi}O_2F_4], 4\ H_2O$
$M_2[Mo^vOF_5]$	$K_2[Mo^vOF_5], H_2O$	$Cu[Mo^vOF_5], 4\ H_2O$
$M_2[Nb^vOF_5]$	$K_2[Nb^vOF_5], H_2O$	$Cu[Nb^vOF_5], 4\ H_2O$
		$Cu[X^{iv}F_6], 4\ H_2O$
		($X^{iv} = $ Si, Ti, Sn.)

(4) *Hexagonal*   (5) *Regular*

$M''[Mo^{vi}O_2F_4], 6\ H_2O$	$(NH_4)_3[Mo^{vi}O_3F_3]$
$M''[Mo^vOF_5], 6\ H_2O$	$(NH_4)_3[W^{vi}O_3F_3]$
$M''[Nb^vOF_5], 6\ H_2O$	
$M''[X^{iv}F_6], 6\ H_2O$	$(NH_4)_3[Nb^vOF_6]$
	$(NH_4)_3[Zr^{iv}F_7]$

Fluorotungstates

Several series of these are known: they are made by dissolving tungstates in HF. The main types are $M_2[WO_2F_4]$ (the commonest), $M[WO_2F_3(H_2O)]$, and $M_3[WO_3F_3]$.[1217]

[1214] K. A. Hofmann, *Z. anorg. Chem.* 1896, **12**, 60.
[1215] V. Lenher and A. G. Fruehan, *J.A.C.S.* 1927, **49**, 3076.
[1216] *Neuere Anschauungen*, ed. 5, p. 146.
[1217] See Gmelin, 'Wolfram', p. 158.

Permolybdates

Acid solutions of molybdates when treated with hydrogen peroxide turn yellow or orange, and yield coloured salts which have the typical reactions of H_2O_2, and obviously contain hexavalent molybdenum combined with peroxide —O—O— groups. The simplest of these have the composition M_2MoO_5, but other simple types, such as M_2MoO_6 and M_2MoO_8 are known; and all these acids have the same tendency as the parent molybdic acid to condense, so that many of the salts are highly complex.

In one case the free acid is known; $H_2MoO_5, 1 \cdot 5\,H_2O$ is made by treating MoO_3 with H_2O_2, filtering the deep yellow-red solution, and evaporating *in vacuo*.[1218] It forms a yellow powder which, unlike per-chromic acid, is insoluble in ether.

The salts,[1219] which are numerous, seem by their colours to belong to two classes: (1) yellow, as Na_2MoO_6, and (2) red, as in the numerous salts[1219] M_2MoO_8, which are explosive.

Pertungstates

Tungsten trioxide and the tungstates behave with hydrogen peroxide just like the molybdenum compounds.[1220]

Recent work shows that the per-acids of tungsten are among the stablest per-acids known[1221] (tungsten being the heaviest element, apart from the eccentric uranium, of an even group) though like all per-acids they slowly lose oxygen.

Further investigation shows[1222-3] that with monotungstates, when the hydrogen peroxide is weak, colourless monobasic ions with 2 atoms of active oxygen are formed:

$$[WO_4] + 2\,H_2O_2 \rightleftharpoons [HWO_6] + OH + H_2O.$$

If the H_2O_2 is stronger, the yellow ion with 4 active O atoms is got:

$$[WO_4]^{--} + 4\,H_2O_2 \rightleftharpoons [WO_8]^{--} + 4\,H_2O.$$

Hexatungstates only give the colourless $[HWO_6]^-$ ions:

$$[HW_6O_{21}]^{5-} + 12\,H_2O_2 \rightleftharpoons 6\,[HWO_6]^- + 9\,H_2O + H^+.$$

Molybdenyl Sulphate

It is a sign of the stability of the oxy-salt or 'yl' salt type in this subgroup that even hexavalent molybdenum is able to adopt it, and in a form XO_2'' otherwise practically confined to uranium. There are signs, however, that this form is less stable with tungsten, although it reappears with uranium. Molybdic acid is soluble in sulphuric acid, and this is one

---

[1218] W. Muthmann and W. Nagel, *Ber.* 1898, **31**, 1836.

[1219] K. Gleu, *Z. anorg. Chem.* 1932, **204**, 67; A. Rosenheim, M. Hakki, and O. Krause, ib. 1932, **209**, 175; N. J. Kobosev and N. N. Sokolev, ib. 1933, **214**, 321.

[1220] A. Rosenheim, M. Hakki, and O. Krause, *Z. anorg. Chem.* 1932, **209**, 202.

[1221] K. F. Jahr and E. Lother, *Ber.* 1938, **71**, 894.

[1222] Id., ib. 903.　　　　　　　[1223] Id., ib. 1127.

of the few points that distinguishes it from tungstic. The fact has been used to separate the two, by dissolving out the MoO_3 in a mixture of SeO_2Cl_2 and H_2SO_4.[1224] From the solution of molybdic acid in H_2SO_4 various compounds can be separated, but the simplest is the 'yl' sulphate MoO_2SO_4.[1225] It is very hygroscopic and decomposes on heating. If it is exposed to dust it is superficially reduced and turns blue.

A similar selenate MoO_2SeO_4 has also been obtained.[1226]

Substituted Tungstic Acids

Many derivatives are known of both molybdic and tungstic acids with organic acids, especially oxy-acids, such as citric, mucic, salicylic, gallic, etc., all or most of which owe their stability to the fact that they contain chelate rings.

An interesting series of these is that of the catechol compounds[1227-8]; the acidity of catechol is so weak that they must owe their stability to chelation. They are mainly of two types $M_2[WO_3cat(H_2O)]$ ($M = NH_4$, Tl′), and two similar kinds $(NH_4)_2[WO_2cat_2],H_2O$ and $(NH_4)H[WO_2cat_2]$.

Molybdenum Blue

This is a substance or group of substances about which there has been much discussion. It clearly contains molybdenum in two valency states, of which one is vi and the other probably v.

The first product of the reduction of molybdenum trioxide is commonly a blue substance known as molybdenum blue (discovered by Berzelius in 1826). It is probable that there are several distinct substances included under this name[1229]; they are stable only when they contain water as well as Mo and O. One formula which seems often to satisfy the analyses is Mo_3O_8,xH_2O or perhaps more exactly Mo_8O_{23},xH_2O.[1230] All sorts of reducing agents will produce these substances, Cu and HCl, Zn, Al, Fe, hydrazine, H_2S, etc.; they can also be made by the oxidation of pentavalent molybdenum, or air or diluted nitric acid. The solid substance is nearly black, but it is very soluble in water to form a deep-blue solution, which, as its X-ray pattern suggests, is probably colloidal.[1230] It forms compounds with various acids, such as phosphoric, and also with bases, including the alkalies; the products are always complicated in composition, and often colloidal. For possible structures see reference [1231].

[1224] H. B. Merrill, *J.A.C.S.* 1921, **43**, 2383.

[1225] J. Meyer and V. Stateczny, *Z. anorg. Chem.* 1922, **122**, 19.

[1226] E. Wendehorst, ib. 1928, **176**, 233.

[1227] L. Fernandes, *Gaz.* 1925, **55**, 434.

[1228] R. Weinland, A. Babel, K. Gross, and H. Mai, *Z. anorg. Chem.* 1926, **150**, 177.

[1229] See further M. Guichard, *C.R.* 1900, **131**, 389, 419; V. Auger, ib. 1936, **202**, 1180; V. Auger and N. Ivanov, ib. 1937, **204**, 1424, 1815.

[1230] F. B. Schirmer, L. F. Audrieth, S. T. Gross, D. S. McClennan, and L. J. Seppi, *J.A.C.S.* 1942, **64**, 2543.

[1231] W. D. Treadwell and Y. Schaeppi, *Helv. Chim. Acta*, 1946, **29**, 771.

Tungsten Blue

This seems to be very similar. The gentle reduction of WO_3 or tungstates gives blue products, which are no doubt compounds of WO_3 with lower oxides.[1232] If WO_3 is left in sunlight under water it turns blue. The formation of a blue colour on addition of stannous chloride and HCl is a very sensitive test for a tungstate. (See also under W_2O_5, p. 1049).

PENTAVALENT MOLYBDENUM AND TUNGSTEN

THE compounds of pentavalent molybdenum are usually formed by the electrolytic reduction of the trioxide. The main results of the fall in valency are (1) the production of colour: while the hexavalent compounds are usually colourless the pentavalent are usually green or red, and (2) the disappearance of the acidic properties of the oxide. The pentavalent molybdenum atom nearly always forms covalent molecules (including, of course, complex ions) or rarely salts of the 'yl' type $[MoO_2]X$.

With tungsten, while there is no doubt of the existence of pentavalent compounds, their number is much more limited than with molybdenum; apart from the pentachloride and pentabromide it is confined to the complex salts, which very closely resemble those of molybdenum.

Molybdenum Pentachloride

This is the only known pentahalide of molybdenum. It is made[1233-4] by heating the powdered metal in chlorine. It consists of dark green almost black crystals, m. pt. 194°, b. pt. 268°, giving a dark red vapour whose density is normal at 350°. Electron diffraction shows[1236] that $MoCl_5$ is a trigonal bipyramid, with all the Mo—Cl distances 2·27 A (theory 2·35). In the fused state it is practically a non-conductor, the conductivity being $1·9 \times 10^{-6}$ at 216°.[1235] It is very hygroscopic and sensitive to moisture; even moist air turns the blue-black surface green; when heated in dry air it is oxidized to the white hexavalent oxychloride MoO_2Cl_2, while it reacts violently with water to give the green pentavalent oxychloride $MoOCl_3$.[1237] Its formation of green and conducting solutions in certain solvents is due to traces [1238] of moisture forming the oxychloride $MoOCl_3$, which is green. If the solvents are thoroughly dried they either react, as the alcohols do, with evolution of HCl, or they give red solutions which do not conduct. The only exception is pyridine, which gives a brown conducting solution, but it has been shown that this is due to the reduction by the pyridine of the pentavalent molybdenum to tetravalent, and the formation of compounds of the composition $MoCl_4, x$py. In ether the pentachloride forms a black co-ordination compound $MoCl_5, 2 Et_2O$.

[1232] O. Glemser and H. Sauer, *Z. anorg. Chem.* 1943, **252**, 144, 160.

[1233] A. Voigt and W. Biltz, ib. 1924, **133**, 299.

[1234] O. Hönigschmid and G. Wittmann, ib. 1936, **229**, 65.

[1235] For the magnetic properties see W. Klemm and H. Steinberg, ib. **227**, 193.

[1236] R. V. G. Ewens and M. W. Lister, *Trans. Far. Soc.* 1938, **34**, 1358.

[1237] P. Klason, *Ber.* 1901, **34**, 148; I. Nordenskjold, ib. 1575.

[1238] W. Wardlaw and H. W. Webb, *J.C.S.* 1930, 2100.

$MoCl_5$ reacts with phenols in carbon disulphide[1239] to replace some of the chlorine, giving $MoCl_2(O \cdot C_6H_5)_3$: dark red needles, insoluble in cold water, easily soluble in CS_2 and in benzene.

Tungsten Pentachloride

This is made by heating the hexachloride, or distilling it in hydrogen. It forms dark green needles, m. pt. 248°, b. pt. 276°. It gives a greenish-yellow vapour, of which the density is normal for WCl_5. Its electrical conductivity is $0 \cdot 67 \times 10^{-6}$ at 250°.[1240] It is less stable in air than the hexachloride; it burns in air to $WOCl_4$ (hexavalent); it is very hygroscopic. It is hydrolysed by water, acids, or alkalies to a greenish-blue solution, which ultimately becomes colourless, through oxidation to WO_3.

Tungsten Pentabromide[1241-2]

This is very like the pentachloride. It is made from bromine and tungsten at a red heat, or by passing HBr over WCl_6 at 250–300°. It forms dark brown or black needles, m. pt. 276°, b. pt. 333° with some decomposition; the vapour is dark brown. It is soluble in ether, CCl_4, chloroform, and ligroin. It decomposes even in a vacuum to bromine and the lower bromides. It is hydrolysed by water to the blue oxide.

Oxyhalides

Pentavalent oxyhalides are unknown both with molybdenum and with tungsten, but complexes derived from them have been made (see below).

Molybdenum Pentoxide

This can be made by heating a mixture of the trioxide and the metal in the right proportions, or by precipitating a solution of pentavalent molybdenum with ammonia, when the hydrate $MoO(OH)_3$ comes down and can be dried to Mo_2O_5.[1243] It is a dark violet powder, insoluble in water, slightly soluble in sulphuric and hydrochloric acids. Its specific resistance at the ordinary temperature[1244] is less than that of the dioxide ($r \times 10^4 = 12 : MoO_2$ 31).

The hydroxide $MoO(OH)_3$[1245] which is precipitated from Mo^v solutions by ammonia, is soluble to some extent in water (2 g./litre) but not in presence of ammonium chloride, probably because the solution is colloidal.

[1239] A. Rosenheim and C. Nernst, *Z. anorg. Chem.* 1933, **214**, 209.

[1240] A. Voigt and W. Biltz, ib. 1924, **133**, 301.

[1241] E. Defacqz, *C.R.* 1899, **128**, 1233; *Ann. Chim. Phys.* 1901, [7] **22**, 249.

[1242] F. W. Bergstrom, *J.A.C.S.* 1925, **47**, 2317, 2322.

[1243] For more recent work see E. Friederich and L. Sittig, *Z. anorg. Chem.* 1925, **145**, 137; W. Wardlaw and F. H. Nicholls, *J.C.S.* 1925, **127**, 1487. The existence of this oxide is denied by Gmelin, but the later work quoted above, and especially the determination of the electrical conductivity, seem to make it certain that it exists.

[1244] Friederich and Sittig, loc. cit.   [1245] P. Klason, *Ber.* 1901, **34**, 150.

Tungsten Pentoxide

While the existence of molybdenum pentoxide is fairly well established, that of the tungsten analogue is very doubtful indeed. It may possibly occur as a solid solution in WO_3 in the tungsten blue already described, but it is more likely that this is a definite compound W_4O_{11}.[1246-7] The so-called wolfram blue, or mineral blue, which is formed by the gentle reduction of WO_3 or of tungstates, has a composition according to recent analyses somewhere between W_2O_5 and W_4O_{11} ($= W_2O_{5.5}$). Later work suggests that there may be a W_4O_{11} which is violet-blue, and a solid solution (or new compound) of this with more WO_3 which is pure blue.[1247-9]

Molybdenum Pentasulphide

This is prepared by reducing a solution of ammonium molybdate in 20 per cent. sulphuric acid with zinc until it is wine-red, which shows that the molybdenum is pentavalent, and then saturating with H_2S. A dark brown precipitate of $Mo_2S_5, 3 H_2O$ is formed. This is insoluble in water but soluble in acids with evolution of H_2S; if it is heated in a stream of H_2S it is converted into $Mo_2S_5, 3 H_2S$. If carefully heated in CO_2 it loses its water and becomes Mo_2S_5.[1250]

A similar selenide exists.

Tungsten, just as it will not form a pentoxide, will not form a penta-sulphide or a pentaselenide, although both sulphides and selenides of hexavalent and of tetravalent tungsten exist.

Salts of Pentavalent Molybdenum and Tungsten

These scarcely exist at all. The only salts formed by Mo^v with acids are oxy- or 'yl' salts, and apparently these are only known in the sulphates. The existence of the simple sulphate $Mo_2O_3(SO_4)_2$ is rather doubtful,[1251] though there is a series of double salts derived from it, such as

$$(NH_4)[MoO_2(SO_4)],H_2O.$$

In the same way pentavalent tungsten does not seem to give any simple salts, except that the W^v compounds can be dissolved in concentrated H_2SO_4 or HCl to give blue solutions, which may contain such salts. But most likely these are complex too: the solution if saturated with HCl deposits the complex $M_2[WOCl_5]$.

COMPLEXES OF PENTAVALENT MOLYBDENUM

These are numerous and varied; the most important are (1) the oxy-halides, (2) the cyanides, (3) the thiocyanates, and (4) certain chelate organic derivatives, such as those of catechol.

[1246] See J. A. M. van Liempt, *Rec. Trav.* 1931, **50**, 343, who brings forward evidence to show that W_2O_5 does not exist, but that W_4O_{11} does.

[1247] See further F. Ebert and H. Flasch, *Z. anorg. Chem.* 1935, **226**, 65.

[1248] E. Tarjan, *Naturwiss.* 1931, **19**, 166.

[1249] L. Wöhler, Z. Shibata, and R. Kunst, *Z. Electrochem.* 1932, **38**, 811.

[1250] F. Mawrow and M. Nikolow, *Z. anorg. Chem.* 1016, **95**, 191.

[1251] F. H. Nicholls, H. Saenger, and W. Wardlaw, *J.C.S.* 1931, 1443.

Complex Oxyhalides

Though no free oxyhalides of molybdenum occur, complexes with fluorine, chlorine, and bromine are all known.

Oxyfluorides

The salts belong to various types,[1252] such as $K_2[MoOF_5],H_2O$, which is blue. $M_2[Mo^vOF_5]$ can crystallize with $M_2[Mo^{vi}O_2F_4]$, and similarly $M_5[Mo^v{}_3O_3F_{14}]$ with $M_5[Mo^{vi}{}_3O_6F_{11}]$.

Oxychlorides

These have been much more extensively examined, especially by Wardlaw and his co-workers.[1253-6] The solution of pentavalent molybdenum is conveniently made by reducing the molybdate with a platinized platinum cathode (a polished Pt cathode gives Mo^{iii}). From this the oxychlorides can be made. The chief type is $M_2[MoOCl_5]$, where $M = NH_4$, K, Rb, py, quin, etc. These chlorides, as well as the bromides, and their tungsten analogues, all have magnetic moments corresponding to one unpaired electron (and see later p. 1055). They have any colour from white to amber or green,[1257] and are soluble in water, the concentrated solution being reddish-brown, and changing on dilution first to orange and then to yellow; the cause of this became evident when the freezing-points and the conductivities of the solutions were measured, for both of these properties showed that there was practically complete hydrolysis to MCl, HCl, and hydrated Mo_2O_5. A similar series of salts is $M[MoOCl_4,H_2O]$, which is also green. The corresponding bromides are known in both series, and are even more easily hydrolysed and oxidized than the chlorides.

Oxybromides

These complexes are of two types, $M[MoOBr_4]$, usually hydrated, and $M_2[MoOBr_5]$, usually anhydrous.[1258-9] Alkaline, alkaline earth, and pyridinium salts are known. They are from dark red to green.

Oxy-halogen Complexes of Pentavalent Tungsten

These are formed with chlorine and bromine but not with fluorine.

Tungsten trioxide dissolved in concentrated HCl can be reduced, either electrolytically[1260] or by bismuth amalgam[1261] to a definite pentavalent state, which is bright blue: the solutions are unstable and oxidize in the

[1252] E. F. Smith and V. Oberholtzer, *J.A.C.S.* 1893, **15**, 26; *Z. anorg. Chem.* 1893, **4**, 243.

[1253] R. G. James and W. Wardlaw, *J.C.S.* 1927, 2145.

[1254] Id., ib. 1928, 2726.   [1255] H. M. Spittle and W. Wardlaw, ib. 2742.

[1256] F. G. Angell, R. G. James, and W. Wardlaw, ib. 1929, 2578.

[1257] C. F. Hiskey and V. W. Meloche, *J.A.C.S.* 1940, **62**, 1819; 1941, **63**, 964.

[1258] R. F. Weinland and W. Knöll, *Z. anorg. Chem.* 1905, **44**, 81.

[1259] A. Rosenheim and M. Koss, ib. 1906, **49**, 148.

[1260] O. Collenberg and J. Backer, *Z. Electrochem.* 1924, **30**, 232.

[1261] K. Someya, *Z. anorg. Chem.* 1925, **145**, 173; 1927, **163**, 207.

air. From these solutions a whole series of salts of the alkalies and of organic bases have been obtained[1262]; they are of two types: $M_2[WOCl_5]$ and $M[WOCl_4]$, both anhydrous and hydrated.* The first class, whether hydrated or not, is a fine green: the second is bright brown when it is anhydrous: the only hydrated salts of this second type, Et_4N and $Pr_4N[WOCl_4],H_2O$ are blue-green.

These salts are stable in dry air; in moist air or in water they are hydrolysed and oxidized, going first blue and finally white. Oxidizing agents such as Cl_2, $KMnO_4$, HNO_3, and H_2O_2 readily and completely convert them into compounds of hexavalent tungsten. The pentavalent oxychlorides $M_2[WOCl_5]$ undergo a remarkable reaction with potassium cyanide, in which they are converted into the octacyanides of tetravalent tungsten, $K_4[WCy_8]$: molybdenum behaves in the same way. It was thought[1263] that oxygen was evolved, but Young has shown [1264] that with tungsten (and no doubt with molybdenum too) this is not so, but the corresponding quantity of tungstate is formed; the essential cause of the reaction is the very remarkable stability of these octacyanides of W^{iv} (and of Mo^{iv}), which is discussed later.

Complex Tungsten Bromides

The salts $M_2[WOBr_5]$ (M = Rb, Cs, NH_4), $Et_4N[WOBr_4],H_2O$, and $(pyH)[WOBr_4]$ have been prepared[1265] in exactly the same way as the chlorides described above; they have the same crystalline form, but are more brownish-yellow in colour. They are stable in dry CO_2, but are more easily hydrolysed than the chlorides; their solutions in concentrated HBr are green, while those of the chlorides in concentrated HCl are blue.

Complex Pentavalent Molybdenum Cyanides

Complex cyanides are highly characteristic of certain valencies, especially 4, of both molybdenum and tungsten, the stable form being the octacyanide $M_4[MoCy_8]$. These have been converted[1264,1266] into the pentavalent molybdenum cyanides by oxidizing the solution with $KMnO_4$, and isolating the product as the silver salt. This was then converted into the K salt $K_3[Mo^vCy_8]$, and also, by the action of HCl, into the free acid $H_3Mo^vCy_8, 3H_2O$. The reaction is very peculiar, because in all other cases permanganate oxidizes the molybdenum to the hexavalent state; the fact that here the oxidation proceeds no farther than the pentavalent must be due to the great stability of this 8-covalent complex of Mo^v, as compared,

* A pyridine salt $(pyH)_2[WOCl_5]H_2O$ is formed when pyridine reacts with WCl_6 in CCl_4 in presence of moisture: the excess of pyridine seems to be chlorinated and so reduce the tungsten. This salt is green.

[1262] See further O. Collenberg, *Z. anorg. Chem.* 1918, **102**, 259; O. Collenberg and A. Guthe, ib. 1924, **134**, 322.
[1263] W. R. Bucknall and W. Wardlaw, *J.C.S.* 1927, 2988.
[1264] R. C. Young, *J.A.C.S.* 1932, **54**, 4515.
[1265] H. Paulssen von Beck, *Z. anorg. Chem.* 1931, **196**, 85.
[1266] O. Olsson, *Ber.* 1914, **47**, 917; *Z. anorg. Chem.* 1914, **88**, 49.

that is, with that of a corresponding Mo^{vi} complex. The pentavalent octacyanides are yellow, very sensitive to light, and very easily reduced.

Complex Pentavalent Tungsten Cyanides

These show exactly the same peculiarities as the molybdenum cyanides. Tungsten forms no simple cyanides at all, nor any complex cyanides of any valencies except 4 and 5 (molybdenum is the same). Here again the only known types are the octacyanides $M_3[WCy_8]$ and $M_4[WCy_8]$. Here too, the tetravalent form is oxidized by permanganate no farther than to the pentavalent state in H_2SO_4 solution, although this reagent oxidizes tungsten in all other known compounds (as it does molybdenum) to the hexavalent state.[1267] Various salts of the pentavalent series are known, as well as the free acid: they are made much in the same way as with molybdenum. If the tetravalent $M_4[WCy_8]$ solution is oxidized and treated with silver nitrate, the red silver salt $Ag_3[WCy_8]$ is precipitated. If this is treated with HCl the free acid $H_3[WCy_8]$, 6 aq. is formed. This consists of orange-yellow crystals and is unstable in air.

Complex Thiocyanates: Molybdenum

These are formed by both elements, and are entirely different in type from the cyanides, never having covalencies above 6. The molybdenum thiocyanates have been examined by James and Wardlaw.[1268] A delicate test for molybdenum is that the solution turns deep red on addition of KCNS, and that the colour is soluble in ether. The nature of this compound was quite unknown. James and Wardlaw were able, by treating the complex Mo^v oxychloride $M_2[MoOCl_5]$ with a thiocyanate, to replace all the Cl atoms by CNS, and obtained two series of salts (1) a red-brown series $M_2[MoO_2(SCN)_3]$, and (2) a dark green series $M_2[MoO(SCN)_5]$. On acidifying the solution and extracting with ether a red ethereal solution was obtained, which on evaporation left behind a red oil, solidifying to an almost black solid. This is the free acid $H_2[MoO_2(SCN)_3]$, 2 H_2O.

All these compounds are highly hydrolysed in water, though thiocyanic acid is a far stronger acid than hydrocyanic.

Tungsten Complex Thiocyanates

So far as they are known these seem to be similar to the molybdenum compounds. Solutions of pentavalent tungsten on addition of thiocyanates give red solutions from which a few salts have been isolated, such as two pyridine salts, apparently $(pyH)_2[WO_2(SCN)_3]$ and $(pyH)_2[WO(SCN)_5]$.[1269]

Chelate Organic Derivatives

These have been investigated with molybdenum, but apparently not with tungsten. Molybdenyl oxalates with pentavalent molybdenum, of

[1267] O. Olsson, *Ber.* 1914, **47**, 917.
[1268] R. G. James and W. Wardlaw, *J.C.S.* 1928, 2726.
[1269] O. Olsson, *Ber.* 1913, **46**, 578.

the type $M[MoO_2Ox]$, xH_2O are known.[1270] The barium and pyridine salts are both red, and are fully hydrolysed in water.

Rosenheim[1271] has made a series of complex salts with catechol and with salicylic acid, etc., of the types

$$M_3[MoOcat_3], x \text{ aq., and } M_2[Mo(OH)_3cat_2], x \text{ aq.}$$

Very similar salts are formed by pentavalent niobium. If the catechol is replaced by a monohydric phenol, such as phenol itself or cresol, the products are of quite a different type, being covalent compounds of the composition $MoCl_2(O \cdot Ar)_3$.

TETRAVALENT COMPOUNDS
Tetrahalides

A TETRAFLUORIDE MoF_4 was reported by Berzelius, but it has not been confirmed.

Molybdenum tetrachloride $MoCl_4$ can be made by heating molybdenum dioxide with a solution of Cl_2 in CCl_4 in a sealed tube at 250°,[1272] or by heating the trichloride $MoCl_3$ to a red heat in a stream of CO_2,[1273] when it is converted into the 'divalent' Mo_6Cl_{12}, which stays behind, and $MoCl_4$ which distils over.

$MoCl_4$ is a brown powder which is easily volatile, forming a yellow vapour. It is not stable. If it is heated in a sealed tube it is partly disproportionated into $MoCl_3$ and $MoCl_5$. It is sensitive to air, light, moisture, and heat. It will not keep even in carbon dioxide. It reacts with water with hissing, and is soluble in, but not decomposed by alcohol: in these hydrolyses it splits up into $MoCl_3 + MoCl_5$ or their decomposition products.

The tetrabromide and tetraiodide have been described, but are not confirmed.

Oxyhalides of tetravalent molybdenum do not seem to have been made.

Tungsten Tetrahalides

While the fluoride and bromide are unknown, not only the chloride but also the iodide have been prepared.

Tungsten tetrachloride can be made by distilling the hexachloride in hydrogen at a sufficiently high temperature. It forms a loose grey-brown mass, and is non-volatile and infusible. It is hygroscopic and hydrolysed by water. If it is heated in air it is converted into the volatile WCl_5 and the non-volatile WCl_2 or W_6Cl_{12}.

Tungsten tetrabromide is unknown, though the divalent, the complex trivalent, and the penta- and hexavalent bromides of tungsten are all

[1270] R. G. James and W. Wardlaw, *J.C.S.* 1927, 2145.
[1271] A. Rosenheim and C. Nernst, *Z. anorg. Chem.* 1933, **214**, 209.
[1272] A. Michael and A. Murphy, *Am. Ch. J.* 1910, **44**, 379.
[1273] See W. Biltz and C. Fendius, *Z. anorg. Chem.* 1928, **172**, 390.

known: and on the other hand the tetraiodide is known, though no other iodide of tungsten except the divalent has been made.

Tungsten tetraiodide WI_4 can be made[1274] by heating WCl_6 with liquid HI in a bomb. It is black, infusible, and not volatile without decomposition. It is reduced by hydrogen below a red heat. Chlorine expels iodine from it in the cold, and bromine at 100° (no doubt forming the penta- or hexahalide). It is insoluble in ether and chloroform, and also in water, which slowly attacks and hydrolyses it. It is decomposed by acids.

Molybdenum Dioxide, MoO_2

This can be obtained by the careful oxidation of molybdenum, or by the action of steam on ignited molybdenum, or by the reduction of the trioxide by passing hydrogen over it at 470°; or by the reduction of molybdates with zinc or in other ways.

It is a brown-violet powder with a copper reflex; the solid is a fairly good conductor of electricity, but not so good as Mo_2O_5. At high temperatures it is oxidized by carbon dioxide,[1275] and it is converted by CCl_4 into the tetrachloride. It takes up chlorine to form the hexavalent oxychloride MoO_2Cl_2, but unlike MoO_3 it will not add on HCl. Also unlike MoO_3 it will not dissolve in alkaline or acid solutions, but it is oxidized by nitric acid, and by silver nitrate (with separation of silver) to MoO_3.

A hydrated form, approximately $Mo(OH)_4$, is precipitated when a molybdate is reduced with hydrogen and palladium[1276]: this on careful drying is converted into MoO_2.

Tungsten Dioxide, WO_2

This is formed by the feeble reduction of the trioxide, as by hydrogen at a low red heat or by heating in CO_2, or with carbon to 1,000°, tungsten blue being usually formed as an intermediate product.

It is a brown powder which melts in an atmosphere of nitrogen at 1,500–1,600°,[1277] and boils at about 1,700°.[1278] Its crystal structure is of the rutile type, as is that of MoO_2.[1279] The distance W—O is 2·00 A (theory 2·03). It is easily oxidized back to WO_3, and is reduced by hydrogen at high temperatures to the metal. Chlorine converts it into the hexavalent WO_2Cl_2, and CCl_4 at 250° into WCl_4. HCl and H_2SO_4 have no action on the dioxide: nitric acid converts it into the trioxide WO_3.

Molybdenum Disulphide, MoS_2

This is molybdenite, the chief ore of molybdenum. The crystal forms a giant molecule with a layer-lattice, in which each Mo has 6 S atoms at

1274 E. Defarqz, *C.R.* 1898, **127**, 510; *Ann. Chim. Phys.* 1901, [7] **22**, 259.

1275 C. Friedheim and M. K. Hoffmann, *Ber.* 1902, **35**, 792.

1276 C. Paal, ib. 1914, **47**, 2214; C. Paal and H. Büttner, ib. 1915, **48**, 220.

1277 E. Friederich and L. Sittig, *Z. anorg. Chem.* 1925, **145**, 134.

1278 E. Alterthum and F. Koref, *Z. Elektrochem.* 1925, **31**, 508.

1279 V. M. Goldschmidt, *Trans. Far. Soc.* 1929, **25**, 259.

the points of a trigonal prism; the distances are Mo—S 2·35 (theory 2·40); Mo···Mo 3·15; S···S 3·08 A.[1280]

The mineral is found in Norway, but mainly in America (especially Colorado and Arizona), and in Queensland. The compound can be made from its elements, from the action of H_2S on the trioxide, or by fusing the trioxide with sulphur and potassium carbonate.

Molybdenum disulphide has a metallic conductivity, at any rate above 200°[1281]; this increases when it is exposed to light. On heating it decomposes to sulphur and molybdenum.[1282]

A similar selenide $MoSe_2$ is known.

Tungsten Disulphide, WS_2

This is formed by heating the trisulphide in the absence of air, or by fusing the trioxide with sulphur and K_2CO_3, or by passing sulphur over tungsten or its trioxide.

It is a soft, dark-grey powder, with the same crystal structure as MoS_2.[1283] It is insoluble in water, and burns in air to WO_3. If it is heated *in vacuo* it loses sulphur at 1,200° and above, and forms metallic tungsten.

A similar selenide has been prepared.[1283]

A dark-grey diamagnetic telluride WTe_2 can be made from the elements at 700°.[1284]

COMPLEXES OF TETRAVALENT MOLYBDENUM AND TUNGSTEN

These are almost confined to the cyanides and a few 'ato' compounds.

Complex Chlorides

If a solution of WO_3 in concentrated HCl is suitably reduced (for example, with tin) it can be made to give the chloride $K_2[W^{IV}(OH)Cl_5]$,[1285] which is a dark-green solid giving a red solution. The solutions are remarkably stable, and can be kept exposed to air for some days, even when very dilute, without change.

No complex bromides are known.

The corresponding molybdenum compounds do not seem to have been prepared.

Complex Tetravalent Cyanides: Molybdenum

These complexes are very characteristic of the tetravalent state of both the elements. This is especially true of the octacyanides $M_4[XCy_8]$. With

[1280] R. G. Dickinson and L. Pauling, *J.A.C.S.* 1923, **45**, 1466; O. Hassel, *Z. Krist.* 1925, **61**, 92 (confirms Dickinson and Pauling).

[1281] C. Tubandt and M. Haedicke, *Z. anorg. Chem.* 1927, **160**, 306.

[1282] N. Parravano and G. Malquori, *Atti R. Linc.* 1928, [vi] **7**, 109.

[1283] V. M. Goldschmidt, *Trans. Far. Soc.* 1929, **25**, 279.

[1284] A. Morette, *C.R.* 1943, **216**, 566.

[1285] A. Rosenheim and R. F. Bernhardi-Grisson, *7th Internat. Congr. Ap. Chem.* 1910, **10**, 123, 125.

molybdenum there are[1286-9] three series of salts: (1) yellow $M_4[MoCy_8]$; (2) red-violet $M_4[MoO_2Cy_4]$, x aq.; (3) a blue series which are obtained by the hydrolysis of salts of series (2), and so must contain tetravalent molybdenum: they probably are $M_3[Mo(OH)_3Cy_4(H_2O)]$, x aq. The first series (in which the central atom has the inert gas number) are remarkably stable,[1287-8] especially among 8-covalent compounds. They are formed from trivalent or pentavalent molybdenum by the action of a large excess of KCN. The potassium salt $K_4[MoCy_8]$ 2 H_2O is yellow, and with concentrated HCl gives the free acid $H_4[MoCy_8]$ 6 H_2O, also yellow. Type (2) is formed with a smaller excess of KCN. See further reference [1291]. They are diamagnetic.[1290]

This is the first 8-covalent complex whose shape has been determined. X-ray investigation showed[1292] that the anion of $K_4[Mo^{iv}(CN)_8]$, 2 H_2O is not a cube or a twisted cube (antiprism), but is dodecahedral[1293-4] (for figure see original paper).

Hölzl[1289] finds that if the octacyanide is treated with methyl sulphate it is methylated: this is a way of saying that it is converted into a co-ordination compound of MeNC, which, as a fact, is of a different type, being $[MoCy_4(CH_3 \cdot NC)_2(OH_2)_2]$, 4 H_2O. When treated with KCN this is reconverted into the octacyanide.

Complex Cyanides of Tetravalent Tungsten

These are very similar to the molybdenum compounds. The main series are the octacyanides $M_4[WCy_8]$, which are yellow, stable to air, and in solution neutral to litmus. The remarkable fact that these octacyanides of tetravalent molybdenum or tungsten are oxidized by permanganate in acid solution only up to the pentavalent stage has been disputed, but it has been confirmed.[1295-7]

Complex Tetravalent Thiocyanates

These have been prepared with molybdenum, and, as with the pentavalent compounds, they are entirely different to the cyanides, and do not go beyond a co-ordination number of 6.

[1286] A. Rosenheim, *Z. anorg. Chem.* 1907, **54**, 97.

[1287] O. Collenberg, ib. 1922, **121**, 298.

[1288] W. R. Bucknall and W. Wardlaw, *J.C.S.* 1927, 2981.

[1289] F. Hölzl and G. I. Xenakis, *Mon.* 1927, **48**, 689.

[1290] W. Klemm and H. Steinberg, *Z. anorg. Chem.* 1936, **227**, 193.

[1291] H. H. Willard and R. C. Thielke, *J.A.C.S.* 1935, **57**, 2609.

[1292] J. L. Hoard and H. H. Nordsieck, ib. 1939, **61**, 2853.

[1293] For the theory of the structure of $[Mo(CN)_8]^{4-}$ see C. Racah, *J. Chem. Phys.* 1943, **11**, 214.

[1294] For 8-co-ordination in general see L. E. Marchi, *J.A.C.S.* 1943, **65**, 2257.

[1295] O. Olsson, *Ber.* 1914, **47**, 917; *Z. anorg. Chem.* 1914, **88**, 54.

[1296] A. Rosenheim and E. Dehn, *Ber.* 1915, **48**, 1170.

[1297] O. O. Collenberg (this is the same person as O. Olsson), *Z. anorg. Chem.* 1922, **121**, 281, 298.

The compounds $M_2[Mo(SCN)_6]$ can be made[1298-9] by oxidizing the corresponding compounds of trivalent molybdenum with potassium ferricyanide.

Complex Oxalates

These are known in the molybdenum series: they differ from most of the other complexes in that they are oxy-salts ('yl' salts), with some oxide-oxygen attached to the molybdenum. They are all highly complex, containing 3 or 4 atoms of molybdenum in the molecule[1300]; even the apparently simple molybdenyl oxalate, with the composition $MoO(C_2O_4)$, $3H_2O$ has been shown[1300] to be really complex, and probably triple, with the formula $H_2[Mo_3O_4(C_2O_4)_3]$, $8H_2O$, this being the form from which many of the salts are derived. This complexity is also supported by the conductivities of the salts.

TRIVALENT MOLYBDENUM
Trihalides

THE trifluoride MoF_3 is not certain. Complex salts derived from it are well known (see below, p. 1059).

Molybdenum Trichloride

This can be made by passing the vapour of the pentachloride over heated molybdenum, or more conveniently[1301] by heating the pentachloride to 250° in a stream of hydrogen. It forms dark-red crystals which are insoluble in water and are not hydrolysed by it in the cold, so that the crude product can be freed from other chlorides by grinding with water.

An aqueous solution of the trichloride can be obtained by electrolysing a solution of molybdenum trioxide in HCl; it is purplish-red, and alkaline chlorides precipitate red complex salts such as $K_3[MoCl_6]$ (p. 1059).

$MoCl_3$ is almost non-volatile; at a red heat in dry CO_2 it is converted into the tetrachloride $MoCl_4$ and the dichloride Mo_3Cl_6. In dry air it is slowly oxidized and, if the air is not quite dry, slowly hydrolysed.

It forms ammines with ammonia, methylamine, and pyridine, mostly of the form $MoCl_3 + 2$ or 3 molecules amine.

Molybdenum Tribromide, $MoBr_3$

This can be made from the elements, best at 350–400°.[1301] It forms dark-green or black needles. It is insoluble in ordinary solvents, but easily dissolves in pyridine to form a dark-brown solution, from which the compound $MoBr_3$, 3 py can be obtained. Gaseous ammonia completely converts it, even at low temperatures, into metallic molybdenum.

[1298] A. Rosenheim and A. Garfunkel, *Ber.* 1908, **41**, 2386.
[1299] G. A. Barbieri, *Atti R. Linc.* 1930, [6] **12**, 55.
[1300] H. M. Spittle and W. Wardlaw, *J.C.S.* 1929, 792.
[1301] A. Rosenheim, G. Abel, and R. Lewy, *Z. anorg. Chem.* 1931, **197**, 200.

Oxyhalides of Trivalent Molybdenum

These are formed by all the three lighter halogens, and are hydrated to the same extent, forming $MoO(hal)$, $4 H_2O$.

The fluoride $MoOF$, $4 H_2O$ is made[1302] by treating the chlorine compound with ammonium fluoride.

$MoOCl$, $4 H_2O$. This occurs in two presumably stereomeric forms, one brown and the other green.[1303-4] They are both made by reducing MoO_3 electrolytically and precipitating with acetone in an atmosphere of CO_2 in complete absence of air. The freezing-points in water and the conductivities of the solution show that both forms first dissolve in water as non-electrolytes, and then slowly hydrolyse, the green form rather quicker than the brown.

The brown form is easily oxidized in the air, and easily soluble in water; the solution reduces cupric and mercuric salts to cuprous and mercurous, ferric to ferrous, and silver nitrate to metallic silver. The green form behaves in much the same way, but is far more reactive. Wardlaw points out that if we assume an octahedral arrangement of the 6-covalent $O \leftarrow Mo — Cl$, $4 H_2O$, a *cis* and a *trans* structure are possible; from the behaviour of the two forms with sodium salicylate[1304] he concludes that the green is the *trans* form.

$MoOBr$, $4 H_2O$. This is similar to the chloride, but only the brown form is known.[1304-5]

Molybdenum Sesquioxide, Mo_2O_3

The existence of this oxide has been doubted,[1306] but it is fairly certain that it or its hydroxide exists. Alkalies precipitate from a solution of trivalent molybdenum a black powder which has a composition very near to $Mo(OH)_3$; it is very slightly soluble in acids, and is oxidized by the air to MoO_3.[1307]

Molybdenum Sesquisulphide, Mo_2S_3

This cannot be made by the reduction of the disulphide with hydrogen, as that proceeds the whole way to the formation of the metal; but it can be prepared by heating the disulphide in an electric furnace either alone, or mixed with lime and calcium fluoride.[1308] It consists of steel-grey needles.

A similar selenide is known.

[1302] W. Wardlaw and R. L. Wormell, *J.C.S.* 1927, 1089.
[1303] Id., ib. 1924, **125**, 2370.
[1304] Id., ib. 1927, **130**, 1090.
[1305] W. Wardlaw and A. J. I. Harding, ib. 1926, 1592.
[1306] M. Guichard, *Ann. Chim. Phys.* 1901, [7] **23**, 549.
[1307] W. Muthmann and W. Nagel, *Ber.* 1898, **31**, 2012; C. Paal and H. Büttner, ib. 1915, **48**, 220.
[1308] W. Muthmann and A. Mai, *Ann.* 1907, **355**, 111.

Oxy-salts of Trivalent Molybdenum

The electrolytic reduction of solutions of MoO_3 in H_2SO_4 gives rise to red and green solutions.[1309] The difference between these is obscure, but the green solution is further reduced 2,000 times as quickly as the red.[1310] In the same way a sulphate $Mo_2O(SO_4)_2$, $5 H_2O$ can be made, as well as other more complex compounds.

An oxy-oxalate $Mo_2O(C_2O_4)_2$, $6 H_2O$ is also known.[1311]

Trivalent Tungsten

All the trivalent compounds we have so far discussed have been compounds of molybdenum. Now it is a general rule that in any A subgroup as the atomic weight increases the lower valencies become less stable. This effect is very marked with tungsten; the difference in stability between molybdenum and tungsten is small when their valencies are 6, 5, or even 4, but considerable in the trivalent compounds. The trivalent tungsten compounds are confined to the complexes, and these are of a complicated kind, with two tungsten atoms in the molecule.

Trivalent tungsten forms no halides, no oxide,[1312] and no sulphide. In fact, there are no tungsten analogues to any of the trivalent molybdenum compounds which we have so far discussed. The only known tungsten compounds of this valency are a group of salts of the acid $H_3W_2Cl_9$, which are usually regarded as complexes derived from an (unknown) chloride W_2Cl_6, which is assumed to be a polymer of WCl_3, and so to contain trivalent tungsten. On the other hand, the complex compounds of trivalent molybdenum, which are fairly numerous, do not include this type of complex at all, but like the tetravalent complexes are mainly the halides (of the usual types), the cyanides, and the thiocyanates.

COMPLEXES OF TRIVALENT MOLYBDENUM

Complex Halides

Fluorides. These are of the type of $K[MoF_4]$, H_2O, which is pale violet: the ammonium salt is similar. They are made by adding the alkaline fluoride to a solution of MoO_3 which has been reduced electrolytically.[1313]

Chlorides. These are got in the same way by adding HCl and an alkaline chloride to an electrolytically reduced MoO_3 solution. They are of two types (not including the above fluoride type) $M_3[MoCl_6]$ and $M_2[MoCl_5, H_2O]$.[1314] They are both brick-red, and in solution are strong reducing agents.

[1309] W. Wardlaw and N. D. Sylvester, *J.C.S.* 1923, **123**, 971.

[1310] G. Bredig and J. Michel, *Z. physikal. Chem.* 1922, **100**, 136.

[1311] W. Wardlaw and W. H. Parker, *J.C.S.* 1927, 1312; see also Wardlaw *et al.*, ib. 512, 519.

[1312] See J. A. M. van Liempt, *Rec. Trav.* 1931, **50**, 343.

[1313] A. Rosenheim and H. J. Braun, *Z. anorg. Chem.* 1905, **46**, 320.

[1314] F. Foerster and E. Fricke, *Z. angew. Chem.* 1923, **36**, 458.

The conductivities and freezing-points in water show that these salts first dissolve according to the formulae given above, and then slowly hydrolyse[1315] like MoOCl itself (p. 1058).

Some of these trivalent molybdenum complexes are isomorphous with ferric compounds.[1316] Both the potassium and the ammonium salts $M_2[MoCl_5, H_2O]$ are isomorphous with those of M_2FeCl_5, H_2O; further, the potassium salts form solid solutions containing up to 17 per cent. of the molybdenum compound, and the ammonium up to 10 per cent.

Trivalent Molybdenum Thiocyanate Complexes

The double salts $M_3[Mo(SCN)_6]$ are obtained by the electrolytic reduction of MoO_3 solution in presence of KCNS: they are yellow, and some of them are isomorphous with the chromic compounds.

Cyanides

If the chloride $K_3[MoCl_6]$ is treated with KCN solution in air-free water in an atmosphere of nitrogen, the salt $K_4[Mo(CN)_7, H_2O]$ separates.[1317] It is interesting to see how here, too, the CN group (apparently alone of acid radicals) is able to raise the co-ordination number of the molybdenum to 8.

Complex Halides of Trivalent Tungsten

If sodium tungstate is reduced electrolytically in HCl strong enough to prevent hydrolysis of the products, a series of salts can be got of the formula $M_3[W_2Cl_9]$.[1318-19] The free acid is known only in solution; this is obtained by the action of HI on the thallous salt. It is a strong acid which expels CO_2 from a carbonate, and it is green. The salts are numerous, and can be divided into several groups.

1. $M_3[W_2Cl_9]$: M = NH_4, K, Rb, Cs, Tl'. These are greenish-yellow, and can be recrystallized from water or dilute HCl: they are anhydrous, and are fairly stable when dry. The solubility falls off rapidly from NH_4 to Tl', which last is almost insoluble.

2. Salts of ammine-cations such as $Co(NH_3)_6'''$, $Cr(NH_3)_6'''$, and $Ag(NH_3)_2'$. These are stable also when dry, but are slowly hydrolysed by water, in which they are only slightly soluble. This slow hydrolysis, and a slow oxidation by air, are common to both types of salts.

It has been shown by Young[1320] that these salts undergo two remarkable reactions. If the aqueous solutions, say of the potassium salt of type 1, is heated, the salt decomposes the water with the evolution of hydrogen, and the formation of a higher valency of the tungsten: a black solid is

[1315] See W. R. Bucknall, S. R. Carter, and W. Wardlaw, *J.C.S.* 1927, 515.

[1316] G. Carobbi, *Gaz.* 1928, **58**, 35.

[1317] R. C. Young, *J.A.C.S.* 1932, **54**, 1402.

[1318] O. Olsson, *Ber.* 1913, **46**, 566.

[1319] O. Olsson-Collenberg and K. Sandved, *Z. anorg. Chem.* 1923, **130**, 16.

[1320] R. C. Young, *J.A.C.S.* 1932, **54**, 4517.

precipitated, which is said to be W_5O_9 (valency 3·6). The same reaction occurs in the cold in the presence of KOH, but unless the concentration of the KOH is at least 50 per cent., the reaction is not complete.

The second curious reaction is that when $K_3[W_2Cl_9]$ is treated with KCN in an atmosphere of nitrogen, it is oxidized to the tetravalent tungsten compound $K_4[WCy_8]$ no hydrogen is evolved, but the required oxygen is got from the HCN, which is hydrolysed to formic acid and this partly reduced to formaldehyde, which can actually be detected.

These compounds, as has been said, are peculiar to tungsten. Their existence and their reactions obviously depend on the structure of the W_2Cl_9''' ion. This has lately been examined by X-ray methods. Brosset[1321] has shown that the salts $M_3[W_2Cl_9]$, where M = NH_4, K, Rb, Cs, and Tl', which are coloured, but not very strongly, are all isomorphous; the shape of the anion is this:

It is formed of two WCl_6 octahedra, with a face in common. The W··W distance is only 2·46 A, which is even less than that (2·74) in metallic tungsten. These results have been confirmed by Jürg Waser in Pauling's laboratory.[1322] The substance is diamagnetic. From the very short W··W distance Pauling concludes[1322] that there is a covalent link, between single and double, joining the two tungsten atoms, which in that case would be at least tetravalent, so that trivalent tungsten would disappear; he also points out the remarkable similarity in structure between this ion and the carbonyl $Fe_2(CO)_9$ (VIII. 1369).

DIVALENT MOLYBDENUM AND TUNGSTEN

THE existence of these valencies is based on the 'dihalides' of the compositions MoX_2, WX_2, which are certainly polymerized, and whose molecular weights and constitutions have only recently been established.

Divalent Molybdenum

The so-called dichloride and dibromide of molybdenum are very remarkable substances; one-third of their halogen is much more easily removed than the rest, as was pointed out by their discoverer Blomstrand,[1326] so that the formulae must be multiplied at least by 3, which would give

[1321] C. Brosset, *Nature*, 1935, **135**, 874; Id., *Arkiv Kemi, Min., Geol.* 1936, **12 A**, no. 4. [This latter paper gives the data on which the crystal structure is based.]
[1322] L. Pauling, *Chem. and Eng. News*, 1947, 2970 (Oct. 13).
[1323] I. Koppel, *Z. anorg. Chem.* 1912, **77**, 289.
[1324] K. Lindner, E. Haller, and H. Helwig, ib. 1923, **130**, 209.
[1325] W. Biltz and C. Fendius, ib. 1928, **172**, 389.
[1326] C. W. Blomstrand, *J. prakt. Chem.* 1859, **77**, 89, 97; 1861, **82**, 437.

$Mo_3X_4(Cl_4)$.[1323-5] Recent work[1322,1329-30] has shown that the polymerization is really sixfold, and the formulae are $Mo_6X_8[X_4]$; the structure of this complex cation has been determined.

Molybdenum dichloride Mo_6Cl_{12} is made by the action of the halogen on the heated metal, or by heating the trichloride $MoCl_3$ in a stream of CO_2, when it breaks down into $MoCl_4$ which volatilizes, and Mo_6Cl_{12} which stays behind.[1325] Another rather remarkable but very effective method[1324] is to heat metallic molybdenum in phosgene at 630°.

Mo_6Cl_{12} is a yellow powder, infusible and non-volatile, which is quite insoluble in water but reacts with it slowly; it is also insoluble in toluene, ligroin, and acetic acid, but soluble in alcohol and ether.

The compounds are remarkable for their extraordinary stability, especially to oxidation; they are not acted on by dilute acids, and they have, even in solution, practically no reducing power. The bromide, as we shall see, is even more inert than the chloride.

The looser attachment (presumably ionic) of one-third of the halogen atoms is shown in various ways. Thus the chloride dissolves, to give a yellow solution, in concentrated HCl, HBr, and HI, and from the solution can be obtained $[Mo_6Cl_8](hal)_4$, $6 H_2O$, where 'hal' is the halogen of the acid used, Cl, Br, or I. So, too, when the chloride is treated with silver nitrate, instead of the silver being reduced to the metal, as we should expect, double decomposition occurs, with the formation of the nitrate $[Mo_6Cl_8](NO_3)_4$.[1324] It also dissolves in alkali, and the hydroxide

$$[Mo_6Cl_8](OH)_4, 14 H_2O$$

crystallizes out, or can be precipitated with CO_2 or acetic acid: this consists of yellow crystals, and two of the water molecules appear to form part of the complex, since only the rest can be removed in a desiccator.

From the HCl solution can also be crystallized a compound of the composition Mo_6Cl_{12}, $2 HCl$, $8 H_2O$ which is probably to be written $H_2[Mo_6Cl_8]Cl_6$, $8 H_2O$, as a double chloride of hydrogen and the complex cation, as is shown by its forming the pyridine salt[1324]; the acid is stable in an atmosphere of HCl, but soon loses HCl in air.

Molybdenum dibromide, also discovered by Blomstrand, is very similar to the chloride; it is made[1327] by heating the metal in bromine vapour in a stream of nitrogen; since the higher bromides are decomposed between 600° and 700°, it is more easily got pure than the chloride.

It is a yellow-red amorphous powder, infusible, and even more indifferent to acids than the chloride: it is not soluble in the halogen hydrides, as the chloride is, nor is it perceptibly decomposed even by boiling aqua regia. This difference is probably due to a difference in solubility rather than in chemical characteristics. The bromide is soluble in alkalies, and on adding excess of HBr the hydrated bromide Mo_6Br_{12}, $6 H_2O$ crystal-

[1327] K. Lindner and H. Helwig, *Z. anorg. Chem.* 1925, **142**, 181.

lizes out; this is very similar in behaviour to the hydrate of the chloride. The bromide, like the chloride, behaves as the dihalide of a weak tetra-acid base $[Mo_6Br_8](OH)_4$, which can actually be prepared (with 16 H_2O), as can also a whole series of derivatives $Mo_6Br_8X_4$, x H_2O, where X = F, Cl, NO_3, or X_2 = SO_4, CrO_4, MoO_4, C_2O_4.

The iodide MoI_2 or Mo_6I_{12} described by Berzelius, was probably a mixture.[1328]

The structure of this $[Mo_6X_8]^{4+}$ cation has been elucidated by the X-ray examination by Brosset[1329] of $[Mo_6Cl_8](OH)_4$, 14 H_2O and $[Mo_6Cl_8]Cl_4$, 8 H_2O (see further refs. [1322,1330]). In the cation the 8 chlorine atoms are at the corners of a cube, with the 6 molybdenum atoms slightly above the centres of the 6 faces. Presumably each Cl has the

links Cl⟨→, and each Mo is divalent and 4-covalent with an E.A.N. of 48.

The Mo··Mo distance is, however, only 2·64 A, which certainly suggests that there may be an Mo—Mo link (theory 2·72); this would make the molybdenum trivalent.

Tungsten Dihalides

These are very like the molybdenum compounds, but are much less stable.

Tungsten Dichloride. This is formed by reducing the hexachloride WCl_6 with hydrogen or with 3 per cent. sodium amalgam, or by heating the tetrachloride WCl_4.[1331-2]

It is a grey powder, non-volatile and infusible. It is unstable in air, evolves hydrogen with water, and in general behaves as a strong reducing agent: for example, if it is heated in the vapour of nitric acid it produces large quantities of ammonium salt. This is quite unlike the molybdenum dihalides, which have practically no reducing power at all: in fact the resemblance between the dihalides of the two elements goes no further than that both are non-volatile and infusible: but there is greater resemblance between the complexes, which makes it fairly certain that the tungsten dihalides have the same sixfold structure as those of molybdenum and are $W_6(hal)_{12}$.

Tungsten Dibromide. This can be made by reducing the pentabromide with hydrogen at the temperature of a zinc chloride bath (Roscoe). It behaves just like the chloride.[1333] With potassamide it forms a peculiar compound $W(NK)_2NH_2$, also produced from WBr_5.[1334]

Tungsten Di-iodide. It is curious that although the dihalides of tungsten are much less stable than those of molybdenum, tungsten will form a

[1328] M. Guichard, *C.R.* 1896, **123**, 821; *Ann. Chim. Phys.* 1901, [7] **23**, 565.
[1329] C. Brosset, *Arkiv. Kem. Min. Geol.* 1945, **20** A, No. 7; 1946, **22** A, No. 11.
[1330] H. M. Powell, *Ann. Rep. Chem. Soc.* 1946, **43**, 95.
[1331] K. Lindner and A. Köhler, *Ber.* 1922, **55**, 1461; *Z. anorg. Chem.* 1924, **140**, 357.
[1332] W. Biltz and C. Fendius, ib. 1928, **172**, 388.
[1333] H. A. Schaffer and E. F. Smith, *J.A.C.S.* 1896, **18**, 1098.
[1334] F. W. Bergstrom, ib. 1925, **47**, 2317, 2322.

di-iodide which molybdenum probably will not. Tungsten di-iodide is made by passing iodine vapour over red-hot tungsten, or HI over WCl_6 at 400–450°.[1335-6] It is a brown powder, which is not fusible and cannot be volatilized without decomposition. It is insoluble in cold water: hot water at once hydrolyses and oxidizes it. Aqueous HF or HCl attack it slowly, alkaline solutions at once.

Monoxides of Molybdenum and Tungsten

It is very improbable that either of these compounds exist, at any rate as separable substances. The black precipitate which Blomstrand obtained by the action of alkalies of solutions of derivatives of molybdenum dihalides, was really a trivalent molybdenum compound. Also the spectrum of MoO_3 gives no indication of the presence of a monoxide.[1337]

Tungsten monoxide WO, according to Langmuir,[1338] may exist in the film of oxide formed on the surface of a hot tungsten wire in O_2.

Divalent Molybdenum Complexes[1339]

These are all derivatives of the 'dihalides' Mo_6X_{12}, and are formed from the Mo_6Cl_8 ion by co-ordination; but until the X-ray data are available we cannot say exactly what their structures are. They are formed by the dichloride and dibromide alike. The acid

$$H_2[Mo_6Cl_{14}(H_2O)_2],\ 6\,H_2O$$

made by treating a solution of the dichloride with hydrochloric acid has two molecules of water much more firmly attached than the other six. In water it gives at first a clear yellow solution, in which, however, it is hydrolysed, and a sudden precipitate containing all the molybdenum separates. A series of salts can be obtained from this chloro-acid. It forms a very stable pyridine salt $(pyH)_2[Mo_6Cl_{14}(H_2O)_2]$.

The pyridine salts obtained from alcoholic solution

$$(pyH)_6[Mo_6Cl_{18}),\ 6\,ROH\ (R\ =\ CH_3,\ C_2H_5,\ C_5H_{11}),$$

give on heating $(pyH)_2[Mo_6Cl_{14}]$. Again, if the acid is treated in HCl with alkaline chlorides it forms a series of derivatives

$$M_2[Mo_6Cl_{14}(H_2O)_2],\ 4\,H_2O\ (M\ =\ K,\ NH_4,\ urea + H,\ M_2\ =\ en + 2H).$$

These are the main complex salts of divalent molybdenum. It is possible to prepare the corresponding bromides, and in the chlorides it is easy to replace all the halogen atoms but eight by bromine, as in the salt $M_2[Mo_6Cl_8Br_6]$. It is obvious that the complex anion has a core $Mo_6(hal)_8$, to which 6 Cl, 6 Cl$+$2 H_2O, or 10 Cl are attached in the different salts.

[1335] E. Defacqz, *C.R.* 1898, **126**, 962; *Ann. Chim. Phys.* 1901, [7] **22**, 259.

[1336] A. Rosenheim and E. Dehn, *Ber.* 1915, **48**, 1168.

[1337] G. Piccardi, *Atti. R. Linc.* 1933, [vi] **17**, 654.

[1338] *Phys. Z.* 1914, **15**, 520.

[1339] K. Lindner, E. Haller, and H. Helwig, *Z. anorg. Chem.* 1923, **130**, 214.

Complexes of Divalent Tungsten

As with divalent molybdenum, these are formed only by the chlorides and bromides, and are all built up on a basis $[W_6(hal)_8]^{4+}$, forming most commonly the type $M_2[W_6Cl_{14}, 2 H_2O]$, or the corresponding bromine compound.

In the preparation of these complexes WCl_6 is reduced either by heating with aluminium with the addition of silica to moderate the reaction,[1340-2] or by sodium amalgam.[1342] The product is extracted with HCl and evaporated: the residue is saturated with HCl gas, and the hydrogen compound (the 'chloro-acid') separates in yellow needles. The acid is most probably[1341] $H_2[W_6Cl_{14}(H_2O)_2]$, 6 H_2O, like the molybdenum compound. Its only certain salt is that of pyridine: this smaller stability of the tungsten complexes as compared with those of molybdenum is to be expected in the divalent state. The acid in a desiccator easily loses all its water molecules but two, together with two HCl, giving W_6Cl_{12}, 2 H_2O. The acid is more reactive than the molybdenum compound, the chlorine being much more easily hydrolysed, with a break up of the complex.[1342] It is soluble in water and slowly hydrolysed. The smaller stability as compared with molybdenum is shown by its behaviour with alcoholic silver nitrate; with this reagent the molybdenum acid loses 6 HCl and gives $Mo_6Cl_8(NO_3)_4$: but the tungsten acid has all its chlorine precipitated, and is then oxidized by the excess of $AgNO_3$ with separation of silver. The tungsten compound is more stable to sulphuric acid, which only oxidizes it above $100°$: below that temperature it acts like the molybdenum acid, and has two chlorines replaced to give $W_6Cl_8(SO_4)_2$.

The action of alkalies on the acid is very instructive. They first dissolve it to form a yellow solution, but very soon the complex breaks up, and at the same time the tungsten is oxidized, with evolution of hydrogen; it is clear that the tungsten can only remain in this state of valency so long as this complex with six tungsten atoms persists; when the alkali breaks it up by removing the chlorine atoms the separate tungsten atoms are at once oxidized by the water (even in alkaline solution).

Thus the tungsten complex resembles its molybdenum analogue very closely: they both have the same behaviour on heating, the same preferential ionization of one-third of the halogen atoms, and the same slow hydrolysis by water and stability to HCl. The main difference is the greater instability of tungsten to alkalies: the amphoteric hydroxide $[Mo_6Cl_8(H_2O)_4](OH)_4$ is stable to and dissolves in alkalies, while the corresponding tungsten compound is at once broken up and destroyed. This difference is in agreement with that observed between the dichlorides themselves, that the molybdenum compound is so stable that it has no reducing properties, while W_6Cl_{12} is able even to reduce water, with evolution of hydrogen.

[1340] K. Lindner and A. Köhler, *Ber.* 1922, **55**, 1464.
[1341] Id., *Z. anorg. Chem.* 1924, **140**, 358.
[1342] J. B. Hill, *J.A.C.S.* 1916, **38**, 2385.

Bromine Complexes of Divalent Tungsten

The mixed chlorine-bromine complexes mentioned above can be made from the chloro-acid by treatment with concentrated boiling HBr.[1343] On cooling, the acid $H_2[W_6Br_8Cl_6(H_2O)_2]$, $18\ H_2O$ crystallizes out. Its solubility, its hydrolysis, and its instability to alkalies are almost identical with those of the chlorine compound. A pyridine salt $(pyH)_2[W_6Br_8Cl_6]$ can be prepared, though (like the chlorine compound) not directly.

MOLYBDENUM AND TUNGSTEN CARBONYLS

THESE compounds belong to the same type as the chromium carbonyl $Cr(CO)_6$ already described; they no doubt have the same structure; they have the same E.A.N. of the next inert gas, and the same general properties, though they are not quite so stable.

Molybdenum Carbonyl, $Mo(CO)_6$

This compound was first made[1344] by the action of carbon monoxide under not less than 150 atm. on molybdenum at 200°. Klemm[1345] showed that it definitely had the formula $Mo(CO)_6$. Hieber[1346-8] made it like the chromium compound (p. 1026) by the action of carbon monoxide on the chloride in the presence of phenyl magnesium bromide.

The carbonyl is driven over from the products with steam.

$Mo(CO)_6$ boils at 156·4°,[1347] but has a considerable vapour pressure well below its boiling-point, and can be sublimed in hydrogen or CO_2 at 30° or 40°. The vapour begins to decompose about 150°. With oxidizing agents, and especially with halogens, CO is evolved and molybdenum salts are formed.

Like other carbonyls it readily forms ammines[1348] by the replacement of successive carbonyl groups by amines: thus we get

$Mo(CO)_3py_3$	$Mo(CO)_4Phthr.$	$Mo(CO)_3py,Phthr.$	$Mo_2(CO)_6en_3$
Yellow-brown	Deep red	Red-black	Pale yellow
	[Phthr. = o-phenanthroline]		

It is remarkable that of these amines the one which has the weakest power of co-ordination is ethylene diamine: while pyridine acts on $Mo(CO)_6$ at 80–85°, ethylene diamine will only expel CO above 180°. Ethylene diamine is normally one of the strongest amminating agents; but that is when it attaches itself to one central atom as a chelate group, and has the stability which chelation involves. Here we see its natural weakness when it has to link two groups, and does not form a ring.

[1343] K. Lindner and A. Köhler, *Z. anorg. Chem.* 1924, **140**, 364.

[1344] L. Mond, H. Hirtz, and M. D. Cowap, *J.C.S.* 1910, **97**, 808; *Z. anorg. Chem.* 1910, **68**, 217.

[1345] W. Klemm, H. Jacobi, and W. Tilk, ib. 1931, **201**, 14.

[1346] W. Hieber and E. Romberg, ib. 1935, **221**, 321.

[1347] Id., ib. 332.   [1348] W. Hieber and F. Mühlhauer, ib. **337**.

Tungsten Carbonyl, $W(CO)_6$

This was first made by Job[1349] like the chromium compound, by the action of $\Phi \cdot Mg \cdot Br$ on WCl_6 in solution in ether and benzene, in an atmosphere of CO. Hieber[1350-1] showed that at low temperatures a 20 per cent. yield can be obtained. He examined[1351] the thermal properties of the three carbonyls.

$W(CO)_6$ is a colourless crystalline solid, which begins to sublime at 50° and boils at 175° C.[1351] It is decomposed by heating, especially if it is impure, and also by fuming nitric acid, but not by water or by ordinary acids.

In almost every point the tungsten compound behaves like the other two, although like the molybdenum compound it is not quite so stable as the chromium carbonyl. But it is clearly more stable than either the nickel compound $Ni(CO)_4$, or the iron $Fe(CO)_5$.

Summary: Molybdenum and Tungsten

A brief comparison of these two similar elements in their various valencies may be useful.

Hexavalent Compounds. This is the most stable state for both. Of the halides molybdenum gives only MoF_6, while we have WF_6, WCl_6, and WBr_6; a stronger affinity for bromine than for the lighter halogens often distinguishes tungsten from molybdenum though the sizes of the ions (1·36 : 1·37 A) are practically the same. The oxyfluorides of molybdenum are more and the oxychlorides less stable than those of tungsten.

The trioxides and their derivatives—acids, thio-acids, etc.—are very similar for both.

Pentavalent Compounds. These are definitely less stable with tungsten than with molybdenum. There are no pentafluorides, but molybdenum gives $MoCl_5$, and tungsten WCl_5 and WBr_5; but while there is probably an Mo_2O_5 and certainly an Mo_2S_5, there is no W_2S_5, and probably no W_2O_5. There are oxyfluoride complexes of molybdenum but not tungsten; oxychlorides of both; oxybromides of tungsten but not molybdenum. Both elements give octacyanide complexes, so stable that permanganate will not oxidize them to the hexavalent state.

Tetravalent Compounds. Here there is very little difference between the two elements. Tetrahalides, dicalcides, oxyhalides, and octacyanides are given by both, and in each type the two are about equally stable.

Trivalent Compounds. Here on the contrary there is scarcely any likeness between molybdenum and tungsten. Trivalent molybdenum forms non-volatile trihalides, an oxide, sulphide, and selenide; also complex halides, and 8-covalent double cyanides $M_4[Mo(CN)_7OH_2]$: all these are quite definite, though they are easily oxidized.

[1349] A. Job and J. Rouvillois, *C.R.* 1928, **187**, 564.
[1350] W. Hieber and E. Romberg, *Z. anorg. Chem.* 1935, **221**, 321.
[1351] Id., ib. **332**.

Trivalent tungsten forms none of these compounds at all; it only occurs in a group of salts of the complex acid $H_3[W_2Cl_9]$, to which there are no molybdenum analogues.

Divalent Compounds. With both elements these are confined to the 'dihalides' $(A_6hal_8)hal_4$ and their derivatives, including the salts

$$M_2[A_6hal_{14}(H_2O)_2].$$

All these occur with both, and the structure of the group A_6hal_8'''', which is known with molybdenum, must be the same with tungsten. But this group is much less stable with tungsten than with molybdenum.

URANIUM

URANIUM is of unusual interest, for several reasons. Except for radium and thorium, whose chemical properties are almost wholly ionic, it is (or was until lately) the only element in the last period whose chemistry is known in any detail, and this is in many ways different from that of the other members of the VIth Group. In addition, its nuclear transformations, especially under bombardment, are of fundamental importance; they include the phenomenon of atomic fission—the breaking up of the nucleus into fragments nearly of the same size—making part of the nuclear energy available as a source of power or for the atomic bomb; and they lead to the formation of the trans-uranium elements 93–6 (93 neptunium, 94 plutonium, 95 americium, 96 curium), which for the first time give clear evidence of the opening of the 'second rare earth series', the 'uranides', through the expansion of the fifth quantum group from 18 towards 32.

The nuclear transformations of uranium are partly spontaneous, giving neighbouring elements, and partly induced by collision, leading sometimes to atomic fission, and sometimes to the formation of the trans-uranium elements 93–6. These new elements will be discussed after uranium, and all the nuclear changes of uranium (and its isotopic constitution) will be dealt with along with them (p. 1090).

The extreme importance of uranium as a source of atomic energy both for peace and for war has led to a very large amount of work being done in the last few years on the physical and chemical properties of this and the succeeding elements; some of this work has been or is being published, but much of it has not yet been released for publication. I have tried to bring the following account up-to-date as far as possible, and I am very much indebted to Dr. C. D. Coryell, of the Massachusetts Institute of Technology, and to Dr. M. W. Lister, of Harwell, for the help they have given me; but new papers are appearing almost daily,* and many of the statements will need modification and amplification by the time they are in print.

Uranium was discovered by Klaproth in 1789, and named after the planet Uranus, which had been discovered by Herschel in 1781. Its chief ore is pitchblende, which is U_3O_8 containing small quantities of other oxides. This can be converted by treatment with concentrated nitric acid into uranyl nitrate $UO_2(NO_3)_2$, which can be purified by recrystallization and on heating leaves a residue of the trioxide UO_3. Pitchblende is found in Cornwall, in St. Joachimsthal in Czechoslovakia, in Colorado, near the Bear Lake in Canada, and in the Belgian Congo; many other sources have been discovered in the last few years. Except as a source of atomic energy and of radium, uranium is of small practical use. The metal is not used

---

* A series were read at the Chicago meeting of the American Chemical Society at Easter 1948, abstracts of which were issued by the Society. So far as these have not appeared in their journal they are referred to here by their numbers, as *J.A.C.S.* 1948, T.S. 10.

at all; the salts and the oxide are used to colour glass for illumination, and the carbide UC_2 as a catalyst in Haber's ammonia synthesis.

Uranium Metal

Uranium is a very heavy (density, 18·7), silver-white metal, hard, but not so hard as steel, which melts at 1,150°[1352] (not, as previously supposed, 1,690°), a very low temperature in comparison with the rest of the group, and is more volatile than iron. The solid has two sharp transition points at 662° and 772° C., the heats of transition being 0·680 and 1·165 k.cals. per g.-atom.[1353] It is reactive; it burns in air on warming to give U_3O_8; it catches fire in fluorine, giving mainly the tetrafluoride; it catches fire in chlorine at 180°, and combines with bromine at 210° and with iodine at about 260°. Dry hydrogen chloride attacks it at a dull red heat; sulphur combines with it at 500°, and nitrogen at 1,000°. Its normal potential probably comes between those of manganese and zinc. In a finely powdered state it is attacked by cold water; acids readily dissolve it to form hydrogen and tetravalent uranium salts, nitric acid reacting only slowly, because uranium, like the other metals of the subgroup, is made passive by it. Alkalies have no action on it.

Uranium Hydride, UH_3[1354]

At 500–600° under 120 atm. pressure of hydrogen uranium forms a hydride UH_3; the composition is quite definite and is confirmed by X-ray measurements, and the compound will not take up more hydrogen or more uranium. It is a brittle substance but conducts electricity like a metal; it does not melt or decompose (under a high pressure of hydrogen) up to far above 600°.

The X-ray results show that each U has 6 nearest U's at 3·32 A. It is not an interstitial compound; there are no U—U bonds (theory for U—U 2·98 A) and there are no ions. It is a metal-like hydride of a new type, and must contain some kind of U—H—U link. A similar deuteride can be made. The crystal structure has been discussed in detail by Pauling and Ewing,[1355] who support these conclusions.

Uranium and Carbon

Two, if not three, carbides of uranium have been prepared. UC can be made from its elements[1356]; they will combine at 2,100°: or from uranium powder and carbon tetrachloride at 650°.[1357] It has a sodium chloride

[1352] H. D. Smyth, *Atomic Energy for Military Purposes*, Princeton University Press (the official American report, also published by the British Government as a white paper).

[1353] G. E. Moore and K. K. Kelley, *J.A.C.S.* 1947, **69**, 2105.

[1354] R. E. Rundle, ib. 1719.

[1355] L. Pauling and F. J. Ewing, ib. 1948, **70**, 1660.

[1356] R. E. Rundle, N. C. Baenziger, A. S. Wilson, and R. A. McDonald, ib. 99.

[1357] L. M. Litz, A. B. Garrett, and F. C. Croxton, ib. 1718.

structure, and is miscible in the solid state with the nitride UN and probably with the oxide UO also. A carbide U_2C_3 seems to exist above 2,000°.

UC_2 is formed by heating oxides of uranium with carbon,[1358-9] or from uranium with excess of carbon at 2,400°.[1357] It looks like bismuth, is crystalline, melts at 2,425°, and is calculated to boil at 4,100°. It forms brilliant sparks when it is hit; it catches fire when it is ground in a mortar, and anyhow in air at 400°; it is decomposed by cold water and violently by hot, giving a mixture of various hydrocarbons.[1360] Its crystal structure is like that of calcium carbide CaC_2,[1357] which suggests an acetylide of divalent uranium which should give acetylene with water; but it might possibly be $U^{iv}[C=C]$, and if so the C—C distance should be longer than in $Ca[C\equiv C]$. (Compare the MC_2 carbides of La, Ce, Pr, and Nd, though La could scarcely be either divalent or tetravalent.)

Uranium and Nitrogen

Uranium absorbs nitrogen when it is heated. Various compounds have been described, some of which (such as U_3N_4) are probably solid solutions.[1361] The most certain[1356,1362] are UN, with a sodium chloride lattice, U_2N_3, which is isomorphous with Mn_2O_3, and UN_2; this last, which has a fluorite structure, can only be made and is only stable under a high pressure (over 100 atm.) of nitrogen.

The compound U_3N_4, which is probably a solid solution of U_2N_3 and UN, can be made from its elements, or by passing ammonia over UCl_4, or by heating a mixture of U_3O_8 and magnesium in nitrogen. It is dark brown or black; it decomposes *in vacuo* above 1,400°; it burns slowly in air to U_3O_8, and is insoluble in water, concentrated hydrochloric or sulphuric acid, but easily soluble in nitric acid. Boiling potassium hydroxide solution has no effect on it, but fusion with the hydroxide decomposes it with evolution of ammonia.[1361]

Uranium and Phosphorus

Heimbrecht, Zumbusch, and Biltz[1363] find by investigation of the system $U+P$ that the phosphides UP_2, U_3P_4, and UP exist; they discuss their structures.

HEXAVALENT URANIUM

THIS is the most stable state of valency of uranium; it is also that in which the element most clearly shows its group properties, and its resemblance to the typical and the B elements of Group VI, such as sulphur and selenium, as well as to molybdenum and tungsten. It is represented by

[1358] O. Ruff and A. Heinzelmann, *Z. anorg. Chem.* 1911, **72**, 64.
[1359] O. Heusler, ib. 1926, **154**, 366.
[1360] J. Schmidt, *Z. Elektrochem.* 1934, **40**, 170.
[1361] R. Lorenz and J. Woolcock, *Z. anorg. Chem.* 1928, **176**, 302.
[1362] R. E. Rundle, N. C. Baenziger, and A. S. Wilson, *J.A.C.S.* 1948, T.S. 56.
[1363] M. Heimbrecht, M. Zumbusch, and W. Biltz, *Z. anorg. Chem.* 1940, **245**, 391.

three types of compounds, (1) UF_6 and UCl_6, (2) UO_3 and its salts with metals, the uranates, and (3) the salts with acids of the divalent uranyl radical $[UO_2]^{++}$ or $[O{=}U{=}O]^{++}$, which is almost peculiar to this element and its immediate successors, is very stable, and also has a strong tendency to form complexes.

Uranium Hexafluoride[1364-6]

This can be made by the action of fluorine on uranium or its carbide in presence of a little chlorine, which acts as a catalyst and causes the reaction to go to the hexafluoride, whereas without it it is liable to stop at the tetrafluoride.[1364-5] It can also be made by the action of fluorine or even hydrogen fluoride on the pentachloride UCl_5.

The electron diffraction[1367] and the Raman spectra[1368] show that the molecule is octahedral, and the dipole moment is zero[1369]; it is feebly paramagnetic.[1366] It forms pale yellow crystals, melting at $64 \cdot 05°$ C. under 1,137 mm. pressure, and having a vapour pressure of 1 atm. at $56 \cdot 5°$.[1370-1] It is interesting to compare the boiling-points of the hexafluorides of Group VI:

SF_6	SeF_6	TeF_6	$[CrF_6]$	MoF_6	WF_6	UF_6
$-64°$ subl.	$-46 \cdot 6°$	$-39°$	[none]	$+35°$	$+17 \cdot 5°$	$+56 \cdot 5°$ subl.

The heat of evaporation of UF_6 is $10 \cdot 36$ k.cals.[1364] It is not acted on by dry air, oxygen, nitrogen, carbon dioxide, chlorine, or iodine, but hydrogen reduces it to the tetrafluoride even in the cold. It is very hygroscopic, fumes in moist air, and reacts violently with water to form UO_2F_2 or with excess of water UO_3; it behaves in the same way with alcohol. It is very reactive: it reacts vigorously with benzene, toluene, or xylene, with evolution of HF and separation of carbon, and slowly even with CS_2 and paraffin oil. It is soluble (apparently without reaction) in $(CHCl_2)_2$, CCl_4, and nitrobenzene.

The chloride UCl_6 has recently been made by disproportionation, by subliming the pentachloride; it begins to lose chlorine at 100°, and is the most reactive of the uranium chlorides.[1372]

The oxyhalides of hexavalent uranium are really uranyl salts $[UO_2](hal)_2$, and as such are described later (p. 1075).

[1364] O. Ruff and A. Heinzelmann, *Z. anorg. Chem.* 1911, **72**, 64.

[1365] A. v. Grosse and P. Kronenberg, ib. 1932, **204**, 184.

[1366] P. Henkel and W. Klemm, ib. 1935, **222**, 70.

[1367] H. Braune and P. Pinnow, *Z. physikal. Chem.* 1937, **B 35**, 239.

[1368] J. Bigeleisen, M. G. Mayer, P. C. Stevenson, and J. Turkevich, *J. Chem. Phys.* 1948, **16**, 442.

[1369] C. P. Smyth, Princeton University Report no. A 2130, quoted in reference [1368].

[1370] B. Weinstock and R. H. Crist, ib. 436.

[1371] F. G. Brickwedde, H. J. Hoge, and R. B. Scott, ib. 429.

[1372] C. H. Prescott jr., *J.A.C.S.* 1948, T.S. 48.

Uranium Trioxide

This can be made by the careful heating of uranyl nitrate $UO_2(NO_3)_2$, or ammonium uranate, or peruranic acid, or the hydrated trioxide $UO_2(OH)_2$ (uranic acid) precipitated by acids from the solution of a soluble uranate.

UO_3 forms an orange or brick-red powder which, according to Goldschmidt, is isotropic and shows no signs of crystalline structure. It is not volatile and on heating loses oxygen to form U_3O_8. It is amphoteric in behaviour, forming uranyl salts with acids (for example, $[UO_2]Cl_2$ with HCl) and uranates with metallic oxides or carbonates; this latter reaction begins at a temperature depending on the metal, from 125° for the strontium to 450° for the manganous salt.[1373]

A peroxide UO_4 is formed reversibly by the action of hydrogen peroxide on a uranyl salt $[UO_2]X_2$[1374]; it is relatively insoluble, and can be used for the separation of uranium.

Uranium and Sulphur

Biltz *et al.*[1375] examine the system U+S by phase-rule methods, and tensimetric and X-ray measurements. In addition to US_2 and U_2S_3 they get US_3 from US_2+S at 600–800°, with evolution of 40 k.cals. per U atom, the excess of sulphur being removed with CS_2, or by heating *in vacuo*. M. Zumbusch[1376] examines a subsulphide found by Biltz: it has a face-centered cubic lattice of U atoms, indicating U_4S_n: from the densities n is found to be 3. The lattice is of the NaCl type with U for Na and S for Cl, but a quarter of the Cl places are unoccupied. U—S distance is 2·75, U···U 3·88 A (theory U—S 2·53; [U]·[S] 2·79; U—U 2·98).

Uranic Acid

The hydrates of uranium trioxide are the uranic acids. Three of these are known[1377] as well as a colloidal form: written as acids they are, (1) H_2UO_4; (2) H_2UO_4, H_2O; (3) $H_2U_2O_7$. The first of these forms orange-yellow crystals, insoluble in water; the second is lemon yellow, unchanged in air, losing water over H_2SO_4 to go into (1); 0·16 g. dissolves in a litre of water at 27°. The compound (2) is amphoteric in behaviour, and though an acid is also a base, forming salts with acids; with nitric acid it gives uranyl nitrate $UO_2(NO_3)_2$, evolving 12·38 k.cals. (Gmelin).

Uranates

A large number of these are known, of various types. Their tendency to condense is much smaller than that of the molybdates or the tungstates, and scarcely greater than that of the chromates. The commonest type is

[1373] G. Tammann and W. Rosenthal, *Z. anorg. Chem.* 1926, **156**, 20.
[1374] C. E. Larson, *J.A.C.S.* 1948, T.S. 47.
[1375] E. F. Strotzer, O. Schneider, and W. Biltz, *Z. anorg. Chem.* 1940, **243**, 307.
[1376] M. Zumbusch, ib. 322.
[1377] G. F. Hüttig and E. v. Schroeder, ib. 1922, **121**, 250.

that of the di-uranates $M_2U_2O_7$, corresponding to the dichromates; the next commonest is the simple M_2UO_4; but tri-, tetra-, penta-, and even hexa-uranates are known, though none of the more complicated forms like the meta-tungstates: nor can uranium replace molybdenum and tungsten in the 6-, 9-, and 12-hetero-poly-acids.

All uranates, even those of the alkalies and ammonium, are insoluble. Ammonia will precipitate from a solution of a uranyl salt the di-uranate $(NH_4)_2[U_2O_7]$, a yellow powder practically insoluble in water, but easily soluble in ammonium carbonate solution: this salt can be used to estimate uranium, but it is liable to go over into the colloidal state.

(Thiouranates do not seem to occur.)

Peruranates

Uranic acid, like the corresponding acids of chromium, molybdenum, and tungsten, reacts with hydrogen peroxide to give peroxide —O—O— derivatives.

If a concentrated solution of uranyl nitrate or acetate is treated with H_2O_2, a yellow precipitate of UO_4, $2 H_2O$ comes down. These precipitates are hard to dry, and the existence of this particular hydrate has been denied.[1378] If dilute H_2O_2 is used the precipitates are easier to filter, and on analysis the ratio of uranium to active oxygen is found to be 1:7.[1379]

This substance, which is quite stable, and does not begin to lose oxygen until about 100°, is often called peruranic acid, but it does not form salts directly with bases, and though the peruranates do exist, they are not the salts of UO_4, $2 H_2O$.

If, however, this compound is treated at once with alkali and H_2O_2, or if a uranyl salt is treated with H_2O_2 or Na_2O_2 solution, peruranates are produced. These contain more than 1 atom of active oxygen to 1 U: those of the alkalies and alkaline earths are of the type of $K_4[UO_8]$, $10 H_2O$, while those of the heavy metals seem to be mainly of the type $M_2'[UO_5]$. $M_2[UO_6]$, $x H_2O$ also occurs.[1380-1]

The constitution of the peruranates has been re-examined lately,[1380-1] and it has been definitely shown that the so-called peruranic acid UO_4, $2 H_2O$ is not ionized, and is not the parent of the salts, in which the ratio of active oxygen to uranium is not, as in the 'acid' 1:1, but 1·5–3:1.

Uranium Reds

These are a curious series of brilliant red compounds, formed from the uranates by treatment with alkali and hydrogen sulphide in presence of air. They always contain sulphur, and either ammonium or a metal: thus a possible composition of one of them is $U_3O_8(OK)(SK)$. According

[1378] But it is reasserted by A. Rosenheim and H. Daehr, *Z. anorg. Chem.* 1929, **181,** 177.

[1379] A. Sieverts and E. L. Müller, ib. 1928, **173,** 299.

[1380] A. Rosenheim and H. Daehr, ib. 1932, **208,** 92.

[1381] R. Schwarz and F. Heinrich, ib. 1935, **233,** 391.

to V. Kohlschütter[1382] they always contain U:S:alkali in the ratio 5:2:5, and with acids half the sulphur comes off as H_2S and the other half as free sulphur, indicating that the sulphur is present as —S—S—.[1383] As the 'metallic' component we can have K, NH_4, Ba, and hydrazinium $H_2N \cdot NH_3$. In many ways these compounds resemble the ultramarine compounds of aluminium.

Uranyl Compounds

All the salts formed by hexavalent uranium with acids are salts of this uranyl ion $[UO_2]^{++}$, which behaves like a compound metal. It also has a strong tendency to form complex salts.

The structure of this ion, as of all the compounds in which one of these heavier elements has two of its valencies saturated by an oxygen atom, is uncertain. These are the two possibilities of a double link and a co-ordinate link. With the uranyl ion, as it has two oxygen atoms, there are thus three possible structures:

$$[O \leftarrow U \rightarrow O]^{++} \qquad [O \leftarrow U = O]^{++} \qquad [O = U = O]^{++}$$

Val Gp. $\qquad$ (8),$\underline{4}$ $\qquad\qquad$ (8),$\underline{6}$ $\qquad\qquad$ (8),$\underline{8}$

The true structure is presumably some kind of resonance hybrid; the U—O distance is 1·90 A, which supports this (theory 2·09).

According to Dittrich[1384] the uranyl salts, like the mercuric, but like no others, are dissociated to much the same extent as the acids from which they are derived. This seems to imply that both the ion and the covalent form are stable.

The uranyl ion has a strong tendency to increase its covalency by complex formation either by adding two amine molecules, as in $[(H_3N)_2UO_2]Cl_2$, or by forming a complex salt with alkaline salts, as in $K_2[UO_2Cl_4]$.

Uranyl Halides

It must be noticed that these compounds $UO_2(hal)_2$ are definitely salts, and are quite unlike the covalent oxychlorides, with corresponding formulae, produced by sulphur and chromium, such as SO_2Cl_2 or CrO_2Cl_2. This is shown most conclusively by their non-volatility (SO_2Cl_2 b. pt. 69·3°, CrO_2Cl_2 116·7°).

UO_2F_2. This is obtained by evaporating down a solution of UO_3 in HF. It is said to contain water, but this is uncertain and anyhow the water can probably be removed. It is extraordinarily hygroscopic, and if heated in air is converted into U_3O_8 or UO_3. It is easily soluble in water and ethyl alcohol, but insoluble in ether, and (unlike the other uranyl halides) in amyl alcohol.

[1382] *Ann.* 1901, **314**, 311.
[1383] This, however, is denied by V. Auger, *Bull. Soc. Chim.* 1919, [4] **25**, 351; V. Auger and J. N. Longinescu, *C.R.* 1926, **182**, 970.
[1384] C. Dittrich, *Z. physikal. Chem.* 1899, **29**, 449.

UO_2Cl_2. The anhydrous form is prepared by the action of Cl_2 on the dioxide UO_2, or on a mixture of U_3O_8 and carbon, at a red heat. The hydrated form separates[1385] from a solution of UO_3 in HCl as UO_2Cl_2, $3 H_2O$, in yellow crystals which cannot be dehydrated without decomposition: it is stable in dry air, but is very hygroscopic. It is very soluble in water, of which 100 g. will dissolve 740 g. of the trihydrate at 18°, and in alcohol and ether. The aqueous solution is very considerably hydrolysed.

UO_2Br_2. This is only known as the hydrate with $7 H_2O$, obtained from the dioxide and bromine, or from the trioxide and HBr, in yellow-green crystals. It is very hygroscopic: it is easily soluble in water to form a yellow solution, in which it is hydrolysed to the trioxide UO_3.

UO_2I_2. This is most conveniently made by precipitating the nitrate $UO_2(NO_3)_2$ in ethereal solution with barium iodide. It forms red crystals, and is very unstable, being very easily hydrolysed by water and oxidized by air.

Uranyl Nitrate, $UO_2(NO_3)_2$

This is the best-known of the uranyl salts. It is made by dissolving an oxide of uranium in nitric acid. It occurs with 0, 2, 3, and 6 molecules of water. The hexahydrate forms yellow prisms soluble in water, alcohol, and (rather surprisingly for a hexahydrated nitrate) in ether. The trihydrate forms yellow crystals; the dihydrate is greenish, and the anhydrous compound is a yellow powder. The saturated solution in ether contains 22 per cent. at 0° and 8·8 per cent. at 20°.[1386] It is also soluble in acetone, but not in CS_2, benzene, toluene, or chloroform. The aqueous solution, which can hold up to 56 per cent. of anhydrous salt at 25°, has the conductivity of a salt solution: it is about 6 per cent. hydrolysed at 25° in a normal solution.[1387]

Uranyl Chlorate is known only in solution.

Uranyl Perchlorate, $UO_2(ClO_4)$, $6 H_2O$: yellow crystals, melting at 90°, very deliquescent.

Uranyl Iodate is known only in the form of hydrates with $2 H_2O$ and $1 H_2O$ (two modifications of the latter). It cannot be dehydrated without decomposition.[1388] It is only slightly (about 1 per cent. at 100°) soluble in water.

Uranyl Formate $UO_2(HCO_2)_2$, 0 and $1 H_2O$: soluble 7·2 per cent. in water at 15°.

Uranyl Acetate, 0 and $2 H_2O$: highly fluorescent. Decomposes at 275°: 7·7 g. anhydrous salt dissolve in 100 g. of water at 15°. This salt is one of the most usual sources of uranium compounds.

The most important of the uranyl salts of dibasic acids are these:

[1385] W. Oechsner de Coninck, *Ann. Chim. Phys.* 1904, [8] **3**, 500; *C.R.* 1909, **148**, 1769.
[1386] P. Misciattelli, *Gaz.* 1930, **60**, 839.
[1387] H. Ley, *Z. physikal. Chem.* 1899, **30**, 249.
[1388] P. Artmann, *Z. anorg. Chem.* 1913, **79**, 330.

Uranyl Sulphide, $[UO_2]S$. This can be made as a brown precipitate by adding ammonium sulphide to a solution of a uranyl salt. It is soluble in dilute acids, and in moist air is readily hydrolysed to uranic acid $UO_2(OH)_2$. It can also be made in the dry way by fusing UO_3 with sulphur and KCNS. It then forms black crystals, much more resistant to acids, and only dissolved by HCl if it is hot[1389]: when ignited in air it burns to SO_2 and U_3O_8.

Uranyl Sulphate. This is formed by evaporating a solution of uranyl nitrate in H_2SO_4. It gives hydrates with 0, 1, 2, and 3 H_2O. The trihydrate loses water in air; sol^y 17·4/15·5°. This like all uranyl salts readily forms complex salts, but it does so more easily than some, since a free complex acid $H_2[UO_2(SO_4)_2]$, 2 H_2O can be obtained, and there is evidence of the existence of complex ions in a solution of uranyl sulphate itself.[1390]

Uranyl Carbonate, UO_2CO_3. This occurs in the pure state in E. Africa as the mineral Rutherfordine, formed by the weathering of pitchblende. It is difficult if not impossible to make in the laboratory.

Uranyl Oxalate. The compound $UO_2(C_2O_4)$, 3 H_2O is 0·5 per cent. soluble in water at 20°.

There are also many uranyl derivatives, probably largely chelate, of organic acids, oxy-acids, and the like, for example, of malic acid,[1391] salicylic acid,[1392] and of β-diketones.[1393]

These last show a curious co-ordinate unsaturation. Biltz[1394] prepared the uranyl acetonylacetonate as an orange-yellow solid with the composition UO_2A_2, H_2O. Hager[1393] showed that if it is formed in presence of a base, the resulting products—all orange-yellow solids—are, when B the base is NH_3, methylamine, or aniline, UO_2A_2, HA, B and when it is pyridine or quinoline UO_2A_2, B, with no extra diketone molecule. Hager suggests that the compounds of the first type may be salts $BH[UO_2A_3]$.

Complex Uranyl Compounds

The uranyl group has a very strong tendency to form complexes, and complex salts corresponding to nearly all the simple uranyl salts are known. There are also a certain number of diammines of the type of $(H_3N)_2UO_2Cl_2$: thus one molecule of uranyl chloride or bromide will form an addition compound with two molecules of ether, aniline, pyridine, nitrosodimethyl-aniline, etc.; and uranyl nitrate forms similar compounds of the composition $UO_2(NO_3)_2$, 2 B, where B is NH_3, pyridine, or quinoline.

But the great majority of these complexes are double salts; they are

[1389] J. Milbauer, ib. 1904, **42**, 448.
[1390] A. Colani, *C.R.* 1927, **185**, 273; *Bull. Soc. Chim.* 1928, [iv] **43**, 754.
[1391] L. W. Andrews, *Proc. Iowa Acad. Sci.* 1925, **32**, 299.
[1392] R. Weinland and K. Hager, *Z. anorg. Chem.* 1927, **160**, 193.
[1393] K. Hager, ib. **162**, 82.
[1394] W. Biltz and J. A. Clinch, *Z. anorg. Chem.* 1904, **40**, 221.

formed in very large numbers by all kinds of metals[1395]; the following
account deals mainly with the salts of the alkali metals and ammonium
compounds with more than one uranium atom in the molecule are usually
omitted.

Fluorides. These are of three types (the most obvious one $M_2[UO_2F_4]$
does not seem to occur):

1. $M[UO_2F_3]$; Na, 4 H_2O
2. $M_3[UO_2F_5]$; K_3, 0; $(NH_4)_3$, 0.
3. $M_4[UO_2F_6]$; Li_4, 0; Na_4, 0; K_4, 0.

F. Olsson[1396] has shown that the alkyl and aryl ammonium bases have
a strong tendency to form double salts with uranyl fluoride; they are of a
peculiar type (although parallels could be found among other substituted
ammonium salts) in that they have only one ammonium fluoride molecule
to 1, 2, or 3 of UO_2F_2, for example (B = ammonia or substituted ammonia): $BH[UO_2F_3]$; $BH[U_2O_4F_5]$; $BH[U_3O_6F_7]$.

Chlorides. Almost the only simple type is: $M_2[UO_2Cl_4]$; Na_2, 0 H_2O;
K_2, 0, 2; $(NH_4)_2$, 2; Rb_2, 2; Cs_2, 0.

Bromides. These are similar: $K_2[UO_2Br_4]$, 2 H_2O; $(NH_4)_2$, 2.

Nitrates. These are of two types:

1. $M[UO_2(NO_3)_3]$ (e.g. K, NH_4, Rb, Cs) all anhydrous but most of them
   very hygroscopic, and also:
2. $M_2[UO_2(NO_3)_4]$; K_2, 0; $(NH_4)_2$, 2 H_2O.

Iodate. $K[UO_2(IO_3)_3]$, 3 H_2O.

Acetate. Most of these are of the type $M[UO_2Ac_3]$: e.g. Li, 3 and 5 H_2O;
Na, 2 and 0; K, 5 and 1; NH_4, 3 and 0. They crystallize very well and
have a brilliant green fluorescence.

Cyanides. There is a double cyanide $K_2[UO_2(CN)_4]$ which is of interest
in view of the importance of the cyanides among the molybdenum and
tungsten compounds, because this seems to be the only cyanide of any
kind known to be formed by uranium: there are no known simple
cyanides, and no other double cyanide formed with any of the alkali
metals or ammonium.

Sulphates. The usual type is $M_2[UO_2(SO_4)_2(OH_2)_2]$; Li_2, 4 H_2O (including the two in the ion): Na_2, 3; K_2, 2; Rb_2, 2; Cs_2, 2; $(NH_4)_2$, 2. (These
last four afford strong evidence that there are two molecules of water in
the anion.) There is also at least one salt of a different type $K_4[UO_2(SO_4)_3]$,
2 H_2O.

Carbonates. $(NH_4)_4[UO_2(CO_3)_3]$, 2 H_2O; yellow; solubility 5 g. in 100 g.
of water at 5°. Also Na_4, 0; $(NH_4)_4$, ? 0; Rb_4, 0.

Oxalates. According to Wyrouboff[1397] there are four types of these salts:

1. $M_2[UO_2Ox_2]$.   3. $M_6[U_2O_4Ox_5]$.
2. $M_4[UO_2Ox_3]$.   4. $M_2[U_2O_4Ox_3]$.

[1395] See Gmelin, 'Uranium' (1936), pp. 186–237.
[1396] *Z. anorg. Chem.* 1930, **187**, 112.
[1397] G. Wyrouboff, *Bull. Soc. Min.* 1909, **32**, 340; see also A. Colani, *Bull. Soc. Chim.* 1925, [4] **37**, 861.

Of (1) and (2) there are the following examples:

1. Li$_2$, 5·5 H$_2$O; Na$_2$, 5 and 3; K$_2$, 3; (NH$_4$)$_2$ 3 and 0; Rb$_2$, 2; Cs$_2$, 2. (The H$_2$O is obviously attached to the oxalate group in the last two salts.)
2. (NH$_4$)$_4$[UO$_2$Ox$_3$].

Uranoso-uranic Oxide, U$_3$O$_8$

This compound, which is presumably composed of hexavalent and tetravalent uranium, perhaps UO$_2$, 2 UO$_3$, is for some reason remarkably stable. It is probably a solid solution of the di- and trioxide, and its stability is due to its dissociation tension being very near that of the oxygen in the atmosphere. It constitutes, of course, the mineral pitch-blende. It can be made by strongly heating the dioxide or the trioxide in air, or by igniting in air the uranyl salts of volatile acids, or ammonium uranate.[1398] It forms dark-green to olive-green crystals; its crystal structure is not known except that it is different from that of the dioxide UO$_2$. Unlike the dioxide it can be sublimed at 1,300°, but at 1,240° its vapour pressure is only 1·4 mm.[1398] When strongly heated it gives off oxygen, forming apparently first a solid solution of UO$_2$ in U$_3$O$_8$: it is only at very high temperatures that the conversion into UO$_2$ is complete. By heating in hydrogen it is completely converted into the dioxide UO$_2$. It is slightly soluble in HCl and readily in HF. If heated with concentrated H$_2$SO$_4$ it is slowly converted into uranyl sulphate UO$_2$(SO$_4$) and U(SO$_4$)$_2$.

This oxide seems also to form a hydrate, which can be made by exposing a uranyl salt solution, containing an oxidizable substance such as alcohol, aldehyde, or glucose, to sunlight,[1399] i.e. by partly reducing the hexavalent to pentavalent uranium. This hydrate is a violet powder, and seems to go black on drying. It oxidizes in air very readily.

PENTAVALENT URANIUM

This valency occurs in the pentafluoride and pentachloride, in the UO$_2^+$ ion which is found in solution, and probably in the pentoxide U$_2$O$_5$.

Uranium pentafluoride UF$_5$ occurs in two modifications, which are distinguished by their X-ray patterns.[1400]

Uranium pentachloride UCl$_5$[1401] is formed along with the tetrachloride when uranium oxide and carbon are heated in chlorine, and can be separated because the pentachloride is the more volatile of the two; the temperature of formation is about 500–600°.

It forms long needles, green by reflected, and red by transmitted light; it is unstable and loses chlorine even at the ordinary temperature, so that

[1398] W. Biltz and H. Müller, *Z. anorg. Chem.* 1927, **163**, 260.

[1399] J. Aloy, *Bull. Soc. Chim.* 1900, [3] **23**, 369; J. Aloy and E. Rodier, ib. 1920, [4] **27**, 104; J. Zehenter, *Mon.* 1900, **21**, 237.

[1400] P. Agron, A. Grenall, R. Kunin, and S. Weller, *J.A.C.S.* 1948, T.S. 45.

[1401] O. Ruff and A. Heinzelmann, *Z. anorg. Chem.* 1911, **72**, 64.

it can only be kept in an atmosphere of chlorine. It is volatile at 70° under low pressures,[1402] but its molecular weight has never been determined, so that it may be U_2Cl_{10}, with one atom of hexavalent and one of tetravalent uranium.

It is excessively hygroscopic: the aqueous solution deposits $U(OH)_4$. It is soluble in alcohol, acetone, and benzonitrile, and slightly soluble in CCl_4 and chloroform.

All attempts to make UBr_5[1403] have failed.

The pentoxide U_2O_5 has been prepared[1404]; it is orthorhombic. The pentavalent uranyl ion $[UO_2]^+$ is present in hydrolysed solutions of the pentahalides.

TETRAVALENT URANIUM

THE remarkably stable tetravalent state of uranium is very important as a sign of the beginning of the uranide series of elements (see p. 1091).

The hydroxide $U(OH)_4$ has no acidic properties whatever, but only basic. Moreover, it seems to be unable to form covalent compounds, other than perhaps the hydroxide itself, unless it has a negative charge, i.e. unless it forms part of a complex anion. Thus all the simple tetravalent uranium compounds are salts, even the halides; the tendency to form complexes is fairly strong. They are, on the whole, less stable than the compounds of hexavalent uranium, but are more stable than any of the lower valencies.

The resemblance of the tetravalent uranium salts to those of thorium is very striking; it is ordinarily somewhat concealed because it is easy to separate the uranium by changing its valency, while that of thorium cannot change. The likeness is so great that Fleck,[1405] when he was working out the isotopic relations of the radioactive elements, raised the question whether they are not related as a kind of isotopes, and tested this by seeing whether the salts (he used the fluorides) of thorium and tetravalent uranium could be separated by their solubilities when the uranium was kept throughout in the tetravalent state: he showed that in spite of their similarity this separation could be effected.

In the following account the properties of the thorium salts are briefly appended for comparison.

Borohydrides

Schlesinger and Brown[1406] have shown that when uranium tetrafluoride is treated with aluminium borohydride it gives $U(BH_4)_4$, [$Th(BH_4)_4$ has recently been obtained]. When this is treated with boron trimethyl it gives $U(BH_4)_3BH_3Me$ and $U(BH_3Me)_4$. The ethyl derivatives were also

[1402] H. Martin and K. H. Eldau, *Z. anorg. Chem.* 1943, **251**, 295.
[1403] W. Biltz and H. Müller, ib. 1927, **163**, 295.
[1404] R. E. Rundle, N. C. Baenziger, and A. S. Wilson, *J.A.C.S.* 1948, T.S. 56.
[1405] A. Fleck, *J.C.S.* 1914, **105**, 250.
[1406] H. I. Schlesinger and H. C. Brown, *J.A.C.S.* 1948, T.S. 50.

obtained. These are the most volatile of all known uranium compounds except UF_6, having the vapour pressures:

$U(BH_4)_4$	0·33 mm. at 35°	2·27 mm. at 55°
$U(BH_4)_3BH_3Me$	2·83 ,, ,,	11·89 ,, ,,
$U(BH_3Me)_4$	0·16 ,, ,,	0·58 ,, ,,

The first two are dark-green solids in the cold, the third is dark violet. They all seem stable in the cold in the absence of air but react slowly with air, and quickly with water, alcohol, and hydrochloric acid. At 80–100° the reversible reaction

$$2\,U(BH_4)_4 \rightleftharpoons 2\,U(BH_4)_3 + B_2H_6 + H_2$$

occurs.

Uranium Dioxide, UO_2

This is formed when UO_3 or U_3O_8 is heated in hydrogen, and also by the action of water on the chlorides or double chlorides of tetravalent uranium. It is a brown or black* powder melting at 2,176° [thorium dioxide has a very high melting-point, as we all know from its use in gas mantles] and is so stable that Klaproth thought it was the element. It has the same crystal structure (CaF_2 lattice) as ThO_2[1404]; it dissolves with difficulty in acids (like ThO_2) (except in nitric acid, which oxidizes it to uranyl nitrate $UO_2(NO_3)_2$), and forms U^{iv} salts. If it is heated in air or steam it is oxidized to U_3O_8, and it takes up chlorine at a red heat to form UO_2Cl_2. The form which is precipitated from U^{iv} salts is hydrated, and is green or red. It oxidizes in air to UO_3, $3\,H_2O$.

Uranium Disulphide, US_2

This is made from the elements, or by passing hydrogen and sulphur vapour over UCl_4 or Na_2UCl_6 at 500°. It is a dark-grey crystalline powder which when heated *in vacuo* neither melts nor decomposes below 1,100°; at 1,300° it begins to dissociate. It is attacked very slowly by water, more rapidly by hydrochloric acid, and violently by nitric acid.

Tetrahalides

Uranium tetrafluoride UF_4 is the usual product of the action of fluorine on uranium; it can also be made by treating the yellow solution of UO_2F_2, made by dissolving U_3O_8 in hydrofluoric acid, with stannous chloride, or by the action of hydrofluoric acid on uranium tetrachloride.[1407] It can also be made[1409] by the reaction

$$2\,CF_2Cl_2 + UO_3 = UF_4 + CO_2 + CO + 2\,Cl_2$$

which goes at 400°.[1408] It is a green solid which melts about 1,000°, and is stable up to 1,100°[1409]; it is insoluble in water. [ThF_4 is also a high-melting solid; it forms a hydrate ThF_4, $4\,H_2O$.] If heated in air UF_4 is

* Other colours—red and blue—have been attributed to it, but these products may have contained a slight excess of oxygen.

[1407] O. Ruff and A. Heinzelmann, *Z. anorg. Chem.* 1911, **72**, 64.
[1408] H. S. Booth, W. Krasny-Ergen, and R. E. Heath, *J.A.C.S.* 1946, **68**, 1969.
[1409] V. G. Chlopin and M. L. Jaschtschenko, *Bull. Acad. Sci. U.R.S.S.* 1942, 87.

converted into U_3O_8; if heated in hydrogen it gives a red-brown compound which perhaps is UF_3. Its solubility in water is 0·0053/25°, apparently as the acid $H_2[UF_4(OH)_2]$; it forms hydrates with $\frac{1}{2}$, 2, and $2\frac{1}{2}$ H_2O.[1409] It is hardly attacked at all by acids, but is converted by boiling with alkaline hydroxide solution into the hydroxide $U(OH)_4$.

U_2F_9: this remarkable substance was discovered by R. Livingston[1411] in 1943; its formula was established by analysis.[1412] It is a black substance which turns green on exposure to air. The crystal structure has been examined by Zachariasen.[1410] He finds that it is cubic, with each U atom surrounded by 9 F's at the average distance of 2·31 A (theory U—F 2·13, [U](F)⁻ 2·38). The uranium atoms, though they must be half penta- or a quarter hexavalent and the rest tetravalent, are all equivalent, and presumably are all in resonance.

Uranium Tetrachloride UCl_4 is formed from the elements: from the pentachloride on standing; from the action of carbon tetrachloride on U_3O_8, or of chlorine on a mixture of U_3O_8 and carbon at a low red heat; or by the action of phosgene on uranium dioxide. [$ThCl_4$, m. pt. 820° (it begins to sublime below this) is made in the same way from carbon tetrachloride and ThO_2.]

UCl_4 is the stablest of the chlorides of uranium; it forms dark-green crystals with a metallic glance. It melts at 567° and boils at 618° (very like $ThCl_4$); the electrical conductivity of the fused tetrachloride at 570° is 0·34, i.e. is that of a salt[1413] [$ThCl_4$ 0·61/814°]. UCl_4 is very hygroscopic (the compounds of uranium must have more hygroscopicity between them than those of any other element); it dissolves in water with a large evolution of heat [so does $ThCl_4$], and gives a green solution which is very largely hydrolysed.

It is soluble in acetone, ethyl acetate, and ethyl benzoate, giving a pale-green solution. It is insoluble in ether, chloroform, and benzene.

Uranium Tetrabromide is very like the tetrachloride, but less stable. It is made by passing bromine vapour in carbon dioxide or nitrogen over heated U_3O_8 mixed with carbon: it can also be got by the action of HBr on the tetrachloride.

Brown or black crystals: its vapour density at a red heat is normal, so that the substance boils undecomposed [$ThBr_4$ boils at 725°]. It is very hygroscopic and hydrolysed by water; in moist air it is at once oxidized to the oxybromide UO_2Br_2.[1414]

Uranium Tetraiodide, UI_4, is made from its elements[1415] or by the action of iodine on the dioxide and carbon at a red heat, or by reducing UO_2I_2 with HI in sunlight.[1416] It is similar to UCl_4, but less stable. It forms

[1410] W. H. Zachariasen, *J. Chem. Phys.* 1948, **16**, 425.

[1411] R. Livingston and W. Burns, *Manhattan Project Report* CN 982, Oct. 1943.

[1412] S. Weller, A. Grenall, and R. Kunin, Report A—3326, March 1945.

[1413] A. Voigt and W. Biltz, *Z. anorg. Chem.* 1924, **133**, 281.

[1414] See T. W. Richards and B. S. Merrigold, ib. 1902, **31**, 254.

[1415] M. Guichard, *C.R.* 1907, **145**, 921.

[1416] J. Aloy and E. Rodier, *Bull. Soc. Chim.* 1922, [4] **31**, 247.

black needles melting at about 500°. It is deliquescent in moist air [ThI_4 is also deliquescent] and hydrolysed by it, and then oxidized to the oxyiodide.

Oxyhalides of Tetravalent Uranium

Oxyfluoride. The hydrate UOF_2, 2 H_2O is made by treating U_3O_8 with excess of 30 per cent. HF: or by reducing UO_2Cl_2 solution to the tetravalent stage and adding HF.[1417] It is a green solid which can be dried at 100°. It can be used to estimate uranium.[1418] [$ThOF_2$ is known.]

Oxychloride. This is formed by the photochemical reduction of UO_2Cl_2 in ether.[1419] It is very pale green, very soluble in water and alcohol. The grass-green solution soon darkens, especially on warming, and precipitates $U(OH)_4$. [$ThOCl_2$ is readily formed, and hydrolyses easily.]

Other Salts of Tetravalent Uranium

These salts, which are less stable than the uranyl salts, are all green, and usually are easily soluble in water; the oxalate, however, is nearly insoluble even in acids, and also is more stable than most of the salts. Most of the salts are considerably hydrolysed in water (as we should expect the salts of a tetravalent base to be, and as the thorium salts are) and they are very easily oxidized: the hydroxide $U(OH)_4$ formed by hydrolysis (and precipitated by alkalies) is no doubt covalent, and as such is more readily oxidized than the ion.

They form complex salts (especially the oxalate) but not quite so readily as the uranyl salts.

Nitrate. No neutral nitrate is known, but only the basic nitrate $UO(NO_3)_2$.[1419] This is pale green, and can be dried at 100°. [Thorium does form a normal nitrate $Th(NO_3)_4$, 12 and 5 H_2O. But if it is dissolved in water a basic compound separates out.] (We must remember that nitric acid though classed as a strong acid is really much weaker than HCl, not to say $HClO_4$.)

Chlorate and Perchlorate. These can be made in solution by dissolving the hydroxide $U(OH)_4$ in acid, but they decompose on evaporation.

Formate and Acetate. The normal salts UAc_4 and also the basic salts $UOAc_2$ are known.

Sulphates. These can be made by the action of sunlight on a solution of U_3O_8 in H_2SO_4. There are certainly two hydrates, $U(SO_4)_2$, 4 H_2O and $U(SO_4)_2$, 8 H_2O. Thorium sulphate forms the same hydrates, which are both isomorphous with these uranium salts, and which resemble the uranium salts also[1420] in showing the most peculiar behaviour in solution. Thus the solubilities in g. anhydrous salt to 100 g. water are:

$$U(SO_4)_2,\ 4\ H_2O:10\cdot9/24°,\ 6\cdot7/63°$$
$$U(SO_4)_2,\ 8\ H_2O:11\cdot3/18°,\ 58\cdot2/62°.$$

[1417] F. Giolitti and G. Agamennone. *Atti R. Linc.* 1905, [5] **14**, i. 114, 165.
[1418] F. Giolitti, *Gaz.* 1904, **34**, ii. 166.
[1419] A. Benrath, *Z. Wiss. Phot.* 1917, **16**, 258.
[1420] F. Giolitti and G. Bucci, *Gaz.* 1905, **35**, ii. 162.

This indicates an unparalleled degree of metastability in the octahydrate at the higher temperature. The explanation was finally given by R. J. Meyer,[1421] who showed that the salts were isomeric even in solution, and that in water (or strictly speaking in the presence of dilute acid, added to repress hydrolysis) the molecular weight of the tetrahydrate was twice as great as that of the octahydrate.

Phosphates. Ortho-, meta-, and pyrophosphates of tetravalent uranium are known.

Oxalates. If a solution of a uranyl salt containing oxalic acid is exposed to sunlight the uranium is reduced, and uranous oxalate precipitated. $U(C_2O_4)_2$ is dark green, and insoluble in water and dilute acids; it is easily soluble in alkaline oxalate solution with the formation of a double oxalate.

[Thorium forms a similar oxalate, which is hydrated, $ThOx_2$, 6 H_2O. It also is almost insoluble in water, but readily soluble in solutions of alkaline oxalates or ammonium oxalate, forming double salts.]

Complexes of Tetravalent Uranium

These are numerous, though not nearly so numerous as the uranyl complexes. The following are some of the more important. The thorium analogues are added in square brackets.

Fluorides.[1422] $K[UF_5]$; $NH_4[UOF_3]$. [$KThF_5$, $\frac{1}{2} H_2O$; K_2ThF_6, 4 H_2O.]

Chlorides. $M_2[UCl_6]$; M = Li, Na, K, Rb, Cs. [$Cs_2[ThCl_6]$.]

Bromides. $Na_2[UBr_6]$; $K_2[UBr_6]$. [$(pyH)_2[ThBr_6]$.]

It will be noticed that all these complex U^{iv} halides (though not quite all the thorium compounds) are anhydrous.

The hydrogen halides seem to be the only monobasic acids which form tetravalent uranium complexes; but several polybasic acids do so.

Sulphates. On adding sulphuric acid to an electrolytically reduced solution of UO_2Cl_2 the acid $H_2[U(SO_4)_3]$, 10 H_2O is formed.[1423] Salts of it are also known such as $K_2[U(SO_4)_3]$, 2 H_2O and also another type, $(NH_4)_4[U(SO_4)_4]$. [$Na_2[Th(SO_4)_3]$, 6 H_2O : $K_4[Th(SO_3)_4]$, 2 H_2O.]

Sulphites. No simple uranous sulphites are known, but a complex $(NH_4)_4[U(SO_3)_4]$[1424] and also more complicated salts have been prepared.

Phosphate. A complex phosphate $Na_2[U(PO_4)_2]$ is known. [Also the corresponding Th salt $Na_2[Th(PO_4)_2]$.]

Oxalates. The insoluble simple oxalate of tetravalent uranium is very soluble in solutions of alkaline oxalates, owing to the formation of double salts.[1425] Such are $K_4[UOx_4]$, 5 H_2O, grey; $(NH_4)_4[UOx_4]$, 7, 6, and 0 H_2O; $Ba_2[UOx_4]$, 6 H_2O, red-violet.

[1421] R. J. Meyer and H. Nachod, *Ann.* 1924, **440**, 186.

[1422] For the crystal structure of the complex fluorides of tetravalent uranium see W. H. Zachariasen, *J.A.C.S.* 1948, **70**, 2147.

[1423] F. Giolitti and G. Bucci, *Gaz.* 1905, **35**, ii. 168.

[1424] A. Rosenheim and M. Kelmy, *Z. anorg. Chem.* 1932, **206**, 39.

[1425] See L. E. Marchi, W. C. Fernelius, and P. J. MacReynolds, *J.A.C.S.* 1943, **65**, 329, 333.

[Various complex oxalates of thorium, such as $Na_2[Th(C_2O_4)_3]$ are known.]

TRIVALENT URANIUM

THERE seems to be no doubt that trivalent uranium exists. There are the trihalides, a trivalent sesquisulphide U_2S_3, and a trivalent ion in solution: and although the molecular weight of none of these compounds is known, since all but the last are infusible and non-volatile, and the ion is very probably complex, the alternative suggestion that they contain divalent and quadrivalent uranium is improbable since divalent uranium, if it exists at all, is extremely unstable.

Uranium borohydride, $U(BH_4)_3$. As we have seen (p. 1080) tetravalent uranium borohydride is converted into the trivalent $U(BH_4)_3$ at 80–100°. Unlike the dark-green volatile $U(BH_4)_4$ this compound is brownish-red and non-volatile, and detonates violently.[1406]

A *nitride* UN has recently been established on X-ray evidence[1404]; it has a sodium-chloride lattice.

Uranium sesquisulphide, U_2S_3, can be made by heating the tribromide in hydrogen sulphide for 8–10 hours in complete absence of oxygen.[1426] It consists of grey crystals, which decompose in air with evolution of hydrogen sulphide.

Trihalides

Uranium trifluoride, UF_3. If the tetrafluoride is heated in hydrogen, it gives off hydrogen fluoride, and a red-brown solid, insoluble in water, is formed: it is scarcely attacked by any acids except nitric. This is presumably the trifluoride UF_3.[1427] Its existence has recently been confirmed.[1412]

Uranium trichloride, UCl_3, is made by reducing the tetrachloride with hydrogen; it was discovered by Peligot in 1842; for recent work see references [1372,1428-9]. It can also be made by subliming the tetrachloride in nitrogen.[1430] For the crystal structure of this and of the isomorphous trihalides of the lanthanide and the actinide elements see Zachariasen.[1431]

It forms dark-red needles, scarcely volatile at all and very hygroscopic. It is more stable in air than the pentachloride, but as hygroscopic as the tetrachloride. It dissolves easily in water to give a purple-red liquid, which at once begins to evolve hydrogen, turns green, and deposits what is probably the tetravalent $U(OH)_4$. It dissolves in hydrochloric acid with evolution of 40·6 k.cals. per g.-atom uranium, and forms a red solution (which can also be got by reduction of a solution of higher valency), which is rather more stable than the solution in water.

Uranium tribromide, UBr_3, can be made by distilling the tetrabromide

[1426] G. Alibegoff, *Ann.* 1886, **233**, 134.
[1427] H. C. Bolton, *Z. Chem.* 1866, [2] **2**, 353; *Bull. Soc. Chim.* 1866, [2] **6**, 450.
[1428] A. Rosenheim and H. Loebel, *Z. anorg. Chem.* 1908, **57**, 235.
[1429] W. Biltz and C. Fendius, ib. 1928, **172**, 386.
[1430] O. Hönigschmid and W. E. Schilz, ib. **170**, 148.
[1431] W. H. Zachariasen, *J. Chem. Phys.* 1948, **16**, 254.

in nitrogen,[1432] or by the action of hydrogen on the tetrabromide at its melting-point, when the reduction goes to trivalent uranium, but no further.

It forms dark-brown, very hygroscopic crystals; the volatility is too small for the vapour density to be measured. It dissolves in water with great ease and a hissing sound to give a purple-red solution, in which it slowly oxidizes on standing.

[U_2O_3: according to Biltz (see under U_2O_5) this does not exist.]

Trivalent Uranium Sulphate

Rosenheim[1433] showed that a sulphate of trivalent uranium undoubtedly exists. It is made by precipitating the reduced solution of trivalent uranium by fairly concentrated H_2SO_4. He gives it the formula $H[U(SO_4)_2]$, which has an improbable unhydrated acidic hydrogen; attempts to prove the formula by preparing its salts failed, because the substance is so easily oxidized. It forms red crystals which are very easily oxidized—even during washing—to the tetravalent state. In water it is at once oxidized to U^{iv} with evolution of hydrogen.

DIVALENT URANIUM

THE only good evidence for this valency is the monoxide UO. There is a very dubious monosulphide which has not been seen for over fifty years; a difluoride UF_2 has got into the literature, but only through a misprint, as was pointed out by Sieverts.[1434] Recent work on the halides[1400] has given no evidence of divalent uranium compounds.

Uranium monoxide, UO, can be made from its elements[1356,1404]; it is very difficult to get it free from carbide and nitride; the dioxide is only completely converted into the monoxide at a very high temperature. It has a sodium chloride lattice.

Uranium monosulphide, US. According to Alibegoff (1886) this can be made by heating the sesquisulphide U_2S_3 to a red heat in hydrogen. But Flatt and Hess[1435] failed to repeat his work, and got no evidence for the existence of compounds of divalent uranium.

[1432] O. Hönigschmid, *C.R.* 1914, **158**, 2005; *Mon.* 1915, **36**, 68.
[1433] A. Rosenheim and H. Loebel, *Z. anorg. Chem.* 1908, **57**, 237.
[1434] A. Sieverts, ib. 1928, **170**, 191.
[1435] R. Flatt and W. Hess, *Helv. Chim. Acta*, 1938, **21**, 525.

NUCLEAR FISSION AND NUCLEAR ENERGY[1436-53]

In 1937 it was found, mainly by Otto Hahn and his co-workers,[1437] that the bombardment of uranium by neutrons gave a whole series (10) of radioactive products, whose chemical properties showed that they were not isotopes of any element from 84 Po to 92 U; as no case was then known where bombardment caused more than a small change in atomic number, it seemed that these must be the elements following uranium, with atomic numbers 93 to 97, and their isotopes. Early in 1939, however, Hahn showed[1438-9] that one of the supposed new elements was barium, and he suggested that the uranium nucleus was broken up into barium plus krypton $(56 + 36 = 92)$. Further work confirmed this, and showed that the nuclei of heavy elements like thorium and uranium can be broken by nuclear bombardment into a few large pieces. These 'fission' products usually themselves change further, so that the number of products that have been identified is large. A complete list of the 160 known fission products of uranium (including isotopes), with their various radiations, has been given by the Plutonium Project.[1440] Recent work[1441] has shown that not only thorium (which behaves very like uranium) but also tantalum, platinum, thallium, lead, and bismuth when bombarded with α-particles, neutrons, or deuterons of 100–400 m.e.v. energy undergo fission with the formation of gallium, bromine, strontium, ruthenium, etc.

Now Aston showed in 1927[1442] that the masses of the atoms are not exact multiples of the unit $^{16}O/16$; those of the lightest elements, especially hydrogen, and those of the heaviest being rather greater, while those of the intermediate elements are smaller, with a minimum at about Ti—Ni. This can be seen by plotting against the atomic weight the 'packing fraction': if an isotope with a mass-number N is found to weigh $N + f$ times the unit, the packing fraction is $(f/N) \times 10^4$. Examples of its values are H $+81\cdot2$; He $+9\cdot8$; Ti $-7\cdot24$; Cr $-8\cdot18$; U $+5\cdot0$. Hence if a heavy atom undergoes fission the products will weigh less than it did. Now Einstein showed that when mass is converted into energy the latter has

[1436] British White Paper on the Atomic Bomb, 1945.

[1437] O. Hahn, L. Meitner, and F. Strassmann, *Ber.* 1937, **70**, 1374.

[1438] O. Hahn and F. Strassmann, *Naturwiss.* 1938, **26**, 755.

[1439] Id., ib. 1939, **27**, 11.

[1440] Plutonium Project, *J.A.C.S.* 1946, **68**, 2411.

[1441] I. Perlman, R. H. Goeckermann, D. H. Templeton, and J. J. Howland, *Phys. Rev.* 1947, ii. **72**, 352.

[1442] F. W. Aston, *Mass Spectra and Isotopes*, ed. 2, 1942, p. 81.

[1443] N. Bohr, *Nature*, 1939, **143**, 330; *Phys. Rev.* 1939, ii. **55**, 418.

[1444] N. Bohr and J. A. Wheeler, ib. **56**, 426.

[1445] N. Bohr, ib. 1940, ii. **58**, 654.

[1446] G. T. Seaborg, *Chem. Eng. News*, 1945, **23**, 2190.

[1447] Id., ib. 1946, **24**, 1192.   [1448] E. Fermi, ib. 1357.

[1449] F. Daniels, ib. 1514.   [1450] G. T. Seaborg, ib. 3160.

[1451] H. G. Harvey, H. G. Heal, A. G. Maddock, and E. L. Rowley, *J.C.S.* 1947, 1010.

[1452] G. T. Seaborg and A. C. Wahl, *J.A.C.S.* 1948, **70**, 1128.

[1453] G. T. Seaborg, *Chem. Eng. News*, 1947, **25**, 358.

the enormous value $e = mc^2$, where c is the velocity of light. This gives $2 \cdot 2 \times 10^{10}$ k.cals. as the equivalent of a mass of 1 g. This does not mean that all mass can be converted into energy: as far as we know, protons or neutrons cannot be so converted, and the only part of the atomic mass that can be turned into energy is that shown by the differences of the packing fraction. Hence it is theoretically possible that a part of the nuclear energy might be liberated by transforming either the lightest or the heaviest of the elements into others of medium weight. The first method occurs in the conversion of 4 atoms of hydrogen into 1 of helium, which is the source of most of the energy of the stars (see Group 0, p. 3); as this requires atomic collisions at a temperature of about 40 million °C. it is not likely to be achieved artificially. The second method, the fission of heavy atoms, is that used in the atomic bomb, and is the only one we have for obtaining atomic energy. The fission of 1 g. of ^{235}U or ^{239}Pu involves the loss of about 1 mg. of mass, and so the liberation of 2×10^7 k.cals. of energy.

The process used for the fission depends on the fact that heavier atoms have a larger proportion of neutrons than lighter, and so their fission might be expected to lead to the liberation of several neutrons. Thus if ^{235}U with $235 - 92 = 143$ neutrons, broke up into two atoms of even the heaviest isotope of palladium (each with $110 - 46 = 64$ neutrons), there would be $143 - 128 = 15$ extra neutrons set free. Most of these extra neutrons remain, however, in the nuclei produced, which emit β-rays and so increase their atomic numbers. The neutrons, being uncharged, have very long free paths, and unless the mass of material is large they will escape from it without causing a fission; there must, however, be some critical size at which the neutrons liberated by the fission of one atom can on the average break up one atom more; above this size they can each break up more than one atom. This is the principle of the atomic bomb, in which two pieces of the fissile material, each a little below the critical size, are suddenly brought together (by the explosion of a small charge), when the rate of fission increases with enormous rapidity, and the whole energy of a large fraction of the mass that is lost is released in about a millionth of a second.

The critical size for ^{238}U, broken up only by fast neutrons, is calculated to be about 40 tons, which for practical purposes is prohibitive; for ^{235}U, which is broken by slow neutrons much more easily, it is not more than a few kilograms. The separation of the ^{235}U from the 140 times as abundant ^{238}U is, however, like all isotopic separations, extremely laborious; it involves either a lengthy diffusion of volatile uranium compounds if they can be found, or the use of something like a giant mass spectrograph. This has to some extent been carried out, but another source of energy has been found in plutonium, ^{239}Pu. The theory of atomic fission worked out by Bohr and Wheeler[1443-5] (and verified experimentally) showed that both ^{235}U and ^{239}Pu would be broken up by slow neutrons. Now ^{239}Pu can be made from the abundant ^{238}U by bombardment with neutrons of moderate speed (about 5 e.v.), and it has the great advantage that it can be separated by chemical means; for example, it can be co-precipitated in the reduced (IV) state, and then oxidized to the hexavalent state to remove the carrier.

It is for the production of this ^{239}Pu that the atomic 'piles' were constructed. In these, pure (usually metallic) uranium is embedded in graphite; the fast neutrons (usually started by casual cosmic rays) are reduced to thermal (gas-kinetic) speeds of about 0·025 e.v. by passing through 40 cm. of graphite, and some of them break up other ^{235}U atoms, while others are absorbed by ^{238}U atoms which they convert through ^{239}U into ^{239}Np and so into ^{239}Pu. The working of the pile depends on the conditions being such that the neutrons given by one ^{235}U fission on the average break up exactly one more ^{235}U. If the number is below this the chain dies down, and if above, it leads to an explosion. The regulation is effected by inserting rods of a material which absorbs neutrons, such as cadmium; these can be pushed in or pulled out as required.

The immense scale on which this work was carried out in America during the war (with 125,000 workmen at a cost of 2×10^9 dollars, the target aimed at being between 1 kg. of plutonium per month and 1 kg. per day[1352]) made it possible to obtain from the piles some of the other products, such as ^{237}U and ^{237}Np, and further to obtain by the bombardment of the plutonium the last two elements americium and curium—all these in weighable quantities.

THERE are three natural isotopes of uranium, whose mass numbers and abundances are:

Mass numbers	234^a	235	238
Abundance per cent.	0·008	0·7	99·3

$$a = {}^{1436}$$

They undergo the following spontaneous changes:*

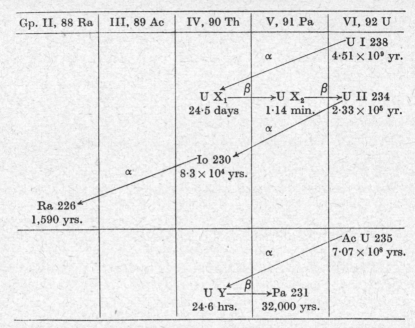

Gp. II, 88 Ra	III, 89 Ac	IV, 90 Th	V, 91 Pa	VI, 92 U

U I 238
4·51 × 10⁹ yr.

α

U X₁ —β→ U X₂ —β→ U II 234
24·5 days   1·14 min.   2·33 × 10⁵ yr.

α

Io 230
8·3 × 10⁴ yrs.

α

Ra 226
1,590 yrs.

Ac U 235
7·07 × 10⁸ yrs.

α

U Y —β→ Pa 231
24·6 hrs.   32,000 yrs.

Of the artificial isotopes of uranium[1446-7,1449] ^{237}U is made from ^{238}U by $(n, 2n)$; it goes in 7 days to ^{237}Np, which can be isolated from the products of the big piles.

^{239}U is formed by the action of resonance neutrons of about 5 e.v. on ^{238}U, and goes in 23 minutes by a β-ray change to ^{239}Np.

Trans-uranium Elements and their Production

93 Neptunium. Seaborg and Perlman[1454] find that the amount of neptunium in pitchblende is certainly less than 1 part in 10⁹, and there is no evidence that there is any. 93 was the first trans-uranium element to be discovered (E. M. McMillan and P. A. Abelson, Berkeley, 1940). There are three isotopes, 237, 238, 239.

^{237}Np is made through ^{237}U by bombarding ^{238}U with moderately fast neutrons, and also from ^{235}U by double neutron capture; it is formed in the pile to about 1/1,000 of the plutonium, and can be isolated if required.

* The times given throughout are those of half-life. In the bombardments described later the symbols in brackets, such as (d, n), give the nature of the bombarding particle followed by that of the particle or ray emitted on bombardment.

This is by far the stablest of the isotopes, and is the one to be used for working out the chemistry of the element. Its half-life is $2 \cdot 25 \times 10^6$ years (α-change, to ^{233}Pa).

^{238}Np is got from ^{238}U by d, $2n$; it goes by a β-change in 2 days to ^{238}Pu.

^{239}Np is formed spontaneously (β, 23 min.) from ^{239}U. It goes by a β-change in $2 \cdot 3$ days to ^{239}Pu.

94 Plutonium. Seaborg and Perlman[1454] find 1 part in 10^{14} of ^{239}Pu in a pitchblende concentrate from the Great Bear Lakes in Canada.

^{238}Pu, made from ^{238}Np as above, was discovered by Seaborg *et al.*[1446]; its half-life (α) is about 40 years; it changes into ^{234}U.

^{239}Pu is made from ^{238}U by neutrons of about 5 e.v.; it has an α-ray change with a half-life of 24,110 years. Hence it occurs in nature, and it has been separated from pitchblende and from carnotite, in both of which it occurs to about 1 part in 10^{14} (this means 1/100 microgram per ton). ^{239}Pu is the material used along with ^{235}U in the atomic bomb.

^{241}Pu is formed by the change α, n from ^{238}U. It has a slow β-change to give ^{241}Am.

95 Americium. ^{241}Am was first made by G. T. Seaborg, R. A. James, and L. O. Morgan in 1944, by bombarding ^{239}Pu with 40 m.e.v. α-particles in the Berkeley 60-inch cyclotron. It is an α-emitter with a half-life of 500 years. It is also formed as above by a spontaneous β-change from ^{241}Pu.

^{242}Am is formed by the action of slow neutrons on ^{241}Am; it undergoes a spontaneous β-change in 18 hours into ^{242}Cm.

96 Curium was discovered in 1944 by G. T. Seaborg, R. A. James, and A. Ghiorsi. Two isotopes are known, 240 and 242. ^{240}Cm is made (α, $3n$) by the action of 44 m.e.v. α-particles on ^{239}Pu. Its natural half-life is 1 month.

^{242}Cm is made as described above from ^{239}Pu or ^{241}Am; it is an α-emitter with the short life of 160 days.

PROPERTIES OF THE URANIDE ELEMENTS

The question whether the fifth quantum group of electrons which is completed up to 18 in gold begins to expand towards 32, as the fourth does in cerium, and if so where, has now been settled by the chemical properties of these newly discovered elements. In the lanthanides the beginning of the expansion is marked by the main valency becoming and remaining 3. With these later elements of the seventh period there is scarcely any sign of valencies other than those of the group until we come to uranium. Thorium is practically always tetravalent (very unstable trihalides have recently been obtained); it is particularly remarkable that it is so even in the nitride, which is Th_3N_4, though the existence of the very stable nitrides VN, ZrN, and HfN shows that in this type of molecule the trivalent state is greatly stabilized. Up to and including uranium, the group valency is always the stablest, but beyond this no further rise of valency occurs, such

---

[1454] G. T. Seaborg and M. L. Perlman, *J.A.C.S.* 1948, **70**, 1571.

as we find in rhenium and osmium. Hence the point of departure of the new series of structures (corresponding to lanthanum in the first series) is obviously uranium, and the series should be called the uranides.

With the succeeding elements the lower valencies become increasingly stable, these lower valencies being 4 for 93 and 94, and 3 for 95 and 96; it is doubtful whether 96 Cm has any valency other than 3. The valencies are given in the following table, the most stable being doubly, and the next most stable singly, underlined.

89 Ac		3			
90 Th		(3)	4̲		
91 Pa				5̲	
92 U		3	4̲	5	6̲
93 Np		3	4̲	5	6
94 Pu		3	4̲	5	6
95 Am	2̲	3̳	4	?5	
96 Cm		3̳			

The atomic structures of the isolated atoms are not certain (see Meggers[1455]), as is true also to some extent of the lanthanide elements, but from the chemical point of view this is of less importance, since the energies of the alternative orbits do not greatly differ. We may compare for the (not always realizable) trivalent ions the number n of electrons in the penultimate quantum group (assuming that there are 8 in the outermost group) in the two series:

Lanthanides .	57 La	58 Ce	59 Pr	60 Nd	61 Il	62 Sm	63 Eu	64 Gd
'Actinides' .	89 Ac	90 Th	91 Pa	92 U	93 Np	94 Pu	95 Am	96 Cm
Number n .	18	19	20	21	22	23	24	25

The chemical development is not wholly dissimilar in the two series. Among the lanthanides cerium has the tetravalency of a fourth group element almost as strongly marked as its trivalency, but this higher valency vanishes in the succeeding members of the period; in the elements of the seventh period the group valency is maintained as the most stable up to 6* in uranium, and then this fades out, the trivalency of the third group being ultimately regained. The position of curium should be noticed; it has as many electrons in its outer groups as gadolinium, the penultimate group in the trivalent ion being 25 in both—i.e. half-way between 18 and 32. This implies great stability, which as we have seen (III. 450) is supported for gadolinium by the valency being only 3, while the preceding element europium can be di- and the succeeding element terbium tetravalent. With curium we have in the same way 3 as the only valency, while the preceding element americium can be divalent like europium.

* It was pointed out by Bohr (*Theory of Spectra and Atomic Constitution*, 1922) that the f electrons will be less firmly held in the fifth than in the fourth quantum group; hence we might expect the valencies to be higher here than in the corresponding lanthanides.

[1455] W. F. Meggers, *Science*, 1947, **105**, 514.

These elements resemble the lanthanides in other ways as well. The successive members show a contraction like that of the lanthanides (III. 445) due to the smaller screening effect of the electrons in the f subgroup. Zachariasen[1456] has shown by X-ray measurements that this occurs with the radii of the trivalent and tetravalent ions, as well as with the A—O distances in the hexavalent $[AO_2]^{++}$ ions. The figures are:

| | Radius of | | A—O distance in hexavalent $[AO_2]^{++}$ |
	Trivalent ion	Tetravalent ion	
Ac	1·13	..	..
Th	..	1·10	..
Pa	..	..	..
U	1·04	0·89	1·91
Np	1·02	0·88	1·90
Pu	1·01	0·86	1·89
Am	1·00	0·85	..
Cm	..	..	..

The paramagnetism also is similar: in the table, n is, as before, the number of electrons in the penultimate quantum group; the paramagnetic susceptibilities are multiplied by 10^3; they show a change corresponding to the 'first hump' in the lanthanides (III. 442).

n					
18	Th^{iv}, U^{vi}	Dia.		La^{iii}, Ce^{iv}	Dia.
19	Np^{vi}	+2·45		Ce^{iii}	+2·35
20	U^{iv}				
20	Np^{v}	+4·0		Pr^{iii}	5·05
20	Pu^{vi}				
21	Np^{iv}	+3·9		Nd^{iii}	5·05
22	Pu^{iv}	+1·5		..	..
23	Pu^{iii}	+0·35		Sm^{iii}	1·0
24	Am^{iii}	+0·3		Eu^{iii}	3·60

The absorption spectra again have the remarkable 'rare earth' characteristic (III. 443) of being composed of very narrow bands, often at low temperatures only some 5 A broad.

A brief account of the chemistry of the individual trans-uranium elements follows.

Neptunium has the oxidation states VI, V, IV, and III, with a shift of stability towards the lower states as compared with uranium. The pentavalent state is fairly stable with neptunium, more so than with uranium or plutonium. The oxidation of the tetra- to the hexavalent state is much easier with neptunium than with plutonium; it can be effected by cold permanganate with the former but not with the latter.[1452]

All four states have been obtained in water[1457]; strong oxidizing agents

[1456] W. H. Zachariasen, *J.A.C.S.* 1948, T.S. 57.

[1457] L. B. Magnusson, J. C. Hindman, and T. A. LaChapelle, ib. T.S. 88.

will give the hexavalent neptunyl acetate $Na[NpO_2(O \cdot CO \cdot CH_3)_3]$, and electrolytic reduction in an atmosphere of nitrogen gives the trivalent form.

There is a borohydride $Np(BH_4)_4$.

The chief oxide is NpO_2, which can only be oxidized to Np_3O_8 with difficulty; an oxide NpO has also been described.

Halides of the type NpX_3, NpX_4, and NpX_6 are known; the fluoride (and also the iodate) of the reduced neptunium is insoluble in water, while that of the oxidized (presumably $[NpO_2]^+$ or $[NpO_2]^{++}$) is soluble.[1452]

Plutonium. Its chemistry was examined by Seaborg and Wahl[1452] and by Harvey *et al.*[1451] in Canada, with about 5 mg. of ^{239}Pu from an atomic pile; their results essentially agree. The plutonium was separated by the co-precipitation of its trifluoride with lanthanum trifluoride, and was then removed from the latter by oxidation to a soluble hexavalent fluoride, presumably PuO_2F_2.

Plutonium has three well-marked valencies of III, IV, and VI, of which IV is the most stable, though the compounds easily disproportionate to III+VI, the latter appearing as $[PuO_2]^{++}$.

Trivalent plutonium is a much weaker reducing agent than trivalent uranium, which liberates hydrogen from water; tetravalent plutonium is reduced to trivalent by trivalent uranium, as well as by hydroxylamine, sulphur dioxide, iodine ion, etc. Pu^{iii} is stable in solution in absence of air (and forms a hydrated ion, as is shown by the absorption spectrum)[1458]; in presence of air it is slowly oxidized to Pu^{iv}; permanganate in acid solution oxidized Pu^{iii} to Pu^{iv} in the cold, but to Pu^{vi} at 60°. Pu^{iii} salts are blue; ammonia precipitates $Pu(OH)_3$ as a dirty-blue solid very easily oxidized by air; PuF_3 is insoluble. Pu^{iii} salts form complexes very readily; there is a series of double sulphates $M[Pu(SO_4)_2]$, $4\,H_2O$ as with the lanthanide metals; for the crystal structure of $NaPuF_4$ see Zachariasen.[1459]

Tetravalent plutonium salts are pink or greenish; PuO_2 (insoluble) is brown, $Pu(OH)_4$ brownish-green, and PuF_4 (insoluble) yellow. They form complexes very readily; complex (or at least double) thiocyanates, oxalates, and sulphates are known; for the crystal structure of the complex salts $M[PuF_5]$ (M = Na, K, and Rb) see reference [1459]. A Pu^{iv} salt can be removed from aqueous solution by adding acetyl acetone and extracting with benzene.

Pentavalent plutonium[1460] is unstable (though more stable than pentavalent uranium), and goes to a mixture of Pu^{vi} with Pu^{iv} or Pu^{iii}. It occurs as the ion $[PuO_2]^+$.

Hexavalent plutonium. Plutonium is not oxidized to this by hydrogen peroxide, as uranium is to U^{vi}, but it is by other strong oxidizing agents, such as dichromate, permanganate, ceric salts, and electrolytic oxidation. The Pu^{vi} compounds include the slightly soluble ammonium plutonate

[1458] J. C. Hindman, *J.A.C.S.* 1948, T.S. 89.
[1459] W. H. Zachariasen, ib. **70**, 2147.
[1460] R. E. Connick, ib. 1949, **71**, 687.

(presumably $(NH_4)_2PuO_4$) and a series of mostly brown or orange plutonyl salts PuO_2X_2. The plutonyl salts are usually orange, and pink in dilute solution. They are very like the uranyl salts, except in their oxidizing power. The nitrate $PuO_2(NO_3)_2$ is soluble in ether; the complex sodium acetate is isomorphous with its uranium analogue.

Among the individual plutonium compounds the following should be mentioned.

Plutonium hydride and deuteride.[1461] At 400–500° under 350 mm. pressure of hydrogen PuH_2 and PuH_3 are formed; they give solid solutions in one another; the heat of formation of PuH_2 is 32·5 k.cals. per mole. Deuterium behaves in the same way, but the dissociation pressure is 1·5 times as great as with hydrogen.

A borohydride $Pu(BH_4)_4$ or perhaps $Pu(BH_4)_3$ has been obtained.

The oxides PuO, PuO_2, and perhaps Pu_2O_5 have been made. Pu^{iv} forms two differently coloured peroxides, with the probable compositions $2\,Pu^{iv}$, $1\,O_2$, $1\,OH$ (brown), and $2\,Pu^{iv}+2\,O$—O (red)[1462]; equilibria indicate that both have 2 Pu atoms in the molecule; there is no sign of a peroxide with 1 Pu.[1462] Thorium behaves in much the same way.[1451]

The known halides are of the types PuX_3 and PuX_4.[1463] At 900° PuF_4 forms PuF_3 and free fluorine. The tetrafluoride does not react with dry oxygen up to 600°, but at this temperature the trifluoride undergoes the reversible reaction

$$4\,PuF_3 + O_2 = 3\,PuF_4 + PuO_2.$$

Americium.[1464] In water[1465] this is mainly trivalent, and is very like the corresponding lanthanide europium. Only very powerful oxidizing agents such as sodium hypochlorite or alkaline hydrogen peroxide will oxidize trivalent americium, and even these have no effect on trivalent curium. Divalent americium can be got by the action of a powerful reducing agent such as sodium amalgam on the trivalent element; this resemblance to europium is emphasized by the fact that $AmSO_4$ can be co-precipitated with $EuSO_4$. Pentavalent americium probably occurs. The oxides AmO, Am_2O_3, and AmO_2 occur. AmO_2 is stable in air; $Am(OH)_3$ when ignited in air at 900–1,400° goes to AmO_2, which is reduced by hydrogen at 800° to AmO.

Halides. Only those of the type AmX_3 are known. AmO_2 is converted into the corresponding halide by hydrogen fluoride at 600°, by CCl_4 at 850°, by $AlBr_3$ at 500°, and by AlI_3 at 500°. X-rays show all these trihalides to be isomorphous with the corresponding plutonium compounds.[1466]

[1461] I. B. Johns, ib. T.S. 54.
[1462] R. E. Connick and W. H. McVey, ib. T.S. 91.
[1463] S. Fried and N. R. Davidson, ib. T.S. 53.
[1464] See further B. B. Cunningham, ib. T.S. 42.
[1465] S. G. Thompson, R. A. James, and L. O. Morgan, ib. T.S. 43.
[1466] S. Fried, ib. T.S. 55.

Curium.[1465,1467] The trivalent is certainly the stablest and probably the only valency state of curium, as it is of its lanthanide analogue gadolinium.

The only known oxide is Cm_2O_3, and the trifluoride CmF_3 is co-precipitated with lanthanum or other rare earth trifluorides, from which it can only be separated with difficulty.

[1467] L. B. Werner and I. Perlman, *J.A.C.S.* 1948, T.S. 44.

GROUP VII

THE HALOGENS

F Cl Br I 85(At)

Mn Tc Re [93 Np]

IN this group we have the extreme case of the resemblances among the later groups of the typical to the B elements. The halogens F—Cl—Br—I form the most perfect series we have, more so even that the alkali metals, since their behaviour is more diverse, not being so much confined to that of the simple ions. The resemblance of this series to the A elements Mn—Tc—Re is limited to the heptavalent compounds of the perchlorate-permanganate type. This limitation we now realize to be an inevitable result of the atomic structures; but it makes it desirable to treat the two sections of Group VII separately.

The Halogens, F, Cl, Br, I, At

The chief characteristic of these elements is their marked univalency, which is due to the atom having one electron less than the next inert gas. The most important classes of compounds of all these elements are (a) the simple univalent anions, and (b) the 1-covalent compounds. As the size of the atom increases we find, as we should expect, that the second class (b) tend to become more important than (a).

Apart from these compounds, the covalency can be increased by co-ordination, and further, with all but fluorine, the valency group is capable of expansion. The actual distribution of covalency maxima among the halogens is remarkable; it is as follows, the theoretical maxima being added in brackets: fluorine 1, or at most 2 (4); chlorine 4 (6); bromine 5 in BrF_5, otherwise 3 (6); iodine 7 (8). Fluorine never, so far as we know, exceeds a covalency of 2; it only attains this in the polymerized hydrogen fluoride, and only if a hydrogen bond is a covalency; in all other non-ionized compounds apart from possible resonance forms its covalency is 1.

In chlorine, on the other hand, where the maximum valency group is 12, it is only very rarely that a group of more than 8 is found, perhaps only in the unstable salts of the anion Cl_3^-, and in chlorine trifluoride ClF_3. But by co-ordination as donor the octet of chlorine very readily reaches a covalency of 4, as in the very stable perchlorates.

In bromine again the expansion of the octet is very rare, and seems to be confined to the tri- and pentafluorides BrF_5 and BrF_3, and certain perhalide ions as Br_3^- and $BrCl_2^-$; but here the limit of the covalency appears to be less than in chlorine, and seldom exceeds 3: the bromates are formed but not the perbromates. This is another example of the limitation of the covalency in the first long period, as we have already seen in chromium, arsenic, etc.

In iodine, as we should expect, high covalencies are frequent, rising to 6 in H_5IO_6 and 7 in the heptafluoride IF_7.

The differences in this series of elements are distributed in the usual way; chlorine and bromine are very similar to one another, but differ markedly from fluorine on the one side and iodine on the other. The changes in physical constants as we go along the series are shown in the Table which follows; the various heats of linkage (heats of formation from the atoms)[2] are given, and for each halogen the mean A—hal of all the known values for the covalent links that it forms.

	F	Cl	Br	I
At. wt. 1948 . . .	19·000	35·457	79·916	126·92
Rad. of atom .	0·64	0·99	1·14	1·33 A.U.
Rad. of ion (V.M.G. 1927)	1·33	1·81	1·96	2·20 ,,
Electron affinity[a] . .	98·5	92·5	87·1	79·2
				(k.cals./atom)
B. pt.	−187·9°	−34·11°	+58·8°	187°
M. pt.	−223°	−101·04°	−7·3°	113·7°
Abundance g./ton, crust .	270	480	[ca. 30]	0·3
Colour . . .	Pale yellow	Green-yellow	Brown	Violet
Thermal | 1,000° K. .	?	0·035%	0·23%	2·8%
Dissocn. / 2,000° K. .	?	52%	72·4%	89·5%
Normal potl. to H .	+2·8 v.	+1·36 v.	+1·08 v.	+0·58 v.
Mob. of ion/18° .	46·6	65·5	67·6	66·5
D.E.C. liquid . .	1·56/−184° C.	1·94/10°	3·15/25°	11·08/118°
Condy. liq. in mhos at m. pt. . . .	. .	10^{-16}	$5·5 \times 10^{-10}$	$5·2 \times 10^{-5}$
Trouton constant . .	18·8	20·4	21·9	22·9
Sol[y] in water g./100 g. 20°, 1 atm. .	(reacts)	0·59	3·6	0·018
Heats of linkage:[b]				
Hal—hal . . .	33·3	57·8	53·8	51·2 k.cals.
A—hal . . .	86·4	80·0	65·5	52·0 ,,

$$a = {}^1, \ b = {}^2.$$

As usual the heat of linkage to hydrogen falls off (132·4, 102·7, 87·3, 71·4) comparatively rapidly as the atomic weight of the halogen increases. In every case, with one significant exception (F—F; see note, p. 1146), the values fall for any given element from fluorine to iodine. The stability of the HXO_3 acids ('ate') is in the order $IO_3 > BrO_3 > ClO_3$. The readiness to form oxides is greatest with iodine, and the iodine oxides are by far the most stable; but the next readiest is chlorine, of which at least four oxides are known, which are easy to make, although they are very unstable. Until a few years ago it was thought that fluorine and bromine could not form oxides at all. This is now known to be untrue, but the oxides are difficult to make, and most, though not all, of them are very unstable.

Fluorine differs in so many respects from the other halogens that it will be convenient to treat it separately first, and then discuss chlorine, bromine, and iodine together.

[1] Pauling, *Chemical Bond*, p. 341.   [2] See Introduction, p. xxxi.

FLUORINE[3,4]

FLUORINE is in some ways the most interesting of the halogens. It is almost as widely distributed in the earth's crust as chlorine itself. According to V. M. Goldschmidt[5] the proportions in grammes per ton (parts per million) are F 270, Cl 480, making the former 56 per cent. of the latter. In sea-water the proportion of F to Cl is very small, about 7×10^{-5}.[6] In spite of this our knowledge of the properties of fluorine was until lately very scanty, and is still small in comparison with its interest and its abundance. This is mainly due to two causes. Firstly, the enormous affinity of fluorine for silicon makes both free fluorine and fluorine ion attack silica and silicates, so that vessels of glass or quartz cannot be used in working with them; in experiments involving elementary fluorine, since this attacks many metals, the choice of containing vessels is still further limited. Certain metals, especially platinum and copper, can be used if the temperature is not too high, as they become covered with a protective film of fluoride; for higher temperatures the vessels can be made out of powdered fluorite CaF_2[7]; sintered corundum Al_2O_3 can also be used; the fluorine acts on this superficially, but the AlF_3 layer formed, not being volatile, protects the Al_2O_3 from further attack.[8] Secondly, the quantitative estimation of fluorine is of great practical difficulty, owing to the absence of suitable insoluble fluorides, and the great solubility of the silver salt. This deficiency of knowledge about the compounds of fluorine has been to a considerable extent made up during recent years, especially by the work of Ruff on the inorganic compounds, and that of Swarts, and recently Midgley and his collaborators, on the organic.

The most remarkable characteristics of fluorine, which it is not always easy to refer to a common cause, are:

1. Its extreme electronegativity.

2. Its large heat of ionization, and of covalency formation (Table VI B, p. xxxi). Where the heats of linkage A—F and A—Cl are both known for the same element A, A—F is on the average 15 k.cals. greater than A—Cl. Since the heat of linkage in the molecule of elementary fluorine is only 33·3, 24·5 k.cals. less than in Cl_2 (57·8), it is obvious why fluorine has such an enormously greater chemical activity than the other halogens. In particular, its links to boron, hydrogen, silicon, and carbon are among the strongest of known covalent bonds.

3. Its low covalency, never, so far as we know, exceeding 2, and perhaps never reaching it.

4. *Per contra*, fluorine has tendency to bring out the highest covalency

[3] H. J. Emeleus (*J.C.S.* 1942, 441) has a general lecture on Fluorine.

[4] For an account of fluorine chemistry in general, especially on the technical side, see *J. Ind. Eng. Chem.* 1947, **39**, 236–434.

[5] *J.C.S.* 1937, 656.

[6] T. G. Thompson and H. J. Taylor, *J. Ind. Eng. Chem.* (*Anal.*), 1933, **5**, 87.

[7] O. Ruff and A. Riebeth, *Z. anorg. Chem.* 1928, **173**, 373.

[8] O. Hennebohn and W. Klemm, ib. 1936, **229**, 340.

of the atom to which it is attached, as we see in $[HF_2]^-$, $[SiF_6]^{--}$, SF_6, and OsF_8. The only known compounds of the types MA_8 and MA_7 are OsF_8 and IF_7, the only compounds of the type MA_6 in which A is not fluorine are UCl_6, WCl_6, and probably WBr_6. This peculiarity is no doubt connected with the small size of the covalent fluorine atom (two-thirds of chlorine and less than half of iodine), and with the large heat of linkage A—F.

5. The weakness of the true (as well as the apparent) acidity of hydrogen fluoride, and its remarkable tendency to polymerize.

6. The abnormal solubilities of many of its salts as compared with those of the other halogens, as, for example, with silver and the alkaline earths.

7. The tendency for the fluoride to be ionized when the other halides are not, as with aluminium, tin, mercury, etc. This results on Fajans' principles from the small size of the fluorine ion; but the magnitude of the effect is remarkable.

The differences to be expected from the structure of fluorine and its position in the periodic table are those due to its small size, and the limitation of the valency group to 8, which latter cuts out a series of types of compound formed by the heavier halogens; but these are clearly insufficient to explain all the differences observed in practice. Often the most we can do is to emphasize and collect the peculiarities, in the hope that they will some day be explained.

Elementary Fluorine

[For physical properties see Table, p. 1098].

Fluorine was of course not isolated until long after the other halogens.* Its affinity for other elements is so strong that it can only be separated from its compounds by the most vigorous means, and even then, unless special precautions are taken, it will combine with its surroundings. Free fluorine is produced in a few reactions, as by the action of heat on the double lead fluoride K_3PbF_7 (which can be made from lead dioxide and potassium fluoride), or on AgF_2, PtF_4, OsF_8, CoF_3, etc.; but either the yields are small, or the decomposition temperature is so high that no containing vessel will resist the fluorine, or the compounds themselves can only be made by the use of elementary fluorine; so that the only practical method of preparing it is by means of electrolysis. It was by this method that fluorine was originally isolated by Moissan[9] in 1886, by electrolysing a solution of potassium hydrogen fluoride KHF_2 in hydrogen fluoride at a low temperature (about $-25°$) with platinum electrodes. All the subsequent methods of preparation are based on this, though the details have been modified.[10] Moissan used not more than 25 per cent. of KHF_2 in HF

---

* The discoverers, and dates of discovery, of the free halogens are: fluorine, Moissan, 1886; chlorine, Scheele, 1774; bromine, Balard, 1826; iodine, Courtois, 1811.

[9] H. Moissan, *C.R.* 1886, **102**, 1543; **103**, 202, 256.

[10] See O. Ruff, *Ber.* 1936, **69**, A 181, a general lecture on fluorine from which much of this is taken.

at $-23°$ to $-30°$, with platinum electrodes: others have used KH_3F_4 (m. pt. 65°) at 50–200° with a nickel anode (Lebeau,[11] Cady[12]) (this method, at as low a temperature as possible, is probably the best): or KHF_2 (m. pt. 227°) at 240–250° with a copper cathode and a graphite anode.[13-16] Dennis[17] avoided a diaphragm by using a V-shaped copper vessel; this was modified by Henne.[18]

Physical Properties of Elementary Fluorine

(and see p. 1098)

Concordant measurements of electron diffraction[19,20] show the F—F distance to be $1·44±0·01$ A, giving the (purely covalent) radius as $0·72$ A, 12 per cent. longer than that ($0·64$) derived from its compounds, where the link is partly ionic. The D.E.C. is $1·56$ at $-183°$; the dipole moment is zero.[21] A saturated solution of [solid] chlorine in liquid fluorine at $-195°$ contains $1·04$ per cent. Cl_2.[21]

Chemical Properties of F_2

Fluorine is quite exceptionally reactive. It is the most electronegative of the elements; the ion has the strongest electroaffinity; its heat of hydration is greater than that of any other halogen ion, or of any alkaline cation.[22]

Solid fluorine explodes when brought in contact with liquid hydrogen at $-252·5°$ C.* Fluorine has no action on oxygen or ozone, on the rare gases, or on nitrogen; otherwise it reacts with practically all elements, though some of them must be heated, because the fluorine forms a protective layer of fluoride on the surface.

Fluorine reacts with water with the utmost ease, giving oxygen mixed with ozone, hydrogen peroxide, and apparently other oxidizing substances which have not yet been isolated.[23] The solution of fluorine in water or alkaline solutions is a very strong oxidizing agent.

Both elementary fluorine and, rather surprisingly, fluorine ion are highly

---

* It will be shown later, however (p. 1102), that in the complete absence of catalysts this does not happen.

[11] P. Lebeau and A. Damiens, *C.R.* 1925, **181**, 917.

[12] G. H. Cady, *J.A.C.S.* 1934, **56**, 1431.

[13] W. L. Argo, F. C. Mathers, B. Humiston, and C. O. Anderson, *J. Phys. Chem.* 1919, **23**, 348.

[14] F. Meyer and W. Sandow, *Ber.* 1921, **54**, 759.

[15] G. H. Cady and J. H. Hildebrand, *J.A.C.S.* 1930, **52**, 3839.

[16] K. Fredenhagen, D.R.P. 493, 873 (1928).

[17] L. M. Dennis, J. M. Veeder, and E. G. Rochow, *J.A.C.S.* 1931, **53**, 3263.

[18] A. L. Henne, ib. 1938, **60**, 96.   [19] L. O. Brockway, ib. 1348.

[20] M. T. Rogers, V. Schomaker, and D. P. Stevenson, ib. 1941, **63**, 2610.

[21] E. Kanda, *Bull. Chem. Soc. Japan*, 1937, **12**, 458.

[22] K. Fajans, *Naturwiss.* 1921, **9**, 733.

[23] See F. Fichter and W. Bladergroen, *Helv. Chim. Acta*, 1927, **10**, 549, 555, 559, 560; F. F. and E. Brunner, *J.C.S.* 1928, 1862; *Helv. Chim. Acta*, 1929, **12**, 214, 305; F. F. and A. Goldach, ib. 1930, **13**, 378.

poisonous.[24-5] It is said, however,[26] that fluorine ion in concentrations less than 1 p.p.m. in the water-supply is not harmful to health, and may even be beneficial.

Of the compounds of fluorine many have already been dealt with under the other elements they contain. But there remain to be discussed (1) hydrogen fluoride and its salts, (2) organic compounds with fluorine attached to carbon, and (3) the oxides of fluorine.

HYDROGEN FLUORIDE

THIS is one of the most remarkable of the compounds of fluorine, and in some ways it is unique. The action of hydrogen fluoride as a catalyst in organic reactions is discussed below (p. 1132), in the C—F section.

The affinity of hydrogen for fluorine is very great; the heat of formation of the H—F link (132·4 k.cals.)[27] is probably greater than that of any other single link, with the exception of B—F (140·6 k.cals.); even the double C=C link only involves 146 k.cals.

Moissan and Dewar found that when solid fluorine is brought in contact with liquid hydrogen at −252·5° (F_2, m. pt. −223°; H_2, b. pt. −252·7°) it explodes. The heat evolved by the combustion of one litre of the gases in question is for H_2+F_2 2,860 cals., for H_2+Cl_2 980 cals., for H_2 and O_2 1,740 cals., roughly in the ratio $3:1:2$.

At the same time there is evidence that the combination does not proceed at all rapidly in the absence of catalysts. Eyring has shown[28] that even at the ordinary temperature the two gases on mixing do not normally react; but occasionally, especially in the presence of impurities, they explode violently. Theory would lead us to expect a heat of activation of 50 k.cals., while a chain reaction, like that between hydrogen and chlorine, should not begin below 150°. These conclusions are supported by Bodenstein who found[29] that in magnesium vessels at the ordinary temperature there is practically no reaction even in ultraviolet light, not even when chlorine is added. This supports the view that the reaction, exactly like those of chlorine and bromine, goes through the atoms, but that the reaction chains are exceptionally easily broken on the walls of the vessel. It must be remembered that the reaction between hydrogen and chlorine is rapid only because of the great length of the reaction chains.

Hydrogen fluoride is commonly made by the action of strong sulphuric acid on calcium fluoride in lead vessels. But for its preparation in quantity it is better to heat the 'acid' fluoride KHF_2.[30] As it is very difficult to

[24] See E. Deussen, *Deutsch. Z. f. ges. Med.* 1923, **2**, 14.
[25] See K. Roholm, *Fluorine Intoxication* (especially among cryolite workers), Lewis and Co., London, 1937. Reviewed in *Nature*, 1937, **140**, 483.
[26] M. S. Nichols, *Amer. J. Public Health*, 1939, **29**, 991.
[27] H. v. Wartenberg and H. Schütza, *Z. anorg. Chem.* 1932, **206**, 65.
[28] H. Eyring and L. S. Kassel, *J.A.C.S.* 1933, **55**, 2796.
[29] M. Bodenstein and H. Jokusch, *Z. anorg. Chem.* 1927, **231**, 24.
[30] For details of its preparation in quantity see W. Klatt, ib. 1935, **222**, 236.

dehydrate the acid, the anhydrous substance is best prepared by first dehydrating the salt KHF_2 by electrolysis.[31] The apparatus for working with it should be made wholly of metal, and by preference of platinum, gold, or silver. The pure acid produces very painful and dangerous wounds on the skin, which, however, can be healed if they are immediately treated with magnesium or calcium hydroxide.[32-3]

Physical Properties of Hydrogen Fluoride[34-47]

These are some of the more important (with the water values added for comparison): b. pt. $+19.54°$ C.[40]; m. pt. $-83.7°$[46]; crit. temp. $230.2°$[37] (water $374°$). Heat of fusion 1.094 k.cals. for 20 g. (water 1.44 k.cals./18 g.). Heat of evaporation of HF[42]: (1) to saturated vapour $(HF)_{3.5}$ 1.78 k.cals., (2) to monomeric HF gas 7.80 k.cals., for 20 g. (water 9.70 k.cals. for 18 g.); Trouton 26.6 (water 26.0). For its thermodynamic values generally see reference [51]. For the spectra see [57-60]. Diamagnetic susceptibility [52]. The viscosity is 0.570 centipoises at $-50°$, and 0.256 at $0°$, almost the same as

[31] J. H. Simons, *Chem. Rev.* 1931, **8**, 213.

[32] K. Fredenhagen and M. Wellmann, *Z. angew. Chem.* 1932, **45**, 537.

[33] W. Klatt, *Z. anorg. Chem.* 1935, **222**, 238.

[34] J. H. Simons, *J.A.C.S.* 1924, **46**, 2179.

[35] J. H. Simons and J. H. Hildebrand, ib. 2183.

[36] R. T. Birge and O. R. Wulf, *Phys. Rev.* 1928, ii. **31**, 917. (Theory for the hydrogen halides, based on the energy levels.)

[37] P. A. Bond and D. A. Williams, *J.A.C.S.* 1931, **53**, 34. (Critical temperature.)

[38] J. H. Simons and J. W. Bouknight, ib. 1932, **54**, 129. (Density and surface tension.)

[39] J. Dahmlos and G. Jung, *Z. physikal. Chem.* 1933, B **21**, 317. (Heat values.)

[40] K. Fredenhagen, G. Cadenbach, and W. Klatt, ib. 1933, **164**, 176. (Some physical properties, but mainly on HF as a solvent.)

[41] K. Fredenhagen, *Z. anorg. Chem.* 1933, **210**, 210. (Vapour density and heats of evaporation.)

[42] K. Fredenhagen, W. Klatt, H. Kunz, and U. Butzke, ib. 1934, **218**, 161. (Dissociation isotherms at the ordinary temperature: heats of dissociation.)

[43] G. Briegleb, *Z. physikal. Chem.* 1942, B **52**, 368. (Same subject.)

[44] E. O. Salant and D. E. Kirkpatrick, *Phys. Rev.* 1934, ii. **46**, 318. (Rotation spectrum.)

[45] Id., ib. 1935, ii. **48**, 945. (Same subject.)

[46] G. H. Cady, *J.A.C.S.* 1934, **56**, 1431.

[47] K. Fredenhagen and J. Dahmlos, *Z. anorg. Chem.* 1928, **178**, 272.

[48] S. H. Bauer, J. Y. Beach, and J. H. Simons, *J.A.C.S.* 1939, **61**, 19.

[49] F. Günther, K. Holm, and H. Strunz, *Z. physikal. Chem.* 1939, B **43**, 229.

[50] Id., ib. B **44**, 474.

[51] G. M. Murphy and J. F. Vance, *J. Chem. Phys.* 1939, **7**, 806.

[52] P. Ehrlich, *Z. anorg. Chem.* 1942, **249**, 219.

[53] N. B. Hannay and C. P. Smyth, *J.A.C.S.* 1946, **68**, 171.

[54] A. J. Weith, M. E. Hobbs, and P. M. Gross, ib. 1948, **70**, 805.

[55] H. A. Benesi and C. P. Smyth, *J. Chem. Phys.* 1947, **15**, 337.

[56] R. A. Oriani and C. P. Smyth, *J.A.C.S.* 1948, **70**, 125.

[57] A. M. Buswell, R. L. Maycock, and W. H. Rodebush, *J. Chem. Phys.* 1939, **7**, 856.

[58] Id., ib. 1940, **8**, 362.   [59] A. L. Wahrhaftig, ib. 349.

[60] L. A. Woodward and H. J. V. Tyrrell, *Trans. Far. Soc.* 1942, **38**, 513.

that of ethyl ether.[63] The dielectric constant is 174·8 at −73°, 83·6/0° (water 87·9/0°).

The electron diffraction of the vapour[48] indicates that there are no 6-rings, but zigzag polymers, probably of several kinds. Distances are: in monomeric HF 1·00±0·06 (theory 0·94); F··H··F 2·55±0·03; angle F···F···F 140±5°; the hydrogen atoms are within 15° of the line joining the 2 F atoms. Debye-Scherrer photographs of solid HF at −182°[49-50] indicate tetragonal crystals, with 4 [HF]$_4$ molecules in the unit cell. Each [HF]$_4$ is a zigzag with F··H··F 2·7 A, and the F···F···F angle about 134°.[62]

Measurements of the dielectric polarization of the monomeric gas at lower pressures and higher temperatures gives $\mu = 1·91$ D[53,56]; very similar values are got in non-polar solvents.[54] As the pressure increases a mixture of open-chain polymers (not one only) is formed[55]; but there are signs that cyclic non-polar polymers are produced at still higher pressures.

Clusius[64-5] has shown that the specific heats of solid HF (like those of NH_3 and H_2O, and unlike those of HCl, HBr, HI, PH_3, and H_2S) do not indicate that at any temperature the oscillations (which seem to be those of H_2F_2 molecules) pass into rotations.

Electrical Conductivity. The lowest value reached[61] was $1·4 \times 10^{-5}$ reciprocal ohms; this was only obtained when special precautions were taken to secure purity; but probably the true conductivity is much less than this, and more of the order of that of water (4×10^{-8}); there are obvious difficulties in the purification, and the affinity for water in particular is enormous, the partition coefficient at low water concentrations for water between liquid and gas being greater than 100,000, and in hydrogen fluoride water acts as a strong electrolyte.

Hydrogen fluoride is miscible with water in all proportions, evolving much heat. The heat of mixture of HX with 400 H_2O is in k.cals./HX.

HX =	HF	HCl	HBr	HI
	11·6	17·2	19·9	19·2

But in solvents such as hydrocarbons its solubility is very small, even near its boiling-point. Thus in benzene and octane at 25° with HF vapour at 1 atm. pressure, the solubilities are as follows[66] (the normality in the gas, with a mean molecular weight of (HF)$_{3·45}$, is 0·045):

	Benzene	*n-Octane*
Grammes HF/litre . .	1·50	0·42
Norm. of soln. . .	0·0217	0·0061
Partn.: soln./gas . .	0·486	0·137

[61] K. Fredenhagen and G. Cadenbach, *Z. anorg. Chem.* 1928, **178**, 289.

[62] For a theoretical discussion of the configuration and potential energy of the (hypothetical) gaseous H_2F_2, see G. E. Evans and G. Glockler, *J. Chem. Phys.* 1948, **16**, 325.

[63] J. H. Simons and R. D. Dresdner, *J.A.C.S.* 1944, **66**, 1070.

[64] K. Clusius, *Z. Elektrochem.* 1933, **39**, 598.

[65] K. Clusius, K. Hiller, and J. V. Vaughen, *Z. physikal. Chem.* 1930, B **8**, 427.

[66] J. H. Simons, *J.A.C.S.* 1931, **53**, 83.

Hydrogen fluoride is more highly associated than any other known substance. From the vapour-pressure measurements of Thorpe and Hambly,[67] confirmed and extended by Fredenhagen,[41-2] it appears that at 1 atm. pressure and $19 \cdot 5°$ C. (the b. pt. of the liquid) hydrogen fluoride has in the vapour an association factor of $3 \cdot 45$, but that it is converted practically entirely into single HF molecules if either the pressure is lowered at this temperature of $19 \cdot 5°$ to 20 mm., or the temperature is raised at 1 atm. to $80°$ C. The heat absorbed when 20 g. of the vapour (of mean association factor $3 \cdot 45$) is converted wholly into monomeric HF is $6 \cdot 02$ k.cals.[42] Various ring-polymers have been suggested, such as H_6F_6[35,70] and H_4F_4,[68] but none of them could be confirmed,[41,66] and the electron diffraction results already mentioned[48] are all in favour of the vapour containing only a series of open-chain polymers, as was originally suggested by E. Baur in 1904.[71-2] An examination of the solid hydrates of HF has only given the series 1 $H_2O + 1$, 2, and 4 HF.[69] In view of the undoubted existence of $[HF_2]$ ions in solution in water, it should be noticed that Fredenhagen's results[41] give no indication of any special stability of a double polymer H_2F_2.

The state of liquid hydrogen fluoride, which is obviously polymerized, will be discussed later. That of the solid has been discussed already (p. 1104).

Hydrogen Fluoride in Water

The behaviour of hydrogen fluoride as an acid in aqueous solution has been the subject of numerous investigations,[73-7] and is very remarkable. It is certainly a weak acid, in the sense that in decinormal solution it is only some 10 per cent. ionized. But the dissociation constant calculated from the conductivity measurements falls continuously with dilution. It was shown by Pick[73] that these results could be explained by assuming that the solution contains, in addition to the monomeric HF and its ions H^+ and F^-, the ions F_2H^- as the anions of a strong acid, i.e. without there being any undissociated HF_2H present. This agrees with the great stability of the 'acid' fluorides, such as KHF_2. We thus have two equilibria, (a) between the undissociated monomeric acid HF and its ions:

$$HF \rightleftharpoons H^+ + F^-$$

[67] T. E. Thorpe and F. J. Hambly, *J.C.S.* 1889, **55**, 163.

[68] J. F. T. Berliner and R. M. Hann, *J. Phys. Chem.* 1928, **32**, 1142.

[69] G. H. Cady and J. H. Hildebrand, *J.A.C.S.* 1930, **52**, 3843.

[70] R. W. Long, J. H. Hildebrand, and W. E. Morrell, ib. 1943, **65**, 182.

[71] E. Baur, *Z. physikal. Chem.* 1904, **48**, 488.

[72] See further J. Kreuzer, ib. 1943, B **53**, 213.

[73] H. Pick, *Nernst Fertschrift* (*Z. phys. Chem.*), 1912, 360.

[74] C. W. Davies and L. J. Hudleston, *J.C.S.* 1924, **125**, 260.

[75] J. D. C. Anthony and L. J. Hudleston, ib. 1925, **127**, 1122.

[76] K. Fredenhagen and M. Wellmann, *Z. physikal. Chem.* 1932, **162**, 454.

[77] W. A. Roth, H. Pahlke, A. Bertram, and E. Börger, *Z. Elektrochem.* 1937, **43**, 350.

giving the equation $\quad\dfrac{[H^+].[F^-]}{[HF]} = K_1,$

and (b) between the F^- ion and its complex with HF

$$F^- + HF \rightleftharpoons F_2H^-$$

$$\dfrac{[F_2H^-]}{[F^-].[HF]} = K_2.$$

For K_1 Pick obtained the value $7\cdot2\times10^{-4}$; for K_2 $5\cdot5$. Pick's conclusions were entirely confirmed by Davies[74] from the transport numbers in aqueous hydrofluoric acid, and by Anthony and Hudleston[75] from the freezing-points of solutions of HF in water. For the second equilibrium constant K_2 they got the value $4\cdot7$, so that we may take the mean value $5\cdot1$ as being very near the truth. Measurements by Roth[77] of the heats of dilution of aqueous solutions of HF have further confirmed these conclusions.[78] E.M.F. measurements in concentration cells have given the fairly concordant values K_1 $6\cdot7\times10^{-4}$, K_2 $3\cdot96$.[78]

We may, therefore, take it that in water hydrogen fluoride is present partly as the strong (completely dissociated) acid $H[F_2H]$, with an equilibrium constant $5\cdot1$ for the formation of the anion from F^- and HF: and partly as a half-strong acid HF, with an Ostwald dissociation constant of $7\cdot2\times10^{-4}$, about half as strong as monochloracetic acid ($K = 15\cdot5\times10^{-4}$). The proportions of these various molecular species present in water at various concentrations are given below, being expressed (1) as normalities, and (2) as percentages of the total stoichiometric concentration of hydrogen fluoride.

Total stoich. norm. of HF	HF		F^-		F_2H^-		H^+	
	norm.	%	norm.	%	norm.	%	norm.	%
0·100	0·088	88	0·006	6	0·003	3	0·009	9
1·000	0·890	89	0·010	1	0·050	5	0·060	6

These relations are very peculiar, and are not found in any other known substance. In the first place the weakness of the simple acid HF is in startling contrast to the behaviour of the other halogen acids HCl, HBr, and HI, which are all strong electrolytes. This contrast agrees with the observation that the solubilities of the alkaline halides all fall as we go from lithium to caesium, except for the fluorides, where the change is in the opposite direction, as it is with the alkaline salts of all weak acids (see p. 95). This much greater relative stability of the covalent form in hydrogen fluoride is presumably connected with the much greater heat of formation of the link (H—F 132; H—Cl 103; H—Br 87; H—I 71 k.cals.). This weakness of HF as an acid is perhaps its most remarkable characteristic. But the occurrence of $[F_2H]^-$, the anion of the dimeric acid, is

[78] H. J. Broene and T. De Vries, *J.A.C.S.* 1947, **69**, 1644.

almost as remarkable, for two reasons. Firstly, it shows the very strong tendency of the fluorine ion F^- to take up HF, that it will do so in preference to water even in dilute aqueous solution.[79] Thus, in the decinormal solution above, where a third of the total ionized fluorine is thus combined, the stoichiometric concentration of H_2O is more than 600 times that of HF. Secondly, while HF is found to be weak acid, weaker than monochloracetic, $H[F_2H]$ is as strong an acid as hydrochloric. Why the tendency of the link in H—F to ionize should be so much increased by the combination of the fluorine with another HF molecule in $H[F\cdots H—F]$ we do not know.

This peculiar method of ionization of hydrogen fluoride in water is of special interest in relation to the very singular properties of liquid hydrogen fluoride as a solvent, which are discussed in the next section. For the boiling-point curves of the system HF—H_2O see Fredenhagen.[80]

Liquid Hydrogen Fluoride

The condition of hydrogen fluoride in the liquid state is very difficult to determine. It is undoubtedly polymerized or associated, as is shown, for example, by the high boiling-point, more than 100° higher than that of hydrogen chloride (−85°). This association (which is necessary in view of the association of the vapour) is supported by many other properties: by the high molecular heat of fusion,[39] by the small temperature coefficient of the surface tension (Eötvös constant): by the low and inconstant value[38] of the parachor, which is 34 at −80° and 36 at +20° (theory 42·8); the parachor values for associated liquids are usually low, and, as we should expect, rise with the temperature. Fredenhagen claims[41] to have determined the association factor as 3·5 from the elevation of the boiling-point by dissolved substances, but this of course gives the association not of the liquid but of the vapour, for which it provides a useful confirmation of the value (3·45) obtained (p. 1105) from the vapour density.

Liquid Hydrogen Fluoride as a Solvent

The behaviour of liquid hydrogen fluoride as a solvent is very remarkable and instructive; we owe our knowledge of it mainly to the work of Fredenhagen and his collaborators during the last twenty years.[81-2,84-6,91]

[79] For the theory of the formation of this ion see M. Davies, *J. Chem. Phys.* 1947, **15**, 739.

[80] H. Fredenhagen and E. Kerck, *Z. anorg. Chem.* 1944, **252**, 280.

[81] K. Fredenhagen and G. Cadenbach, ib. 1929, **178**, 289.

[82] Id., *Z. physikal. Chem.* 1930, **146**, 245.

[83] P. A. Bond and V. M. Stowe, *J.A.C.S.* 1931, **53**, 30.

[84] K. Fredenhagen, *Z. Elektrochem.* 1931, **37**, 684.

[85] K. Fredenhagen, G. Cadenbach, and W. Klatt, *Z. physikal. Chem.* 1933, **164**, 176.

[86] K. Fredenhagen and G. Cadenbach, ib. 201.

[87] W. Klatt, *Z. anorg. Chem.* 1935, **222**, 225.   [88] Id., ib. 289.

[89] Id., ib. 1937, **232**, 393.   [90] A. Hantzsch, *Ber.* 1930, **63**, 1789.

[91] H. Fredenhagen, *Z. anorg. Chem.* 1939, **242**, 23.

If the solvent power and the ionizing power of a liquid depended on its physical properties alone, we should expect to find a close parallel between hydrogen fluoride and water, both associated, and with nearly the same very high dielectric constant (83·6 and 87·9 at 0°). As a fact,[85] although liquid hydrogen fluoride surpasses even water in its ability to dissolve organic and inorganic compounds, and to form highly conducting solutions, its behaviour is in many ways quite different from that of water. This is a conclusive proof, as Fredenhagen says, that the power of a liquid to bring about both solution and ionization is not wholly determined by its physical properties, but depends on its chemical behaviour as well, and especially on its chemical reactions with the solute. The facts are as follows.[82,84-6,91]

Of all those substances, both organic and inorganic, which will dissolve in any solvents in the cold—of which the natural solubility is not too small—a very great majority will dissolve in liquid hydrogen fluoride, often to a large extent; in this respect it is a better solvent than water. Nearly everything which dissolves to more than a minute extent gives a solution of high and often very high conductivity, sometimes greater than that of the potassium halides in water; this is true of neutral organic substances such as alcohols and aldehydes as well as of salts, and also of water.

The cations present in these conducting solutions may be of the most diverse kinds, far more so than in water, including such ions as $[CH_3 \cdot OH_2]^+$ and $[H_2NO_3]^+$, but, in striking contrast to the behaviour of aqueous solutions, there is with very few exceptions only one kind of anion that can exist in a solution in liquid HF, and this is the anion derived from the solvent (as though the only anion in water was hydroxyl). This anion is always assumed to be $[F]^-$, but it is important to notice that, in view of the strong tendency of the fluoride ion to take up HF and form $[F_2H]^-$, it must be assumed to be this 'acid fluoride' anion $[F_2H]^-$. For simplicity, however, we may usually write it as $[F]^-$, as we write $[H]^+$ in water for $[H_3O]^+$.

A very few substances, mainly organic, will dissolve in hydrogen fluoride without ionization, but nearly all solutes conduct, and with these the following types of reaction occur.

1. With inorganic fluorides there is simple ionization to give $M^+ + F^-$.

2. Salts of other acids (and hydroxides) are converted into fluorides with liberation of the acid (or of water):

$$MA + HF = M^+ + F^- + HA.$$

The HA so liberated may either (a) be insoluble in the liquid and so be evolved (HCl, HCN, etc.), or (b) if it is an oxy-acid it nearly always forms an oxonium ion such as $[H_2NO_3]^+$: thus with KNO_3 4 ions are produced:

$$KNO_3 + 2 HF = K^+ + H_2NO_3^+ + 2 F^-.$$

3. With water or organic oxygen compounds similar oxonium fluorides are formed, such as $[H_3O]^+ + F^-$; alcohols, ketones, etc., as well as some

organic compounds free from oxygen, behave in the same way; with organic compounds the ionization is not always complete.

4. With a very few exceptionally strong oxy-acids and their salts (such as perchlorates) the anions remain as such in the solution.

5. Some acids react further with the solvent; thus sulphuric acid gives HSO_3F and chromic CrO_2F_2.

These various cases may be considered further.

Solutes which form non-conducting solutions include[84,88] acyl fluorides, some nitriles, trichloracetic acid (acetic acid ionizes), and some hydrocarbons such as benzene, as well as a few presumably covalent inorganic compounds such as mercuric cyanide and azide, and silver azide.

1. Metallic fluorides.[82-3] Those of monatomic metals dissolve easily (KF 38 g. in 100 c.c. solution at $0°$; LiF 5·3 g., 20 times as much as in water); the order for the alkalies is $Li < Na < K < Rb < Cs$, the same as in water. Fluorides of divalent metals dissolve slightly, and those of trivalent not at all, except AlF_3, which is very soluble. The MF salts behave as strong electrolytes, reaching a maximum molecular conductivity of about 260 at about $V = 40$.

2. That other salts form fluorides with liberation of their acids is proved by the precipitation of the fluoride if it is insoluble, by the facts that the cation cannot be precipitated by the salts of other acids, and that a metallic fluoride will not neutralize the free acid as the hydroxide would in water:

$$HA + MF = M^+ + A^- + HF;$$

further the conductivity of the salt is the exact sum of the conductivities of equivalents of the acid and the fluoride.

As to the behaviour of the acids thus liberated, (a) those which are insoluble and so expelled include HCl, HBr, HI, HCN, and HN_3. With HCl 0·1 g. KCl was dissolved[82] in 5 c.c. HF, with evolution of HCl. After a few seconds water was added and then $AgNO_3$: no turbidity was produced, though a concentration of 10 mg. to the litre would have caused it; at $-10°$ however, a supersaturated solution of HCl persists for a short time.[91] HBr and HI are similar,[83] and so are HCN and HN_3, though some of their metallic derivatives dissolve without ionizing.[92] (b) The formation of oxonium ions by many oxyacids is shown by the conductivities (see below), which indicate that 4 ions are produced. With water it has been shown by E.M.F. measurement that its addition to HF increases the concentration of fluoride ions; the elevation of the boiling-point shows[93] that $[H_3O]F$ has a dissociation constant of 0·06, so that in a normal solution it is about 25 per cent. ionized. The nitronium cation $[H_2NO_3]^{+*}$ was shown by Hantzsch to exist as nitrate in nitric acid, and to explain the high conductivity of the absolute (100 per cent.) acid.

---

* This has since been shown to be present largely in the unhydrated form $[NO_2]^+$, related to it as $[H]^+$ is to $[H_3O]^+$ (see V. 690).

[92] W. Klatt, *Z. physikal. Chem.* 1939, **185**, 306.
[93] K. and H. Fredenhagen, *Z. anorg. Chem.* 1939, **243**, 59.

3. For the behaviour of organic compounds in general see references [84-5,87-9]. Alcohols and phenols are only half-strong electrolytes, the former some 60 per cent. dissociated at about $V = 500$, and the phenols much less.[93] Aldehydes, ketones, and alkyl ethers conduct well; carboxylic acids partly give oxonium ions $R \cdot CO_2H_2^+$ and partly acyl fluorides, which do not ionize.[88] In the chloracetic acids the ionization falls off, and by trichloracetic has practically disappeared.

Of the oxygen-free compounds, amines react violently to give fully dissociated fluorides. Thioalcohols and thioethers behave like the oxygen compounds. Of the hydrocarbons[94] the paraffins are insoluble, but benzene gives a colourless 2·2 per cent. non-conducting solution; anthracene gives a 3·1 per cent. green solution, whose conductivity indicates a 59 per cent. ionized salt.

4. The salts of a few very strong acids ($HClO_4$, HBF_4, and perhaps HIO_4) can form their own anions in hydrogen fluoride, instead of going to $F^- + HClO_4$, etc. The reluctance of the ClO_4 ion to co-ordinate with hydrogen, which is the cause of its great strength as an acid, is apparently even greater than that of HF; if HF could easily form H_2F^+ the pure acid would conduct owing to the presence of

$$[H_2F]^+[F_2H]^- \text{ (as of } [H_2NO_3] \cdot [NO_3] \text{ in } HNO_3).$$

But it seems that if a hydrogen ion, which cannot exist alone, has only the choice between combining with ClO_4^- or HF_2^-, it takes the latter. Hantzsch has shown[90] that anhydrous perchloric acid will absorb HF vapour in the cold to give a colourless crystalline compound of the composition HF, $HClO_4$, m. pt. 56°, which must be $[H \cdot FH] \cdot [ClO_4]$; its high melting-point recalls that of the hydrate, m. pt. 50°, which is shown by X-ray analysis to be $[H_3O] \cdot [ClO_4]$. The only alternative, $[H_2ClO_4]^+F^-$ is very improbable, not only because $HClO_4$ is so reluctant to assume the covalent state, but also because such a salt would certainly be $[H_2ClO_4] \cdot [F_2H]$. In the same way BF_3 combines with HF to give a salt of the composition and presumably the structure $[H \cdot FH] \cdot [BF_4]$, very like the perchlorate. From the behaviour of periodates in HF it seems that HIO_4 is similar.

5. Several of the oxy-anions react further with HF, replacing OH by F; thus H_2SO_4[91] gives HSO_3F, which dissolves without ionization; hence K_2SO_4 is shown to give more than 4 (probably 5 or 6) ions:

$$K_2SO_4 + 4HF = 2K^+ + HSO_3F + H_3O^+ + 3F^-.$$

In the same way chromates give CrO_2F_2. Chlorates and bromates, unless they are kept very cold, decompose with evolution of oxygen and chlorine dioxide or bromine.

The experimental evidence for these conclusions is largely based on the conductivities (see especially the apparatus of Fredenhagen and Cadenbach[82]). The molecular conductivity usually reaches a limit at about $V = 40$, and for a great many solutes (e.g. H_2O, KF, AgF, EtOH, acetic acid) this limit is close to 260. This must mean that the mobility of the

[94] W. Klatt, *Z. Anorg. Chem.* 1937, **234**, 189.

constant ion F^-, or better F_2H^-, like that of OH^- in water, is much greater than those of the cations, so that the differences of the latter can be neglected. This enables us to tell how many ions are in the solution; with KNO_3 for example, the limit is 520 (4 ions).

These values are on the whole in agreement with the results of the elevation of the boiling-point[84]; the constant (for 1 mole/1,000 g. HF) was found to be 1·91 as the mean of concordant results with benzoyl fluoride, benzonitrile, and trichloracetic acid, which dissolve without ionization. This value agrees well with the heat of evaporation of 6·15 k.cals. found[38] for $(HF)_{3.45}$ at 19·5°.

To sum up. The behaviour of hydrogen fluoride as an ionizing solvent is mainly due to two factors: (1) its great tendency to form the very stable anion F_2H^-, if the hydrogen ion of this acid $H[F_2H]$ can be found a place, and (2) the great reluctance of hydrogen ions to form a covalent link with a fluorine atom already attached to hydrogen, either in the neutral HF (or its polymers) or in the $[F_2H]$ anion, this last being the reason why $H[F_2H]$ is a strong acid. Hence there is a great tendency for any substance which can take up a hydrogen ion (such as an oxygen compound that can go to the oxonium state), to take it up, even if (like a ketone) it is one which ordinarily does not do so. It is only when there is present a still stronger acid, i.e. one which is more reluctant than $H[F_2H]$ to co-ordinate with its hydrogen ion, that the $[H_2F]^+$ cation is formed.

The almost complete insolubility of the other halogen hydrides in hydrogen fluoride appears less unusual if it is remembered that they are unassociated substances of low boiling-point (HCl will only dissolve up to 1·50 g. per litre in benzene at 25°[95]), while hydrogen fluoride is perhaps the most highly associated substance known. The anomaly is in this difference, and not in the solubility, which is merely the result of it. Hydrogen fluoride, with its high boiling-point and its high internal pressure, is a bad solvent for all non-associated substances that are not solvated by it; thus it is immiscible with paraffins. In much the same way HCl is only slightly soluble in H_2SO_4. A substance which does not itself associate is likely to be insoluble in so highly associated a liquid, and one which does associate with itself is likely to be able to take up a hydrogen ion, so that we can see why the acid liberated when a salt is dissolved in hydrogen fluoride nearly always is either expelled from the solution or converted into an oxonium cation.

There still remains the question why the ion

is so stable, and $[H—F—H]^+$ so unstable. Here it can only be said that this is in accordance with the general reluctance of fluorine to form a second covalency; the H of H—F must form a hydrogen bond with the F of another H—F in polymerized hydrogen fluoride, but we have no direct

[95] J. H. Simons, *J.A.C.S.* 1931, **53**, 83.

evidence of a definitely dicovalent fluorine atom either as A—$\overset{+}{\text{F}}$—A or
A—$\overset{+}{\text{F}}$—$\overset{-}{\text{B}}$. The fact that fluorine directs substitution in benzene to the
ortho-para positions like chlorine, does, however, suggest that it may have
a resonance form

like the 'back co-ordinated' form which certainly occurs with chlorine

in which it is dicovalent. The firmness with which fluorine is attached to
the benzene ring (p. 1131) points in the same direction.

INORGANIC FLUORIDES

THE simple derivatives of the four halogens are very similar to one
another, but the fluorides are sufficiently different from the rest to deserve
separate treatment. The main division of the halides is of course into
ionized and covalent compounds. With the former, the boiling-points
[and melting-points] are very high, and fall with increase of atomic weight
of the halogen, as the following values of the boiling-points [and melting-
points] of the alkaline halides show:

B. pt. diff. MF—MCl	*Fluoride*		*Chloride*		*Bromide*		*Iodide*	
+288° Li	1,670°	[840°]	1,382°	[606°]	1,310°	[535°]	1,189°	[450°]
+275° Na	1,705°	[992°]	1,430°	[803°]	1,393°	[740°]	1,300°	[653°]
+ 87° K	1,498°	[846°]	1,411°	[768°]	1,376°	[748°]	1,330°	[693°]
+ 25° Rb	1,408°	[775°]	1,383°	[717°]	1,350°	[681°]	1,304°	[638°]
− 70° Cs	1,253°	[684°]	1,303°	[638°]	1,300°	[681°]	1,280°	[621°]

This is obviously because the work required to separate the ions is less as
they get larger.

With covalent halides, on the other hand, in which the external field
of the molecule is much weaker, and the work of separation correspondingly
less, the melting- and boiling-points are low, and increase with a rise in
the atomic weight of the halogen, as is shown in the following table:

B. pt. diff. XF_n—XCl_n	*Boiling- and melting-points*			
	F	Cl	Br	I
+104·5° H	+ 19·5° [− 83·7°]	−85·0° [−114·2°]	−66·8° [−87·0°]	−35·5° [− 51°]
−204·4° C	−128° [−185°]	+76·4° [− 22·9°]	.. [+93·7°]	.. [+171°]
−153·5° Si	− 96° [− 90·2°] (sbl.)	+57·5° [− 70·4°]	154·6° [+ 5·2°]	290° [123·8°]
−118·5° Ge	− 35° [− 15°]	+83·5° [− 51·8°]	185·9° [+26·1°]	.. [145°]

This is the normal behaviour of the halides. But they, and especially the fluorides, often show abnormalities of various kinds. The fluoride ion from its small size should be peculiarly able to resist the tendency to assume the covalent state, and we find that the fluorides of some elements such as tin and aluminium are more salt-like than the other halides. The same tendency is shown, though in a less degree, by some other elements, as may be seen from the following table, which gives the boiling-points and [melting-points] as before. It is particularly interesting to see how with tin and lead the alkyl- and aryl-halides follow the simple binary halides in behaviour.

	Fluoride	Chloride	Bromide	Iodide
SnX₄ . .	704° [..]	114·1° [−36°]	203·3° [+33°]	346° [146·2°]
Tol₃SnX .	.. [305°]	.. [97·5°]	.. [98·5°]	.. [120·5°]
AlX₃ .	1,260° [1,260°+]	160° [192·5°]	255° [97·5°]	381° [191°]
GaX₃ .	950° [..] (sbl.)	201·3° [77·9°]	279° [121·5°]	346° [212°]
InX₃ .	1,200° [1,170°]	.. [586°]	.. [436°]	.. [210°]
ZnX₂ .	1,500° [..]	720° [313°]	670° [390°]	.. [446°]
CdX₂ .	1,748° [..]	964° [568°]	863° [585°]	ca. 710° [387°]
HgX₂ .	360° [645°] (sbl.)	302° [277°]	320° [238°]	350° [257°]
Hg₂X₂ .	.. [570°]	383° [543°]	340° [340°+]	310° [290°]
PbX₂ .	1,285° [818°]	945° [498°]	916° [373°]	.. [412°]
Aryl₂PbX₂ Alkyl₂PbX₂	.. [ca. 300°]	.. [v. low]	.. [v. low]	.. [v. low]
UX₄ .	.. [1,000°]	618° [567°]	.. ..	.. ..
CrF₂ .	1,300+[1,100°]	?	?	.. [793°]

The boiling-points of the trihalides of the elements of Group V B show that with the smaller elements the triple charge makes even the fluorides covalent, but as the radius of the central atom increases the fluorine ion becomes stable before the chlorine: the boiling-point of MF_3 suddenly rises with arsenic, and the antimony and bismuth trifluorides are less volatile than the chlorides:

Boiling-points of Trihalides

	N	P	As	Sb	Bi
MF₃ . . .	−129°	− 95°	+ 63°	319°	Over red heat (say 600°)
MCl₃ . .	+ 71°	+ 76°	+130°	221°	447°
Diff., MCl₃—MF₃	+200°	+171°	+ 67°	− 98°	−150° say

Solubilities

The fluorides often show a marked difference from the other halides in their solubility in water. Where their melting- and boiling-points are abnormally high we should expect the solubilities to be correspondingly small, and this often is so, as in the salts of the alkalies, the alkaline earths, and divalent lead. Sometimes, however, the solubility of the fluoride is abnormally high, as with AgF and TlF; in Group II B we get both effects, low solubilities for the zinc and cadmium salts, and high for the mercuric and mercurous. The results are given in the following tables, the solubilities being in g. anhydrous salt to 100 g. water at a temperature near 20°.

Alkalies

	F	MCl/MF	Cl	Br	I
Li . .	0·15	539	80·8	163	165·5
Na . .	3·94	9·1	35·9	88·7	177·7
K . .	96·5	0·36	34·4	65·0	144·6
Rb . .	Very big	..	91·2	108·3	156·4
Cs . .	..	..	185·8	..	ca. 70

Alkaline Earths

	Be	Mg	Ca	Sr	Ba	Ra
MF_2 .	Very big	0·013	0·004	0·074	0·121	..
MCl_2 .	Very big	54·1	81·5	55·5	37·2	24·5
Ratio Cl/F	..	4,160	20,400	750	307	..

Heavy Metal Halides

Ratio Cl/F		Fluoride	Chloride	Bromide	Iodide
157	PbX_2	0·0069	1·079	0·955	0·073
265	ZnX_2	1·59	420·7	471·4	437·6
25·4	CdX_2	4·35	110·6	112·3	86·2
Small	HgX_2	Very big	7·31	0·616	0·006
Very small	Hg_2X_2	Very big	$0·47 \times 10^{-4}$	39×10^{-6}	2×10^{-8}
1/126,000	AgX	181·5	143×10^{-5}	$26·3 \times 10^{-5}$	$0·54 \times 10^{-5}$
1/224	TlX	359	1·6	5·7	0·56

In the same way bismuth trifluoride is practically insoluble in water and scarcely affected by it, while the other halides of bismuth are of course very soluble in water and largely hydrolysed.

The relatively high solubility of the fluoride which is found in the thallous salts is repeated in the dialkyl-thallium halides (III. 464) of which the fluorides are excessively soluble in water and insoluble in benzene, while the chlorides, bromides, and iodides are soluble in benzene and only slightly in water. Here, however, it is clear that the fluorides are ionized and the other halides covalent, whereas the thallous and argentous halides are ionized in the crystal.

Acyl Fluorides

The fluorides of organic and inorganic acids, such as acetyl fluoride $CH_3 \cdot CO \cdot F$ and nitrosyl fluoride NOF, and the monofluorides of dibasic acids, such as $H \cdot SO_3F$, seem at first sight to be sometimes more and sometimes less reactive than the chlorides. They are usually at least as readily hydrolysed as the chlorides and perhaps more so (the reactions are very rapid and there are no quantitative data); this is so at any rate with those of the carboxylic acids and of nitrous and nitric acids.

On the other hand, certain acid fluorides show a remarkable stability, especially the mono- and difluorides of sulphuric acid, fluorosulphonic acid HSO_3F and its salts, and sulphuryl fluoride SO_2F_2.* This last is not acted on by water even if the two are heated together in a sealed tube at 150°, and is only slowly absorbed even by potash. The acid HSO_3F is stable to heat up to 900°, and is only slowly and incompletely (reversibly) hydrolysed by water, with which chlorosulphonic acid reacts almost explosively. Its salts are correspondingly stable; while the chlorosulphonates are rapidly hydrolysed in solution, the fluorosulphonates are quite stable to water and can be recrystallized from it. The alkyl and aryl sulphonyl fluorides $R \cdot SO_2 \cdot F$ show a similar inactivity.

This remarkable inertness seems to be largely thermodynamical, i.e. due to the strength of the S—F link. The fluoride and the fluoro-acid are obviously covalent compounds like their chlorine analogues, as is indicated by their boiling-points $(SO_2F_2 - 52°$; $SO_2Cl_2 + 69·3°$; HSO_3F 162·6°; HSO_3Cl 151°). The reversible hydrolysis of the acid is evidence of the thermodynamic stability of the S—F link, but the extreme inertness, especially of sulphuryl fluoride, does seem to need some further explanation.† It is very remarkable that the selenium compound SeO_2F_2 shows no such inertness, but is just as reactive as its chlorine analogue.

Something of the same slowness to hydrolyse is shown by the fluorophosphoric acids H_2PO_3F and $H \cdot PO_2F_2$, though not by POF_3; here probably the main cause is again thermodynamic, i.e. is the strength of the P—F linkage. For this, however, we have no thermochemical data.

'Acid' Fluorides

The considerable class of 'acid' fluorides are the salts of the acids $H[F_nH_{n-1}]$, with n usually 2. These polymerized forms of HF are all monobasic acids, so that the salts are not really acid salts, and the fluorine atoms of the anion are obviously united through hydrogen bonds. The ordinary acid fluorides or bifluorides $M[F_2H]$ may thus be written

---

* See Group VI, Sulphur, p. 933.

† Especially as the values of the heats of linkage scarcely seem to support it. The heat of formation from the atoms (Ha) of SF_6 gives for S—F 71·4 k.cals. To judge by the values of P—Cl in PCl_3 (77·1) and PCl_5 (62·0) we should expect a higher value of S—F where the covalency was lower. The value for S—Cl can be got roughly in two ways. Ha for S_2Cl_2 (these values of course are all for the gaseous state) is 196·1, and for S—S in S_8 63·8: the difference, 132·3 for 2(S—Cl) gives us S—Cl 66·2; again the difference between Ha for SO_2Cl_2 (395·8) and SO_2 (255·4), is 140·4, giving 70·2 for S—Cl: we may perhaps take the mean value of 68 k.cals. as approximately true. For S—Br we have Ha (S_2Br_2) 177·1 − 63·8 = 113·3, giving S—Br as 56·7. So we have S—F 71·4; S—Cl 66; S—Br 57. The difference is striking, and in accord with the usual behaviour of fluorine; but in the hydrolysis of the halide the heat of the reaction depends on the difference between the heat values of H—hal and S—hal, and this difference is in the wrong direction:

$$(H—F) - (S—F) = 61·0$$
$$(H—Cl) - (S—Cl) = 36·6$$
$$(H—Br) - (S—Br) = 30·1$$

M[F—H··F]. The nature of the bond is discussed above under hydrogen bonds (I. 26). Crystal structure measurements have given values of from 2·26 to 2·50 for the F···F distance in these salts ; while the expected distance for two F—H links, i.e. for a structure F—H—F should be

$$2 (0·64 + 0·30) = 1·88.$$

[See Pauling, *Chemical Bond*, pp. 277 sqq.] See further references [70–1,96].

Similar but more complex salts, MF, 2HF and MF, 3HF, or as they should be written M[F$_3$H$_2$] and M[F$_4$H$_3$], are also known, such as AgF$_4$H$_3$.

Tananaev[97] obtained from the system KF—HF—H$_2$O at 0°, 20°, and 40°, the solid fluorides KF; KF$_2$H; KF$_3$H$_2$; KF$_4$H$_3$; KF$_5$H$_4$; and 2 KF, 5 HF.

With rubidium the salts RbF, 2 HF; RbF, 3 HF; and RbF, 3·5 HF were obtained.[98]

With caesium the melting-point curve of the system CsF—HF indicated the salts CsF, HF (m. pt. 170·6°), CsF, 2HF (50·2°), CsF 3HF (32·6°), and CsF, 6HF (−42·3°).[99]

ORGANIC COMPOUNDS OF FLUORINE[99a]

THE organic compounds of fluorine, though few in comparison with those of the other halogens, are fairly numerous, and they show in a high degree the great differences between fluorine and the other members of the group.

Our knowledge of these compounds comes largely from the work which Swarts carried on in Belgium for forty years from 1897, and that of Midgley and his collaborators in Columbus, Ohio, who examined in particular the fluorine and other halogen substitution products of methane, ethane, and ethylene, partly with a view to their uses as refrigerants, and partly from their intrinsic interest. Swarts has published two very useful summaries of his work in 1901[100] and in 1924.[101]

The peculiarities of the organic fluorine compounds are mainly due to the exceptionally large energies of formation of the links of fluorine to hydrogen (132·4) and to carbon (103·4 k.cals.). In consequence the heats of reaction of fluorine compounds differ greatly from those of the other halides ; these are some examples (the corresponding chlorine values follow in brackets):

—C—H + F$_2$	= —C—F	+ HF + 103.7 k.cals.	[Cl + 23·1]
—C—H + H—C— + F$_2$ = —C—C—	+ 2HF + 115·5	[Cl + 31·6]
—C—C— + F$_2$	= 2—C—F	+	91·9	[Cl + 16·6]
—C=C— + F$_2$	= —CF—CF— +	109·1	[Cl + 33·8]
—C—F + H$_2$O	= —C—OH	+ HF −	0·3	[Cl − 4·0]

[96] G. Glockler and G. E. Evans, *J. Chem. Phys.* 1942, **10**, 607.

[97] I. Tananaev, *J. Appl. Chem. Russ.* 1938, **11**, 214.

[98] K. R. Webb and E. B. R. Prideaux, *J.C.S.* 1939, 111.

[99] R. V. Windsor and G. H. Cady, *J.A.C.S.* 1948, **70**, 1500.

[99a] For further details see F. Smith, *Ann. Rep. Chem. Soc.* 1947, **44**, 86.

[100] F. Swarts, *Mem. Acad. Roy. Belg.* 1901, **61** (94 pp.). It is abstracted at some length in *Chem. Centr.* 1903, i. 11–14.

[101] Id., *Bull. Soc. Chim.* 1924, [4] **35**, 1533–63.

Owing to the large heats of reaction of elementary fluorine, and its tendency to remove hydrogen as HF, direct fluorination is very difficult, and was long thought to be impossible. Solid methane (m. pt. $-184°$) explodes violently on treatment with liquid fluorine,[102] and other organic compounds, even sodium acetate, behave in the same way[103-4]; even when this can be avoided the products are usually mixtures of black tars with hydrogen fluoride and sometimes carbon tetrafluoride. The use of unstable fluorine compounds like lead tetrafluoride as source of fluorine was also found[105-6] to give very small yields. This is the more important since indirect methods of introducing fluorine atoms, which succeed with other halogens, often fail with fluorine. The action of hydrogen fluoride on alcohols is very slow below 170°, and even at equilibrium there is less than 50 per cent. of the fluoride present. Attempts to add HF to the double-carbon link for a long time failed, which is not surprising since the ease of the reaction falls off in the order HI > HBr > HCl; hydrofluoric acid readily reacts with ethylene oxide or epichlorhydrin, but normally only to catalyse the hydrolysis of the cyclic ether, and no trace of fluoride is formed. More recently, however, Grosse and Linn[107] have shown that under pressures up to 25 atm. the addition is easy; it is promoted by the presence of lead dioxide (i.e. PbF_4)[108] and of boron trifluoride.[109] See further reference [110]. The phosphorus fluorides react with alcohols mainly to form phosphorus esters.

More recently also, the reaction of direct fluorination has been brought under control. One of the first to do this was Ruff, who showed[111] that fluorine acts on fluoroform CHF_3 to give CF_4 and C_2F_6. The main work on direct fluorination was due to Bigelow et al. (*J.A.C.S.* 1934–41)[112-21]; they have shown under what conditions this reaction can be made to give definite products. The best way seems to be to pass the vapour of the organic substance mixed with fluorine and if necessary diluted with

[102] H. Moissan and G. Chavanne, *C.R.* 1905, **140**, 407.

[103] B. Humiston, *J. Phys. Chem.* 1919, **23**, 573.

[104] F. Fichter and K. Humpert, *Helv. Chim. Acta*, 1926, **9**, 694.

[105] O. Dimroth and W. Bockemüller, *Ber.* 1931, **64**, 516.

[106] W. Bockemüller, ib. 522.

[107] A. V. Grosse and C. B. Linn, *J. Org. Chem.* 1938, **3**, 26.

[108] A. L. Henne and T. P. Waalkes, *J.A.C.S.* 1945, **67**, 1639.

[109] A. L. Henne and R. C. Arnold, ib. 1948, **70**, 758.

[110] R. Y. Thompson, P. Tarrant, and L. A. Bigelow, ib. 1946, **68**, 2187.

[111] O. Ruff, *Ber.* 1936, **69**, 299.

[112] L. A. Bigelow and J. H. Pearson, *J.A.C.S.* 1934, **56**, 2773.

[113] W. D. Miller, J. D. Calfee, and L. A. Bigelow, ib. 1937, **59**, 198.

[114] J. D. Calfee and L. A. Bigelow, ib. 2072.

[115] N. Fukuhara and L. A. Bigelow, ib. 1938, **60**, 427.

[116] J. D. Calfee, N. Fukuhara, and L. A. Bigelow, ib. 1939, **61**, 3552.

[117] J. D. Calfee, N. Fukuhara, D. S. Young, and L. A. Bigelow, ib. 1940, **62**, 267.

[118] E. H. Hadley and L. A. Bigelow, ib. 3302.

[119] D. S. Young, N. Fukuhara, and L. A. Bigelow, ib. 1171.

[120] N. Fukuhara and L. A. Bigelow, ib. 1941, **63**, 788.

[121] L. A. Bigelow, *Chem. Rev.* 1947, **40**, 51.

nitrogen over copper gauze; the copper acts as a catalyst, but is only slightly attacked. In this way they have succeeded in fluorinating numerous aliphatic and aromatic substances, such as methane,[118] ethane,[114,116,119] ethyl chloride,[117] hexachloroethane,[113] acetone,[120] benzene[115] hexachlorobenzene,[112] silver cyanide,[149,150] etc. The fluorine replaces hydrogen and chlorine, adds on to double links, and can also cause both the breakdown and the building up of carbon chains (see further Miller, 1940[122]).

The indirect methods normally used for the preparation of the organic fluorine compounds are different according as these are aliphatic or aromatic.

With the paraffin derivatives the methods consist in substituting a fluorine atom for one of another halogen by treating the organic halide with a metallic fluoride, and by preference that of a less electro-positive metal. Moissan used anhydrous silver fluoride. Swarts showed that mercurous fluoride, made from mercurous carbonate and HF, was more effective than silver fluoride, especially in presence of a trace of iodine (see further reference [158]). Another effective reagent much used both by himself and by others, is antimony trifluoride. In the absence of a catalyst this is usually inert, though it can sometimes react, as with benzal chloride and benzotrichloride, and with trichloromethyl ether[141]; it becomes far more active in presence of a trace of bromine, or of a small quantity of antimony pentachloride.[124,142] The active molecule is probably the pentahalide, the reactions being, with bromine:

$$SbF_3 \quad + Br_2 \quad = SbF_3Br_2$$
$$SbF_3Br_2 + 3\,R\cdot Br = 3\,R\cdot F + Br_2 + SbBr_3$$

[122] W. T. Miller, *J.A.C.S.* 1940, **62**, 341.

[123] F. Swarts, *Bull. Soc. Chim. Belge*, 1927, **36**, 323.

[124] T. Midgley and A. L. Henne, *J. Ind. Eng. Chem.* 1930, **22**, 542.

[125] O. Ruff and R. Keim, *Z. anorg. Chem.* 1930, **192**, 249.

[126] R. M. Buffington and W. K. Gilkey, *J. Ind. Eng. Chem.* 1931, **23**, 254.

[127] W. K. Gilkey, F. W. Gerard, and M. E. Bixler, ib. 364.

[128] F. R. Bichowsky and W. K. Gilkey, ib. 366.

[129] R. M. Buffington and J. Fleischner, ib. 1290.

[130] R. M. Buffington and W. K. Gilkey, ib. 1292.

[131] O. Ruff and R. Keim, *Z. anorg. Chem.* 1931, **201**, 245.

[132] H. S. Booth, W. L. Mong, and P. E. Burchfield, *J. Ind. Eng. Chem.* 1932, **24**, 328.

[133] H. S. Booth and E. M. Bixby, ib. 637.

[134] W. Cawood and H. S. Patterson, *J.C.S.* 1932, 2180.

[135] H. S. Booth, P. E. Burchfield, E. M. Bixby, and J. B. McKelvey, *J.A.C.S.* 1933, **55**, 2231.

[136] F. Hovorka and F. E. Geiger, *J.A.C.S.* 1933, **55**, 4759.

[137] W. Menzel and F. Mohry, *Z. anorg. Chem.* 1933, **210**, 257.

[138] O. Ruff and O. Bretschneider, ib. 173.

[139] N. V. Thornton, A. B. Burg, and H. I. Schlesinger, *J.A.C.S.* 1933, **55**, 3177.

[140] E. G. Locke, W. R. Brode, and A. L. Henne, ib. 1934, **56**, 1726.

[141] H. S. Booth, P. E. Burchfield, and H. M. Elsey, ib. 1935, **57**, 2069.

[142] W. B. Whalley, *J. Soc. Chem. Ind.* 1947, **66**, 427, 430.

and the pentachloride behaving in a similar way. Booth[132] gets better yields under pressure; thus in making the di- and trifluoro-derivatives of hexachloro-ethane 2·6 kg. of antimony trifluoride, 80 g. of the penta-chloride, and 1·7 kg. of C_2Cl_6 are heated in an autoclave for 7 hours at 320° and 60 atm. Henne[140] finds that the ready formed SbF_3Cl_2 is better than a mixture of the trifluoride and pentachloride.

A new and more powerful fluorinating agent is mercuric fluoride,[146] made (in a 75 per cent. yield) by the action of fluorine on powdered mercuric chloride. This reagent has little action on chlorides, but it reacts readily with bromides, and with iodides even violently, unless they are in solution. In some cases this reagent will carry the fluorination farther than the antimony halides. Thus Henne[155] made fluoroform CHF_3 from bromo-form by first converting this into CHF_2Br with bromine and excess of SbF_3 at 4 atm. pressure (this is as far as that reagent will take it) and then treating the product with mercuric fluoride.

Other methods have sometimes been found useful. Iodine penta-fluoride will fluorinate carbon tetrachloride,[131] but not benzene. Methyl fluoride can be made by the simple process of heating tetramethyl ammonium fluoride (Collie, 1889).[159,134]

Hydrogen fluoride will add on to a triple $C \equiv C$ link (though not to a double $C = C$), the addition following Markownikoff's rule.[160-1]

Rules of Substitution

As we have seen, the preparation of the aliphatic fluorine compounds almost always begins with the replacement of other halogens by treatment with a metallic or semi-metallic fluoride. The particular inorganic fluoride used for this purpose sometimes determines the extent to which the replacement will go, and the relative ease with which different halogens are replaced (thus mercuric fluoride is far more efficient with a bromide or an iodide than with a chloride, and with these will carry the reaction further than antimony trifluoride, which, however, acts as well with a chloride as with the other halides); but it does not seem to affect the relation between the position of the halogen atom and its ease of replace-ment.

[143] A. L. Henne and E. C. Ladd, *J.A.C.S.* 1936, **58**, 402.
[144] A. L. Henne and D. M. Hubbard, ib. 404.
[145] A. L. Henne and T. Midgley, ib. 882. [146] Id., ib. 884.
[147] A. L. Henne and M. W. Renoll, ib. 887. [148] Id., ib. 889.
[149] O. Ruff and M. Giese, *Ber.* 1936, **69**, 598. [150] Id., ib. 604.
[151] O. Ruff, O. Bretschneider, W. Luchsinger, and G. Miltschitzky, ib. 299.
[152] K. L. Ramaswamy, *Proc. Ind. Acad. Sci.* 1935, **2**, 364.
[153] L. O. Brockway, *J. Phys. Chem.* 1937, **41**, 185.
[154] Id., ib. 747. [155] A. L. Henne, *J.A.C.S.* 1937, **59**, 1200.
[156] Id., ib. 1400. [157] J. H. Simons and L. P. Block, ib. 1407.
[158] A. L. Henne and M. W. Renoll, ib. 1938, **60**, 1060.
[159] J. N. Collie, *J.C.S.* 1889, **55**, 110.
[160] A. L. Henne and E. P. Plueddeman, *J.A.C.S.* 1943, **65**, 587.
[161] A. V. Grosse and C. B. Linn, ib. 1942, **64**, 2289.

Swarts points out[101] that antimony trifluoride never causes the replacement of a halogen except in compounds which have two halogens attached to one carbon.* Thus $CH_2Br \cdot CH_2Br$ is not affected, but $CHBr_2 \cdot CH_2Br$ readily loses one, and even more readily two of the bromine atoms of the $-CHBr_2$ group to give $CHF_2 \cdot CH_2Br$, so that it would seem that the bromine is more readily replaced in $-CHFBr$ than in $-CHBr_2$; in the meantime the Br of the $-CH_2Br$ is unaffected. In the same way[146] mercuric fluoride reacts with ethylidene bromide to give a little $CH_3 \cdot CHFBr$ and much $CH_3 \cdot CHF_2$. Further, as is shown below, $-CCl_3$ reacts more readily than $-CHCl_2$. When, however, there are two F atoms and one Cl or Br on a carbon, the latter cannot be replaced, except with benzotrichloride, which is readily converted not only into $C_6H_5 \cdot CF_2Cl$, but also into the trifluoride by SbF_3, even in the absence of a catalyst; this must be the effect of the proximity of the benzene ring. If the chlorine is directly attached to the benzene nucleus it is of course in the absence of ortho- or para-nitro groups unaffected by any of these reagents, even by HgF_2.[146]

A more detailed account of the course of these substitutions is given by Henne and Midgley.[145] Their discussion of the stability relations of the products will be dealt with later. The effect of structure on the ease of substitution is shown by the behaviour of hexachloroethane C_2Cl_6 on treatment with antimony trifluoride and pentachloride. The successive products are (1) $CCl_2F \cdot CCl_3$; (2) $CCl_2F \cdot CCl_2F$; (3) $CClF_2 \cdot CCl_2F$; (4) $CClF_2 \cdot CClF_2$; after which at the ordinary temperature the fluorination stops; no isomers are formed in the course of this reaction. This shows, (*a*) that the CCl_3 group can be fluorinated, and (*b*) that the successive fluorine atoms go by preference to the carbon atoms which have least fluorine. That the presence of fluorine discourages fluorination is shown by the fact that the reaction of SbF_3 on C_2Cl_6 goes by itself without a catalyst as far as the trifluoride (3 above), but to get the tetrachloride one must use SbF_3Cl_2 at 140–150°; nothing will introduce a fifth or sixth fluorine atom.

Although CF_2Br is less easily fluorinated than $CHFBr$, CCl_3 goes more easily than $CHCl_2$. Hence, $CHCl_2 \cdot CCl_3$ gives first $CHCl_2 \cdot CCl_2F$ and then $CHCl_2 \cdot CClF_2$ easily. At this point the further replacement on the first carbon is difficult owing to the presence of the hydrogen, and on the second because of the protective effect of the two fluorine atoms; but it is possible with difficulty to get $CHClF \cdot CClF_2$ and then $CHF_2 \cdot CClF_2$. So too, $CHCl_2 \cdot CHCl_2$ gives $CHClF \cdot CHCl_2$, and then $CHF_2 \cdot CHCl_2$, and then the action stops; further treatment with SbF_3 either has no effect or it converts the last product into $CF_3 \cdot CH_2Cl$. In the same way $CH_2Cl \cdot CCl_3$ gives $CH_2Cl \cdot CCl_2F$, and then $CH_2Cl \cdot CClF_2$ and stops; $CH_2Cl \cdot CHCl_2$ gives $CH_2Cl \cdot CHClF$, and $CH_2Cl \cdot CHF_2$, and there the reaction stops.

Mercuric fluoride, although it follows the same general lines, is more efficient; thus $-CH_2Cl$ cannot be fluorinated by SbF_3, but it can by HgF_2. This effect is, however, to some extent hindered by the presence of

* Mercuric fluoride can, however, do this with the halogens in $-CH_2Br$ and $-CH_2I$, though not in $-CH_2Cl$.[146]

other halogen atoms on the next carbon. Thus mercuric fluoride fluorinates ethyl chloride easily, but $CH_2Cl \cdot CHClF$ very little, and $CH_2Cl \cdot CHF_2$ not at all; so too it fluorinates ethyl bromide easily, but $CH_2Br \cdot CHF_2$ not at all; it reacts with ethyl iodide violently, but with $CH_2I \cdot CHF_2$ it needs a long time at 160°, and then only gives a 60 per cent. yield of $CH_2F \cdot CHF_2$. In general, mercuric fluoride gives the same products as antimony trifluoride. The fluorination of methyl chloroform $CH_3 \cdot CCl_3$ can be carried right through to $CH_3 \cdot CF_3$.

These remarkable relations can be reduced to the following rules.

1. The replacement by fluorine of another halogen is very difficult when there are not at least two halogen atoms on the carbon in question; it is in that case impossible with SbF_3, although it can be done with HgF_2 if there is no more easily replaceable halogen in the molecule.

2. Fluorination is easier with the $C(hal)_3$ group than with $CH(hal)_2$, provided the halogens in question are not fluorine. But the presence of a fluorine atom on a carbon makes other halogen atoms on that carbon less easy to replace, and the presence of two fluorines makes the replacement impossible with antimony trifluoride, though it can be done with mercuric fluoride. This effect of a CF_2 group in hindering substitution sometimes extends to the next carbon atom. For further work on the preparation and chlorination of fluoro-paraffins and fluoro-alkylenes see Henne *et al.*[162-7]

Organo-fluorine Compounds: Physical Properties

Numerous values of the heat properties (including the boiling- and melting-points) of paraffins with the hydrogen wholly or partially replaced by fluorine and chlorine are given in the following papers (see p. 1118).

C_1.[126-30,137,168-72,184]

C_2.[135-6,143-4,147-8,168-75,185,190]

C_3.[123,176-80,186-9]

Monofluorides of alkyls C_1–C_4.[180]

1,1 and 2,2 difluorides of C_1–C_7.[181]

Perfluorides C_xF_y.[157,182-3]

The values for the C_1 and C_2 compounds, for the alkyl fluorides (12) and the perfluorides (14) follow on the next page.

[162] A. L. Henne, T. Alderson, and M. S. Newman, *J.A.C.S.* 1945, **67**, 918. (Preparation of perfluorinated carboxylic acids.)

[163] A. L. Henne and J. B. Hinkamp, ib. 1194. (Chlorination of difluoropropane.)

[164] Id., ib. 1197. (The same for α, α, α trifluorobutane.)

[165] A. L. Henne and W. J. Zimmerschied, ib. 1235. (Fluoro-derivatives of cyclopentane and -pentene.)

[166] A. L. Henne, J. B. Hinkamp, and W. J. Zimmerschied, ib. 1906. (Chlorination of aliphatic fluorides.)

[167] A. L. Henne and T. P. Waalkes, ib. 1946, **68**, 496. (Fluorinated propanes and propenes.)

[168] A. Benning and R. C. MacHarness, *Ind. Eng. Chem.* 1939, **31**, 912.

[169] Id., ib. 1940, **32**, 497.

[170] Id., ib. 698. [171] Id., ib. 814. [172] Id., ib. 976.

I

C_1 *Cpds.*	$CHClF_2$	$CHCl_2F$	CCl_3F	CF_4
B. pt.	$-40\cdot8°a$	$+8\cdot9°a$	$+23\cdot8°a$	$-128°b$
Crit. temp.[a]	$96\cdot8°$	$178\cdot5°$	$198\cdot0°$	..
M. pt.	..	..	$-110\cdot5°c$	$-184°b$

II

C_2	CH_3CF_2Cl	$CCl_2F\cdot CCl_2F$	$CCl_3\cdot CF_3$	$CCl_3\cdot CClF_2$	$CClBrF\cdot CClBrF$
B. pt.	$9\cdot21°d$	$47\cdot6°a$	$45\cdot9°e$	$91\cdot5°e$	$139\cdot9°e$
M. pt.	..	$24\cdot7°g$	$14\cdot2°e$	$40\cdot6°e$	$32\cdot8°e$

	$CCl_2Br\cdot CBrF_2$	$CCl_2F\cdot CClF_2$	C_2F_6	$CCl_3\cdot CCl_2F$
B. pt.	$138\cdot9°e$	$47\cdot7°f$	$-78\cdot2°b$	..
M. pt.	$45\cdot5°e$	$-36\cdot6°f$	$-100\cdot6°b$	$+99\cdot9°g$

$$a = {}^{169}, b = {}^{181}, c = {}^{184}, d = {}^{185}, e = {}^{174}, f = {}^{175}, g = {}^{173}.$$

Monofluorides:[180]

	$Me\cdot F$	$Et\cdot F$	$1—Pr\cdot F$	$2—Pr\cdot F$	$Sec\cdot Bu\cdot F$	$Iso—Bu\cdot F$	$TertBu\cdot F$
B. pt.	$-78\cdot5°$	$-37\cdot7°$	$-2\cdot5°$	$-9\cdot4°$	$+25\cdot1°$	$+12\cdot1°$	$+44\cdot8°$
M. pt.	$-141\cdot8°$	$-143\cdot2°$	$-159°$	$-133\cdot4°$	$-121\cdot4°$	$-77°$	$-12\cdot1°$

Perfluorides[183]. From paraffins:

	CF_4	C_2F_6	C_3F_8	$n\text{-}C_4F_{10}$	$iso\text{-}C_4F_{10}$	$n\text{-}C_7F_{16}$	$n\text{-}C_{16}F_{34}$
B. pt.	$-128°$	$-78\cdot2°$	$-38°$	$-4\cdot7°$	$-3\cdot0°$	$+82°$	$240°$
M. pt.	$-184°$	$-100\cdot6°$	$-183°$	..	..	..	$115°$

[173] J. Bernstein and W. T. Miller, *J.A.C.S.* 1940, **62**, 948.
[174] A. L. Henne and E. G. Wiest, ib. 2051.
[175] L. Riedel, *Z. Ges. Kälte-Ind.* 1938, **45**, 221.
[176] A. L. Henne and M. W. Renoll, *J.A.C.S.* 1937, **59**, 2434.
[177] A. L. Henne and E. C. Ladd, ib. 1938, **60**, 2491.
[178] A. L. Henne and M. W. Renoll, ib. 1939, **61**, 2489.
[179] A. L. Henne and J. V. Flanagan, ib. 1943, **65**, 2362.
[180] A. V. Grosse, R. C. Wackher, and C. B. Linn, *J. Phys. Chem.* 1940, **44**, 275.
[181] A. L. Henne, M. W. Renoll, and H. M. Leicester, *J.A.C.S.* 1939, **61**, 938.
[182] J. H. Simons and L. P. Block, ib. 2962.
[183] A. V. Grosse and G. H. Cady, *Ind. Eng. Chem.* 1947, **39**, 367.
[184] D. W. Osborne, C. S. Garner, R. M. Doescher, and D. M. Yost, *J.A.C.S.* 1941, **63**, 3496.
[185] L. Riedel, *Z. Ges. Kälte-Ind.* 1941, **48**, 105.
[186] A. L. Henne and F. W. Haeckl, *J.A.C.S.* 1941, **63**, 3476.
[187] A. L. Henne, A. M. Whaley, and J. K. Stevenson, ib. 3478.
[188] A. L. Henne and A. M. Whaley, ib. 1942, **64**, 1157.
[189] E. T. McBee, H. B. Hass, R. M. Thomas, W. G. Toland, and A. Truchan, ib. 1947, **69**, 944.
[189a] M. T. Rogers, ib. 457.
[190] A. L. Henne and R. P. Ruh, ib. 1948, **70**, 1025.
[190a] N. J. Leonard and L. E. Sutton, ib. 1564.

	From naphthenes		Ethylene	Benzene	Toluene
	C_5F_{10}	C_6F_{12}	C_2F_4	C_6F_6	C_7F_8
B. pt.	22°	52°	− 76·3°	82°	103·5°
M. pt.	− 12°	+50°	− 142·5°	− 12°	− 70°

Dipole Moments

The dipole moments of various organic fluorides, along with those of the other halides, have been determined or collected (for references see original) by Rogers[189a]; they were all measured in benzene solution at 25°:

R	R·F	R·Cl	R·Br
Methyl . . .	1·60	1·65	1·45
Ethyl . . .	1·70	..	1·85
n-Amyl . . .	1·85	..	1·95
tert. Amyl . . .	1·95	2·14	2·25
Benzyl . . .	1·77	1·85	1·85

See further reference [190a].

Refractive Power and Volatility

The replacement of hydrogen by fluorine has relatively little effect on either of these properties. For example, the change in refractive power caused by replacing a hydrogen atom by a group X is on the average as follows:[101,152]

X =	CH_3	NO_2	Br	Cl	F
Paraffins . . .	+4·61	+5·41	+7·79	+4·97	−0·09
Aromatics . . .	+4·84	+6·44	+7·79	+4·94	−0·174

In the same way the boiling-points are often little affected by the same replacement when there is only one halogen on the carbon. Thus we have the series C_6H_6 80·2°; C_6H_5F 86·5°; $C_6H_4F_2$ 88·9°; $CH_3 \cdot C_6H_5$ 110°; $CH_3 \cdot C_6H_4F$ ortho 113·9°, para 102°; C_6H_5OH 183°; $F \cdot C_6H_4 \cdot OH$ ortho 151°; para 185·6°. But when this replacement gives rise to CF_2 or still more to CF_3 groups—i.e. to what are, as we shall see the characteristically stable groups, the boiling-points are lowered. Examples of this are:

Compound	X = F	X = H	Diff.
$CHXF_2$ . . .	− 82·2°	− 51·6°	− 30·6°
CXF_3 . . .	−128·0°	− 82·2°	− 45·8°
$CHFXCl$ . . .	− 40·7°	− 0·9°	− 39·8°
$CHXFBr$ . . .	− 14·5°	+ 19°	− 33·5°
$CHXFI$ . . .	+ 21·6°	+ 53·4°	− 31·8°
$CX_3 \cdot COOH$ . .	72·4°	117·1°	− 44·7°
$CX_3 \cdot CO \cdot NH_2$ . .	122·8°	162·5°	− 39·7°
$CX_3 \cdot COF$ . .	− 59°	+ 20·5°	− 79·5°
$CX_3 \cdot CN$ . . .	− 61·5°	+ 81·6°	−144°
$CX_3 \cdot CO \cdot CH_3$ . .	22°	56°	− 34°

The perfluorides are less volatile than the hydrocarbons up to C_3, but more so above this; the differences are, for $CF_4+36°$, for $C_3H_8+7°$, for $C_4F_{10}\pm0°$, but for $C_7H_{16}-16°$.[183]

Reactivity of the Aliphatic Fluorine Compounds

This is largely determined by the great affinity of fluorine for hydrogen and for carbon; the latter makes it much more difficult to remove fluorine from carbon than any other halogen; in fact in the reactions of the organic fluorides it is exceptional for the fluorine to react. The affinity for hydrogen makes many of the fluorides lose hydrogen fluoride readily within the molecule. Thus[101] the fluorides of secondary alkyl groups are converted into the alkylene and HF on distillation (and sometimes at the ordinary temperature), which the corresponding chlorides and bromides are not. So too cyclohexyl fluoride is too unstable to isolate: it breaks up into hydrogen fluoride and cyclohexene.

The evidence is that when a carbon atom carries only one fluorine atom and no other negative group, its reactivity is not very different from that of chlorine; but that if there is also on the carbon a negative group such as carboxyl, or still more another halogen, or most of all another fluorine, the reactivity is greatly reduced.[139,151] In general, fluorine shows an inactivity not wholly explained by the heats of linkage: thus in the reaction between alkyl halides and sodium vapour at 200° Polyani[191] found these values for the relative lives of the various halides under the same conditions (the heats of formation of the C—X links are added for comparison):

	Alk—F	Alk—Cl	Alk—Br	Alk—I
Relative lives . .	10^6	104	50	1
Heat of C—X . .	107	66·5	54	45·5 k.cals.

Again, though the heat of reduction by hydrogen varies little

$$(C—X + H_2 = C—H + HX: \text{ for F } 24·4, \text{ for Cl } 19·1 \text{ k.cals.}),$$

the aliphatic fluorides are not as a rule reduced by nascent hydrogen, or by hydrogen gas and platinum black, as the other alkyl halides are.

The reactivity of the fluorides is closely related to the ease or otherwise of their formation by the replacement of other halogens on treatment with inorganic fluorides (p. 1120). An important preparative reaction is the removal of a molecule of halogen from the fully halogenated ethanes on treatment with zinc in alcoholic solution, forming a tetra-substituted ethylene. Midgley and Henne[145] show that this goes easily and quantitatively with the following halides, a chlorine atom being in each case removed from each carbon atom: $CCl_2F \cdot CCl_3$, $CCl_2F \cdot CCl_2F$, $CHCl_2 \cdot CCl_2F$, $CH_2Cl \cdot CHClF$, $CHCl_2 \cdot CHClF$, $CH_2Cl \cdot CCl_2F$. With all these, one at least of the chlorine atoms removed is in a position where it is easily replaceable by fluorine on treatment with SbF_3. On the other hand, with the following halides it is quite difficult to carry out this reaction with zinc

191 H. v. Hartel, N. Meer, and M. Polyani, *Z. physikal. Chem.* 1932, B **19**, 139.

and only small yields are got (one halogen atom always comes from each carbon, and this is chlorine if possible, but in the second and third examples one of the halogen atoms is a fluorine): $CCl_2F \cdot CClF_2$, $CH_2Cl \cdot CHF_2$, $CHCl_2 \cdot CHF_2$, $CH_2Cl \cdot CClF_2$. The difficulty of reaction here arises from the fact that in each case a halogen has to be removed from a carbon carrying two fluorines, which as we have seen is the most strongly stabilizing group. In the same way it was found to be impossible to get any yield of tetra-fluorethylene $CF_2{=}CF_2$ from $CClF_2 \cdot CClF_2$ under ordinary conditions, and even at 70 atm. only a 30–35 per cent. yield was obtained.

In general, when the carbon atom has one fluorine atom attached to it and no other halogen, the reactivity is not very different from that of a chloride. The alkyl fluorides $C_nH_{n+1} \cdot F$ are quite easily hydrolysed (more easily by acids than by alkalies: the tertiary fluorides most and the primary least); from C_5 upwards they readily lose HF on heating and form an olefine. The monofluorides also have not the complete physiological inertness of the other fluorides (see further p. 1129). When the molecule has two monofluoride groups it becomes still less stable; $CH_2F \cdot CH_2F$ loses hydrogen fluoride spontaneously at $0°$, and is completely converted into glycol by passing through water; 1,2-difluoro-cyclohexane behaves in the same way.

The presence of other negative groups on the same or even the next carbon atom stabilizes the link to fluorine in a remarkable degree. The alcohol and carboxyl groups CHOH and COOH have this effect: fluorethyl alcohol $CH_2F \cdot CH_2OH$ and fluoroacetic acid $CH_2F \cdot COOH$ are quite stable. But the strongest effect is produced by the halogens themselves, and among them especially by fluorine. Among the methane derivatives[156] the difluorides are much more stable than the mono, and have very little physiological action (see later). Methyl fluoride is no more stable than methyl chloride, but methylene chlorofluoride CH_2ClF is more stable than methylene chloride, and the fluorine atoms in methylene fluoride CH_2F_2 are scarcely affected by anything. So too while ethylene difluoride $CH_2F \cdot CH_2F$, as we have seen, hydrolyses and decomposes with the greatest ease, ethylidene difluoride $CH_3 \cdot CHF_2$ resists hydrolysis, and is so stable that animals can breathe a 50 per cent. mixture with air without hurt. In CCl_2F_2 not only are the two fluorine atoms themselves very firmly bound, but they fix the chlorine atoms too, and the molecule is far more stable than CH_2Cl_2 or CCl_2Br_2.[126] This stabilizing influence extends to the next carbon atom or even to the next but one.[145] Thus $CH_2Br \cdot CH_2F$ is easily converted into glycol, but in $CH_2Br \cdot CHF_2$ the bromine is so firmly held that it is only hydrolysed by mercuric oxide and water at $150°$: the fluorine atoms only begin to hydrolyse with this reagent at $200°$. In the same way the fluorine of the CH_2F group is much more stable in $CH_2F \cdot CHF_2$ than it is in $CH_2F \cdot CH_2F$. So too magnesium has no action on $CHF_2 \cdot CHBr_2$.

It is thus clear that the CF_2 group[192] not only has the links to the

[192] For the physical properties of compounds with the CF_2 group, see A. L. Henne and E. G. DeWitt, *J.A.C.S.* 1948, **70**, 1548.

fluorine exceptionally strong, but also holds a third halogen on the same carbon atom much more firmly, and even strengthens a C—F link on a neighbouring carbon atom.

Many other examples could be given of the stability of the CF_2 and CF_3 groups, which often causes the compounds to behave as if the hydrogen had never been replaced by fluorine. Thus di-fluoro-ethyl alcohol $CHF_2 \cdot CH_2OH$ is almost identical in properties with ethyl alcohol.[101,193] While the chloro- and bromo-alkylamines are so unstable that they can only be obtained as salts, $CHF_2 \cdot CH_2 \cdot NH_2$ is quite a stable compound, and can be kept unchanged for years. This stability makes some unusual reactions possible. Thus Swarts was able to make trifluoroacetic acid $CF_3 \cdot COOH$ by oxidizing $F_3C \cdot C_6H_4 \cdot NH_2$ with chromium trioxide.

Again, CF_2Cl_2[124] is not affected by heating in the dry state to 175° for a month, and is markedly non-inflammable. If it is forced to react with metals by heating, it is the chlorine which is removed, and not the fluorine.

The considerable reactivity of the alkyl chlorides and bromides, though it is much diminished by the presence of the fluorine, still leaves the mixed halides some possibilities of reaction. Thus $CHFBr \cdot COOH$ is hydrolysed even by water, and its salts are very unstable, the acid being converted into glyoxylic acid $CHO \cdot COOH$. The most remarkable inertness is found in molecules which have no halogens except fluorine. Such are the two gases hexafluorethane C_2F_6, (b. pt. $-78 \cdot 1°$) and tetrafluorethylene C_2F_4, (b. pt. $-76 \cdot 3°$).[138] Neither of these is affected by water, sodium hydroxide, or concentrated sulphuric acid; metals like sodium attack them only at a red heat. C_2F_4 adds on Br_2 and also is absorbed by oleum. C_2F_6, being saturated, is still more inert. Water, molybdenum, molybdic and tungstic acids, and potassium iodide do not react with it below 500°; lead oxide PbO does not do so below 1,000°.

When we come to the —CF_3 group the stability is still further increased.[151] A remarkable example is fluoroform CHF_3, which can be made from bromoform or iodoform by treatment with mercurous fluoride[151] or antimony trifluoride.[155] This undergoes no change on heating even with potassium iodide to 1,150°. Oxidizing agents have little effect on it; nitric acid, either alone, or with concentrated sulphuric acid, or oxides of nitrogen or silver nitrate, has no action in 15 days at 150°; Mn_2O_7 has no action on it at 25°; when it is oxidized it is converted into COF_2 and HF. Its extra-ordinary physiological inertness is described below.

The —CF_3 group is so stable that it is easy to convert one of its compounds into another without disturbing the CF_3. Thus Gilman and Jones[194] convert $CF_3 \cdot CO \cdot OEt$ into the amide, the nitrile, the amine $CF_3 \cdot CH_2 \cdot NH_2$, and the diazo-compound $CF_3 \cdot CHN_2$; and Simons[198] into

[193] For the preparation and physical properties of the fluoroalkyl ethers see J. D. Park, D. K. Vail, K. R. Lea, and J. R. Lacher, *J.A.C.S.* 1948, **70**, 1550.
[194] H. Gilman and R. G. Jones, ib. 1943, **65**, 1458. [195] Id., ib. 1948, **70**, 1281.
[196] Id., ib. 1943, **65**, 2037. [197] A. L. Henne, ib. 1938, **60**, 2275.
[198] J. H. Simons and E. O. Ramler, ib. 1943, **65**, 389.

the acyl halides, trifluoroacetophenone, and many of its substitution products. The main points to be noticed in the chemistry of these compounds are as follows.[199]

$CF_3 \cdot CH_2 \cdot NH_2$ is a very weak base[194]; its conversion by nitrous acid into the diazo-compound $CF_3 \cdot CHN_2$ is a most unusual reaction.[194] $CF_3 \cdot CH_2I$ reacts with magnesium but gives no Grignard compound, forming MgIF and $CH_2{=}CF_2$.[196] (In the same way $CHF_2 \cdot CH_2I$ with magnesium gives vinyl fluoride $CH_2{=}CHF$).[197] Simons and Ramler[198] found that $CF_3 \cdot COCl$ reacts with benzene in presence of $AlCl_3$ to give trifluoroacetophenone $CF_3 \cdot CO \cdot C_6H_5$; this is a sign of the great stability of the CF_3 group, since in general $AlCl_3$ reacts with organic fluorides to give chlorides and AlF_3. Russell *et al.*[200] determined the heat capacity of trifluoroethane $CF_3 \cdot CH_3$ from 12° K. to 220° K.; their results showed a barrier of 3·45 k.cals. to rotation of the CH_3. They also found the heats of fusion and evaporation to be 1·48 and 4·582 k.cals., giving a Trouton constant of 20·29. See further 2,2,2-trifluoroethanol.[195]

This great stability of the CF_2 and CF_3 groups is remarkable in view of the electron diffraction measurements of Brockway,[153-4] who found that the halogen derivatives of methane fell into two classes, in one of which the C—F distance was (within experimental error) 1·41, and in the other 1·36 A (theory 1·41); moreover, all the compounds of the first class had only one fluorine atom on the carbon, while all those of the second had two. The values are:

A			B		
CH_3F	. . .	$1·42\pm0·02$	CH_2F_2	. . .	$1·36\pm0·02$
CH_2FCl	. . .	1·40 3	CHF_2Cl	. . .	1·36 3
$CHFCl_2$	. . .	1·41 3	CF_4	. . .	1·36 3
$CFCl_3$	. . .	1·40 4	CF_2Cl_2	. . .	1·35 3

Though the increased stability of the linkage extends to the chlorine, no evidence was obtained that the C—Cl link is shortened in these compounds.

The reason suggested by Brockway for the shortening of the C—F link in these compounds is this. We know that the M—Cl distance is shortened in $SiCl_4$, $GeCl_4$, etc., owing to resonance with a doubly linked M←Cl structure, but that there is no shortening in CCl_4 because this structure is impossible here, since the carbon already has its maximum number of valency electrons. For the same reason the shortening of the C—F link in these substituted methanes cannot be due to the structure

Brockway therefore suggests that with fluorine, since the C—F bond

[199] A. L. Henne and M. S. Newman, ib. 1938, **60**, 1697.
[200] H. Russell, D. R. V. Golding, and D. M. Yost, ib. 1944, **66**, 16.

probably has in any case a considerable degree of ionic character,* we may have to reckon with a form in which one fluorine is completely ionized, giving rise to a shortened double link of carbon to fluorine.

Benzotrifluoride $C_6H_5 \cdot CF_3$ (b. pt. $102 \cdot 3°$)[201] shows a similar inactivity of the CF_3 group. But the presence of electron-donor groups in the ortho or para positions makes it much more reactive; the *o*- or *p*-phenol loses HF readily to alkali, and the amine, *p*-aminobenzotrifluoride, loses it even on distillation, and to some extent in the reduction of the nitro-group.[202]

C_2F_6 (b. pt. $-78 \cdot 2°$, Trouton $22 \cdot 2$, barrier to rotation of CF_3 $4 \cdot 35$ k.cals.)[203] does not react with silica below $600°$, and the homogeneous decomposition of the vapour begins above $800°$.[203]

Finally carbon tetrafluoride is as inert as SF_6 itself.[125] Prolonged sparking, either alone or in presence of hydrogen, has no effect, though the reaction $C—X + H_2 = C—H + HX$ is more highly exothermic with fluorine than with any other halogen. According to v. Wartenberg[204] the heat of formation of carbon tetrafluoride from graphite and elementary fluorine is 231 k.cals., which gives for C—F the unusually high value of 117 k.cals. (usual value $103 \cdot 4$). At the ordinary temperature none of the liquids examined, which included concentrated sulphuric acid and concentrated sodium hydroxide, had any action on it. The gas was heated with an enormous number of solids, including silver, bismuth, copper, lead, arsenic, sulphur, iron, lime, boron trioxide, P_2O_5, CrO_3, KOH, potassium iodide, up to the softening point of glass without any reaction occurring.

In its influence on other groups in an organic molecule fluorine has an even stronger acidifying effect than the other halogens, as may be seen by comparing the dissociation constants of the substituted acetic acids $CH_2X \cdot COOH$.[101]

$100K$ (*Classical*) for $CH_2X \cdot COOH$ at $25°$

X =	H	F	Cl	Br	I
	0·0018	0·218	0·156	0·158	0·076

So too $CHFBr \cdot COOH$ is an acid strong enough to expel HCl from NaCl on heating. On the other hand the fluorine-substituted compounds seem to be more stable than their chlorine analogues. This is especially marked in the fluoroalcohols, which are quite stable compounds, while the chloroalcohols are relatively unstable, easily hydrolysed and easily oxidized.

* According to Pauling (*Chemical Bond*, p. 74) the C—F link is 44 per cent. ionic.

[201] F. H. Field and J. H. Saylor, *J.A.C.S.* 1946, **68**, 2649.
[202] R. G. Jones, ib. 1947, **69**, 2346.
[203] E. L. Pace and J. G. Aston, ib. 1948, **70**, 566.
[204] H. v. Wartenberg, *Nachr. Ges. Wiss. Gött.* 1946, 57.

Trifluoroisopropyl alcohol[205] $CF_3 \cdot CHOH \cdot CH_3$ (made by the reduction of the corresponding acetone) is quite stable in presence either of acids or of alkalies, so that we can observe the effect on the properties of the alcoholic hydroxyl group of the accumulation of negative atoms on the next carbon. This trifluoroethyl alcohol is definitely acidic, in the same sense as, but more so than, a phenol, having a dissociation constant of 2×10^{-7} (phenol 10^{-10}, 2,4-dichlorophenol $1 \cdot 3 \times 10^{-8}$), and forms a stable potassium salt with potassium carbonate in water. It also resembles the phenols in reacting with phosphorus tribromide to give primarily not the alkyl bromide but the phosphorous ester

$$CF_3 \atop CH_3 \!\!\!\Big\rangle CH \cdot O \cdot PBr_2',$$

which, however, can be made on treatment with more bromine to give the expected bromide $CF_3 \cdot CHBr \cdot CH_3$.

Toxicity

The toxicity of many of the fluorine derivatives of methane and ethane has been measured, in view of their possible use as refrigerants. Considering how chemically inert many of them are, we might have expected their toxicity to be small, but we could scarcely have expected it to be as small as it is, particularly as many of the chlorine analogues, such as chloroform, carbon tetrachloride, and trichloroethane $C_2H_3Cl_3$ have a strong physiological action, and fluoride ion is a violent poison.

The simplest way of expressing the physiological activity of an organic compound is to give the maximum percentage concentration by volume of the vapour that animals (mostly guinea-pigs) can stand for long periods without damage. For CO_2 the maximum tolerated concentration is 2–3 per cent.; for ammonia and for chlorine about 0·01 per cent.; for the chlorinated methanes, ethanes, and ethylenes it ranges from about 0·1 per cent. for ethylene dichloride and 0·8 per cent. for ethylidene chloride $CH_3 \cdot CHCl_2$[207] to about 1 per cent. for methylene chloride.[206] For methyl chloride CH_3Cl it is 0·1 per cent., showing that this has considerable toxic power. The replacement of hydrogen in methyl chloride by fluorine considerably diminishes the toxicity but does not destroy it; many monofluorides with no other halogen are highly toxic, especially the fluoroacetates.[208] The effect increases rapidly with the number of fluorine atoms introduced. If there is only one of these, then, like the chemical reactivity, the toxicity is not enormously reduced: the compounds $CHFCl_2$ and CH_2FCl have a maximum tolerated concentration of about 4 per cent.[133] With the difluorides $CHClF_2$ and CH_2F_2 the inertness is increased, and the maximum is 20 per cent.[119] If the hydrogen is all

[205] F. Swarts, *Bull. Soc. Chim. Belge*, 1929, **38**, 99.
[206] *Toxicity of Industrial Solvents*, Medical Research Council, London, 1937.
[207] F. Flury and F. Zernik, *Schädliche Gase*, Berlin.
[208] H. McCombie and B. C. Saunders, *Nature*, 1946, **158**, 382.

replaced by halogens, the toxicity is less (this happens to some extent in the absence of fluorine, too: compare $CHCl_3$ 0·37 and CCl_4 0·70): CF_2Cl_2 can be breathed in 40 per cent. concentration for hours without danger.

The extreme case is fluoroform CHF_3 which is particularly striking owing to the great toxicity of its analogue chloroform. It was shown[155] that a guinea-pig put into a 50 per cent. air-fluoroform mixture (by weight over 70 per cent. CHF_3) did not know that the gas was there, and another in a mixture of 80 vols. CHF_3 and 20 vols. O_2 (93 per cent. CHF_3 by weight, 63 per cent. fluorine) gave no sign of discomfort. The same is true for a mixture of 80 vols. $CH_3 \cdot CF_2 \cdot CH_3$ and 20 vols. oxygen.[176] This is a physiological inactivity only paralleled by nitrogen and the inert gases. Even saturated hydrocarbons have a very considerable toxic effect, approaching that of the chloromethanes; thus with cyclohexane the maximum tolerable concentration is about 1·3 per cent. (*Toxicity of Industrial Solvents*, p. 120); with chloroform $CHCl_3$ it is 0·37 per cent.

Aromatic Fluorine Compounds

In the aromatic compounds fluorine as we should expect behaves very differently according as it is attached to the nucleus or a side chain. The side-chain derivatives show that the presence of the aromatic ring has an effect on the behaviour of the substituents in this chain,* and in general, increases their activity. The fluorination of the methyl group is easier in toluene than in a paraffin.

The Ar—C—F group is unusually unstable (this is overcome by the stability of the CF_3 group in $Ar \cdot CF_3$); $\Phi \cdot CH_2F$ loses HF very readily to form a polymer $—[CH\Phi]_n—$[209]; Φ_3CF is hydrolysed with exceptional ease.[210] $\Phi \cdot CHF_2$[211] is more stable, but is readily hydrolysed[212]; Ar_2CFBr[101] is very readily hydrolysed to the ketone; Φ_2CF_2[212] is much more stable than $\Phi \cdot CH_2F$, but much less so than $\Phi \cdot CF_3$. This last is reduced by hydrogen only in the ring, giving $C_6H_{11} \cdot CF_3$; it cannot be hydrolysed, and can be heated at 150° with 10 per cent. HCl for 3 days without change.

Compounds with Fluorine attached to the Ring

These are the aromatic fluorine compounds in the stricter sense. The methods of preparation used in the aliphatic series are not as a rule available here; the aromatic halides necessarily only have one halogen atom attached to a carbon, which makes replacement difficult, and also of course they have the halogen very firmly fixed; in presence of ortho- and para-nitro-groups, however, the chlorine can be replaced by fluorine[213] (though

* For a general discussion of the effect of fluorine on the reactivity of aromatic compounds see p. 1132 and Ingold.[85-6]

[209] C. K. and E. H. Ingold, *J.C.S.* 1928, 2249.
[210] F. F. Blicke, *J.A.C.S.* 1924, **46**, 1515.
[211] T. van Hove, *Bull. Acad. Roy. Belge*, 1913, 1074.
[212] A. L. Henne and H. M. Leicester, *J.A.C.S.* 1938, **60**, 864.
[213] H. B. Gottlieb, ib. 1936, **58**, 532.

the yield is not good) by treatment with potassium fluoride at 200°. But as a rule the aromatic fluorine compounds must be made through the diazo-compounds. This can be done by coupling the diazo-compound with a secondary amine such as piperidine and decomposing the diazo-amino-compound with concentrated hydrofluoric acid:[214-15]

$$2\,HF + Ar \cdot N{=}N{-}NHC_5H_{10} = Ar \cdot F + N_2 + C_5H_{10}NH \cdot HF.$$

But the yields are not good. The best method is to convert the diazo-compound into the borofluoride, and decompose this by heat (Balz and Schiemann[216]). The necessary fluoroboric acid HBF_4 is easily made by dissolving boric acid in concentrated hydrofluoric acid solution. The reaction

$$Ar \cdot N_2 \cdot BF_4 = Ar \cdot F + N_2 + BF_3$$

goes quite smoothly and quietly, and there are no by-reactions. These diazonium borofluorides can even be analysed quantitatively by decomposing them with strong sulphuric acid and measuring the nitrogen evolved.[217] The borofluorides are easy to handle; they are only slightly soluble in water, and can even be recrystallized from it. They are not explosive and so can be handled in quantity; the yields are good, and often quantitative. By means of this reaction a long series of aromatic fluorine compounds (phenyl, biphenyl, and naphthyl) have been made and investigated[217-29] mainly by Schiemann and his collaborators.

The quietness and smoothness of the reaction is probably due to the fact that the heat which is absorbed in breaking up the very stable BF_4 complex compensates for that which is evolved in the decomposition of the diazo-group.[217]

The fluoro-aromatic compounds in general have the properties we should expect. They show how firmly the fluorine is attached to the ring. See further references [221-2]. On the whole the evidence is that fluorine is more firmly attached to the benzene ring than any other halogen. It can,

[214] O. Wallach, *Ann.* 1886, **235**, 233; O. Wallach and Fr. Heusler, ib. 1888, **243**, 219.

[215] F. Swarts *et al.*, *Rec. Trav.* 1908, **27**, 120.

[216] G. Balz and G. Schiemann, *Ber.* 1927, **60**, 1186.

[217] G. Schiemann and R. Pillarsky, ib. 1929, **62**, 3035.

[218] G. Schiemann and E. Bolstad, ib. 1928, **61**, 1403.

[219] G. Schiemann, ib. 1929, **62**, 1794.

[220] G. Schiemann and W. Roselius, ib. 1805.

[221] Id., ib. 1931, **64**, 1332.

[222] G. Schiemann and R. Pillarsky, ib. 1340.

[223] G. Schiemann, W. Gueffroy, and W. Winkelmüller, *Ann.* 1931, **487**, 270.

[224] G. Schiemann and W. Roselius, *Ber.* 1932, **65**, 737.

[225] G. Schiemann and W. Winkelmüller, ib. 1933, **66**, 727.

[226] G. Schiemann and T. B. Miau, ib. 1179.

[227] G. Schiemann, R. Pillarsky, W. Winkelmüller, T. B. Miau, and H. G. Baumgarten, *J. pr. Chem.* 1934, [ii] **140**, 97. This paper contains a full bibliography and a discussion of the technique of the borofluoride method of making the aromatic fluorides.

[228] G. Schiemann, W. Winkelmüller, E. Baesler, and E. Ley, ib. 1935, [ii] **143**, 18.

[229] G. C. Finger and F. H. Reed, *J.A.C.S.* 1944, **66**, 1972.

however, be removed quantitatively from fluorobenzene by heating with sodium in a sealed tube.[230] Gilman and Heck have shown[231] that magnesium does not act on fluorobenzene under ordinary conditions at all; after 6 months no Grignard reagent was found to have been formed, and after 18 months very little. (Chlorine shows a somewhat similar reluctance to form Grignard compounds.) The alkyl fluorides form Grignard compounds with magnesium, though not always very readily. Para-fluoro-bromo-benzene[222] is readily converted into the compound $F \cdot C_6H_4Mg \cdot Br$, and the usual products of the reactions of this compound, without the fluorine atom being disturbed.

On the other hand with alkalies, and even with alcoholic potash, the fluorine can react. The conversion of a fluoride into a methyl ether by treatment with potassium hydroxide in methyl alcohol can be made to go even with fluorobenzene itself[232]; the reaction becomes quite easy when the ring has a nitro-group in the ortho[219] or para[233] position to the fluorine.

In aromatic compounds fluorine, like the other halogens, directs further substitution to the ortho and para positions; the ratio para/ortho is larger for fluorine than for chlorine, this quantity diminishing in the order $F > Cl > Br > I$.[206,234]

B. Jones[235] finds that on the rate of chlorination of the anilides fluorine and chlorine in the para positions have about the same effect; with the ethers the relative rates for F, Cl, Br are ortho 43, 37, 44; and para 19, 10, 10.

Hydrogen Fluoride as an Organic Catalyst

It has recently been shown, largely by J. H. Simons (*J.A.C.S.* 1938–43[236–49,255–6,258–64]) that hydrogen fluoride is a valuable catalyst in a number of organic reactions. It will usually[240] catalyse the same reactions as aluminium chloride, sulphuric acid, or boron trifluoride; but it will bring

[230] J. Piccard and C. Buffat, *Helv. Chim. Acta*, 1923, **6**, 1047.

[231] H. Gilman and L. L. Heck, *J.A.C.S.* 1931, **53**, 377, 378.

[232] B. Tronow and E. Kruger, *J. Russ. phys. chem. Ges.* 1926, **58**, 1270.

[233] H. Rouche, *Bull. Acad. Roy. Belge*, 1922, [5] **7**, 534.

[234] C. K. Ingold and C. C. N. Vass, ib. 2262.

[235] B. Jones, *J.C.S.* 1938, 1414.

[236] J. H. Simons, G. H. Fleming, F. C. Whitmore, and W. E. Bissinger, *J.A.C.S.* 1938, **60**, 2267.

[237] J. H. Simons and S. Archer, ib. 2952.   [238] Id., ib. 2953.

[239] J. H. Simons, S. Archer, and E. Adams, ib. 2955.

[240] J. H. Simons, S. Archer, and H. J. Passino, ib. 2956.

[241] J. H. Simons and S. Archer, ib. 1939, **61**, 1521.

[242] J. H. Simons, D. I. Randall, and S. Archer, ib. 1795.

[243] J. H. Simons, S. Archer, and D. I. Randall, ib. 1821.

[244] J. H. Simons and S. Archer, ib. 1940, **62**, 451.

[245] J. H. Simons, S. Archer, and D. I. Randall, ib. 485.

[246] J. H. Simons and S. Archer, ib. 1623.

[247] J. H. Simons and H. J. Passino, ib. 1624.

[248] J. H. Simons, *J. Ind. Eng. Chem.* 1940, **32**, 178.

about some reactions that they will not, such as the addition of an aliphatic halide to an olefine. It has the advantage over aluminium chloride that it does not form tars, and over sulphuric acid that it does not substitute. It is also very easily removed after the reaction by distillation and in other ways.

For a general account of this see Simons,[248] from which much of the following is taken.

Anhydrous hydrogen fluoride is now (1940) made commercially in the U.S.A. by the controlled action of sulphuric acid on calcium fluoride, and is purified by distillation; it then contains from 0·1 to 0·5 per cent. of water, and from 0·01 to 0·1 per cent. of silicon tetrafluoride, and sells at 1 dollar per lb. for a few lbs., and 20 cents a pound in quantity. It is made, purified, and stored in steel vessels, which are not seriously attacked, although owing to the catalytic effect of iron, the organic reactions should as a rule be carried out in copper vessels. No chemical reagent will dry hydrogen fluoride; calcium chloride, sulphuric acid, and phosphorus pentoxide all react with it, and it can only be dried by electrolysis. For many organic reactions, however, traces of water do not matter.

The organic reactions which hydrogen fluoride catalyses may be divided into polymerizations, alkylations, acylations, and certain special reactions.

Polymerizations.[248] These occur even with rubber: tubes and stoppers are converted in contact with HF into a hard brittle mass. All kinds of unsaturated compounds from ethylene to linseed or Soya-bean oil are polymerized by it; so too are many aldehydes, but *not* aromatic hydrocarbons.[260]

Alkylations. Alkyl groups can be introduced, especially into aromatic hydrocarbons, with olefines,[237,241,249,252] alkyl halides,[238,251-2,258] esters,[252] or alcohols.[241,246,249,252] The reactions can be done in steel vessels, mostly at 0°–20°, using 25–50 per cent. of anhydrous HF. It is to be noticed that benzene condenses with propylene to give isopropyl benzene,[237] but with cyclopropane to give normal propyl benzene.[239] In the condensation with alcohols there are two curious points,[246] (1) with HF alcohols react better

[249] J. H. Simons and G. C. Bassler, *J.A.C.S.* 1941, **63**, 880.
[250] A. V. Grosse and C. B. Linn, *J. Org. Chem.* 1938, **3**, 26.
[251] W. S. Calcott, J. M. Tinker, and V. Weinmayr, *J.A.C.S.* 1939, **61**, 949.
[252] Id., ib. 1010.
[253] L. F. Fieser and E. B. Hershberg, ib. 1940, **62**, 49.
[254] Id., ib. 1939, **61**, 1272.
[255] J. H. Simons and A. C. Meunier, ib. 1943, **65**, 1269.
[256] J. H. Simons and E. O. Ramler, ib. 1390.
[257] V. N. Ipatiev, H. Pines, and R. E. Schaad, ib. 1944, **66**, 816.
[258] J. W. Sprauer and J. H. Simons, ib. 1942, **64**, 648.
[259] J. H. Simons and A. C. Werner, ib. 1356.
[260] S. M. McElvain and J. W. Langston, ib. 1944, **66**, 1759.
[261] W. H. Pearlson and J. H. Simons, ib. 1945, **67**, 352.
[262] H. Pines and V. N. Ipatiev, ib. 1631.
[263] H. Pines, A. Edeleanu, and V. N. Ipatiev, ib. 2193.
[264] E. B. Butler, C. B. Miles, and C. S. Kuhn, *Ind. Eng. Chem.* 1946, **38**, 147.

than halides, but with aluminium chloride the reverse holds; (2) secondary and tertiary alcohols react at the ordinary temperature, but primary only do so with difficulty at temperatures below 100°. Further,[247] while ethyl and the higher alkyls can be introduced into benzene in this way, methyl alcohol, methyl acetate, and methyl iodide will not react, though with aluminium chloride methyl chloride readily reacts, and even methyl alcohol will do so. The alkylation by alcohols and olefines cannot be due to the intermediate formation of alkyl fluoride, as the reaction goes more slowly with the alkyl fluoride itself than with the doubly linked C=C group.[249]

The production of new rings goes especially well with hydrogen fluoride; thus[251] perylene (see figure) is formed from phenanthrene, acrolein, and HF.

Acylation.[253-4] This can be done[242] with acids, anhydrides, esters,[243] or acyl halides, usually in a bomb at 80–100°. Unlike aluminium chloride HF gives as good a yield with the free carboxylic acid as with the acyl halide or ester, and sometimes a better one. Thus toluene+acetic acid gives *p*-methyl acetophenone.

Carboxylation. *n*-Propyl alcohol reacts with 90 per cent. formic acid in presence of hydrogen fluoride at 100° to give *n*-butyric acid; the same product is obtained in presence of hydrogen fluoride from primary propyl chloride and nickel carbonyl.[250]

Special Reactions. A curious shortening of the carbon chain by splitting off a carbon atom can occur. Thus[236] tertiary amyl chloride with HF at 0° gives 10–17 per cent. of tertiary butyl chloride, along with more complicated products (hexyl, heptyl, undecyl chlorides, etc.); the production on alkylation with AlCl₃ of tertiary butyl groups from higher (amyl, hexyl, octadecyl) halides was noticed by Gilman. In the same way[244] di- and tri-isobutylene split up when treated with HF and phenol, and give *p-tert.* butyl phenol.

Similarly hydrogen fluoride can bring about various inter- and intra-molecular rearrangements: thus[245] *tert.* butyl benzene+phenol gives *tert.* butyl phenol+benzene: benzophenone oxime gives benzanilide (Beckmann reaction): phenyl acetate gives *p*-acetyl phenol[248]:

$$\bigcirc\!\!-O-CO-CH_3 \longrightarrow CH_3-CO-\bigcirc\!\!-OH.$$

The number of additions that can be made to C=C in presence of HF is especially large. Hydrocarbons, phenols, alcohols, acids, and alkyl halides[255] can be added on in this way; benzene reacts with butadiene in HF to give α-, β-diphenyl butane $CH_3 \cdot CH_2 \cdot CH\Phi \cdot CH_2\Phi$.[256] Condensations are also frequently produced by it, as when acetophenone gives dypnone

$$\begin{matrix} CH_3 \\ \diagdown \\ \diagup \\ \Phi \end{matrix}C\!\!=\!\!CH \cdot CO \cdot \Phi.\text{[257]}$$

See further references [261-4].

OXIDES OF FLUORINE

IT was long believed that fluorine was incapable of combining with oxygen, to give either an oxide or an oxy-acid. We now know that it can certainly form two oxides, F_2O and F_2O_2 (a third, FO, has been described, but in error); whether it can also form an oxyacid is very doubtful.

Fluorine monoxide F_2O was first obtained by Lebeau[265-6], best by passing fluorine gas slowly through 2 per cent. NaOH solution; the gas so produced contains about 70 per cent. of F_2O. This is the method which is now always used for its preparation. The reaction is not understood: in pure water only a small quantity of F_2O is produced,[274] while in concentrated sodium hydroxide the whole of the F_2O is decomposed.

A more complete investigation of its properties was made by Ruff and his collaborators.[267-9] The fullest and most accurate account is in the last of these. The gas was carefully purified by fractional distillation, and was shown by analysis to contain 99·8 per cent. F_2O.

Fluorine monoxide F_2O is a colourless gas, condensing to a yellow-brown liquid. B. pt. −144·8° C. (128·3° K.), m. pt. −223·8° C. (49·3° K.); this is the lowest melting-point recorded for any compound (unless we include HD, m. pt. 13·95° K.). Critical temp. −81° C. The heat of evaporation is 2·65 k.cals., and hence the Trouton constant 20·65.[269] The density at the melting-point is found by extrapolation to be 1·90.

The infra-red spectrum indicates an $O{\Large\langle}{ \atop }$ molecule with an angle of

100°.[275]

Fluorine monoxide has a peculiar smell, rather like that of elementary fluorine. It is even more poisonous than fluorine itself[269]; it penetrates more deeply into the lungs, and its full effect is only felt after a time. The results can be mitigated by inhaling 1 per cent. solutions of calcium chloride and magnesium sulphate.

F_2O is an endothermic compound, its heat of formation from gaseous fluorine and oxygen being −4·6±2 k.cals.[267] Hence its heat of formation from its atoms is

$$F_2 + \tfrac{1}{2}O_2 = F_2O - 4\cdot6$$

$$33\cdot3 \quad 59\cdot1 \qquad 87\cdot8$$

[265] P. Lebeau and A. Damiens, *C.R.* 1927, **185**, 652.

[266] Id., ib. 1929, **188**, 1253.

[267] O. Ruff and W. Menzel, *Z. anorg. Chem.* 1930, **190**, 257.

[268] O. Ruff and K. Clusius, ib. 267.

[269] O. Ruff and W. Menzel, ib. 1931, **198**, 39.

[270] F. Ishikawa, T. Murooka, and H. Hagisawa, *Bull. Inst. Phys. Chem. Res. Tokyo*, 1933, **12**, 742.

[271] Id., *Sci. Rep. Tohuku*, 1934, **23**, 431.

[272] F. Ishikawa, H. Sato, and T. Takai, *Bull. Inst. Phys. Chem. Res. Tokyo*, 1934, **13**, 1053, 1058.

[273] W. Koblitz and H. J. Schumacher, *Z. physikal. Chem.* 1934, B **25**, 283.

[274] G. H. Cady, *J.A.C.S.* 1935, **57**, 246.

[275] G. Hettner, R. Pohlman, and H. J. Schumacher, *Z. f. Physik.* 1935, **96**, 203.

87·8 k.cals., showing that the heat of formation of the F—O link is 43·9 k.cals. According to Pauling's theory, the very small heat effect of the formation of the oxide from the gaseous elements is a sign that the links in F_2O are almost purely covalent.

Fluorine monoxide does not attack glass in the cold, and although it is slightly endothermic has never been found to explode at temperatures below its boiling-point. Mercury pumps cannot be used with it, as it corrodes the mercury; cooled charcoal must be used, and with care, since if the gas is at too high a pressure when it is brought into contact with the charcoal, violent explosions may occur.

Fluorine monoxide breaks up into its elements on heating. Koblitz and Schumacher[273] measured the decomposition by means of the change of pressure. The reaction

$$2\,F_2O = 2\,F_2 + O_2$$

involves a 50 per cent. increase in pressure. At 260° C. the change takes up to 5 hours or so; the pressures used varied from 80–760 mm.

The reaction was carried out with the pure gas, and also in presence of varying amounts of other gases, such as nitrogen, helium, argon, oxygen, and silicon tetrafluoride. The rate of decomposition is given approximately by the equation

$$\frac{dx}{dt} = K \cdot [F_2O]([F_2O] + [X] + [Y]...)$$

where [X], [Y], etc., are the concentrations of the added gases. This indicates that the reaction is really monomolecular, but that the life of a molecule activated by collision (either with another F_2O or with a molecule of an added gas) is very short (less than 10^{-12} sec.), so that it always breaks up before it is deactivated, as happens at very low pressures in other monomolecular reactions.

In general[269] fluorine monoxide is less active than fluorine, and often (e.g. with many metals) will not react below a rather high temperature, where the real reagent may be the liberated fluorine. In dry systems it usually fluorinates; in presence of water (see further below) it is an oxidizing agent. But it was shown by L. M. Dennis that the traces of free oxygen in the crude gas can be completely removed by exposure to yellow phosphorus.

Its reaction with water is of interest. This is so highly exothermic:

$$F_2O + H_2O_{gas} = O_2 + 2\,HF + 74 \cdot 8 \text{ k.cals.}$$

that we should expect it to occur very readily. As a fact, however, it does not. The gas can be kept over water unchanged for four weeks.[269] In the absence of liquid water the reaction is still slower; no change was found to occur in the moist gas in a year.[270-2] The solubility of the gas in water at 0° is 68 c.c. per litre[269] (at 0° a litre of water dissolves hydrogen 22 c.c., nitrogen 23, oxygen 49, argon 53); the solution obeys Henry's law.[270]

In the presence of alkali on the other hand, especially if it is concentrated, the decomposition is rapid and complete. The gas is quickly absorbed with liberation of oxygen, and the production of an oxidizing solution[276-7]; what this may contain is not certain, but it was shown[277] that it is not potassium ozonate, as had been suggested.[278]

Fluorine monoxide has an inertness, especially to water, similar to, but rather less than, that of nitrogen fluoride and to be explained in the same way. The complex

$$\begin{matrix} F \\ \\ F \end{matrix} \Big\rangle O \cdot \cdot H - O - H$$

can be formed just as

$$\begin{matrix} Cl \\ \\ Cl \end{matrix} \Big\rangle O \cdot \cdot H - O - H$$

can with Cl_2O, but the further stage of the elimination of HOF (as Cl_2O gives HOCl) is impossible because HOF does not exist.

Ruff[269] failed to find any higher fluoride (e.g. OF_4) in the residue from the distillation of F_2O. This is natural, since oxygen cannot have more than a valency octet.

Fluorine Dioxide, F_2O_2

The second oxide of fluorine F_2O_2 was discovered by Ruff and Menzel in 1933.[279] It is formed when a mixture of fluorine and oxygen, cooled with liquid air, is exposed to the electric discharge. It is a brown gas, condensing to a cherry-red liquid and an orange solid.[279] It begins to decompose at about $-100°$ into what was thought to be another oxide FO, but is now known to be a mixture of F_2 and O_2 (see below). At $-100°$ and below, the gas has the vapour density and composition corresponding to F_2O_2. It can be purified by distillation at $-115°$ under a pressure of a few mm., the decomposition products F_2 and O_2 being continuously pumped off. Its physical properties are[280]: v.p. (measured with quartz spiral) 10 mm. at $-119.5°$; 50 mm. at $-101°$; at about $-95°$ (v.p. *ca.* 80 mm.) decomposition begins. Extrapolation gives the b. pt. $-57°$ C.; heat of evaporation 4·57 k.cals., Trouton constant 21·2. M. pt. $-163.5°$ C. ($109.6°$ K.). Density: solid at m. pt. 1·912, liquid at b. pt. extrapolated 1·44. For the infra-red absorption spectrum see reference [286].

[276] L. M. Dennis and E. G. Rochow, *J.A.C.S.* 1932, **54**, 832.
[277] Id., ib. 1933, **55**, 2431.
[278] F. Fichter and W. Bladergroen, *Helv. Chim. Acta*, 1927, **10**, 549.
[279] O. Ruff and W. Menzel, *Z. anorg. Chem.* 1933, **211**, 204.
[280] Id., ib. 1934, **217**, 85.
[281] P. Frisch and H. J. Schumacher, ib. 1936, **229**, 423.
[282] Id., *Z. physikal. Chem.* 1936, B **34**, 322.
[283] O. Ruff, *Ber.* 1936, **69**, A 191.
[284] P. Frisch and H. J. Schumacher, *Z. Elektrochem.* 1937, **43**, 807.
[285] H. J. Schumacher and P. Frisch, *Z. physikal. Chem.* 1937, B **37**, 1.
[286] P. H. Brodersen, P. Frisch, and H. K. Schumacher, ib. 25.

On warming, the gas decomposes, and in so doing doubles its volume. This is compatible with either of the two reactions:

$$F_2O_2 = 2\,FO \text{ or } = F_2 + O_2.$$

The product was at first supposed to be a new oxide FO, because it was found that on vigorous shaking it was completely absorbed by 30 per cent. hydriodic acid; this seemed to exclude the possibility that it contained free oxygen. Frisch and Schumacher,[281] however, showed that the decomposition product gave an absorption spectrum identical with that of a mixture of F_2 and O_2; they further found that 30 per cent. hydriodic acid is able to absorb oxygen under the conditions of Ruff's analysis. Ruff[283] agrees that there is no reason to think that FO exists.

As the dioxide is only stable below $-95°$, there is little to say about its chemical properties except with respect to its decomposition into its elements. This reaction is conveniently measured between $-25°$ and $60°$.[282,284-5] It is a homogeneous reaction of the first order, with a heat of activation of 17·0 k.cals.

As to the structure of F_2O_2 we have no evidence whatever; it may be either F—O—O—F or $\underset{F}{\overset{F}{\diagdown}}O\rightarrow O$. The readiness with which it breaks up into its elements makes the examination of its structure very difficult.

Fluorine Perchlorate, $F \cdot ClO_4$

This remarkable substance is made[287] by passing fluorine over cold 72 per cent. aqueous perchloric acid. It is a colourless gas melting at $-167·5°$ and boiling at $-15·9°$. It is explosive even down to its freezing-point. It is obviously analogous to the nitrate $F \cdot NO_3$ described above (V. 703). As will be shown later (VII. 1242), there is reason to think that the iodide $I \cdot ClO_4$ is formed by the action of iodine on silver perchlorate, although only its decomposition products can be isolated.

[287] G. H. Rohrback and G. H. Cady, *J.A.C.S.* 1947, **69**, 677.

CHLORINE, BROMINE, AND IODINE

MANY of the physical properties of these elements are given in the table on p. 1098.

Elementary Chlorine

Chlorine is the most abundant of the halogens, especially in sea water, a ton of which contains in grammes chlorine 15,000, bromine 97, iodine 0·17 (ratio $10^6 : 6,000 : 1$). Its preparation depends on the discharge of its ion, either directly (i.e. electrolytically) or by oxidation. The older methods of oxidation (by manganese dioxide or by air in presence of certain catalysts) have now been replaced for technical purposes by the electrolysis of sodium chloride, which is primarily for the production of caustic soda, the chlorine being a by-product; the chloroparaffins which are now so much used as solvents were developed to utilize this chlorine.

Chlorine has two isotopes of masses 34·979 and 36·978[288] in the proportions 75·4, 24·6.[289] They have been separated almost completely by thermal diffusion in a 20-m. tube (Clusius and Dickel[290-1]); their electrolytic separation factor is 1·006 on platinum electrodes, or 1·007 on graphite.[292] The boiling- and melting-points data (p. 1098) are given by Giauque.[293] For the high purification of chlorine by distillation and freezing see reference [294]. The dipole moment of chlorine is zero.[295]

Chemically chlorine is extremely reactive, though less so than fluorine. Water absorbs about twice its volume of the gas at 25°. It is present in the solution partly as such, and partly as what may be called the hydrolytic products HCl and HOCl. In an N/40 solution of chlorine in water about one-half is present as the two acids. On standing, and more rapidly in sunlight, this 'chlorine water' evolves oxygen through the conversion of HOCl into HCl.

Chlorine can also form with water at low temperatures a crystalline hydrate, which has a dissociation tension of Cl_2 of 760 mm. at 9·6°.[296] Faraday gave this hydrate the formula $Cl_2, 10\ H_2O$. Recent work indicates that it is $Cl_2, 6\ H_2O$,[297] or 8 H_2O.[298]

Atomic Chlorine

This highly active monatomic form of chlorine, analogous to those of hydrogen, oxygen, and nitrogen, was discovered simultaneously by

[288] S. Okuda, K. Ogata, K. Aoki, and Y. Sugawara, *Phys. Rev.* 1942, **58**, 578.
[289] A. O. Nier and E. E. Hanson, ib. 1936, **50**, 722.
[290] K. Clusius and G. Dickel, *Naturwiss.* 1939, **27**, 148.
[291] Id., ib. 487.
[292] H. L. Johnston and D. A. Hutchison, *J. Chem. Phys.* 1942, **10**, 469.
[293] W. F. Giauque and T. M. Powell, *J.A.C.S.* 1939, **61**, 1970.
[294] P. M. Fye and J. J. Beaver, ib. 1941, **63**, 1268.
[295] E. Kanda, *Bull. Soc. Chem. Japan*, 1937, **12**, 473.
[296] G. Tammann and J. G. R. Krige, *Z. anorg. Chem.* 1925, **146**, 192.
[297] A. Bouzat and L. Aziniéres, *C.R.* 1923, **177**, 1444; S. Anwar-Ullah, *J.C.S.* 1932, 1172.
[298] I. Harris, *Nature*, 1943, **151**, 309.

Rodebush[299] and by Schwab.[300-1] It is formed by the action of the electric discharge on chlorine gas at low temperatures. The metal of the electrode is liable to catalyse the recombination of the atoms. Hence Rodebush used external electrodes, while Schwab found that internal water-cooled electrodes of iron were more effective. Below 1 mm. the gas can be atomized up to some 20 per cent. The atoms recombine rapidly; the rate—or rather the amount of uncombined atoms left—may be measured by the heat evolved on a thermo-junction inserted in the gas at varying distances from the source, in a tube along which the gas is passing at a known rate. At about 0·1 mm. pressure the mean life in a glass tube was found to be 6×10^{-3} second.[300] The combination[301-3] occurs only on the walls of the tube. It is promoted by magnesium and by copper, and still more by silver, but platinum has no more effect than the glass. Methane 'kills' the catalytic power of the glass, presumably by occupying the surface. Carbon monoxide promotes it.

Atomic chlorine is highly reactive, combining slowly with sulphur and red phosphorus, rapidly with copper and chromium sesquioxide. It also can be shown to start the long chains in a mixture of hydrogen and chlorine.

Elementary Bromine

Bromine has two natural isotopes 79 and 81, present in nearly equal amounts (50·6 and 49·4: Blewett[304]). It is remarkable for giving at least five artificial isotopes, two of which are isobaric.[305-11] Their masses and life periods are[305-6]:

Mass numbers	78	80 a	80 b	82	83
Half-life	6·4′	18·5′	4·54 hr.	33·9 hr.	2·54 hr.

For work on isotopic exchange see p. 1098.

For boiling-points, etc. (p. 1098) see reference [313]. The dielectric constant is 3·33 at 0°.[314] Bromine is the only element except mercury that is liquid at the ordinary temperature.

Bromine is practically always made from a solution of a natural halide containing it (commonly 'bitterns', the mother liquor from the

[299] W. H. Rodebush and W. C. Klingelhoefer, *J.A.C.S.* 1933, **55**, 130.
[300] G. M. Schwab and H. Friess, *Naturwiss.* 1933, **21**, 222.
[301] Id., *Z. Elektrochem.* 1933, **39**, 586.
[302] E. J. B. Willey and S. G. Foord, *Proc. Roy. Soc.* 1934, **147**, 309.
[303] G. M. Schwab and H. Friess, *Z. physikal. Chem.* 1936, **178**, 123.
[304] J. P. Blewett, *Phys. Rev.* 1936, **49**, 900.
[305] A. H. Snell, ib. 1937, **52**, 1007.
[306] R. Fleischmann, *Z. Phys.* 1937, **107**, 205.
[307] E. Friedmann, A. K. Soloman, and N. T. Werthessen, *Nature*, 1939, **143**, 472.
[308] C. S. Lu and S. Sugden, *J.C.S.* 1939, 1273.
[309] J. E. Willard, *J.A.C.S.* 1940, **62**, 256.   [310] Id., ib. 3161.
[311] A. Berthelot, *Ann. Physique* 1944 [xi] **19**, 117, 219.
[312] P. M. Doty and J. E. Mayer, *J. Chem. Phys.* 1944, **12**, 323.
[313] F. E. C. Scheffer and M. Voogd, *Rec. Trav.* 1926, **45**, 217.
[314] D. Doborzynski, *Z. Phys.* 1930, **66**, 657.

manufacture of common salt), by treatment with chlorine followed by distillation or extraction with air or a hydrocarbon solvent such as benzene. It has been calculated that there are in Germany 6×10^{10} tons of carnallite (KCl, $MgCl_2$, $6 H_2O$) containing 0·2 per cent., that is 120 million tons, of bromine.

The use of lead tetraethyl as an anti-knock in petrol enormously increased the demand for bromine, as ethylene dibromide had to be added (along with the dichloride) to the petrol to remove a deposit of lead from the cylinders. About 600 g. of bromine are needed per ton of petrol; this meant in Britain in 1938 500 tons, and in the U.S.A. in 1936 12,000 tons—three times the total previous annual consumption. New sources of bromine were found, partly in salt lakes and salt deposits with a considerable bromine content, but especially in the sea water, which contains 97 g. per ton. This is extracted commercially at Wilmington, N. Carolina. The large volume of extracted water must be returned to the sea in such a way that it does not dilute the intake. On this coast there is a steady southward current, and the works is on a tongue of land between the sea and the estuary of a river flowing southwards, so that the water is taken in from the sea, and the debrominated exhaust sent into the river, from which the current carries it away to the south. The sea water is slightly acidified with H_2SO_4, and treated with the exact amount of chlorine required, the acidity and the free halogen content being closely controlled by means of a hydrogen electrode and a 'redox' electrode. The liquid then falls through a counter current of air, which removes 90 per cent. of the free bromine. The air is stripped of its bromine by concentrated sodium carbonate solution, and when this is acidified the bromine separates as a liquid layer, and is at once combined with ethylene to give ethylene dibromide.

Solid bromine is isomorphous with iodine; it has a molecular structure, with a separation of $2·27 \pm 0·10$ A.U. between the atoms[315] (theory 2·28); this result agrees with the value 2·26 obtained[316] from the band spectrum of the gas, and that of 2·27 got by electron diffraction of the vapour.[317] It retains an intense orange colour even in liquid hydrogen at $-252°$.[318]

Liquid bromine is of course deeply coloured, but its colour (like that of chlorine but unlike that of iodine) is little affected by the solvent, the absorption bands having much the same position in the vapour, in water, in chloroform, and in carbon tetrachloride.[319]

Chemically elementary bromine is of course very reactive, its behaviour being like that of chlorine, but less violent. Thus in the cold it attacks gold but not platinum.

Liquid bromine is a fairly good solvent, especially for halides; sometimes,

[315] B. Vonnegut and B. E. Warren, *J.A.C.S.* 1936, **58**, 2459.
[316] M. C. Neuberger, *Gitterkonstante*, 1931.
[317] R. Wierl, *Phys. Z.* 1930, **31**, 366, 1028.
[318] K. Clusius, *Z. Naturforsch.* 1947, **2 b**, 244.
[319] See Gmelin, *Brom*, p. 89.

as with ammonium halides, and also certain organic solutes such as benzamide[320] and the ethers,[321] the solutes are more or less ionized. Its conductivity is extraordinarily minute, less than that of pure water, being about 0.16×10^{-8} mhos at $18°$,[322] that of the purest water being 4×10^{-8}, so that the pure liquid can scarcely be ionized at all.

Atomic Bromine

Bromine vapour can be dissociated by sparks[323] and recombines on standing. It is also dissociated by heat[312] and by light; in the last event the product is a normal and an excited atom, as is usual with covalent molecules (Franck and Sponer); the heat of thermal dissociation has been found to be 48.1 k.cals. (theory 53.8).

It can be dissociated by the electric discharge in exactly the same way as chlorine, with the use of water-cooled iron electrodes in the vapour at a pressure of 0.1 mm.[324] The degree of atomization, as with chlorine, is from 10 to 40 per cent. Recombination of the atoms is much more rapid than with chlorine (though the heat evolved is less), occurring whenever an atom hits the wall (with chlorine only about 1 in 12 of such collisions is effective); unlike chlorine this is only slightly slowed down by adding methane. Hence it is very difficult to observe the reactions of atomic bromine. Recombination of the atoms in the gas itself is much slower, because a triple collision is necessary to get rid of the energy of combination; of the double Br+Br collisions only about 1 in 10^9 is fruitful.[325] In the presence of a considerable amount of a foreign gas the homogeneous reaction is quicker; it can then be measured[326] by adding hydrogen, and observing the rate of formation of hydrogen bromide, which is a measure of the concentration of bromine atoms; in this way the power of different gases to cause the recombination can be determined. Further measurements of the same kind have been made by using the intensity of the absorption as a measure of the concentration of the bromine molecules.[327]

Bromine and Water

Bromine is miscible with the ordinary organic solvents, but its solubility in water is limited, and that of water in bromine still more so. At $22°$ bromine will dissolve only 0.046 per cent. of water[328]; water dissolves 3.5 per cent. of bromine, the amount being nearly constant from $6°$, the melting-point of the hydrate, to $55°$, where the saturated solution, or the

[320] W. Finkelstein, *J. Russ. Phys. Chem. Soc.* 1926, **58**, 565.

[321] B. P. Bruns, *Z. anorg. Chem.* 1927, **163**, 120.

[322] M. Rabinovitsch, *Z. physikal. Chem.* 1926, **119**, 81; W. Finkelstein, ib. **121**, 47.

[323] J. J. Thomson, *Proc. Roy. Soc.* 1887, **42**, 345.

[324] G. M. Schwab, *Z. physikal. Chem.* 1934, B **27**, 452.

[325] V. Kondratjev and A. Leipunsky, *Z. Phys.* 1929, **56**, 353.

[326] K. Hilferding and W. Steiner, *Z. physikal. Chem.* 1935, B **30**, 399.

[327] E. Rabinovitsch and H. L. Lehmann, *Trans. Far. Soc.* 1935, **31**, 689.

[328] M. Wildermann, *Z. physikal. Chem.* 1893, **11**, 413.

two-liquid system, boils under atmospheric pressure.[329] There is a solid hydrate of bromine which is stable in contact with the solution from the cryohydric point of $-0.3°$ up to about $+6.2°$, where it melts to give two liquid layers. Its composition probably[330-3] is $Br_2, 8 H_2O$.

Bromine reacts with water like the other halogens, giving hydrobromic and hypobromous acids, but the reaction is more complicated than with chlorine since polybromides, Br_3^-, and some Br_5^-, and perhaps even higher compounds, are formed. It has been found[334] that the proportions of the various products in a saturated solution of bromine in water at 25° are, in millimoles per litre:

Br_2	HOBr	H^+	Br^-	Br_3^-	Br_5^-
20·68	1·7	1·71	0·37	1·21	0·13

Elementary Iodine

Iodine is the rarest of the halogens. One ton of average rock contains 0·3 g., and 1 ton of sea water 17 mg.[335] It has long been obtained from kelp, the ashes of certain species of seaweed, which contain from 0·1 to 3 per cent. of iodine, but it is more readily got from Chile saltpetre ($NaNO_3$) which contains up to 1 per cent. of iodine as iodate. The world production in 1929 was 1,650 tons of which 80 per cent. came from Chile.

Solid iodine has a molecular lattice of I_2 molecules, isomorphous with solid bromine. Its molecular weight in neutral (non-ionized) solution is always that of I_2.

Liquid iodine has a perceptible conductivity of 5.22×10^{-5} at 117°, just above its melting-point.[336] It is remarkable that this, like the conductivity of a metal, diminishes with rise of temperature, being only 3.95×10^{-5} at 155°. The rise in conductivity with atomic weight in the halogens is remarkable; the following are the values for the liquids near their boiling-points.

Cl	Br/Cl	Br	I/Br	I
Less than 10^{-16}	5,500,000	5.5×10^{-10}	95,000	5.22×10^{-5}

Iodine may here be showing something of a metallic character.

Gaseous iodine dissociates on heating more readily than any of the other halogens; its heat of dissociation is 36·1 k.cals./I_2[337]; for the rate of

---

[329] H. W. Bakhuis Roozeboom, *Rec. Trav.* 1884, **3**, 73; 1885, **4**, 71; 1886, **5**, 380, 393; *Z. physikal. Chem.* 1888, **2**, 452, 477; F. H. Rhodes and C. H. Bascom, *Ind. Eng. Chem.* 1927, **19**, 480.

[330] H. W. Bakhuis Roozeboom, *Rec. Trav.* 1884, **3**, 84.

[331] H. Giran, *C.R.* 1914, **159**, 246.

[332] I. W. H. Harris, *J.C.S.* 1932, 582.

[333] J. d'Ans and P. Höfer, *Z. angew. Chem.* 1934, **47**, 71.

[334] W. C. Bray and E. L. Connolly, *J.A.C.S.* 1911, **33**, 1487; G. Jones and M. L. Hartman, *Trans. Amer. Electrochem. Soc.* 1916, **30**, 295.

[335] I. Masson, *Nature*, 1938, **141**, 227.

[336] M. Rabinovitsch, *Z. physikal. Chem.* 1926, **119**, 82.

[337] M. L. Perlman and C. K. Rollefson, *J. Chem. Phys.* 1941, **9**, 362.

recombination of the atoms see reference [338]. Under 1 atm. pressure the dissociation begins to be perceptible at 600°, is 36 per cent. at 800°, 80 per cent. at 900°, and practically complete at 1,000°.

Iodine is black or grey in the solid state, practically black in the liquid, and a fine violet (whence the name) in the vapour. The colour of its solution varies in a very curious way with the nature of the solvent. This phenomenon has been the subject of numerous investigations.[339] The fundamental fact is that iodine in solution is sometimes violet and sometimes brown, and less often has an intermediate red colour. Iodine chloride, bromide, and cyanide behave in the same way (see later, pp. 1153, 1155). Violet solutions, of much the same colour as the vapour, are formed in such solvents as the paraffins and many of their halogen-substitution products, red in the aromatic hydrocarbons (and also in concentrated hydrochloric and nitric acids) and brown in water and the alcohols.[340] The colours of the solutions are often affected by temperature, low temperatures usually favouring brown, and high temperatures violet. Thus the brown solution in ethyl stearate or oleate becomes violet if heated to 80°.

The absorption spectra[341] are practically identical in their general form in the visible. There is one main absorption band, of which the maximum is with the violet solutions at about 5,400 A, with the red about 5,200 A, and with the brown about 4,700 A. The extinction coefficient (for the range 4,300–6,800 A) is almost constant for the violet solutions at 0·42; for the brown solutions it is less, and varies from 0·23 to 0·30 (except for the brown solution in nitrobenzene, where it is again 0·42). The violet solutions obey Beer's law, but the brown do not, although the precise character of their departure from it has not been investigated.

When the difference of colour was first discovered it was supposed to be due to a difference in molecular weight of the dissolved iodine. This, however, has been definitely disproved, mainly through the work of Beckmann. He showed[342] that the results which appeared to support the difference in molecular weight were usually vitiated in the boiling-point experiments by the volatility of the iodine, and in the cryoscopic work by the formation of solid solutions. When allowance was made for these complications, the molecular weight of the solute was always found to be that of I_2.

[338] O. K. Rice, ib. 258.

[339] For the earlier work, especially on the molecular weight of the dissolved iodine, see Abegg, *Iod* (1913), pp. 378–91. The whole literature of the subject up to 1931 is discussed in Gmelin, *Iod*, pp. 111–29.

[340] For a full list of solvents of these three kinds see Gmelin, pp. 111–14. A. Lachman (*J.A.C.S.* 1903, **25**, 50) after trying 60 solvents could only distinguish two colours, violet in saturated solvents. The work of Getman[341] favours this view to some extent, but indicates that the aromatic hydrocarbons have an intermediate colour.

[341] F. H. Getman, ib. 1928, **50**, 2883.

[342] E. Beckmann, *Z. physikal. Chem.* 1890, **5**, 76; E. Beckmann and A. Stock, ib. 1895, **17**, 107.

If the change of colour is not due to a difference in the molecular weight it must be caused by solvation. This conclusion is supported by the whole behaviour of these solutions. The vapour shows that the colour of the pure I_2 molecule is violet. This colour persists in those solvents which are of a saturated character, and so are least likely to combine with the iodine. The resemblance in colour between the vapour and the violet solutions does not depend merely on visual observation. The extinction of coefficients have been measured for the vapour and for the solution in CCl_4 by E. Rabinovitsch and W. C. Wood,[343] who find that the wave-length for maximum extinction is the same for both (5,200 A) and that even the absolute magnitudes of the coefficient are nearly the same. This violet colour is also favoured by a rise of temperature, which would tend to break up a solvate. The brown colour is found with solvents of a more unsaturated or associated kind, and is favoured by low temperatures, which might be expected to promote solvation. This view, that the violet solutions contain unsolvated, and the brown solvated I_2 molecules, is supported by a variety of other considerations. The violet solutions have the same extinction coefficients whatever the solvent, and obey Beer's law; this is because the coloured substance is the I_2 molecule, which is not affected either by the solvent or by concentration. On the other hand, the brown solutions have different extinction coefficients, and also do not obey Beer's law; this again is to be expected since the brown molecules contain solvent, and as the solvents are usually associated, the colour may well not obey Beer's law. Again it was found by Lachman[340] that the colour of a violet solution is changed by the addition of even a small amount of a solvent of the unsaturated or associated type; the violet solution in chloroform is turned red by 0·4 per cent. of alcohol; while a brown solution must be largely diluted with a non-associated solvent before a violet colour appears.

With the red solution in benzene we have definite evidence of solvation. For this Williams[344] found an iodine moment of 1·2 D. This was confirmed by Müller and Sack,[345] who further showed that in hexane and in cyclohexane the moment of iodine is zero. Hence the iodine molecule itself is non-polar, and the moment in benzene is due to some kind of combination with the solvent. This shows not only that in the red solution in benzene the iodine is solvated, but also, as we should expect, that the solvation is very imperfect. The moment of a co-ordination compound, such as those of the aluminium halides investigated by Ulich and Nespital[346] (see under Al, III. 433) is somewhere about 4 D, so that we should conclude from the moments that in benzene about 25 per cent. of the I_2 is solvated. (See also ref. [347].)

---

[343] *Trans. Far. Soc.* 1936, **32**, 545.
[344] J. W. Williams, *Phys. Z.* 1928, **29**, 174.
[345] H. Müller and H. Sack, ib. 1930, **31**, 815.
[346] H. Ulich and W. Nespital, *Z. angew. Chem.* 1931, **44**, 750; W. Nespital, *Z. physikal. Chem.* 1932, B **16**, 221.
[347] F. Fairbrother, *Nature*, 1947, **160**, 87.

Iodine has a small solubility in water, rising rapidly with the temperature. In g. per litre this amounts to 0·16 at 0°, 0·34 at 25°, and 3·3 at 100°. It reacts with water in a rather complicated way, giving iodide and hypoiodite, of which the former takes up more iodine to form polyiodide ions such as I_3^-, while the latter, in presence of alkalies, is converted into iodide and iodate. These reactions, and the general question of the hydrolysis of the halogens, are discussed below under the oxyacids of the halogens. The well-known deep blue colour which free iodine gives with starch paste must be due to the formation of some addition compound. See references [348-9].

INTER-HALOGEN COMPOUNDS

THE halogens form a surprisingly large number of compounds with one another, all of which are well defined, covalent, and practically non-associated substances; they are usually formed slowly from their elements. This peculiarity of the halogens is obviously due to their being the only series of electronegative elements which can form acyclic molecules without double links, and hence such combination is not restricted to the lightest members of the group. There are no less than 11 inter-halogen compounds known, in addition to the 4 halogens themselves, so that we can draw some general conclusions as to the conditions of their existence.

These compounds are all of the type AB_n, where $n = 1, 3, 5$, or 7. None of them contains more than two different halogens, or more than one atom of the heavier of these. When n is greater than 1, B is always either fluorine or chlorine: when it is greater than 3, B is always fluorine. It is evident that all the B atoms are directly joined to the single A. It is also clear that the heavier A is, the more B's it can carry, and the lighter B, the more B's can combine with a single A. These obvious steric effects are, however, not the only factors of stability in these compounds. For example, among the AB compounds it would seem that they are less stable, the greater the difference in atomic number (or size) between A and B; thus BrF is very much less stable than ClF, and IF has never been obtained.

These relations can only be explained by reference to the heats of linkage concerned. These, so far as they are known, are given in the table on p. 1147; they are all derived from molecules of the A_2 or AB type; how the values differ in the compounds of higher valency, such as AB_3, in most cases we do not know, but we have evidence that as the covalency increases the heats of linkage diminish somewhat, but not much, except when the steric relations interfere, and the B atoms are too many or too large for the space.

It will be seen that with the single exception of the high Cl—F link* (the

* This indicates the tendency of all links to F to have large heats except that of F to F, which alone is purely covalent.

[348] R. S. Stein and R. E. Rundle, *J. Chem. Phys.* 1948, **16**, 195.
[349] G. A. Gilbert and J. V. R. Marriott, *Trans. Far. Soc.* 1948, **44**, 84.

only known value for a link of fluorine to another halogen), they are all of the same order of magnitude, as is shown by the heats of formation from the diatomic gaseous elements, which are: $ClF+25\cdot7$; $BrCl+0\cdot7$; $ICl+3\cdot5$; $IBr+1\cdot2$ k.cals.

	F	Cl	Br	I
F	33·3	71·3	..	..
Cl	71·3	57·8	52·7	51·0
Br	..	52·7	53·8	42·9
I	..	51·0	42·9	51·2

But when in the formation of one of these compounds an atom assumes a higher valency, the total number of links is increased, so that heat is evolved. Thus in the reaction $A_2+3B_2 = 2AB_3$ the number increases from 4 to 6, involving, if we take the value of these links to be on the average about 50 k.cals., the production of 100 k.cals. of heat. So generally, in the reaction $A_2+nB_2 = 2AB_n$ the number of links increases from $n+1$ to $2n$. Hence there will always be a tendency to form the compounds with the highest valency, unless for some other reason (such as the considerations of space) these are unstable. This is what actually happens. For example, the instability of BrF is not due to the weakness of the Br—F link; if it were, the molecule would break down into Br_2+F_2. It does not do this, but goes over into Br_2 together with BrF_3 and BrF_5, thus increasing the number of links present:

$$3\,BrF = Br_2 + BrF_3$$
$$3 \qquad 1 \qquad 3 = 4$$

$$5\,BrF = 2\,Br_2 + BrF_5$$
$$5 \qquad 2 + 5 = 7$$

It is therefore evident that there will be a tendency for the heavier atom to accumulate as many B atoms on itself as it has room for; the compound of higher valency will be unstable if the B atoms are getting too crowded, and those of lower valency if there is room for more.

This perhaps explains why it is that though we get inter-halogen compounds with 4, 6, and even 8 halogen atoms in the molecule, we never find a pure halogen molecule with more than 2, such as $Br \cdot Br_3 = Br_4$ or $Cl \cdot Cl_5 = Cl_6$; presumably the central atom is not large enough to carry three or more atoms of its own size.

The valency groups of the central atom in these types of molecule are:

Type	AB	AB$_3$	AB$_5$	AB$_7$
Val. gp. of A . .	6, 2	(2)2, 6	(2) 10	14

It follows that AB$_3$ and AB$_5$ molecules can only be formed when A can have an inert pair of electrons, so that the formation of such compounds is evidence of the inertness: and that AB$_7$ is only possible when A is iodine, since chlorine and bromine are limited to a covalency of 6.

COMPOUNDS OF THE TYPE AB

These compounds are obviously of the same type as the halogens themselves. Of the six possible compounds all are known except IF. The following table gives the values of the boiling-points, [m. pts.] and (Trouton constants) for these substances, the pure halogens being added for completeness.

AB Compounds

Boiling-points, [M. pts.] and (Trouton constants)

	F	Cl	Br	I
F	−188° [−219°] (18·8)	.. .. ..	.. .. ..	.. .. ..
Cl	−100·8° [−156°] (13·2)	− 33·7° [−102·3°] (18·4)	.. .. ..	.. .. ..
Br	+ 20° [− 33°] (20·5)	+ 5° [− 66°] ..	+ 58·8° [− 7·2°] (23·1)	.. .. ..
I	.. .. ..	+ 97·4° [a: 27·2°] [b: 13·9°] (27·5)	116° [36°] ..	185° [114°] (32·6)

Chlorine Fluoride, ClF

B. pt. −100·8°[352]; m. pt. −156°[355]; critical temperature −14°[352]; density of the liquid at its boiling-point 1·62°.[354] Heat of evaporation 2·27 k.cals.; Trouton constant 13·2 [?].[352]

This substance is formed[350] by the action of slightly moist chlorine on fluorine at the ordinary temperature; if the gases are dry they do not react below 250°. The reaction is exothermic (like practically all the reactions of elementary fluorine), evolving 25·7 k.cals.[353] per ClF. Fredenhagen[356] found that if a mixture of fluorine and chlorine is sparked, a yellow flame goes through the tube, followed by an explosion. This is no doubt due to the formation of chlorine fluoride. If the gases are dried, nothing happens on sparking. It will be noticed that the energy produced by the combination of chlorine with fluorine is more than 16 per cent.

[350] O. Ruff, J. Fischer, F. Luft, E. Ascher, F. Laass, and H. Volkmer, *Z. angew. Chem.* 1928, **41**, 1289.
[351] O. Ruff and E. Ascher, *Z. anorg. Chem.* 1928, **176**, 258.
[352] O. Ruff and F. Laass, ib. 1929, **183**, 214.
[353] O. Ruff and W. Menzel, ib. 1931, **198**, 375.
[354] O. Ruff, F. Ebert, and W. Menzel, ib. 1932, **207**, 46.
[355] O. Ruff and A. Braida, ib. 1933, **214**, 82.
[356] K. Fredenhagen and O. T. Krefft, *Z. physikal. Chem.* 1929, **141**, 221.

greater than that produced by the same volume of chlorine on combination with hydrogen (25·7 in place of 22·1 k.cals.).

Chlorine fluoride is an almost colourless gas, forming a yellow liquid and a colourless solid. It has a characteristic odour; it reacts just like fluorine, but even more readily.[351]

Bromine Fluoride, BrF

Gaseous bromine and fluorine react[357] very slowly at 0°; at +50° the reaction is quicker, but the BrF which is presumably the primary product reacts further, forming the trifluoride and the pentafluoride, together with free bromine. This goes on so readily that the monofluoride has never been got pure, and so its physical properties are only approximately known.

By allowing the components to react at about +10°, and fractionating the product at 150 mm. a yield of nearly 50 per cent. can be obtained.

Bromine monofluoride is a pale-brown gas, condensing to a dark-red liquid, which freezes to crystalline leaflets of the shape of boric acid and the colour of potassium dichromate. By extrapolation the boiling-point is found to be +20°, and the melting-point −33°. The Trouton constant is 20·5. It is remarkable that while the three bromine fluorides BrF, BrF_3, and BrF_5 are all miscible with one another, none of them has more than a very slight natural solubility with bromine.

Chemically bromine monofluoride behaves like the other fluorides of bromine, but it is more reactive. It is continuously changing into a mixture of Br_2, BrF_3, and BrF_5, and if it is warmed to 50° this conversion is complete.

[Iodine monofluoride IF is unknown, presumably going at once to IF_5 and IF_7: IF_3 is also unknown.]

Bromine Chloride

Bromine monochloride has a curious history. Balard, who discovered bromine in 1826, noticed in that year that when bromine is mixed with chlorine the colour diminishes,[358] but this observation, though it was also made by C. Löwig in 1829 (Diss., Heidelberg) and by Schönbein in 1863[359] was disregarded for a century. Then in 1928 G. M. B. Dobson noticed the same thing when he was using the mixture as a light filter for observing the ozone bands in the atmosphere, and he further noticed that this loss of colour takes time (of the order of a minute); this was confirmed by Barratt and Stein[366] with the spectrophotometer. Meanwhile in 1906

[357] O. Ruff and A. Braida, *Z. anorg. Chem.* 1933, **214**, 81.

[358] A. J. Balard, *Ann. Chim. Phys.* 1826, **32**, 371.

[359] C. F. Schönbein, *J. pr. Chem.* 1863, **88**, 483.

[360] P. Lebeau, *C.R.* 1906, **143**, 589.

[361] B. J. Karsten, *Z. anorg. Chem.* 1907, **53**, 365.

[362] K. H. Butler and D. McIntosh, *Proc. Nova Scot. Inst. Sci.* 1927, **17**, 23.

[363] G. S. Forbes and R. M. Fuoss, *J.A.C.S.* 1927, **49**, 142.

[364] N. W. Hanson and T. C. James, *J.C.S.* 1928, 1955.   [365] Id., ib. 2979.

[366] S. Barratt and C. P. Stein, *Proc. Roy. Soc.* 1929, **122**, 582.

Lebeau[360] had measured the freezing-point curves for the system Cl_2-Br_2, and Karsten in 1907[361] had worked out the complete phase-rule diagrams both for the boiling-points and for the melting-points of this system; they agreed on the facts, and both concluded from the results that no compound was formed. Butler and McIntosh[362] confirmed these measurements for the freezing-points, and drew the same conclusion. These facts, which are not in dispute, show what care must be exercised in interpreting this kind of phase-rule diagram. All the 4 curves obtained (vapour and liquid for the boiling-points and liquid and solid for the melting-points) are continuous, and without break, or maximum, or minimum. These are certainly the general forms which would occur if the two elements formed no compound, but were completely miscible in the solid and liquid states. They are, however, equally compatible with the existence of a compound, if this is partly dissociated, and also forms in the solid state a continuous series of solid solutions with both of its components, which in view of the identity of molecular type of the three substances Br_2, BrCl, and Cl_2 is not improbable. The melting-points and boiling-points of the system I_2-Br_2 (described below) are very similar, though they do give indications of the presence of the compound IBr.

The existence of the compound ClBr has been established in several ways, of which the most important quantitatively is by spectrophotometric measurements. Earlier results,[366-8,371] based on the assumption that at the wave-length of 5,690 A (maximum of the bromine band) BrCl has no absorption, did not give very concordant values. It was pointed out by Vesper and Rollefson[375] that this assumption is quite unsupported, and greatly affects the calculations. For example, on this assumption Gray and Styles's results[368] give values of the constant

$$K = \frac{[Br_2] \cdot [Cl_2]}{[BrCl]^2}$$

at different pressures of 0·162 and 0·125: but if the absorption of BrCl is 1·24 per cent. of that of Br_2, the K values from both experiments are 0·111. Using the light of the green lines of the helium discharge (round 5,020 A), and assuming here the ratio of the absorption of BrCl to that of Br_2 to be 0·11, they get concordant values of $0·107\pm0·002$.

This agrees with the value of 0·12–0·14 got by Yost[374] in CCl_4 solution from the partial pressures of the halogens in this solvent, and the calculation of the thermodynamical constants. Vesper and Rollefson further find that in the dark the reaction between the elements takes from 16 to 60

[367] A. E. Gillam and R. A. Morton, *Proc. Roy. Soc.* 1929, **124**, 604.
[368] L. T. M. Gray and D. W. G. Style, ib. 1930, **126**, 603.
[369] H. Lux, *Ber.* 1930, **63**, 1156.
[370] T. W. J. Taylor and L. A. Forscey, *J.C.S.* 1930, 2272.
[371] W. Jost, *Z. physikal. Chem.* 1931, **153**, 143.
[372] Id., ib. 1931, B **14**, 413.   [373] S. Anwar Ullah, *J.C.S.* 1932, 1176.
[374] C. M. Blair and D. M. Yost, *J.A.C.S.* 1933, **55**, 4489.

minutes to reach equilibrium; in the light they used this is reached in 2 minutes.

In water a very different value of 0·00032 was obtained by Forbes and Fuoss,[363] by the determination of the E.M.F. of solutions of chlorine in HCl solutions containing a bromide.

The existence of BrCl is also supported by the behaviour of a mixture of bromine and chlorine with unsaturated organic compounds. Hanson and James[364-5] found that such a mixture adds on to unsaturated acids and esters much more rapidly than either element separately, and gives a mixture of the α-chloro-β-bromo- and α-bromo-β-chloro-compounds. Taylor and Forscey[370] found the same for the reaction with diazo-acetic ester in carbon tetrachloride, which gave mainly the chloro-bromo-acetate; this reaction has the advantage that it is practically instantaneous, and may be supposed to give a true measure of the proportion of BrCl present; on this hypothesis they find it to be (by molecules) 80 per cent., giving in this solvent $K = 0·015$.

As a result of measurements of the equilibrium between mixtures of Cl_2 and Br_2 and their solid salts (KCl and KBr) Schütza[377] calculates the constant $K = 0·140/800°$ C. See also reference [376]. From spectroscopic measurements of the rate of change, which is of the order of 15″ for half change at the ordinary temperature, and of the equilibrium, at different temperatures, W. Jost[371-2] finds the heat of reaction in the gaseous state to be 0·95 k.cals., and the heat of activation 14·0 k.cals.

The physical properties of BrCl are little known, since at the ordinary temperature the pure substance is changing into its components (the trichloride $BrCl_3$ has not been found to exist, so there is no question of its undergoing disproportionation like BrF); but Lux[369] claims to have obtained BrCl by the slow distillation of a mixture of bromine and chlorine, as a yellow solid melting at −54°.

According to Anwar Ullah[373] if chlorine is passed into bromine under water at temperatures below 18° the solid hydrate BrCl, 4 H_2O separates, which is more stable than the hydrate of chlorine or bromine.

Iodine Chloride

Iodine monochloride was discovered by Davy and by Gay-Lussac in 1814. It is formed by the direct combination of the elements, or by the oxidation of an iodide in hydrochloric acid. It is best made in quantity by adding a weighed amount of solid iodine to excess of liquid chlorine; the excess is then driven off by warming, and the residue weighed. It always contains more chlorine than corresponds to ICl, and enough iodine is added to bring the proportions back to that point; the product is then kept above its melting-point—say at 35°—for 24 hours to ensure complete combination.[389]

[375] H. G. Vesper and G. K. Rollefson, ib. 1934, **56**, 620.
[376] G. Brauer and E. Victor, *Z. Elektrochem.* 1935, **41**, 508.
[377] H. Schütza, *Z. anorg. Chem.* 1938, **239**, 245.

Iodine monochloride is a remarkable example of dimorphism; the stable form α melts at 27·2°,[380] and the unstable β at 13·9°; there is no reason to think that the difference is anything more than in the arrangement of identical molecules. The phase-rule diagram for the system I_2—Cl_2* was worked out in detail by Stortenbeker in 1888.[378-9] The boiling-point of ICl is 100±3°, with slight dissociation into iodine and ICl_3. This dissociation begins at low temperatures; it is 0·42 per cent. at 25° and 1·58 per cent. at 100°.[389] The Trouton constant is 27·5,[389] and cannot be seriously affected by the slight dissociation. The cause of this high value is not explained; it is very nearly the mean for those of iodine (32·6) and chlorine (18·4): (18·4+32·6)/2 = 25·5: obs. 27·5. The dipole moment of ICl is 0·5 D.[393]

The specific conductivity of ICl has been found to be $4·6 \times 10^{-3}$ mhos at 35°, but further purification would no doubt lower it still further. The liquid is an ionizing solvent in which KCl has a molecular conductivity of 28·8 at $V = 2$, 30·4 at $V = 16$, and apparently about 31·3 at infinity.[389]

The absorption spectrum of ICl has a series of bands[381-3,386-7,390,392] in which the effect of the two chlorine isotopes can be detected.

The heat of formation of the ICl molecule has been determined in a variety of ways. Thomsen's thermochemical results give

$$\tfrac{1}{2}I_{2\text{gas}} + \tfrac{1}{2}Cl_{2\text{gas}} = ICl_{\text{gas}} + 3·53 \text{ k.cals.}$$

McMorris and Yost[391] have determined the equilibrium

$$I_2 + Cl_2 = 2\,ICl$$

at various temperatures, (1) by adding to the system solid barium chloroplatinate which gives at every temperature a known vapour pressure of chlorine, and (2) from the reaction

$$2\,NOCl + I_2 = 2\,NO + 2\,ICl.$$

In this way they find H_f to be 3·46 k.cals., in close agreement with Thomsen. The corresponding value of H_a, the heat of formation from the atoms, is 49·6 k.cals. From the spectrum Wilson[382] found H_a to be 49·65, and Cordes[390] 47·13. Darbyshire's value of 65·68 k.cals.[392] presumably refers to excited atoms.

* See Findlay, *Phase Rule*, ed. 7, p. 194 (1931).

[378] W. Stortenbeker, *Rec. Trav.* 1888, **7**, 152.
[379] Id., *Z. physikal. Chem.* 1889, **3**, 11.　　[380] G. Oddo, *Gaz.* 1901, **31**, 146.
[381] G. E. Gibson and H. C. Ramsperger, *Phys. Rev.* 1927, ii. **30**, 598.
[382] E. D. Wilson, ib. 1928, ii. **32**, 611.
[383] A. E Gillam and R. A. Morton, *Proc. Roy. Soc.* 1929, **124**, 604.
[384] F. A. Philbrick, *J.C.S.* 1930, 2254.
[385] A. E. Gillam and R. A. Morton, *Proc. Roy. Soc.* 1931, **132**, 152.
[386] W. E. Curtis and O. Darbyshire, *Trans. Far. Soc.* 1931, **27**, 77.
[387] W. E. Curtis and J. Patnowski, *Nature,* 1931, **127**, 707.
[388] J. H. Faull and S. Baeckström, *J.A.C.S.* 1932, **54**, 620.
[389] J. Cornog and R. A. Karges, ib. 1882.
[390] H. Cordes, *Z. Phys.* 1932, **74**, 34.
[391] J. McMorris and D. M. Yost, *J.A.C.S.* 1932, **54**, 2247.
[392] O. Darbyshire, *Phys. Rev.* 1932, **39**, 162; revised ib. **40**, 366.

Iodine monochloride when once melted can remain liquid below its melting-point for weeks. At ordinary temperatures it is the stable α-form which crystallizes out; the β-form slowly separates if the liquid is suddenly chilled to −5°. This metastable β-form can be kept below 0° for days, but on addition of a crystal of the α-form it at once goes over.

The α- (stable) form of ICl consists of red transparent crystals: the crystals of the β are brown. The liquid is brownish-red; the vapour has the colour of bromine, and a very similar absorption spectrum. Iodine monochloride is a very active substance. It has a choking smell like a mixture of I_2 and Cl_2; it strongly attacks the nose and eyes, and causes bad burns on the skin. It also attacks cork and rubber violently. It is used commercially as an iodinating agent, usually in solution either in concentrated aqueous hydrochloric acid, or in some organic solvent with which it does not react, such as ether or CCl_4.[395]

The colour of iodine chloride in solution shows differences exactly like those of iodine.[385] In all solvents in which iodine is violet (such as CCl_4) ICl is brown, the absorption spectrum having in the visible one band with a maximum at 4,600 A or close to it. In all solvents in which iodine is brown (e.g. in chloroform containing a trace of alcohol, in acetic acid, in ethyl acetate, in ether, and in water) ICl is yellow. In these last solvents the absorption in the visible is again a single band, but the maximum is shifted to 3,600—3,500 A (in aqueous HCl rather further, to 3,430 A). The colour of the vapour exactly corresponds: just as I_2 vapour is violet, like its solution in CCl_4, so ICl vapour is brown, like its solution in the same solvent. It is obvious that with both substances the change of colour is due to solvation.

In pure water ICl is hydrolysed to HCl+HOI, and the latter then changes to iodic acid with separation of iodine. If the water contains not less than fifth normal HCl the hydrolysis is completely stopped. The ICl then forms a stable yellow solution, with the absorption band in nearly the same position as in ethyl acetate and other solvents of the second kind (maximum 3,430 A), but with an extinction coefficient about twice as great; an increase of the HCl concentration from this 0·2 normal up to 10 times normal does not change the position or the intensity of the absorption.[385] Further, an alkaline chloride such as NaCl has the same power of preventing hydrolysis as HCl, and the same effect on the colour, the absorption maximum being at 3,420 A.[385] The two most important facts about these solutions are:

1. That NaCl can replace HCl, and

2. That it is impossible to extract the ICl from its solution in aqueous HCl with solvents like CCl_4, benzene, or nitrobenzene.[384,394] The suggestion that the ICl is dissociated into I^+ and Cl^- is sufficiently disproved by

[393] K. F. Luft, *Z. Phys.* 1933, **84**, 767.

[394] F. A. Philbrick, *J.A.C.S.* 1934, **56**, 1257.

[395] For its curious solubility curve in CCl_4 see J. Cornog and L. E. Olson, ib. 1940, **62**, 3328.

the fact that the addition of 0·14–normal ICl to n HCl does not increase the conductivity, but diminishes it by about 0·7 per cent.; moreover, on electrolysis none of the iodine goes to the cathode.[388] The suggestion (Philbrick[394]) that the real reaction in the aqueous HCl is the formation of ICl_2^- ions seems to fit all the facts. The formation of undissociated $HICl_2$ (Gillam and Morton[385]) is improbable because (1) the addition of ICl to HCl should cause a proportional fall in the conductivity instead of a very small one; (2) an undissociated $HICl_2$ might be able to be extracted by benzene or CCl_4; (3) if a solution of ICl in CCl_4 is saturated with HCl gas, the colour and the position of the absorption band do not change[385]; (4) a corresponding undissociated sodium compound $NaICl_2$, in the sodium chloride solutions is impossible. If we suppose that ICl has a strong tendency to attach itself to Cl^- ions, and that $[H]ICl_2$ is a strong acid, all these phenomena can be explained. The absence of reaction between ICl and HCl in CCl_4 is due to there being nothing to solvate the hydrogen ions (compare $HF+SiF_4$). The equilibrium in the reaction

$$ICl + Cl^- = ICl_2^-$$

must be very far to the right-hand side, for as we have seen the absorption of a solution of ICl in 0·2n HCl is not changed when the HCl concentration is raised to 10 times normal, so that the formation of the complex ion must be sensibly complete in fifth normal acid.

Iodine Monobromide, IBr

Iodine monobromide was discovered by Balard, and is formed like the other compounds by the direct combination of the elements. In the system I_2—Br_2[396] the S—L curves indicate a continuous series of solid solutions from I_2 to Br_2, but at 50 molecules per cent. the solidus and liquidus curves touch. The V—L boiling-point curves approach at this concentration, but do not actually touch, showing that there is considerable dissociation in the vapour at this temperature (116°). These curves, especially those for the freezing-points (given in Gmelin, *Iod*, p. 630), though they give clear evidence of the existence of the compound, are not unlike those for the system Br_2—Cl_2 (above, p. 1154).

Iodine monobromide forms crystals of the colour of iodine, which melt at 42°[403] to a nearly black liquid which boils at 116° to give a red, partially dissociated, vapour. The degree of dissociation at 25° was found to be 8 per cent. in the vapour and 9·5 per cent. in CCl_4 solution[402]; at 300° it

[396] P. C. E. Meerum-Terwogt, *Z. anorg. Chem.* 1905, **47**, 209.

[397] W. A. Plotnikow and W. Rokotjan, *Z. physikal. Chem.* 1913, **84**, 365 (= *J. Russ. Phys. Chem. Ges.* 1913, **45**, 193; *Chem. Centr.* 13, i. 1809).

[398] W. Müller, *Z. physikal. Chem.* 1926, **123**, 24.

[399] R. M. Badger and D. M. Yost, *Phys. Rev.* 1931, ii. **37**, 1548.

[400] J. McMorris and D. M. Yost, *J.A.C.S.* 1931, **53**, 2625.

[401] H. W. Cremer and D. R. Duncan, *J.C.S.* 1932, 2031.

[402] D. M. Yost, T. F. Anderson, and F. Skoog, *J.A.C.S.* 1933, **55**, 552.

[403] A. E. Gillam, *Trans. Far. Soc.* 1933, **29**, 1132.

is about 20 per cent.[398] The chemical properties of IBr are intermediate between those of its component elements. The heat of dissociation into atoms (in the gas) was found from the spectrum by Badger[399] to be 41·5 k.cals. (confirmed by Cordes[390]), which makes the heat of formation in the gaseous state from $I_2 + Br_2$ 2·30 k.cals. McMorris and Yost[400] by thermo-chemical methods find the latter value at 25° to be 1·27. The value in CCl_4 solution is much the same as in the vapour.

Liquid iodine monobromide appears to be partly ionized. The measurements by Plotnikow and Rokotjan[397] of the conductivity of solutions of iodine in bromine are very difficult to explain, but they indicate that the maximum ionization does not exceed one part in 10,000.

In its solutions iodine bromide shows the same changes of colour as I_2 and ICl.[401,403] The relations are precisely similar to those with I_2 or ICl. We find two classes of solvents, each with its own characteristic colour. Thus:

1. I_2 violet, ICl red-brown, IBr red
   Vapour: solutions in CCl_4, $CHCl_3$, hexane, benzene, toluene, CS_2

2. I_2 brown, ICl yellow, IBr yellow-orange
   Solutions in MeOH, EtOH, lower esters, ethers, formic and acetic acids, acetone

As examples of the wave-lengths, we may take the positions of the bands in CCl_4 and in alcohol:

Compound	I_2	IBr	ICl
CCl_4 . . .	5,200 A	4,940 A	4,600 A
Alcohol . . .	4,470 A	3,900 A	3,550 A
Diff. . . .	−730 A	−1,040 A	−1,050 A

As with iodine a small amount of a solvent of the second kind has a great effect on the colour in one of the first kind; the addition of 1 per cent. of ethyl alcohol to a solution of IBr in CCl_4 has a visible effect. The effect is obviously in all these cases due to solvation. Cyanogen iodide $I \cdot CN$[403] shows something of the same kind of colour change, but the effect is much smaller.

COMPOUNDS OF THE TYPE AB_3

In these compounds the central atom has the valency group (2), 2, 6, and so the central atom must be able to have an inert pair of electrons. The known compounds of this type, with their boiling- and melting-points are:

	ClF_3	BrF_3	ICl_3
B. pt. . . .	+12·1°	+127°	(decp.)
[M. pt.] . .	[−82·6°]	[+ 8·8°]	[101° under pressure]

The small number of compounds of this type is evidently due to their existence being limited on both sides; the B atoms must not be too large; only fluorine can act as B unless A is iodine, when chlorine can also act as B; on the other hand, the B atoms must not be too small, or the compounds of higher valency will become the more stable, as in IF_5.

Chlorine Trifluoride, ClF_3

This compound is of special interest since it is almost the only isolable compound in which chlorine definitely shows that two of its valency electrons can become inert, and chlorine is the only element of the second short (subtypical) period which can be shown to have this property. The pair must also be inert in the ion Cl_3^-, but this has not been isolated in the form of salts (with one or two exceptions) though there is evidence for its existence in solution.

Chlorine trifluoride was discovered by Ruff and Krug in 1930,[404] originally as an impurity in the monofluoride. It is made by passing a mixture of chlorine or chlorine monofluoride with excess of fluorine through a tube heated to 250°, condensing with liquid air, and purifying by distillation. The reaction $ClF + F_2 = ClF_3$ is reversible, and at equilibrium at 250° the amount of ClF is greater than that of ClF_3.

Chlorine trifluoride[405] is a colourless gas, which condenses to a pale green liquid, and then forms a white solid. It boils at $+12 \cdot 1°$ and melts at $-82 \cdot 6°$.

This compound is remarkable for the extraordinary vigour with which it reacts, which is even greater perhaps than that of fluorine itself. It destroys glass and quartz glass except at low temperatures; glass wool catches fire in the vapour immediately. Organic substances (including the picenes or high vacuum oils) if they can be fluorinated at all, react at once with inflammation; one drop of the liquid sets fire to paper, cloth, or wood. Most elements are attacked explosively, and if not they can be lighted by a fragment of charcoal; many oxides behave in the same way. Liquid ClF_3 reacts with water with a noise like the crack of a whip; if water is allowed to enter the flask which contains the gas some of it is thrown out by the violence of the reaction.

Bromine Trifluoride, BrF_3

Moissan observed that fluorine combines with bromine, but the trifluoride was first isolated by Lebeau,[406] and was further examined by Prideaux.[407] A more detailed investigation of it was made by Ruff and Braida.[408-9] It is made from its elements, and purified by distillation. It is a pale yellow-

---

[404] O. Ruff and H. Krug, *Z. anorg. Chem.* 1930, **190**, 270.

[405] O. Ruff, F. Ebert, and W. Menzel, ib. 1932, **207**, 46.

[406] P. Lebeau, *C.R.* 1905, **141**, 1018; *Ann. Chim. Phys.* 1906, [8] **9**, 248.

[407] E. B. R. Prideaux, *J.C.S.* 1906, **89**, 316.

[408] O. Ruff and A. Braida, *Z. anorg. Chem.* 1932, **206**, 59.

[409] Id., ib. 1933, **214**, 91.

green liquid at the ordinary temperature, and solidifies to long prisms. It melts at 8·8°, and boils at 127°.[409] From the change of vapour pressure with temperature the heat of evaporation at the boiling-point is 10 k.cals., and hence the Trouton constant 25·3.[409] At the melting-point the density of the solid is 3·23, and that of the liquid 2·843.[408]

Bromine trifluoride is formed, as we have seen, by the decomposition of BrF. It fumes strongly in air, and attacks quartz at 30°, giving bromine, oxygen, and silicon tetrafluoride.

[Iodine trifluoride: Ruff and Braida[410] made a special search for a lower fluoride of iodine than IF_5, but in vain.]

Iodine Trichloride, ICl_3

This compound, which was discovered by Gay-Lussac in 1814, is formed (but slowly) by the direct combination of the elements. It is best prepared either[411] by condensing chlorine in excess on iodine at $-80°$, leaving it some hours in the freezing mixture, and evaporating off excess of chlorine,[412] or by passing chlorine over iodine until this is converted into ICl, and then raising the temperature to 100° and increasing the stream of chlorine, when the trichloride distils over and can be condensed.

ICl_3 forms lemon-yellow needles, which melt at 101° under their own (dissociation) vapour pressure of 16 atm., to a reddish brown liquid. The solid is very volatile, and loses weight in a stream of dry air even at $-12°$.[413] Its vapour pressure reaches 1 atm. at 64°. The vapour density shows[414] that the compound dissociates completely into $ICl+Cl_2$ at 77°. In solution the dissociation seems to be complete even at the ordinary temperature. The absorption spectrum of ICl_3 in CCl_4 is identical with the sum of those of ICl and Cl_2.[415] Stortenbeker's $L—V$ curves give no sign of the presence of ICl_3 in the liquid (and incidentally no indication of a pentachloride at all).

From the vapour pressures and the equilibria in the reaction

$$ICl + Cl_2 \rightleftharpoons ICl_3$$

Nies and Yost[416] find the heat evolved, with ICl and Cl_2 gaseous, but ICl_3 solid, to be 25·3 k.cals. From the heat of formation of ICl it follows that the heat of the reaction

$$\tfrac{1}{2}I_{2\,gas} + 3/2Cl_{2\,gas} = ICl_{3\,solid}$$

is 36·9 k.cals. Assuming for ICl_3 a heat of fusion of 4 k.cals., and of evaporation of 9·5 k.cals. (for a boiling-point of about 380° K. and a Trouton constant of 25) we get for the H_f of ICl_3 (all gaseous) 23·4 and for its H_a

[410] Id., ib. 1934, **220**, 43.
[411] E. Birk, *Z. angew. Chem.* 1928, **41**, 751.
[412] E. C. Truesdale and F. C. Beyer, *J.A.C.S.* 1931, **53**, 164.
[413] W. Stortenbeker, *Rec. Trav.* 1888, **7**, 163; *Z. physikal. Chem.* 1889, **3**, 12.
[414] P. Melikoff, *Ber.* 1875, **8**, 490.
[415] A. E. Gillam and R. A. Morton, *Proc. Roy. Soc.* 1929, **124**, 606.
[416] N. P. Nies and D. M. Yost, *J.A.C.S.* 1935, **57**, 306.

(from the atoms) 128·2, with an error of perhaps $\pm 2\cdot 5$ k.cals. The heat of formation of the I—Cl link in ICl_3 is one third of this, or $42\cdot 7 \pm 0\cdot 8$, rather less than for the link in I—Cl, which is $51\cdot 0$: this fall in the heat value with a rise in covalency is usually found, for example, in the P—Cl link in PCl_3 and PCl_5. But in spite of it the gaseous reaction

$$ICl + Cl_2 = ICl_3$$

(with an increase from two covalencies to three) evolves some 20 k.cals.

COMPOUNDS OF THE TYPE AB_5

This type is only possible when the ratio of the radii A/B is large enough, and in fact only occurs in the fluorides of bromine and iodine.

Bromine Pentafluoride, BrF_5

This was first made by Ruff and Menzel in 1931,[417] by passing fluorine through bromine trifluoride at 90–100°, and heating the issuing gas to 200°, most conveniently in a copper vessel. The reaction

$$BrF_3 + F_2 = BrF_5$$

appears to go at this temperature to completion.

BrF_5 is a colourless liquid, which fumes strongly in air. Its vapour density is normal. The melting-point is $-61\cdot 3°$, and the boiling-point $+40\cdot 5°$; the heat of evaporation from the v.p./T curves is 7·44 k.cals., and hence the Trouton constant 23·7.

It is remarkably stable to heat; if it is passed through a copper tube at 460° C. no trace of free fluorine can be detected in the issuing gas, even by the smell. It reacts readily with metals, sometimes in the cold, and always on heating; it reacts in the cold with charcoal, arsenic, sulphur, selenium, iodine, and alkaline chlorides, bromides, and iodides, the reaction always being violent, and the substance usually catching fire.

If a few drops of the liquid are allowed to fall into water, Br_2 vapours are evolved, and there is an explosion. If moist nitrogen is passed through the liquid, all the oxygen of the water is evolved as such, while HF, HBr, and probably BrF_3 are formed.

Iodine Pentafluoride, IF_5

This was first obtained by Gore,[418] by the reaction

$$5\,AgF + 3\,I_2 = 5\,AgI + IF_5.$$

Later it was got by Moissan[419] by the direct combination of the elements; see also Prideaux.[420] It can also be made by the action of fluorine on

[417] O. Ruff and W. Menzel, *Z. anorg. Chem.* 1931, **202**, 49.
[418] G. Gore, *Phil. Mag.* 1871, [4] **41**, 309.
[419] H. Moissan, *C.R.* 1902, **135**, 563.
[420] E. B. R. Prideaux, *J.C.S.* 1906, **89**, 316.

heated I_2O_5.[423] A more detailed examination of its properties is due to Ruff and his co-workers.[421-2] They made it by passing fluorine over iodine. If the fluorine is kept cool by dilution with 3 times its volume of nitrogen a quartz vessel can be used. In presence of oxygen some oxyfluoride IOF_3 crystallizes out. Any of the more volatile heptafluoride IF_7 can be removed by distillation: this is best done under 10 mm. pressure, when it comes over at about $-10°$.

Iodine pentafluoride is[422] a colourless liquid melting at $+9·6°$. Boiling-point extrapolated $98\pm1·5°$. It dissolves iodine (giving a brown solution) and bromine. It is stable to heat up to over $400°$ C. It fumes strongly in the air, and reacts at once with water to form HF and iodine pentoxide; with glass it reacts slowly in the cold, and quickly at $100°$, to give $SiF_4+I_2O_5$. Most metals (e.g. silver, copper, mercury, iron) react with it only slowly, but sulphur, red phosphorus, silicon, bismuth, tungsten, and arsenic react at once, usually with incandescence. Organic compounds react violently[421] usually carbonizing, and often catching fire.

With carbon tetrachloride iodine pentafluoride reacts slowly, to give mainly CCl_3F, with a residue of ICl and ICl_3.

COMPOUNDS OF THE TYPE AB₇

Of this type the molecule IF_7 is the only representative, not only among the inter-halogen compounds, but in chemistry generally.

Iodine Heptafluoride, IF₇

Fluorine has no action on IF_5 in the cold, but on heating the heptafluoride is formed reversibly.[423] Fluorine is passed through liquid IF_5 at $90°$, and the vapours are then led through a platinum tube heated to $270°$; the yield seems to be better the higher the temperature, but at $300°$ the tube is attacked. The issuing gases are condensed, and the IF_7 purified by distillation. A yield of over 80 per cent. can be obtained.

Iodine heptafluoride is a colourless gas, which condenses on cooling either to a colourless liquid boiling (slightly supercooled) at $+4·5°$ C. (boiling-point of IF_5 extrapolated $98°$), or to a snow-white solid, melting at $+5–6°$. The heat of evaporation is 7·33 k.cals., and the Trouton constant 26·4.

IF_7 behaves in general like ClF_3, but is less violent: it usually loses 2F to give the more stable IF_5. It seems to be curiously stable to water (it has no 'lone pair' of electrons): Ruff says 'water dissolves the gas without violence: the gas can even be blown through the liquid water with the formation of clouds, but with only partial decomposition. The solution can be shown to contain periodate and fluoride ions.'

[421] O. Ruff and R. Keim, *Z. anorg. Chem.* 1931, **201**, 245.
[422] O. Ruff and A. Braida, ib. 1934, **220**, 43.
[423] O. Ruff and R. Keim, ib. 1930, **193**, 176.

HYDROGEN HALIDES

THE hydrides of chlorine, bromine, and iodine are very similar to one another, and are all sharply distinguished from hydrogen fluoride in being non-associated.

HYDROGEN CHLORIDE, HCl

Hydrogen and chlorine in the gaseous state combine with the evolution of 22·06 k.cals.[424] heat (theory 21·9) under the influence of light, or heat, or other agents. This change as brought about by light is the classical example of a photochemical reaction, and has been more thoroughly examined than any other, ever since the days of Bunsen. The kinetics of the reaction are too complicated to allow of any full discussion here, but some of the main points may be mentioned.[425]

The reaction is brought about by light which is absorbed by the chlorine. The quantum yield is enormous; in complete absence of oxygen one quantum of light will cause the formation of 7·6 million molecules of HCl.[426] To account for these facts Nernst[427] proposed a mechanism which, though not complete, may probably be taken to represent the main lines of the reaction. He assumes the following series of reactions:

$$1.\ Cl_2 + h\nu\ =\ 2\ Cl$$
$$2.\ Cl\ + H_2\ =\ HCl + H$$
$$3.\ H\ + Cl_2\ =\ HCl + Cl.$$

We thus have a chain reaction, which can proceed indefinitely far through (2) and (3) without any fresh absorption of light. The chain can be broken by any of the reactions

$$2\ Cl\ =\ Cl_2$$
$$2\ H\ =\ H_2$$
$$H + Cl\ =\ HCl.$$

It has been found that the presence of small quantities of various substances interferes with the reaction, no doubt by breaking the chains. These substances are of two kinds, (a) those that permanently slow down the reaction, and (b) those that merely cause a delay ('induction period') before the reaction begins.[428] This difference is clearly due to the fact that substances of the second kind, such as ammonia, are destroyed by the chlorine in the presence of light, so that they disappear in time from the

[424] W. F. Giauque and R. Overstreet, *J.A.C.S.* 1932, **54**, 1731. (From spectroscopic data.)

[425] For a full discussion see Hinshelwood, *Chem. Reactions in Gaseous Systems*, ed. 3, 1933, pp. 100–6; *Kinetics of Chemical Change* (1940), pp. 100–13. See also N. Semenoff, *Chemical Kinetics and Chain Reactions*, 1933, pp. 89–122. Also N. S. Bayliss, *Trans. Far. Soc.* 1937, **33**, 1339.

[426] J. E. Cremer, *Z. physikal. Chem.* 1927, **128**, 285.

[427] W. Nernst, *Z. Elektrochem.* 1918, **24**, 335.

[428] See for example C. H. Burgess and D. L. Chapman, *J.C.S.* 1906, **89**, 1399; D. L. Chapman and L. K. Underhill, ib. 1913, **103**, 496; D. L. Chapman and J. R. H. Whiston, 1919, **115**, 1264.

system, while the others such as oxygen[429-30] are not removed, and their influence therefore persists.

The thermal synthesis is a chain reaction depending on the walls. At 200° the chain length is about 10^4, as compared with 10^6 for the photo-reaction: hence it is less inhibited by oxygen.[431]

Hydrochloric acid was formerly made by the action of sulphuric acid on sodium chloride; this reaction, like that in which nitric acid is made, goes in two stages, the second of which, the action of sodium hydrogen sulphate on sodium chloride, occurs only at a red heat. It is now made on the large scale almost entirely from the combination of the hydrogen and the chlorine liberated when sodium chloride solution is electrolysed for the manufacture of caustic soda.

Properties of Hydrogen Chloride

Hydrogen chloride is a colourless gas, melting at $-114\cdot2°$ C., and boiling at $-85\cdot0°$; the heat of evaporation is $3\cdot86$ k.cals., and, accordingly, the Trouton constant $20\cdot5$.

The solid has a molecular lattice. As happens with many molecular crystals there is a temperature above which the molecules rotate, while below it they only oscillate. The change from one state to the other may or may not be accompanied by a change of phase (true dimorphism), but it can in any case be detected by the measurement of the specific heats. In hydrogen chloride this change leads to a definite dimorphism, with a transition temperature of 98° K. ($-175°$ C.); hydrogen bromide is similarly dimorphic; in hydrogen iodide there is a transition point marked by the specific heats, but no true dimorphism.[432] In hydrogen fluoride, owing to the association, the molecules never rotate.[433]

As would be expected from the large heat of formation, hydrogen chloride is very stable to heat. Nernst[434] has calculated the percentage dissociation into H_2+Cl_2 as follows:

Temp. abs.	500° K.	1,000° K.	2,000° K.	3,000° K.
Per cent. diss.	$1\cdot92\cdot10^{-8}$	0·00134	0·41	1·30

It can also be dissociated by ultraviolet light; the light of a quartz lamp that would cause a 35 per cent. dissociation of SO_3 into SO_2 and oxygen only causes 0·25 per cent. dissociation of HCl.[435]

The dielectric constant of hydrogen chloride at the critical point ($+51°$) is $2\cdot83$.[436] The specific conductivity of the liquid near its boiling-

[429] M. Bodenstein, *Z. physikal. Chem.* 1941, B **48**, 239.
[430] M. Bodenstein and H. F. Launer, ib. 268.
[431] J. C. Morris and R. N. Pease, *J.A.C.S.* 1939, **61**, 391, 396.
[432] Th. Neugebauer, *Z. physikal. Chem.* 1937, B **35**, 136.
[433] K. Clusius, K. Hiller, and J. V. Vaughen, ib. 1930, B **8**, 427.
[434] W. Nernst, *Z. Elektrochem.* 1909, **15**, 691.
[435] A. Coehn and A. Wassiljeva, *Ber.* 1909, **42**, 3183; cf. A. Coehn and K. Stuckardt, *Z. physikal. Chem.* 1916, **91**, 733.
[436] W. Herz, ib. 1922, **103**, 269.

point is 0.1×10^{-6} mhos.[437] Most chlorides (K, Li, NH_4, Cu′, Cu″, Au, Pb, etc.) are insoluble in it; stannic chloride dissolves, giving a non-conducting solution.

The dipole moment of hydrogen chloride is definitely lower in the gas than in non-polar solvents. In the gas it is 1.03[439] or 1.06[438]; by the beam method it was found[440] to be 0.91 D. In solution the moment is about 1.3, being according to Fairbrother[441-2] 1.26 in cyclohexane (dielectric constant at 25° 2.01) and 1.32 in benzene (2.27) and in carbon tetrachloride (2.23).

Chemical Properties

Hydrogen chloride gas, like the bromide and iodide, has a curious power of forming solid compounds of definite composition with certain anhydrous salts of oxy-acids, especially the sulphates, phosphates, and phosphites of di- and trivalent (mainly transitional and B) metals.[443] Many of these are formed at the ordinary temperature, and do not decompose below 200°, where the HCl compounds lose their HCl, but those of HBr and HI usually have the anion of the oxy-acid reduced, with liberation of the halogen. These compounds have as many molecules of halogen hydride to one metal atom as the latter has valencies: thus salts $M′′′PO_4$ have 3 molecules, but $M′′SO_4$, $M′′HPO_4$, and $M′′(HPO_2)_2$ only 2 molecules of the halide to 1 M.

Hydrogen chloride, which, like the bromide and iodide, is covalent in the pure state, remains covalent and unsolvated in non-ionizing solvents such as the hydrocarbons and, accordingly, has the minute solubility to be expected of a gas of so low a boiling-point. For example, the solubilities in g. per litre at 25° are hexane 6.20, benzene 13.7, o-nitro-toluene 18.0,[444-5,447] chloroform at 0° 10. In such solutions Henry's law is obeyed.[446] From the vapour pressures the heat of solution of the acid can be calculated[447-8]; it is in benzene 4.3, in chloroform 3.0, in ethylene dibromide 3.2 k.cals./mole.

On the other hand, the solubility in water is enormously greater (770 g. per litre of solution at 20° and 1 atm.), while the vapour pressure rises much more rapidly than the concentration. Roscoe and Dittmar's results (1859) for water and HCl at 20° give these values of p, the pressure of the

[437] E. H. Archibald, *J.A.C.S.* 1907, **29**, 1418.

[438] H. Braune and T. Ascher, *Z. physikal. Chem.* 1931, B **14**, 18.

[439] C. T. Zahn, *Phys. Rev.* 1926, **27**, 455.

[440] H. Scheffers, *Phys. Z.* 1940, **41**, 89.

[441] F. Fairbrother, *J.C.S.* 1932, 43.

[442] Id., *Trans. Far. Soc.* 1934, **30**, 862.

[443] F. Ephraim, *Ber.* 1925, **58**, 2262; 1926, **59**, 790; F. Ephraim and A. Schärer, ib. 1928, **61**, 2161.

[444] S. J. O'Brien, C. L. Kenny, and R. A. Zuercher, *J.A.C.S.* 1939, **61**, 2504.

[445] S. J. O'Brien and C. L. Kenny, ib. 1940, **62**, 1189.

[446] S. J. O'Brien and J. B. Byrne, ib. 2063.

[447] S. J. O'Brien, ib. 1941, **63**, 2709.

[448] J. J. Howland, D. R. Miller, and J. E. Willard, ib. 2807.

gas in mm., and *c*, the concentration of the liquid in g./litre, with those of *c/p*, which would be constant if Henry's law held:

p	.	.	.	60	500	1,300 mm. Hg
c	.	.	.	613	782	895 g./l.
c/p	.	.	.	10·3	1·56	0·68

In the same way Wrewsky[449] shows that to raise the solubility from 8 to 16 mols. per cent. at 25° the pressure must be increased more than 100 times. See further Wynne-Jones.[450]

Ether, in which the solubility is 220 g./l. at 20°, is intermediate between the other two classes of solvents, owing to the formation of the oxonium compound.

In water at ordinary concentrations the hydrogen chloride is practically all present as the hydrated ions. The infra-red absorption bands characteristic of HCl, and shown by the liquid hydride and its solutions in non-ionizing solvents, do not appear in the aqueous solutions.[451] In dilute solutions the conductivities agree with the Debye–Hückel–Onsager formula.

But the large vapour pressures of the very concentrated solutions show that they contain a considerable amount of undissociated hydrogen chloride, and that in the general equation for ionization

$$M—A \rightleftharpoons M[A] \rightleftharpoons [M]^+ + [A]^-$$

(where according to Debye the middle term M[A] represents only a limiting case) with hydrogen chloride the covalent H—Cl though negligible at low concentrations becomes quite considerable at high. This behaviour must be contrasted, on the one side, with that of weak acids like acetic, where the unionized form always predominates except at extreme dilutions, and, on the other, with salts like the alkaline halides, where this first (unionized or covalent) term must be entirely absent, since the salt can be shown to be ionized in all states, solid, liquid, and gaseous.

On the other hand, the halogen acids HCl, HBr, and HI, though they appear in dilute aqueous solution to be among the strongest acids, and to be as highly dissociated as any, go over into the covalent form more easily than such acids as perchloric if the conditions become less favourable to ionization, either through the increase of concentration or when the water is replaced by a less powerfully ionizing solvent. Of the familiar strong acids the first to 'shut up' in this way is nitric, the next the halogen hydrides (other than HF, which is quite peculiar), and the last perchloric acid. These facts were first pointed out by Hantzsch[452] and have been entirely confirmed by later work. Thus Hartley finds[453] that E.M.F. measurements of solutions of HCl even in methyl alcohol show the ionization to be less complete than in water.

[449] M. Wrewsky, *Z. physikal. Chem.* 1924, **112**, 113.
[450] W. F. K. Wynne-Jones, *J.C.S.* 1930, 1064.
[451] W. West and R. T. Edwards, *J. Chem. Phys.* 1937, **5**, 14.
[452] See especially *Z. Elektrochem.* 1923, **29**, pp. 221–46.
[453] Sir H. Hartley and J. W. Woolcock, *Phil. Mag.* 1928, vii. **5**, 1133.

Hydrogen chloride is often used in non-aqueous solvents as a condensing agent. It can be used in some reactions in the place of hydrogen fluoride. Simons[454] has carried out a series of alkylations of aromatic hydrocarbons using initial pressures of hydrogen chloride of 7–27 atm., and working at 75–235°. As with hydrogen fluoride the products are always para-compounds. Thus tert. butyl chloride reacts with toluene giving with either hydrogen chloride or fluoride only the para-di-derivative, whilst with aluminium chloride only 30–35 per cent. of para is formed, along with 65–70 per cent. of meta.

HYDROGEN BROMIDE

The heat of formation of gaseous HBr from H_2 and gaseous Br_2 is 4·82 k.cals., so that the compound is exothermic, but only slightly so. The dynamics of the formation of hydrogen bromide from its elements has been studied by a variety of people.[455] The reaction is complicated, but the main process, as was shown by Christiansen,[456] Polanyi,[457] and Herzfeld,[458] consists essentially of four reactions:

$$
\begin{aligned}
1. &\quad Br_2 &=&\quad 2\,Br \\
2. &\quad Br + H_2 &=&\quad HBr + H \\
3. &\quad H + Br_2 &=&\quad HBr + Br \\
4. &\quad H + HBr &=&\quad H_2 + Br
\end{aligned}
$$

The first three exactly correspond to the 'Nernst chain' for the formation of hydrogen chloride from its elements. The first stage, the dissociation of the bromine, can be brought about by tne action of heat or of light. With heat we have the thermal reaction of hydrogen and bromine; this is much slower than with chlorine, and unless the gases are heated to a rather high temperature (about 500° C.[459]) a reaction initiated at one point in the mixture, e.g. by local heating, is not able to spread owing to the small evolution of heat. The thermal reaction does not go with a measurable velocity below 200° C.; between 200° and 300° it has been examined in detail by Bodenstein and Lind.[460]

The essential difference between the reaction of bromine with hydrogen and that of chlorine is that reaction (2) above

$$X + H_2 = HX + H$$

which with chlorine is exothermic, with bromine absorbs about 16 k.cals. Hence the probability that a bromine atom will react with a hydrogen molecule on collision is $e^{-16,000/RT}$, which at 177° C. is $1·75 \times 10^{-8}$. Thus

[454] J. H. Simons and H. Hart, *J.A.C.S.* 1944, **66**, 1309.

[455] For a full account see Hinshelwood, 1933, p. 107; Semenoff, *Chain Reactions*, p. 140; Gmelin, *Brom*, 1931, pp. 168–80.

[456] J. A. Christiansen, *Dansk. Vid. Math. Phys. Medd.* 1919, **1**, 14.

[457] M. Polanyi, *Z. Elektrochem.* 1920, **26**, 49.

[458] K. F. Herzfeld, ib. 1919, **25**, 301.

[459] A. B. Sagulin, *Z. physikal. Chem.* 1928, B **1**, 282.

[460] M. Bodenstein, ib. 1904, **49**, 61; M. Bodenstein and C. S. Lind, ib. 1907, **57**, 168.

on the average such a bromine atom will only react after 10^8 collisions or 0·01 second after it has been produced. This length of life gives it more than one chance of combining with another bromine atom. Hence the reaction chains are very short, and many bromine atoms must disappear before they have started a chain at all.

The photochemical reaction differs from the thermal only in the way in which the bromine atoms are formed; the subsequent changes are the same in both. For the reasons given above, the rate of combination is here also much slower than with chlorine, and the quantum yield, instead of amounting to many thousands or even millions, is often less than unity.

On heating, hydrogen bromide dissociates to some extent into hydrogen and bromine, and does so more readily than hydrogen chloride; the percentage dissociation[461] is 0·5 at 1,024° C., 0·73 at 1,108°, and 1·08 at 1,222°.

Owing to the small heat of formation of hydrogen bromide it is scarcely practical[462] to produce it by the direct combination of the elements, and its formation is therefore usually supported by some other form of chemical energy, as by combining the bromine with phosphorus or aluminium and treating the product with water: by the action of bromine on an organic substance, such as benzene or naphthalene, when, of course, half the bromine goes to brominate the hydrocarbon: or by treating a salt of HBr with a strong acid (best with phosphoric, as this does not oxidize the HBr produced).

Hydrogen bromide reacts to some extent with P_2O_5 and with H_2SO_4, forming free bromine and other volatile products; it can be dried by anhydrous $CaBr_2$[463] or by dried (but not ignited) alumina.[464]

Hydrogen bromide boils at $-66\cdot7°$ and melts at $-81\cdot6°$; its critical temperature is 89·8°. The solid is trimorphic.[466] The heat of evaporation is 4·21 k.cals.,[465] giving a Trouton constant of 20·4. The vapour density is normal, and the liquid shows no signs whatever of association.[467]

The dipole moment in the gaseous state is 0·78 D[468], it is markedly larger than this in non-ionizing solvents; thus Fairbrother[469] found (at 20°) 0·96 in CCl_4 and 1·01 in benzene. The dielectric constant of the liquid is 6·29 at $-80°$, and 3·82 at $+24\cdot7°$.[470] The electric conductivity at $-80°$ is $0\cdot8 \times 10^{-8}$.[471]

[461] K. Vogel v. Falckenstein, ib. 1909, **68**, 278; cf. A. Eucken and F. Fried, *Z. Phys.* 1924, **29**, 49.

[462] See, however, *Inorganic Syntheses*, vol. i, p. 154.

[463] G. P. Baxter and R. D. Warren, *J.A.C.S.* 1911, **33**, 340.

[464] F. M. G. Johnson, ib. 1912, **34**, 911.

[465] W. F. Giauque and R. Wiebe, ib. 1928, **50**, 2198.

[466] K. Clusius, *Z. Naturf.* 1946, **1**, 142.

[467] For an enumeration of all the physical properties which support this conclusion (with references) see Gmelin, *Brom*, 1931, p. 194.

[468] C. T. Zahn, *Phys. Rev.* 1926, **27**, 455.

[469] F. Fairbrother, *Trans. Far. Soc.* 1934, **30**, 862.

[470] O. C. Schaefer and H. Schlundt, *J. Phys. Chem.* 1909, **13**, 671.

[471] D. McIntosh, *Trans. Amer. Electrochem. Soc.* 1912, **21**, 121.

Bromine vapour undergoes complete radioactive exchange with gaseous HBr at room temperature in 2 minutes.[472] This may be due to the formation of HBr_3.[473]

Hydrogen bromide resembles the chloride very closely in its general behaviour, the only marked difference being the ease with which it is oxidized. Like the chloride and the iodide it behaves as a covalent compound when it is by itself or in non-ionizing solvents, and hence, owing to its volatility, dissolves in these solvents only to a small extent[474]; in ionizing solvents, especially water, it dissolves very readily, and mainly—almost entirely except at high concentrations—in the ionized form.

In organic solvents containing oxygen (alcohols, acids, esters, ethers, ketones) HBr usually dissolves readily, with a considerable evolution of heat; the solution of 1 mole in 24 moles of ethyl alcohol (giving a 6·8 per cent. solution) evolves 23·1 k.cals.[475]; this is due to the formation of the solvated ions of the oxonium bromide $[Et \cdot OH_2]$ (Br); very little alkyl bromide is formed.

In solvents free from oxygen the solubility of HBr at the ordinary temperature is very small and usually unknown. In benzene[476] it obeys Henry's law, the pressure of HBr in atmospheres divided by the molarity of the solution being 16·1/30° and 24·35/50° (extrapolated 14·0/25°). The heat of solution in benzene is 4·20 k.cals. per mole. At lower temperatures the solubility increases, and benzene at −4° will dissolve 14 per cent.[477] A saturated solution in CCl_4 at the ordinary temperature contains about 0·8 g. in 100 c.c. At lower temperatures solid phases are formed which have the composition of addition compounds of HBr and the solvent[477]; such are $HBr, 2 C_6H_5 \cdot CH_3$ (m. pt. −86·5°), $HBr, C_6H_5 \cdot C_2H_5$ (m. pt. −105·5°) and $HBr, 2 C_6H_5 \cdot C_2H_5$ (m. pt. −103·8°); these are presumably merely crystal aggregates or van der Waals compounds.

There can be no doubt that in these solvents HBr is present essentially in the covalent form. But it is remarkable that Topley and Weiss[478] showed that if a well-dried solution of hydrogen bromide in carbon tetrachloride was treated with radioactive bromine, there was a complete exchange of activity in a few minutes at room-temperature. This cannot have been due to the dissociation of the bromine into atoms, as this at so low a temperature would have been too minute,[479] nor does it seem likely that enough water would have been left after 5 days over P_2O_5 to cause ionization. Hence, they suggest that undissociated HBr_3 may be formed in sufficient quantities to cause the exchange, although no evidence of its formation in the system HBr—Br_2, solid, liquid, or gaseous, has been

[472] L. C. Liberatore and E. O. Wiig, *J. Chem. Phys.* 1940, **8**, 165.
[473] W. F. Libby, ib. 348.
[474] S. J. O'Brien and E. G. Bobalek, *J.A.C.S.* 1940, **62**, 3227.
[475] M. Berthelot, *Ann. Chim. Phys.* 1876, [5] **9**, 347.
[476] A. F. Kapustinski and V. A. Maltzev, *J. Phys.-Chem. Russ.* 1940, **14**, 105.
[477] O. Maass and J. Russell, *J.A.C.S.* 1918, **40**, 1564.
[478] B. Topley and J. Weiss, *J.C.S.* 1936, 912.
[479] A. R. Gordon and C. Barnes, *J. Chem. Phys.* 1933, **1**, 692.

obtained by phase rule methods.[480] As we saw above (p. 1166) a similar exchange was found later to occur in the gaseous state, and was similarly explained.

Hydrogen bromide is of course very soluble in water of which a litre dissolves under 1 atm. pressure 2,212 g. at 0° and 1,930 g. at 25°, the latter solution being about 16-normal. It forms hydrates with HBr to 4 H_2O (m. pt. $-56\cdot8°$), 3 H_2O ($-48°$), 2 ($-11\cdot2°$), and 1 (incongruent).[481] The partial pressure of the HBr changes in the same way as with HCl, being minute at low concentrations, but rising rapidly when the concentration much exceeds 10 n.[482-3]

Radioactive exchange between the halogen hydride or its salts and the free halogen occurs completely and rapidly in aqueous solution with bromine,[484] chlorine,[485] and iodine.[486] This is no doubt due to the formation of the polyhalide ions X_3^-.

HYDROGEN IODIDE, HI

Hydrogen iodide differs from the bromide mainly in being much more readily oxidized. The reaction

$$H_2 + I_2 = 2\,HI.$$

if H_2 and HI are gaseous and I_2 solid, involves the absorption of $12\cdot2$ k.cals.: if the iodine also is gaseous it is just exothermic, but only gives out $1\cdot4$ k.cals. As a result hydrogen iodide acts in many cases as a reducing agent, and a concentrated aqueous solution is often used for this purpose in organic chemistry. Owing to this relatively feeble affinity of hydrogen for iodine reaction chains cannot occur in the formation of HI. The dynamics of the formation have been studied in great detail especially by Bodenstein,[487] by sealing up known quantities of hydrogen and iodine in glass bulbs, which were then heated for a known time to a fixed temperature, chilled, broken under oxygen-free water, and the contents analysed. The reaction is homogeneous and of the second order; the heat of activation calculated from the temperature co-efficient of the velocity is 40 k.cals. The absolute rate of reaction calculated from this value of the activation

[480] E. H. Buhner and P. J. Karsten, *Akad. Amst. n Versl.* 1909, **17**, 502; *Proc. Acad. Amst.* 1909, **11**, 506. See also E. Beckmann and P. Waentig, *Z. anorg. Chem.* 1910, **67**, 48.

[481] S. U. Pickering, *Phil. Mag.* 1893, [5] **36**, 119; H. W. Bakhuis Roozeboom, *Rec. Trav.* 1885, **4**, 111, 334; 1886, **5**, 332, 374; *Z. physikal. Chem.* 1888, **2**, 454, 457.

[482] S. J. Bates and H. D. Kirschman, *J.A.C.S.* 1919, **41**, 1998.

[483] M. Wrewsky, N. Sawariski, and L. Scharlow, *J. Russ. Chem. Soc.* 1924, **54**, 367; *Z. physikal. Chem.* 1924, **112**, 103.

[484] A. v. Grosse and M. S. Agruss, *J.A.C.S.* 1935, **57**, 591.

[485] F. A. Long and A. R. Olson, ib. 1936, **58**, 2214.

[486] D. E. Hull, C. H. Shiflet, and C. S. Lind, ib. **55**, 535.

[487] M. Bodenstein, *Ber.* 1893, **26**, 2610; *Z. physikal. Chem.* 1894, **13**, 56, 110; 1897, **22**, 1; 1899, **29**, 295. See Hinshelwood, *Kinetics of Chemical Change* (1940), p. 47, etc.

energy is at 700° 0·14 (per sec. per mole per litre) while the observed rate is 0·064.[488]

This reaction is also interesting in relation to the theory of Eyring and Polyani[489] that the essential use of the heat of activation is to bring the atoms into the positions required for forming the new molecules. While the quantitative calculation of this effect depends on factors which are not fully known, it is possible in this way to show that the reaction of hydrogen with iodine must go more easily through the molecules, and those with chlorine and bromine through the atoms.[490]

The photosynthesis of hydrogen iodide depends on a different mechanism, the dissociation of the I_2 molecules into atoms, as with bromine and chlorine. With iodine as with bromine the difficulty arises in the second stage of the reaction.

$$I + H_2 = IH + H - 32·0 \text{ k.cals.}$$

Owing to the highly endothermic character of this reaction, the iodine atom will only be able to react if it has a high kinetic energy, and so light waves can only bring about the reaction if they are very short[491]. Coehn and Stuckardt[492] found that a mixture of hydrogen and iodine reaches equilibrium in light of a wave-length shorter than 2,200A, but that if the wave-length was longer than this there was no sign of the formation of hydrogen iodide.

On heating, hydrogen iodide dissociates largely into its constituent elements. The equilibrium in the reaction

$$H_2 + I_2 = 2 HI$$

lies almost wholly on the right-hand side, but since the formation of HI in the gaseous state evolves heat, the dissociation is favoured by a rise of temperature. At any temperature near the ordinary the reaction is very slow; equilibrium is not reached at 100° in 3 months. The proportions at equilibrium have been found[493-4] to be:

At			600° K.	700° K.	800° K.	1,490° K.
Per cent. diss.		.	19·1	22·2	24·9	35·6

At the highest temperatures the equilibrium is to some extent affected by the dissociation of the iodine molecules into atoms.[495]

[488] W. C. M. Lewis, *J.C.S.* 1918, **113**, 471.

[489] H. Eyring and M. Polanyi, *Z. physikal. Chem.* 1931, B **12**, 279; H Eyring, *J.A.C.S.* 1931, **53**, 2537.

[490] A. Wheeler, B. Topley, and H. Eyring, *J. Chem. Phys.* 1936, **4**, 178, have calculated by the methods of statistical mechanics the absolute rates of reaction of iodine, bromine, and chlorine with H_2, HD, and D_2, and have shown that the results are in accordance with observation.

[491] See E. J. Bowen, *J.C.S.* 1924, **125**, 1237, where the whole question of the photochemistry of the combination of the halogens with hydrogen is discussed.

[492] A. Coehn and K. Stuckardt, *Z. physikal. Chem.* 1916, **91**, 722.

[493] M. Bodenstein, ib. 1899, **29**, 296.

[494] K. Vogel v. Falckenstein, ib. 1909, **68**, 279; **72**, 113.

[495] See further A. H. Taylor and R. H. Crist, *J.A.C.S.* 1941, **63**, 1377; they measure equilibrium and rates for I_2+H_2, and for I_2+D_2.

The photodissociation of HI has been shown to give a normal neutral hydrogen atom and an excited neutral iodine atom, as would be expected from a covalent H—I molecule.[496]

Hydrogen iodide boils at −35·4 and melts at −50·8°.[497] Its critical temperature is 150·8°. The heat of evaporation at the boiling-point is 4·724 k.cals., giving a Trouton constant of 19·9. The heat of fusion at the melting-point is 0·686 k.cals./mole.[497]

Solutions of HI, as of HBr and HCl, are divided into those in which the molecule remains covalent, as in hydrocarbons, and those in which it is ionized, as in water. The non-ionized solutions have been very little investigated, but they resemble those of HCl and HBr in the same solvents; the solubility is always very small. In organic solvents containing oxygen, hydrogen iodide is readily soluble owing to the formation of oxonium iodides.

In water hydrogen iodide is very soluble: the three halogen hydrides have almost the same molar solubility in water, a litre of which, at 10° and under a gas pressure of 1 atm., will dissolve 14 moles of HCl, 15 of HBr, and 12 of HI.[498] Solid hydrates with

$$4 \; H_2O \; [\text{m. pt.} \; -36·5°], \; 3 \; H_2O \; [-48°], \; \text{and} \; 2 \; H_2O \; [ca. \; -43°]$$

are known; a monohydrate has not been isolated.[499]

In water hydrogen iodide is of course a strong acid. Attempts have been made to determine the relative strength of the three halogen acids in water; but the results[500] are inconclusive.

Aqueous solutions of hydriodic acid decompose very readily, as we should expect from the heat relations. In complete absence of oxygen they can be kept indefinitely, even in the light, but in presence of oxygen the reaction

$$O_2 + 4 \, HI = 2 \, H_2O + 2 \, I_2 + 112·2 \; \text{k.cals.}$$

goes on spontaneously, and is hastened by light.

The chemical reactions of the solution are in general those of a strong acid, and those of a reducing agent. A great many—in fact most—organic substances of the most varied types, aliphatic and aromatic alike, if they are heated at 250–300° with saturated aqueous hydriodic acid, are reduced to saturated hydrocarbons. The strength of the reducing agent can be maintained by adding elementary phosphorus, which reacts with the liberated iodine in the presence of the water to regenerate HI. With this reagent CS_2 can be reduced to methane and hydrogen sulphide.

All ordinary oxidizing agents will liberate iodine from hydriodic acid—ozone, oxygen, nitric acid, arsenates, antimonates, vanadates (reduced to the quadrivalent state), chromates, permanganates, chlorine, bromine, ferric salts, etc.

[496] J. Franck and H. Kuhn, *Z. Phys.* 1927, **43**, 164 (*B.C.A.* 1927, A, 711).

[497] W. F. Giauque and R. Wiebe, *J.A.C.S.* 1929, **51**, 1445.

[498] R. Abegg and G. Bodländer, *Z. anorg. Chem.* 1899, **20**, 468.

[499] S. U. Pickering, *Ber.* 1893, **26**, 2309.

[500] A. Hantzsch and A. Weissberger, *Z. physikal. Chem.* 1927, **125**, 256.

BINARY CHLORIDES, BROMIDES, AND IODIDES

Much of the properties of these compounds have already been discussed along with the inorganic fluorides (Fluorine, p. 1112). Something more may be said about properties of the halides which bear on the question of ionization or covalency. The covalent have low boiling-points, which rise with the atomic weight of the halogen; the salts have high boiling-points, falling in this order. The electric conductivities of the fused substances are high with salts, and low or very low with covalent halides.

The conductivities of the fused halides have been determined mainly by Biltz and Klemm,[501] who in particular have measured nearly all the known chlorides. They cannot all be measured at the same temperature, and this has therefore usually been done just above the melting-points. Since the melting-points of ionized compounds are higher than those of covalent, and the conductivities all increase with temperature, this exaggerates the differences in conductivity between the two classes of compounds, but the conductivities vary over so wide a range (in the ratio of 10^8 to 1) that the temperature effect is only of secondary importance. Out of 60 chlorides of 53 elements examined by Biltz and Klemm, 31 were found to have conductivities (in reciprocal ohms near the melting-point) lying between 10 and 0·1, and are obviously ionized, while for 26 the value was less than 2×10^{-6}, showing that these are covalent. Only 3 ($BeCl_2$, $ZnCl_2$, $HgCl_2$) gave intermediate values (32, 24, and $0·82 \times 10^{-4}$).

A further distinction between halides is their behaviour with water. This can be of four kinds. (1) Ionization; (2) hydrolysis to HX and the hydroxide of the other element; (3) no action at all; (4) hydrolysis to the hydride of the second element and hypohalous acid HOX.

As we have seen, which of these occurs depends on the nature of the atom A. (1) Ionization is favoured by low valency, a large cation, especially when this has an inert gas structure, and a small anion. When these conditions are not fulfilled, ionization does not occur, but one of the alternatives (2), (3), or (4). (2) is then the normal behaviour if A has a valency group of less than the maximum size for that atom (BCl_3, $SiCl_4$, etc.); (3) inactivity is found where A has its maximum valency group and this is fully shared (CCl_4, SF_6, SeF_6); (4) hydrolysis to the hypohalous acid occurs when the valency group of A is of the maximum size but is not fully shared: among the binary halides this normally happens only with those of nitrogen and oxygen, and the elementary halogens themselves.*

COMPLEX HALIDES (INCLUDING FLUORIDES)[502]

There are more known types of complex halides than of any other kind of complex salt, and almost as many as for the rest put together. The existence of four halogens, and the absence of complications due to other

---

* For its occurrence among organic halides (with C-hal) see below, p. 1189.

[501] See especially W. Biltz, *Z. anorg. Chem.* 1924, **133**, 312; W. Biltz and W Klemm, ib. 1926, **152**, 267.

[502] See N. V. Sidgwick, *J.C.S.* 1941, 441.

atoms attached to the donor, make the relations comparatively easy to detect.

Complexes have been described with every number of halogen atoms from 2 to 8 on the central atom (those with more than one central atom are not discussed here, as their structures are often uncertain). Usually the only evidence we have for their constitutions is the composition of the solid, but it is only when the crystal structure is known that we can be sure we are dealing with a single salt and not a crystal aggregate. This danger is not imaginary. For example, X-ray analysis has shown that the salt $K_2CuCl_4,2 H_2O$ is really an aggregate of planar molecules of $CuCl_2,2 H_2O$ with K^+ and Cl^- ions (I. 163): that $CsAuCl_3$ (with apparently divalent gold) is $Cs_2Au^iAu^{iii}Cl_6$, and is made up of Cs^+ with 2 kinds of anions, linear $Au^iCl_2^-$ and planar $Au^{iii}Cl_4^-$ (I. 190); and that Cs_3CoCl_5 is made up of Cs^+, Cl^-, and $CoCl_4^{--}$ (VIII. 1389). With most complex salts we have better evidence (for example from the solubilities) that they contain complexes, than what these complexes exactly are; but it is to be presumed that usually they are not aggregates of this kind, and the composition may be taken at its face value.

The influence of the halogen on the formation and stability of the complexes is marked. In simple compounds, as we have seen, the heats of formation of the links are always in the order

$$A—F > A—Cl > A—Br > A—I,$$

the mean relative values with some 20 observed A atoms being 1·47, 1, 0·84, 0·69. The increased covalencies of the A atom in the complex will diminish these, but not much, as is shown by these relative values:

Al—Cl in $AlCl_3$	1	P—Cl in PCl_3	1
Al—Cl in Al_2Cl_6	0·80	P—Cl in PCl_5	0·85
Sb—Cl in $SbCl_3$	1	I—Cl in ICl	1
Sb—Cl in $SbCl_5$	0·82	I—Cl in ICl_3	0·82

so that, as all the values will be diminished in the complexes similarly, the order of the heats of formation of the A—hal links is not likely to be changed. Experimentally so far as is known the order of stability of the complex halides is usually $Cl > Br > I$. But while the fluoride is sometimes more stable than the chloride (as we should expect it to be), it is sometimes less so. Possible causes of its being less are (1) that the simple fluoride does not exist, (2) that it is very insoluble, and (3) that it is highly hydrolysed by water. The data show that there are some 22 central atoms whose complex fluorides are more stable than the chlorides, and 34 where the fluoride is less stable or is unknown. The following table gives the number of each kind which come under the headings (1), (2), and (3): 'normal' are those to which none of these causes apply.

Binary fluoride	*1. Non-exist.*	*2. Insol.*	*3. Hydrol.*	*4. Normal*
Stability of }F > Cl (22)	2	1	2	17
complex }F < Cl (34)	17	4	9	4

No satisfactory generalizations can be made about the effect of the nature of the central atom on the size and stability of the complex; but the following list may be useful. The symbols X 6, Cl 4, etc., are written for the complex ions AX_6, ACl_4, etc. X = F, Cl, Br, I.[503]

Group I (VII. 1105) *Hydrogen.* H[F—H··F], with a hydrogen bond. No chloride.

    Alkali Metals. None (too strongly ionized).

p. 147. Cu′, Ag′, Au′: X 2, X 3, rarely X 4. Only fluoride $M_2[AgF_3]$. Stability Cl > Br > I: Cu′ > Ag′ > Au′.

p. 161. Cu″. F > Cl, Br > I: X 3, 4, rarely 5, no more.

p. 176. [Ag″. None, as cation oxidizes anion.]

p. 190. Au‴. No F: Cl, Br, I, always X 4.

Group II

p. 217. Be. F 4 very stable. Cl 4 doubtful.

p. 242. Mg. F 3 and 4. Ca, Sr, Ba none.

pp. 284, 331. Zn, Cd, Hg. All give stable complexes: $F \ll Cl > Br > I$: with F, Zn > Cd > Hg. All give X 3 and 4: Cd also X 6.

Group III

p. 409. Boron. F 4 very stable: no others.

p. 435. Al. F 4, ? 5, 6. No others except X 4 in Al_2Cl_6 and Al_2Br_6.

p. 441. Sc and rare earth metals. Very few, if any, except Sc: F 4 and F 6.

p. 476. Ga. F 4, 5, 6: no Cl, Br, or I.

p. 476. In. No F: Cl and Br, 4 and 5.

p. 476. Tl. No F: Cl 4 and 5.

Group IV

    [Carbon none.]

p. 614. Si^{iv}. F 6: no Cl, Br, I.

p. 615. Ge^{iv}. The same.

p. 616. Sn^{iv}. X 6 and X 8 stable: F = Cl > Br > I.

p. 616. Pb^{iv}. Cl, Br, I all 6.

p. 618. Ge″. Cl 3.

p. 622. Sn″. Cl 3 and 4; ? I 4.

p. 626. Pb″. Cl, Br, I: 4–6.

Group IV. A

p. 644. Ti^{iv}. $F \gg Cl$, Br, I: all 6: stability in the order Si > Ti > Zr.

p. 645. Zr^{iv}. Similar but less stable; F 5, to 8.

p. 646. Th^{iv}. F 5, 6: Cl 5.

p. 651. Ti‴. F 5, 6: Cl 5.

Group V

p. 756. P^{v}. F 6 stable.

p. 799. As^{v}. F 6.

[503] Gmelin, *Fluor*, 1926, pp. 59–72 gives a complete list to date of the double fluorides, with references. In *Chlor*, 1927, p. 223; *Brom*, 1931, p. 285; *Iod*, 1933, p. 431, are given lists only of the complex acids.

p. 799. Sb^v. F, Cl, Br all 6; stability of F 6 P > As > Sb
[Bi^v no complexes.]
[P^{111} none: no inert pair.]

p. 798. As^{111}. Cl 4: Br 4, 5. Not very stable.

p. 798. Sb^{111}. X 4, 5, 6; ? F 7.

p. 799. Bi^{111}. X 4, 5, (6): F only 4.

p. 817. V^v. Only oxy-halides, as $M[VOF_4]$.

p. 839. Nb^v. F 6, 7, and oxy. Cl only oxy, unstable.

p. 848. Ta^v. F 6, 7, 8: no oxy.

p. 822. V^{iv}. F 4, 5, 6.

Group VI

p. 989. Se. Only Se^{iv}: Cl, Br 6: no F or I: rather unstable.

p. 993. Te^{iv}. Similar: no F, Cl, Br, I 5 and 6: unstable.

p. 1008. Cr^v. Oxy, as $M_2[CrOCl_5]$ and $M[CrOCl_4]$.

p. 1050. Mo^v. Similar. F < Cl > Br.
[W^v. None.]

p. 1055. [No Cr^{iv} or Mo^{iv}] W^{iv} only type $M_2[W(OH)Cl_5]$.

p. 1021. Cr^{111}. Very stable with F, Cl, Br: no I. X 5, and 6.

p. 1059. Mo^{111}. F 4: Cl 4. (No Br or I).

p. 1060. [W^{111}. None except $M_3[W_2Cl_9]$.]
[Cr^{11}. None.]

p. 1064. [Mo^{11}. Only derivs. of Mo_6hal_{12}.]
[W^{11}. None.]

p. 1078. U^{vi}. All are uranyl, UO_2: F 3, 5, 6; Cl 4.

p. 1084. U^{iv}. Very like Th: F 5, Cl 6, Br 6.

Group VII

p. 1190. Halogens: perhalides as $M[X_3]$, $M[X_5]$ etc.: practically no F.
For central atom Cl < Br < I.

p. 1198. $M[ICl_4]$, planar.

p. 1274. Mn^{iv}. F 6, Cl 6: fairly stable.

p. 1282. Mn^{111}. F 5, Cl 5: hydrolysed by water.

p. 1287. Mn^{11}. X 3, 4, 6. F < Cl > Br. Not very stable.

p. 1305. Re^v. Oxyhalides as $M_2[ReOCl_6]$: unstable.

p. 1308. Re^{iv}. F, Cl, Br, I: all 6. Very stable.

p. 1313. Re^{111}. Cl 4, Br 4.

Group VIII.

p. 1366. Fe^{111}. F < Cl > Br: no I. F 4–6, Cl 4–7.

p. 1367. Br 4 and 5.

p. 1348. Fe^{11}. Few, only F and Cl 3 and 4.

p. 1413. Co^{111}. No pure complex halides, only ammine-halides.

p. 1389. Co^{11}. F < Cl > Br > I. X 3–6, especially 4.

p. 1448. Ni^{11}. F > Cl > Br > I. F 4, Cl 3, and ? 4.

p. 1477. Ru^{iv}. Cl, Br, no F or I. All X 6 or X 5 OH.

p. 1473. Ru^{111}. Cl > Br: no F or I. X 4–7.

p. 1502. Os^{vi}. None pure, only oxy- with Cl and Br, as $K_2[OsO_2Cl_4]$.

p. 1497. Os[iv]. X 6. F, Cl > Br > I.

p. 1493. Os[iii]. Cl 6, very unstable.

p. 1510. Os[ii]. None pure, only $M_2[Os(NO)X_5]$; X = Cl, Br, I; Cl very stable.

p. 1525. Rh[iii]. No F: Cl > Br > I. X 5–7. Stable.

p. 1545. Ir[iv]. X 6. F > Cl > Br. No I.

p. 1540. Ir[iii]. X 6. Cl > Br. No F or I.

p. 1576. Pd[iv]. Cl, Br 6; no F or I. Rather stable.

p. 1561. Pd[iii]. Cl 5, very unstable.

p. 1568. Pd[ii]. Cl, Br, I, all 4. Fairly stable.

p. 1622. Pt[iv]. All 4 halogens X 6: F little known. Very stable.

p. 1609. Pt[iii]. Cl 5, very unstable.

p. 1605. Pt[iv]. No F, the rest all X 4; Cl, Br > I.

ORGANIC CHLORIDES, BROMIDES, AND IODIDES

THESE organic derivatives are far better known than those of fluorine, and only a few of their more important properties can be discussed.

The methods of preparation are by addition to the double link or by substitution; the conditions may be summarized thus.

A. Addition to double and triple links, the addendum being either (*a*) halogen, or (*b*) halogen hydride. (The addition of HO+Cl is discussed under HOCl, p. 1213).

B. Replacement of other atoms or groups by halogen.

The other group may be

(*a*) Hydrogen. This is direct halogenation, the reagent being either the halogen itself or some compound which yields it, such as an iodide chloride $Ar \cdot ICl_2$.

(*b*) Hydroxyl: this is done by

    1. Hydrogen halide.

    2. Phosphorus tri- or pentahalide.

(*c*) NH_2: this is confined to the aromatic amines, which react through the diazo-compounds.

These are the most important methods, though there are others that are sometimes used. These methods may be taken in order.

A. *Addition Reactions*

(*a*) *Addition of Halogens to Multiple Links*

Addition can take place to double or to triple links, but much more is known about the former. The addition of chlorine or bromine (not of iodine, save in exceptional cases like that of cyclopropane[504]) occurs readily in presence of catalysts such as salt-like surfaces, and of light; the photochemical reaction, like that of hydrogen with the halogens, is homogeneous and inhibited by oxygen; it gives a quantum yield of 10^6 with chlorine and 10^5 with bromine.[505] When ethylene and bromine are brought together in

504 R. A. Ogg and W. J. Priest, *J. Chem. Phys.* 1939, **7**, 736.

505 H. Schmitz, H. J. Schumacher, and A. Jäger, *Z. physikal. Chem.* 1942, B **51**, 281.

the gas, the reaction takes place almost entirely on the glass walls.[506] Norrish[507] found that the rate of combination is much greater when the walls are 'polar' (as with glass); if they are covered with solid paraffin the combination is almost stopped, whereas with stearic acid it is quicker than with glass alone. The relative amounts of combination in 4 minutes with various substances on the walls are:

Paraffin	Cetyl Alc.	Glass	Stearic acid
3·8	13·3	19·0	21·9

The addition in carbon tetrachloride solution is accelerated by light.[508] It goes several times as quick when the liquid is moist as when it is carefully dried. It also goes, curiously, much quicker at 0° than at 25°, and this temperature effect is increased as much as 100 times when the system is dried.

The effect of substituents (especially methyl groups) in the ethylene both on the heat and on the rate of reaction have been measured. The heat of reaction of C=C with Br_2 was measured in the vapour at 80°, being catalysed by dry calcium bromide, both for the substituted ethylenes[509-10] and for the unsaturated cycloparaffins[511]; the results may be compared with the heats of hydrogenation[512-13]:

Hydrocarbon	C=C+Br$_2$	C=C+H$_2$
$H_2C=CH_2$	29·1	32·6 k.cals.
$CH_3 \cdot CH=CH_2$	29·4	30·1 ,,
$CH_3 \cdot CH_2 \cdot CH=CH_2$	29·6	30·3 ,,
$CH_3 \cdot CH=CHCH_3$ trans	29·1	27·6 ,,
$CH_3 \cdot CH=CHCH_3$ cis	30·2	28·6 ,,
$(CH_3)_2C=CHCH_3$	30·4	26·9 ,,
Cyclopentene	28·6	··
Cyclohexene	33·6	28·6 ,,
Cycloheptene	30·4	26·5 ,,
Cyclooctene	29·3	23·5 ,,
Normal heptene	30·2	··

These results with the ethylenes give a thermodynamic basis for Markownikoff's rule (below, p. 1177), and also show why in substitution the bromine replaces by preference the hydrogen on the most highly substituted carbon.

The whole of this evidence makes it probable that these small differences depend on the hindrance to free rotation, and that this hindrance is due to atomic (or link) repulsion, so that the energy content is greater in the eclipse position.

[506] T. D. Stewart and K. R. Edlund, *J.A.C.S.* 1923, **45**, 1014.

[507] R. G. W. Norrish, *J.C.S.* 1923, **123**, 3006.

[508] H. S. Davis, *J.A.C.S.* 1928, **50**, 2769.

[509] J. B. Conn, G. B. Kistiakowsky, and E. A. Smith, ib. 1938, **60**, 2764.

[510] Id., ib. 1939, **61**, 1868.   [511] M. W. Lister, ib. 1941, **63**, 143.

[512] G. B. Kistiakowsky, J. R. Ruhoff, H. A. Smith, and W. E. Vaughan, ib. 1936, **58**, 137.

[513] Id., ib. 1935, **57**, 876.

The replacement of the hydrogen atoms in ethylene by methyl groups is found[508] to increase the rate of addition of halogen; thus with the dried system in the dark ethylene needs some days for fairly complete combination, methyl ethylene some hours, and trimethyl ethylene only a few minutes. On the other hand, negative groups (such as halogen atoms or carboxyl groups) diminish the rate: the relative rates of addition of bromine in methylene chloride at $-35°$ were found by Ingold[514] to be:

$CH_2=CH_2$	.	.	1·0	$CH_2=CH \cdot COOH$ . . 0·03	
$(CH_3)_2C=CH_2$	.	.	5·5	$CH_2=CHBr$ . . . 0·04	
$(CH_3)_2C=C(CH_3)_2$	.	.	14		

In the same way tetraphenyl ethylene will not react with bromine at all,[515-16] and though it does add on chlorine, it easily loses it again.[517-18]

An interesting question[519] is how far addition to the double link takes place in the *cis* and how far in the *trans* position. Earlier workers, including van 't Hoff and Wislicenus, made the natural assumption that the addition must be in the *cis* position. It is, however, well established now that both kinds of addition occur, and it is indeed probable that the *trans* addition predominates. Thus it has been shown that acetylene on addition of bromine gives a mixture of *cis* and *trans* dibromo-ethylene[520]; fumaric acid takes up chlorine to give about 80 per cent. meso (*trans*) and 20 per cent. racemic dichlorosuccinic acid,[521] and maleic anhydride with chlorine gives 80 per cent. racemic and 20 per cent. meso-acid,[522] in both cases the *trans* addition predominating.

When the unsaturated molecule contains two double links in the conjugate position, there is the possibility that the halogen will not add either to one or to the other of the double links, but to the 1 and 4 positions, giving a new double link:

$$C=C-C=C \longrightarrow \underset{\underset{Br}{|}}{C}-C=C-\underset{\underset{Br}{|}}{C}$$

It was to account for such reactions as this that Thiele put forward his theory of conjugate double links.[523] Later work has shown that with such a system 1,4-addition often occurs, but by no means always. With the halogens it would seem that the addition is normally to the 1 and 2 positions[524]; but in the particular case of butadiene the quantum mechanism

---

[514] C. K. and E. H. Ingold, *J.C.S.* 1931, 2354; see also S. V. Anantakrishnan and C. K. Ingold, ib. 1935, **984**, 1396.

[515] A. Behr, *Ber.* 1870, **3**, 751.   [516] H. Bauer, ib. 1904, **37**, 3317.

[517] H. Finkelstein, ib. 1910, **43**, 1533.

[518] J. F. Norris, R. Thomas, and B. M. Brown, ib. 2940.

[519] See W. Hückel, *Theor. Grundl. d. org. Chemie*, 1931, Bd. i, 290.

[520] G. Chavanne, *C.R.* 1912, **154**, 776.

[521] R. Kuhn and T. Wagner-Jauregg, *Ber.* 1928, **61**, 519.

[522] B. Holmberg, *J. pr. Chem.* 1911, **84**, 145.

[523] J. Thiele, *Ann.* 1899, **306**, 87.

[524] Cf. W. Hückel, *Theor. Grundl. d. org. Chemie*, 1931, Bd. i, p. 307.

of the addition has been studied by Eyring,[525-6] who concluded that 1,4-addition should occur, and that the reaction should be catalysed by the walls; an experimental investigation by Heisig and Wilson[527] fully confirmed these conclusions.

Bartlett and Tarbell[528] show that in general the addition of halogen occurs in two stages, the first being the formation of a complex cation $[C\!=\!C\!\cdot\!\cdot X]^+$, which Robinson[529] writes

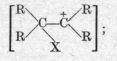

this has been attacked on the ground that *cis* and *trans* olefines would then give the same products. But it has been pointed out[530] that there should be co-ordination (at least in a resonance form) to the cyclic structure

which overcomes this difficulty. See further reference [531].

A. (b) *Addition of Hydrogen Halides*

This is in general less easy than the addition of the halogens, but takes place more readily the heavier the halogen. The heats evolved in these reactions in the gaseous state are:

$$C\!=\!C + HCl = CH\!-\!CCl + \quad Q.$$
$$41{\cdot}4 \quad 102{\cdot}7 \quad 87{\cdot}3 \quad 66{\cdot}5 + 9{\cdot}7 \text{ kc.}$$

$$+ HBr = CH + CBr$$
$$41{\cdot}4 \quad 87{\cdot}3 \quad 87{\cdot}3 \quad 54{\cdot}0 + 12{\cdot}6 \text{ kc.}$$

$$+ HI - CH\!-\!CI$$
$$41{\cdot}4 \quad 71{\cdot}4 \quad 87{\cdot}3 \quad 45{\cdot}5 + 20{\cdot}0 \text{ kc.}$$

When the double link is unsymmetrically placed in the organic molecule, a new question arises as to which way the hydrogen halide attaches itself

$$R_2C\!=\!CR_2' + H\cdot hal \begin{cases} R_2CH\!-\!CR_2'hal \\ R_2Chal\!-\!CR_2'H \end{cases}.$$

Markownikoff in 1870[532] stated his well-known rule that the halogen

[525] H. Eyring, *Science*, 1933, **77**, 158.
[526] H. Eyring, A. Sherman, and G. E. Kimball, *J. Chem. Phys.* 1933, **1**, 586.
[527] G. B. Heisig and J. L. Wilson, *J.A.C.S.* 1935, **57**, 859.
[528] P. D. Bartlett and D. S. Tarbell, ib. 1937, **59**, 407.
[529] R. Robinson, 'Electronic Theory of Organic Reactions', *Inst. of Chem.* 1932.
[530] I. Roberts and G. E. Kimball, *J.A.C.S.* 1937, **59**, 947.
[531] K. Nozaki and R. A. Ogg, ib. 1942, **64**, 704, 709.
[532] W. B. Markownikoff, *Ann.* 1870, **153**, 256.

attaches itself to the carbon which has the least number of hydrogen atoms (this is the basis of Michael's 'positive–negative' rule[533]) to which he added a second rule, that in the addition to vinyl chloride CH_2=$CHCl$, or to α-chloro-propylene $CH_3 \cdot CH$=$CHCl$, the halogen of hydrogen chloride or iodide goes to the carbon which already carries a chlorine atom.[534]

These rules are substantially true, but in 1933 a new and so far unexplained influence on these reactions was discovered by Kharasch.[535] He showed that in some of these cases the orientation of the product was determined, considerably if not wholly, by the presence or absence during the reaction of oxygen or certain peroxides. Thus allyl bromide which has been exposed to the air, and can be shown to contain peroxidic impurities, rapidly takes up HBr and forms mainly 1,3-dibromopropane:

$$CH_2Br \cdot CH\!\!=\!\!CH_2 + HBr \longrightarrow CH_2Br \cdot CH_2\!\!-\!\!CH_2Br.$$

But if the peroxides are removed and the reaction carried out in the absence of air, the addition is slow, and 80 per cent. of the product is the 1,2-dibromide $CH_2Br \cdot CHBr \cdot CH_3$. If oxygen is passed through a peroxide-free specimen for 10 minutes, 70 per cent. of the 1,3-product is again obtained. In presence of 'antioxidants', substances which remove oxygen or peroxides (such as diphenylamine or quinol), only the 1,2-dibromide is formed.

This discovery led to much further work, and the results up to date have been summarized by J. C. Smith.[536-7] A most remarkable result is that while this 'Kharasch effect' is undoubtedly true, it is strictly limited, and is confined (1) almost to terminal double links, and (2) quite to the addition of HBr. For a further discussion and a suggested explanation of these phenomena see reference [538]. It has been shown that the addition of a hydrogen halide to a molecule CH_2=$CH \cdot R$ takes place as follows:

Hydrogen Chloride adds slowly (oxygen or no oxygen), always giving CH_3—$CHCl \cdot R$ (Markownikoff's first rule). See further references [539-40,546].

Hydrogen Bromide: in the absence of oxygen or a peroxide the HBr adds on slowly, giving again the 2-halide CH_3—$CHBr \cdot R$, as with HCl: this is

[533] A. Michael, *J. prakt. Chem.* 1899, **60**, 341; *Ber.* 1906, **39**, 2138.

[534] For a discussion of the causes of these reactions see H. B. Watson, *Modern Theories of Org. Chemistry*, ed. 2, 1941, p. 145.

[535] M. S. Kharasch and F. R. Mayo, *J.A.C.S.* 1933, **55**, 2468.

[536] J. C. Smith, *Chem. and Ind.* 1937, 833; 1938, 461.

[537] Id., *Ann. Rep. Chem. Soc. for 1939*, **36**, 219.

[538] F. R. Mayo and C. Walling, *Chem. Rev.* 1940, **27**, 375, and W. A. Waters, *Chemistry of Free Radicals*, 1946, p. 180.

[539] M. S. Kharasch, S. C. Kleiger, and F. R. Mayo, *J. Org. Chem.* 1939, **4**, 428.

[540] M. S. Kharasch, C. Walling, and F. R. Mayo, *J.A.C.S.* 1939, **61**, 1559.

[541] M. S. Kharasch, H. Engelmann, and F. R. Mayo, *J. Org. Chem.* 1937, **2**, 288, 400.

[542] M. S. Kharasch, J. A. Norton, and F. R. Mayo, ib. 1938, **3**, 48.

[543] M. S. Kharasch, M. Z. Fineman, and F. R. Mayo, *J.A.C.S.* 1939, **61**, 2139.

[544] M. S. Kharasch, W. R. Haefele, and F. R. Mayo, ib. 1940, **62**, 2047.

[545] W. E. Vaughan, F. F. Rust, and T. W. Evans, *J. Org. Chem.* 1942, **7**, 477.

[546] M. S. Kharasch, J. Kritschevsky, and F. R. Mayo, ib., 1938, **2**, 489.

the 'normal' reaction. In presence of oxygen or a peroxide the addition takes place rapidly, with the formation of the other product CH_2Br—$CH_2 \cdot R$: this is the 'abnormal' reaction. See further references [541-2].

Hydrogen Iodide always adds on rapidly, and always, oxygen or no oxygen, gives the normal product CH_3—$CHI \cdot R$.

The rate of addition both of HBr and of Br_2 to cyclopropane is greatly increased by the presence of oxygen or peroxides.[543] The bromination of toluene is greatly accelerated by peroxides, both the thermochemical reaction in solution giving benzyl bromide, and the photochemical in the vapour, when the bromine goes into the nucleus.[547] Some other reactions are affected in the same way, such as the Cannizzaro reaction (formation of acid+alcohol) with benzaldehyde,[537] which is stopped by the addition of an antioxidant. Other catalysts, such as powdered iron[544] or nickel, and even ultra-violet light[545] have the same influence on the addition of hydrogen bromide. Ferric chloride hastens the addition of hydrogen chloride or bromide to a terminal C=C group, but does not affect its direction.[539]

The real active agent is probably elementary oxygen, and peroxides (benzoyl peroxide, perbenzoic acid, etc.) are only active so far as they give off oxygen. From the rapidity of the catalysed 'abnormal' reaction, it is evidently a chain reaction, and presumably it involves bromine atoms; but beyond this its mechanism is still obscure (see refs. [537-8]).

The addition of hydrogen bromide to the triple link in acetylene is very slow in the absence of a catalyst, and hydrogen chloride will not go on at all. But in presence of mercuric salts (which seem to be specific for a triple link) HCl forms monochlorethylene CH_2=$CHCl$, and with mercuric bromide HBr forms both monobromethylene CH_2=$CHBr$ and ethylidene dibromide CH_3—$CHBr_2$.

B. *Replacement Reactions*

(a) *Replacement of Hydrogen: Direct Halogenation*

This is commonly effected by means of the halogens themselves. The heat of the reaction Q will be different according as there is or is not water present to absorb the hydrogen halide (ht. of soln.: HCl 17·7, HBr 20·0, HI 19·3 k.cals.). The following table gives the values of Q dry and Q wet— i.e. with or without water to absorb the HX produced.

$$Q\ dry \quad Q\ wet$$

$$\begin{array}{ccccc}
\text{C—H} + & \text{Cl}_2 & = & \text{C—Cl} + \text{H—Cl} \\
87 \cdot 3 & 57 \cdot 8 & 66 \cdot 5 & 102 \cdot 7 & +24 \cdot 1 + 41 \cdot 8
\end{array}$$

$$\begin{array}{ccccc}
\text{C—H} + & \text{Br}_2 & = & \text{C—Br} + \text{H—Br} \\
87 \cdot 3 & 46 \cdot 2 & 54 \cdot 0 & 87 \cdot 3 & + 7 \cdot 8 + 27 \cdot 8
\end{array}$$

$$\begin{array}{ccccc}
\text{C—H} & \text{I}_2 & = & \text{C—I} & \text{H—I} \\
87 \cdot 3 & 37 \cdot 6 & 45 \cdot 5 & 71 \cdot 4 & - 8 \cdot 0 + 11 \cdot 3
\end{array}$$

The reaction often takes place under very different conditions according as the hydrogen replaced is aliphatic or aromatic. It does not occur with

[547] M. S. Kharasch, P. C. White, and F. R. Mayo, ib. **3**, 33.

iodine at all, unless the hydrogen iodide produced is removed, for example by adding iodic acid HIO_3 (which forms I_2+H_2O) or mercuric oxide. With chlorine or bromine it is very slow at the ordinary temperature if it is unassisted, but it can be much hastened by the addition of a suitable catalyst, by exposure to light, or by a rise of temperature. Kharasch finds[549] that in the cold cyclohexane and isobutane are brominated by bromine in the absence of light and oxygen only about 1 per cent. per month; with O_2 in the dark, or with light and no O_2, about 10 per cent.; with both together far more than 20 per cent. Peroxides have no effect. Much the same occurs with $C(CH_3)_4$,[550] where, however, peroxides are active at 50°.

With the paraffins it has been shown[548] that the photochemical reaction (which occurs with toluene and even benzene as well as with the paraffins) is essentially of the same kind as that between chlorine and hydrogen, with the production of long chains, not quite so long as with hydrogen, but of 10^4 to 10^3 links. In the methane series the length of the chain (the quantum yield) falls from 10^4 to 10^3 as the amount of chlorine in the molecule increases, and we go from CH_4 to $CHCl_3$. The photochemical reaction, both with paraffins and with aromatic hydrocarbons, is often, especially with chlorine (see Kharasch, refs. [549-50] above) much delayed by the presence of oxygen, just as is the reaction with hydrogen. The thermal reaction seems to be in many ways similar to the photochemical.

The chlorination of the natural paraffins has recently assumed great technical importance, as these hydrocarbons, obtained from natural gas and separated from one another by fractional distillation, are the sources of a large number of commercial products. The conditions of their chlorination and the nature of the products have recently been examined in great detail by Hass and his colleagues.[551-2] They studied the photochemical and the thermal reactions, both in the liquid and in the gaseous phase; the general conclusions are much the same whichever method of reaction is used. The process is liable to be complicated by the occurrence of a second reaction, known as pyrolysis, which is promoted by high temperatures and long exposures, in which an olefine is formed (usually by the splitting off of a halogen hydride from a halogenated product, but as the temperature approaches that of cracking other groups, even hydrocarbon groups, may be broken off), and this then adds on a molecule of the halogen:

$$CH—C \cdot hal \longrightarrow C{=}C + H \cdot hal \longrightarrow C \cdot hal—C \cdot hal.$$

Assuming that the temperatures are such that pyrolysis is excluded, the results may be summed up as follows.

No rearrangements of the carbon skeleton take place during either

[518] See N. Semenoff, *Chem. Kinetics and Chain Reactions*, 1935, p. 122.

[549] M. S. Kharasch, W. Hered, and F. R. Mayo, *J. Org. Chem.* 1941, **6**, 818.

[550] M. S. Kharasch and M. Z. Fineman, *J.A.C.S.* 1941, **63**, 2776.

[551] H. B. Hass, E. T. B. McBee, and P. Weber, *J. Ind. Eng. Chem.* 1935, **27**, 1190.

[552] Id., ib. 1936, **28**, 333.

thermal or photochemical chlorination, and every possible monochloride is formed. So far as is known, the same is true of the polychlorides as well. The rate of replacement of hydrogen atoms is greatest when they are tertiary and least when they are primary; for chlorination in the vapour at 300° the ratio is 1ry:2ry:3ry: $= 1\cdot00:3\cdot25:4\cdot43$. As the temperature rises this ratio approaches unity both in the liquid and in the vapour. Chlorination in the liquid gives the same order, but the ratio is much nearer to unity. The effect of drying, or of adding coke as a catalyst, or of exposure to light, is to increase the absolute rates of reaction, but to leave the relative values unchanged. For the mechanism of chlorination and bromination see further references [553-4].

The dichloro-compounds are formed in two ways, by loss of HCl followed by addition of chlorine, and by progressive chlorination. Slow chlorination in the vapour, with its long exposures, tends to promote the first kind (pyrolytic), and rapid chlorination in the liquid the second.

When the chlorination is carried out in the vapour, the presence of a chlorine atom on a carbon tends to prevent the replacement of another hydrogen on the same carbon, and to some extent[555] on the next carbon; on the other hand, when $CH_3\cdot CF_2\cdot CH_3$[556] or $CH_3\cdot CCl_2\cdot CH_3$[557] is chlorinated, one CH_3 is converted into CH_2Cl, $CHCl_2$, and CCl_3 before the other is attacked. See further references [558-9].

A variety of catalysts can be used to promote halogenation.[560] These consist mainly of elements (or the halides of elements) which form more than one type of halide. The most important are iron and its halides, the pentachlorides of antimony, molybdenum, and phosphorus, iodine monochloride, and aluminium and its halides. The same catalysts are used for chlorination and for bromination. Iron and its halides promote the halogenation both of aliphatic and of aromatic hydrocarbons; according to Victor Meyer (1891-2) every normal paraffin can be made by treatment with bromine and iron wire to take up one bromine atom on each carbon.

The effect of various catalysts is not the same on paraffins as on aromatic hydrocarbons. Iron seems to be effective with both, but aluminium and its halides have more effect on the paraffins (or on hydrogen atoms in a side chain). The familiar statement that the replacement of hydrogen is easier with an aromatic than with an aliphatic hydrocarbon (which is generally taken to be an important element in the aromatic character) is probably true of halogenation, but the position is not quite simple. In the cold, and in the absence of light and catalysts, substitution is very slow with hydrocarbons of either kind. The influence of light is greater with

[553] H. A. Taylor and W. E. Hanson, *J. Chem. Phys.* 1939, **7**, 418.
[554] A. Guyer and A. Rufer, *Helv. Chim. Acta*, 1940, **23**, 533.
[555] F. F. Rust and W. E. Vaughan, *J. Org. Chem.* 1941, **6**, 479.
[556] A. L. Henne and M. W. Renoll, *J.A.C.S.* 1937, **59**, 2434.
[557] A. L. Henne and E. C. Ladd, ib. 1938, **60**, 2491.
[558] M. S. Kharasch and M. G. Berkman, *J. Org. Chem.* 1941, **6**, 810.
[559] J. Stauff and H. J. Schumacher, *Z. Elektrochem.* 1942, **48**, 271.
[560] See, for example, Houben-Weyl, Bd. ii (1922), p. 430.

aliphatic,[561-2] and that of catalysts on the whole with aromatic hydro-carbons; in the thermal reaction, which is common to both, no direct comparisons seem to have been made.

The bromination of benzene in light has been studied by W. Meidinger[563] (see also ref. [559]), who finds that two simultaneous reactions occur, the normal substitution of hydrogen, and an addition of bromine Br_2 to form presumably $C_6H_6Br_2$, which, however, immediately combines with more bromine to give the hexabromide $C_6H_6Br_6$. This tendency of benzene to pass into a cyclohexane derivative by taking up three halogen mole-cules seems to be exhibited under two sets of conditions, (1) under the influence of light, where in the vapour phase it is the main reaction, and (2) in the presence of a hypohalous acid, HOCl or HOBr[564]; the halogen is added to a caustic soda solution on the top of which a layer of benzene is floating; as soon as excess of halogen has been added to the alkali, reaction takes place with the benzene, and the hexahalide is formed in good yield. The further discussion of this belongs, however, rather to benzene than to the halogens.

In direct halogenation it is possible to use in place of the elementary halogen some compound which evolves it, such as an aryl iodide chloride $Ar \cdot ICl_2$ (see later p. 1247). Complex plumbichlorides such as

$$(NH_4)_2[PbCl_6]$$

can also be used.[565]

In the halogenation of aliphatic ketones and acids a peculiar mechanism has been found. Acetone in aqueous solution is converted by halogens at a measurable rate into the monohalide, such as bromacetone

$$CH_3 \cdot CO \cdot CH_2Br.$$

Lapworth[566] showed that this reaction is catalysed by hydrogen ion; but in presence of a constant excess of acid the rate is proportional to the concentration of the acetone, and independent of that of the halogen. Moreover, the velocity constant at fixed concentrations is the same for chlorine and also for iodine[567] as for bromine.

Hence the reaction whose velocity is being measured is one in which the halogen plays no part. The halogenation of the acetone must take place in two stages, first, a slow reaction in which the halogen is not concerned, and then a rapid reaction of the product with the halogen to give the halogeno-acetone.

The first (slow) stage must be the conversion of the ketone into the enol

[561] H. C. Andersen and E. R. van Artsdalen, *J. Chem. Phys.* 1944, **12**, 479.

[562] G. B. Kistiakowsky and E. R. van Artsdalen, ib. 469.

[563] W. Meidinger, *Z. physikal. Chem.* 1929, B **5**, 29.

[564] F. E. Matthews, *J.C.S.* 1898, **73**, 243.

[565] A. Seyewetz and M. Biot, *C.R.* 1902, **135**, 1120; A. Seyewetz and P. Trawitz, ib. **136**, 240.

[566] A. Lapworth, *J.C.S.* 1904, **85**, 30.

[567] H. M. Dawson and M. S. Leslie, ib. 1909, **95**, 1860. For further work by Dawson and his collaborators on this subject see *J.C.S.* from 1910 onwards.

$CH_3 \cdot C(OH) {=} CH_2$, which being unsaturated should readily (as other enols are known to do) add on the halogen: enolization is often catalysed by hydrogen ion. The product will then add a molecule of the halogen to the double $C{=}C$ link, and the resulting dihalide of the enol will lose hydrogen halide to give the halogeno-ketone, these last two reactions being rapid:

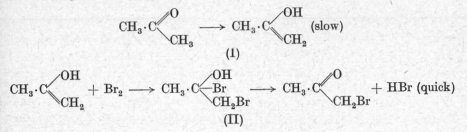

Thus the halogenation of acetone is not the direct substitution that it seems to be, but involves the addition of the halogen molecule to a double link.

A somewhat similar mechanism will explain the peculiar phenomena observed in the bromination of a fatty acid like acetic.[568-70]

B. (b) Replacement of Hydroxyl

Together with the replacement of hydrogen, this is the most important method of making the halides in the aliphatic series. It is effected by the action either of the hydrogen halide, or of a halide of phosphorus, or of thionyl chloride. The behaviour of these reagents is different according as the hydroxyl to be replaced is alcoholic or acidic. The hydrogen halides can only be used for the alcohols; their reaction even with them is rather unexpectedly slow as compared with the rate of esterification by oxy-acids (see further IV. 527, and ref. [571]), and involves heating the reagents together (usually under pressure) for a considerable time; the formation is also incomplete, since the reaction is reversible, unless the products are removed. Phosphorus halides, on the other hand, (chloride, bromide, iodide) react with alcohols immediately and completely. They do the same also with acids, giving the acyl halides, such as acetyl chloride $CH_3 \cdot CO \cdot Cl$, which cannot be prepared by the use of hydrogen halides, since the equilibrium is too far over on the side of the acid.

Phenolic hydroxyl cannot be satisfactorily replaced by the use of phosphorus halides, because the reaction gives mainly the phosphorous or phosphoric esters, the halogen attaching itself rather to the hydrogen than to the aryl radical; a better yield of the aryl halide is got from the nitrophenols. Aromatic halides are therefore usually made either by direct halogenation in presence of a catalyst, or through the diazo-reaction.

[568] J. Volhard, *Ann.* 1887, **242**, 141.
[569] H. B. Watson, *J.C.S.* 1925, **127**, 2067; *Chem. Rev.* 1930, **7**, 173; *Mod. Theories*, p. 119.
[570] H. B. Watson and E. H. Roberts, *J.C.S.* 1928, 2779.
[571] C. N. Hinshelwood, ib. 1935, 599.

The oxygen atom of a ketone can of course be replaced by two halogen atoms by treatment with the phosphorus pentahalide. This reaction is, however, liable[572] to a variety of complications, due partly to the tendency of many ketones to react in the enolic form, and partly to the breaking up of the pentahalide into the trihalide and free halogen, each of which has its own specific reactions.

B. (c) *Replacement of* NH_2

This is confined to compounds in which the NH_2 is attached to an aromatic ring, and always goes through the diazo-compound. It proceeds with all four halogens. With iodine it goes directly without the use of a catalyst; potassium iodide is added to the diazo-solution, and the diazonium iodide which is formed decomposes either spontaneously or on warming to give the aryl iodide:

$$Ar \cdot NH_2 \longrightarrow Ar \cdot N_2[I] \longrightarrow Ar \cdot I + N_2.$$

With the other halogens a catalyst must be used; for fluorination, as we have seen, the diazopiperidide $ArN_2 \cdot NHC_5H_{10}$ can be made and broken up by concentrated HF, or still better the borofluoride can be decomposed by heat:

$$Ar \cdot N_2[BF_4] \Longrightarrow Ar \cdot F + N_2 + BF_3.$$

With chlorine or bromine the reaction can be carried out by Sandmeyer's method with cuprous halide or by the similar Gattermann method, using (in presence of the hydrogen halide) copper powder.

Physical Properties of the Organic Chlorides, Bromides, and Iodides

These halides, like the fluorides, are typical covalent non-associated compounds. Their boiling-points (see Table of boiling- and melting-points on next page) rise with the atomic weight of the halogen; according to Klemm[573] the average differences between the boiling-points are:

RH—RF	RF—RCl	RCl—RBr	RBr—RI
ca. 0°	−50°	−20°	ca.—30°

Among the dihalides the relative positions of the two halogen atoms has a considerable influence on the boiling-point; thus the ethylidene dihalides always have lower boiling-points than their ethylene isomers, the differences being (see table) $-F_2$ 34·7°, $-Cl_2$ 26·4°, $-Br_2$ 22·5°.

From the examination of the freezing-point curves of the binary systems, Klemm concludes that their mutual solubility is in the order

$$R \cdot H > R \cdot F > R \cdot Cl > R \cdot Br > R \cdot I$$

but that the gap between $R \cdot F$ and $R \cdot Cl$ is much greater than that between $R \cdot Cl$ and $R \cdot Br$, or $R \cdot Br$ and $R \cdot I$, and is about as large as that between

---

[572] W. Taylor, *J.C.S.* 1937, 304.

[573] L. Klemm, W. Klemm, and G. Schiemann, *Z. physikal. Chem.* 1933, 165, 379.

the fluoride and the parent hydrocarbon.[574] The percentage mutual solubilities of ethylene dibromide and water have been found to be[575] $C_2H_4Br_2$ in water 0·25/0°, 0·78/75°; water in $C_2H_4Br_2$ 0·35/0°, 1·86/75°.

Boiling- [and melting-] points of Organic Halides

X =	F	Cl	Br	I
CH_3X	− 78·5°	− 24·2°	+ 4·5°	42·5°
	[141·8°]	[− 97·7°]		[− 66·5°]
C_2H_5X	− 37·7°	+ 13·1°	38·4°	72·3°
	[−143·2°]	[−138·7°]	[119°]	[−110·9°]
$n\text{-}C_3H_7X$	− 2·5°	46°	70·5°	101·9°
	[−159°]	[−122·8°]	[−199·9°]	[−101·4°]
C_6H_5X	86·5°	132·0°	156·2°	188·6°
	[− 41°]	[− 45°]	[− 30·6°]	[− 31°]
CH_2X_2	− 51·6°	+ 41·6°	+ 98°	169°
		[− 96·7°]		
$CH_3 \cdot CHX_2$	− 24·7°	+ 57·3°	109°	178°
		[− 96·7°]		
$CH_2X \cdot CH_2X$	+ 10·0	83·7°	131·5°	
		[− 35·5°]	[+ 10·0°]	[81·2°]
CHX_3	− 82·2°	+ 61·3°	147°	(extrap. 218°)
		[− 63·5°]	[+ 7·5°]	[121°]
CX_4	−128°	76·6°	190°	[171°]
	[−184°]	[− 23°]	[+ 93·7°]	

Electron diffraction measurements show[576] that in chloro- and 1,1-dichloro-cyclopropane the C—Cl link forms an angle of $56 \pm 2°$ with the plane of the ring; the distances are normal.

The well known effect of the halogens in raising the dissociation constants of organic acids is shown by the following figures[577]; the first two sets are the classical (Ostwald) values; the last (benzoic acids) are the thermodynamic, which, however, are only a few per cent. smaller than the classical.

Values of K (class.) $\times 10^5$

X =	H	F	Cl	Br	I
$X \cdot CH_2 \cdot COOH$	1·82	217	155	138	75

Effect of distance along the chain: $10^5 K$ (class.) for $Cl \cdot (CH_2)_n COOH$:

$n =$	1	2	3	4	[No Cl.]
$10^5 K$	155	8·5	ca. 3·0	ca. 2·0	[1·8]

[574] Much the same is true of the halogen ions. H. G. Grimm has shown (see Geiger-Scheel, *Handbuch*, Bd. xxiv (1927), p. 58) that among the salt halides the chloride and bromide always give a continuous series of solid solutions, the bromide and iodide nearly always, but the fluoride and the chloride very seldom.

[575] M. E. Schostakovski and I. G. Drushinin, *J. Gen. Chem. Russ.* 1942, **12**, 42.

[576] J. M. O'Gorman and V. Schomaker, *J.A.C.S.* 1946, **68**, 1138.

[577] Quoted from Watson, *Modern Theories*, pp. 36, 207.

Substituted benzoic acids: $K \times 10^5$ thermodyn.

	H	F	Cl	Br	I
Ortho . . .	6·27	54·1	114·0	140·0	137·1
Meta . . .	6·27	13·65	14·8	15·4	14·1
Para . . .	6·27	7·22	10·5	10·7	..

Dipole Moments

The dipole moments of the C—hal links have an obvious bearing on such questions as back co-ordination and reactivity. If we confine ourselves to the monohalogen derivatives of the hydrocarbons we can be sure that the moment of the molecule is very nearly that of the C—hal link it contains. The following are some values.

Dipole Moments (values in $D = 10^{-18}$ E.S.U.)

	F	Cl	Br	I
CH_3 . . .	1·82	1·87	1·80	1·64
C_2H_5 . . .	..	2·05	2·01	1·87
$n—C_3H_7$ . . .	..	2·10	2·13	2·01
$n—C_4H_9$ . . .	..	2·11	2·15	2·08
C_6H_5 . . .	1·57	1·56	1·52	1·34
$\alpha \cdot C_{10}H_7$ . . .	1·42	1·50	1·48	1·43
$\beta \cdot C_{10}H_7$ . . .	1·49	1·57	1·69	1·56

1,2,3-trichlorobenzene 2·31: pentachlorobenzene 0·87.[578]

Radioactive Exchange in Organic Halides

The conditions of exchange of halogen atoms with free halogens, with halogen ions, and with inorganic halides have been examined by the use of radioactive isotopes. The reaction between alkyl bromides and free bromine,[579-80] or alkyl iodides and iodide ion,[581] is bimolecular, with a heat of activation of about 20 k.cals. The rate is much greater in anhydrous than in aqueous acetone,[579] and increases with the size of the alkyl.[581] See further references [582-5].

With aluminium bromide the exchanges are much quicker, the heat of activation being about 11 k.cals.,[586-7] and alkyl bromides react much more rapidly than aryl; $SnBr_4$ and $SbBr_3$ (which have complete octets) exchange much more slowly than aluminium bromide.

[578] J. A. A. Ketelaar, *Rec. Trav.* 1940, **59**, 757.
[579] L. J. Le Roux and S. Sugden, *J.C.S.* 1939, 1279.
[580] G. A. Elliott and S. Sugden, ib. 1836.
[581] H. A. McKay, *J.A.C.S.* 1943, **65**, 702.
[582] W. Koskoski, H. Thomas, and R. D. Fowler, ib. 1941, **63**, 2451.
[583] L. C. Bateman and E. D. Hughes, *J.C.S.* 1937, 1187.
[584] F. Juliusburger, B. Topley, and J. Weiss, *J. Chem. Phys.* 1935, **3**, 437.
[585] D. E. Hull, C. H. Shiflett, and S. C. Lind, *J.A.C.S.* 1936, **58**, 535, 1822.
[586] N. Breshneva, S. Roginski, and A. Schilinski, *J. Phys.-Chem. Russ.* 1937, **9**, 752; **10**, 367.
[587] G. B. Kistiakowsky and J. R. van Wazer, *J.A.C.S.* 1943, **65**, 1829.

Chemical Properties

In their general chemical activity the organic halides may be divided into three classes, which, in the order of increasing reactivity, are:

1. Aryl halides, and vinyl compounds, with the group C=C—hal.
2. Alkyl halides.
3. Acyl halides.

1. The simple aryl halides can scarcely be made to lose their halogen to anything less active than sodium. The presence, however, of negative groups like a halogen atom or NO_2 in the ortho or para (but not meta) position makes the halogen more mobile, until finally with three nitro-groups in the ortho and para positions we get picryl chloride, which behaves like an acyl chloride, and loses its chlorine to water, giving picric acid, and to ammonia, giving picramide.

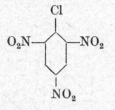

The very similar stability of compounds like the vinyl halides

$$CH_2=CH \cdot hal,$$

in which the halogen is again joined to a doubly linked carbon, is clearly due to the same cause as the stability of the aryl halides. This strengthening of the link of halogen to carbon must be a result of resonance between the ordinary structure and one with a double link from the halogen to the carbon C≤hal. For this view, as we have seen, there is evidence of very various kinds, such as the interatomic distances in the halides of the fourth group elements (IV. 606), the dipole moments or the aryl halides quoted above, and the force constants of such compounds as tetrachloroethylene.

2. *Alkyl Halides.* Here the removal of the halogen is much easier. It can lead to (*a*) the formation of free alkyls, usually dimerizing to R·R; (*b*) the loss of HX (giving C=C); (*c*) the replacement by other halogens (as in R·Cl+KI→R·I); or (*d*) combination with amines to R_4NX; or replacement by hydrolysis, usually (*e*) to give R·OH+HX, but sometimes (*f*) R·H+HOX.

The removal of halogen (*a*, *b*) can be effected thermally, photochemically, or by the action of alkali metals (as in the Wurtz-Fittig synthesis). The thermal reaction goes, for example, with ethyl bromide at 395.[589] It is of the first order and probably begins with simple dissociation into alkyl+ halogen atoms; the ultimate product is mainly ethylene and hydrogen bromide, with some butane. Photochemically the alkyl iodides are broken

[588] F. Fairbrother, *J.C.S.* 1941, 293.
[589] P. Fugassi and F. Daniels, *J.A.C.S.* 1938, **60**, 771.

up by radiation of wave-length from 2,500 to 2,000 A,[590] in the same way as by heat (to alkyls and halogens), as the spectrum shows; the ultimate products are paraffins and olefines.

The action of alkali metals was investigated by Polyani et al.,[591] who allowed a very dilute stream of sodium vapour to diffuse into the vapour of the halide, and measured the rate at which the sodium disappeared by means of its absorption spectrum; they could thus determine the number of collisions needed to decompose one organic molecule; this was for the various halides:

10^6	10^4	50	1
CH_3F	CH_3Cl	CH_3Br	CH_3I
..	C_2H_5Cl	C_2H_5Br	C_2H_5I
..	C_6H_5Cl	C_6H_5Br	C_6H_5I

The results show the expected difference between the different halogens, but none between the alkyl and the aryl halides (contrast this with the action of $AlBr_3$).[588] This is in accordance with the view given above (p. 1187) that the stability of the aryl halides in general is due to back co-ordination (to $>C \leftrightharpoons X$); the positive charge on the carbon will thus be less than in the alkyls, as the dipole moments (alkyl halide ca. 2·0, aryl halide ca. 1·5) indicate. This change will make the saponification, i.e. the attack by a negative hydroxyl ions, more difficult, but not the attack by a neutral sodium atom in Polanyi's experiments.

The relative rates of exchange of halogens when potassium iodide acts on the chlorides $\Phi \cdot C \equiv C(CH_2)_n Cl$ in acetone solution has been found[592] to be:

$$n = 0 \qquad 1 \qquad 2 \qquad 3$$
$$\text{Rate} \quad 0 \qquad 782 \qquad 0·48 \qquad 1·9$$

and also (on a different unit of rate) for

$$\Phi \cdot CH = CH \cdot CH_2 Cl \qquad CH_2 = CH \cdot CH_2 Cl \qquad CH_3 \cdot CH_2 \cdot CH_2 \cdot CH_2 Cl$$
$$1370 \qquad\qquad\qquad 78 \qquad\qquad\qquad 1$$

Reactions with amines. Menschutkin[593] determined the influence of solvents on the rate of the reaction

$$EtI + NEt_3 = [NEt_4]I$$

He found the slowest rate (4·92 moles./sec./litre at 100°) in hexane, and the fastest (6·93 × 10³ in the same units: 1,400 times as fast) in benzyl alcohol. More recently Tronov[594] has shown that in their reactions with pyridine and piperidine, the rates of the halides are in the order $Cl > Br > I$.

[590] W. West and L. Schlessinger, *J.A.C.S.* 1938, **60**, 961.
[591] See M. Polyani, *Atomic Reactions*, 1932, p. 54.
[592] M. J. Murray, *J.A.C.S.* 1938, **60**, 2662.
[593] B. Menschutkin, *Z. physikal. Chem.* 1890, **6**, 41.
[594] B. V. Tronov, *J. Russ. Chem. Phys. Soc.* 1926, **58**, 1278.

A phenyl group or a double link, if it is next to the halogen, greatly slows down the rate, but if it is farther off it increases it. Negative groups such as carboxyl and still more nitro-groups increase the rate.

Hydrolysis by Alkalies to Alcohols: $R \cdot X + MOH = R \cdot OH + MX$. The halogens stand in the same order for this reaction too, but there is a marked distinction between their behaviour with a hydroxyl ion and with an organic base.[595-7] With the hydroxyl ion the rate is very nearly that calculated from the heat of activation and the collision frequency—the 'temperature-independent factor' is nearly 1—while with bases it is much smaller.

With any given type of alkyl halide the change from methyl to ethyl, and from ethyl to propyl and beyond increases the rate of hydrolysis[598]; there is a much greater increase as we pass from a primary to a secondary, and still more to a tertiary halide; thus tertiary butyl halides are extremely reactive,[599] and triphenyl-methyl chloride is hydrolysed even by alcohol. The rate of hydrolysis with some of these compounds is independent of the concentration of the alkali: this is so with benzyl chloride and benzotrichloride,[600] with Φ_2CHCl,[601] with isopropyl and tertiary butyl chloride in 60 per cent. aqueous acetone,[602-4] and in formic acid.[604] This indicates that the slow reaction which is measured is one in which the alkali plays no part, and it might be either a slow ionization of the halide ($R \cdot Cl \rightarrow R^+ + Cl^-$) or a slow reaction of the halide with the solvent. Ingold and Hughes[602-4] adopt the first view, to which, however, it may be objected that we have no direct evidence that ionization (apart from tautomeric change) can ever be slow. Taylor[599,605] takes the second view, and he has shown[605] that in the hydrolysis of tertiary butyl chloride in formic acid the reaction that is measured is actually the formation of tertiary butyl formate, which he has isolated. He assumes that a similar slow reaction occurs with water.

Hydrolysis to Hydride and Hypohalous Acid, $R \cdot X - R \cdot H + HOX$. This alternative form of hydrolysis, which occurs as we have seen with nitrogen halides and other compounds with halogen attached to trivalent nitrogen,[606-7] such as $CH_3 \cdot CO \cdot N\Phi Cl$ and $\Phi \cdot SO_2NHCl$, and with chlorine monoxide Cl_2O, is also found with halogens attached to carbon atoms when these latter also carry certain other negative groups. Carbon tetrachloride

[595] A. E. Moelwyn-Hughes, *Proc. Roy. Soc.* 1938, **164**, 295.
[596] G. H. Grant and C. N. Hinshelwood, *J.C.S.* 1933, **258**, 1351.
[597] C. N. Hinshelwood and A. R. Legard, ib. 1935, 587.
[598] J. A. Mitchell, ib. 1937, 1792.　　　　[599] W. Taylor, ib. 1938, 840.
[600] S. C. J. Olivier and A. P. Weber, *Rec. Trav.* 1934, **53**, 869.
[601] A. M. Ward, *J.C.S.* 1927, 2285.
[602] E. D. Hughes and C. K. Ingold, ib. 1935, 244.
[603] E. D. Hughes, *Trans. Far. Soc.* 1937, **34**, 175.
[604] L. C. Bateman and E. D. Hughes, *J.C.S.* 1937, 1187; see also Hughes *et al.*, ib. 1177, 1183.
[605] W. Taylor, ib. 1852.　　　　[606] F. D. Chattaway, ib. 1905, **87**, 1881.
[607] E. Schmidt, W. v. Knilling, and A. Ascherl, *Ber.* 1926, **59**, 1279.

will not give this reaction, perhaps because the atoms are less crowded, but the tetrabromide is converted into bromoform by alkalies, and the tetraiodide into iodoform even by water.[609]

More effective groups (see ref. [608]) are those containing double links, especially (in order of increasing efficiency) $C=C$, $—CO·OAlk$, $C=O$, and NO_2, as in the compounds tribromophenol bromide (I), dibromomalonic ester (II), dibromodiketohydrinone (III), and bromonitroform (IV):

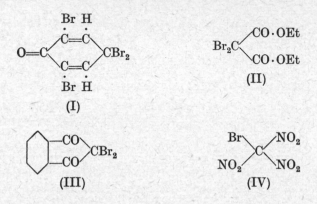

(I)

(II)

(III)

(IV)

An important condition is that the hydrogen which replaces the halogen should be acidic and capable of tautomeric (e.g. keto-enolic) change.

Many of these halides will react directly with unsaturated compounds in water, alcohols, or acids, to add to $C=C$ the groups $R·O$ and halogen, where R = hydrogen, alkyl, or acyl. See later, pp. 1221 sqq.

Other acidic groups are capable of a similar hydrolysis if they replace the halogens in these compounds; thus tetranitromethane when treated with alkali gives nitroform $H·C(NO_2)_3$ and a nitrate, and cyano-trinitro-methane $(NO_2)_3·C·CN$ gives nitroform $H·C(NO_2)_3$ together with cyanic acid or its derivatives.

3. *Acyl Halides* $R—C\overset{O}{\underset{hal.}{\diagdown}}$ These hydrolyse to the free acid+halogen hydride with the greatest ease, the aliphatic more easily than the aromatic, probably because they are more soluble in water. For their thermal decomposition (mostly at 100–400°) see references [610-11].

PERHALIDES

THE perhalides or polyhalides, of which CsI_3 is an example, are really complex halides with a halogen as the central atom of the anion. They have long been known; crystalline salts of organic bases of this type have been made up to the ennea-iodide $M[I_9]$. In aqueous solution we have definite

[608] E. Schmidt, W. v. Knilling, and A. Ascherl, *Ber.* 1926, **59**, 1876.
[609] J. U. Nef, *Ann.* 1899, **308**, 329.
[610] J. H. Simons, T. K. Sloat, and A. C. Meunier, *J.A.C.S.* 1939, **61**, 435.
[611] J. L. Jones, ib. 3284.

evidence of[612] a series of ions of the type $[hal_3]^-$, and probably $[hal_5]^-$; there are indications of still more complex ions such as $[I_7]^-$ and $[I_9]^-$.[613]

The compounds may be divided into (1) salts of HX_3, the largest and best-known class; (2) similar compounds MX_5, MX_7, and MX_9; (3) certain mixed types, like CsI_4, which is dimeric and presumably $Cs_2[I_3 \cdot I_5]$; (4) a peculiar group of salts $M[ICl_4]$, whose properties indicate a different kind of structure from (1) and (2); to this group the salts $M[ICl_3F]$ probably belong.

1. With the $M[X_3]$ salts Werner pointed out[614] that the stability of the complex depends essentially on the heaviest halogen atom it contains; thus, compounds containing at least one iodine atom are much more stable than those without it, and while there are many salts $MICl_2$, and quite a number $MBrCl_2$, there are scarcely any MCl_3. This, as he said, is to be expected if the ion has the structure $[B—A—C]^-$, in which A is performing a different function from B and C, and if for some reason the power of performing it increases with the atomic weight.

Modern work fully confirms this. X-ray examination shows that the B—A—C anion is linear, with the heaviest halogen atom in the middle (e.g. $Cs[Cl—I—Cl]$), and clearly the two outside atoms (B, C) are in the 1-covalent state which is usual for a halogen, with the valency group 6, $\underline{2}$; while the central atom A, on the other hand, has a valency group of 10 $(7+2+1)$ electrons, of which 4 are shared, giving 2,4,$\underline{4}$, i.e. it has an inert pair. Hence, while any halogen atom might occupy a B or C position (the behaviour of fluorine is discussed later) only those halogens can act as central atoms which can have two of their electrons inert. This is not possible with fluorine at all, so far as we know; it is very rare with chlorine, though it does occur as in ClF_3; it is more stable with bromine and much more stable with iodine. Hence the heaviest atom, since it assumes the inert pair state most readily, will always be the central atom. Isomerism should thus be impossible in these trihalide anions, and this agrees with experiment: supposed cases of isomerism[615] have been proved erroneous.[616]

X-ray evidence that the ion is linear, with the heaviest atom in the middle, and the inter-halogen distances those to be expected for ordinary single links, has been obtained for CsI_3, KI_3, $CsIBr_2$, and $CsICl_2$[617]; in more detail for $CsICl_2$ by Wyckoff[618] and by Hassel[619]; for $NH_4[I_3]$,[620-1] $NH_4[Cl \cdot I \cdot Br]$,[622] $Cs[Cl \cdot I \cdot Br]$,[623] $NMe_4[I_3]$,[621] and $NMe_4[ICl_2]$.[624]

[612] R. W. Dodson and R. D. Fowler (*J.A.C.S.* 1939, **61**, 1215), using radioactive halogens, have shown that Br^- ions $+Br_2$, and also I^- ions $+I_2$, exchange in water at room temperature.

[613] H. M. Dawson, *J.C.S.* 1908, **93**, 1308.

[614] *Neuere Anschauungen*, ed. 3, 1913, p. 110.

[615] F. Ephraim, *Ber.* 1917, **50**, 1082.

[616] H. W. Cremer and D. R. Duncan, *J.C.S.* 1931, 1857; ib. 1933, 181; see also C. L. Jackson and I. H. Derby, *Amer. Chem. J.* 1900, **24**, 30.

[617] G. L. Clark and W. Duane, *Proc. Nat. Acad. Wash.* 1923, **9**, 117; *Phys. Rev.* 1923, ii. **21**, 380.

Composition and Stability of Trihalide Ions

F_3 ions are impossible, since fluorine cannot expand its octet and act as a central atom. But though there is no apparent reason why fluorine should not act as one of the outer atoms, it very seldom does so. CsIBrF has been described,[625] made by the action of IBr on dry CsF; it does not appear to have been analysed, but its properties, and the concentration of IBr which it gives to carbon tetrachloride, seem probable. Otherwise the only fluorine trihalides known are a series of salts of $H[ICl_3F]$, but these probably have structures analogous to that of $M[ICl_4]$, and are described along with the latter (p. 1198).

The other trihalide ions are of the types $[ClB_2]$, $[BrB_2]$, and $[IB_2]$, where B is a halogen atom not heavier than the central atom.

The first, therefore, can only be $[Cl_3]$. Of this two salts have been described (made by treating the simple chlorides with chlorine), the trimethyl sulphonium salt $Me_3S[Cl_3]$, which, however, seems doubtful,[626] and the tetramethyl ammonium salt $Me_4N[Cl_3]$,[627] which loses chlorine rapidly in air. Solids of this type are evidently very unstable. The existence of the $[Cl_3]$ ion in solution has, however, been established[628] from the effect of hydrogen chloride on the solubility of chlorine in water, the effect of the hydrogen ion being eliminated by experiments with sulphuric acid. The value found for the dissociation constant

$$K = \frac{[Cl_3^-]}{[Cl^-]\cdot[Cl_2]}$$

was 0·01 at 25°. For an estimate of the rate of formation of $[Cl_3]$ ions ($> 4 \times 10^5$ in litres, moles, minutes) see reference [629].

All the trihalide ions that can be formed by chlorine, bromine, and iodine have been shown to be formed, not only in the solid state but also in solution: the evidence is based on the freezing-points, conductivity, solubility of the halogen, partition with non-ionizing liquids, etc. The free acids must exist in solution, and are shown to be strong electrolytes, though they have never been isolated.[630] It was shown[631] that halogens will never combine with hydrogen halide in the gaseous state to give the

[618] R. W. G. Wyckoff, *J.A.C.S.* 1920, **42**, 1100.

[619] O. Hassel, *Tidskr. Kemi Bergvesen*, 1931, **11**, 92.

[620] R. C. L. Mooney, *Z. Krist.* 1935, **90**, 143.

[621] Id. *Phys. Rev.* 1938, ii. **53**, 851.   [622] Id., ib. 1935, ii. **47**, 807.

[623] R. C. L. Mooney, *Z. Krist.* 1938, **98**, 324.   [624] Id., ib. 1939, **100**, 519.

[625] H. W. Cremer and D. R. Duncan, *J.C.S.* 1931, 2249.

[626] L. Dobbin and O. Masson, *J.C.S.* 1885, **47**, 67.

[627] F. D. Chattaway and G. Hoyle, ib. 1923, **123**, 654.

[628] M. S. Sherrill and E. F. Izard, *J.A.C.S.* 1931, **53**, 1667.

[629] R. S. Halford, *J.A.C.S.* 1940, **62**, 3233.

[630] H. W. Cremer and D. R. Duncan (*J.C.S.* 1931, 1857) obtained from IBr+concentrated HBr a dark-red viscous liquid of composition $HIBr_2$, 1·02 H_2O (6 per cent. water); and from ICl+concentrated HCl a dark-brown liquid of composition $HICl_2$, 2·76 H_2O; neither would freeze in ice and salt.

[631] M. Trautz and F. A. Henglein, *Z. anorg. Chem.* 1920, **110**, 279.

perhalide acid, any more than SiF_4 will with HF, owing to there being no water to hydrate the hydrogen ion.

By various methods (see refs. [630-9] above) the stability of most of these ions (all except $Br \cdot Cl_2$) in water has been measured. The values of

$$K = \frac{[AB_2^-]}{[A^-] \cdot [B_2]}$$

at or near 25° are given in the table: for convenience the linking atom of the complex is given first.

Ion	K	Ref.	Ion	K	Ref.
$Cl \cdot Cl_2$	0·01	628	$I \cdot ICl$	2·10	637
$Br \cdot Br_2$	17·8	635, 639	$I \cdot Br_2$	370	632
$Br \cdot BrCl$	1·39	636	$I \cdot BrCl$	43·5	632
$I \cdot I_2$	725	633–4	$I \cdot Cl_2$	167	632
$I \cdot IBr$	11·9	637			

From these figures the great importance of the central atom is obvious. The geometrical means of the constants for the ions of which the heaviest atom is chlorine, bromine, and iodine are 0·01, 4·97, and 60·7. For the three pure trihalides the differences of the relative values are even greater: the ratios for $Cl_3^- : Br_3^- : I_3^-$ are 1 : 1,780 : 72,500.

In each class the stability seems to be greater (1) the nearer the terminal atoms are in mass to the central atom, and (2) the nearer they are to one another. Thus we have:

(1)　$I \cdot I_2$ 725; $I \cdot Br_2$ 370; $I \cdot Cl_2$ 167.

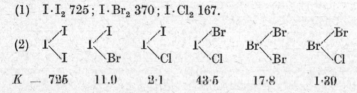

(2)

$K -$　725　　11·9　　2·1　　43·5　　17·8　　1·39

[632] J. H. Faull, *J.A.C.S.* 1934, **56**, 522. A variety of methods were used, mainly partition with CCl_4.

[633] Grinnell Jones and B. B. Kaplan, ib. 1928, **50**, 1854. Mainly by E.M.F., and by partition with pure water through air (Grinnell Jones's 'equilibrator'); they find 715 at 25° and 1,390 at 0°. Gmelin, *Iod*, p. 426, quotes 7 values of K for I_3^- at 25°, of which the mean gives $K = 725$, which is accepted in the table.

[634] J. S. Carter, *J.C.S.* 1928, 2227.

[635] G. Jones and M. L. Hartmann, *Trans. Amer. Electrochem. Soc.* 1917, **30**, 323. Similar methods; they find 19·6. P. Job (*C.R.* 1926, **182**, 633; *Ann. Chim.* 1928, [10] **9**, 146), from measurements of the absorption of light, got 28·6.

[636] Mean of the fairly concordant results of A. Jakowkin, *Z. physikal. Chem.* 1896, **20**, 30; E. A. Dancaster, *J.C.S.* 1924, **125**, 2039; P. Ray and P. V. Sarkar, ib. 1922, **121**, 1453.

[637] A. v. Kiss and A. Urmanczy, *Z. anorg. Chem.* 1931, **202**, 189.

[638] Value got at 20° by C. Winther, *Z. physikal. Chem.* 1929, B **3**, 303.

[639] R. O. Griffith, A. McKeown, and A. G. Winn, *Trans. Far. Soc.* 1932, **28**, 101. This value of 17·8 is a mean; the constant is to some extent affected by the ionic strength of the solution. They quote and discuss previous workers' results.

The stability of the solid salts, and their ease of separation, are largely influenced by the nature, and especially the size, as they are fully ionized,[640] of the cation.

The anions being linear with the B···B distance from $1.98\,(Cl_3^-)$ to $2.66\,(I_3^-)$ and hence the length (about 1 atomic diameter more) from 3·8 to 4·8 A.U., the lattice is naturally more stable with large (e.g. organic) cations than with the alkalies, whose ionic diameters are from 1·2 to 2·6 A.U. The perhalides of organic bases are especially numerous. The first perhalide discovered (1819) was strychnine tri-iodide.[641] Others are known of quinoline and isoquinoline[642]; of secondary, tertiary, and quaternary ammonium bases[627]; and of the diazonium bases.[643] In addition to the nitrogenous bases phosphonium, arsonium, stibonium, sulphonium, and even iodonium[644] hydroxides form perhalides, the order of stability being

$$N > P > As > Sb > S.$$

As we saw, one of the two known trichlorides is that of dimethyl sulphonium, and the other that of tetraethyl ammonium.

The inorganic perhalides are relatively few, and are almost, though not quite, confined to the alkali metals (the largest monatomic cations), and to the heaviest and largest among these. Those without iodine (i.e. with a central atom of bromine) are confined to rubidium and caesium, of which the salts MBr_3, MBr_2Cl, and $MBrCl_2$ are known.

The tri-iodides, though they are more stable, are scarcely formed by anything but the largest alkaline ions. Lithium forms no tri-iodide,[655] nor does sodium, though NaI_4, $2\,H_2O$ is known[645] (see later). KI_3, usually regarded as the typical trihalide, is formed at 15°,[646] but at 25° only the hydrated forms (KI_3, H_2O, and $2\,H_2O$ α and β),[647-8*] which break up at 70° into $KI+I_2$.[649] (For the hydration of $KIBr_2$ see ref. [650]) On the other hand, rubidium,[651-2] caesium,[653] and ammonium[654] readily form anhydrous tri-iodides.

* The water no doubt makes the cation up to the necessary size.

[640] A. A. Jakowkin, *Z. physikal. Chem.* 1896, **20**, 34; H. M. Dawson, *J.C.S.* 1901, **79**, 238; M. Le Blanc and A. A. Noyes, *Z. physikal. Chem.* 1890, **6**, 401.

[641] B. Pelletier and J. B. Caventou, *Ann. Chim. Phys.* 1819, [2] **10**, 164.

[642] K. Gleu and W. Jagemann, *J. prakt. Chem.* 1936, [2] **145**, 257.

[643] A. Hantzsch, *Ber.* 1895, **28**, 2754.

[644] M. O. Forster and J. H. Schaeppi, *J.C.S.* 1912, **101**, 382.

[645] G. H. Cheeseman, D. R. Duncan, and I. W. H. Harris, *J.C.S.* 1940, 837.

[646] M. Auméras and A. Ricci, *Bull. Soc. Chim.* 1939, [5] **6**, 849.

[647] T. R. Briggs, K. D. G. Clack, K. H. Ballard, and W. A. Sassaman, *J. Phys. Chem.* 1940, **44**, 350.

[648] N. S. Grace, *J.C.S.* 1931, 594.

[649] T. R. Briggs and W. F. Geigle, *J. Phys. Chem.* 1930, **34**, 2250.

[650] G. H. Cheeseman and J. H. Martin, *J.C.S.* 1932, 586.

[651] T. R. Briggs, G. C. Conrad, C. C. Gregg, and W. H. Reed, *J. Phys. Chem.* 1941, **45**, 614.

[652] T. R. Briggs and E. S. Patterson, ib. 1932, **36**, 2621.

[653] T. R. Briggs and S. S. Hubard, ib. 1941, **45**, 806.

[654] T. R. Briggs, K. H. Ballard, F. R. Alrich, and J. P. Wikswo, ib. 1940, **44**, 325.

The relative stability of the solid perhalides has been determined from their dissociation pressures, and from the concentration of the halogen (pure or mixed) dissolved out from the solid salt by such a solvent as carbon tetrachloride. The stability must depend on the formation constant K of the perhalide ion, the lattice energy of the crystal, and the volatility of the halogen that is split off.

In the decomposition the halogen atom which remains as an ion attached to the cation is always without exception the lightest in the molecule (and hence never, except with the pure perhalides, that which was the central atom). This must, therefore, be the reaction which absorbs the least energy. Now the heats of formation of the pure and mixed halogens (see above, p. 1147) do not differ much, but the lattice energy of the simple halide which remains will obviously be greater (since it depends on the electrostatic attraction) the smaller the halogen ion, as the boiling-points of the simple alkaline halides show.

The dissociation pressures were measured by Ephraim,[656] who found the temperatures at which those of the various rubidium and caesium salts reached 1 atm. He showed that if this temperature on the absolute scale is divided by the square root of the atomic volume of the alkali metal,* the result ($T/\sqrt{v}$), or (which follows from this) T_{Cs}/T_{Rb}, is practically the same for the Rb and Cs salts of any particular trihalide ion.

In the following table t_{760} is the temperature in °C., and T the absolute temperature at which the dissociation pressure is 1 atm.

Temperatures of 1 atm. dissociation of Perhalides

Salt	t_{760}	$T/\sqrt{v}$.	Halogen lost
CsI_3	250° C.	62·5	I_2
RbI_3	192°	62·2	I_2
$CsBr_3$	147·5°	50·2	Br_2
$RbBr_3$	105·5°	50·6	Br_2
CsI_2Br	201·5°	56·7	IBr
$CsIBr_2$	242·5°	61·8	IBr
$RbIBr_2$	186·5°	61·5	IBr
$CsICl_2$	209°	57·6	ICl
$RbICl_2$	151°	56·8	ICl

[MI_2Cl: neither of these salts can be made.]

$CsBr_2Cl$	124°	47·4	Br_2
$RbBr_2Cl$	81°	47·7	Br_2
$CsBrCl_2$	138°	49·1	BrCl
$RbBrCl_2$	93°	49·0	BrCl

The relative stabilities of the different perhalide ions are given by the

* The value he uses for caesium is 70·7.

655 R. Abegg and A. Hamburger, *Z. anorg. Chem.* 1906, **50**, 414. [No LiI_3 seems to have been found since.]
656 F. Ephraim, *Ber.* 1917, **50**, 1069.

ratios of their T temperatures. The rubidium and caesium salts give very similar results; the mean values are:

Salt	Rel. stability T_{salt}/T_{MI_3}	Salt	Rel. stability T_{salt}/T_{MI_3}
MI$_3$	[1]	MBr$_3$	0·81
MIBr$_2$	0·99	MBr$_2$Cl	0·76
MICl$_2$	0·92	MBrCl$_2$	0·79
MI$_2$Br	0·90	..	..

Though the relative differences are so much smaller, the results agree closely with those already given (p. 1193) for the stability of the ions in water.

Cremer and Duncan[657] measured the concentration of halogen produced in CCl$_4$ on leaving it in contact with the solid salt; equilibrium is established in about a day, but actually they were left together for about a week. The following table gives the normality of the CCl$_4$ solution at 25°.

Cation	MBr$_3$	MI$_3$	MI$_2$Br	MIBr$_2$	MIBrF	MIBrCl	MICl$_2$
K	..	..	..	0·0473	..	0·61	0·029
Rb	..	0·0059	..	0·0010	..	0·0108	0·00035
Cs	0·0438	0·00075	0·0155	0·00014	0·01	0·00035	0·00006
NH$_4$	..	0·0120	..	0·00842	..	0·122	0·0057
NH$_3$CH$_3$	..	..	..	0·00134	..	..	..
NH$_2$(CH$_3$)$_2$	..	..	..	0·00004	..	..	..
NH(CH$_3$)$_3$	..	..	..	0·0029	..	..	..
N(CH$_3$)$_4$	..	..	..	0·00004	..	..	..

The relative stability of the perhalide anions is much the same as we got before. That of the unique fluoride CsIBrF is interesting, and comes between those of MI·BrCl and MI·IBr. The order of stability of the cations is Na < K < NH$_4$ < Rb < Cs, being that of the sizes; with the methyl-amines it is NMe$_4$,NH$_2$Me$_2$ > NH$_3$Me > NHMe$_3$ > NH$_4$, increasing on the whole with the size of the ion, while symmetry seems to have as great an effect with the cation as we found it to have with the anion.

Inorganic perhalides other than those of the alkalies have very rarely been isolated in the solid state. Even from the alkaline earths they have not been obtained, presumably owing to their high solubility; Rivett[658] has examined the system BaI$_2$—I$_2$—H$_2$O at −15·8° and +90°, and found over this range the solids BaI$_2$, 7½ H$_2$O, 2 H$_2$O and 1 H$_2$O, but no solid periodides, although the solution obviously contains the ions of one, since when it is saturated with BaI$_2$ and I$_2$ at 90° it contains to 1 kg. water, 8·6 moles (3·36 kg.) of BaI$_2$, and 43 moles (10·9 kg.) of iodine, corresponding to Ba[I$_6$]$_2$. Another possible periodide is the compound TlI$_3$; this does not behave like a thallic compound, and has the colour and instability to

657 H. W. Cremer and D. R. Duncan, *J.C.S.* 1931, 2243.
658 A. C. D. Rivett and J. Packer, ib. 1927, 1342.
659 H. L. Wells and S. L. Penfield, *Am. J. Sci.* 1894, **47**, 463 (*Ber.* 1894, **27**, R 494).

be expected of the thallous salt Tl[I·I₂].[659] Biltz[660] has tried to prepare perhalides by the addition of iodine or other halogens to stannic iodide, and to the tri-iodides of arsenic, antimony, and bismuth, but in vain.

A remarkable characteristic of the perhalides is their strong tendency to solvation; the effect of hydration in stabilizing the perhalides of the lighter alkali metals has been pointed out (p. 1194).

More peculiar are the solvates formed with some organic molecules, especially benzonitrile, nitrobenzene, and benzene itself; oxidizable addenda like alcohols cannot be used, as they reduce the perhalides. If a mixture of the simple iodide and iodine is recrystallized[661] from benzonitrile (not, however, from acetonitrile or benzyl cyanide), solid solvation products may be obtained of the tri-iodides of Na, K, Li, and even hydrogen, with the compositions (and melting-points) which follow (N = $C_6H_5 \cdot CN$): $HI_3, 4N$ (97°); $LiI_3, 4N$ (92·5°); $NaI_3, 2N$ (67°); $KI_3, 2N$ (53°).

Dawson and his colleagues[662-5] find that in nitrobenzene, while potassium iodide is quite insoluble, and iodine only dissolves (at 20°) up to 0·2 moles per litre, each shows a considerable solubility in presence of the other, that of the potassium iodide rising to 1·5-normal, while the iodine can rise to 4 molecules of I_2 to every KI; the results suggest that the lowest iodide that can exist in nitrobenzene solution is KI_3, and the highest KI_7, both of them no doubt solvated. These nitrobenzene solutions have a considerable electrical conductivity,[662] about one-fifth of that of an aqueous solution of potassium iodide of the same normality, although the viscosity of nitrobenzene is almost exactly twice that of water (at 20°, nitrobenzene 0·0198, water 0·0101). The only salt which was isolated was, curiously, the sodium salt, $NaI_5, 2 C_6H_5 \cdot NO_2$, green deliquescent crystals, decomposed by organic solvents such as benzene.

Other alkali metals, and ammonium and substituted ammoniums, can replace the potassium,[655] and nitroaryls and nitroalkyls the nitrobenzene.[654]

2. Higher halides MI_5, MI_7, and MI_9 are known; they are less stable than the trihalides, and nearly all are iodides, though one or two bromides are known. (The types $MICl_4$ and $MICl_3F$ are treated separately later.) They are formed by the alkalies from potassium onwards, and especially (up to $-I_9$) by the tetra-alkyl ammonium salts.[627,679] In solution we have evidence of $[I_7]^-$ and $[I_9]^-$,[599] as well as $[Br_5]^-$[658]; the dissociation of the ions $[Br_5]^-$[635] and $[I_5]^-$[666] has been measured by the methods described above (p. 1193); the values got for

$$K_2 = \frac{[Br_5^-]}{[Br^-] \cdot [Br_2]^2}$$

[660] W. Biltz and K. Jeep, *Z. anorg. Chem.* 1927, **162**, 46.
[661] J. H. Martin, *J.C.S.* 1932, 2640.
[662] H. M. Dawson and R. Gawler, ib. 1902, **81**, 524.
[663] H. M. Dawson, ib. 1904, **85**, 467.
[664] H. M. Dawson and E. E. Goodson, ib. 796.
[665] H. M. Dawson, ib. 1908, **93**, 1308.
[666] J. N. Pearce and W. G. Eversole, *J. Phys. Chem.* 1924, **28**, 245.

at 25° are 40·7 for this pentabromide, and $1·85 \times 10^5$ (4,550 times as great) for the corresponding pentaiodide constant. From the form of the equation these values are not directly comparable with those for the trihalides (p. 1193), but they are with one another, and they show the much greater stability of the iodide.

These higher halides are even more readily solvated than the trihalides. Thus we have KI_7,H_2O[647] and a variety of solid addition compounds with benzene (= B): KI_5, 2 B,[668] KI_7, 2 B,[648] KI_9, 3 B[667]: RbI_7, 2 B[667] and 4 B,[669] RbI_9, 2 B[667]: CsI_9, 3 B[667]; and KI_7 in nitrobenzene solution is shown (p. 1197) to combine with the solvent.

The structures of these higher halide ions must be built up on the type

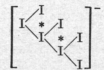

and in similar ways, the starred atoms having a covalency of 3 (2, 2, 6) as they have in $C_6H_5 \cdot ICl_2$; this unusual and so presumably unstable structure explains why these ions nearly always contain iodine.

3. Some of the higher halides have the unexpected composition MX_4 (practically all MI_4): thus we have NaI_4, 2 H_2O,[645] KI_4,O and 2 H_2O,[646] and CsI_4,[653,670-1] with a similar ammonium salt NH_4I_4,HI,H_2O.[654] CsI_4 decomposes at 136° to CsI_3 and iodine, and this at 211° gives CsI and more iodine.[672]

It is obvious that the formulae of these salts must be doubled, and that CsI_4 is Cs_2I_8, probably a crystal aggregate of CsI_3 and CsI_5; this is put beyond doubt by the fact that it is diamagnetic,[673] which is impossible for an 'odd' ion $[I_4]^-$.

4. The salts derived from $HICl_4$ have many peculiarities, which distinguish them from the other pentahalides like $M[I_5]$.

Unlike any of the other types, this gives a free acid $HICl_4$, 4 H_2O, separating in crystals when chlorine is passed into a suspension of iodine in concentrated hydrochloric acid at 0°; it is very unstable even at 0°, but has the same absorption spectrum as the solution of an alkaline salt $MICl_4$.[674]

Again, while the ordinary perhalides are formed only by the heavier

[667] N. S. Grace, *J. Phys. Chem.* 1933, **37**, 347.

[668] J. A. Fialkov and A. B. Polischtschuk, *Ber. Inst. Chem. Akad. Wiss. Ukraine*, 1940, **7**, 95.

[669] H. W. Foote and M. Fleischer, *J. Phys. Chem.* 1940, **44**, 633.

[670] N. Rae, *J.C.S.* 1931, 1579.

[671] T. R. Briggs, J. A. Greenawald, and J. W. Leonard, *J. Phys. Chem.* 1930, **34**, 1951.

[672] T. R. Briggs, ib. 2260.   [673] S. S. Hubard, ib. 1942, **46**, 227.

[674] V. Caglioti, *Atti R. Linc.* 1929, [6] **9**, 563.

[675] Filhol, *J. Pharm.* 1839, **25**, 431, 506.

OXIDES OF CHLO...

WITH the oxides there is muc...
and iodine—especially betwe...
we have hitherto met, and...
three halogens separately.

OXID...

At least eight oxides of...
Cl_2O_3, certainly does not exi...
its existence seems to be req...
Cl_2O and ClO_2; two more, $Cl...$
pair (like NO_2 and N_2O_4); a...
important properties of the...

	Colour	M...
Cl_2O	Brown	—
[ClO	..	
ClO_2	Yellow-green	
$ClO_3 \rightleftharpoons Cl_2O_6$	Brown	+
Cl_2O_7	Colourless	—
ClO_4 ?	Colourless	

a...

These oxides are all, so fa...
quite all of them when pre...
explosive.

Chlo...

This is the anhydride of...
behaviour. It can be made...
with anhydrous calcium nit...
of chlorine on a solution of...

KClO...

or by the action of chlorine...
that the reversible hydroly...
hypochlorite is carried to co...
forming the insoluble and...

HgC...
hgClO...

[687] See C. F. Goodeve...
[688] From Bichowski...
[689] C. F. Goodeve an...

alkali metals, these salts are formed by all of them: $CsICl_4$, $RbICl_4$,[676-7] $KICl_4$,[675] $NaICl_4$, 0 and 2 H_2O,[677,682] $LiICl_4$, 4 H_2O.[677] But as with the trihalides the salts with the smallest cations (here Li and Na), are much less stable in air than the others.

The trihalides, as we have seen, rarely have cations of a valency greater than 1. But a whole series[678] of divalent metallic cations form tetra chloroiodides, though trivalent metals, such as Al, Fe′′′, Cr′′′, and Bi will not do so. The divalent salts are all of the type $M''[ICl_4]_2$, 8 H_2O; many of them are fairly stable.[682-3] They are formed by Co′′, Ni′′, Mn′′ (the stablest of the series), Zn, Be (very hygroscopic and extremely unstable), Mg, Ca, Sr; the last three are all fairly stable; they are all to some extent dissociated into their components in solution, and as ICl_3 is hydrolysed by pure water to iodic acid, the solution must be acidified with HCl when the iodate of the metal in question is insoluble, or this will be precipitated. The instability of the Be salt shows that in these compounds also the stability is affected by the size of the cation.

This is also indicated by the large number of salts of this type which are formed by organic bases[679-81]; they are easily made by adding iodine to a solution of the base in concentrated hydrochloric acid, and passing in chlorine. The golden-yellow salts are all fairly soluble in water and stable in presence of a solution of ICl_3 in HCl. They melt sharply with decomposition; they are stable when dry. They are formed by a very great variety of bases: mono- to tetra-alkyl ammonium, guanidine (m. pt. 163°: very stable), pyridine (235°), quinoline (195°), and numerous methyl-, chloro-, and nitro-derivatives of pyridine and quinoline, caffeine, piperidine ($C_5H_{10}NH$, $HICl_4$, H_2O, dimorphic, m. pt. 102°), and many others.

The diazonium salts[681] are remarkably stable, the cations as well as the anions. They melt sharply (e.g. benzene-diazonium 88°, *p*-toluene 95°, tribromobenzene 135°) with decomposition, but only occasionally with explosion; they can be kept indefinitely in sealed tubes or in an atmosphere of chlorine. They give the usual diazo-reactions, and concentrated aqueous ammonia converts them into the azide and nitrogen iodide.

The existence of a free acid in the crystalline state: of salts of the lightest alkali metals: of a stable series of salts of divalent metals: all distinguish the tetrachloroiodides sharply from the other perhalides. It is further remarkable that no tetrabromoiodides have been made. Chattaway and Hoyle[679] made a series of perhalides of bases, with any odd number of halogen atoms in the anion up to 9; these included the tetrachloroiodides

[676] H. L. Wells and S. L. Penfield, *Am. J. Sci.* 1892, [3] **43**, 17; *Z. anorg. Chem.* 1892, **1**, 85.

[677] H. L. Wells, H. L. Wheeler, and S. L. Penfield, ib. [3] **44**, 42; ib. 1893, **2**, 255.

[678] R. F. Weinland and Fr. Schlegelmilch, ib. 1902, **30**, 134 (C. 02. i. 845).

[679] F. D. Chattaway and G. Hoyle, *J.C.S.* 1923, **123**, 654.

[680] F. D. Chattaway and F. L. Garton, ib. 1924, **125**, 183.

[681] F. D. Chattaway, F. L. Garton, and G. D. Parkes, ib. 1980.

[682] M. G. do Celis and E. Moles, *Anal. Fis. Quim.* 1932, **30**, 540.

[683] M. G. de Celis, ib. 1935, **33**, 203.

and three other p[...]
mixed halogens of[...]
structure suggeste[...]

the replacement of[...]
an increase in stab[...]

This question h[...]
crystal structure c[...]
four chlorine aton[...]
2·34±0·03 A. (no[...]
(1) that this is the[...]
electrons having 4[...]
agrees with the ge[...]
the total number[...]
unshared pairs be[...]
unoccupied).

To the same ty[...]
Rb[ICl₃F], meltin[...]
action of chlorine c[...]
are orange-yellow.[...]
they both begin to[...]
to exist.

A similar series[...]
the action of ICl₃[...]
and the approxima[...]
Et₂NH (85°); Me[...]
310°); pyridine (m[...]
seen, the tetramet[...]
and the methylan[...]
than the alkaline[...]

The extreme ra[...]
stability of these[...]
M[ICl₄] type.

[684] R. C. L. Moon[...]
[685] H. S. Booth, C[...]
[686] H. S. Booth, V[...]

It is commonly prepared by passing chlorine gas over dry mercuric oxide, which is often mixed with sand to moderate the reaction. The gas is condensed in a freezing mixture not below $-20°$, so that the excess of chlorine passes on.[690-1] Cork and rubber must be avoided, as they cause explosive decomposition.

Chlorine monoxide is a brownish gas, looking like nitrogen peroxide; the liquid is dark brown. It melts at $-116°$ and boils at $+2°$; the Trouton constant is 22·5.[692] For the results of electron diffraction see p. 1205. The vapour density of the gas is normal. It attacks the eyes and the mucous membrane. It is highly explosive; the gas explodes on heating, and sometimes at the ordinary temperature; the liquid is liable to explode on pouring from one vessel to another, or when it is allowed to boil. It is a violent oxidizing agent, converting most metals into a mixture of their oxides and chlorides. It reacts with water[693-4] to give HOCl, or in presence of HCl chlorine and water.

The decomposition of Cl_2O, both photochemical and thermal, has been the subject of much investigation. The thermal decomposition[691,695-8] can be examined at 100–140°. There is an induction period followed by an essentially second-order reaction; Hinshelwood[698] concludes that the very complex reaction must include at least two consecutive reactions with about the same heat of activation (about 21 k.cals.). It is remarkable that the reaction has the same velocity, with the same temperature coefficient and apparently the same mechanism, in CCl_4 as in the gas.[697]

The photochemical decomposition of Cl_2O has been examined by Bowen,[699] Bodenstein,[700] and Schumacher.[701-2] Bowen showed that the effective light was that absorbed by chlorine (of which some is practically always present as an impurity) and that for every quantum absorbed 2 molecules of the Cl_2O are decomposed. His results were confirmed by Bodenstein. Schumacher pointed out that the results can be explained by a series of reactions

$$1.\ Cl_2 + h\nu = 2\ Cl$$
$$2.\ Cl + Cl_2O = Cl_2 + ClO$$
$$3.\ 2\ ClO = Cl_2 + O_2$$

The intermediate compound ClO has never been isolated, but the assump-

[690] M. Bodenstein and G. Kistiakowski, *Z. physikal. Chem.* 1925, **116**, 373.
[691] C. N. Hinshelwood and C. R. Pritchard, *J.C.S.* 1923, **123**, 2730.
[692] C. F. Goodeve, ib. 1930, 2733.
[693] C. H. Secoy and G. H. Cady, *J.A.C.S.* 1940, **62**, 1036.
[694] W. A. Roth, *Z. physikal. Chem.* 1942, **191**, 248.
[695] C. N. Hinshelwood and J. Hughes, *J.C.S.* 1924, **125**, 1841.
[696] J. J. Beaver and G. Stieger, ib. 1931, B **12**, 93.
[697] E. A. Moelwyn-Hughes and C. N. Hinshelwood, *Proc. Roy. Soc.* 1931, **131**, 177.
[698] C. N. Hinshelwood, *Gas Reactions*, ed. 3, p. 87.
[699] E. J. Bowen, *J.C.S.* 1923, **123**, 2328.
[700] M. Bodenstein and G. Kistiakowski, *Z. physikal. Chem.* 1925, **116**, 371.
[701] H. J. Schumacher and C. Wagner, ib. 1929, B **5**, 199.
[702] W. Finkelnburg, H. J. Schumacher, and G. Stieger, ib. 1931, B **15**, 127.

tion of its existence enables us to explain not only this reaction, and the chlorine sensitized photodecomposition of ozone, but also that of ClO_2; the question is further discussed below under that compound.

[*Chlorine Sesquioxide*, Cl_2O_3

This anhydride of chlorous acid does not really exist; the substance that was taken for it, which is formed by the reduction of potassium chlorate in presence of acid, or by the action of chlorine on silver chlorate, was shown[703-4] to be a mixture of ClO_2 and oxygen.]

Chlorine Dioxide, ClO_2

This was first obtained by Chenevix in 1802, by the action of H_2SO_4 on $KClO_3$; when so made it contains both free chlorine and free oxygen. It is highly endothermic ($-23\cdot5$ k.cals.) and can only be made by the reduction of chlorine in a higher state of oxidation, commonly the chlorate. Chloric acid when treated with concentrated H_2SO_4 breaks up mainly according to the equation

$$3\ HClO_3 \xrightarrow{\ H_2SO_4\ } 2\ ClO_2 + HClO_4 + H_2O$$

It is also formed (along with CO_2) when chloric acid is reduced with oxalic. It is usually prepared by the action of concentrated H_2SO_4 on $KClO_3$; the two are gently warmed, and the evolved gas is condensed in such a way that the Cl_2 and O_2 can pass on. For details of its preparation see reference [705].

Chlorine dioxide is an orange-yellow gas which liquefies at $+11°$ to a reddish-orange liquid, and freezes at $-59°$ to crystals looking like potassium dichromate. As would be expected of an 'odd molecule' it is paramagnetic.[706]

The vapour density of the gas is normal, and there are no signs of its associating to form 'even' molecules in the liquid state or in solution. The surface tension of the liquid has the temperature coefficient required on the Ramsay-Shields theory for a non-associated liquid.[707] The freezing-point of the aqueous solution indicates that the solute is not associated, and the partition between water and CCl_4 is practically independent of the concentration (C_{CCl_4}/C_{H_2O} is $1\cdot2$ at $0°$, and $1\cdot64$ at $25°$) which shows that it is monomeric in CCl_4 as well.[708]

Chlorine dioxide either as a gas or as a liquid explodes violently on the smallest provocation. In the dark its solution in carbon tetrachloride usually decomposes slowly, but if it is quite free from Cl_2O (traces of which can be removed by treatment with baryta) it remains unchanged for a

[703] F. E. King and J. R. Partington, *J.C.S.* 1926, 926.
[704] C. F. Goodeve and F. D. Richardson, *C.R.* 1937, **205**, 416.
[705] E. Schmidt *et al.*, *Ber.* 1921, **54**, 1861; 1923, **56**, 25.
[706] N. W. Taylor and G. N. Lewis, *Proc. Nat. Acad. Wash.* 1925, **11**, 456; N. W. Taylor, *J.A.C.S.* 1926, **48**, 855.
[707] C. H. Cheeseman, *J.C.S.* 1930, 35.
[708] W. Bray, *Z. physikal. Chem.* 1906, **54**, 583.

long time.[709] It is acted on by light, giving not only chlorine and oxygen, but also Cl_2O_6 and apparently Cl_2O_7. Its absorption spectrum[710] shows that it is first broken up into ClO and oxygen; the positions of the bands make it possible to calculate the energy of the linkage, and lead to the unusual result that more energy is required to remove the first oxygen than the second, the stages being

$$ClO_2 \xrightarrow[66 \cdot 6 \text{ k.cals.}]{} ClO \xrightarrow[57 \cdot 0 \text{ k.cals.}]{} Cl + O.$$

See further p. 1205.

The further course of the photodecomposition depends on the nature of the medium. In the gas, and in CCl_4,[711] the ClO reacts with itself and with the ClO_2, the products in CCl_4 being mainly Cl_2+O_2, and in the gas Cl_2O_6 and perhaps Cl_2O_7 as well.[712] In water[713] the ClO does not react with the excess of ClO_2, presumably because it is attacked by the water; we may suppose it combines with it to form an (unknown) acid H_2ClO_2, which then reacts further, giving:

$$ClO + H_2O = H_2ClO_2$$
$$H_2ClO_2 + ClO = HCl + HClO_3,$$

which would give a quantitatively accurate explanation of the observed reaction products.

Chlorine dioxide is very soluble in water; it forms a yellow crystalline hydrate, probably $ClO_2,8\ H_2O$, which is stable up to $18°$.[708] The aqueous solution is stable in the dark, and the gas can be expelled from it again. In light it is slowly converted, as we have seen, mainly into $HCl+HClO_3$. With alkalies it forms (but only slowly) a chlorite and a chlorate.

ClO_2 is extremely reactive; it is very easily reduced[708] to chlorous acid $HClO_2$, which itself very easily passes into $HCl+HClO_3$. It reacts with most substances, often explosively. $KMnO_4$ oxidizes it only up to the chlorate stage.

ClO_2 is an 'odd' molecule, and so cannot be given a normal formula. We may write it with two single bonds, as in

in this the chlorine has a valency group of only seven electrons; this defect will be shared with the oxygens, so that the molecule will be a resonance hybrid of the forms

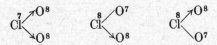

[709] R. Luther and R. Hoffmann, *Z. physikal. Chem.* Bodenstein Festschrift, 1931, 755.

[710] W. Finkelnburg and H. J. Schumacher, ib. 704.

[711] E. J. Bowen, *J.C.S.* 1923, **123**, 1199.

[712] See E. A. Moelwyn-Hughes, *Reactions in Solutions*, Ed. i (1933), p. 66.

[713] E. J. Bowen and W. M. Cheung, *J.C.S.* 1932, 1200.

When one oxygen is split off, the remaining ClO will have its resonance diminished, since now only two forms are possible, $\overset{7}{Cl} \rightarrow O^8$ and $\overset{8}{Cl} - \overset{7}{O}$, and presumably it is this loss of resonance energy which makes the absorption of heat in the change $ClO_2 \rightarrow ClO + O$ (66·6 k.cals.) greater than in $ClO \rightarrow Cl + O$ (57.0 k.cals.).

But from electron diffraction measurements Brockway and Sutton[714-15] find that the Cl—O distance in ClO_2 is only 1·53 A, while in Cl_2O it is 1·68 (theory 1·65 A). This shortening would suggest that there is some resonance with a doubly linked form

$$\overset{9}{Cl}\underset{\searrow O^8}{\overset{\nearrow O^8}{}},$$

since the Cl is not limited to an octet; also the value found for the valency angle in ClO_2 was rather large, though it could not be measured very accurately ($137° \pm 15° : Cl_2O$ $115°$). Some double-link character in ClO seems needed to explain why its heat of formation is 57·0 k.cals., while that of the Cl—O link in Cl_2O is only 49·3.

A singular derivative of ClO_2 is ClO_2F, made by the direct union of ClO_2 with F_2 diluted with N_2 at 0°; it boils at about −6° and melts at about −115°.[716]

Chlorine Trioxide, $ClO_3 \rightleftharpoons Cl_2O_6$

The formation of a brown liquid when ClO_2 is exposed to light had been observed by many people,[717] but the isolation from it of a new oxide of chlorine was the work of Bodenstein and his colleagues.[718-20] It is formed[718] as a brown viscous layer on the walls of the vessel when sunlight or other bright light acts on chlorine and ozonized oxygen (some Cl_2O_7 being produced at the same time).[721] It is best made[720] by allowing ClO_2 to act on ozone, and freezing out the product with ice; this reaction has a very small heat of activation of about 1 or 2 k.cals., which means that about one collision in every 1,000 is fruitful. In this way brown drops are formed, which are a solution of ClO_2 in Cl_2O_6; the ClO_2 can then be distilled off, and the Cl_2O_6 which remains purified by distillation at a very low pressure.

Cl_2O_6 is a dark-red liquid, which solidifies at +3·5° to a solid looking like potassium dichromate.[722] It is the least volatile of the oxides of chlorine; its vapour pressure is 0·31 mm. at 0° C. The boiling-point extrapolated from the vapour-pressure curve is 203°,[723] but even at 0° the

[714] L. O. Brockway, *Proc. Nat. Acad. Sci.* 1933, **19**, 868 (ClO_2).

[715] L. E. Sutton and L. O. Brockway, *J.A.C.S.* 1935, **57**, 473.

[716] H. Schmitz and H. J. Schumacher, *Z. anorg. Chem.* 1942, **249**, 238.

[717] e.g. by E. Millon, *Ann.* 1843, **46**, 312, and E. J. Bowen, *J.C.S.* 1923, **123**, 2330.

[718] M. Bodenstein, P. Harteck, and E. Padelt, *Z. anorg. Chem.* 1925, **147**, 233.

[719] M. Bodenstein and H. J. Schumacher, *Z. physikal. Chem.* 1929, B **5**, 233.

[720] H. J. Schumacher and G. Stieger, *Z. anorg. Chem.* 1929, **184**, 272.

[721] A. C. Byrns and G. K. Rollefson, *J.A.C.S.* 1934, **56**, 2245.

[722] J. Farquharson, C. F. Goodeve, and F. D. Richardson, *Trans. Far. Soc.* 1936, **32**, 790.

[723] C. F. Goodeve and F. D. Richardson, *J.C.S.* 1937, 294.

vapour begins to decompose into $Cl_2 + O_2$ (the heat of activation of this is $11 \cdot 5$ k.cals.[720]).

The molecular weight in the gaseous state is that of ClO_3, since when it is decomposed by heat into Cl_2 and O_2 its volume is found to be doubled (observed increase $2 \cdot 03$, $1 \cdot 97$, $2 \cdot 04$, $1 \cdot 95$[722-3]);

$$2 ClO_3 = Cl_2 + 3 O_2.$$

On the other hand, in the liquid state it is practically entirely polymerized to Cl_2O_6. This is suggested by the very low vapour-pressure, and proved by the fact that the molecular weight has been found cryoscopically in CCl_4 to be only 10 per cent. less than that required for the double molecules (found 153, 156; calc. for Cl_2O_6 167).[719,724] Further, the liquid has been shown to be diamagnetic, though less than Pascal's theory requires, which may be due to its containing a small admixture of the paramagnetic ClO_3.[722]

The substance fumes in air, and soon decomposes, being converted successively into Cl_2O_7, Cl_2O, ClO_2, and ultimately $Cl_2 + O_2$. If it is added to liquid water it explodes (it is always liable to do this), but if the gas is mixed with water vapour and cooled, crystals of the monohydrate of perchloric acid $HClO_4$, H_2O, separate out, the main reaction being

$$Cl_2O_6 + H_2O = HClO_3 + HClO_4.$$

We have no direct evidence as to the structure of these molecules ClO_3 and Cl_2O_6. It seems most probable that ClO_3 is ClO_2 with an extra co-ordinated oxygen, and should be written

$$Cl \overset{\nearrow O}{\underset{\searrow O}{\rightarrow} O},$$

with a septet of electrons on one atom, no doubt shared by resonance between the four; in the bimolecular form it is very likely that the union is between the chlorine atoms, giving

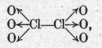

the symmetry of which has been supposed (though it is not easy to say why) to explain why this is the least volatile oxide of chlorine. This structure is also analogous to that of N_2O_4, which shows considerable resemblance to Cl_2O_6 in many ways, especially in its ready interconversion with the monomeric odd-molecule form.

Chlorine Heptoxide, Cl_2O_7

This is the anhydride of perchloric acid, and as such can be made by dehydrating the acid; it is also formed, along with Cl_2O_6, when blue light acts on a mixture of chlorine and ozonized oxygen.[721] It is usually prepared by leaving anhydrous or highly concentrated aqueous perchloric

[724] M. H. Kalina and J. W. T. Spinks, *Canad. J. Res.* 1938, **16**, B 381.

acid in contact with P_2O_5 for a day at $-10°$ or below, and then distilling carefully *in vacuo*; after one such fractionation it can be redistilled at the ordinary pressure.[725-6]

It is a colourless volatile oil (Cl_2O_7 and the doubtful ClO_4 are the only oxides of chlorine which are not coloured); m. pt. $-91·5°$, b. pt. (extrapolated) $+80\pm1°$; Trouton constant $23·4$.[726] It explodes violently under a blow, or in contact with flame or iodine, but on the whole it is the stablest oxide of chlorine, as we should expect from the behaviour of the perchlorates. It has no action in the cold on sulphur or phosphorus, or on wood or paper. With water it is slowly converted into $HClO_4$. It is endothermic ($-63·4$ k.cals.).[727] Its dipole moment in CCl_4 at $20°$ is $0·72\pm0·02$ D.[728] The Raman spectrum indicates that it has two ClO_3 groups joined by an oxygen bridge, with the O angle $128°$.[728]

Chlorine Tetroxide, $(ClO_4)_n$

The existence of this oxide is not certain. Its preparation was claimed by Gomberg[729-30] by the action of iodine on a solution of silver perchlorate in an organic solvent. If the solvent is an aromatic compound such as chloro- or nitro-benzene, the ultimate reaction is of the type

$$C_6H_5X + I_2 + AgClO_4 = C_6H_4XI + HClO_4 + AgI.$$

This reaction was further examined by Birckenbach,[731] who ascribes it to the intermediate formation of $I \cdot ClO_4$. But in anhydrous ether little of the solvent is attacked by the iodine, and Gomberg considers the main reaction to be

$$I_2 + 2 AgClO_4 = 2 AgI + 2 ClO_4.$$

The molecular weight of this compound is unknown, and it has never been isolated, so that the only evidence we have for its existence is the properties of the ethereal solution prepared in the way just described. These, except the oxidation of metals without evolution of hydrogen, and the oxidation of hydrogen iodide (which is denied by Birckenbach) could all be due to perchloric acid.

Until we have more evidence of it, the existence of this oxide must be regarded as very doubtful. If it does exist, its colourlessness seems to make it certain that it cannot be the odd molecule ClO_4, but must be Cl_2O_8.

OXIDES OF BROMINE

Apart from a few false alarms, no oxides of bromine were known until 1928. We now have good evidence of three, a gaseous Br_2O, analogous to

[725] A. Michael and W. T. Conn, *Am Chem. J.* 1900, 23, 445; 1901, 25, 92.
[726] C. F. Goodeve and J. Powney, *J.C.S.* 1932, 2078.
[727] C. F. Goodeve and A. E. L. Marsh, ib. 1937, 1161.
[728] R. Fonteyne, *Natuurwet. Tijds.* 1938, 20, 275.
[729] M. Gomberg, *J.A.C.S.* 1923, 45, 398.
[730] M. Gomberg and H. R. Camrath, *Trans. Far. Soc.* 1934, 30, 24.
[731] L. Birckenbach and J. Goubeau, *Ber.* 1932, 65, 395.

Cl_2O, a solid of the composition Br_3O_8, but of unknown molecular weight, and a recently discovered BrO_2. There is no reason at present to suppose that any other oxide of bromine exists.

Bromine Monoxide, Br_2O

Zintl and Rienäcker[732] showed that if bromine vapour is led over mercuric oxide (which should be precipitated at 50° and dried at 110°) it reacts at temperatures from 50° to 100°, and the product contains up to 4 per cent. of Br_2O, reckoned on the total bromine. The vapours were frozen out, and the product analysed by determining (*a*) the oxidizing power of its solution in alkali, and (*b*) the total bromine present after reduction with SO_2 to the bromide ion.

In 1935 it was found[733-4] that if a solution of bromine in CCl_4 is shaken with mercuric oxide the resulting solution may contain up to 40 per cent. of its bromine in the form of Br_2O.

Bromine monoxide was isolated by Schwarz and Wiele,[735] who made it by warming the dioxide BrO_2 *in vacuo*; it is brown, and melts at $-17\cdot5°$ to a liquid which slowly decomposes even at $-16°$ with evolution of oxygen. In CCl_4 it gives a green solution which is stable below 0°, and the freezing-point of which indicates that it is monomeric, with perhaps slight association. It oxidizes iodine to the pentoxide.

The structure $\begin{matrix} Br \\ Br \end{matrix}\!\!\!\diagdown\!\!\!\diagup O$ is probable from the analogy of the chlorine compound.

Bromine Dioxide, BrO_2

This is made[736] by the action of the electric discharge on a mixture of bromine vapour and oxygen, in a vessel cooled with liquid air; it deposits as a yellow mass on the sides. A yield of 80 per cent. can readily be got. Any ozone formed is removed by reducing the pressure, and then the deposit is warmed to $-30°$ and the excess of bromine sublimed away. This shows that BrO_2 like Br_2O is less volatile than bromine.

Bromine dioxide is an egg-yellow solid; it does not melt, but at about 0° decomposes spontaneously and vigorously to bromine and oxygen; it was analysed in this way (found Br:O $= 1:1\cdot97, 1\cdot98$).

Later work shows[735] that BrO_2 is stable below $-40°$, but slowly decomposes above it. Warm sodium hydroxide gives $NaBrO_3$, $NaBrO_2$, $NaBrO$, and $NaBr$. If it is warmed *in vacuo* it gives the brown Br_2O, along with a colourless solid which may be Br_2O_7, but could not be isolated or further examined.

[732] E. Zintl and G. Rienäcker, *Ber.* 1930, **63**, 1098.

[733] W. Brenschede and H. J. Schumacher, *Z. physikal. Chem.* 1935, B **29**, 356.

[734] Id., *Z. anorg. Chem.* 1936, **226**, 370.

[735] R. Schwarz and H. Wiele, *J. prakt. Chem.* 1939, [ii] **152**, 157.

[736] R. Schwarz and M. Schmeisser, *Ber.* 1937, **70**, 1163.

Tribromine Octoxide, Br_3O_8

This oxide was discovered by Lewis and Schumacher, who found[737] that the kinetics of the decomposition of ozone by bromine required the assumption of an intermediate oxide of bromine, and by evaporating the mixture at low temperatures obtained a solid which apparently was this oxide. Later[738-9] it was examined in more detail. It is formed by the action of ozone on bromine at temperatures from $-5°$ to $+10°$; at $+10°$ the reaction takes 5 to 10 minutes; but unless special precautions are observed the product decomposes, often explosively. The material must be carefully freed from (especially oxidizable) impurities; the ozone must be in the proportion of about $5\ O_3$ to $1\ Br_2$, because in the formation of the compound much of it is converted into oxygen. Above $-80°$ the oxide is only stable in presence of ozone. If the pressure of this is lowered, the deposit vanishes in 2 or 3 minutes, but it can be re-formed by adding more ozone although the reaction is not properly speaking reversible; when the oxide breaks up it does not give ozone but oxygen, and so if the oxide is kept in contact with ozone, this is being continuously decomposed.

Br_3O_8 (no name seems to have been given to it as yet) is dimorphic, with a transition point at $-35°\pm3°$; near this point the change is very slow. The oxide was analysed by decomposing it by heat, and measuring the ratio $Br_2:O_2$ in the product.

In water the oxide gives a colourless solution which contains no bromine ions, but is acidic and oxidizes potassium iodide. Titration with baryta shows that the ratio of hydrogen ions to bromine atoms is $1·34:1$. That of bromine to active oxygen is $1:2·48$. An acid $H_4Br_3O_{10}$ would give very nearly these results (Br$:H^+$ = $1:1·33$; Br: active O = $1:2·5$). Lewis and Schumacher[739] suggest the following series of reactions:

$$Br_3O_8 + 2\ H_2O = \qquad H_4Br_3O_{10}$$
$$H_4Br_3O_{10} \qquad = \qquad 2\ HBrO_3 + H_3BrO_4$$
$$2\ H_2BrO_4 \qquad = HBr + HBrO_3 + H_2O + 2\ O_2$$

which would agree with the observations.

The structure of Br_3O_8 is quite unknown, and as we have no evidence of its molecular weight it should properly be written $(Br_3O_8)_n$, though we have no reason to expect n to be large.

OXIDES OF IODINE

In its oxides, as in many of its compounds, iodine differs more from bromine than bromine does from chlorine, and no oxide of iodine analogous to any oxide of any other halogen has been shown to exist. The oxides of iodine so far as they are known are all solid and practically non-volatile,

[737] B. Lewis and H. J. Schumacher, *Z. physikal. Chem.* 1928, **138**, 462.
[738] Id., *Z. Elektrochem.* 1929, **35**, 651.
[739] Id., *Z. anorg. Chem.* 1929, **182**, 182.

and though some eight have been described, there are only three for which there is satisfactory evidence, I_2O_4, I_4O_9, and I_2O_5.

Derivatives of I_2O are known, such as $[py \cdot I]NO_3$ and $[py \cdot I]_2O$ (see p. 1241). So too, there are derivatives of I_2O_3 such as the acetate $I(OCO \cdot CH_3)_3$. But neither of these oxides has been isolated. The oxides $I_{10}O_{19}$ of Millon[740] and I_6O_{13} of Kämmerer[741] have been shown[743] to be impure I_2O_4. Finally the evidence for I_2O_7, which is given below, is very unsatisfactory.

Iodine Tetroxide, I_2O_4

This can be made[742-4] by the oxidation of iodine with HNO_3, or H_2SO_4[742]; on long heating with H_2SO_4 a solid crust is formed which is probably a sulphate, and which after washing with water, alcohol, and ether leaves behind the tetroxide in 30 per cent. yield.

This substance forms lemon-yellow crystals which do not melt, but decompose above 130° into their elements; it is practically insoluble in all solvents except slowly and with decomposition, and in this respect is in marked contrast to the very hygroscopic I_4O_9. It dissolves slowly in alkali to give a mixture of iodide and iodate:

$$3 I_2O_4 + 6 KOH = KI + 5 KIO_3 + 3 H_2O.$$

When heated with SO_3 or oleum it is partly oxidized to the pentoxide I_2O_5, and partly converted into a sulphate, probably $I_2O_4, 3 SO_3$, a pale-yellow hygroscopic substance, stable below 130°.

As this oxide is neither volatile nor soluble, its molecular weight is unknown, and it should strictly be written $(IO_2)_n$. The non-volatility shows that n must be greater than 1, especially since ClO_2 and BrO_2 are both gases. It is commonly written I_2O_4, partly because this makes it possible to formulate it as a basic iodate of trivalent iodine $(IO)IO_3$. This may be correct, but it does not explain the insolubility; I_4O_9, which is fairly certainly the neutral iodate of trivalent iodine, $I(IO_3)_3$, is very hygroscopic and at once decomposed by water.

I_4O_9: ? Iodine Tri-iodate

This was first made by Ogier in 1878, and examined later by Fichter.[745] It is formed by the action of ozone at the ordinary temperature on iodine, or better on its solution in chloroform. A better method[746-7] is to warm powdered iodic acid with dehydrated ortho-phosphoric acid H_3PO_4; on standing I_4O_9 separates, and oxygen is evolved.

It is a yellow-white solid which begins to evolve iodine at 75°. It is

[740] E. Millon, *Ann. Chim. Phys.* 1844, [iii] **12**, 333.
[741] *J. prakt. Chem.* 1861, **83**, 65.
[742] M. M. P. Muir, *J.C.S.* 1909, **95**, 656.
[743] H. Kappeler, *Ber.* 1911, **44**, 3496.
[744] R. K. Bahl and J. R. Partington, *J.C.S.* 1935, 1258.
[745] F. Fichter and F. Rohner, *Ber.* 1909, **42**, 4093.
[746] F. Fichter and H. Kappeler, *Z. anorg. Chem.* 1915, **91**, 142.
[747] F. Fichter and S. Stern, *Helv. Chim. Acta*, 1928, **11**, 1256.

very hygroscopic; in presence of moisture it deliquesces, turns red or brown, and is ultimately converted into iodine and iodic acid HIO_3. This oxide is almost certainly the iodate of trivalent iodine $I(IO_3)_3$; in its strong attraction for water, and in the way that it is decomposed by it with separation of iodine, it closely resembles the triacetate $I(OCO \cdot CH_3)_3$ of Schutzenberger[748] which in the same way liberates acetic acid. The reactions that occur when the oxide is treated with water are presumably:

$$I(IO_3) + 3\,H_2O = I(OH)_3 + 3\,HIO_3$$
$$3\,I(OH)_3 = HI + 2\,HIO_3 + 3\,H_2O$$
$$HIO_3 + 5\,HI = 3\,I_2 + 3\,H_2O.$$

It seems to be generally assumed that the iodate must be ionized, but there is no particular evidence of this. The whole behaviour of the compound is very like that of boron triacetate $B(OCO \cdot CH_3)_3$, which is similarly hydrolysed by water, though of course the boric acid is stable. An ion I^{+++} would have the unusual structure (core) (18) (4) with two inert pairs, which may occur in $M[ICl_4]$ but is not found elsewhere. See later under the compounds of trivalent iodine.

Iodine Pentoxide, I_2O_5

This is the anhydride of iodic acid and behaves as such, being formed from it by dehydration and reconverted into it by water. Unlike most of the oxides of the halogens (and all the oxides of chlorine) iodine pentoxide is exothermic (+48 k.cals. for I_2O_5). In spite of this, all attempts to make iodine combine with oxygen in presence of any catalysts, at any temperature from 100° to 500°, have failed; though it is probable that the pentoxide is formed by the electric discharge in ozonized oxygen in presence of potassium iodide (Ogier, 1878).

Iodine pentoxide is formed by dehydrating iodic acid at 195°. It can also be made by oxidizing iodine with nitric acid or nitrogen pentoxide; it is formed directly from iodine and N_2O_5 on warming[749] and the reaction goes very rapidly even at 0° in chloroform solution.[750] According to Moles[751] the best method of preparation is to heat iodine with fuming nitric acid at 70–80° under reflux until the mixture goes yellow.

Iodine pentoxide[752-8] is a colourless, odourless, crystalline substance of

[748] P. Schutzenberger, *J. prakt. Chem.* 1863, **88**, 1.

[749] M. Guichard, *C.R.* 1909, **148**, 925; *Ann. Chim. Phys.* 1917, [9] **7**, 28.

[750] H. Eyring and F. Daniels, *J.A.C.S.* 1930, **52**, 1489.

[751] E. Moles and A. P. Vitoria, *Z. physikal. Chem.* 1931, Bodenstein Festschrift, 583.

[752] M. S. Shah and T. M. Oza, *J.C.S.* 1931, 32.

[753] E. Moles and A. P. Vitoria, *An. Fis. Quim.* 1932, **30**, 99.

[754] E. Moles and A. Parts, ib. 1933, **31**, 618.

[755] E. Moles and P. Villan, ib. 1936, **34**, 787.

[756] G. P. Baxter and G. S. Tilley, *J.A.C.S.* 1909, **31**, 205, 207; *Z. anorg. Chem.* 1909, **61**, 299.

[757] L. Clarke and E. K. Bolton, *J.A.C.S.* 1914, **36**, 1902.

[758] A. Gautier, *C.R.* 1898, **126**, 793, 931; 1899, **128**, 487; *Ann. Chim. Phys.* 1901, [7] **22**, 20.

high density $(5 \cdot 28)$[755] which is non-volatile; it can neither be melted nor sublimed without decomposition[756-7]; in the absence of light it does not begin to decompose below $275°$.[751] It is soluble only when it reacts with the solvent. Water converts it into iodic acid, evolving $2 \cdot 1$ k.cals. per HIO_3[753]; it dissolves in nitric acid (see further under iodic acid),[751] from which it crystallizes out as I_2O_5 if the solvent contains more than 50 per cent. HNO_3.[754] It is a strong oxidizing agent, and with oxidizable substances sometimes detonates (H. Davy, 1815).

Iodine pentoxide oxidizes carbon monoxide to the dioxide, being itself reduced to iodine. This reaction goes at the ordinary temperature extremely slowly, but practically to completion; at $65°$ and above it is rapid.[758] This is known as Ditte's reaction (A. Ditte, 1870). It is used (commonly in presence of H_2SO_4) both for the quantitative estimation of carbon monoxide, and also in respirators for its removal from air.[759]

Nitric oxide also reduces iodine pentoxide slowly at $80°$ and quickly at $120°$, giving iodine and the higher oxides of nitrogen.[752]

Iodine Heptoxide, I_2O_7

This compound would be the anhydride of periodic acid. It has been said to occur,[760-1] but it has never been properly characterized, and no recent workers have been able to prepare it, so that the balance of probability is against it.

OXY-ACIDS OF THE HALOGENS

THESE are of four types (X = Cl, Br, I).

1. $HXO = H—O—X$: Hypohalous acid, hypohalites (Cl, Br, I).
2. $HXO_2 = H—O—X—O$: Halous acid, halites. (Cl, ? Br, no I).
3. $HXO_3 = H—O—X\genfrac{}{}{0pt}{}{\nearrow O}{\searrow O}$: Halic acid, halates. (Cl, Br, I).

4. $HXO_4 = H—O—\underset{\downarrow}{\overset{\uparrow}{X}}\to O$: Perhalic acid, perhalates. (Cl, I, no Br).

with O above and below the X.

The structures assigned to the acids above must be combined with doubly linked structures as resonance forms. In addition to these acids there are certain derivative forms, produced from them by hydration (e.g. H_5IO_6) or by condensation (e.g. $M_4I_2O_9$).

Hypohalous Acids, $H—O—X$

These acids, which in the undissociated form obviously have the structure $H—O—X$, occur with all three halogens, and are formed by the action

[759] For full references see Gmelin, *Iod*, 1933, p. 440.
[760] J. Ogier, *C.R.* 1878, **88**, 722.
[761] A. Michael and W. T. Conn, *Am. Chem. J.* 1900, **23**, 446.

of water on the elementary halogen, which leads (at any rate primarily) to a reversible hydrolysis of the type

$$X_2 + H_2O \rightleftharpoons HX + HOX.$$

The three acids show a marked gradation in properties, which is especially clear with the most important of these, the completeness of the hydrolytic reaction by which they are formed, their strength as acids, and the tendency, which is common in varying degrees to all of them, to change over into the halide and the halate. The approximate values of the constants of these three reactions are given below, the temperature being 25° C. unless otherwise stated.

	Chlorine	*Bromine*	*Iodine*
$K_1 = \dfrac{[H^+] \cdot [X^-] \cdot [HOX]}{[X_2]}$	*ca.* 3×10^{-4}	$5 \cdot 8 \times 10^{-9}$	3×10^{-13}
K_2, Classical dissociation constant	$3 \cdot 2 \times 10^{-8}$	2×10^{-9}	3×10^{-11}
K_3 for reaction $3\,HOX \rightarrow 2\,HX + HXO_3$ (relative)	1	100	30,000

Hypochlorous Acid, H—O—Cl

This acid, known only in aqueous solution, is formed by the action of water on chlorine, a reaction which is rapid but not instantaneous, equilibrium being reached at 0° only after some hours; the velocity has been measured by the streaming method of Hartridge and Roughton.[762-3] The rate-determining reaction

$$Cl_2 + OH^- = HOCl + Cl^-$$

has a velocity constant of 5×10^{14} (litre, second) both at $1 \cdot 2°$ and at $17 \cdot 6°$, showing that there is practically no heat of activation. This rate is approximately that of collision. The hydrolysis is reversible; the equilibrium constant,

$$K = \frac{[H^+] \cdot [Cl^-] \cdot [HOCl]}{[Cl_2]}$$

was found by Jakowkin,[764] from the conductivity, and the partition coefficient with CCl_4 to be $1 \cdot 56 \times 10^{-4}$ at 0°, and $10 \cdot 0 \times 10^{-4}$ at 70° (about 3×10^{-4} at 25°). The effect of a change in the concentration of the free chlorine, or of the hydrogen or chlorine ion, was in accordance with the law of mass action. Water saturated with chlorine at 25° under 1 atm. pressure is about 0·06 molar in total chlorine, and about half of this is present as $HCl + HOCl$, the rest being free Cl_2.

[762] E. A. Shilov and S. M. Solodushenkov, *C.R. Acad. Sci. U.S.S.R.* 1936, **3,** 15.
[763] J. Carrell Morris, *J.A.C.S.* 1946, **68,** 1692.
[764] A. A. Jakowkin, *Z. physikal. Chem.* 1899, **29,** 613.

When hypochlorous acid is made in this way, the attainable concentration is sharply limited by the small solubility of chlorine in water; but the yield can be increased if the hydrochloric acid is removed, since this sends the reaction to completion and more chlorine dissolves. This is usually done by adding the insoluble oxide or carbonate of an element which forms a sparingly soluble or sparingly ionized chloride, the commonest being mercuric oxide. Another method is to complete the hydrolysis by adding alkali (i.e. to absorb the chlorine in soda solution or milk of lime), and then acidify and distil; the hypochlorous acid is stable enough to come over mostly unchanged. Thus the mixture of KCl and KOCl may be treated with H_2SO_4 and distilled; or bleaching powder Ca(Cl)OCl may be distilled either in a stream of CO_2[765] (carbonic acid is about 100 times as strong an acid as hypochlorous) or after treatment with boric acid.[766]

The acid can also be made by the action of water on chlorine monoxide Cl_2O, which is accompanied by the evolution of 4 k.cals. of heat per mole HOCl formed.[767] It is also produced by the hydrolysis of compounds with chlorine attached to nitrogen such as NCl_3; this is an example of the effect of co-ordination on the reactivity (see p. 1170).

Hypochlorous acid is a very weak acid, far weaker than acetic. On account partly of this weakness, and partly of its instability and chemical reactivity, the value of the dissociation constant is not certain; but the more recent results are fairly consistent: for the classical dissociation constant multiplied by 10^8 they give 3·5 at 18°,[768] 3·7 at 18–20°,[769] 3·2 at 15°,[770] and 3·16 at 20°[771]; these are supported by the value 3·7 at 17° found earlier by Sand[772]; hence a probable value is 3×10^{-8}, about 1/600 of the strength of acetic acid, and 25 times that of hydrocyanic; this implies that in a decinormal solution of the acid the dissociation is about 1/170 of 1 per cent.

Hypochlorous acid is not measurably associated in water; this is shown by the freezing-points[764]: by the facts[773-4] that the ratio of the concentrations of HOCl in the liquid and the vapour is independent of the total concentration, and[775] that the aqueous solution of HOCl gives the same absorption spectrum as a solution of ethyl hypochlorite in ligroin, but quite different from that of the alkaline solution. Hence the acid must have the simple HOCl structure, since the ester is known to be monomeric.

If a highly concentrated (25 per cent.) aqueous solution of HOCl is

[765] J. W. Mellor, *J.C.S.* 1902, **81**, 1291.
[766] R. L. Taylor and C. Bostock, ib. 1912, **101**, 451.
[767] W. A. Roth, *Z. physikal. Chem.* 1929, **145**, 289.
[768] J. W. Ingham and J. Morrison, *J.C.S.* 1933, 1200.
[769] G. F. Davidson, *Shirley Institute Memoirs*, 1933, **12**, 1.
[770] H. T. S. Britton and E. N. Dodd, *Trans. Far. Soc.* 1933, **29**, 537.
[771] E. A. Schilov, *J.A.C.S.* 1938, **60**, 490.
[772] J. Sand, *Z. physikal. Chem.* 1904, **48**, 610.
[773] F. G. Soper, *J.C.S.* 1924, **125**, 2227.
[774] J. Ourisson and M. Kastner, *Bull. Soc. Chim.* 1939, [v] **6**, 1307.
[775] K. Schaefer, *Z. Elektrochem.* 1915, **21**, 187; *Z. physikal. Chem.* 1919, **93**, 316.

evaporated at very low pressure, pure chlorine monoxide Cl_2O comes off, so that the hydration of the monoxide is to some extent reversible:

$$2\,HClO \rightleftharpoons Cl_2O + H_2O.$$

For the equilibrium constant of this equation:

$$K = \frac{[Cl_2O]}{[HClO]^2}.$$

St. Goldschmidt[776] found the value $9 \cdot 6 \times 10^{-4}$ at $0°$, which shows that in a normal (about 5 per cent.) solution of HOCl the concentration of Cl_2O is only millinormal.

Hypochlorous acid is obviously thermodynamically unstable, though it usually reacts rather slowly, as is shown by its distilling without much decomposition. But it can decompose in two ways:

(1) $2\,HOCl = 2\,HCl + O_2$

(2) $3\,HOCl = 2\,HCl + HClO_3.$

These reactions occur both with the free acid and with its ions, though the latter appear to be the more stable. Both reactions are greatly accelerated by light, which, however,[777] affects only the ions and not the undissociated acid. For further details on the rate of decomposition of hypochlorous acid in water see Pierron.[778]

The first of these reactions makes hypochlorous acid a strong oxidizing agent, and it is to this that chlorine water owes its bleaching power. Hypochlorous acid will oxidize phosphorus, arsenic, antimony, sulphur, selenium, and their hydrides to the corresponding acids, and hydrogen chloride to chlorine, as in the reversal of the hydrolysis of the latter. The reduction of chlorine to hydrogen chloride by hydrogen peroxide is essentially a reaction of hypochlorous acid; for its kinetics see Connick.[779] Innumerable other examples, both inorganic and organic, might be given.

The hypochlorite ion, or a solution of a soluble hypochlorite, is much slower to decompose at the ordinary temperature than the free acid; an aqueous solution of NaOCl is half decomposed in the cold in about 3 years. Nevertheless the equilibrium in the reaction

$$2\,ClO^- = 2\,Cl^- + O_2$$

is so far over to the right-hand side that an immeasurably large pressure of oxygen would be required to shift it perceptibly towards the left. Accordingly this reaction, both with the acid and with its ion, can be greatly accelerated by a variety of catalysts. As with the decomposition of hydrogen peroxide, the evolution of oxygen gas is greatly hastened by the addition of angular fragments such as powdered glass; platinized (but not bright) platinum has the same effect, both on this reaction

[776] *Ber.* 1919, **52**, 753.

[777] A. J. Allmand, P. W. Cunliffe, and R. E. W. Maddison, *J.C.S.* 1925, **127**, 822; 1927, 655.

[778] P. Pierron, *Bull. Soc.* 1943, [v] **10**, 445.

[779] R. E. Connick, *J.A.C.S.* 1947, **69**, 1509.

and also on the formation of chlorate.[780] The separation of oxygen is also much accelerated by the addition of metallic oxides, such as those of cobalt[781] and nickel[782]; these oxides are actually present as higher oxides, into which they are at once converted by the hypochlorite. Sodium hypochlorite can be used for some organic oxidations in place of permanganate.[783]

The formation of chlorate is essentially due to interaction between the ion and the undissociated acid[784]

$$ClO^- + 2\ HOCl = ClO_3^- + 2\ H^+ + 2\ Cl^-$$

with the possible intermediate formation of the chlorite ion ClO_2^-. The velocity being proportional to the square of the concentration of the undissociated acid, in order to prevent it from occurring (which would diminish the bleaching power of the solution), the concentration of HOCl must be as far as possible reduced, by adding a small excess of alkali; thus in a normal solution of NaOCl the concentration of HOCl, due to hydrolysis, is $5 \cdot 2 \times 10^{-4}$: if a $0 \cdot 01$ normal excess of NaOH is added, this concentration of HOCl is reduced to 1/20, and therefore the rate of formation of chlorate to 1/400 of their previous values. The velocity shows the normal increase of $2 \cdot 5$ for $10°$; that is why when the chlorate is being made the Cl_2 is passed into a hot alkaline solution.

Hypochlorous acid and its ion have two characteristic reactions with organic substances, in addition, of course, to that of oxidation; the first, which occurs with saturated compounds, is direct chlorination, and the second is the addition of HO+Cl to the double C=C link to form a chlorhydrin.

The chlorination of phenols by HOCl[785] takes place essentially between the phenoxide ion Ar—O⁻ and undissociated HOCl; hence phenol ethers cannot be chlorinated by HOCl, though they can, readily, by chlorine. The rate of chlorination by HOCl is greater, the greater the ionization of the free phenol.

With unsaturated compounds, especially ethylenic derivatives, the chlorhydrins are formed:

$$C{=}C + HO{-}Cl = \begin{matrix} C{-}C{-}Cl \\ | \\ OH \end{matrix}$$

In accordance with 'Markownikoff's rule' (1875) the hydroxyl attaches itself to the carbon that has least hydrogen[786]; thus propylene gives

[780] E. Müller, *Z. Elektrochem.* 1902, **8**, 429.

[781] O. R. Howell, *Proc. Roy. Soc.* 1923, **104**, 134. See also Moelwyn-Hughes, *Reactions in Solution*, ed. 2, p. 359.

[782] E. Chirnoaga, *J.C.S.* 1926, 1693.

[783] J. Weijlard, *J.A.C.S.* 1945, **67**, 1031.

[784] F. Foerster and F. Jorre, *J. prakt. Chem.* 1899, [2] **59**, 53; F. Foerster, ib. 1901, [2] **63**, 147.

[785] F. G. Soper and G. F. Smith, *J.C.S.* 1926, 1582.

[786] See A. Michael, *J. prakt. Chem.* 1899, [2] **60**, 454; A. Michael and V. L. Leighton, *Ber.* 1906, **39**, 2157.

β-chloro-isopropyl alcohol $CH_3 \cdot CHOH \cdot CH_2Cl$; this reaction has been much used in the terpene series.[787] The hypochlorous acid need not be made beforehand; the hydrocarbon and the chlorine can be passed into water at the same time. This method is now used on a large scale for making ethylene glycol from ethylene.[788] The direct addition of chlorine may occur at the same time, but this can be diminished by adding 0·1 to 1 per cent. of certain catalysts, such as cupric or ferric chloride.[789] For the kinetics of the addition of hypochlorous acid see references [790-1].

Salts of Hypochlorous Acid

The only solid salts of this acid which have been isolated are those of some of the alkali metals (Na, K) and alkaline earths (Ca, Sr, Ba); only those of sodium and calcium have been accurately characterized. Sodium hypochlorite[792] forms a hepta- and a pentahydrate, m. pts. 19° and 45°. The calcium salt is of special interest in relation to bleaching powder (chloride of lime, Chlorkalk), the most technically important derivative of hypochlorous acid. The structure of bleaching powder, which is of course made by the action of chlorine on slaked lime, has long been disputed. Its composition approaches that of $CaCl_2 + Ca(OCl)_2$, but it always contains a certain amount (up to 20 per cent.) of free calcium hydroxide. The original idea that it is a mixture of calcium chloride and hypochlorite was attacked by Odling (1861), who pointed out that it is not hygroscopic, as it should be if it contained $CaCl_2$; it was also shown later that though $CaCl_2$ is soluble in alcohol, it is not extracted by alcohol from bleaching powder. Odling therefore proposed the formula of a double salt $Ca(Cl)OCl$, which has been widely accepted. More recently the question has been investigated in great detail,[793] both by phase-rule investigations and also by X-ray examination of the solid phases. The authors do not find Odling's salt in any form; the only solid phases (between 25° and 40°) are: (1) $Ca(OCl)_2$ 3 aq.; (2) $3 Ca(OCl)_2, 2 Ca(OH)_2, 2 H_2O$; (3) $Ca(OCl)_2, 2 Ca(OH)_2$; (4) $CaCl_2, 6 H_2O$; (5) $CaCl_2, Ca(OH)_2, H_2O$; (6) $CaCl_2, Ca(OH)_2, 12 H_2O$.

In bleaching powder the chloride seems to be present as the non-hygroscopic salt (5), and the hypochlorite probably mainly as a double salt (such as (2) or (3)) with the hydroxide.

Esters of Hypochlorous Acid

These esters are formed very readily, best by the action of chlorine on a cooled solution of the alcohol in about 10 per cent. aqueous sodium

[787] See for example, G. G. Henderson *et al.*, *J.C.S.* 1921, **119**, 1492; 1923, **123**, 1155; 1924, **125**, 102.

[788] For details of the manufacture see *Brit. Chem. Abstr.* 1929, B 805.

[789] E. D. G. Frahm, *Rec. Trav.* 1931, **50**, 261 (*Brit. Chem. Abstr.* 1931, A 598). In this paper the various methods of preparation are discussed.

[790] E. A. Schilov and N. P. Kanzaev, *J. Phys.-Chem. Russ.* 1934, **5**, 654.

[791] E. A. Schilov, S. N. Soloduschenkov, and A. N. Kurakin, ib. 1939, **13**, 759.

[792] M. P. Appleby, *J.C.S.* 1919, **115**, 1107.

[793] C. W. Bunn, L. M. Clark, and I. L. Clifford, *Proc. Roy. Soc.* 1935, **151**, 141.

hydroxide.[795-6] They can also be prepared by the action of alcohol on a concentrated aqueous solution of HOCl,[794] or by passing Cl_2O into the alcohol and then precipitating the liquid ester with water.[794]

They are yellow volatile liquids with a very irritating vapour. Boiling-points: $CH_3 \cdot OCl$ 12°/726 mm.[795]; ethyl 36°/752 mm.; tertiary butyl 79·6°/750 mm.[796] This last is monomeric both in the vapour and by the freezing-point in benzene solution.

The alkyl hypochlorites are unstable, and explode when brought in contact with a flame or exposed to a bright light; in the absence of flame or light they all, except the tertiary compounds (which are much more stable), decompose fairly easily on standing (e.g. EtOCl undergoes 25 per cent. decomposition in ligroin at −15° in 14 hours), mainly to give the aldehyde +HCl. They are less unstable in the complete absence of hydrogen chloride.[800] The first product of the action of chlorine on ethyl alcohol[797] (the ultimate product being of course chloral) is ethyl hypochlorite, which then decomposes further to acetaldehyde. Secondary esters decompose in the same way to give ketones:

$$R \cdot CH_2 \cdot OCl = R \cdot CH{=}O + HCl$$
$$RR_1CH \cdot OCl = RR_1C{=}O + HCl.$$

The tertiary esters, as has been said, are much more stable,[796] no doubt because they cannot undergo a similar decomposition without breaking the carbon chain; if they are heated this change actually occurs, with the production of an alkyl chloride:

$$RR_1R_2C \cdot OCl = RR_1C{=}O + R_2 \cdot Cl.$$

They will react with olefines, alcohols, and phenols to give chlorhydrin esters and ethers.[801]

In general the esters, like the free acid, are strong oxidizing and chlorinating agents. They explode in contact with copper powder, but do not attack carbon in the cold. It was shown by St. Goldschmidt[798] that with unsaturated (ethylene) derivatives they usually behave like the acid, forming the chlorhydrin

the hydrogen being presumably derived from casual moisture. Phenyl acetylene reacts remarkably with the ethyl ester in carbon tetrachloride to give dichloroacetophenone[798-9]:

$$C_6H_5 \cdot C{\equiv}C \cdot H \longrightarrow C_6H_5 \cdot \underset{\underset{O}{\|}}{C}{-}CHCl_2$$

[794] T. Sandmeyer, *Ber.* 1885, **18**, 1767.   [795] Id., ib. 1886, **19**, 859.
[796] F. D. Chattaway and O. G. Backeberg, *J.C.S.* 1923, **123**, 3000.
[797] Id., ib. 1924, **125**, 1097.
[798] S. Goldschmidt, R. Endres, and R. Dirsch, *Ber.* 1925, **58**, 572.
[799] E. L. Jackson, *J.A.C.S.* 1934, **56**, 977.

apparently by addition of 2 HOCl followed by loss of water. See further for the reactions of ethyl hypochlorite Mousseron.[802]

Hypobromous Acid, H—O—Br

This acid is similar in formation, decomposition, and behaviour to hypochlorous acid, but the quantitative differences are of special interest.

Like HOCl, HOBr can be got only in solution, and as it is less stable than its chlorine analogue the solution can never be obtained free from the decomposition products bromic acid and elementary bromine. HOBr is formed by the hydrolysis of bromine, and so is present in bromine water. The composition of this solution is complicated by the presence of the perhalide ions Br_3^- and Br_5^-. The amount of HOBr at equilibrium is far less than that of HOCl. The equilibrium was examined[803-5] by the determination of the electrical conductivity, and of the partition of the free bromine between the solution and another solvent (in one case[805] pure water, separated from the solution by a layer of air). The results are reasonably concordant, and give for the various constants the following values at 25°.

For the hydrolysis proper

$$\frac{[H^+] \cdot [Br^-] \cdot [HOBr]}{[Br_2]} = 5 \cdot 8 \times 10^{-9}.$$

(This constant has a high temperature coefficient): its value $\times 10^9$ is 0·7 at 0°, and 11·3 at 35°.[804] For the perhalide ions Br_3^- and Br_5^- we have at 25° the equilibria

$$\frac{[Br_3^-]}{[Br_2] \cdot [Br^-]} = 16 \cdot 0: \qquad \frac{[Br_5^-]}{[Br_2]^2 \cdot [Br^-]} = 40 \cdot 0.^{[805]}$$

Hence a saturated solution of bromine in water at 25° (0·2141 molar in total bromine content) must contain the following concentrations, in millimoles per litre, of the various molecular species:

Br_2	HOBr	HBr	Br_3^-	Br_5^-
211·8	1·92	1·92	0·26	0·0021

Hypobromous acid can be made in the same way as hypochlorous, but owing to the much less favourable position of the hydrolytic equilibrium, and the much more rapid decomposition, the maximum attainable concentration is very low. According to Pollak[806] the strongest solution that can be made by the action of mercuric oxide on bromine and water is 0·1 normal, largely on account of the solubility of the mercuric bromide;

[800] H. T. Comastri, *Anal. Asoc. Quim. Argentina*, 1939, **27**, 41.

[801] C. F. Irwin and G. F. Hennion, *J.A.C.S.* 1941, **63**, 858.

[802] M. Mousseron and P. Froger, *Bull. Soc.* 1945, [v] **12**, 69.

[803] W. C. Bray and E. L. Connolly, *J.A.C.S.* 1911, **33**, 1487.

[804] H. A. Liebhafsky, ib. 1934, **56**, 1500.

[805] Grinnell Jones and S. Baeckström, ib. 1517.

[806] F. Pollak and E. Doktor, *Z. anorg. Chem.* 1931, **196**, 89.

though this is only about 1/15 as soluble as mercuric chloride, it produces more effect, because of the much smaller hydrolytic constant. To prepare a stronger solution a substance with a less soluble bromide must be used, such as silver nitrate; on distillation at 20–25° under 11–12 mm. pressure very little of the nitric acid comes over, and a 0·3 normal hypobromite solution is obtained. This still contains elementary bromine and as a decomposition product bromic acid, of which the former can be blown away by a stream of nitrogen, but the latter cannot be removed.

Hypobromous acid is a much weaker acid than hypochlorous, though it is much stronger than hypoiodous; K at 20° is about 2×10^{-9} [807-8] (less than a tenth of that of HOCl). It undergoes the same two decomposition reactions as HOCl:

$$(1)\ 5\ HOBr\ =\ HBrO_3 + 2\ H_2O + 2\ Br_2$$

$$(2)\ 4\ HOBr\ =\ O_2 + 2\ H_2O + 2\ Br_2.$$

In comparing this with the behaviour of hypochlorous acid, which in both of these reactions gives, along with the chlorate or the oxygen, not elementary chlorine but HCl, it must be remembered that with bromine the hydrolytic equilibrium is so far over on the side of the free element that the reaction

$$HOX + HX\ =\ H_2O + X_2$$

is far more important.

These two decompositions both occur much more readily than with chlorine.[805] Reaction (1) is the most important in the dark; it probably goes through bromous acid $HBrO_2$:

$$(1a)\ 3\ HOBr \qquad\quad =\ HBrO_2 + H_2O + Br_2$$

$$(1b)\ HBrO_2 + 2\ HOBr\ =\ HBrO_3 + H_2O + Br_2$$

but the bromous acid never attains a measurable concentration.

In a weakly alkaline solution the rate of formation of bromate is 100 times as fast as that of chlorate, but 30,000 times slower than that of iodate.[809] As with the chlorate the change is due to the interaction of the ion with the undissociated hypohalous acid:

$$BrO^- + 2\ HOBr\ =\ BrO_3^- + 2\ H^+ + 2\ Br^-,$$

and in the same way it is greatly accelerated by a rise of temperature, which not only raises the velocity constant but also much increases the concentration of the undissociated acid, which in the alkaline solution is due to hydrolysis.

The reactions of hypobromous acid and its ions, like those of hypochlorous, consist largely of oxidations and brominations. Copper salts, which catalyse the decomposition of hypobromites to bromide and

---

[807] M. Kiese and A. B. Hastings, *J.A.C.S.* 1939, **61**, 1291.

[808] E. A. Schilov, ib. 1938, **60**, 490.

[809] H. Kretzschmar, *Z. Elektrochem.* 1904, **10**, 798.

oxygen,[810] also cause the oxidation of manganous ions to proceed to the permanganate, instead of stopping at MnO_2.[811] The acid, like HOCl but apparently even more so, can add on to C=C; thus[812] if the halogen is added to a suspension of finely divided cinnamic acid in water, a mixture of the dihalide and the hydroxy-halide or halohydrin is formed,

$$\Phi \cdot CHX \cdot CHX \cdot COOH + \Phi \cdot CH(OH) \cdot CHX \cdot COOH,$$

of which the latter is always in excess. With chlorine it is 91 per cent. of the whole, and with bromine 98 per cent.

No solid hypobromite seems to have been isolated, but a bromine analogue of bleaching powder is known, which is remarkable for having a reddish-orange colour; this is said to be due to the adsorption of bromine on the surface of the powder.

Hypobromous Esters

Unlike their chlorine analogues these esters have not been isolated, but there is abundant evidence that they are formed as intermediate products in certain reactions in methyl alcohol solution, in which free bromine, or a molecule with a reactive 'positive' bromine atom (replaceable by hydrogen) (see p. 1189), in contact with an unsaturated organic compound, adds on $Br + O \cdot CH_3$ to the double link.

Dimroth pointed out that certain brominations go especially well in methyl or ethyl alcohol solution,[813] including K. H. Meyer's bromine-titration of enols,[819] and he suggested that in these reactions the real reagent is the alkyl hypobromite: thus with enols

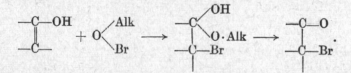

Many unsaturated compounds react with bromine in methyl alcohol to give methoxy-bromides,[815-16] as in water they give hydroxy-bromides.[812] Further, many organic compounds containing 'positive' bromine can replace the bromine in this reaction.[814,817-18] Thus with bromotrinitro-methane

$$Br \cdot C(NO_2)_3 + -CH=CH- \longrightarrow \begin{array}{c} -CH-CHBr- \\ | \\ O \cdot CH_3 \end{array} + CH(NO_2)_3 :$$

[810] P. Fleury, *C.R.* 1920, **171**, 957.
[811] K. M. Filimonovitsch, *Amer. Chem. Abstr.* 1931, **25**, 5640.
[812] J. Read and A. C. P. Andrews, *J.C.S.* 1921, **119**, 1774.
[813] O. Dimroth, E. Schultze, and F. Heinze, *Ber.* 1921, **54**, 3041.
[814] E. Schmidt, W. Bartholoméx, and A. Lübke, ib. 1922, **55**, 2099.
[815] J. B. Conant and E. L. Jackson, *J.A.C.S.* 1924, **46**, 1728.
[816] E. L. Jackson, ib. 1926, **48**, 2168.
[817] E. Schmidt, W. v. Knilling, and A. Ascherl, *Ber.* 1926, **59**, 1279.
[818] Id., ib. 1876.

a reaction like that of tetranitromethane [823]

$$C(NO_2)_4 + \text{—CH=CH—} \longrightarrow \begin{array}{c} \text{—CH—CH(NO}_2)\text{—} \\ | \\ O \cdot Alk \end{array} + CH(NO_2)_3.$$

The result can be shown[820-1] not to be due to the subsequent replacement of a bromine in the dibromide by the alkoxy-group.

Many other compounds with bromine atoms that are replaceable by hydrogen behave in the same way, for example the other bromonitromethanes $Br_2C(NO_2)_2$ and Br_3CNO_2[818] (CBr_4 is inactive, though it gives $CHBr_3$ with alkali). The nitro-groups can be replaced by carbonyls, and even by carboxy-alkyls, as in $\begin{array}{c} NO_2 \\ \diagdown \\ Br \diagup \end{array} C(CO \cdot OEt)_2$ and (rather weakly) $Br_2C(CO \cdot OEt)_2$; if they are part of a ring they are more effective, as in di-methyl-dibromo-dihydro-resorcin, with the grouping $CO\text{—}CBr_2\text{—}CO$, and even tribromophenol bromide with $C\text{=}CH\text{—}CBr_2\text{—}CH\text{=}C\text{—}$, where double links serve the same purpose. The N—Br compounds are of course especially active in this way, such as acetobromamide $CH_3 \cdot CO \cdot NHBr$.[817]

The kinetics of the reaction of bromine on a methyl alcohol solution of stilbene $C_6H_5 \cdot CH\text{=}CH \cdot C_6H_5$ were studied by Bartlett and Tarbell.[822] They showed that the results could be explained by supposing (on the general lines of Robinson's theory) that the primary reaction is the addition of one bromine atom to the $\diagup C\text{=}C\diagdown$ double link, giving Br^- and a complex organic cation, which attracts the Br^- anion present and also reacts with the methyl alcohol, so that there is a competition between these two: thus getting the scheme

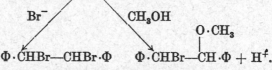

$$\Phi \cdot CH\text{=}CH \cdot \Phi + Br_2 \longrightarrow \Phi \cdot CHBr\text{—}\overset{+}{C}H \cdot \Phi + Br^-$$

$$Br^- \diagup \qquad \diagdown CH_3OH$$

$$\qquad \qquad \qquad \qquad \qquad O \cdot CH_3$$
$$\qquad \qquad \qquad \qquad \qquad |$$
$$\Phi \cdot CHBr\text{—}CHBr \cdot \Phi \qquad \Phi \cdot CHBr\text{—}CH \cdot \Phi + H^+.$$

If so, the reactive bromine compound must be able to form a positive monobromo-cation, and so leave behind a negative complex

$$R \cdot Br + \diagup C\text{=}C\diagdown = R^- + \diagup C\text{—}\overset{|}{C}\text{—}Br^+$$

which could then take up hydrogen, i.e. it must contain 'positive' bromine, as it is in fact found to do.

Hypoiodous Acid, HOI

This acid and its salts are undoubtedly the first products of the action of water or alkalies on iodine; they are also formed by the oxidation of the

[819] K. H. Meyer, *Ann.* 1911, **380**, 212.
[820] K. Meinel, ib. 1934, **510**, 129.   [821] Id., ib. 1935, **516**, 237.
[822] P. D. Bartlett and D. S. Tarbell, *J.A.C.S.* 1936, **58**, 466.
[823] E. Schmidt, R. Schumacher, W. Bäjen, and A. Wagner, *Ber.* 1922, **55**, 1751.

iodine ion, and by the reduction of iodates and periodates; so far the acid is the analogue of hypobromous and hypochlorous acids, but it differs from them very markedly, especially in three ways: it is a much weaker acid, it is much more readily converted into the halate (iodate), and also it is present to a much smaller extent in the hydrolysis of the elementary halogen by water. In all these respects (p. 1213) it acts as the last member of the series HOCl—HOBr—HOI; but in some its position is so extreme that the accurate determination of the constants is very difficult.

The equilibrium constant for the hydrolysis

$$\frac{[HOI] \cdot [H^+] \cdot [I^-]}{[I_2]}$$

is about 3×10^{-13} [824-5]; it is thus 1/5,000 of that for bromine, and $0 \cdot 7 \times 10^{-9}$ of that for chlorine.

The dissociation constant of hypoiodous acid is very small, and its value is very difficult to determine, especially as in any solution containing iodine ions there must be I_3^- and I_5^- ions as well. The most probable value[826] of the dissociation constant at $25°$ is

$$\frac{[H^+] \cdot [IO^-]}{[HOI]} = 4 \cdot 5 \times 10^{-13},$$

which would make it about 1/70,000 of that of HOCl. The acid is a very weak acid, and a very weak base in the sense that it forms compounds with groups which are able to act as the anions of acids, though whether they are actually ionized in their iodine compounds is doubtful (see later, under monovalent iodine derivatives, p. 1242). It can also act as a definite base, with $K_b = 3 \cdot 2 \times 10^{-10}$.[826] Hypoiodous acid is so unstable that it is usually only a transient intermediate product, rapidly changing, even in the cold, into the iodate. The free acid is even more unstable than its alkaline solution,[827] and neither it nor its salts can be isolated. It is more stable in dilute solution, but even then most of it is changed into iodate in 15 minutes. The alkaline solution, though it is more stable than this, is far less so than that of a hypobromite or hypochlorite: it was found[828] that of a solution of potassium hypoiodite more than 30 per cent. had decomposed in an hour in the cold (NaOCl is only 50 per cent. decomposed after 3 years in solution in the cold). It also has a tendency to be reduced to the iodide, which is much weaker than the tendency to go over into the iodate but yet is sufficient to make it an even stronger bleaching agent than the hypobromite or hypochlorite ions. For the kinetics of the hypoiodite decomposition see reference [827].

[824] W. C. Bray and E. L. Connolly, *J.A.C.S.* 1911, **33**, 1485.

[825] A. Skrabal, *Mon.* 1912, **33**, 99.

[826] Id., *Ber.* 1942, **75**, 1570.

[827] For the kinetics of this change see C. H. Li and C. F. White, *J.A.C.S.* 1943, **65**, 335.

[828] K. J. P. Orton and W. L. Blackman, *J.C.S.* 1900, **77**, 830.

Halous Acids, HXO_2 and Halites

Acids of this type are the least stable of the oxy-acids of the halogens. With chlorine there is no doubt of the existence of the salts $M[ClO_2]$, a whole series of which have been prepared, and it is at least probable that the acid can exist in solution. With bromine neither the acid nor its salts have been isolated, but it is quite possible that the salts can occur in solution. With iodine there seems to be no reason for assuming the occurrence of iodites either as acid or as salts.

Chlorous Acid, $HClO_2$

This acid has not been isolated, though numerous salts are known. It is presumed[880] to be an intermediate product in the action of water on chlorine dioxide:

$$2\ ClO_2 + H_2O\ =\ HClO_2 + HClO_3,$$

but it is rapidly decomposed. Its ions are certainly formed in the analogous action of alkali on the dioxide

$$2\ ClO_2 + 2\ OH^-\ =\ H_2O + ClO_2^- + ClO_3^-.$$

It can also be made, free from chlorate, by treating chlorine dioxide with sodium peroxide or an alkaline solution of H_2O_2[831]:

$$2\ ClO_2 + Na_2O_2\ =\ 2\ NaClO_2 + O_2.$$

The acid can be got in solution by adding a strong acid to a solution of a chlorite; if H_2SO_4 is added to the barium salt a colourless solution is obtained, which, however, begins in 1 minute at $15°$ or 10 minutes at $0°$, to turn yellow from the formation of chlorine dioxide[832]:

$$4\ HClO_2\ =\ 3\ ClO_2 + \tfrac{1}{2}\ Cl_2 + 2\ H_2O.$$

The solution does not give the yellow colour of ClO_2 for more than an hour if it is completely freed from chloride and hypochlorite ions.

The acid itself in aqueous solution is colourless, and is shown by the minute conductivity to be very weak; but it is much more stable as a salt than as an acid, and as it shows this greater stability in sodium bicarbonate solution, it must at least be a stronger acid than carbonic.[830] It has a strong and rapid oxidizing action, converting, for example, iodide into iodate; but the ion $[ClO_2]^-$ only reacts relatively slowly.

A large number of salts of chlorous acid have been prepared,[833] for example those of the alkalies, alkaline earths, amines, Cu″, Ag, Zn, Cd, Hg, Pb″, Co″, Ni. The solid salts practically all explode when struck or heated, but otherwise they are stable in the dark for weeks; our knowledge of them

[830] W. C. Bray, *Z. physikal. Chem.* 1906, **54**, 463, 569; *Z. anorg. Chem.* 1906, **48**, 217.

[831] A. Reychler, *Bull. Soc.* 1901, **25**, 659.

[832] G. Lasègue, *C.R.* 1912, **155**, 158.

[833] For a list with references see Gmelin, *Chlor*, 1927, p. 300.

is largely due to G. R. Levi *et al.*[834] The salts are mostly very soluble, often in alcohol as well as in water, especially those of the alkalies and alkaline earths. Almost the only exceptions are the salts of lead and silver; the solubilities in water in g. per 100 g. solution at 0° are: $Ba(ClO_2)_2$ 30·5; $Pb(ClO_2)_2$ 0·035; $AgClO_2$ 0·17.

On heating, the salts are converted into a mixture of chloride and chlorate; the solution when treated with chlorine is converted into the chloride with evolution of ClO_2.[835]

Bromous Acid, $HBrO_2$

It is doubtful whether this acid or its salts exist at all. The acid was supposed to be an intermediate product in the conversion of HOBr into $HBrO_3$, but Pollak and Doktor have shown[836] that though it may be formed it never attains a measurable concentration. There is rather more evidence for the existence of the bromite ion BrO_2^-, though no salts have been isolated. The decomposition of the hypobromite ion to BrO_3^- seems to be bimolecular, and perhaps the first stage is

$$2\ BrO^- = BrO^- + Br^-.$$

Further,[837] if in the partly decomposed solution the hypobromite ion is removed by ammonium salts or urea, it can oxidize an arsenite in the cold in presence of alkali, which $[BrO_3]^-$ cannot.

Iodous Acid HIO_2 and the iodites do not appear to exist at all.

Halic Acids, HXO_3 and the Halates, $M[XO_3]$

These are comparatively stable,[838] and are known with all three halogens. On the whole their resemblance is close. They are all strong acids (unlike the HOX and HXO_2 acids) and are strong oxidizing agents. Their stability is generally in the order $HClO_3 < HBrO_3 < HIO_3$, the opposite to the order of the hydracids; thus $HClO_3$ will oxidize HI to the iodate. The free acids are extremely soluble in water; they lose water on heating, so much so that the first two cannot be obtained in the anhydrous state; HIO_3 is known, as a hygroscopic solid. Iodic acid differs considerably from the other two (as periodic does from perchloric) especially in its tendency to polymerize; there is evidence that in water it is mainly the dibasic acid $H_2I_2O_6$: there are even signs that the IO_3 ion can itself polymerize.

The structure of all three XO_3 ions has been determined by X-ray

---

[834] See for example, G. Bruni and G. R. Levi, *Gaz.* 1915, **45**, ii. 169; G. R. Levi, *Atti R. Linc.* 1922, [v] **31**, i. 52, 212; 1923, **32**, i. 38, 165, 623; 1930, [vi] **11**, 1005; 1932, **16**, 632; *Gaz.* 1922, **52**, i. 207, 417; 1923, **53**, 40, 105, 200, 245, 522.

[835] G. R. Levi and M. Tabet, ib. 1935, **65**, 1138.

[836] F. Pollak and E. Doktor, *Z. anorg. Chem.* 1931, **196**, 89.

[837] J. Clarens, *C.R.* 1913, **156**, 1999.

[838] A. Polesitzki (*C.R. Acad. U.R.S.S.* 1939, **24**, 540) using radioactive Br and I, shows that there is no halogen exchange between Br^- and BrO_3^-, or I^- and IO_3^-.

examination of the crystals. It is found that the ion is pyramidical, with the X atom above the plane of the three oxygens.[839-43]

This is supported for ClO_3 by the Raman spectra of aqueous solutions of the Ca, Sr, Zn, and Cd, salts, and for BrO_3 by those of Mg and Zn.[844] It is found by X-ray analysis of the α-form of HIO_3[845]; some of the metallic iodates seem to have a more complicated structure. For example, KIO_3 has each iodine surrounded octahedrally by 6 oxygens (perowskite structure).[846]

Chloric Acid, $HClO_3$ and the Chlorates

Chloric acid cannot be obtained in the pure state, since the aqueous solution, if it is concentrated beyond 40 per cent. $HClO_3$ ($= HClO_3, 7 H_2O$), begins to decompose with evolution of chlorine and oxygen, and formation of perchloric acid. The acid is usually made by treating a solution of the barium salt with sulphuric acid, filtering, and evaporating.

This concentrated aqueous solution is a colourless, oily liquid, which is a strong oxidizing agent, reacting violently with organic materials.

The dilute aqueous solution of $HClO_3$ is quite reasonably stable, and can be heated to its boiling-point without decomposition; in the cold it slowly decomposes, being mainly converted into the perchlorate.

Chloric acid is a strong acid, and a strong oxidizing agent, converting concentrated hydrogen chloride into chlorine, and iodine into the iodate; it is quantitatively reduced by aluminium to the chloride.

Its salts, the chlorates, are made either by the action of chlorine on hot alkali or by the electrolytic oxidation of the chloride ion.[847] In the formation from chlorine and alkali at any temperature the hypochlorite is always the first product, and as long as the solution remains alkaline very little chlorate is produced; but as soon as it becomes acid, i.e. as soon as undissociated HOCl is present, the chlorate formation becomes rapid.[848]

Salts of Chloric Acid

A large number of chlorates are known[849]; they are mostly very soluble in water, the potassium salt being less so than most, especially in the cold: the solubilities in g. per 100 g. water are: $NaClO_3$ 101/20°; $KClO_3$ 3·3/0°, 7·3/20°, 56·0/100°. They are usually prepared from the calcium salt, made by passing chlorine into hot milk of lime, by double decomposition.

[839] R. G. Dickinson and E. A. Godhue, *J.A.C.S.* 1921, **43**, 2045.

[840] N. H. Kolkmeier, J. M. Bidvoet, and A. Karssen, *Z. Phys.* 1923, **14**, 291; **20**, 82.

[841] A. Karssen, *Rec. Trav.* 1923, **42**, 904.

[842] W. H. Zachariasen, *Z. Krist.* 1929, **71**, 517.

[843] S. v. Náray-Szabó and J. Pocza, ib. 1942, **104**, 28.

[844] M. Rolla, *Gaz.* 1939, **69**, 779.

[845] M. T. Rogers and L. Helmholz, *J.A.C.S.* 1941, **63**, 278.

[846] Wells, *S.I.C.*, p. 273.

[847] For details of the electrolytic methods see Gmelin, *Chlor*, pp. 214–18.

[848] F. Foerster and F. Jorre, *J. prakt. Chem.* 1899, [2] **59**, 53; F. Foerster, ib. 1901, **63**, 141.

[849] For a list with references see Gmelin, *Chlor*, p. 339.

All alkaline chlorates are decomposed on heating into chloride and perchlorate:

$$4 \, KClO_3 = 3 \, KClO_4 + KCl,$$

and at the same time to some extent into chloride and oxygen:

$$2 \, KClO_3 = 2 \, KCl + 3 \, O_2.$$

With potassium chlorate the first reaction takes place at 395°, along with a little of the second. As is well known, the second of these reactions is greatly hastened by certain catalysts, especially manganese dioxide, which makes it go just above 200°.

Bromic Acid, $HBrO_3$ *and the Bromates*

In general, bromic acid resembles chloric acid very closely. It can be made by the electrolytic oxidation of bromide solutions, or by the action of bromine on water in the presence of bases. In the latter reaction, as with chlorine, the first stage is the formation of the hypohalous acid HOBr. In the conversion of this into the bromate only a few per cent. of oxygen are lost[850]; the reaction is on the same general lines as the formation of chlorate or iodate, but *ceteris paribus* the rate with bromine is 100 times as fast as with chlorine, and 1/30,000 times as fast as with iodine.[851] In the electrolytic preparation E. Müller has found[852] that if a small quantity of potassium chromate is added to the liquid, a nearly quantitative yield is got.

Free bromic acid, like free chloric acid, cannot be obtained in the anhydrous state, as its aqueous solution begins to decompose at a certain limiting strength, which is nearly the same as for chloric acid, being about 50 per cent., corresponding to the formula $HBrO_3$, $7 \, H_2O$ (as with $HClO_3$). Bromic acid is a strong acid, as the electrical conductivity shows.[853] It is a strong oxidizing agent; it is rather slow to act, but the ion has nearly the same oxidation potential as the chlorate ion.

The salts of bromic acid are well known[854]; they are easily made, colourless, usually hydrated when the valency of the cation is more than 1; the salts of univalent ions except lithium are anhydrous, Na, K, Tl', Ag, Hg'; those of divalent cations are hydrated up to $6 \, H_2O$; those of the rare-earth metals all have $9 \, H_2O$. They are usually easily soluble, the potassium salt, however, being an exception. On heating they decompose to oxygen and the bromide (or with less positive metals to the oxide and free bromine); some, such as the NH_4 and Pb'' salts, are explosive. The rare-earth salts are mostly well defined, and have been found useful in separating these elements.[855] Some of the solubilities, in g. anhydrous salt in 100 g. solution (for references see Gmelin, p. 324) at temperatures of 18–25° are:

[850] A. Skrabal, *Sitzb. Wien. Akad.* 1907, **116**, 215; 1911, **120, 27**.

[851] H. Kretschmar, *Z. Elektrochem*, 1904, **10**, 879.   [852] Ib. 1899, **5**, 469.

[853] W. Ostwald, *J. prakt. Chem.* 1885, [2] **32**, 311.

[854] For a list, with crystallographic and other properties, including solubilities, see Gmelin, *Brom*, pp. 323–4.

[855] See, for example, J. K. Marsh, *J.C.S.* 1929, 2387.

Li, H_2O 60·5; Na, 27·7; K, 6·45; Tl, 0·345; Ag, 0·192; Mg″, 6 H_2O 42; Ca, H_2O 63; Sr, H_2O 30; Ba, H_2O 0·652; Zn, 6 H_2O 59; Pb″, H_2O 1·32.

The ion has the same shape as ClO_3.[856]

Iodic Acid and the Iodates

Iodic acid can be made by the action of water on iodine pentoxide; by the oxidation of iodine with nitric acid, or with chlorine if the HCl formed is removed with silver oxide; by the action of a strong acid on an iodate; or by the action of a chlorate on iodine.

It is a colourless, dimorphic solid; there is also a so-called 'anhydro-acid' HI_3O_8. HIO_3 is extremely soluble in water, the saturated solution containing 76·3 per cent. of acid at 25°, and 86 per cent. at 110°, where the solid HIO_3 changes with partial melting into HI_3O_8; at 195° this latter goes over into I_2O_5 and water.

Iodic acid is a strong acid, but in many ways it behaves as if it were polymerized. Though the evidence on this question is to some extent conflicting (see, for example, Gmelin, *Iod*, p. 490) the most probable conclusion is that the anion of the ordinary iodates is the simple IO_3^-: that iodic acid in dilute solution has the simple formula $H[IO_3]$ and is a strong electrolyte; but that at higher concentrations the free acid polymerizes to a considerable extent, and is at least a dibasic acid $H_2I_2O_6$.

The iodates MIO_3 behave in solution in most ways like chlorates and bromates.[857] But there is a series of acid salts, such as $(NH_4)HI_2O_6$ and $KH_2I_3O_9$, which suggest polymerization,* and also the free acid behaves in a curious way. The freezing-points of the aqueous solution of the acid indicate a van't Hoff 'i' differing but little from 1 over a large range of concentrations from high values down to 3 per cent. which for a highly ionized acid is not compatible with a formula HIO_3 (for which i should be nearly 2), but it is compatible with a highly ionized dibasic acid $H_2I_2O_6$, for which i would be one-half of 2 to 3—i.e. from 1 to 1·5.[858] So too the molecular conductivity at $V = 2$ is only half that of chloric acid.[857] But in dilute solution[859] the ionization is as complete, or almost as complete, as that of HCl.

Weitz and Stamm[860] claim to have shown that in other ways also iodic acid behaves like a dibasic acid. Their evidence, however, refers not to the free acid but to the ions of its salts, which seem unlikely to polymerize; and it has been shown[861] that some of their effects are confined to very concentrated solutions.

---

* These peculiarities of the iodates are also shown in their crystal structure: see references [864-7].

[856] W. H. Zachariasen, *Phys. Rev.* 1931, [2] **37**, 105.
[857] A. Rosenheim and O. Liebknecht, *Ann.* 1899, **308**, 40.
[858] E. Groschuff, *Z. anorg. Chem.* 1905, **47**, 331.
[859] C. A. Kraus and H. C. Parker, *J.A.C.S.* 1922, **44**, 2439.
[860] E. Weitz and H. Stamm, *Ber.* 1928, **61**, 1144.
[861] H. B. Weiser and E. B. Middleton, *J. phys. Chem.* 1920, **24**, 50.

A curious difference between the ions of iodic and those of chloric or bromic acids has been stated by Hevesy[862]; the diffusion coefficients of ions are roughly proportional to the reciprocal of the electrovalency, presumably owing to the increase with the charge of the size of the solvated ion. The only exceptions among monobasic anions seem to be F^- and IO_3^-. The values for the ionic mobilities at 18°, which for univalent ions are proportional to the diffusion coefficients, are given below: the difference for the iodate, though not large, is quite perceptible; the values for the simple halide ions show the small effect of the atomic number of the halogen in that series:

Ionic Mobilities at 18°

	ClO_3^-	BrO_3^-	IO_3^-
	55·0	48·2	33·8

F^-	Cl^-	Br^-	I^-
46·6	65·5	67·7	66·5

This effect, unlike those of Weitz and Stamm, seems to show that the ion behaves not like a divalent ion I_2O_6'', but rather like an ion IO_3 with a charge greater than 1. If the differences in mobility are significant, the IO_3 ion must be exceptionally large in its hydrated form. This may well be so: the behaviour of periodic as compared with perchloric acid shows that iodine compounds tend to assume a high covalency (and so presumably a greater degree of solvation) than their bromine and chlorine analogues.

A further indication of this power of combination in the IO_3 ion is given by the existence of acid iodates of the general types $MIO_3 + n(HIO_3)$, or $n(I_2O_5)$,[863] and of compounds of the IO_3 ion with other acidic oxides such as SeO_3 and MoO_3.

The iodates are much more stable than the chlorates and bromates, but they will explode if mixed with carbon or organic material and heated; they are also far less soluble in water. Sodium iodate occurs in nature in Chile saltpetre, which is the chief source of iodine.

The iodate ion oxidizes hydrogen iodide to iodine and water

$$IO_3^- + 5\, I^- + 6\, H^+ = 3\, H_2O + 3\, I_2.$$

This reaction needs the presence of free hydrogen ion, and so can be used to estimate this, especially when the solution must not become alkaline during the titration, as with some keto-enolic tautomers.

A large number of complex salts are known which contain iodic acid or its anion; examples are $KHSO_4$, KIO_3; $2\, KIO_3$; $2\, SeO_3$, H_2O; and others. For the crystal structures of iodates see further references [864-8].

[862] G. v. Hevesy, *Z. physikal. Chem.* 1930, **149**, 474.
[863] U. Croatto and G. Bryk, *Gaz.* 1941, **71**, 590.
[864] W. H. Zachariasen, *Skr. Akad. Oslo*, 1928, **4**, 99.
[865] W. H. Zachariasen, and F. A. Barta, *Phys. Rev.* 1931, **37**, 1628 (LiIO$_3$).
[866] M. T. Rogers and L. Helmholz, *J.A.C.S.* 1940, **62**, 1537.
[867] C. H. MacGillavry and C. L. Panthaleon van Eck, *Rec. Trav.* 1943, **62**, 729.
[868] I. Náray-Szabó and J. Neugebauer, *J.A.C.S.* 1947, **69**, 1280.

Fluoroiodic Acid, HIO_2F_2

Salts of this acid can be made by dissolving iodates (as KIO_3) in con-centrated hydrofluoric acid, when they crystallize out. The iodine atom has the valency decet 2, 8 if we write it $F_2I(\rightarrow O)_2$. Helmholz and Rogers[866] have examined the crystal structure of KIO_2F_2. They find that the anion has the distances I—O 1·93; I—F 2·00 (theory I—O 1·99; I—F 1·97). The shape is that of an octahedron with two *cis*-places vacant, the F—I—F angle being 180°, and the two O's in a plane perpendicular to this, with the O—I—O angle 100° [this is very near to the expected value, of a trigonal bipyramid with two polar F atoms, and two equatorial O atoms, with O—I—O 120°]. Compare the structure of tellurium tetrachloride (VI. 992).

Perhalic Acids, HXO_4 or H_5XO_6

Only chlorine and iodine give acids of this type. The absence of a perbromic acid $HBrO_4$ is one of the examples of the reluctance of elements in the first long period to assume covalencies which are reached by their neighbours both above and below; other examples are the absence of hexahalides of chromium and of a pentachloride of arsenic (see p. 791).

The two members of this series of acids which do occur are strikingly different from one another. Perchloric acid shows no tendency to form an 'ortho'-acid of higher basicity by combination with water, as meta-phosphoric HPO_3 forms the ortho-acid H_3PO_4; the hydrates which per-chloric acid forms are really hydronium salts, as $(H_3O)[ClO_4]$. On the other hand, periodic acid scarcely reacts in the simple HIO_4 form at all, but nearly always as H_5IO_6 (as telluric reacts as H_6TeO_6).

Perchloric acid is the strongest of the ordinary 'strong' acids, and remains ionized in solvents of smaller ionizing power than water, in which nitric and even hydrochloric acid go into the covalent state.[869-70]

Perchloric Acid, $HClO_4$

Perchloric acid[871] and its derivatives occur in two forms, a stable ionized state, and an unstable and often explosive covalent one. The anhydrous acid belongs (at least mainly) to the latter type, and the hydrated acid to the former; according to Abegg 'there is probably no acid which differs so much as this does in its anhydrous and in its hydrated states'. The anhydrous acid can be made from the aqueous solution by distillation under reduced pressure, but it is better to distil a mixture of $KClO_4$, or the concentrated aqueous acid, with sulphuric acid, which last must be from 90 to 92 per cent. acid, as a stronger acid decomposes the perchloric acid. Pure $HClO_4$ melts at $-112°$, and according to Hantzsch the extrapolated boiling-point is about 130°. It can, however, be distilled only *in vacuo*, and like H_2SO_4 it breaks up to some extent into the anhydride

[869] A. Hantzsch, *Z. Elektrochem.* 1923, **29**, 221; *Ber.* 1927, **60**, 1939.
[870] Id., *Z. physikal. Chem.* 1928, **134**, 406.
[871] For heat of formation see C. F. Goodeve and A. E. L. Marsh, *J.C.S.* 1937, 1816.

Cl_2O_7 and water (really the hydrated acid),[872] the distillate containing about 57 per cent. of anhydride. If it is heated under ordinary pressure it breaks up into water, oxygen, chlorine dioxide, etc., often explosively (see further ref. [873]). It is a colourless liquid, rather more mobile than water; it is unstable, and on keeping, even in the cold, soon begins to decompose. It is a violent oxidizing agent; with organic materials such as wood and paper, and with most organic compounds, the anhydrous acid reacts explosively.

Perchloric acid reacts vigorously with water; it gives a series of six solid hydrates, some of which form solid solutions with one another. These compounds, with their melting-points, are[872]: $HClO_4$, $-112°$; $HClO_4, H_2O$ $+50°$; $HClO_4, 2 H_2O$ $-17·8°$; $HClO_4, 2·5 H_2O$ $-29·8°$; $HClO_4 +3 H_2O$, (*a*) $-37°$, (*b*) $-43·2°$; $HClO_4 +3·5 H_2O$ $-41·4°$. The most remarkable of these is the monohydrate, melting more than 160° higher than the anhydrous acid; it is very stable, and can be heated nearly to its boiling-point (110°) without decomposition; the liquid is 10 times as viscous as the anhydrous acid. It forms a hygroscopic solid, which has practically the same crystal lattice as ammonium perchlorate, showing that it really is the hydronium salt $(H_3O)[ClO_4]$. Its saturated solution in water at 25° contains 27 per cent. by molecules or 65 per cent. by weight of the acid.

In aqueous solution perchloric acid is practically completely dissociated, and its properties, apart from the acidity, are those of its salts, i.e. of the perchlorate ion. This ion is remarkable for its extreme stability; it is not reduced by SO_2, H_2S, HCl, or HI, nor by metallic iron or zinc (which merely form their perchlorates with evolution of hydrogen), nor by aluminium or nitrous acid: nearly all of these reagents will reduce chloric acid. It is, however, reduced by trivalent titanium in acid solution, by some of the lower valencies of vanadium and molybdenum, and slowly by chromous salts.

We may consider first the constitution of the acid itself. ClO_4^- is a very stable ion, extremely reluctant to go over into the covalent state; its structure is well established; the four oxygen atoms are joined by single co-ordinate links to the central chlorine (with the usual possibility of resonance with Cl==O), and are arranged tetrahedrally round it. The great stability of this molecule, so far exceeding even that of its immediate predecessor ClO_3^-, may be due to the symmetry, and to the fact that the chlorine atom has all its valency electrons shared, and is surrounded on all sides by the oxygens, which, as their refractivity shows, are very resistent to deformation, and hence are slow to form covalent links. The covalent form (which is

[872] H. J. van Wyk, *Z. anorg. Chem.* 1902, **32**, 115; 1906, **48**, 1.
[873] W. Dietz, *Angew. Chem.* 1939, **52**, 616.

shown by its Raman spectrum to have the four oxygen atoms still tetra-hedrally arranged, with the hydrogen attached to one of them[874,876]) is very much less stable (the esters are even less stable, being among the most explosive substances known). This instability is proved by the way in which the acid always dissociates when there is anything present which can take up its hydrogen, since a 'naked' hydrogen ion cannot exist. Thus it will convert nitric acid into what was supposed to be the nitronium base $[H_2NO_3]\cdot[ClO_4]$[874] but is probably a mixture of $[NO_2]ClO_4$ and $[H_3O]ClO_4$, and even compel the reluctant hydrogen fluoride to solvate its hydrogen ion, in $[H_2F]\cdot[ClO_4]$ (p. 1110).

The covalent form has a series of Raman lines[874-6,878] quite different from those of the ClO_4 ion, and some of them identical with lines of Cl_2O_7.[879] The anhydrous acid shows these covalent lines with none of the lines of ClO_4, indicating that there is no association (as the low viscosity also suggests), and no formation of an acidium cation such as in $[H_2ClO_4]\cdot[ClO_4]$. On addition of water the ClO_4^- lines first appear at 97 per cent., but the $HClO_4$ lines continue down to about 75 per cent. acid,[876-8] though $[H_3O]\cdot[ClO_4]$ corresponds to 85 per cent. acid; hence the fused oxonium perchlorate must contain some of the covalent acid.

Perchlorates

The general properties of the perchlorate ion have already been described, but the salts have a variety of peculiarities which are worth considering.

The first point—as with most salts—is the solubility.[879] The per-chlorates are remarkable in that they are practically all either excessively soluble, or only sparingly soluble, in water; the salts that form hydrates all belong to the first class (average of 15, 62/25°),* and those that do not, including the salts of organic amines though not that of ammonium, to the second (average of 8, 5·0/25°). Of the alkaline salts those of lithium and sodium are hydrated and very soluble (37·4 and 67·7 at 25°), while those of potassium, rubidium, and caesium are anhydrous and only slightly soluble (2·02, 1·32, and 1·93 at 25°). The amines usually form very insoluble perchlorates, and for this reason the acid is often used in organic chemistry for their separation.

Many of these perchlorates are as remarkable for their solubilities in oxygen-containing organic solvents as for those in water. The following table, taken largely from the work of Willard and Smith,[880] gives some of the values.

* Solubilities are expressed as usual in g./100 g. water.

[874] A. Simon and H. Reuther, *Naturwiss.* 1937, **25**, 477.
[875] D. R. Goddard, E. D. Hughes, and C. K. Ingold, *Nature*, 1946, **158**, 480.
[876] A. Simon, H. Reuther, and G. Kratzsch, *Z. anorg. Chem.* 1938, **239**, 329.
[877] A. Hantzsch, *Ber.* 1925, **58**, 941.
[878] R. Fonteyne, *Naturwet. Tijds.* 1938, **20**, 112.
[879] See especially Gmelin, *Chlor*, 1927, p. 397.
[880] H. H. Willard and G. F. Smith, *J.A.C.S.* 1923, **45**, 286.

Solubilities of Perchlorates at 25° (g./100 g. solvent)

Salt	Water	MeOH	EtOH	Acetone	Ethyl acetate	Ether
LiClO$_4$ . . .	27·2	64·6	60·3	57·7	48·8	53·2
LiClO$_4$, 3 H$_2$O . .	..	61·0	42·2	49·0	26·4	0·196
NaClO$_4$ . . .	67·7	33·9	12·8	34·1	8·80	0
KClO$_4$ . . .	1·32	0·105	0·012	0·155	0·0015	0
CsClO$_4$ . . .	1·93	0·093	0·011	0·150	0	0
Mg(ClO$_4$)$_2$ . . .	49·9	34·1	19·3	30·02	41·5	0·29
Ca(ClO$_4$)$_2$ . . .	65·4	70·4	62·4	38·2	43·1	0·26
Ba(ClO$_4$)$_2$ . . .	66·5	68·5	55·5	55·5	53·0	0

The anhydrous perchlorates of the alkali metals and of some amines are dimorphic; they change on heating from the ordinary rhombic to a regular form, at lower temperatures the larger the cation[881]: for example, Na 308°, K 300°, Rb 279°, Cs 219°, NH$_4$ 240°. X-ray photographs indicate that this is due to the rotation of the anions at the higher temperatures.[882]

The strong affinity of some of these salts for water makes them valuable as dehydrating agents. This is especially true of the magnesium salt, which is used commercially for this purpose. Mg(ClO$_4$)$_2$ occurs in the anhydrous form, and also forms hydrates with 2, 3, 4, and 6 molecules of water.[883-5] The hexahydrate melts at 146°; in a month in the cold over P$_2$O$_5$ it is converted into the trihydrate, and this, if it is heated in dry air at 170–250°, loses the rest of its water and forms the anhydrous salt.[883] This is as good a drying agent as phosphorus pentoxide; even the trihydrate is as effective as P$_2$O$_5$ at 0°, though not at higher temperatures.[883]

The perchlorates are remarkably stable to heat, as is shown by the methods which can be used for their dehydration, and the alkaline perchlorates will stand temperatures of 300° (Li) to 400° (K) without decomposition.

The most remarkable of the perchlorates is the silver salt.[886-7] This salt, in spite of having a univalent cation, is extremely soluble in water, the saturated solution containing 74 per cent. of the salt at the cryohydric point of —58·2°, and 84·8 per cent. (557 g. to 100 of water) at 25°[887-8]; in 60 per cent. aqueous perchloric acid this is reduced to 5·63 per cent. (one fifteenth). It forms a monohydrate AgClO$_4$, H$_2$O which is stable from the cryohydric point up to 43°.[887] It is also soluble in many organic solvents free from oxygen, including hydrocarbons with many of which it forms

[881] D. Vorländer and E. Kaascht, *Ber.* 1923, **56**, 1157.
[882] C. Finbak and O. Hassel, *Z. physikal. Chem.* 1936, B **32**, 130.
[883] H. H. Willard and G. F. Smith, *J.A.C.S.* 1922, **44**, 2255.
[884] J. H. Yoe, R. W. McGahey, and W. T. Smith, *Ind. Eng. Chem.* 1928, **20**, 656.
[885] G. F. Smith, O. W. Rees, and V. R. Hardy, *J.A.C.S.* 1932, **54**, 3513.
[886] A. E. Hill, ib. 1921, **43**, 254.
[887] Id., ib. 1922, **44**, 1163.
[888] G. F. Smith and F. Ring, ib. 1937, **59**, 1889.

solid compounds.* Some of the values are given in the table that follows, with the compositions of the solid phases present.[886,889-92]

Solubilities of Silver Perchlorate at 25°

Solvent	Water[a]	Aniline	Pyridine	Benzene[b]	Toluene[c]
G. salt to 100 g. solvent .	577	5·3	26·4	5·3	101
Mols. salt to 100 mols. solvent　　. . .	48·2	2·42	10·0	2·03	44·8
Solid phase (S = AgClO$_4$)　. .	S, H$_2$O	S, 6 $\Phi \cdot$ NH$_2$	S, 4 py.	S, C$_6$H$_6$	(S, C$_7$H$_8$ below 22.6°)

$$a = {}^{888}, b = {}^{889}, c = {}^{892}$$

The much greater solubility in toluene than in benzene suggests that the toluene compound is very stable in solution. These solid compounds are all liable to explode, especially the benzene compound, which, though normally stable up to 145°, sometimes explodes with great violence when struck, even in the cold.[893] Silver perchlorate is also easily soluble in glycerol, acetic acid, nitromethane (see later), nitrobenzene, and chlorobenzene. In benzene solution it is monomeric (by the freezing-point) when dilute, but as the concentration increases it polymerizes up to 2 or 3 times.[886] In the same way the dipole moment increases greatly with dilution; in $n/200$ solution it is already high, being 4·70 D at 25°,[894] but on further dilution to $n/5000$ it increases to 10·7 D,[895] which is very nearly the theoretical value for the ion-pair [Ag]·[ClO$_4$] ($4\cdot80 \times 2\cdot25 = 11\cdot9$).[895-6] This strongly suggests that at these very low concentrations the salt is present as ion-pairs, which as the concentration increases collect together into larger aggregates, with a fall in the molecular polarization, as occurs with many quaternary ammonium salts in chloroform (Walden) or in benzene.[895]

Silver perchlorate is readily soluble in nitromethane (in which most salts will not dissolve), and the solution has a high conductivity,[897] so that in this solvent (with the dielectric constant 37) the ions seem to separate.

Lead perchlorate Pb(ClO$_4$)$_2$ is said[898] to be readily soluble in organic solvents; but the alcoholic solution exploded so violently that the salt was not further investigated.

* But benzene will not extract a perceptible amount from an aqueous solution weaker than 2·3-normal, which shows that such solutions have no measurable concentration of unionized salt.

[889] A. E. Hill, *J.A.C.S.* 1922, **44**, 1163.
[890] A. E. Hill and R. Macy, ib. 1924, **46**, 1132.
[891] R. Macy, ib. 1925, **47**, 1031.
[892] A. E. Hill and F. W. Miller, ib. 2702.
[893] S. R. Brinkley, ib. 1940, **62**, 3524.
[894] J. W. Williams, *Phys. Z.* 1928, **29**, 174.
[895] G. S. Hooper and C. A. Kraus, *J.A.C.S.* 1934, **56**, 2265.
[896] W. F. Luder, P. B. Kraus, C. A. Kraus, and R. M. Fuoss, ib. 1936, **58**, 255.
[897] C. P. Wright, D. M. Murray-Rust, and H. Hartley, *J.C.S.* 1931, 199.
[898] H. H. Willard and J. L. Kastner, *J.A.C.S.* 1930, **52**, 2391.

The perchlorates of the diazonium bases are readily made[899]; they are relatively insoluble in water (most diazonium salts are extremely soluble), for example the phenyl compound 1·4 per cent. and the o-tolyl 0·82 per cent. at 0°; unlike the diazonium salts of some other strong acids, such as fluoroboric, they are violently explosive.

A nitrosyl salt $[NO] \cdot [ClO_4]$ can be made[900-1] by heating the very concentrated acid with nitrous fumes. It is fairly stable, and does not decompose below 108°. It is decomposed by water with evolution of brown fumes; in solution in nitromethane it has the high conductivity of a salt.[901]

Owing to the exceptional tendency of perchloric acid to ionize (i.e. to its great strength) it can form normal salts (BH) $[ClO_4]$ even with very weak organic bases such as isatin or azobenzene, and as these are usually only slightly soluble they are often used to purify and separate such bases.[902] The effect of aryl groups in weakening the basicity of ammonia, i.e. its tendency to go into the quaternary ammonium cation, culminates in the triaryl amines, which have scarcely any basicity left, and form no normal salts except the perchlorates, $[Ar_3NH] \cdot [ClO_4]$. But there is also a series of abnormal 'tetravalent' nitrogen salts of the type $[Ar_3N] \cdot [ClO_4]$, which are odd molecules. If tritolylamine is treated with an ethereal solution of silver perchlorate and iodine (which perhaps contains the ClO_4 radical: see p. 1207), a deep blue solution is formed, from which the violet salt $[Tol_3N] \cdot [ClO_4]$ separates.[903-4] It melts at 123°, and only explodes above this; it is not very soluble in water, but gives a blue solution, which has the reactions of the perchlorate ion, and precipitates insoluble perchlorates.

Perchloric Esters

The ethyl ester was made by Hare and Boyle in 1841, and then by Roscoe in 1862,[905] in both cases by distilling barium ethyl sulphate with barium perchlorate; Hare and Boyle say that it is incomparably more explosive than any other known substance, which still seems to be very nearly true. Later work[906] shows that this method of preparation is the best, though others can be used, such as the action of the alcohol or of diazomethane on the anhydrous acid, or of the alkyl iodide on the dry silver salt. Meyer and Spormann[906] say that the explosions of the perchloric esters are louder and more destructive than those of any other substance; it was necessary to work with the minimum quantities, under the protection of thick gloves, iron masks, and thick glasses, and to handle the vessels with long holders.

They thus made the methyl (b. pt. 52°), ethyl (b. pt. 89°), and propyl

[899] K. A. Hofmann and H. Arnoldi, *Ber.* 1906, **39**, 3146.
[900] K. A. Hofmann and A. Zedwitz, ib. 1909, **42**, 2031.
[901] A. Hantzsch and K. Berger, *Z. anorg. Chem.* 1930, **190**, 321.
[902] K. A. Hofmann, A. Metzler, and K. Höbold, *Ber.* 1910, **43**, 1080.
[903] E. Weitz and H. W. Schwechten, ib. 1926, **59**, 2307.
[904] Id., ib. 1927, **60**, 545.   [905] H. E. Roscoe, *Ann.* 1862, **124**, 124.
[906] J. Meyer and W. Spormann, *Z. anorg. Chem.* 1936, **228**, 341.

esters. These esters are miscible with alcohol or ether, and are insoluble in water but are slowly hydrolysed by it.[907]

The very peculiar trichloromethyl ester $CCl_3 \cdot O \cdot ClO_3$ is formed by the action of silver perchlorate on carbon tetrachloride at the ordinary temperature, in presence of a little hydrogen chloride.[908-9] The pure salt does not react with the pure liquid even in months, but if even as little as 1 part of HCl to 4,000 of $AgClO_4$ is added a slow reaction occurs in the cold, giving some 60–70 per cent. yield of this ester in 3 weeks.

$CCl_3 \cdot O \cdot ClO_3$ is a colourless, mobile liquid melting at $-55°$, and stable enough to be distilled *in vacuo*; it is so explosive, that it can only be made in minute quantities, and could not be completely purified. It begins to decompose at 40°; it is miscible with CCl_4; it reacts with ethylene dibromide and phosphorus oxychloride. Molecular weights by the freezing-point in CCl_4 were 3 times that of the simple ester, but the material was only about 90 per cent. pure; the analysis is that to be expected for a mixture of $CCl_3 \cdot ClO_4$ with about 5 per cent. of CCl_4.

It is evident that the exceptionally explosive character of the alkyl perchlorates is due partly to the instability of the covalent form of the perchlorates, which is shown by the anhydrous acid, and partly to the extra energy of decomposition provided by the alkyl group, owing to the excess of oxygen in the ClO_4, which has one more atom of oxygen than is needed for the combustion of a methyl group:

$$2\ CH_3 \cdot ClO_4 \longrightarrow 3\ H_2O + 2\ CO_2 + Cl_2 + \tfrac{1}{2}O_2.$$

The general relations are much the same as with nitric acid and the nitrates, except that with the perchlorates the explosions are much more easily produced, and much more violent when they occur.

Periodic Acid

While $HClO_4$ shows no tendency to increase its basicity by hydration (e.g. to give H_3ClO_5 or H_5ClO_6), periodic acid is more stable in the form H_5IO_6 (less correctly written HIO_4, $2\ H_2O$), though the simple form HIO_4 occurs also, both as the free acid and in the salts. The relation of this acid to perchloric is exactly like that of telluric to sulphuric and selenic acids, but the difference is less marked in Group VII; the simple form being better known and more stable with iodine than with tellurium. The effective atomic numbers and the valency groups of the central atoms are identical in Groups VI and VII:

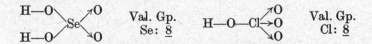

[907] For more of these esters see K. A. Hofmann, A. Zedwitz, and H. Wagner, *Ber.* 1909, **42**, 4390.

[908] L. Birckenbach and J. Goubeau, *Naturwiss.* 1930, **18**, 530.

[909] Id., *Ber.* 1931, **64**, 218.

$$\begin{matrix} H-O \\ H-O \\ H-O \end{matrix}\!\!\!>\!Te\!\!<\!\!\!\begin{matrix} O-H \\ O-H \\ O-H \end{matrix} \qquad \text{Val. Gp.} \atop \text{Te:}\underline{12} \qquad\qquad \begin{matrix} H-O \\ H-O \\ H-O \end{matrix}\!\!\!>\!I\!\!<\!\!\!\begin{matrix} O-H \\ O-H \\ O \end{matrix} \qquad \text{Val. Gp.} \atop \text{I:}\underline{12}$$

The change must be due to an increase in the relative stability of the higher covalency in the heavier element.

Periodic acid is much weaker than perchloric, and as a result of the number of hydroxyl groups, and their small ionizing power, tends to form condensed acids, such as the 'pyro' acid $H_4I_2O_9$, of which a series of salts is known.

Free periodic acid is made from its salts, and since these are stable to heat, many of their methods of preparation depend on the use of high temperatures. Periodates can be made by igniting the iodates of the alkaline earths or of many heavy metals:

$$5\,Ba(IO_3)_2 = Ba_5(IO_6)_2 + 4\,I_2 + 9\,O_2:$$

or by igniting a mixture of sodium peroxide and iodine, or of barium peroxide with barium iodide or iodine: or even by heating barium or sodium[910] iodide in the air. A common method of preparation is in the wet way, by the oxidation of an iodate (or of iodine and an alkaline hydroxide) with chlorine. The free acid can be made by the action of sulphuric acid on the lead or barium salt, or of hydrochloric acid on the silver salt.

Periodic acid occurs certainly in two and probably in three forms, all of which are colourless. When the aqueous acid is evaporated the 'ortho'-acid H_5IO_6 crystallizes out. If this is heated to 100° under 12 mm. pressure it loses water and goes over into the meta-acid HIO_4[911-12]; an intermediate product of the composition $H_4I_2O_9$ is formed at 80°.[912] On further heating, the meta-acid HIO_4 is not converted into its anhydride I_2O_7, which does not seem to exist, but it begins to sublime at 100°, and at 138° it loses oxygen and is converted into iodic acid HIO_3. The ortho-acid H_5IO_6 melts at 122°; it is hygroscopic, and is readily soluble in water, the solubility being 112/25°[913]; it is readily soluble in alcohol, and less so in ether. That the ortho-acid really has the 6-covalent structure and is not a hydrate $HIO_4, 2\,H_2O$, is proved by the numerous salts (see next section) in which two or more of the hydrogen atoms are replaced by metals, and also by the infra-red spectrum which contains no H_2O bands.[914]

Periodic acid is not nearly so strong an acid as perchloric, even in water. The ortho-acid H_5IO_6 is for practical purposes a dibasic acid, with a first dissociation constant of about 0·023 (dichloracetic acid has $K = 0·05$), and a second of the order of 10^{-6}.[915] Hence it loses its 'activity' as an acid very readily, even in alcohol (in sharp contrast to $HClO_4$).

[910] E. Zintl and W. Morawcitz, *Z. anorg. Chem.* 1940, **245**, 20.
[911] A. B. Lamb, *Amer. Chem. J.* 1902, **27**, 135.
[912] J. R. Partington and R. K. Bahl, *J.C.S.* 1934, 1088.
[913] A. E. Hill, *J.A.C.S.* 1928, **50**, 2678.
[914] A. E. van Arkel and C. P. Fritzius, *Rec. Trav.* 1931, **50**, 1043.
[915] N. Rae, *J.C.S.* 1931, 876.

Periodic acid is easily reduced to iodic acid by hydrochloric, sulphuric, or sulphurous acids, or hydrogen sulphide; most organic substances are oxidized by the solid periodic acid at once. It is found that while simple alcohols and mono-hydroxy-acids are not oxidized by the acid in the cold, α-diols (containing the group —C(OH)—C(OH)—) readily give ketones and acids.[916]

All attempts to prepare an ester of periodic acid have failed.[917] Presumably the alkyl periodates are even more unstable than the perchlorates.

Periodates

Periodic acid readily gives condensed forms, with several iodine atoms in the molecule. Except for the pyro-acid $H_4I_2O_4$[912] these are only known in the form of salts, of which the following are among the more important types: $M_5'IO_6$ ortho, $M_4'I_2O_9$ pyro, $M_3'IO_5$ meso, $M_8'I_2O_{11}$ di-ortho, $M'IO_4$ meta.

The conversion of one form into another is usually easy and rapid. In water all these salts are considerably hydrolysed, and as a rule the salts separating from water have not got more than two of their hydrogen atoms replaced by metals. In the absence of water the higher salts are relatively stable, especially to heat, the ortho more so than the meta. It is remarkable that while many periodates are converted by heat into iodates, certain iodates (for example, the barium or sodium salt) if ignited in air are converted into the periodates.[910]

In striking contrast to the perchlorates, the periodates are as a rule only slightly soluble in water. The study of the 3-component systems alkaline hydroxide, I_2O_7, H_2O at 25°[918] shows that the solid phases at this temperature are with sodium, $NaIO_4$ 3 H_2O (= NaH_4IO_6, H_2O); $Na_2H_3IO_6$; $Na_3H_2IO_6$. With potassium they are KIO_4 and $K_4I_2O_9$, 9 H_2O (= $K_2H_3IO_6$, 3 H_2O). There seems to be no tendency to produce addition compounds of the salt and the acid—'acid' salts like the acid iodates, such as KHI_2O_6; on the contrary, the solubility of the periodates is decreased by adding periodic acid. The solubilities of some of these salts, in g. of anhydrous salt to 100 g. solvent, are as follows; those of the corresponding perchlorates are added below them:

	$NaIO_4$, 3 H_2O	KIO_4	$RbIO_4$	$CsIO_4$	$(NH_4)IO_4$	$K_4I_2O_9$, 9 H_2O
	12·6/25°	0·51/25°	0·65/13°	2·15/15°	2·70/16°	12·3/25°
$MClO_4$	67·7	2·02	1·52	1·93	19·95	..

It will be seen that of the potassium salts the pyro is some 24 times as soluble as the ortho.

Periodic acid forms a series of hetero-poly-acids with the oxides of molybdenum and tungsten, of the normal hetero-poly-acid type, with one

[916] P. Fleury and J. Lange, *C.R.* 1932, **195**, 1395.
[917] A. Hantzsch, *Ber.* 1927, **60**, 1940.
[918] A. E. Hill, *J.A.C.S.* 1928, **50**, 2678.

molecule of periodate to 6 or more of the other oxide, for example, M_5IO_6, 6 MoO_3.

The structure of the IO_4 ion has been determined by X-ray analysis[919-20]; it has the four oxygen atoms arranged symmetrically round the iodine at the points of a regular tetrahedron. The I—O distance is 1·79 A[920] (theory I—O 1·95, I=O 1·81).

The 'paraperiodate' $(NH_4)_2H_3IO_6$ has been shown[921] to have this formula, and not to be the hydrate $(NH_4)_4I_2O_9$, 3 H_2O; the iodine has an octahedron of 6 Os with I—O 1·93; each O has 3 oxygen neighbours (in other octahedra), 2 of them 3·02 A away and the third (no doubt with a hydrogen bond) at 2·60 A.

SUPPOSED POSITIVE HALOGEN IONS

THE idea that one form that a halogen atom can assume is that of a positive ion seems to have originated in the hypothesis that when a halogen is hydrolysed the molecule breaks up into positive and negative ions, of which the former combines with the negative hydroxyl and the latter with the positive hydrogen ion:

$$X_2 = X^+ + X^-$$
$$X^+ + OH^- = X \cdot OH$$
$$X^- + H^+ = X \cdot H$$

As we have seen, a combined halogen atom usually decomposes in the second of these ways, to give the halogen hydride, but there are many which react in the other way, forming the hypohalous acid and being replaced by hydrogen instead of hydroxyl (e.g. NCl_3, $Br \cdot C(NO_2)_3$ etc.). It is an obvious suggestion that a halogen atom in a compound may be either positive or negative; that if it is negative it forms the halogen hydride and if positive the hypohalous acid.

If the phrase 'positive halogen' (there is no doubt about the existence of negative halogen ions) is only meant to indicate this kind of behaviour, it is harmless and perhaps useful. If, however, it implies the actual existence of positively charged monatomic halogen ions, the question needs further inquiry, and the results of this are on the whole unfavourable.

In the first place, nearly all the attempts to get definite evidence for the existence of positive halogen ions have failed. Thus Philbrick[922] and Faull and Baeckström[923] find that the amount of iodine cations in an aqueous solution of ICl is negligible; Soper and Smith[924] show that the kinetics of the chlorination of phenols gives no support to the idea of positive chlorine ions. Fuoss and his co-workers,[925] from a study of the oxidation potentials

[919] See P. P. Ewald and C. Hermann, *Strukturbericht*, 1913–26, p. 348.
[920] E. A. Hazlewood, *Z. Krist.* 1938, **98**, 439.
[921] L. Helmholz, *J.A.C.S.* 1937, **59**, 2036.
[922] F. A. Philbrick, ib. 1934, **56**, 1257.
[923] J. H. Faull and S. Baeckström, ib. 1932, **54**, 620.
[924] F. G. Soper and G. F. Smith, *J.C.S.* 1926, 1582.
[925] G. S. Forbes, S. W. Glass, and R. M. Fuoss, *J.A.C.S.* 1925, **47**, 2903.

of chlorine, iodine monochloride, and iodine trichloride, concluded that it is unnecessary to assume the existence of positive iodine ions. Noyes and Wilson,[926] though they maintain that positive chlorine ions are present in chlorine water, admit that they can get no electrometric evidence of their presence.

Again, in many reactions in which the presence of positive halogen ions is assumed, there is no real necessity for the assumption. Most of the evidence adduced by W. A. Noyes in a long series of papers really overlooks the distinction between electrovalent and covalent links (as he is inclined to admit[927]), and proves no more than that a halogen atom in certain positions is replaced on hydrolysis by hydrogen and not by hydroxyl. Again, the kinetics of the addition of bromine to double carbon links in alcoholic solution, as we have seen (p. 1221), although it requires the assumption of a positive monobrominated ion

does not provide any proof of the separate existence of positive bromine ions.

If we confine ourselves to considering the behaviour of the halogens in water, where the most satisfactory evidence of the ionic condition is to be obtained, there is one overriding condition which must be satisfied. The halogens (we are not now dealing with fluorine) all form hypohalous acids HOX, which, as acids, can to some extent dissociate into $[X—O]^-$ and $[H]^+$. If positive halogen ions can exist, HOX must also be able to dissociate into $[X]^+$ and $[OH]^-$. But the product of the concentrations of $[H]^+$ and $[OH]^-$ which it gives cannot exceed K_w, the product of $[H]$ and $[OH]$ in water at the temperature in question ($1 \cdot 01 \times 10^{-14}$ at $25°$), or the acid will lose water and go over to the oxide X_2O. Hence, if we know the value of K_a, the (classical) acidic dissociation constant for these acids, we can calculate an upper limit for K_b, the dissociation constant of XOH as a base, which will make $[H^+] \cdot [OH^-] = K_w$ at any given dilution V. It is easy to show that at this dilution

$$[H] = \sqrt{\frac{K_a}{V}} \quad \text{and} \quad [OH] = \sqrt{\frac{K_b}{V}}.$$

Hence since $[H] \cdot [OH]$ is equal to K_w, K_b cannot exceed $(K_w^2 \times V^2)/K_a$. As the values of K_a for HOCl, HOBr, and HOI are approximately known, we can calculate at $25°$ for any given dilutions (say at $V = 1$ and $V = 100$ litres) the maximum value of K_b and the maximum concentration of positive halogen ions which is possible if the acid is not to go over to the oxide X_2O. The results are given below, first the values of K_a and then,

[926] W. A. Noyes and T. A. Wilson, *J.A.C.S.* 1922, **44**, 1630.
[927] Ib. 1934, **56**, 1819.

for each dilution, (*a*) the maximum possible value of the basic dissociation constant, and (*b*) the concentration (normality) of X, the positive halogen ion, which this constant will give at that dilution:

		HOCl	HOBr	HOI
	K_a	3.4×10^{-8}	ca. 10^{-9}	3×10^{-11}
$V = 1$	$\{K_b$ max.	3×10^{-21}	10^{-19}	3×10^{-18}
	$[X^+]$	5.5×10^{-11}	3.2×10^{-10}	1.7×10^{-9}
$V = 100$	$\{K_b$ max.	3×10^{-17}	10^{-15}	3×10^{-14}
	$[X^+]$	5.5×10^{-10}	3.2×10^{-9}	1.7×10^{-8}

It will be seen that, at any rate in water, the concentration of the positive halogen ions can never be more than minute. (See further, Robertson and Waters.[928])

If, however, these positive ions are stabilized by co-ordination, for example, with pyridine, they can exist in quantity. Thus if silver nitrate is treated with chlorine in a dry mixture of pyridine and chloroform, a white solid separates of the composition of the salt $[Cl, py_2]^+(NO_3)$; this melts with decomposition at $77.8°$ C., and is soluble in water, pyridine, and chloroform, but not in ligroin.[929] An exactly similar bromine compound can be made.[930] These are no doubt true salts of the co-ordinated halogen cation; solubility in chloroform is quite common with organic salts. The bromine compound is very reactive; it adds on to cyclohexene to form the saturated bromo-nitrate

Carlsohn[931-2] confirmed the existence of this nitrate,[932] and from the compound $AgClO_4$, 2 py made the corresponding perchlorate $[Br, py_2](ClO_4)$, which is easier to handle as it is not hygroscopic, and not very soluble in water. With sodium hydroxide this gives[933] a yellow solid of the composition of Br_2O, H_2O, py, which he suggests may be a hypobromite with the structure

$$\left[Br\diagdown_{py}^{OH_2} \right]^+ (OBr).$$

With iodine, compounds of this type seem to be more numerous, but they are known only through Carlsohn's work quoted above. The salts obtained were of three kinds, and included the following examples:

(1) $[I, py_2]X : X = NO_3, ClO_4$.

(2) $[I, py]X : NO_3$, acetate, benzoate, etc.

(3) $[I, py]_2X$: succinate, phthalate.

[928] A. Robertson and W. A. Waters, *J.C.S.* 1947, 492.

[929] M. I. Uschakov and V. O. Tchistov, *Bull. Soc.* 1936, [v] **3**, 2142.

[930] Id., *Ber.* 1935, **68**, 824.

[931] See H. Carlsohn, *Diss. Leipzig*, 1924 (unprinted); *Habilitationsschrift Leipzig*, 1932. This last is quoted fairly fully in Gmelin, *Iod*, 1933, 454.

[932] H. Carlsohn, *Ber.* 1935, **68**, 2209.   [933] Id., ib. 2212.

In place of pyridine, picoline, lutidine, and collidine can be used. These compounds must be true salts of an iodine cation since when the nitrate is electrolysed in an organic solvent, the iodine migrates to the cathode. The corresponding bases seem to occur, but they have been little investigated.

It thus appears that the halogens can form cations when these are co-ordinated, but that except in presence of solvents of greater co-ordinating power than water, these positive halogen ions scarcely exist at all. There is no intrinsic improbability in such ions being formed in any ionizing—that is, solvating—solvent. The bare hal$^+$ ion will be unstable because it has only a valency sextet, but by co-ordination, for example, to form $[hal \leftarrow OH_2]^+$, the octet is completed, much as in the ion $[(CH_3)_3Sn \leftarrow OH_2]^+$, which, however, is more stable as the octet is fully shared.

Another series of halogen derivatives which have been supposed to establish the existence of positive halogen ions consists of those in which the halogen atom is united to the anion of a strong acid. But these are almost certainly not true salts but covalent compounds. Much of our knowledge of them is due to the work of Birckenbach and his colleagues[934] on 'pseudo-halogens', that is, compounds behaving like free halogen molecules, including both mixed compounds such as cyanogen bromide Br·CN, and those free from halogens such as cyanogen NC·CN.

A remarkable example is iodine perchlorate, or rather its decomposition products, since the compound itself cannot be isolated. When silver perchlorate in solution is treated with iodine, silver iodide is immediately precipitated.[935] Presumably the compound I·ClO$_4$ (ionized or covalent) is formed at the same time, but this at once reacts with the solvent whatever this may be. Even with so inert a solvent as CCl$_4$ reaction occurs (p. 1236):

$$Ag[ClO_4] + I_2 = AgI + I \cdot ClO_4$$

$$I \cdot ClO_4 + CCl_4 = I \cdot Cl + CCl_3 \cdot ClO_4$$

with the production of trichloromethyl perchlorate. With solvents containing hydrogen attached to carbon this hydrogen is replaced by iodine:

$$-C-H + I \cdot ClO_4 = -C-I + H \cdot ClO_4.$$

This reaction is of practical importance for iodination in organic chemistry, but the perchloric acid must be at once removed as it is a powerful oxidizing agent, especially in the anhydrous state; this can easily be done by adding magnesium or calcium oxide, which forms the perchlorate of the metal and at the same time absorbs the water so produced.

In presence of an unsaturated compound such as cyclohexene there is

[934] L. Birckenbach *et al.*, 'Pseudohalogene', i. *Ber.* 1925, **58**, 786; xxxii, ib. 1936, **69**, 723. Mostly in *Ber.*: some in *Ann.* and *Z. anorg. Chem.*

[935] L. Birckenbach and J. Goubeau, *Ber.* 1932, **65**, 395.

direct addition of $I+ClO_4$ to the double link.[936] This reaction is quite general; addition according to the scheme

$$Ag \cdot X + I_2 \longrightarrow [Ag \cdot I + I \cdot X] \longrightarrow \begin{array}{c} -C-C- \\ | \quad | \\ I \quad X \end{array}$$

to the double link of cyclohexene occurs with a whole series of silver salts, where $X = Cl$, NO_2 acetate, benzoate, etc. This seems to be specific for the silver, mercuric, and aurous salts; the salts of other metals will not react in this way.[937]

The replacement of halogen by hydrogen instead of hydroxyl (see pp. 1189, 1222), is as we have seen no evidence for positive halogen ions at all. It is noticeable that while this replacement is very marked when the carbon atom carrying the halogen is attached to CN (or carbonyl or NO_2) groups,[938] it does not occur at all when the halogen itself is directly attached to CN, in the cyanogen halides, such as $Br \cdot CN$; these are hydrolysed by water to hydrogen halide and cyanic acid.

The degree of hydrolysis of compounds of this 'positive halogen' type has been measured by Birckenbach *et al.*[939]

COMPOUNDS OF POLYVALENT HALOGENS

SOME of the most important of these compounds have already been dealt with, in discussing the interhalogen compounds, the perhalides, the oxides, and the oxy-acids. Of those that remain, which are almost restricted to the compounds of iodine and are nearly all organic, the great majority have the halogen in the trivalent state, as in the iodide chlorides, the iodoso- and the iodonium compounds; the pentavalent state is here practically confined to the iodoxy-compounds. The following table gives the valency groups and the absolute valencies for the main types of compound with which we are now concerned; the symbol (2) indicates the inert pair of electrons.

Type	I^{+++}	$a-I{<}^{b}_{b}$	$Ar \cdot I \rightarrow O$	$Ar \cdot I {=} O$	$[Ar_2I]^+$	$Ar \cdot I{<}^O_O$	$Ar \cdot I{<}^O_O$
Val. gp.	4	(2) 2, 6	4, 4	(2) 2, 6	4, 4	2, 6	(2), 8
Absolute valency	3	3	3	3	3	5	5

The compounds with one or two hydrocarbon radicals (never more) attached to the halogen are both numerous and important, but there is a small group of compounds of trivalent halogens which have no carbon attached to the halogen, made by oxidizing a solution or suspension of

[936] Id. and E. Berninger, ib. 1339.

[937] Id., ib. 1933, **66**, 1280; 1934, **67**, 917, 1420; L. Birckenbach, J. Goubeau, and H. Kolb, ib. 1729.

[938] L. Birckenbach and K. Huttner, ib. 1929, **62**, 153.

[939] L. Birckenbach, K. Huttner, and W. Stein, ib. 2065.

iodine in an acid; they have the composition of salts of the trivalent base $I(OH)_3$, a basic form of the non-existant iodous acid HIO_2; the simplest of these is iodine trichloride. They are commonly called salts, but are almost certainly covalent compounds, although they may at least partially ionize in some solvents (see the acetate below); ICl_3 was discovered by Gay-Lussac in 1814, and the nitrate $I(NO_3)_3$ by Millon in 1844.[940] The recent work on the subject is mainly due to Fichter.[941-4] The compounds are all easily decomposed, are very easily hydrolysed by water, and so are difficult to purify; but they seem to be of two kinds, basic 'salts' of the type $OI \cdot A$, fairly stable, and yellow, and neutral compounds IA_3, less stable than the first class, and colourless.

The following are examples of the neutral compounds:

Nitrate, $I(NO_3)_3$. Made by oxidizing iodine with cold very concentrated nitric acid.[942] It is a yellow very unstable powder; on warming, or with moisture, it is converted into iodine, iodic acid, and oxides of nitrogen.

The Iodate, $I(IO_3)_3$ (I_4O_9) has already been described (p. 1210) among the oxides of iodine.

The Acetate, $I(O \cdot CO \cdot CH_3)_3$ (Schützenberger, 1861), is made by oxidizing iodine in acetic anhydride with nitric acid, or in acetic acid with chlorine monoxide. (Its similarity to antimony acetate $Sb(O \cdot CO \cdot CH_3)_3$ is a good example of the effect of the inert pair.) It forms colourless crystals, and is fairly stable in the cold; on heating it begins to decompose at 100°, and explodes at 140°.[945] In acetic anhydride solution this behaves like a salt[944]; the solution conducts electricity, and on electrolysis the iodine migrates to the cathode. It should be noticed that this does not prove the existence of I^{+++} ions: the results can be accounted for by the presence of $[I(O \cdot CO \cdot CH_3)_2]^+$ ions, which are more probable than I^{+++} since in them the iodine has a complete valency octet, while in I^{+++} (if it is not solvated) it only has a quartet.

The perchlorate[943] is unique among these compounds in being hydrated, having the composition $I(ClO_4)_3, 2H_2O$, which perhaps should be written $[I, 2H_2O]^{+++}(ClO_4)_3$. It is made by dissolving iodine in cooled anhydrous perchloric acid, and oxidizing with ozone. The water for the hydration is mainly formed in the reaction

$$I_2 + 6\ HClO_4 + O_3 = 2\ I(ClO_4)_3 + 3\ H_2O.$$

It is very readily decomposed by more water.

Our knowledge of the 'basic' iodous compounds $OI \cdot X$ or $[OI]X$ is

[940] E. Millon, *Ann. Chim. Phys.* 1844, [3] **12**, 330.

[941] F. Fichter and F. Rohner, *Ber.* 1909, **42**, 4092.

[942] H. Kappeler, ib. 1911, **44**, 3496.

[943] F. Fichter and H. Kappeler, *Z. anorg. Chem.* 1915, **91**, 134 (*J.C.S. Abstr.* 1915, ii. 253).

[944] F. Fichter and S. Stern, *Helv. Chim. Acta*, 1928, **11**, 1256 (*B.C.A.* 1929, A. 41).

[945] For other carboxylates $I(O \cdot CO \cdot R)_3$ see J. W. H. Oldham and A. R. Ubbelohde, *J.C.S.* 1941, 368.

mainly due to Masson.[946-9] The sulphate $(IO)_2SO_4$ can be made[946-7] by heating iodine pentoxide with concentrated sulphuric acid, or by dissolving the pentoxide and iodine together in the slightly diluted acid. It is a white crystalline substance, which is hydrolysed by water with the formation of iodous acid or its decomposition products. It has a remarkable effect on substituted benzenes. If the groups already present are ortho-para directing, it gives a quantitative yield of the *p*-iodonium salt $[Ar_2I]X$[949]; if they are meta-directing, as with nitrobenzene, the iodoso-group is introduced into the meta position,[948] which can be done in no other way.

ORGANIC DERIVATIVES OF POLYVALENT IODINE

These are the compounds in which one or two organic radicals (nearly always aromatic) are attached to the iodine; they include the iodide-chlorides, and the iodoso-, iodoxy-, and iodonium compounds. They were discovered by Willgerodt and by Victor Meyer towards the end of the last century; the work up to 1914 was collected by Willgerodt, in his *Organische Verbindungen mit mehrwertigem Iod*.[950] Recently the subject has been re-examined and extended by Masson and his collaborators.[949,951]

The iodide chlorides $Ar \cdot ICl_2$, the first compounds of the group to be discovered (Willgerodt, 1885) are commonly made by the action of chlorine on the aryl iodides (the alkyl compounds, which are few and much less stable, will be described later); they have all the properties of covalent compounds, and must have the formula

$$Ar—I\underset{\diagdown Cl}{\overset{\diagup Cl}{}},$$

the iodine having the valency group (2), 2, 6, with the inert pair. The corresponding fluorides $Ar \cdot IF_2$ are known, and are very similar in properties to the chlorides; the bromides $R \cdot IBr_2$ are unknown in the aromatic series, but curiously have been made in the aliphatic (see p. 1259).

On treatment with alkali the iodide chlorides have the two chlorine atoms replaced by an oxygen to give the iodoso-compounds $Ar \cdot IO$, which perhaps should be written $Ar \cdot I \rightarrow O$. These are the bases from which the iodide chlorides (and other acid derivatives) can be formed. On heating they readily change by 'disproportionation' into a mixture of the iodide and the more highly oxidized iodoxy-compounds:

$$2\,Ar \cdot IO = Ar \cdot I + Ar \cdot IO_2.$$

These latter, though they are formally analogous to the nitro-compounds,

946 I. Masson, ib. 1938, 1708.
947 I. Masson and W. E. Hanby, ib. 1699.
948 I. Masson and C. Argument, ib. 1702.
949 I. Masson and E. Race, ib. 1937, 1718.
950 Enke, Stuttgart, 1914; referred to in what follows as M.I. with page.
951 I. Masson, E. Race, and F. E. Pounder, *J.C.S.* 1935, 1669.

differ from them in many ways. They are amphoteric, weakly basic, and weakly acidic; the structure is probably like that of the nitro-compounds

$$Ar \cdot I \underset{O}{\overset{O}{\diagdown}} .$$

The iodonium compounds have the same relation to the organic iodides that the sulphonium compounds have to the sulphides, or the ammonium salts to the amines; they are true salts of the type $[Ar_2I]X$. They are formed by a variety of rather unexpected reactions; the simplest is the action of moist silver oxide on a mixture of iodoso- and iodoxy-compounds:

$$Ar \cdot IO + Ar \cdot IO_2 + Ag \cdot OH = Ar_2I[OH] + AgIO_3.$$

Some other forms of compound, especially the amphoteric diaryl iodyl hydroxide $Ar_2IO \cdot OH$, have recently been discovered by Masson.

We may now consider each of these groups in more detail, postponing the aliphatic derivatives, and the mixed iodonium compounds, until later.

*Iodide Chlorides**

These were until recently the source from which all the other organic compounds of trivalent iodine were made. The original[952] and still the chief method of preparation is the direct chlorination of the iodide in any solvent that does not react with (and especially remove the chlorine from) the product; the usual solvent is chloroform or carbon tetrachloride, but ligroin can be employed. They are also formed from the aryl iodide with sulphuryl chloride (which is reduced to sulphur dioxide), or from the iodoso- or iodoxy-compounds (chlorine being produced at the same time from the latter) by the action of concentrated hydrochloric acid upon them, or that of PCl_5 on their suspension in chloroform.

Certain substituted phenyl iodides undergo the addition of chlorine with difficulty or not at all. No trivalent iodine compounds have been obtained from o-di-iodo-benzene,[953] though they are formed by the meta and para isomers, and by o-chloro-iodo-benzene; other examples of this are given below.

The cause of this phenomenon is obscure. It does not seem to be steric, since compounds[954] in which the iodide has an ortho-methyl group and an ortho-bromine, or two ortho-bromine atoms, form the whole series of trivalent iodine compounds quite easily.

Highly chlorinated phenyl iodides[955] can no longer form polyvalent iodine compounds when the ring has more than 3 chlorine atoms, and the presence of 2 chlorine atoms in the ortho-positions restricts their formation very greatly. Thus symmetrical trichloro-iodo-benzene forms an iodide

* The iodide-fluorides are described below, p. 1248.

[952] C. Willgerodt, Report of the 58th meeting of the Verein Deutscher Natur-forscher and Aerzte, Strassburg, 1885.
[953] M.I. 43.   [954] J. McCrae, *J.C.S.* 1898, **73**, 691.
[955] C. Willgerodt and K. Wilcke, *Ber.* 1910, **43**, 2746: see M.I. 50.

chloride, but only with difficulty and in bad yield, and the iodide-chloride produced is unstable; the iodoso-compound cannot be obtained from this with alkali but only with alkaline carbonate, since free alkali reduces the iodide chloride to the iodide: the iodide chloride loses its chlorine in a few days in ether: a basic nitrate can be got but not, as is usual, a neutral nitrate: and finally the iodoxy-compound cannot be obtained at all. It is curious that with the corresponding bromine compound, *s*-tri-bromo-iodobenzene, McCrae[954] found no difficulty in making all the derivatives; but he did not examine the reactions in so much detail as Willgerodt.

No trivalent iodine compounds whatsoever can be obtained from 1-iodo-2, 3, 4, 6-tetrachlorobenzene[956] nor from pentachloro-iodobenzene,[957] nor from hexaiodobenzene.[958] The reaction seems to need the presence of unreplaced hydrogen on the ring, since 1-iodo-2, 5-dichloro-3, 4, 6-tri methyl-benzene also forms none of these compounds.[959] Compounds with two ortho-methyl groups, such as iodomesitylene and iodo-chloro-mesitylene, form trivalent iodine compounds, but they are very unstable.[960] Even the 2,3 and 2,5-dibromo-iodobenzene derivatives show considerable instability[961]; the iodoso-compound of the former loses all its oxygen on standing and gives no iodoxy-compound and no iodonium; of the latter the iodide-chloride is so unstable that its chlorine is lost on evaporating the solution unless this is done in a stream of chlorine.

The iodide chlorides[962] are lemon-yellow crystalline substances, fairly easily soluble in organic solvents other than ligroin. They are slightly soluble in water, which, however, hydrolyses them to the iodoso-compound and HCl; this reaction is reversible, and concentrated HCl will convert the iodoso-compound into the iodide chloride. The chlorine is not very firmly held, and can, in fact, be titrated with thiosulphate. Phenyl iodide chloride $C_6H_5ICl_2$ decomposes on heating at about 100° to give phenyl iodide and elementary chlorine.

Hence the iodide chlorides act as oxidizing and chlorinating agents[965]; they convert alcohol into aldehyde, thiophenol into diphenyl disulphide, and sodium malonic and sodium cyanacetic esters into acetylene tetra-carboxylic and dicyanosuccinic esters respectively. They add on Cl_2 to

[956] M.I. 53.   [957] M.I. 54.   [958] E. Rupp, Diss. Heidelberg, 1897.
[959] M.I. 74.   [960] M.I. 75.   [961] Ib.   [962] M.I. 27.
[963] A. Zlaratow, *Z. f. Nahr. u. Genussmittel*, 1913, **26**, 348.
[964] See W. Bockemüller, *Ber.* 1931, **64**, 522, where the references for many of these reactions are given.
[965] See further R. Neu, ib. 1939, **72**, 1505.

the double carbon link (for example, in α,α-diphenyl ethylene and in stilbene $\Phi \cdot CH = CH \cdot \Phi$) in the same way as elementary chlorine does, but more slowly. It has even been proposed[963] to use phenyl iodide chloride for the quantitative estimation of the unsaturated links in fats.[964] In the same way it will convert alkyl iodides into the chlorides and free iodine; the bromides, such as ethyl bromide, do not seem to be affected.

On standing, phenyl iodide chloride chlorinates itself, giving para-chloro-iodobenzene $+ HCl$.

Apart from these reactions, the most characteristic behaviour of the iodide chlorides is their hydrolysis by water or alkali to the iodoso-compound $Ar \cdot IO$.

Iodide Fluorides, $Ar \cdot IF_2$

These were first obtained by Weinland and Stille[966] by the action of concentrated aqueous hydrofluoric acid on the iodoso-compounds. The latter dissolve readily in hydrofluoric acid, obviously to give the fluorides $Ar \cdot IF_2$, just as they give the chlorides $Ar \cdot ICl_2$ with concentrated hydrochloric acid. The iodide fluorides usually melt at low temperatures, and are difficult to get in the crystalline state, but this can sometimes be done from glacial acetic acid. In this way the para-tolyl compound $p\text{-}CH_3 \cdot C_6H_4 \cdot IF_2$ was made: yellow needles, melting-point 112°, decomposing at 115°; sparingly soluble in acetic acid, and completely hydrolysed by water to $Ar \cdot IO$ and HF. The p-bromo-compound, melting-point 110°, is similar.

Since the iodide chlorides act as weaker chlorinating agents than elementary chlorine, the iodide fluorides might be used for fluorination,[964] in place of the very violent elementary fluorine. They will not by themselves add halogen to the double carbon link, but they form loose addition compounds with HF and with SiF_4, and these react, giving, for example, with α,α-diphenyl ethylene $\Phi_2C = CH_2$ a 60 per cent. yield of the difluoride. This suggests that the trivalent iodine atom holds the fluorines more firmly than the chlorines. The nature of these addition compounds is very obscure; the hydrogen fluoride compound is very unstable: if its chloroform solution is evaporated the HF goes away with the solvent. The SiF_4 compounds appear to be solids, but they could not be purified sufficiently to be sure of their composition.

As a fluorinating agent (i.e. for replacement) phenyl iodide fluoride $\Phi \cdot IF_2$ is very vigorous.[967] It will also remove hydrogen; thus it converts acenaphthene into di-acenaphthyl.

[*Iodide Bromides*, $R \cdot IBr_2$. These compounds, which are known in the alkyl but curiously not in the aryl series, are described below, p. 1259.]

Iodoso-compounds, $Ar \cdot I \rightarrow O$

These are of two kinds: the ordinary kind with 'free' iodoso-groups such as iodosobenzene $C_6H_5 \cdot I \rightarrow O$, and a small number of cyclic compounds,

[966] R. F. Weinland and W. Stille, *Ann.* 1903, **328**, 132.
[967] B. S. Garvey, L. F. Halley, and C. F. H. Allen, *J.A.C.S.* 1937, **59**, 1827.

not unlike ketolactones in structure, such as *o*-iodoso-benzoic acid, which can be shown to be

These cyclic compounds, which are very stable, and have various peculiarities of their own, will be dealt with later (p. 1253). We may first consider the true iodoso-compounds with unmodified —I→O groups.

The iodoso-compounds are formed by the hydrolysis of the iodide chlorides; the exact conditions are somewhat different in each case, as the hydrolysis is reversible. Sometimes water is sufficient for the hydrolysis, but often alkaline carbonate or even hydroxide must be used, though if the reagent is too powerful, it may simply remove chlorine and regenerate the iodide. As both the iodide chloride and the iodoso-compound are very slightly soluble in water, the former must be finely ground, and the treatment continued until the solid, after washing with water, no longer shows an acid reaction.

Oxidation of the iodide to the iodoso very rarely occurs except with the much more stable cyclic compounds.[968]

The iodoso-compounds are greyish-white, amorphous substances, with a very characteristic penetrating 'iodoso smell'; the absence of this smell is a conclusive proof[969] that a free iodoso-group is not present.

In organic solvents (other than acids, with which they react) the iodoso-compounds are almost or quite insoluble, but they dissolve to some extent in water (iodosobenzene 0·81 g. per litre at 16°[951]), and also in methyl alcohol. The aqueous solutions are quite neutral, and so cannot contain an acidic form $Ar \cdot I(OH)_2$. The solubilities of different iodoso-compounds seem to vary in a peculiar way: thus, 1,3-di-methyl-4-iodoso-benzene, melting-point 91° is fairly easily soluble in water[970] while *p*-iodoso-ethyl benzene, though it melts at 89°, is quite insoluble in water.[971]

Iodosobenzene is somewhat poisonous[972] (lethal dose about 0·20 g. per kg. for rabbits and dogs, corresponding to about 12 g. for a man); the iodoxy compounds are much less poisonous, and the simple aryl iodides not at all.

The iodoso-compounds are strong oxidizing agents. Though they are neutral to litmus they soon bleach it; they oxidize alcohol to aldehyde and formic acid to carbonic.[973] Iodosobenzene can also replace hypobromous acid in the Hofmann reaction[974] (oxidation of amides to amines $+CO_2$).

Iodoso-compounds, either alone or in water, change slowly in the cold and rapidly on heating into a mixture of the iodoxy-compound and the iodide. Masson[951] has pointed out that this reaction can be simply

[968] C. Harries, *Ber.* 1903, **36**, 2996.   [969] M.I. 2.   [970] M.I. 67.   [971] M.I. 71.
[972] M.I. 233.   [973] M.I. 32.   [974] J. Tscherniac, *Ber.* 1903, **36**, 218.

expressed as a result of the dipole association of the iodoso-molecules:

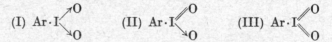

Iodoso 'Salts'

The iodoso-group behaves with acids like a diacid base, giving, for example, as we have seen, the iodide chloride with HCl and the iodide fluoride with HF. Other acids, both inorganic and organic, behave in the same way. The products $Ar \cdot IX_2$ are often called salts, but there is evidence that most if not all of them are covalent. They are made by the action of the acid on the iodoso-compound; with strong acids it is often convenient to work in glacial acetic acid.[975] Thus there is a nitrate $C_6H_5I(NO_3)_2$[976]: large greenish-yellow crystals, exploding feebly at 105–106°, hydrolysed by water at once: a chromate $C_6H_5I(CrO_4)$ made with a solution of chromic oxide in acetic acid: orange-red, explodes at 66°; an acetate $C_6H_5 \cdot I(O \cdot CO \cdot CH_3)_2$,[977] colourless crystals, easily soluble in acetic acid, chloroform, and benzene, very slightly in ether: melting-point 156–157°: slowly hydrolysed by water. The propionate and butyrate are similar.

Iodoxy-compounds, $Ar \cdot IO_2$

These are (the only organic) compounds of pentavalent iodine, which-ever of the three possible formulae

$$\text{(I) } Ar \cdot I \!\!\begin{array}{c}\diagup O\\\diagdown O\end{array} \qquad \text{(II) } Ar \cdot I \!\!\begin{array}{c}\diagup O\\\diagdown O\end{array} \qquad \text{(III) } Ar \cdot I \!\!\begin{array}{c}\diagup O\\\diagdown O\end{array}$$

we adopt; no doubt there is resonance between all three.

The iodoxy-compounds are commonly made[978] from the iodoso, which change spontaneously on keeping, especially if they are warmed, into a mixture of iodoxy-compound and iodide.[979] It is usually most convenient to boil the iodoso-compound with water, when the iodide goes off with the steam; the iodoxy-compounds are non-volatile, and can be recrystallized from water or from acetic acid.

They can also be made by oxidizing the iodoso or the iodide chlorides with hypochlorous acid, or with bleaching powder and acetic acid, or directly from the iodides[980] by treating these with bromine and then with alkali; as there are no iodide bromides, the oxidizing agent must be hypobromous acid.

Our knowledge of the properties, both physical and chemical, of the iodoxy-compounds has been much increased, and considerably modified, by the work of Masson[951] and his collaborators.

[975] M.I. 33.　　　　　　　　　　　　　[976] C. Willgerodt, *Ber.* 1892, **25**, 3498.

[977] J. Tscherniac, ib. 1903, **36**, 218.　　　　　　　　　　[978] M.I. 13.

[979] C. Willgerodt, *Ber.* 1893, **26**, 1307; P. Askenasy and V. Meyer, ib. 1356.

[980] M.I. 16.

The iodoxy-compounds, like the iodoso, are usually white substances. Iodoxybenzene can be heated to 230° without either decomposing or melting, and it has no perceptible vapour pressure even at this temperature. It is slightly soluble in water (sol^y 0·274/14°, 1·17/99°; Φ·IO 0·081/16°)[951]; in inert organic solvents it is even less soluble. The insolubility does not appear to be due to polymerization, since the substance is shown by the freezing-points to be monomeric in water[951] and in formic acid.[981] It has been suggested that the substance Ar·IO$_2$ might be the iodonium periodate Ar$_2$I[IO$_4$], but Masson made this salt, which has quite different properties from iodoxybenzene; it forms large colourless crystals; it is several times as soluble in water, and it melts with decomposition at 129°, more than 100° lower than iodoxybenzene. Since iodoxybenzene is neither polymerized nor ionized in solution, its obvious association in the solid is

difficult to explain. A dipole attraction of the $-I\begin{smallmatrix}\nearrow O \\ \searrow O\end{smallmatrix}$ groups has been

suggested (Masson), but it is not clear why this should be greater than with nitrobenzene, which is much more volatile and more soluble. The greater solubility of iodoxybenzene in water and in formic acid suggests that it interacts with those solvents. The instability of the double I$=$O link may be relieved in solution by solvation, e.g. to

$$Ar\cdot I\begin{smallmatrix}\nearrow O \\ \leftarrow O-H \\ \searrow O-H\end{smallmatrix}$$

while in the solid the same end is achieved by the polymerization of the molecules through the formation of I—O—I links. This would not occur with the nitro compounds, because the N—O links are not unstable.

The iodoxy-compounds hold their oxygen more firmly than the iodoso, and they are not such strong oxidizing agents; they will, however, oxidize hydrogen chloride with the production of the iodide chloride and free chlorine. With hydrogen fluoride, where obviously the free halogen cannot be liberated, a pentavalent fluoride Ar·IOF$_2$ is formed,[960] an unstable compound which, like the iodide fluorides, is quantitatively decomposed by water to the iodoxy-compound and hydrogen fluoride.

On heating, the iodoxy-compounds do not melt, but explode at fairly definite temperatures, often with great violence.

Iodoxybenzene is commonly described as neutral, but Masson has shown that it is both a weak acid and a weak base; its compounds with acids and with alkalies are readily hydrolysed. Dilute sulphuric acid has no action on it, but the acid H$_2$SO$_4$, 2 H$_2$O forms a sulphate Φ·IO$_2$, H$_2$SO$_4$ (m. pt. 127°): colourless crystals, insoluble in organic solvents and broken up by water. Iodoxybenzene must be more basic than nitrobenzene, for this sulphate is produced by an acid which is sufficiently diluted to hydrolyse

[981] L. Mascarelli and M. Martinelli, *Atti R.* 1907, [5] **16**, i. 183 (*Chem. Centr.* 07, i. 1322).

the corresponding nitro-derivative $\Phi \cdot NO_2, H_2SO_4$, which also has the much lower melting-point of 12°.[982] With the dihydrate of perchloric acid iodoxybenzene forms a perchlorate, which may have the structure

$$\left[C_6H_5—I \underset{\underset{O}{}}{\overset{\overset{+}{O}}{<}} H \right] (ClO_4) \ ;$$

it is, however, violently explosive, and was not further examined.

The behaviour of the iodoxy-compounds with alkalies is much more complicated and remarkable.[951]

The iodoxy-compound dissolves in the alkali, but can be precipitated at once unchanged by carbon dioxide; it must therefore be a weak acid, and the conductivity shows that K is about 10^{-11}. The freezing-point of the alkaline solution is not affected by the addition of the iodoxy-compound, so that ions of the composition $ArIO_2OH$ must be produced. The structure may well be

$$Ar—I \underset{\underset{O—H}{}}{\overset{\overset{\bar{O}}{}}{\rightarrow}} O \ .$$

Its salts (iodoxylates) were not prepared, as the acid soon decomposes.

After a few hours in the cold, the solution of iodoxybenzene in alkali completely changes; it now contains C_6H_5I, IO_3^- ions, and a new oxidizing substance which was shown not to be C_6H_5IO, IO_4^-, IO_2^-, IO^-, ozone, nor any compound with an —O—O— link. From this solution carbon dioxide precipitates a carbonate, which acetic acid converts into the acetate $\Phi_2IO(O \cdot CO \cdot CH_3)H_2O$, insoluble in water, soluble in benzene and chloroform, melting-point 114° with decomposition. Hence the reaction is:

$$2[Ar \cdot IO_2 \cdot OH]^- = Ar_2IO \cdot OH + IO_3^- + OH^-.$$

This diaryl iodyl hydroxide is a strong oxidizing agent; it is weakly basic and forms the carbonate and acetate described above, but it will not react with strong acids. Hence the products are evidently not true salts but are covalent compounds. The most probable of the formulae suggested by Masson is perhaps this (I = (2) $\underline{10}$).

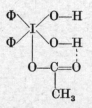

For complex mercuric compounds see references.[987–8]

[982] I. Masson, *J.C.S.* 1931, 3200.
[983] D. Vorländer and H. David, *Ber.* 1937, **70**, 146.
[984] H. Lütgert, ib. 151.

Iodoxybenzene is broken up by alkalies slowly (quickly at 100°) to benzene and sodium iodate. Its derivatives behave in the same way. Hence —IO_2 is a very mobile and also a 'positive' group, one that is replaced by hydrogen, and so it is of a cationoid nature.[951] It should therefore direct substitution to the meta position. This has been difficult to prove, but Masson[951] has shown that under proper conditions iodoxy-benzene can be quantitatively mononitrated by nitric acid, and that 99·5 per cent. of the product is meta. According to the Hammick–Illingworth rule[985] —SbO_2 should be meta-directing, but not —IO_2; so this is a good example of the way in which the 'inert pair' makes an element behave like the one two places before it in the Periodic Table. The mobility of the —IO_2 group is remarkable; it is turned out from *p*-iodoxy-nitrobenzene by dilute nitric acid, silver hydroxide, sodium nitrite, or sodium azide.[983] In ortho-para dinitro-iodoxybenzene the iodoxy group is even more easily removed.[984]

Cyclic Derivatives of Trivalent Iodine

If the iodine in *o*-iodobenzoic acid is converted into the trivalent state, it is liable to react with the carboxyl group with the formation of a ring compound; the first iodoso-compound to be made was of this type, got by the direct oxidation of *o*-iodobenzoic acid,[989] a reaction which will not produce the ordinary 'free' iodoso-groups. Ring-compounds of this kind are known among the derivatives of iodide chlorides and iodoso-compounds, but not of iodoxy-compounds.

According to Willgerodt[990] if *o*-iodobenzoic is chlorinated in glacial acetic acid, two compounds are formed, (*a*) the normal dichloride

$$C_6H_4(COOH)ICl_2$$

sintering at 75–80° and melting at 95°, and (*b*) a substance differing in composition from the first by 1 HCl, which sinters at 100° and melts with decomposition at 115–120°. These must be

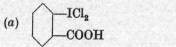   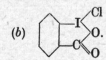

This seems to be the only known cyclic derivative of the aryl iodide chloride type. Thiele has, however,[991] made the corresponding derivatives of chloro-iodofumaric and of α-chloro-iodoacrylic acid:

[985] D. Ll. Hammick and W. S. Illingworth, *J.C.S.* 1930, 2358.

The cyclic iodoso-compounds are much better known. Ortho-iodoso-benzoic acid was made by Victor Meyer[989,992] by the oxidation of ortho-iodobenzoic acid with nitric acid, or with potassium permanganate in presence of sulphuric acid, or from the iodide chloride prepared in chloroform solution (this is undoubtedly the true —ICl_2 compound, Willgerodt's (*a*) form) with alkali, or even with water alone. It forms long colourless needles, melting at 244°; on rapid heating it explodes at about 250°. This must be the cyclic compound A (below) and not the isomeric B because[993]:

(A) (B)

1. It has not got the characteristic iodoso smell.

2. All true iodoso-compounds (with uncombined —IO groups) when heated with water are converted into a mixture of the iodide and the iodoxy, or sometimes (with loss of oxygen) into the iodide alone; this compound on the contrary is entirely unaffected by boiling with water; this is one of the signs of the greater stability of the cyclic compounds.

3. All true iodoso-compounds oxidize alcohol to aldehyde; *o*-iodoso-benzoic acid can be boiled with 50 per cent. aqueous alcohol without change (another sign of its stability).

4. It was shown[992] that whereas normal iodoso-compounds are converted by heating with acetic anhydride into diacetates Ar·$I(OAc)_2$, this compound is wholly converted into a monacetate, melting-point 166–167°, which must be

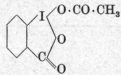

5. Ortho-iodosobenzoic acid is a very weak acid, weaker than carbonic; it only turns litmus reddish-purple, while the *m*- and *p*-acids turn it red. Ostwald[992] found the dissociation constants to be:

$1·32 \times 10^{-3}$ $0·6 \times 10^{-6}$

[987] L. Mascarelli, *Atti R. Linc.* 1905, [5] **14**, ii. 199 (*Chem. Centr.* 05. ii. 893).
[988] See M.I. 38. [989] V. Meyer and W. Wachter, *Ber.* 1892, **25**, 2632.
[990] *J. prakt. Chem.* 1894, **49**, 476.
[991] J. Thiele and W. Peter, *Ann.* 1909, **369**, 119.
[992] V. Meyer and P. Askenasy, *Ber.* 1893, **26**, 1357. [993] See M.I. 134.

(ratio 2,200:1); the compound is obviously far weaker than a true carboxylic acid.

Owing to the cyclic stability it is only a weak oxidizing agent.

It is amphoteric: it forms salts both with acids and with bases; the sodium, calcium, and barium salts are amorphous and highly hydrolysed, and, as we should expect with a very weak acid, there is no ammonium salt. The compounds with acids, such as the nitrate, are at once hydrolysed by water. A whole series of substitution products of o-iodosobenzoic acid have been made, which all have very similar properties; the o-iodo-phthalic acid derivative is a definite but monobasic acid, as we should expect.

o-Iodoxybenzoic acids, which can be made by oxidizing the iodoso-compound with potassium permanganate, or by dissolving in alkali and passing in chlorine,[994] are quite normal. The simple o-iodoxybenzoic acid must have the structure

$$\text{(benzene ring)} \begin{array}{l} -IO_2 \\ -CO \cdot OH \end{array} ;$$

it is easily soluble in water; it is a strong acid and expels CO_2 from carbonates; its salts are normal. On keeping it is partly converted into the iodoso-compound, a very striking proof of the stability of the latter, as iodoso-compounds with normal free —IO groups always go over spontaneously into the iodoxy.

IODONIUM COMPOUNDS

These are the salts of the cations Ar_2I^+. They were originally obtained by Victor Meyer[995] by a peculiar method, the treatment of iodosobenzene with a large excess of sulphuric acid, when apparently the reaction

$$2 \, \Phi \cdot IO \longrightarrow \begin{array}{c} \Phi \\ I \cdot C_6H_4 \end{array} \hspace{-0.3em} > \hspace{-0.3em} I \, [SO_4H] + \text{'O'}$$

occurs; the iodo-iodonium salt is certainly produced: the fate of the extra oxygen 'O' is unknown, but a good deal of resin is formed.

Another method[996] is to treat a mixture of iodoso and iodoxy with moist silver oxide:

$$Ar \cdot IO + Ar \cdot IO_2 + AgOH = Ar_2I(OH) + AgIO_3.$$

Alkali can be used in place of silver oxide, and then on reduction with sulphur dioxide the iodonium iodide is precipitated. In this reaction the diaryl iodyl base $Ar_2IO \cdot OH$ must first be formed, and then reduced to the iodonium salt (see p. 1252).

A quite different reaction,[997] which can synthesize unsymmetrical

[994] V. Meyer and C. Hartmann, *Ber.* 1894, **27**, 1600.
[995] C. Hartmann and V. Meyer, ib. 426.   [996] Id., ib. 504.
[997] C. Willgerodt, ib. 1897, **30**, 56; 1898, **31**, 915.

iodonium bases, is to shake the iodide chloride in the cold with water and mercury diaryl, when a mixture of $Ar \cdot Hg \cdot Cl$ and the double salt $(Ar_2I)_2[HgCl_4]$ is produced. The latter is then extracted with water and decomposed by hydrogen sulphide.

Probably the best method of preparing the iodonium compounds is that of Masson and Race.[998] They find that if benzene, toluene, or chloro-, bromo-, or iodo-benzene is shaken with a cold solution of iodine pentoxide in concentrated sulphuric acid, it dissolves to form a dark solution. After adding cold water and filtering off a small quantity of iodo-compound the filtrate on reduction with sulphur dioxide gives a large yield of the yellow salt $Ar_2I[I]$. In this reaction the iodine always enters in the para position to any methyl or halogen already present; with meta directing substituents like NO_2 only small yields of the iodonium salts are got.

This reaction is obscure, but it can be summarized thus:

$$HIO_3 + 2\ Ar \cdot H + H_2SO_4 = Ar_2I[SO_4H] + 2\ H_2O + \text{`O'}.$$

The state of the oxidizing agent represented by 'O' is not explained, but about 15 per cent. of the aromatic compound is lost, and no doubt is oxidized by this oxygen. Probably the iodine pentoxide is reduced by part of the organic material to the trivalent stage, which in the presence of the sulphuric acid (which is necessary to the reaction) is stabilized as the sulphate; Fichter and Kappeler[999] have shown that such a sulphate of trivalent iodine is formed. We may suppose that this acts in the form of the iodyl ion IO^+ (or much less probably the trivalent I^{+++} ion) thus:

$$IO^+ + 2\ H \cdot Ar = H_2O + Ar_2I^+.$$

The iodine atom in the iodonium ion Ar_2I^+ has a complete octet of electrons and an inert gas number; there is thus no question of the iodonium compounds (except perhaps to a small extent the free base) not being ionized. The ionic structure of the salts, and in particular the halides, is evident. They are fairly soluble in water; they give conducting solutions, as do also the free bases; they form double salts of the types $[Ar_2I]_2PtCl_6$, $[Ar_2I]_2HgCl_4$, and $Ar_2I[AuCl_4]$ (no such double salts are formed by the iodide chlorides). The X-ray measurement of the iodide confirms this conclusion[1000]; the shortest distance between two iodine atoms in diphenyl iodonium iodide is 3·5 A.U.; the theory for the sum of the radii of one iodine atom and one I^- ion is 3·53: for the covalent I—I link (2 atomic radii) 2·7; the I—I distance in NH_4I_3 was found[1001] to be 2·8 A.U.

Further it has been shown[1002] that if inactive $\Phi_2I[I]$ is treated in solution with radioactive sodium iodide, it at once shares half its iodine with the

[998] I. Masson and E. Race, *J.C.S.* 1937, 1718.

[999] F. Fichter and H. Kappeler, *Z. anorg. Chem.* 1915, **91**, 134.

[1000] W. V. Medlin, *J.A.C.S.* 1935, **57**, 1026.

[1001] R. C. L. Mooney, *Phys. Rev.* 1934, **45**, 755.

[1002] F. Juliusburger, B. Topley, and J. Weiss, *J.C.S.* 1935, 1295.

organic salt, but the linking iodine atom is not shared, and if the iodonium is precipitated with excess of inactive sodium iodide it is found to be inactive. This covalent iodine atom is not exchanged at all, even on heating up to its decomposition point. The free iodonium bases $Ar_2I \cdot OH$ are only known in solution, being made from the halides with silver oxide. The solution has a strong alkaline reaction and absorbs CO_2 from the air to form a carbonate (this does not necessitate a higher dissociation constant than about 10^{-5}, since ammonia behaves in this way). The salts are more or less soluble in water; the iodide is the least soluble of the halides and the fluoride the most.[1004] They include a series of perhalides,[1003] such as $\Phi_2I[ICl_2]$, $\Phi_2I[Cl_3]$ (a very rare type), and $\Phi_2I[ICl_4]$, melting-point 119°.

A cyclic iodonium compound, in which the two carbon atoms attached to the iodine are part of the same radical, has been prepared by Mascarelli in the o, o'-diphenylene iodonium salts.[1005] This base was made from the corresponding di-iodo-compound by treating a mixture of its iodoso and iodoxy-compounds with silver oxide. The free base has the structure

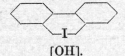

[OH].

It was not isolated, but the solution was found to be strongly alkaline, and to absorb CO_2 from the air. A series of its salts were prepared.[1006] In this compound, as in the cyclic iodoso-compounds, the ring-structure is the cause of exceptional stability. The iodonium compound is formed with the greatest ease, being produced from the corresponding di-iodide chloride or di-iodoso-compound on keeping, and also produced directly when o, o'-diamino-diphenyl is diazotized and treated with alkaline potassium iodide.

When the iodonium iodides are heated, they decompose a little above 100° into two molecules of the iodide:

$$Ar_2I \, [I] = 2 \, Ar \cdot I.$$

Two mechanisms have been suggested for this reaction: (A) that in a first stage one aryl group breaks off from the iodine, and this group then combines with an iodine ion; (B) that the iodine ion substitutes in one ring first, before the scission takes place.

These hypotheses were tested by Lucas[1007] by examining the products of decomposition of di-o-tolyl iodonium iodide, which goes over completely in the solid state in a few minutes at 155°. This substance on mechanism (A) would give (see below) two molecules of o-iodotoluene; on (B), since

[1003] M. O. Forster and J. H. Schaeppi, ib. 1912, **101**, 382.

[1004] H. J. Eméleus and H. G. Heal, ib. 1946, 1126.

[1005] L. Mascarelli, *Atti R. Linc.* 1907, **16**, ii. 562; 1908, **17**, ii. 580; 1912, **21**, ii. 617.

[1006] See M.I. 206.

[1007] J. H. Lucas, E. R. Kennedy, and C. A. Wilmot, *J.A.C.S.* 1936, **58**, 157.

the new iodine atom would presumably enter ortho- or para- to the linking iodine, it would give 1 molecule of ortho- and 1 of meta-iodotoluene:

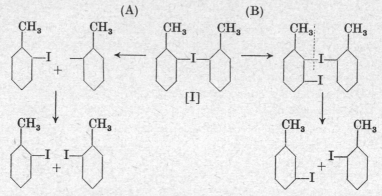

Experiment showed that only ortho-iodotoluene was formed, so the first mechanism appears to be the true one.

The dynamics of this reaction were studied by Fletcher and Hinshelwood.[1008] They determined the rate of decomposition of a saturated solution of phenyl iodonium iodide in phenyl iodide (the reaction took several hours at 111°: sol^y 0·00106/0°, 0·00290/25°, 0·0334/95°). The reaction is probably unimolecular, and the heat of activation 29·5 k.cals. The rate of reaction is between 10^4 and 10^5 times as great as is calculated from the number of collisions with this heat of activation, allowing for two squared terms, and so indicates that the molecule has about 7 degrees of freedom. The rates of decomposition which have been previously measured of the salts of the bases NR_4, PR_4, and SR_3 also show this ratio of about 10^5.

With the unsymmetrical *p*-anisyl-phenyl iodonium chloride and bromide it has been shown[1009-10] that on decomposition the anisyl nucleus remains attached to the iodine, and the phenyl goes to the bromine or chlorine.

ALIPHATIC COMPOUNDS OF TRIVALENT IODINE

These were discovered by Thiele; they are few in number and all unstable. The derivatives with saturated alkyl groups are the least stable; unsaturated radicals such as —CH=CR$_2$ behave more like aryls. The formation of these trivalent iodine compounds, and especially of the iodide chlorides from which the rest are obtained, is opposed by a tendency to three reactions: (1) a redissociation into $R \cdot I + Cl_2$, (2) the chlorination by the —ICl$_2$ group (with its reduction to —I) of some other part of the molecule, and (3) the reaction

$$R \cdot ICl_2 = R \cdot Cl + ICl.$$

The last of these reactions will be less likely to occur the firmer the attachment of the iodine to the hydrocarbon radical, and this attachment is

[1008] C. J. M. Fletcher and C. N. Hinshelwood, *J.C.S.* 1935, 596.

[1009] R. B. Sandin, M. Kulka, and R. McCready, *J.A.C.S.* 1937, **59**, 2014.

[1010] R. B. Sandin, F. T. McClure, and F. Irwin, ib. 1939, **61**, 2944.

strong both with an aryl, and when a doubly linked carbon carries the iodine. In a saturated alkyl iodide it is relatively weak.

Thiele[1011] showed that many alkyl iodides if treated at a low temperature with chlorine in a mixture of carbon tetrachloride and ligroin are converted into iodide chlorides; this was effected with methyl iodide, methylene di-iodide (only one iodine being converted into $-ICl_2$), ethyl, isopropyl, and tertiary butyl iodides. The products are yellow crystalline solids, which are very unstable and even at low (and fairly definite) temperatures decompose into alkyl chloride $+ICl$. The most stable are the methylene compound $I \cdot CH_2 \cdot ICl_2$ (decomposition point $-11 \cdot 5°$); $CH_3 \cdot ICl_2$ ($-28°$); $C_2H_5 \cdot ICl_2$ ($-36°$). The secondary and especially the tertiary compounds are far less stable; the isopropyl compound decomposes only just above $-100°$, and the tertiary butyl far below it. No iodoso- or iodoxy-compounds were obtained from them, but Thiele made, in the same way as the chlorides, methyl iodide bromide $CH_3 \cdot IBr_2$, orange-yellow plates (analysed) decomposing at $-45°$.

The remarkable fact that methyl iodide bromide is not much less stable than the iodide chloride, whereas among the much more stable aryl derivatives the iodide bromides are unknown, may be due to steric causes. It is probable (though not certain) that the three atoms attached to the iodine lie in a plane with it, and there may be room for a methyl, but not for an aryl, in addition to the two bromines.

More stable than these saturated compounds are the vinyl derivatives, containing the group $I-C=C$[1012]; this is no doubt mainly due to the much firmer attachment of the iodine. Thus symmetrical di-iodo- and chloro-iodo-ethylene both give iodide chlorides

$$I \cdot CH=CH \cdot ICl_2 \text{ and } Cl \cdot CH=CH \cdot ICl_2;$$

the first of these decomposes at $+37°$; the second, which is more stable, has a real melting-point of $77°$. This latter is stable enough to be converted by alkalies into the iodoso-compound $Cl \cdot CH=CH \cdot IO$, which has the characteristic 'iodoso smell', and gives the usual derivatives with acids such as a diacetate and a chromate; it is not very stable; it explodes at $63°$; it decomposes on keeping; if it is treated with water at $72-75°$ it is converted in the normal way into the iodoxy-compound and the iodide, i.e. into $Cl \cdot CH=CH \cdot IO_2 + Cl \cdot CH=CH \cdot I$. The iodoxy-compound forms white crystals, which explode with great violence if heated to $135°$, or if struck or rubbed. It dissolves fairly readily in water, but not in the ordinary organic solvents. It dissolves readily in sodium hydroxide solution, evolving acetylene:

$$Cl \cdot CH=CH \cdot IO_2 + H_2O = HIO_3 + C_2H_2 + HCl.$$

A further series of non-aromatic trivalent iodine derivatives are the cyclic fumaric and acrylic compounds already mentioned (p. 1253).

[1011] J. Thiele and W. Peter, *Ann.* 1909, **369**, 149.
[1012] J. Thiele and H. Haakh, ib. 131.

Iodonium salts containing non-aryl radicals were first made by Willgerodt[1013] by the action of an iodide chloride on silver acetylide in presence of water:

$$2 \; Ar \cdot ICl_2 + Ag \cdot C \!=\! CH = Ar \!-\! I \!-\! \underset{\underset{Cl}{|}}{C} \!=\! \underset{\underset{Cl}{|}}{C} \!-\! H + AgCl + ArI.$$
$$[Cl]$$

This reaction was extended by Thiele,[1012] who acted with silver acetylide on the iodide chloride of chloro-iodo-ethylene, and obtained the purely aliphatic iodonium salt with this formula.

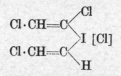

At the same time a certain amount of the iodoso-compound $Cl \cdot CH \!=\! CH \cdot IO$ is undoubtedly formed, and can be recognized by its smell.

These iodonium salts resemble those of the diaryl iodonium bases very closely. Thus the chloride is easily soluble in water, and forms double salts with auric and platinic chlorides. The bromide and iodide are sparingly soluble in water. Treatment of the halides with alkali, in order to obtain the free base, led to complete decomposition.

Attempts to make the iodide chloride from acetyl iodide, and from benzyl iodide, were quite unsuccessful.

ELEMENT NO. 85 (ASTATINE*)[1024]

THERE seems to be no doubt now that this element has been obtained as artificial product of nuclear bombardment. The claim[1014-15] to have identified it among the products of the decay of radium, or perhaps of thorium[1016] or actinium[1017,1020] has been disputed,[1018] and is not yet established. It is, however, probable[1019-21] that it is among the products of radium, being formed from RaA by the loss of a β-particle.

Segré *et al.* found[1022-3] that when bismuth (chosen because the next element polonium is so rare) is bombarded with α-particles of 32 m.e.v. energy, a product is obtained of 7·5 hours half-life, which cannot be identified with Tl, Pb, Bi, Po, or any other known element up to uranium, and so is probably No. 85, though its properties are rather more like those

* This name, meaning unstable, has been suggested for the element.

[1013] *Ber.* 1897, **30**, 56; 1898, **31**, 915.
[1014] H. Hulubei and Y. Cauchois, *C.R.* 1939, **209**, 39.
[1015] Id., ib. 1940, **210**, 696.
[1016] W. Minder, *Helv. Phys. Acta*, 1940, **13**, 144 (*Amer. C.A.* 1940, 7735).
[1017] A. Leigh-Smith and W. Minder, *Nature*, 1942, **150**, 767.
[1018] B. Karlik and T. Bernert, *Naturwiss.*, 1942, **30**, 685.
[1019] S. Flügge and A. Krebs, ib. 1944, **32**, 71.
[1020] B. Karlik and T. Bernert, ib. 44.   [1021] Id., ib. 1946, **33**, 23.
[1022] D. R. Corson, K. R. MacKenzie, and E. Segré, *Phys. Rev.* 1940, ii. **57**, 459.
[1023] Id., ib. ii. **58**, 672.

of polonium. If it is mixed with a bismuth salt it is precipitated with it by hydrogen sulphide; if it is mixed with iodine it is not separated along with it by silver nitrate; it can be deposited electrolytically. One of its few haloid properties is that it is found to be concentrated in the thyroids of guinea-pigs. Paneth points out[1024] that it should be easy to identify it by reduction to the volatile hydride.

The element undergoes further change in an unusual way:

$$\overset{211}{\underset{85}{}} + \overset{0}{\underset{-1}{}}e \xrightarrow{\text{7·5 hours}} \overset{211}{\underset{84}{}} \text{AcC}'$$

$$\overset{211}{\underset{84}{}} \text{AcC}' \xrightarrow{\text{1/300 sec.}} \overset{207}{\underset{82}{}} \text{AcD} + \overset{4}{\underset{2}{}} \text{He}.$$

The first of these two reactions is peculiar, in that the 85 nucleus picks up one of its own K electrons.

[1024] F. A. Paneth, *Nature*, 1942, **149**, 567.

GROUP VII A

	25 Manganese	43 Technetium	75 Rhenium	[93 Neptunium]
At. wt. 1938 .	54·93	(ca. 98)	186·31	
Rad. of atom .	1·18	. .	1·37 A.U.	
Parts per million in earth's crust .	930	0	0·001	

THE distribution of the elements in this subgroup is peculiar. The first member, manganese, is about the tenth commonest element in the earth's crust. It has been known from very early times, and much of its chemistry was described by Scheele in 1774. It remained the only known member of the subgroup for 150 years after this, until in 1925 Noddack and Frl. Tacke announced the discovery of the next two elements 43 and 75, which they called Masurium and Rhenium; they had made a systematic search among what they thought the most probable minerals, and after considerably concentrating any Gp. VII A elements that might be present, claimed to have identified these two by means of their X-ray lines. Since this announcement rhenium has been obtained in some quantity; it is about as abundant in the earth's crust as rhodium or iridium; its chemistry has been worked out in very considerable detail. With masurium, on the other hand, no subsequent work has been reported, so that it must be assumed that it has not yet been shown to be a permanent component of the earth, although recently it has been made by nuclear bombardment, in quantities minute but sufficient for some of its more important chemical properties to be determined. Element 93 (neptunium) has now been made in quantity in the production of plutonium for the atomic bomb, and much of its chemistry is known (see VI. 1094); but as a 'uranide' element it does not belong to Gp. VII any more than cerium does to Gp. IV or praseodymium to Gp. V.

Our chemical knowledge of the members of this subgroup is thus almost confined to the two elements manganese and rhenium.

On the analogy of other A subgroups, we should expect the elements to have valencies ranging from 2 (or possibly 1) to the group valency of 7, and the only compounds showing any resemblance to those of the Gp. VII B elements (the halogens) to be those in which the atom has this group valency of 7, that is, the permanganates and perrhenates as compared with the perchlorates and periodates. Also on going from manganese to rhenium the lower valencies should become less stable as compared with the higher, and in any particular valency the tendency to form cations should become less.

The facts entirely confirm these expectations. Manganese has valencies of 7, 6, 4, 3, 2, and probably 1; rhenium has all these and 5 as well. With manganese the most stable valencies are 7, 4, and 2, the first being that of the permanganates and the last that of the divalent cation. In rhenium the stability of the highest valency of 7 in the perrhenates is markedly greater than that of manganese in the permanganates; the valency of 4 is stable with rhenium also, while the valency of 2 with rhenium, though it does occur in solution, is so unstable that the compounds cannot be isolated.

The greater stability of the highest valency in rhenium is shown in the heptoxide, which boils undecomposed at 350°, while Mn_2O_7 begins to lose oxygen at 0°; in consequence, if a rhenium compound is heated in air, the rhenium sublimes away as the heptoxide (just as osmium does as OsO_4), whereas manganese is ultimately left behind as manganous oxide MnO. So too, while $KMnO_4$ begins to give off oxygen at 200°, $KReO_4$ can be distilled without change at 1,370°.

A striking difference is that rhenium heptoxide and the perrhenates are colourless, apparently because the absorption bands are shifted with rhenium into the ultra-violet. The rhenates M_2ReO_4 are, however, green like the manganates, and many of the rhenium compounds of the lower valencies are coloured.

The other element of this subgroup, masurium 43, can be got only by nuclear bombardment, and so only in minute quantities. Enough, however, is known of its chemistry to show that it resembles rhenium far more closely than manganese; if the active material is mixed with manganese and rhenium and the two are separated, the activity practically always goes with the rhenium. This is to be expected from the behaviour of the previous A subgroups, as may be seen by comparing Ti with Zr and Hf, V with Nb and Ta, Cr with Mo and W, or Fe with Ru and Os.

MANGANESE

MANGANESE is present in the earth's crust to the extent of 930 parts per million[1025] (compare F 270, P 786, S 500, Cl 480, Ba 390; the only commoner elements are, in order of atomic numbers O, Na, Mg, Al, Si, K, Ca, Ti, and Fe, so that manganese is tenth in order of abundance). It is very widely distributed in minerals, and next to iron one of the most frequent constituents of rocks; it is widely distributed also in the vegetable and to a less extent in the animal kingdom. Its most important ore is pyrolusite MnO_2, but there are many others, nearly all of them oxides, such as braunite Mn_2O_3 and hausmannite Mn_3O_4; iron ores nearly always contain a certain proportion of manganese.

Metallic manganese is mainly used (to the extent of more than a million tons per annum) to remove oxygen from iron and steel, being employed in the form of its iron alloys spiegeleisen and ferromanganese. It is also a constituent of certain valuable alloys such as manganin (Cu 84 per cent., Mn 12 per cent., Ni 4 per cent.), which is used in precision instruments for electrical measurements, because its electrical conductivity has only a very small temperature coefficient. Manganese dioxide ('Glassmakers' soap') is used to remove the colour from glass which contains iron; potassium and calcium permanganate are used as disinfectants, and manganous salts such as the chloride and sulphate are employed in agriculture to stimulate the germination of seeds. Manganese deficiency can cause diseases in vegetation.

Manganese occurs in its compounds with the valencies of 7, 6, 4, 3, 2, and 1. In the first two of these states it is acidic and not basic, and occurs only as the strong permanganic acid $H[Mn^{vii}O_4]$ (violet) and the (perhaps less strong) manganic acid $H_2Mn^{vi}O_4$ (green), and their derivatives. Hexavalent manganese is unstable and readily changes (disproportionates) into a mixture of hepta- and tetravalent manganese, e.g. into permanganic acid and manganese dioxide.

Tetravalent manganese is almost wholly acidic as in the manganites, which are the salts derived from the definite though weak acid $(HO)_2MnO$ or H_2MnO_3. The tetravalent manganese compounds are unstable partly because of the readiness with which they hydrolyse and precipitate the very insoluble MnO_2, and partly because they are so easily reduced. In its very few soluble derivatives the Mn^{iv} is always part of a complex anion. While Mn^{vii} is like Cl^{vii} and Mn^{vi} rather like S^{vi}, Mn^{iv}, apart from its changes of valency, more resembles Sn^{iv} or Pb^{iv}.

In its lower valencies of 3 and 2 manganese is no longer acidic, but is in the wider sense basic. It affords a good illustration of the rather ambiguous nature of this word. In both states it is basic in the sense that it replaces the hydrogen of acids; but the divalent derivatives are nearly all simple salts of the monatomic cation Mn^{++}, which is much the most stable ionized form of the element, and more stable than Cr'' or even Fe'', while the only stable compounds of trivalent manganese are complexes in which

[1025] V. M. Goldschmidt, J.C.S. 1937, 656.

the manganese is in the anion; the simple Mn′′′ compounds all decompose practically instantaneously in one or two ways, partly by their ready hydrolysis with the precipitation of Mn_2O_3 or its hydrates, and partly by disproportionation into Mn^{iv} and Mn^{ii}. We also find as usual that while the lower of these two valencies is the more stable in the simple cations, it is the less stable in the covalent state, so that manganous hydroxide $Mn(OH)_2$ precipitated from the stable manganous solution is oxidized by the air to the trivalent condition. In the same way the complexes are more stable in the trivalent state, as they are with cobalt.

Metallic Manganese

This is most conveniently made by reducing the oxide with aluminium (Goldschmidt's method); MnO_2 reacts so violently that it must first be reduced by heating to Mn_3O_4. Reduction with charcoal gives a very impure metal with much dissolved carbon.

Metallic manganese boils at $2,032°$[1026] and melts at $1,247°$.[1027] It is like iron in appearance, but it is harder (not quite so hard as cast iron) and much more brittle, so that it can be powdered in a steel mortar. It occurs in at least two forms,[1027-33] an α-, stable from the ordinary temperature up to about $700°$,[1027,1033] and a β-, stable above this. A supposed third form, γ- or electrolytic manganese, is probably a hydride.[1030]

The crystal structure is extremely complicated. In the α-modification[1030-1] the unit cell contains 58 atoms, whose positions and distances show that they are in at least four different states of valency or linkage, the interatomic distances varying from $2\cdot25$ to $2\cdot95$ A.U. (the ratio, $0\cdot763:1$, is almost the same as that ($0\cdot778:1$) of $C\equiv C$ to $C—C$), but there is much distortion. The structure of β-manganese,[1032] with 20 atoms in the unit cell, is imperfectly made out.

Manganese forms numerous alloys. It gives a continuous series of solid solutions with each of the four elements next after it, iron, cobalt, nickel, and copper. With aluminium and with antimony, especially in the presence of a small amount of copper, it forms the well-known Heusler alloys, which are highly ferromagnetic, although they contain no ferromagnetic element. The addition of a small quantity of silicon makes manganese as hard as steel.

Chemically manganese is a highly reactive and ignoble metal. It decomposes water slowly in the cold and rapidly on heating, and dissolves readily in dilute mineral acids with evolution of hydrogen and formation of the divalent manganous salt. It is converted by fluorine into the

[1026] Extrapolated: E. Baur and R. Brunner, *Helv. Chim. Acta*, 1934, **17**, 958.
[1027] H. Moser, E. Raub, and E. Vincke, *Z. anorg. Chem.* 1933, **210**, 67.
[1028] A. Westgren and G. Phragmén, *Z. Phys.* 1925, **33**, 777.
[1029] A. J. Bradley, *Phil. Mag.* 1925, **50**, 1018.
[1030] A. J. Bradley and J. Thewlis, *Proc. Roy. Soc.* 1927, **115**, 456.
[1031] G. D. Preston, *Phil. Mag.* 1928, [vii] **5**, 1198.   [1032] Id., ib. 1207.
[1033] G. Johannsen and H. Nitka, *Phys. Z.* 1938, **39**, 440.

di- and the tri-fluoride, and by chlorine into manganous chloride $MnCl_2$; if it is heated in nitrogen above 1,200° it burns to form a nitride.

Manganese and Hydrogen

No hydride seems to be known except the spectroscopic hydride MnH[1034] (unless the so-called γ-manganese is a hydride). According to Lorenz and Heusler[1035] the metal has no action on hydrogen at any temperature.

Manganese and Carbon

Fused manganese dissolves carbon just as iron does, ultimately forming a carbide. Various carbides have been described, but the only definite one is Mn_3C; there is also a metastable Mn_4C. They are made by heating manganese with carbon or with methane, or manganous oxide with sugar charcoal.[1036-7] Mn_3C is hydrolysed by water, giving mainly methane and ethane.[1038]

Manganese and Nitrogen

If the metal is heated in nitrogen gas it begins to glow at 1,210–1,220°, and then burns with a flame, absorbing nitrogen more readily even than magnesium. The compound formed is most probably Mn_3N_2, which, however, seems to form a solid solution at least with manganese.[1039] Another compound, probably MnN_2, is got by the action of ammonia on manganese at a white heat; it is distinguished by being [apparently ferro-] magnetic.[1040]

HEPTAVALENT MANGANESE

This valency is confined to the strong acid permanganic acid $HMnO_4$, its anhydride, Mn_2O_7, and its salts. These are all distinguished by brilliant colours, the acid and its salts being purple and the anhydride dark green. In these compounds the manganese has its group valency, i.e. it is sharing all the electrons which it has in excess of the preceding inert gas; it has a core of $25-7 = 18$ electrons, arranged as 2. 8. 8. There is thus a close analogy to the compounds of heptavalent chlorine, such as $HClO_4$, where again the core (2. 8) is made up of complete quantum groups. The permanganates and perchlorates are in general isomorphous, and the potassium salts can form a continuous series of solid solutions with one another. It is in accordance with the behaviour of the earlier groups that in the compounds where it has the group valency manganese should always be acidic (compare H_4TiO_4, H_3VO_4, H_2CrO_4).

[1034] T. E. Nevin, *Proc. Roy. Irish Acad.* 1942, A **48**, 1.

[1035] R. Lorenz and F. Heusler, *Z. anorg. Chem.* 1893, **3**, 225.

[1036] O. Ruff, *Ber.* 1912, **45**, 3139; O. Ruff and E. Gersten, ib. 1913, **46**, 400.

[1037] R. Schenck and K. Meyer, *Z. anorg. Chem.* 1938, **239**, 161.

[1038] W. R. Myers and W. P. Fishel, *J.A.C.S.* 1945, **67**, 1962.

[1039] F. Haber and G. van Oordt, *Z. anorg. Chem.* 1905, **44**, 341.

[1040] E. Wedekind, *Phys. Z.* 1906, **7**, 805; *Z. Elektrochem.* 1906, **12**, 810; *Ber.* 1908, **41**, 3769.

Permanganic Anhydride, Mn_2O_7

Like perchloric acid permanganic acid forms a liquid and volatile anhydride Mn_2O_7, which is, however, far less stable than Cl_2O_7 (which when pure can be distilled at $80°$ under ordinary pressure) owing to its tendency to lose oxygen and go over into the very stable MnO_2.

The heptoxide is made[1041-4] by adding powdered potassium permanganate in quantity to concentrated sulphuric acid, when it separates as a dark oil of high specific gravity (2·4), which can be distilled slowly in a stream of air at 15 mm. pressure at $0°$, and freezes in liquid air to dark green crystals.[1044]

It is stable at $-5°$; at $0°$ it begins to give off oxygen, but the decomposition is very slow up to $+10°$, when it becomes rapid, and soon explosive.[1044] The decomposition is irreversible; its products are MnO_2 and oxygen; the intermediate formation of a trioxide MnO_3 could not be detected.[1044] If it is added to a small quantity of water, the heat evolved (12 k.cals. per Mn_2O_7) decomposes it, but if it is dropped into a large excess of water it forms a purple solution of permanganic acid; the acid can be concentrated by evaporation of the solution up to 20 per cent. $HMnO_4$, but above this strength it decomposes.

The heptoxide is an even stronger oxidizing agent than permanganic acid, and combustible substances take fire when they come into contact with it. It will, however, dissolve without decomposition in acetic anhydride, forming a purple solution (which may contain a mixed anhydride $CH_3 \cdot CO \cdot O \cdot MnO_3$).

Permanganic Acid, $HMnO_4$

This acid has never been isolated, but its solution can be made, for example, by the action of H_2SO_4 on the barium salt. The dilute solution, which has, of course, the purple colour of the $[MnO_4]^-$ ion, is very stable, but if concentrated beyond about 20 per cent. it begins to decompose. Dubois[1045] has obtained a 2·6 molar (24·5 per cent.) aqueous solution, which froze at $-11°$ to a cryohydric mass of crystals of ice, and (no doubt hydrated) permanganic acid. The latter could not be isolated, and in daylight the solid soon began to deposit MnO_2, and evolve ozone.

Conductivity measurements[1043,1046] show that permanganic acid is a strong acid. Hence its reactions are essentially those of the MnO_4' ion, and of its salts.

Permanganates

The permanganates are made by oxidizing manganous salts or manganese dioxide with various oxidizing agents, including atmospheric air,

[1041] B. Franke, *J. prakt. Chem.* 1887, [2] **36**, 31.
[1042] T. E. Thorpe and F. J. Hambly, *J.C.S.* 1888, **53**, 175.
[1043] J. M. Lovén, *Ber.* 1892, **25**, ref. 620.
[1044] A. Simon and F. Fehér, *Z. Elektrochem.* 1932, **38**, 137.
[1045] P. Dubois, *C.R.* 1935, **200**, 1107.
[1046] H. N. Morse and J. C. Olsen, *Amer. Chem. J.* 1900, **23**, 431.

in presence of alkali, the oxidation being carried either directly to the heptavalent state, or to the hexavalent state of the manganates M_2MnO_4. The presence of alkali favours the acidic derivatives of the higher valencies, and a large excess the (dibasic) hexavalent as against the heptavalent stage. Lead dioxide in concentrated sulphuric acid or nitric acid, or periodates will convert manganous salts directly into permanganates. The manganate can be made (see p. 1270) by heating manganese dioxide with alkali in presence of air or potassium nitrate; it is then converted into the permanganate by treatment with acid

$$3\ K_2MnO_4 + 2\ H_2O = 2\ KMnO_4 + MnO_2 + 4\ KOH$$

or by oxidation either with chlorine

$$2\ K_2MnO_4 + Cl_2 = 2\ KMnO_4 + 2\ KCl$$

or electrolytically.

The best known salts are those of the alkalies, particularly potassium; the sodium salt is inconveniently soluble. The potassium salt forms a continuous series of solid solutions with potassium perchlorate: the ammonium salts of these two acids behave in the same way. Potassium permanganate also forms solid solutions with barium sulphate.[1047] For the crystal structure and solubilities of silver permanganate see references [1048-9] respectively.

The solubilities (in g. per 100 g. water) of some of these are: Li, 3 H_2O, 71/16°; Na, 3 H_2O very large; K, 6·34/20°; Rb, 1·1/19°; Cs, 0·23/19°; Ag, 0·92/20°.

The characteristic brilliant colour of the permanganate solutions has always attracted attention. The absorption spectrum shows a series of well-marked bands, of which seven can be detected in the visible region, becoming less intense towards the ultra-violet. In the early days of the ionic theory Ostwald[1050] showed that the positions of the 4 least refrangible of these bands with 13 different permanganates in dilute solution in water were identical. Merton[1051] showed that in a series of solvents, such as water, acetone, methyl acetate, alcohols, acetonitrile, etc., while the relative positions of the bands are scarcely affected, the absolute positions are shifted, the maximum being about 0·5 per cent. (30 A.U.) from water to methyl alcohol. The same holds for the solid solution in $KClO_4$, but the shift is much larger (about 140 A.U., or 2·5 per cent.). This work is supported by that of Hagenbach[1052] and (in solid solution at −180°) of Schnetzler.[1053] Later work[1054-5] carried out at the boiling-point of hydro-

[1047] H. G. Grimm, C. Peters, H. Wolff, *Z. anorg. Chem.* 1938, **236**, 57.
[1048] K. Sasvari, *Z. Krist.* 1938, **99**, 9.
[1049] F. Hein and W. Daniel, *Z. anorg. Chem.* 1937, **234**, 155.
[1050] *Z. physikal. Chem.* 1892, **9**, 579.
[1051] T. R. Merton, *J.C.S.* 1911, **99**, 637.
[1052] A. Hagenbach and R. Percy, *Helv. Chim. Acta*, 1922, **5**, 454.
[1053] K. Schnetzler, *Z. physikal. Chem.* 1931, B **14**, 241.
[1054] J. Teltow, ib. 1938, B **40**, 397.   [1055] Id., ib. 1939, B **43**, 198.

gen (20·4° K.) with the solid solution in $KClO_4$ gives a more detailed analysis of the bands.

Of the chemical reactions of the MnO_4 ion the most important are of course its oxidations, which take place in more ways than one. In very strong alkaline solution $KMnO_4$ evolves oxygen and goes over to the manganate; this is presumably due to the energy evolved by the conversion of a monobasic into a dibasic acid in alkaline surroundings. In moderately alkaline neutral or feebly acid solution, permanganates are reduced by oxidizable substances to MnO_2:

$$2\ KMnO_4 + 6\ H\ =\ 2\ MnO_2 + 2\ KOH + 2\ H_2O.$$

In definitely acid solution the manganese is reduced to the manganous state:

$$2\ KMnO_4 + 3\ H_2SO_4 + 10\ H\ =\ K_2SO_4 + 2\ MnSO_4 + 8\ H_2O.$$

In this way $KMnO_4$ is able to effect an enormous number of oxidations, especially in acid solution; thus it oxidizes ferrous iron, hydrogen peroxide (to oxygen), as well as formic, oxalic, and nitrous acids. It is to be noticed that in the absence of acids it gives a stable solution in pure acetone. The mechanism of these oxidations is very imperfectly understood.

When dry $KMnO_4$ is heated, it begins to give off oxygen at 200°, forming in the first instance potassium manganate and manganese dioxide,[1056-7] which at higher temperatures break down further to Mn_2O_3.

Hein[1058-9] has found that a solution of silver permanganate absorbs hydrogen much more rapidly than the potassium salt; the nature of the products (which contain silver and manganese) is obscure. For the kinetics of the thermal decomposition of silver permanganate (giving silver oxide, manganese dioxide, and oxygen) see reference [1060].

HEXAVALENT MANGANESE

The compounds of this class are confined to manganic acid H_2MnO_4 (known only in solution) and its salts: the supposed anhydride MnO_3 does not seem to exist.

Potassium manganate K_2MnO_4 was made by Scheele by heating MnO_2 with potassium nitrate, and was called by him 'mineral chameleon' because the green solution readily goes purple (from the formation of permanganate) in presence of acids.

Supposed Manganese Trioxide

The claim[1061-2] that a volatile trioxide can be made by heating a solution of $KMnO_4$ in H_2SO_4 as a volatile substance giving a purple vapour has

[1056] G. Rudorf, *Z. anorg. Chem.* 1901, **27**, 58.

[1057] P. Askenasy and A. Solberg, *Nernst-Festschr. Halle*, 1912, p. 53.

[1058] F. Hein, W. Daniel, and H. Schwedler, *Z. anorg. Chem.* 1937, **233**, 161.

[1059] F. Hein, ib. **235**, 25.

[1060] E. G. Prout and F. C. Tompkins, *Trans. Far. Soc.* 1946, **42**, 468.

[1061] B. Franke, *J. prakt. Chem.* 1887, [2] **36**, 31.

[1062] T. E. Thorpe and F. J. Hambly, *J.C.S.* 1888, **53**, 175.

been disproved.[1063] Simon[1064] showed that when manganese heptoxide loses oxygen on warming, it goes straight to the dioxide, with no sign of the intermediate formation of MnO_3.

It would thus appear that the trioxide does not exist.

Manganic Acid, H_2MnO_4, and the Manganates

Manganates can be made from manganese dioxide by heating with alkali, (1) by Scheele's method of oxidizing with potassium nitrate, (2) by oxidation with air alone (this is the method used on the large scale in the manufacture of permanganates), and (3) even in the absence of air, the dioxide being in that case converted into a mixture of the monoxide MnO and the manganate.

The oxidation of manganese dioxide by air in the presence of alkali is never complete. If excess of MnO_2 is used, the reaction stops when 60 per cent. of the potash has been converted into K_2MnO_4[1065]; this appears to be due to the production of a saturated solid solution of 3 parts K_2MnO_4 and 2 parts manganite K_2MnO_3. If the potassium hydroxide is in excess the oxidation is again imperfect, the average ratio of manganese to oxygen being $1:2\cdot6$ (instead of $1:3$), which is supposed[1066] to be due to the formation of a definite compound Mn_5O_{13}.

The manganate is extracted from the green fused mass by water. It would appear that the free acid is very unstable, but the ion MnO_4'' stable; the salt is quite stable in solution so long as an excess of alkali is present, in fact it can then as we have seen become even more stable than the permanganate ion; but in pure water or in presence of acids it readily changes over into the permanganate and manganese dioxide:

$$3\ MnO_4^{--} + 2\ H_2O = MnO_2 + 2\ MnO_4^- + 4\ OH^-.$$

This change occurs in pure water, so that the solution must be readily hydrolysed, and manganic acid a weak acid; but the reaction is obviously promoted by the extremely small (but unmeasured) solubility of the dioxide. If the liquid is boiled, this disproportionation will occur even in alkaline solution (which favours the weak-acid hydrolysis view).

The most important of the manganates is the potassium salt, which is the sole source of potassium permanganate. It forms small dark-green crystals; the absorption bands (Teltow[1054-5]) are very similar to those of the permanganates. It is very soluble in water, but the solubility cannot be measured in pure water, because the salt then changes into $KMnO_4 + MnO_2$; in presence of excess of KOH it is stable, and the solubility in moles of K_2MnO_4 per litre at $20°$ is in 2-N. KOH $1\cdot14$, and in 8-N. KOH $0\cdot078$.

[1063] F. R. Lankshear, *Z. anorg. Chem.* 1913, **82**, 97.

[1064] A. Simon and F. Fehér, *Z. Elektrochem.* 1932, **38**, 137.

[1065] P. Askenasy and S. Klonowsky, ib. 1910, **16**, 104.

[1066] O. Sackur, *Ber.* 1910, **43**, 381, 448; 1911, **44**, 777; F. Bahr and O. Sackur, *Z. anorg. Chem.* 1911, **73**, 101.

If the solid salt is heated above 500° it loses oxygen and is converted into the manganite K_2MnO_3.

The sodium salt occurs with 0, 4, 6, and 8 molecules of water. It is black, and very soluble in water. No other manganates seem to have been got in the pure state, but the pigment known as 'Rosentiehl's Green' is the impure barium salt.

TETRAVALENT MANGANESE

All the compounds of tetravalent manganese may be regarded as derived from the non-existent hydrate $Mn(OH)_4$. The fall in valency necessarily weakens the acidic and strengthens the basic properties of the oxide, and while the oxides of hepta- and hexavalent manganese are acidic and not basic, the tetrahydroxide is both to a small extent, being amphoteric in behaviour; it also very readily forms an extremely insoluble dehydration product in manganese dioxide and its hydrate. As a base it reacts with acids to give salts MnX_4, and as an acid it forms with alkalies the manganites, derived from a weak acid H_2MnO_3 and its condensed forms. Nearly all these compounds are remarkably unstable, at any rate in solution. The salts formed with acids, of the type MnX_4, scarcely exist at all, owing to the ease with which they undergo two reactions: (1) hydrolysis with precipitation of the oxide MnO_2, usually hydrated, but always extremely insoluble, and (2) the discharge of the tetravalent cation Mn^{++++}, i.e. its reduction by the anion or by some other oxidizable substance present. The salts formed with bases, the manganites, are also very unstable in water, for much the same reasons; the manganite ion MnO_3'' is readily reduced, and the weakness of manganous acid as an acid, combined with the great insolubility of the hydrolytic product MnO_2, causes the hydrolysis to go very far.

The general outcome is that the tetravalent manganese compounds are nearly all insoluble substances, almost the only exceptions being the salts of the complex ions such as $K_2[MnCl_6]$, which show an unexpected stability.

Manganese Dioxide, MnO_2

This is the commonest manganese mineral, and is known as pyrolusite, braunstein, psilomelane, etc.

The anhydrous compound is best made[1067] by decomposing manganous nitrate $Mn(NO_3)_2$ by heating it for some hours at 250°, and then at 500° to remove the last traces of oxides of nitrogen. The product is an extremely hard black mass, which is a fairly good conductor of electricity and is used to make 'unattackable anodes' for certain large-scale electrolyses.

Manganese dioxide is a grey-black solid, practically insoluble in water. Like lead dioxide it has a rutile lattice. Its specific conductivity is 0.16 ohm^{-1} at 0°.

Its stability to heat depends greatly on its method of preparation. The

[1067] J. Meyer and R. Kanters, *Z. anorg. Chem.* 1929, **185**, 177.

anhydrous oxide made from the nitrate, which is the purest form of MnO_2, does not begin to lose oxygen below about 530°.[1067] Other forms do so at 300°[1044] or even at 200°.[1067]

Although anhydrous manganese dioxide is very difficult to hydrate (no doubt on account of its insolubility), the form which is precipitated from an aqueous solution, as when a permanganate is reduced with SO_2, is always hydrated, and it is impossible to remove the last traces of water without some loss of oxygen. The water content varies with the method of preparation. It never seems to reach the composition $Mn(OH)_4$, but a monohydrate MnO_2,H_2O or H_2MnO_3 appears to be fairly stable, and is got by dehydrating the washed precipitate at 100°. This compound may be called manganous acid, and it behaves like a weak acid; it reddens blue litmus, and dissolves in alkalies to give definite salts, the manganites (see next section).

Manganese dioxide, in spite of its insolubility, is readily attacked by reducing agents; it oxidizes hydrogen chloride to chlorine:

$$MnO_2 + 4\,HCl = MnCl_2 + Cl_2 + 2\,H_2O$$

and sulphur dioxide to manganous dithionate:

$$MnO_2 + 2\,H_2SO_3 = MnS_2O_6 + 2\,H_2O$$

the manganese being always reduced to the divalent state. The hydrated oxide behaves in the same way, and more readily. When the dioxide is 'fumed' with concentrated sulphuric acid, a violet colour appears, which is due[1068] to manganous ions formed by the reaction

$$2\,MnO_2 + 4\,H^+ = 2\,Mn^{++} + 2\,H_2O + O_2.$$

This formation of dithionate (by which Gay-Lussac discovered dithionic acid in 1819) is unusual; both barium dioxide and lead dioxide with SO_2 only give sulphates. Some manganous sulphate is certainly produced in the reaction,[1069] but the suggestion that this adds on SO_2 to form MnS_2O_6 has been disproved experimentally.[1070] Probably there are two reactions; in the first there is direct combination of MnO_2 and SO_2 to form manganous sulphate, as with lead dioxide; in the second the MnO_2 is reduced by the SO_2 to the sesquioxide Mn_2O_3, which then forms its sulphite $Mn_2[SO_3]_3$, a salt which has been shown to react (like ferric sulphite) to form manganous sulphite + dithionate:

$$Mn_2[SO_3]_3 = MnSO_3 + MnS_2O_6.$$

Putting all this together we should get this equation, which approximately represents the facts

$$2\,MnO_2 + 3\,SO_2 = MnSO_4 + MnS_2O_6.$$

[1068] J. F. G. Hicks and E. Krockmalski, *J.A.C.S.* 1947, **69**, 1970.
[1069] J. Meyer and W. Schramm, *Z. anorg. Chem.* 1924, **132**, 226.
[1070] J. Meyer, *Ber.* 1902, **35**, 3429.

A similar process of alternate oxidation and reduction may explain the catalytic decomposition of hydrogen peroxide by manganese dioxide.[1071]

When manganese dioxide is heated it loses oxygen, as has already been said, and gives successively Mn_2O_3, Mn_3O_4, and MnO.

Manganites

These are the salts of manganous acid, of which MnO_2 is the anhydride. The acid, which in its simplest form is H_2MnO_3, is a very weak acid (owing to the low valency of the manganese), and so its salts are mainly derived (as always happens with weak polybasic acids) from condensed forms, such as $K_2Mn_2O_5$ ($= K_2O, 2 MnO_2$). The number of these forms is very large; calcium, for example, gives compounds containing to 1 CaO, $\frac{1}{2}$, 1, 2, 3, and 5 MnO_2.

The manganites can be made either by the action of aqueous alkali on MnO_2, or by fusing the oxides together. The best defined salts are those which are got by the latter (dry) method, which are crystalline. Manganites made in the wet way are amorphous, are all insoluble in, and yet considerably hydrolysed by water, and are further liable to contain manganese in states of valency lower than 4, so that their identification is very uncertain.

Tetravalent Manganese Salts of Acids

The simple salts of tetravalent manganese as a base can rarely if ever be isolated, though some of them probably exist in solution. They tend to decompose, either by hydrolysis or by reduction. In the form of complex ions, however, they are far more stable. The simple Mn^{4+} ion is evidently less stable than the covalent form, and the complex salts, such as $K_2[MnCl_6]$, will be less liable to reduction, since the higher valencies are always less easily reduced in the covalent state, and also they are less liable to hydrolysis when the manganese is contained in a negatively charged complex, as the attack is mainly by hydroxyl ions.

Of the tetrahalides the fluoride MnF_4 has never been isolated, though it occurs in complexes (see below, p. 1274). The tetrachloride $MnCl_4$ must certainly be assumed to occur in solution, since the dark solution of manganese dioxide in hydrochloric acid does not evolve chlorine at first. The evidence (mainly magnetic) for supposing that in this solution the $MnCl_4$ has gone over into $MnCl_3 + Cl_2$, is not strong. The tetrachloride cannot be separated from its aqueous solution in the solid state, and the solutions very soon give off chlorine unless they contain a high concentration of HCl, i.e. unless the manganese is present mainly in the complex anion. It is stated[1072] that if dry hydrogen chloride is passed through a suspension of MnO_2 in ether at $-70°$, a green solution of $MnCl_4$ is obtained, from which a mixture of CCl_4 and $CHCl_3$ precipitates a black neutral substance which is probably $MnCl_4$, but may contain $MnCl_3$ as well.

[1071] D. B. Broughton and R. L. Wentworth, *J.A.C.S.* 1947, **69**, 741, 744.
[1072] J. H. Krepelka and J. Kubis, *Coll. Czech. Chem. Com.* 1935, **7**, 105.

Complex Salts of Tetravalent Manganese

These include practically all the soluble compounds of tetravalent manganese that are known. Complex halides are formed with fluorine and with chlorine, and they are all of the 6-co-ordinated type $M_2'[MnX_6]$. The hexafluorides, such as K_2MnF_6, can be made by treating either a manganate (with formation of permanganate) or a manganite (by direct replacement) with concentrated HF.

K_2MnF_6 forms small golden-yellow hexagonal crystals. It is hydrolysed slowly by cold and rapidly by hot water, with the precipitation of hydrated MnO_2. The rubidium and probably the ammonium salts have been made, but not the sodium salt (presumably because it is too soluble: order of solubilities with strong acids).

The complex chlorides $M_2[MnCl_6]$ are made by the action of concentrated HCl on a permanganate, chlorine being evolved[1073]:

$$2\ KMnO_4 + 16\ HCl = K_2MnCl_6 + MnCl_2 + 8\ H_2O + 4\ Cl_2.$$

They are dark red in colour.

The corresponding bromides and iodides seem to be unknown, presumably because the halogen ion would be oxidized by the Mn^{iv}. A series of complex iodates $M_2[Mn(IO_3)_6]$, where this danger of reduction by the anion does not occur, has been prepared.

By the action of KCN on $KMnO_4$ in saturated aqueous solution, red crystals are formed which are said[1074] to have the composition $K_4[Mn(CN)_8]$; they are decomposed by water (giving HCN and MnO_2), by acids, and by alcohols. If this is the composition, the salt is presumably a crystal aggregate of $K_2Mn(CN)_6$ and 2 KCN, since the covalency of manganese is limited to 6.

TRIVALENT MANGANESE

In the trivalent state the acidic properties of the oxide have entirely disappeared, and the only form in which the atom can occur with this valency is as a trivalent cation, or as the central atom of an anionic complex. The stability of this state of manganese is in any form small, and (as with cobalt) it is much less stable in the cation than in the complexes. The trivalent Mn^{+++} ion can scarcely exist in water; in presence of mineral acids it changes to a mixture of the dioxide and a manganous Mn'' salt; in the absence of acids it is largely hydrolysed to the weak base $Mn(OH)_3$, which is readily oxidized, even by air.

This tendency of the trivalent manganese compounds to change into either Mn^{iv} or Mn^{ii}, or a mixture of the two, is so strong that it has been suggested that they do not really contain trivalent manganese at all, but a mixture of tetravalent and divalent. This, however, has been disproved by the undoubted existence of trivalent manganic acetylacetonate

[1073] R. F. Weinland and P. Dinkelacker, *Z. anorg. Chem.* 1908, **60**, 173.
[1074] A. Yakimach, *C.R.* 1930, **190**, 681.

$Mn(C_5H_7O_2)_3$, whose molecular weight has been determined (below, p. 1278). Further, it has been shown[1081] that the manganous hydroxide $Mn(OH)_2$ precipitated from a manganous solution by alkali takes up in 3 to 4 days enough oxygen from the air to convert it completely into MnO_2; the trivalent $Mn(OH)_3$, on the other hand, under the same conditions takes up none, and so cannot contain the monoxide. In the same way the trivalent manganese complexes behave very like the trivalent complexes of Cr, Fe, Co, etc., where there is no doubt about the true trivalency of the element.

The trivalent manganese compounds can be made by the oxidation of manganous compounds or the reduction of those of higher valency, but the conditions must be carefully observed if the change is to be arrested at this stage. The preparation by the oxidation of manganous salts is easiest when the products are but slightly soluble, as are the oxide and the phosphate; the oxidation must be carried out in strongly acid solution so as to protect the Mn''' by conversion into the complex state. When they are made by the reduction of more highly oxidized compounds, such as MnO_2 or $KMnO_4$, the best yields are obtained by working in concentrated H_2SO_4, which stabilizes the trivalent manganese in the form of a (probably complex) sulphate; otherwise the reduction goes straight through to the manganous salt.

In solution these compounds are brown or red, according as the complexity varies. Their chemical behaviour is somewhat variable for the same reason.

Manganese Sesquioxide, Mn_2O_3

This occurs in the anhydrous form Mn_2O_3, and also as a hydrate Mn_2O_3, H_2O or $MnO \cdot OH$.

Mn_2O_3 can be made by igniting MnO_2 or manganous salts (i.e. from Mn^{iv} or Mn^{ii}), especially the halides, in air at 500–900°; it is best made from MnO_2 by 20 hours' heating at 700°.[1075]

The hydrated form Mn_2O_3,H_2O or $MnO \cdot OH$ occurs as the mineral manganite; there is no evidence that $Mn(OH)_3$ can be isolated, any more than $Mn(OH)_4$. $MnO \cdot OH$ is left when the moist precipitated sesquioxide is dried at 100°. It is precipitated in the aerial oxidation of manganous chloride solutions in presence of excess of NH_4Cl; the NH_4Cl must be carefully washed out.[1076]

The hydrated oxide is the more active chemically. Its colour varies from grey to brown or black according to the method of preparation. It is used as a brown dye, the manganese being adsorbed by the fibre from a manganous chloride solution, and then oxidized *in situ* by the air.

[1075] R. J. Meyer and K. Rötgers, *Z. anorg. Chem.* 1908, **57**, 104.
[1076] J. Meyer and R. Nerlich, ib. 1921, **116**, 117.
[1077] H. Moissan, *C.R.* 1900, **130**, 622; H. Moissan and Venturi, ib. 1158.
[1078] A. Chrétien and G. Varga, *Bull. Soc.* 1936, [v] **3**, 2385.
[1079] L. Domange, *Bull. Soc. Chim.* 1939, [v] **6**, 1452.
[1080] E. Späth, *Mon.* 1911, **120**, 1117.
[1081] J. Meyer, *Z. anorg. Chem.* 1913, **81**, 385.

If the sesquioxide is heated in hydrogen above 230°, or in air above 940°, it is reduced to Mn_3O_4.

Mn_2O_3 reacts with SO_2 to give manganous sulphate and dithionate[1084]; the first reaction is

$$Mn_2[SO_3]_3 = MnSO_3 + MnS_2O_6$$

and the $MnSO_3$ so formed is then obviously oxidized by Mn''' to the sulphate.

The constitution of Mn_2O_3 is considered later with that of Mn_3O_4.

Mangano-manganic Oxide, Mn_3O_4

This is also known as trimanganese tetroxide and as 'red manganese oxide'. It is the most stable oxide of manganese when heated in air; all the others, the metal itself, and all those salts which contain volatile anions, leave this oxide when heated in air above 940°. The oxide occurs in nature as the mineral hausmannite; it is most conveniently made[1067] by heating one of the higher oxides to 1,000° for 6–8 hours. If alkali is added to a solution containing manganous and manganic salts, or if a manganous salt in solution is oxidized with the right amount of $KMnO_4$, a hydrated form of Mn_3O_4 can be got, but there is no evidence that a definite hydrate exists.

The suggestion that the two oxides Mn_2O_3 and Mn_3O_4 contain no Mn^{iii} but only $Mn^{iv}+Mn^{ii}$ is examined and rejected by J. Meyer[1067,1076] in favour of the more obvious formulae Mn_2O_3 and Mn_2O_3,MnO; the two oxides both dissolve in cold concentrated sulphuric, hydrofluoric, or especially phosphoric acid solutions to give reddish-violet solutions, obviously containing trivalent manganese.

True salts of trivalent manganese are very few, but are rather more numerous than those of the tetravalent element.

Trivalent Manganese Halides

Manganic Fluoride, MnF_3. This is made by the action of fluorine gas on manganous iodide.[1077] It is a red crystalline substance, which breaks up on heating into manganous fluoride MnF_2 and elementary fluorine. With a small quantity of water it forms a red-brown solution which easily becomes supersaturated. On dilution it is decomposed by hydrolysis. It can also be got in solution by dissolving Mn_2O_3, or a suitable mixture of a manganous salt and a permanganate, in HF. It separates from solution in ruby-red crystals of the hydrate $MnF_3, 2H_2O$.

Complex fluorides are known (see below).

Manganic Chloride, $MnCl_3$. The simple chloride is much less stable than the fluoride, and was not isolated until quite recently. It may be contained in the dark coloured solution of MnO_2 in HCl. The solid $MnCl_3$ is said[1072] to be present in the black unstable solid got by saturating a

[1082] J. Meyer and R. Nerlich, *Z. anorg. Chem.* 1921, **116**, 117.
[1083] J. Meyer and W. Schramm, ib. 1922, **123**, 56.
[1084] Id., ib. 1924, **132**, 226.

suspension of MnO_2 in ether with gaseous HCl at $-70°$ and precipitating with CCl_4 and ligroin. Chrétien and Varga[1078] claim to have made it by treating the acetate $Mn(O \cdot CO \cdot CH_3)_3$ with HCl at $-100°$; it forms a brown crystalline mass, giving green solutions in ethyl alcohol, acetyl chloride, and other organic solvents. Cryoscopic measurements in liquid HCl gave the molecular weight corresponding to $MnCl_3$ (we should rather have expected Mn_2Cl_6, like Re_2Cl_6). It decomposes irreversibly at any temperature above $-40°$ into $MnCl_2$ and chlorine.

Manganic Bromide, $MnBr_3$ and *Iodide*, MnI_3 are unknown.

There is a normal *sulphate* $Mn_2(SO_4)_3$ stable up to $300°$[1079] and an acid sulphate (see p. 1278).

The best known of the simple derivatives is the *acetate* $Mn(O \cdot CO \cdot CH_3)_3$, which is often used as the source of other trivalent manganese compounds. This can be made by the oxidation of manganous acetate $Mn(O \cdot CO \cdot CH_3)_2$ with chlorine or potassium permanganate, or by the action of acetic anhydride on manganous nitrate $Mn(NO_3)_2$,[1080] the manganese in the latter reaction being oxidized by the liberated nitric acid. It forms cinnamon-brown crystals with two molecules of water of crystallization; it is hydrolysed by water, but it can be recrystallized from acetic acid, alcohol, or pyridine, and is even somewhat soluble in chloroform.

Complex Manganic Compounds[1081–6]

Trivalent manganese, owing partly to its weakness as a base, has a strong tendency to form complexes, and in these complexes the trivalent state of the element is much stabilized. They are of various kinds, largely chelate, and especially of the 'ato' type.

Complex Mn[iii] *Cyanides*. Though the simple compound $Mn(CN)_3$ is unknown, many of these have been prepared, all of the 6-covalent type $M_3[Mn(CN)_6]$, a type that is very characteristic of the di- and trivalent states of the transitional elements; the most familiar are the ferro- and ferricyanides. The method of formation of the manganicyanides[1081] shows their great stability. If manganous carbonate $MnCO_3$ is dissolved in potassium cyanide solution, a yellow liquid is formed from which the blue complex cyanide of divalent manganese $K_4[Mn(CN)_6]$ crystallizes out. If a current of air is blown through the mixture of solid and mother liquor it slowly turns red, and then orange-red, especially if warmed, forming the manganicyanide $K_3[Mn(CN)_6]$, which goes into solution, and crystallizes out on the addition of alcohol. It can also be made directly by the action of KCN on manganic acetate $Mn(O \cdot Ac)_3$.

Potassium manganicyanide $K_3Mn(CN)_6$ forms dark red crystals, isomorphous with the ferricyanide; the Na, Li, and NH_4 salts are known. They can be recrystallized from KCN solution, but water gradually hydrolyses them with separation of hydrated Mn_2O_3. The dilute solution in KCN solution is yellow, but the concentrated, like the solid salt, is red; the

[1085] J. Meyer and J. Marek, ib. **133**, 325.
[1086] J. Meyer and W. Schramm, ib. 1926, **157**, 190.

formation of a yellow solution in water at great dilutions is common among these Mn‴ complexes; it may possibly be due in some cases to the formation of colloidal manganic hydroxide.

Nitrogen Complexes. Unlike trivalent chromium and cobalt, trivalent manganese has no tendency to co-ordinate with nitrogen to form ammines, nitro-complexes, or in other ways.

Oxygen Complexes. These appear to be all ring-compounds, either chelate, or ato-compounds.

The acetylacetonate $Mn(C_5H_7O_2)_3$[1087-8] is made by the action of acetylacetone on manganic acetate, or on an aqueous suspension of Mn_2O_3. It forms brilliant black crystals which are greenish when powdered; it melts at 172° and is readily soluble in benzene, chloroform, ethyl acetate, etc. Its molecular weight is simple, as determined cryoscopically, and also in the vapour.[1088] This compound gives the most indisputable evidence of the existence of real trivalent manganese.

The ato complexes formed by Mn‴ are numerous, especially with sulphuric, phosphoric, oxalic, and malonic acids.

Complex Sulphates

Among these compounds the alums may be mentioned, although we know now that they are not true complexes. Caesium manganese alum $CsMn(SO_4)_2,12H_2O$ forms coral-red crystals, and is decomposed by water with the precipitation of Mn_2O_3. The Rb, K, and Na salts have been made, but they become increasingly unstable, and can only be prepared at very low temperatures.

These alums, especially the Rb and NH_4 salts, lose water very easily to give the anhydrous double salts $MMn(SO_4)_2$, which may possibly be complex. It is more probable that we have true complexes in the acid $H[Mn(SO_4)_2], 2 H_2O$[1089] and its salts. These complexes are presumably present in the violet solution of the alums in concentrated H_2SO_4, which on dilution first turns red and then brown, and finally precipitates hydrated Mn_2O_3.[1090]

Complex Phosphates

Manganic acetate $Mn(OAc)_3$ dissolves in very concentrated (92 per cent.) H_3PO_4 to give a violet complex acid, which can be shown by transport experiments to have all the manganese in the anion; it is assumed, from the composition of its salts, to be $H_3[Mn(PO_4)_2] H_2O$.[1085] It has, however, only one hydrogen replaceable by metals, and probably should be written $H[Mn(PO_4H)_2(OH_2)_2] H_2O$, with 2 chelate groups

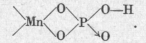

[1087] G. Urbain and A. Debierne, *C.R.* 1899, **129**, 302.
[1088] F. Gach, *Monatsh.* 1900, **21**, 109.
[1089] See, however, H. G. Houlton and H. V. Tartar, *J.A.C.S.* 1938, **60**, 549.
[1090] S. V. Gorbatschev and E. E. Schpitalski, *J. Gen. Chem. Russ.* 1940, **10**, 1961.

On dilution the complex breaks down, with the production of the rather insoluble grey-green simple phosphate $MnPO_4$, H_2O. The structure $M[Mn(PO_4H)_2(OH_2)_2] H_2O$ is exactly like those of the diaquomalonato and diaquo-oxalato salts described below.

Oxalato- and Malonato-complexes

These are in both cases of two types, $M_3[MnA_3]$ and $M[MnA_2(OH_2)_2]$, where A is the divalent anion of the dibasic acid. The oxalato-salts are much less easy to make than the malonato, because the trivalent manganese atom very readily (especially in the light) oxidizes the oxalate ion to give divalent manganese and CO_2. Otherwise the oxalato and malonato complexes are very similar. In the trivalent state many of the neighbouring transitional elements, such as Cr, Fe, Co, Rh, and Ir, behave in the same way.

Oxalato-salts[1086-91]

The trioxalato-salts, such as $K_3[Mn(C_2O_4)_3], 3 H_2O$, are made by reducing $KMnO_4$ with oxalic acid to the manganous stage, and then oxidizing this to the manganic by the addition of more $KMnO_4$, together with enough K_2CO_3 to satisfy the equation

$$5 H_2C_2O_4 + KMnO_4 + K_2CO_3 = K_3[Mn(C_2O_4)_3] + 5 H_2O + 5 CO_2.$$

The salt can also be made[1086] by treating moist hydrated MnO_2 with potassium hydrogen oxalate at $0°$, and precipitating (in red light) with alcohol.

$K_3[MnOx_3], 3 H_2O$ forms small deep red-violet crystals, stable in diffused daylight when dry. It is isomorphous with the ferric compound, and forms mixed crystals with it.[1092] It is very soluble in water; the millimolar solution is yellow-brown, but as the concentration increases the colour changes to cherry-red and then to reddish-purple; the brown colour is evidently due to the replacement of oxalate groups in the complex by water, since the red colour is restored to the dilute solution by excess of potassium oxalate.

Various other trioxalato-salts have been made, such as those of Na, NH_4, Tl', and $[Co(NH_3)_6]^{+++}$; they are mostly very soluble and difficult to purify.

The second series of oxalato-compounds is that of the diaquo-dioxalato-salts $M[MnOx_2(OH_2)_2]$. The trioxalato-manganic complex loses an oxalate radical much more easily than the chromic or cobaltic; silver nitrate or calcium chloride precipitates from the solution the simple silver or calcium oxalate, the complex breaking up. The diaquo-dioxalato-salts are much more soluble than the trioxalato-compounds (with the malonic derivatives the solubilities are in the opposite order). The potassium dioxalato-salt can be made[1086] by treating the dry tetroxalate with MnO_2 suspended in water, or by the action of oxalic acid on $KMnO_4$ in the right proportions[1091]; alcohol will then precipitate from the dark red solution pale

[1091] G. H. Cartledge and W. P. Ericks, *J.A.C.S.* 1936, **58**, 2061.

green crystals of the diaquo-dioxalato-salt. The salt occurs in two isomeric solid forms, one green and the other golden-yellow, which may be the *cis* and *trans* forms, but which both give the same yellow solution. The dilute aqueous solution is soon hydrolysed with separation of manganic hydroxide, but this may be prevented by the addition of centinormal nitric acid. That these oxalato-compounds actually contain trivalent manganese is shown by their giving a red solution in concentrated phosphoric acid.

In a solution of one of these oxalato-salts there is an equilibrium between the two ions:

$$[MnOx_3]^{---} + 2\,H_2O = [MnOx_2(OH_2)_2]^- + [C_2O_4]^{--};$$

this has been measured[1093] by means of the colour, since the trioxalato-compound is red in solution and the dioxalato yellow, the absorption maxima being at 5,200 and 4,500 A.U. respectively. The equilibrium is attained practically at once, and equilibrium constant

$$K = \frac{[MnOx_2(OH_2)_2^-]\cdot[Ox^{--}]}{[MnOx_3^{---}]}$$

is 0·0038 at 0° C.

For the mechanism of the oxidation of oxalate ion by trivalent manganese, and its relation to the formation of these oxalato-complexes, see Duke.[1094]

Malonato-complexes[1083,1095]

These are of the same types as the oxalato-salts, but they are easier to prepare because the anion is not liable to be oxidized by the trivalent manganese. They are, however, much less stable than the oxalato-, or than the chromic and cobaltic malonato-compounds.[1095] The yellow-brown hydrated Mn_2O_3 reacts with malonic acid to give the complex acid $H(H_2O)[Mn(mal)_2(OH_2)_2]$. This is a dark green powder, fairly stable in air and light, but forming in water a yellow solution from which the acid cannot be recovered, and which soon precipitates manganic hydroxide. A solution of an alkaline malonate dissolves manganic hydroxide to give a ruby-red solution (which is the colour of the trimalonato-salt) from which the green complex salt $M[Mn(mal)_2(OH_2)_2]\,H_2O$ separates out. These salts can also be made by reducing a permanganate in presence of a malonate; the first $2\,H_2O$ must be part of the anion, as they are present even when the salt is made in absolute methyl alcohol solution.[1095] The solubilities of the alkaline salts (which are all green) fall off rapidly from Li to Cs.

Concentrated mineral acids, such as sulphuric or phosphoric, give their characteristically coloured manganic salts: they break up the complex but the manganese remains trivalent; but dilute acids at once reduce this to the manganous state: the manganic ion being converted as it always is by

[1092] F. Kehrmann, *Ber.* 1887, **20**, 1595.
[1093] G. H. Cartledge and W. P. Ericks, *J.A.C.S.* 1936, **58**, 2065.
[1094] F. R. Duke, ib. 1947, **69**, 2885.
[1095] G. H. Cartledge and P. M. Nichols, *J.A.C.S.* 1940, **62**, 3057.

an acid into Mn″ and MnO_2, and the latter (which in acid solution is a stronger oxidizing agent than trivalent manganese) being reduced by the liberated malonic acid.

When these green dimalonato-complexes are treated in solution with a further quantity of alkaline malonate the red solution mentioned above of the trimalonato-salt $M_3[Mn(mal)_3]$ is formed. The equilibrium between the di- and trichelate ions in the solution can be measured by means of the colour, and it is found[1095] that the constant

$$K = \frac{[\text{Dichelate ion}] \cdot [\text{Malonate ion}]}{[\text{Trichelate ion}]}$$

is 0·057 at 0° C.

The salts of the di-'ato' series all seem to be green: the manganic, the ferric malonato,[1096] and the iridium oxalato salts.[1097] On the other hand, the colours in the trimalonato series are various: manganic red, ferric emerald-green, cobaltic dark green, chromic dichroic, but predominantly blue. (For a discussion of the colours of manganic compounds, see below.)

A similar series of dichelate salicylic derivatives of trivalent manganese has been described.[1098]

Colours of Trivalent Manganese Compounds

These are various and peculiar; the facts have been collected by Meyer and Schramm.[1083] The solid salts are nearly all green or red, as are many of their solutions, but some of the solutions and a few of the solid salts are yellow-brown. The *green* salts include $MnCl_3$ both solid and in hydrochloric acid solution (but not the complex chlorides $M_2[MnCl_5]$); the simple sulphate, which no doubt is $Mn^{iii}[Mn^{iii}(SO_4)_3]$; the solid phosphate $MnPO_4$ (grey-green), and the diaquo-malonates and diaquo-oxalates in the solid state, though some have a second form which is yellow.

The *red* or *red-violet* complexes include the hydrated fluoride and the complex fluorides, both solid and in solution: the complex chlorides, solid and in solution: the alums: the 'acid sulphate' (a sulphato acid $H[Mn(SO_4)_2] \, H_2O$) and its salts; the mangani-cyanides $M_3[Mn(CN)_6]$. The solutions of trivalent manganese in concentrated phosphoric acid are deep red-violet, a sensitive test for manganese[1082]; the meta and pyrophosphates are said to be violet. Manganic acetylacetonate is dark red; so are the trioxalato and trimalonato-compounds both solid and in solution.

Yellow or *yellow-brown*. These include only the second form of the diaquo-dioxalato-compound and the polynuclear (Mn_2 and Mn_3) acetates,[1099] whose constitution is still very obscure.

No general relations between colour and constitution have so far been suggested for these compounds.

[1096] R. F. Weinland and F. W. Sierp, *Z. anorg. Chem.* 1921, **117**, 59.
[1097] Dufour, *These*, Paris 1912.
[1098] G. A. Barbieri, *Ber.* 1927, **60**, 2421.
[1099] R. F. Weinland and G. Fischer, *Z. anorg. Chem.* 1921, **120**, 161.

Complex Halides

These are remarkable for being confined to the unusual type $M_2[MnX_5]$, often with a molecule of water which presumably completes the co-ordination group of 6; the usual type $M_3[MnX_6]$ does not occur; it is curious that the corresponding rhenium halides are of yet another type $M[ReX_4]$.

The *fluorides* $M_2[MnF_5]$ have been made with the alkalies: Na, 0; NH_4, 0; K, H_2O; all these are red or dark red crystals; the silver salt $Ag_2[MnF_5],4\,H_2O$ is almost black (the distribution of water of crystallization among these salts is very odd).

Complex Chlorides. Though manganic chloride $MnCl_3$ can scarcely be isolated, the complex chlorides are readily prepared by adding alkaline chloride to a solution of Mn_2O_3 in HCl at 0°. They can also be made[1100] by reducing permanganate with concentrated hydrochloric acid, and adding excess of alkaline chloride. They are all of the type $M_2[MnCl_5]$; the K, Rb, and Cs salts are anhydrous, while the NH_4 salt has 1 H_2O. They are hydrolysed by water.

No complex bromides are known, though a solution of $MnBr_3$ can be got by dissolving manganic hydroxide in HBr. No complex iodides are known.

DIVALENT MANGANESE COMPOUNDS

This ion is peculiar in structure (2.8.13), having the d-levels of its third quantum group half filled; this seems to give it abnormal stability, as well as an unusual atomic volume.[1101-2] It is the only stable form of the simple monatomic manganese ion, and accordingly divalent (manganous) salts are always formed when any more highly oxidized compound of manganese is heated with concentrated acid.

The salts are stable, but the covalent hydroxide $Mn(OH)_2$ which is precipitated by alkalies rapidly darkens in air, owing to its oxidation to the trivalent state. This marked difference in stability, the ion being stable in the lower and the covalent compound in the higher valency, is commonly found among the transitional elements.

Solutions of the manganous salts of strong acids do not redden litmus, showing that the hydrolysis is small (as might be expected with a divalent base), but it is sufficient to cause even neutral solutions to precipitate the hydroxide slowly, and the precipitate rapidly darkens owing to its oxidation by the air.

The manganous ion (for its magnetic properties see references [1104-8]) has

[1100] R. F. Weinland and P. Dinkelacker, *Z. anorg. Chem.* 1908, **60**, 173.

[1101] W. Klemm, *Angew. Chem.* 1937, **40**, 524.

[1102] W. Biltz, *Raumchemie d. festen Stoffe, Leipzig,* 1934, pp. 137 et sqq.

[1103] F. C. Tompkins, *Trans. Far. Soc.* 1942, **38**, 131.

[1104] S. S. Bhatnagar, B. Prakash, and J. C. Maheshwari, *Proc. Ind. Acad. Sci.* 1939, **10**, A. 150.

[1105] C. F. Squire, *Phys. Rev.* 1939, ii. **56**, 922.

[1106] H. Bizette, C. F. Squire, and B. Tsai, *C.R.* 1938, **207**, 449.

[1107] H. Bizette and B. Tsai, ib. **209**, 205.

[1108] N. Goldenberg, *Trans. Far. Soc.* 1940, **36**, 847.

a pink colour, which has been ascribed to the presence either of a higher oxidation product of manganese, or of a trace of cobalt compound; but both of these views have been disproved, and there is no doubt that the colour is that of the manganous ion itself.

Sufficiently strong oxidizing agents will oxidize divalent manganese even in acid solution; thus most compounds with the peroxide link, such as the persulphates, precipitate the manganese quantitatively as the hydrated dioxide; ozone will even convert it into $KMnO_4$. It reacts with permanganates to give MnO_2 and hydrogen ion:

$$3\,Mn^{++} + 2\,MnO_4^- + 2\,H_2O = 5\,MnO_2 + 4\,H^+.$$

For the kinetics of this reaction see Tompkins.[1103]

Manganous salts will catalyse a variety of oxidations, such as those of sulphur dioxide, stannous chloride, tartaric and oxalic acids. They also hasten the oxidation of linseed oil, and so are known as 'siccatives'; lead salts have the same effect, but are less active; the most effective agent is a mixture of manganous and plumbous salts.

Manganous salts are usually soluble in water, especially the chloride, nitrate, sulphate, acetate, and thiocyanate; the sulphide, phosphate, and carbonate are insoluble.

As might be expected from its greater basicity, the manganous ion has only a weak tendency to form complexes, but a certain number of them are known, of which the cyanides, especially those of the type $M_4[Mn(CN)_6]$, are the best marked.

Manganous Cyanide, $Mn(CN)_2$, can be precipitated from a manganous solution with potassium cyanide, but it is rapidly oxidized by the air and has never been got in the pure state; the complex cyanides (see below) are much more stable.

Manganous Oxide and Hydroxide

Manganous Oxide, MnO,[1109] occurs in nature as manganosite. It can be made by reducing the higher oxides with hydrogen or carbon monoxide, or by the ignition of manganous carbonate. It is a powder whose colour varies from grass-green to grey, according to the method of production. It has a sodium chloride lattice, with an Mn··O distance of 2·21 A.U. It is practically insoluble in water. It is readily oxidized, especially when it is finely divided, being converted by air, even in the cold, into Mn_3O_4 and Mn_2O_3, but it is not reduced by hydrogen at temperatures below 1,200°.

Manganous Hydroxide, $Mn(OH)_2$, is the mineral pyrochroite. It is precipitated by alkalies (but not by ammonia in presence of NH_4Cl) from a manganous salt solution as a white powder which darkens in air. It has the same crystal structure as $Mg(OH)_2$, the Mn—O distance being 2·30 A. Its solubility product[1110] is $2·2 \times 10^{-13}$ at 25°, giving a solubility of 6×10^{-5}

[1109] For the heats of formation of the (solid) oxides of manganese see H. Siemonsen, *Z. Elektrochem.* 1939, **45**, 637.

[1110] R. Näsänen, *Z. physikal. Chem.* 1942, **191**, 54.

moles per litre. In acid solution it is a strong base, while in alkaline it behaves as an acid, giving $[MnO \cdot OH]^-$ ions.[1111] It is readily oxidized, being converted by air into Mn_2O_3 or MnO_2 (for the kinetics see ref.[1112]); the product formed depends on the state of the oxide as well as the oxidizing agent: thus the colloidal hydroxide, precipitated by alkali from a manganous solution containing gelatine, is oxidized by air up to Mn_2O_3, but by hydrogen peroxide only 80 per cent. as far[1113]; for the reason see reference [1071].

Manganous alkyloxides or *alkylates* have been prepared[1114-15] by the action of sodium alkylate on manganous chloride in alcohol; they form violet crystals, which are at once hydrolysed by water.

Manganous Sulphide, MnS.[1116-18] Manganous salts when treated in solution with ammonium sulphide give a flesh-coloured precipitate of the sulphide, which has an Mn:S ratio between those of MnS and $Mn(SH)_2$, and contains up to 50 per cent. of water. On standing, this changes into greenish-black crystals of the sulphide MnS; the change begins at isolated spots fairly soon, but may take up to 6 years in the cold to complete itself.

Manganous Selenide, MnSe.[1119] This is trimorphic; the α-form has a cubic NaCl structure, is metastable, and goes to the β- (Zn blende type); the γ is hexagonal and has a wurtzite structure.

Salts of Oxy-acids

Manganous Carbonate, $MnCO_3$. This is the mineral manganspat, which is commercially important for making spiegeleisen. The salt can be obtained as a white precipitate by adding $NaHCO_3$ to a solution of a manganous salt; a normal carbonate such as Na_2CO_3 precipitates mainly a basic salt.

The pure crystalline substance is pink. Its stability is largely due to its insolubility; the solubility product $[Mn] \cdot [CO_3]$ is $8 \cdot 8 \times 10^{-11}$ at $25°$, and so the saturated solution is only $9 \cdot 4 \times 10^{-6}$ normal; hence the solid is only slightly hydrolysed, even on boiling, but it slowly darkens on long standing in air, through oxidation. It begins to evolve CO_2 (leaving MnO) below $100°$, and above $330°$ some of the CO_2 is reduced by the MnO to CO.

Of the organic salts the *formate* is a pink salt which crystallizes with $2 H_2O$; sol^y about 7/20°.

The *acetate* $Mn(O \cdot CO \cdot CH_3)_2$, $4 H_2O$ is a stable pink salt; sol^y about 40/20°; the anhydrous salt can be made by heating manganous nitrate with acetic anhydride.

[1111] R. K. Fox, D. F. Swinehart, and A. B. Garrett, *J.A.C.S.* 1941, **63**, 1779.
[1112] A. R. Nichols and J. H. Walton, ib. 1942, **64**, 1866.
[1113] J. Meyer and W. Gulbins, *Z. anorg. Chem.* 1926, **155**, 66.
[1114] B. Kandelaky, I. Setaschwili, and I. Tawberidze, *Kolloid Z.* 1935, **73**, 47.
[1115] J. G. F. Druce, *J.C.S.* 1937, 1407.
[1116] A. Mickwitz and G. Landesen, *Z. anorg. Chem.* 1923, **131**, 101.
[1117] G. L. Landesen and M. Reistal, ib. 1930, **193**, 277.
[1118] H. B. Weiser and W. O. Milligan, *J. Phys. Chem.* 1931, **35**, 2330.
[1119] A. Baroni, *Z. Krist.* 1938, **99**, 336.

The oxalate $Mn(C_2O_4)$ occurs with 3, 2, and 0 H_2O. It is very slightly soluble in water (like all the really simple oxalates of divalent metals): sol^y 0·0312/25°.

Manganous Nitrate, $Mn(NO_3)_2$,[1120-2] forms hydrates with 6, 4, 2, and 1 H_2O; the first of these melts at $+25\cdot8°$, and the last can be dehydrated by warming with nitrogen pentoxide. The salt is colourless and a saturated solution of the hexahydrate at 18° contains 134 g. $Mn(NO_3)_2$ to 100 g. water.

Manganous Sulphate, $MnSO_4$, is one of the most stable of manganous compounds, and is formed by heating almost any compound of manganese with H_2SO_4. It is made technically from MnO_2, either by heating it with concentrated H_2SO_4 (when oxygen is evolved) or by igniting it with anhydrous ferrous sulphate. It forms hydrates[1123-6] with 7, 5, 4, 2, 1, and 0 H_2O. The first of these can crystallize as a vitriol with $ZnSO_4$, 7 H_2O; the second is isomorphous with $CuSO_4$, 5 H_2O.* The solubility of the penta-hydrate at 25° is 68·4 g. to 100 g. water.

The stability of the anhydrous salt to heat is very remarkable; at a red heat, which decomposes ferrous, cobaltous, and nickel sulphates, mangan-ous sulphate is not decomposed at all, and it can be purified from the other sulphates in this way.

Manganous Perchlorate, $Mn(ClO_4)_2$ 6 and 4 H_2O, is very soluble in water, of which at the ordinary temperature 100 g. will dissolve 292 g. of the tetrahydrate (sol^y 136). It is an unstable substance, owing to the tendency of the anion to oxidize the cation; when heated it begins to separate manganese dioxide at 150°, and explodes at 195°.

Manganous Halides

Manganous Fluoride, MnF_2, is made by the action of hydrogen fluoride on metallic manganese or on manganous oxide, or by the fusion of man-ganous chloride with NaF, or in other ways. It forms pink quadratic prisms, which are only slightly soluble in water (1·06 g. in 100 g. water at the ordinary temperature), and gives an unstable tetrahydrate. Fluorine converts it into MnF_3.

Manganous Chloride, $MnCl_2$, can be got in the anhydrous state by the action of hydrochloric acid on heated manganese, or manganous oxide, or carbonate. It forms pink crystals, isomorphous with $CaCl_2$, melting at 650°, and boiling at a red heat to give a vapour with a normal density. It is very soluble in water; it forms hydrates with 6, 4, and 2 H_2O;

* This would suggest that the 4 H_2O molecules attached to the Mn are arranged in a plane.

[1120] W. W. Ewing and C. F. Glick, *J.A.C.S.* 1940, **62**, 2174.
[1121] W. W. Ewing and H. E. Rasmussen, ib. 1942, **64**, 1443.
[1122] W. W. Ewing, C. F. Glick, and H. E. Rasmussen, ib. 1445.
[1123] J. H. Krapelka and B. Rejha, *Coll. Czech. Chem. Comm.* 1931, **3**, 517.
[1124] J. Perreu, *C.R.* 1939, **209**, 167.　　　　　[1125] Id., ib. 311.
[1126] R. Rohmer, ib. 315.

sol^y 73·6/20°. The transition point between the tetrahydrate and the dihydrate in presence of the solution was determined by Richards as a fixed point in thermometry, and found to be[1127] 58·098±0·005°; this result has been confirmed.[1128] The chloride is also soluble in alcohols, with which it forms alcoholates $MnCl_2$, 2 and 3 ROH.[1129]

The *bromide* is very similar; it forms the same series of hydrates; sol^y 144·5/18°.

The *iodide* is also similar: it forms hydrates probably with 9, 6, 4, 2, and 1 H_2O; it is very hygroscopic; the hydrates on warming to 80° begin to lose iodine, but they can be dehydrated in a vacuum in the cold.

According to Wedekind the iodide is ferromagnetic.

Complex Manganous Compounds

With its smaller charge and stronger basicity divalent manganese has much less tendency to form complexes than trivalent.

Among these the *cyanides* are fairly stable; they are probably all of the type $M_4[Mn(CN)_6]$ (corresponding to the ferrocyanides): there is a series of a composition $MMn(CN)_3$, but they should probably be written $M_2Mn''[Mn(CN)_6]$. The free acid $H_4[Mn(CN)_6]$ (presumably with water of crystallization), got by treating the lead salt with H_2SO_4, forms colourless crystals, easily soluble in water, and quickly decomposed by it. Numerous salts (for example, a potassium salt with 3 H_2O) are known; they are fairly soon oxidized by the air (the manganese having lost the protection of its positive charge) to give the manganicyanide $M_3[Mn(CN)_6]$ and Mn_2O_3. They are easily soluble in water and are soon hydrolysed by it, but in a freshly made solution they will undergo double decomposition with other metals; thus they give violet precipitates with zinc or cadmium, and blue ones with aluminium; but these precipitated salts soon decompose.

The complex thiocyanates are very similar.

Ammines. The affinity of Mn^{ii} for nitrogen is not so small as that of Mn^{iii}. The manganous halides can take up as much as 6 NH_3, though the structure of the products is uncertain. The pyridine compound $MnCl_2py_2$ was found[1130] by X-ray methods to be a 4-covalent compound, with the four groups in a plane with the central atom, and at the corners of a square (as we should expect). It is isomorphous with the cobaltous compound.

Oxygen Complexes

These are nearly all chelate, including a series of derivatives of β-diketones and similar substances, of the type MnA_2. As we have seen,[1088] when manganous oxide or carbonate is treated with acetylacetone the derivative of trivalent manganese MnA_3 is produced, the manganese being obviously oxidized by the air. If the reaction is carried out in an atmo-

[1127] T. W. Richards and F. Wrede, *Z. physikal. Chem.* 1907, **61**, 313.

[1128] H. Benrath, *Z. anorg. Chem.* 1934, **220**, 145.

[1129] O. E. Zvjagintzev and A. Z. Tschchenkali, *J. Gen. Chem. Russ.* 1941, **11**, 791.

[1130] E. G. Cox, A. J. Shorter, W. Wardlaw, and W. J. R. Way, *J.C.S.* 1937, 1556.

sphere of nitrogen,[1131] manganous acetylacetonate $Mn(C_5H_7O_2)_2$ is formed. This is a yellow powder, giving a dihydrate and a diammine. Similar compounds were obtained from benzoylacetone, acetoacetic ester, acetone-dicarboxylic ester, and salicylaldehyde. They are all yellow or pale pink solids insoluble in water, soluble (even the hydrates) in organic solvents, including benzene; but their properties were not further examined.

Complex *oxalates* seem to be formed, since the solubility of manganous oxalate (0·0022 of a mole at 25°) rises (to 0·0345 mole) if the solvent contains 0·281-normal ammonium oxalate. Various solid double oxalates are known, such as $K_2[MnOx_2]$, $2H_2O$ and $(NH_4)_2[MnOx_2]$, $2H_2O$.

A series of double nitrates is known, though there is no evidence of their complexity. They are mainly of two types:

1. $Mn''_3[M^{iii}(NO_3)_6]_2$, $24H_2O$: where M^{iii} can be Bi or various rare earth metals, and Mn'' can be replaced by Mg, Zn, Co'', or Ni; these salts crystallize well, and are of great use in separating the rare earths.

2. $Mn''[M^{iv}(NO_3)_6]$, $8H_2O$. Here M^{iv} can be either quadrivalent cerium or thorium.

A series of double sulphates is known, especially with the alkalies. They are all of the type $M_2[Mn(SO_4)_2]$, xH_2O, where x has the following values: 0: Na, K, Rb, Tl'; 2: Na, K, Rb; 4: Na, K; 6: NH_4, Rb, Cs. The distribution of the water of crystallization is curious.

There is no sign that these are true complexes, and the Raman spectrum of a mixed solution of ammonium and manganous sulphates has no lines that are not in the separate solutions, so that no complex appears to be formed.[1132]

Complex Halides

These are of three types, $M[MnX_3]$, $M_2[MnX_4]$, and $M_4[MnX_6]$; the 5-covalent type which is the only one among the complex halides of trivalent manganese does not occur with the divalent compounds at all.

The fluorides seem to be less readily formed than is usual: the only known fluorides belong to the type $M[MnF_3]$.

Chlorides are known of all three types[1133-4]; they are, however, not very stable, and are broken up by water.

The bromide complexes are much less stable, as they are with divalent cobalt; Ephraim could not isolate any alkaline salts, and only one other, a calcium salt $Ca[MnBr_4]_2$, $4H_2O$.

The iodides form no complexes at all.

Univalent Manganese

The oxide Mn_2O probably does not exist,[1135] but the behaviour of the metal[1136] on electrolysis and especially that of manganous solutions on

[1131] B. Emmert, H. Gsottschneider, and H. Stanger, *Ber.* 1936, **69**, 1319.
[1132] H. G. Houlton and H. V. Tartar, *J.A.C.S.* 1938, **60**, 549.
[1133] H. Benrath, *Z. anorg. Chem.* 1934, **220**, 145.
[1134] F. S. Taylor, *J.C.S.* 1934, 699.
[1135] F. Glaser, *Z. anorg. Chem.* 1903, **36**, 1.
[1136] H. Kuessner, *Z. Elektrochem.* 1910, **16**, 758.

reduction give clear evidence that a univalent manganese exists, though the only compound so far isolated is a complex cyanide. Manchot and Gall[1137] showed that a solution of the manganocyanide Na_4 or $K_4[Mn(CN)_6]$ can be reduced in alkaline solution in an atmosphere of hydrogen by aluminium powder. The two salts $Na_5[Mn(CN)_6]$ (very soluble) and $K_5[Mn(CN)_6]$ (less soluble) are both colourless; their solutions reduce lead and cadmium salts to the metal, and on boiling evolve hydrogen, being reconverted to the manganous state. Electrolytic reduction of manganocyanides seems to produce the same result, although the salt $K_2[Mn(CN)_3]$ which was said[1138] to be formed does not seem to exist.[1137,1139]

Nitrosyl Complex of Manganese

If manganous acetate solution is treated with potassium cyanide in an atmosphere of nitric oxide[1140-1] the salt $K_3[Mn(CN)_5NO]$ separates in blue-violet crystals giving a permanganate-coloured solution which soon decomposes, especially in presence of acid or alkali.

In this anion as also in that of $M_5[Mn(CN)_6]$, the E.A.N. of the manganese is $25+3+5+3 = 36$ (as we should expect), and having 24 unshared electrons it must be called univalent.

[1137] W. Manchot and H. Gall, *Ber.* 1928, **61**, 1135.
[1138] G. Grube and W. Brause, ib. 1927, **60**, 2273.
[1139] W. D. Treadwell, O. Gübeli, and D. Huber, *Helv. Chim. Acta*, 1941, **24**, 152.
[1140] W. Manchot and H. Schmid, *Ber.* 1926, **59**, 2360.
[1141] A. A. Blanchard and F. F. Magnusson, *J.A.C.S.* 1941, **63**, 2236.

NO. 43. TECHNETIUM

THE claim of the Noddacks[1142-3] to have found this element, which they called masurium, in 1925, in a mineral (niobite) must be given up, as nothing has been heard of it since, and with it the name masurium. No. 43 was the first otherwise unknown element to be produced artificially, and hence it has been given the name technetium (the artificial one). This was achieved by Segré et al. in 1937[1144-6]; they separated it from a molybdenum plate that had been bombarded for some months with a strong beam of deuterons in the Berkeley cyclotron.* It was shown that the long-period activity which this contained was not due to Mo 42, Zr 40, Nb 41, or Ru 44, and so must be due to No. 43. Further work[1149-58] has shown (see especially Segré[1157]) that among products of the bombardment of molybdenum are at least 5 (possibly 6 [1158]) active isotopes of 43. The total quantities obtained are of the order of 10^{-10} g., but we can identify the product through the lucky chance (rare elsewhere) that one isotope goes over to another with the emission of a γ-ray which expels one of the K electrons, whose return to its place gives the K_α line of 43. For its electrolytic deposition and discharge potentials see Flagg and Bleidner.[1150]

The solid metal has a close-packed hexagonal structure, and is isomorphous with rhodium ruthenium and osmium. Each atom has 6 neighbours at 2·735 A and 6 at 2·704 (average 2·72).[1159] Its chemical properties were examined[1151,1157] by adding manganese and rhenium to the active material, and determining how far the activity remained with one or other of these when they were separated. The general conclusion is that technetium resembles rhenium far more closely than it does manganese, which is what would have been expected on the analogy of the earlier groups. Thus if a little manganese and rhenium salts are added to the active solution, and then hydrogen sulphide is passed through, the activity is precipitated

---

* This isotope can also be made by bombarding ^{98}Mo with neutrons; its mass number is 99, and its half-life $9·4 \times 10^5$ years.[1147] Its mass is 98·913.[1148]

[1142] W. Noddack, I. Tacke, and O. Berg, Sitzber. Preuss. Akad. 1925, 400.
[1143] I. Tacke, Z. angew. Chem. 1925, 38, 1157.
[1144] C. Perrier and E. Segre, Nature, 1937, 140, 193.
[1145] Id., J. Chem. Phys. 1937, 5, 712.
[1146] B. N. Cacciapuoti and E. Segre, Phys. Rev. 1937, ii. 52, 1252.
[1147] E. E. Motta, G. E. Boyd, and Q. V. Larson, ib. 1947, ii. 72, 1270.
[1148] M. G. Inghram, D. C. Hess, and R. J. Hayden, ib. 1269.
[1149] W. Maurer and W. Ramm, Z. Phys. 1942, 119, 334.
[1150] J. F. Flagg and W. E. Bleidner, J. Chem. Phys. 1945, 13, 269.
[1151] C. Perrier and E. Segre, Atti R. 1938, [vi] 27, 579.
[1152] E. Segre and G. T. Seaborg, Phys. Rev. 1938, ii. 54, 772.
[1153] B. N. Cacciapuoti, ib. 1939, ii. 55, 110.
[1154] C. Perrier and E. Segre, J. Chem. Phys. 1939, 7, 155.
[1155] G. T. Seaborg and E. Segre, Phys. Rev. 1939, ii. 55, 808.
[1156] W. Gentner and E. Segre, ib. 814.
[1157] E. Segre, Nature, 1939, 143, 460.
[1158] R. Sagane, S. Kojima, G. Myiamoto, and M. Ikawa, Phys. Rev. 1940, ii. 57, 750.
[1159] R. C. L. Mooney, ib. 1947, 72, 1269.

with the sulphides of manganese and rhenium. From the precipitate dilute hydrochloric acid removes the manganese and leaves the rhenium, which is found to have all the activity. Again, when the molybdenum was converted into the pentoxide, and the whole heated in oxygen, it was found that at 400–500° the rhenium distilled off as the heptoxide (the manganese of course remaining behind) and the activity came off and was condensed with it.

Only one method for separating the active material from rhenium was discovered. If molybdenum pentoxide containing rhenium is dissolved in 80 per cent. sulphuric acid, and moist hydrogen chloride gas is passed through the solution at 200°, the rhenium distils over as a volatile chloride. With active molybdenum the distillate had only a trace of the activity, nearly all of which remained with the manganese in the non-volatile residue. This reaction should make it possible to concentrate natural inactive technetium, if it really occurs in minerals.

75. RHENIUM*

AFTER Hevesy and Coster in 1922 had discovered hafnium, and had shown that its X-ray lines can be detected in almost every zirconium mineral, a search was made by means of the X-ray spectra for the missing elements 43 and 75 in a variety of manganese ores,[1160-1] but in vain. Then W. Noddack and I. Tacke (Frau Noddack) examined a series of minerals of the neighbouring elements such as niobium, molybdenum, tantalum, and the platinum metals. Finally, in 1925[1142-3] they obtained from gadolinite, mainly a basic silicate of beryllium, iron, and the rare earth metals, a fraction in which the element was enriched 100,000 times, which gave five of the X-ray lines of No. 75, to which they gave the name of rhenium.

The properties of the new element 75 make it likely to occur in sulphide ores, and in fact such sulphides as molybdenite (MoS_2) may contain as much as 1, and in two cases as much as 10 and 21 parts of rhenium per million.[1162]

Rhenium has never been found in a higher concentration than 50 parts per million; its average concentration in the earth's crust is given by the Noddacks[1163] as 1×10^{-9} (1 mg./ton), with which Goldschmidt[1164] closely agrees. The only practical sources are a few minerals containing from 10^{-5} to 10^{-7} (10 to 0·1 parts per million) of the element, especially certain gadolinites and alvites ($ca.\ 10^{-6}$), some iron and copper ores (10^{-7}), and some molybdenites ($ca.\ 4 \times 10^{-6}$). The processes of separation are very tedious, and are usually completed by subliming off the rhenium as Re_2O_7 in a stream of oxygen.

Rhenium is made (or was in 1933)[1165] only by one chemical firm at Leopoldshall, in Saxony, from a kupferschiefer containing from 0·1 to 0·01 per cent. of molybdenum, and about a thousandth as much rhenium. In the metallurgy of this mineral for copper, by-products are obtained which are worked up for cobalt, nickel, and molybdenum. These contain on the average 5×10^{-5} (one part in 20,000) of rhenium. This is still further concentrated and then slowly oxidized, whereby the rhenium is converted into perrhenate. In 1933 some 120 kg. of potassium perrhenate were produced.

* The work which has been done on the element and its compounds from its discovery in 1925 up to 1933 has been summarized and discussed by the discoverers I. and W. Noddack in *Das Rhenium*, Voss, Leipzig, 1933; this book is largely quoted below as NN.

[1160] C. H. Bosanquet and T. C. Keeley, *Phil. Mag.* 1924, **48**, 145.

[1161] V. M. Goldschmidt, *Vid. Skrifter I*, 1924, Heft 4, p. 21.

[1162] See NN., p. 10, where the rhenium content of a series of minerals is given.

[1163] NN., p. 20.

[1164] V. M. Goldschmidt, *Geochem. Vert.-ges.* ix (Oslo, 1938), p. 64.

[1165] NN., p. 24.

[1166] For the magnetic properties of rhenium compounds see W. Schüth and W. Klemm, *Z. anorg. Chem.* 1934, **220**, 193. The results are very complicated, and difficult to explain even qualitatively.

[1167] For the parachor of rhenium in its compounds see H. V. A. Briscoe, P. L. Robinson, and A. J. Rudge, *J.C.S.* 1932, 2673.

General Properties of Rhenium[1166-7]

The general properties of rhenium resemble those of manganese in many ways, but all show very significant differences from them. The known valencies are 1, 2, 3, 4, 5, 6, and 7 (the valency of 5 is unknown with manganese). As is usual in passing from a lighter to a heavier element in the same transitional subgroup, the most characteristic differences are (1) that the higher valencies are more stable as compared with the lower, and (2) that the tendency to ionization in the lower valencies is much smaller.

Thus it is found that the highest state of oxidation, the heptavalent, is the most stable that the element can assume. While Mn_2O_7 begins to lose oxygen at $0°$, and $KMnO_4$ at $200°$, Re_2O_7 can be distilled unchanged at $350°$, and $KReO_4$ at $1,370°$. In this valency also rhenium, unlike manganese, is colourless or practically so. A further difference is that in presence of excess of alkali, rhenium forms 'meso-perrhenates' of the type of M_3ReO_5, to which manganese has no analogues; the same difference is shown by telluric and periodic as compared with selenic (or sulphuric) and perchloric acids.

Hexavalent rhenium is practically confined, apart from an oxide ReO_3 and a volatile ReF_6 (there is no MnO_3 or MnF_6), to the rhenates M_2ReO_4. These are similar to the manganates in behaviour, and even in their green colour, but are less stable; they cannot be made from the perrhenates as the manganates can from the permanganates by fusion with excess of alkali.

Pentavalent Rhenium. There is no pentavalent manganese. Even with rhenium this state of valency is unstable, being confined to the pentachloride (there is no pentafluoride) and the hyporhenates, the salts of the weak acid $HReO_3$. The instability of pentavalent rhenium is mainly due to its strong tendency to disproportionate to $Re^{iv}+Re^{vii}$.

Tetravalent Rhenium. As with manganese this is a very stable state, more stable indeed than Mn^{iv} because of the smaller stability of the still lower valencies of rhenium, which makes disproportionation less easy for Re^{iv} than for Mn^{iv}. On the other hand, Re^{iv} is very easily oxidized. The behaviour of ReO_2 on heating shows forcibly the smaller stability of the lower valencies of rhenium as compared with manganese. If manganese dioxide is heated it loses oxygen continuously until it is converted finally into MnO; rhenium dioxide, on the other hand, is oxidized by air (which MnO_2 is not) forming Re_2O_7, and if it is heated in a vacuum to a high temperature it is converted into a mixture of the heptoxide and metallic rhenium. The corresponding tetravalent rhenous acid H_2ReO_3 like manganous acid H_2MnO_3 is a weak acid, and its salts are very readily hydrolysed, and also readily oxidized. The complex halides of Re^{iv}, of the type M_2ReX_6, are unexpectedly stable; the corresponding Mn^{iv} complexes can be made, but they are relatively unstable.

Trivalent Rhenium. These compounds are in some ways more stable than the trivalent manganese compounds, probably for two reasons: (1) because they do not form the unstable simple cation so readily as the Mn^{iii} compounds do, and (2) because the alternative divalent state is much less stable than with manganese, so that the Re^{iii} compounds have less tendency to disproportionate. The trivalent rhenium compounds include the trichloride, which is covalent and polymerized to Re_2Cl_6, like Al_2Cl_6, and Fe_2Cl_6, while $MnCl_3$ is presumably a salt and, probably for that reason, is much less stable. The complex Re^{iii} chlorides are remarkable for being all of the type $MReCl_4$, while the complex halides of Mn^{iii} are all of the unusual 5-covalent type M_2MnCl_5.

Divalent rhenium certainly occurs in solution, but it is very unstable, being oxidized even by water, and no compounds have yet been isolated, whereas divalent manganese gives rise to a whole series of reasonably stable derivatives.

Metallic Rhenium

Rhenium compounds are easily reduced to the metal,[1168] which can be obtained by the ignition of any of them in hydrogen. The metal is usually made either from the perrhenate $KReO_4$ or from the dioxide ReO_2; it can be purified[1169] by oxidizing it to perrhenic acid and reducing this again in hydrogen at 1,000–1,100°. Owing to its infusibility the metal is usually obtained as a powder, but it can be got in a coherent form by heating a very thin platinum or tungsten wire in the vapour of the tetrachloride.[1170]

The melting-point of pure rhenium is 3,137° C.[1170] Its specific resistance is rather high as compared with those of its neighbours.[1170-1] The value in ohms/cm. at 20° is 20×10^{-6}, the others being Mn 4·4, W 5·9, and Os $9·5 \times 10^{-6}$ respectively.

The atomic weight was found from the ratio $AgReO_4:AgBr$ to be 186·31.[1172] It has two isotopes of 185 and 187, which are present in the ratio 1:1·62; it is very rare for the heavier isotope of an element of odd atomic number to be the more abundant.

Chemically[1173] rhenium behaves as a half-noble metal, but its behaviour depends very much on its state of division. The massive metal remains unchanged in the air, while a fine powder may even be pyrophoric. If it is heated in oxygen the heptoxide Re_2O_7 distils off; dry chlorine acts on it below 100° to give volatile chlorides; bromine does so less readily, and iodine not at all. Sulphur converts it into the disulphide ReS_2; nitrogen has no action at any temperature examined (up to 2,000°). Air-free water, either alone, or when it contains HF, HCl, HBr, H_2SO_4, KOH, or ammonia, has practically no action on the metal, which is open to attack chiefly by oxygen (especially in the presence of concentrated acids) and oxidizing agents such as H_2O_2, HNO_3, chlorine water, etc.

[1168] NN., p. 25.   [1169] H. Haraldsen, *Z. anorg. Chem.* 1935, **221**, 397.

[1170] C. Agte, H. Alterthum, K. Becker, G. Heyne, and K. Moers, ib. 1931, **196**, 129.

[1171] W. Meissner and B. Voigt, *Ann. Phys.* 1930, **7**, 915.

[1172] O. Honigschmid and R. Sachtleben, *Z. anorg. Chem.* 1930, **191**, 309.

[1173] NN., p. 33.

The finely divided metal, especially as it is obtained by adsorbing $KReO_4$ solution on clay, drying, and reducing with hydrogen, is an active catalyst for splitting alcohols into hydrogen and the aldehyde[1174-5]; it is less effective for reducing unsaturated hydrocarbons like cyclohexene, and is useless for oxidation reactions, as the rhenium volatilizes away as the heptoxide. If K_2ReCl_6 is reduced in presence of gum, a stable colloidal solution of rhenium is obtained, which catalyses the reduction of maleic and cinnamic acids, and the synthesis of ammonia.[1176]

Rhenium and Carbon[1177]

If methane is heated in contact with rhenium it begins to decompose at 800°, and the separated carbon dissolves in the metal up to 0·9 per cent., but no carbide is formed up to 2,000°. The metallic powder is, however, said to form a carbide when heated in carbon monoxide above 500°; the product contains up to 4·9 per cent. of carbon (about Re_4C_3).

Rhenium and Phosphorus[1178]

Red phosphorus has no action on rhenium up to 750°, even if it is heated with it for days at 40–50 atm. pressure. Above this temperature the elements combine, and the concordant results of measurements of the vapour pressure of the phosphorus, and of X-ray powder diagrams, indicate the formation of definite compounds of the compositions ReP_3, ReP_2, ReP, and Re_2P.

Rhenium and Arsenic[1179]

These elements seem to form only one compound, Re_3As_7, which loses all its arsenic in a vacuum at 1,000°.

HEPTAVALENT RHENIUM

This, which is the group valency, is a particularly stable state for rhenium, even more than for manganese. The tendency of the intermediate valencies to 'disproportionate' with the production of the highest states is even more marked with rhenium than with manganese, and the higher state assumed in this process with rhenium is almost invariably the heptavalent and the lower sometimes the metal.

Heptavalent rhenium occurs in combination with oxygen and sulphur, but scarcely ever with halogens; no heptahalides of rhenium are known, and only a few oxyhalides of this valency such as ReO_3Cl. The heptavalent rhenium compounds are thus practically limited to perrhenic acid

[1174] M. S. Platonov, S. B. Anissimov, and V. M. Krascheninnikova, *Ber.* 1935, **68**, 761; 1936, **69**, 1050.

[1175] M. S. Platonov, *J. Chem. Russ.* 1941, **11**, 683. ReS_2 can also be used for the same purpose.

[1176] C. Zenghelis and C. Stathis, *C.R.* 1939, **209**, 797.

[1177] W. Trzebiatowski, *Z. anorg. Chem.* 1937, **233**, 376.

[1178] H. Haraldsen, ib. 1935, **221**, 397.

[1179] F. Weichmann and M. Heimburg, ib. 1939, **240**, 129.

$HReO_4$ and its derivatives, including the anhydride Re_2O_7, and certain sulphur and selenium derivatives.

Rhenium Heptoxide, Re_2O_7

This substance is always produced when rhenium compounds are ignited in oxygen; it can be made by heating metallic rhenium in oxygen at any temperature above 150°, or by evaporating an aqueous solution of perrhenic acid $HReO_4$ to dryness.

It occurs in two forms, one yellow and the other white. The white form is still very imperfectly understood. It is formed by the direct oxidation of rhenium or of its dioxide, apparently[1180] when the cold gas comes in contact with the hot metal or oxide; it must be isomeric with the yellow Re_2O_7, since at 150°[1181] it changes into the yellow form without any loss of oxygen. This behaviour recalls the dimorphism of phosphorus pentoxide (V. 738).

The ordinary form of rhenium heptoxide is yellow; it darkens on heating, while at -80° it is colourless. There is a striking contrast between the brilliant colours of the heptavalent manganese compounds—the dark green Mn_2O_7 and the purple permanganates—and the nearly colourless derivatives of heptavalent rhenium. This appears to be due to the absorption bands having been shifted out of the visible into the ultra-violet, where the heptoxide and the acid have been shown to have a strong absorption.

Rhenium heptoxide is a solid melting at 304°, and boiling at 350°. The vapour is colourless, stable, and monomeric at least up to 520°. It is easily soluble in water, in which it is reversibly hydrated, alcohol (which it does not oxidize) and acetone, and slightly in ether and CCl_4.

Carbon monoxide and sulphur dioxide reduce Re_2O_7 slowly in the cold and rapidly on heating to the coloured lower oxides; hydrogen reduces it at 300° to the blue-black ReO_2, and at 500° to the metal. H_2S reacts with it slowly in the cold and quickly at 80°, forming a layer of the heptasulphide Re_2S_7 which covers the crystals and prevents further action.

Perrhenic Acid, $HReO_4$

Re_2O_7 is the anhydride of perrhenic acid $HReO_4$, which corresponds to permanganic $HMnO_4$, but differs from it, as periodic does from perchloric, and somewhat as telluric does from selenic and sulphuric, in occurring not only in the monobasic 'meta' form $HReO_4$, but also in a polybasic hydrated form H_3ReO_5, known as meso-perrhenic acid; neither acid can be isolated, but both, especially the first, give rise to numerous salts.

Perrhenates are formed with great ease by the action of oxidizing agents such as hydrogen peroxide on metallic rhenium or its lower oxides and their derivatives. The acid gives in water a colourless solution, which on

---

[1180] NN., p. 43.
[1181] H. Hagen and A. Sieverts, *Z. anorg. Chem.* 1932, **208**, 367.

evaporation loses water continuously until the heptoxide Re_2O_7 is left. If this is mixed with just enough water to give Re_2O_7,H_2O a yellow mass is formed which melts at 150°, but gives no evidence of being a chemical individual.

Perrhenic acid and its salts can be reduced in a variety of ways.[1182-5] In concentrated solution potassium iodide or hydrazine reduces them to ReO_2, with the intermediate formation of the pentavalent hyporhenate $MReO_3$. The reduction in acid solution (it is much hastened by the presence of excess of acid)[1182] usually proceeds directly to the pentavalent stage; this occurs in HCl solution with electrolytic reduction,[1185] with HI,[1185] and with stannous chloride.[1183] In H_2SO_4 solution, on reduction with Fe″ Sn″ or Ti‴, Re^{vi} is formed as an intermediate product, as can be shown both electrometrically and by the colour,[1184] the hexavalent rhenium solution being violet and the pentavalent blue; if the reaction is to be stopped at the hexavalent stage a large excess of H_2SO_4 must be used, and the temperature kept low. With hydriodic acid the reduction goes first to the pentavalent stage, and then further to the tetravalent.[1185]

Perrhenates

A large number of perrhenates are known, of monovalent, divalent, and trivalent bases, some with water of crystallization and some without. They are colourless when the cation is not coloured, the absorption of the anion beginning at 3,800 A.U. The properties, and especially the solubilities, of the solid salts are of interest, particularly in relation to those of the salts of certain other strong monobasic acids with small, roughly spherical, and only slightly deformable anions, such as MnO_4', ClO_4', IO_4', BF_4', and SO_3F'. As we have already seen, a resemblance of this kind often leads to a close similarity in crystal structure and in solubility. It does not necessarily involve any similarity in stability, and in this respect there is a remarkable difference between the perrhenates and the other salts, especially in their resistance to heat. The perrhenates are remarkably stable. $KMnO_4$ begins to lose oxygen at 200°, $KClO_4$ at 400°, KIO_4 at a red heat (say 600°), and KBF_4 begins to dissociate at about 500°; none of these salts can be distilled without decomposition, even in a vacuum, whereas $KReO_4$ melts at 518°,[1186] and distils unchanged under 1 atm. pressure at 1,370°.[1187]

But in the crystalline forms and the solubilities the resemblances are very close. The structure of the ReO_4 ion is as we should expect like that of MnO_4 or ClO_4, with the four oxygens arranged round the rhenium at the points of a tetrahedron.[1188-9] The crystalline forms are indeed different,

[1182] W. F. Jakób and B. Jezowska, *Z. anorg. Chem.* 1933, **214**, 337.

[1183] H. Hölemann, ib. 1934, **217**, 105.

[1184] Id., ib. **220**, 33.   [1185] B. Jezowska, *Rocz. Chem.* 1934, **14**, 1061.

[1186] H. Hölemann and W. Kleese, *Z. anorg. Chem.* 1938, **237**, 172.

[1187] D. Vorländer and G. Dalichau, *Ber.* 1933, **66**, 1534.

[1188] $KReO_4$: E. Broch, *Z. physikal. Chem.* 1929, B **6**, 22.

[1189] $[Cd(NH_3)_4] \cdot (ReO_4)_2$: K. S. Pitzer, *Z. Krist.* 1935, **92**, 131.

the alkaline permanganates and the borofluorides being rhombic, while the perrhenates and periodates are tetragonal, but this is a direct result of the difference in ionic size, as V. M. Goldschmidt has shown.

The solubilities of the perrhenates vary[1190-1] in the same way as those of the other salts mentioned above; we find the same low solubility of the salts of univalent cations (K, Rb, Cs, Tl', Ag') other than Na and Li, and of those of many complicated organic bases such as strychnine and nitron (many more of which are known than of the permanganates, because ReO_4^- is a much less powerful oxidizing agent than MnO_4^-); the much greater solubility of the salts of sodium* and of the simple divalent cations such as Ca, Sr, Cu", Mg, Zn, Cd, Co", Ni; the great diminution of solubility with the tetra- and hexammines of cobalt[1191]; the absence of hydration in the salts of univalent metals and its presence in those of polyvalent. All these peculiarities are shared by the perrhenates with the perchlorates, periodates, borofluorides, and so far as is known the fluoro-sulphonates as well.

The table below gives the solubilities in water in moles per litre at temperatures near the ordinary for a series of these salts.[1190-2] The temperature is always 20° unless otherwise stated.

Solubilities in Water in moles per litre

	ReO_4'	MnO_4'	ClO_4'	IO_4'	BF_4'	SO_3F'
Na . . .	ca. 3·5	Deliqu.	17·28/25°	0·480	..	..
K . . .	0·034	0·404	0·121	0·0022	..	..
Rb . . .	0·031	0·052	0·055	0·023/13°	0·027	..
Cs . . .	0·020	0·009	0·070	0·066/15°	0·047	..
NH_4 . .	0·227	0·580/15°	2·136/25°	0·129/15°	..	..
$Co(NH_3)_6'''$.	0·00051	..	0·013/9°	..	0·016/9°	..
$Cr(NH_3)_6'''$.	0·00073	0·0035/17°	0·0199/17°	..	0·0412/17°	0·063
$Cr(NH_2CONH_2)_6'''$	0·0154	0·084	0·006	..	0·005	0·063
$Ni(NH_3)_6$ in 10-n. aq. NH_3 . .	0·0505/26°	..	0·0134/26°	..	0·0154/26°	..
$Cu(py)_4''$ . .	0·0063	..	0·016/12·5°	..	0·063/12°	0·047/12°
Ag' . . .	0·0089	..	..	..	..	..
Tl' . . .	0·0035	..	..	..	..	..
Ba" . . .	0·235	..	..	..	..	..

Meso-perrhenates

These salts, which are derived from the acid H_3ReO_5, can be made both by alkaline fusion and in the wet way.[1193]

If metallic rhenium or ReO_2 is fused with an alkaline hydroxide with access of air, or in presence of an oxidizing agent such as a peroxide, nitrate, or chlorate, the fused mass turns yellow, or, if it contains much

* The ratio of the solubility of the Na to that of the K salt at 20° (see NN., p. 47) is $MReO_4$ 101 : $MClO_4$ 143 : ($MMnO_4$ large) : MIO_4 22.

[1190] E. Wilke-Dörfurt and T. Gunzert, *Z. anorg. Chem.* 1933, **215**, 369.
[1191] E. Neusser, ib. 1937, **230**, 253.
[1192] W. T. Smith and S. H. Long, *J.A.C.S.* 1948, **70**, 354.
[1193] B. Scharnow, *Z. anorg. Chem.* 1933, **215**, 185.

rhenium, red, from the formation of a meso-perrhenate M_3ReO_5. Salts of this acid can also be made by adding excess of base to solution of a normal perrhenate. Thus the barium salt $Ba_3(ReO_5)_2$ separates as a bright yellow precipitate when barium hydroxide (or an alkaline hydroxide) is added to a solution of barium perrhenate $Ba(ReO_4)_2$. It was shown[1193] that whether the ratio of $Ba(OH)_2$ to $Ba(ReO_4)_2$ taken was 10:1, or 20:1, or 100:1, that of Ba to Re in the product was always the same, and approximately 3:2.

These salts are yellow when cold and red when hot; they give a colourless solution in water because they are at once hydrolysed to the normal or meta perrhenate $MReO_4$; in the same way prolonged washing with water converts a meso into a normal perrhenate.

The barium salt is decomposed by CO_2, with precipitation of $BaCO_3$ and formation of $Ba(ReO_4)_2$, showing the extreme weakness of the second and third dissociation constants of the meso-acid; this is in sharp contrast to the corresponding meso-periodate, where the acid is so much stronger as regards the last two replaceable hydrogen atoms that the barium salt is not converted into the normal periodate by anything weaker than nitric acid.[1194] The strontium salt is similar.

Thioperrhenates

One of the characteristics of heptavalent rhenium is its power of forming compounds in which the oxygen is replaced by sulphur, such as the heptasulphide Re_2S_7 and the thioperrhenates. Feit[1195] showed that if H_2S is passed into a neutral solution of a perrhenate, the colourless solution turns greenish-yellow owing to the production of a thioperrhenate, according to the equation

$$MReO_4 + H_2S = MReO_3S + H_2O.$$

The salt produced is mixed with dark-coloured poly-thio-compounds, but it can be separated from them by fractional precipitation with thallous nitrate of the thallous salt $Tl(ReO_3S)$, which can then be recrystallized from water and alcohol.

In solution these salts are to some extent hydrolysed into H_2S and the perrhenate; silver nitrate precipitates Ag_2S: plumbous cupric and mercuric salts give characteristically coloured precipitates, which are mixtures of the thioperrhenate and the sulphide.

The salts are oxidized by nitric acid, bromine water, or H_2O_2 to perrhenate and H_2SO_4, or if the solution is concentrated to perrhenate and free sulphur. The acidified solution slowly precipitates rhenium heptasulphide:

$$7\,HReO_3S = Re_2S_7 + 5\,HReO_4 + H_2O.$$

The free acid $HReO_3S$ has not been isolated, but conductivities show it to be a strong acid, and accordingly it is not extracted from its aqueous solution by ether. In their solubilities the salts resemble the chlorides

[1194] C. W. Kimmins, *J.C.S.* 1889, **55**, 148.

[1195] W. Feit, *Z. angew. Chem.* 1931, **44**, 65; *Z. anorg. Chem.* 1931, **199**, 262.

rather than the perrhenates: the solubilities of some of them (in g. per litre at 20°) are: Na, very soluble; K, 670; Rb, 143; Cs, 14; Tl′, 1·02; NH$_4$, very soluble.

The prolonged action of H$_2$S on a perrhenate solution seems to lead to the replacement of more oxygens by sulphur.[1196]

Rhenium Heptasulphide, Re$_2$S$_7$

This remarkable compound can be made[1197-1200] by the action of hydrogen sulphide or sodium thiosulphate on an acidified solution of a perrhenate, when it separates as the hydrate Re$_2$S$_7$,H$_2$O. It can be got in the anhydrous form by the action of H$_2$S on dry Re$_2$O$_7$. It is also precipitated by H$_2$S slowly but almost quantitatively from an ammoniacal solution of a perrhenate.[1199]

The anhydrous compound is a fine black amorphous powder easily oxidized by air, sometimes with incandescence. It begins to dissociate below its melting-point, and readily decomposes with evolution of heat into ReS$_2$ and free sulphur. It dissolves only with decomposition, but owing to its fine state of division it is a powerful absorbent. It is not attacked by K$_2$S, HCl, or H$_2$SO$_4$, but is oxidized to perrhenic acid by HNO$_3$, bromine-water, or H$_2$O$_2$.

Rhenium Heptaselenide[1200]

This is very like the heptasulphide, and is made in the same way. It is a fine black powder, which is a strong absorbent, and it breaks up *in vacuo* at 325° into ReSe$_2$ and free selenium.

Oxyhalides of Heptavalent Rhenium

It is remarkable that although no binary halides of heptavalent rhenium are known, at least two oxyhalides have been prepared; this is perhaps on account of the instability of the 7-covalent state.

The chloride ReO$_3$Cl is formed[1201-2] by heating Re$_2$O$_7$ with excess of ReCl$_4$ (or the mixture of ReCl$_5$ and ReCl$_3$: see p. 1308) and fractionating the product. It is a colourless liquid freezing at +4·5°, and boiling at 131°. Water or moist air at once converts it into HReO$_4$+HCl. According to Geilmann[1203] it is very sensitive to light, and in sunlight turns reddish-violet in a few minutes, the colour disappearing again in the dark.

The oxyhalide ReO$_2$Cl$_3$ which has been described does not appear to exist.[1201]

The oxybromide ReO$_3$Br was made by Brukl and Ziegler[1204] by heating

[1196] NN., p. 56.   [1197] I. and W. Noddack, *Z. angew. Chem.* 1931, **44**, 215.
[1198] W. Geilmann and F. Weibke, *Z. anorg. Chem.* 1931, **195**, 289.
[1199] J. H. Müller and W. A. La Lande, *J.A.C.S.* 1933, **55**, 2376.
[1200] H. V. A. Briscoe, P. L. Robinson, and E. M. Stoddart, *J.C.S.* 1931, 1439.
[1201] A. Brukl and K. Ziegler, *Ber.* 1932, **65**, 916.
[1202] H. V. A. Briscoe, P. L. Robinson, and A. J. Rudge, *J.C.S.* 1932, 2673.
[1203] W. Geilmann and F. W. Wrigge, *Z. anorg. Chem.* 1933, **214**, 248.
[1204] A. Brukl and K. Ziegler, *Mon.* 1933, **142**, 539.

metallic rhenium in a mixture of oxygen and bromine vapour, and then distilling the product over Re_2O_7; it is a pure white solid melting at $39 \cdot 5°$, and boiling at $163°$.

HEXAVALENT RHENIUM

The compounds of hexavalent rhenium have a great resemblance to those of hexavalent manganese, but they are definitely less stable. Of all the valency states of rhenium this is the one which has the strongest tendency to disproportionation, according to the equation:

$$3 \text{ Re}^{vi} = \text{Re}^{iv} + 2 \text{ Re}^{vii}.$$

The hexavalent state is not very stable even with manganese, as is shown by the readiness with which a manganate passes into a permanganate, but the change is much easier with rhenium, because of the great stability and large heat of formation of its heptavalent compounds. Thus if a permanganate is fused with excess of an alkaline hydroxide, it loses oxygen and goes over into the manganate, but no corresponding change occurs with a perrhenate.

The compounds of hexavalent rhenium include the trioxide ReO_3 (to which there is no manganese analogue), the salts of rhenic acid H_2ReO_4, whose existence is certain, though they cannot be isolated: like the manganates they are green; a hexafluoride (the only binary halide of rhenium with more than 5 halogen atoms in the molecule), and a few oxyhalides.

Rhenium Trioxide, ReO_3

This is made by heating rhenium with the heptoxide to $200-50°$,[1205] or by burning the metal in a slight defect of oxygen. It is a crystalline powder which may have any colour from dark blue (known as rhenium blue) to copper colour, according to its state of division.[1206]

Its crystal structure is similar to that of CrO_3 and WO_3.[1207] It is not attacked by water, hydrochloric acid (even hot), or dilute sodium hydroxide; it is reduced by acidified potassium iodide with separation of iodine, and is oxidized by nitric acid to $HReO_4$. If it is boiled with concentrated alkali, or heated alone *in vacuo* to $400°$, it is converted into a mixture of the dioxide and heptoxide:

$$3 \text{ ReO}_3 = \text{ReO}_2 + \text{Re}_2O_7.$$

Rhenium trioxide is formally the anhydride of rhenic acid H_2ReO_4, the salts of which can be obtained in solution; but it does not form these salts with alkalies, owing perhaps to the great instability of rhenic acid.

Salts of Rhenic Acid, H_2ReO_4

These salts, which correspond to the green manganates, and are themselves green, have been prepared in solution, but owing to their extreme

[1205] W. Biltz, G. A. Lehrer, and K. Meisel, *Nachr. Ges. Wiss. Gott.* 1931, 191.
[1206] W. Biltz, F. W. Wrigge, and K. Meisel, ib. 1936, i. 161.
[1207] K. Meisel, *Z. anorg. Chem.* 1932, **207**, 121:

instability, and their strong tendency to disproportionate into $Re^{vii} + Re^{iv}$, they have never been isolated.

If a fused alkaline perrhenate is treated[1208] in the absence of air with enough ReO_2 to form the rhenate M_2ReO_4, the yellow mass turns green, and no doubt contains the rhenate, but this cannot be isolated, since both water and alcohol decompose it. If barium perrhenate $Ba(ReO_4)_2$ is fused with ReO_2 and NaOH, and the product extracted with alcohol, impure barium rhenate remains as a green insoluble residue, stable only in presence of excess of alkali, and immediately decomposed by water into the perrhenate $Ba(ReO_4)_2$ and the rhenite $BaRe^{iv}O_3$; it is more stable in the form of pale green mixed crystals with barium sulphate.

Rhenium Hexafluoride, ReF_6

This compound (Ruff[1209,1211-13]) is made by the action of elementary fluorine on rhenium powder at 125°. This must be done in a fluorite (CaF_2) tube, since the product attacks hot quartz; it first reacts with it thus:

$$2\,ReF_6 + SiO_2 = 2\,ReOF_4 + SiF_4$$

and then, with a characteristic disproportionation:

$$3\,ReF_6 + 3\,SiO_2 = ReF_4 + 2\,ReO_3F + 3\,SiF_4$$

the ultimate product containing Re^{iv} and Re^{vii}. The fluorine used must be quite free from oxygen,[1214] and also from chlorine, which last can be removed by condensation and fractionation; the product is condensed with liquid air, and is then practically pure.[1209]

Rhenium hexafluoride is a pale yellow crystalline solid, melting at 18·8° C.[1212] (the melting-point of 25·6° previously given is incorrect) to a pale yellow liquid, of b. pt. 47·6°[1213]; the critical temperature is about 209°. The heat of evaporation is 6·89 k.cals., and the Trouton constant 21·5.[1213] The vapour density is that required for ReF_6.

It is very unstable: it reacts at once with water, fats, glass, and even ligroin; it attacks quartz below 30°, with evolution of bubbles of SiF_4. In practically all these decompositions disproportionation occurs: thus with water the product is $HReO_4$ and the hydrated dioxide.

Rhenium hexafluoride can be reduced by hydrogen at 200°, by CO at 300°, by SO_2 at 400°, and by metallic rhenium at 400–500°; in these reductions it always forms the tetrafluoride ReF_4; at higher temperatures it is reduced to the metal. Oxygen and oxidizing agents convert it into the hexavalent $ReOF_4$ and the heptavalent ReO_3F.

All attempts[1212] to prepare the heptafluoride ReF_7 failed, and the

[1208] NN., p. 58.
[1209] O. Ruff and W. Kwasnik, *Z. anorg. Chem.* 1932, **209**, 113.
[1211] O. Ruff, *Z. angew. Chem.* 1933, **46**, 739.
[1212] O. Ruff and W. Kwasnik, *Z. anorg. Chem.* 1934, **219**, 65.
[1213] Id., ib. **220**, 96.
[1214] For a method for removing oxygen see O. Ruff and W. Menzel, *Z. anorg. Chem.* 1933, **211**, 204.

compound probably does not exist. Further, there is no evidence of the existence of a hexachloride, though a pentachloride is known. The existence and non-existence of these higher halides cannot be explained on stereochemical grounds alone, since the atomic radii of Re, Mo, and W are almost the same ($1\cdot37$, $1\cdot36$, and $1\cdot37$ respectively); all three elements form hexafluorides, but only tungsten a hexachloride, the others stopping at the pentachlorides $ReCl_5$ and $MoCl_5$.

Oxyhalides of Hexavalent Rhenium

Three of these compounds are known, a fluoride and a chloride of the type $ReOX_4$, and a fluoride ReO_2F_2.

$ReOF_4$[1212] is slowly formed by the action of the hexafluoride on quartz or glass; it is best made by passing a mixture of fluorine and oxygen over metallic rhenium at temperatures from $125°$ to $300°$; in either reaction it is mixed with ReF_6, which must be removed by fractional distillation in a high vacuum; the ReF_6 (boiling-point under atmospheric pressure $47\cdot6°$) comes off first, and then the $ReOF_4$ (b. pt. $62\cdot7°$), while a small quantity of ReO_2F_2 remains behind.

$ReOF_4$ is a pure white substance, melting at $+39\cdot7°$, with a heat of sublimation of $9\cdot51$ k.cals., and an extrapolated boiling-point of $62\cdot7°$. Its reactions are just like those of ReF_6, but usually need a rather higher temperature. It is reduced by most organic substances, but is stable to oxidation.

The corresponding chloride $ReOCl_4$[1215] is made by heating the tetra-chloride (or rather the mixture of $ReCl_5$ and $ReCl_3$) with oxygen to $150°$. It is a dark brown solid which melts at $28°$ and gives off a brown vapour on heating. It forms in cold concentrated hydrochloric acid a brown solution, which probably contains the acid H_2ReOCl_6,[1216] but this rapidly changes with the usual disproportionation according to the equation

$$3\ H_2ReOCl_6 + 5\ H_2O = H_2ReCl_6 + 2\ HReO_4 + 12\ HCl.$$

The brown salt K_2ReOCl_6 has been isolated, but it very soon decomposes in this way.

If $ReOCl_4$ is dissolved in organic liquids such as benzene or chloroform, and exposed to moisture, it is hydrolysed with the formation of a blue substance which could not be purified, but seems to have 2 of the 4 chlorine atoms replaced by H or OH.

$ReOCl_4$ reacts violently with gaseous or liquid ammonia. If the product is heated at $300°$ in a stream of ammonia, the NH_4Cl sublimes away, and there remains a solid of the composition $ReO(NH_2)_2Cl_2$. This reacts with water at once to lose both chlorine atoms and form $ReO(NH_2)_2(OH)_2$.[1215]

The last oxyhalide ReO_2F_2 (to which there is no chlorine analogue) is formed as we have seen[1215] in small amount when fluorine and oxygen are

[1215] A. Brukl and E. Plettinger, *Ber.* 1933, **66**, 971.
[1216] I. and W. Noddack, *Z. anorg. Chem.* 1933, **215**, 129.

passed over heated rhenium. When the $ReOF_4$ has been sublimed off it remains as a white powder melting with decomposition at 156° C. In moist air it hydrolyses and turns violet.

Complex *thiocyanates* of hexavalent rhenium appear to be formed,[1217-18] but they have not been isolated.

PENTAVALENT RHENIUM COMPOUNDS

The appearance with rhenium of this valency, which does not occur at all with manganese, is an example of the greater stability of the higher valencies in the heavier atoms of a subgroup. Even with rhenium the pentavalent compounds are few, being confined to the salts of hyporhenic acid* $HReO_3$, the halides and oxy-halides, and a very few cyanide complexes.

The pentavalent rhenium compounds can be made by the action of Re^{iv} on Re^{vii}, and are also formed as the first stage in the disproportionation of Re^{iv}, which gives $Re^{iii} + Re^{v}$.

The instability of the pentavalent rhenium compounds is shown by their great readiness to disproportionate, almost invariably to heptavalent+ tetravalent rhenium. This tendency makes most of the compounds decompose easily, either alone or in solutions which are not strongly acid or strongly alkaline, but it is to some extent checked in presence of excess of either hydroxyl or hydrogen ions, the former giving the hyporhenates, and hydrochloric acid the chloride and the complex oxychlorides.

Hyporhenates, $MReO_3$[1219]

The pentavalent oxide Re_2O_5 has not been prepared. If a perrhenate is fused with ReO_2 and an alkaline hydroxide in the absence of air, the hyporhenate $MReO_3$ can be obtained. The whole behaviour of the rhenium oxides when fused with alkali is peculiar. If rhenium dioxide is fused in this way in absence of air, it is converted into the dark brown rhenite $M_2Re^{iv}O_3$. If air is admitted to the fused mass it first turns yellow from the formation of the hyporhenate MRe^vO_3, then green (rhenate $M_2Re^{vi}O_4$), and then yellow or red (mesoperrhenate $M_3Re^{vii}O_5$). Unless there is enough oxygen present to convert all the rhenium into the mesoperrhenate, a mixture of compounds in the various states of oxidation is produced in proportions depending on the temperature and the amount of oxygen.[1220]

The only hyporhenate hitherto isolated is the sodium salt $NaReO_3$. This forms pale yellow crystals; in the dry state if it is free from alkali it

* Formally this acid is the analogue of the halic acids such as chloric $HClO_3$; but the name of rhenic acid is preoccupied by H_2ReO_4 (so called from manganic acid, there being no $HMnO_3$) to which the halogens have no parallel.

[1217] J. G. F. Druce, *Rec. Trav.* 1935, **54**, 334.
[1218] H. Hölemann, *Z. anorg. Chem.* 1937, **235**, 1.
[1220] I. and W. Noddack, *Z. anorg. Chem.* 1933, **215**, 129.

[1219] NN., p. 61.

very readily goes over into the rhenite $Na_2Re^{iv}O_3$ and the perrhenate $NaRe^{vii}O_4$; in water or in acids it is at once converted into rhenium dioxide and the perrhenate; it is oxidized by the air to the perrhenate (these reactions show the great stability of the heptavalent perrhenate). The solid is fairly stable if it is kept under aqueous or alcoholic soda. Only 0·04 g. dissolves in a litre of 1·8-normal sodium hydroxide at 0°. The solution is yellow, and soon begins to separate the hydrated dioxide; ammonium chloride precipitates the black ReO_2 at once; H_2S reacts slowly to form the thioperrhenate $NaReO_3S$.

Sodium hyporhenate forms mixed crystals with the meta-niobate $NaNbO_3$ and tantalate $NaTaO_3$, in which it is more stable than in the pure state.

The potassium and barium salts were obtained, but they could not be purified; this suggests that hyporhenic acid is a weak acid, with a sodium salt less soluble in water than the potassium salt.

Pentavalent Rhenium Halides

These seem to be confined to the pentachloride, and a certain number of complex derivatives. It is remarkable that no pentafluoride, intermediate between ReF_6 and ReF_4, has been obtained.

Rhenium pentachloride[1221-2] is the chief product of the action of chlorine on metallic rhenium. The product is heated to drive off the volatile $ReOCl_4$, and then further *in vacuo* at 150–250°, when the pentachloride sublimes away, leaving a small residue of the trichloride $ReCl_3$.[1221]

Rhenium pentachloride $ReCl_5$ is a blackish-brown solid giving a dark brown vapour. It decomposes on distillation at the ordinary pressure, and even on melting. If it is distilled in a stream of nitrogen it breaks up into the trichloride and chlorine: no other products are formed; when heated in oxygen it burns with the production of $Re^{vi}OCl_4$ and $Re^{vii}O_3Cl$. If it is heated with potassium chloride it undergoes a remarkable reaction, evolving chlorine and forming the tetravalent complex $K_2Re^{iv}Cl_6$, which can be purified by recrystallization from dilute hydrochloric acid. This complex salt must be exceptionally stable, since it is also formed, with the separation of metallic rhenium, when KCl is heated with rhenium trichloride $ReCl_3$.

In many of its reactions rhenium pentachloride undergoes disproportionation to heptavalent rhenium (perrhenates) and lower states of oxidation. Thus with aqueous sodium hydroxide it gives the hydrated dioxide and the perrhenate: if the temperature is raised the yield of the perrhenate is increased, owing to the oxidation of the dioxide by the air. With water alone $ReCl_5$ reacts violently, giving the hydrated dioxide, perrhenic acid, H_2ReCl_6, and chlorine. With aqueous hydrochloric acid it gives a green solution containing $HReO_4$, H_2ReCl_6, and free chlorine.

No other pentahalides of rhenium are known, and no simple oxyhalides,

[1221] W. Geilmann, F. W. Wrigge, and W. Biltz, *Z. anorg. Chem.* 1933, **214**, 244.
[1222] W. Geilmann and F. W. Wrigge, ib. 248.

and no complex halides; but there is a series of complex oxyhalides described in the next section.

Complex Compounds of Pentavalent Rhenium

Hexavalent rhenium has a certain power of forming unstable complexes of the type of K_2ReOCl_6. With pentavalent rhenium the tendency to form complexes is stronger, and the complexes can in some cases be isolated. It is curious that with pentavalent as with hexavalent rhenium the complex salts are not derived from the binary halides, which are known, but from the oxyhalides which in the pentavalent series do not exist.

The pentavalent rhenium complexes were investigated by Jakób and Jezowska.[1223-5] They showed by E.M.F. measurements[1224] that a solution of $KReO_4$ in aqueous hydrochloric acid is rapidly reduced electrolytically to the Re^v stage, the reduction then proceeding slowly to Re^{iv}.[1225] The pentavalent rhenium solution is greenish, and on addition of KCl precipitates a yellowish-green salt, which on analysis gives figures agreeing fairly well with $K_2[Re^vOCl_5],H_2O$ or $K_2[Re^v(OH)_2Cl_5]$; since the ammonium salt is $(NH_4)_2[ReOCl_5]$ we may assume that the first formula is correct. This salt is stable when dry, but in the presence of moisture darkens and separates the black dioxide (with simultaneous formation no doubt of the perrhenate). The salt differs from the tetravalent compound K_2ReCl_6 in being readily oxidized—by $KMnO_4$, H_2O_2 or nitric acid—to the perrhenate; it is very easily hydrolysed, and if it is warmed in acid solution disproportionates to $K_2ReCl_6+KReO_4$. It is only moderately soluble in very concentrated hydrochloric acid, in which it forms a fairly stable yellow solution; on dilution the colour changes, and in 1:1 HCl is green; on further dilution it becomes greenish-blue, and finally the dioxide is precipitated.[1225]

In cold concentrated hydrochloric acid the salt is not oxidized by air, but on boiling the Re^v is converted into $Re^{vii}+Re^{iv}$; this change is promoted by lowering the concentration of hydrogen ion, and for this reason the base $Re(OH)_5$ and its dehydration product Re_2O_5, cannot be prepared, since they disproportionate at once.

The ammonium salt $(NH_4)_2[ReOCl_5]$ is yellow, and similar to the potassium salt in properties, but it is rather more soluble in aqueous hydrochloric acid.

Cyanide Complexes of Pentavalent Rhenium

A remarkable complex of pentavalent rhenium is the oxy-cyanide salt $K_3[Re^vO_2(CN)_4]$.[1226-7] This is made by treating the tetravalent K_2ReCl_6 with excess of KCN and oxidizing with H_2O_2; the solution is extracted

[1223] W. F. Jakób and B. Jezowska, *Ber.* 1933, **66**, 461.
[1224] Id., *Z. anorg. Chem.* 1933, **214**, 337.   [1225] Id., ib. 1934, **220**, 16.
[1226] W. Klemm and G. Frischmuth, ib. 1937, **230**, 215.
[1227] G. T. Morgan and G. R. Davies, *J.C.S.* 1938, 1858.

with alcohol, the aqueous layer evaporated in the cold, and the residue recrystallized from water. Analysis will not distinguish between

$$K_3[Re^vO_2(CN)_4] \text{ and } K_3[Re^{iii}(OH)_2(CN)_4],$$

but the first formula is established by the oxidizing power and by the fact that this salt is only produced from K_2ReCl_6 when an oxidizing agent is present.

$K_3[ReO_2(CN)_4]$ forms orange crystals, very easily soluble in water; alkalies have no action on the salt, but acids turn it violet.[1228]

Most of the salts of this acid are too soluble to be isolated, but the thallous salt $Tl_3[ReO_2(CN)_4]$ is only slightly soluble in cold water, though easily in hot.

A complex somewhat analogous to this pentavalent rhenium compound is the red complex of tetravalent molybdenum $K_4[MoO_2(CN)_4]$.

COMPOUNDS OF TETRAVALENT RHENIUM

This is a very stable valency with rhenium, even more than with manganese; next to the valency of 7 it is the most stable state for rhenium, while with manganese the lower valencies of 3 and 2 are almost equally important. But even with Re^{iv} disproportionation, with the production of Re^{vii} (together with a lower valency or more often metallic rhenium itself) frequently occurs.

The tetravalent rhenium compounds include the oxide ReO_2 and the rhenites M_2ReO_3, analogous to the manganites: the sulphide ReS_2 and selenide $ReSe_2$, the tetrafluoride ReF_4, and an especially numerous and stable group of complex halides of the type M_2ReX_6, which are formed by all the four halogens.

Rhenium Dioxide, ReO_2

This is made[1229] by burning the metal in an insufficient supply of oxygen, or reducing the higher oxides with hydrogen. The hydrated form is prepared by the electrolytic reduction of acid or alkaline perrhenate solutions, or by the hydrolysis of the salts of tetravalent rhenium.

Anhydrous rhenium dioxide is a black powder which has a great absorptive power for gases and solutes. It is very stable in the absence of oxygen, but at high temperatures it is converted *in vacuo* into a mixture of rhenium heptoxide and metallic rhenium. This is in striking contrast to the behaviour of manganese dioxide, which on heating loses oxygen and is ultimately converted into manganous oxide MnO.

Oxygen on gentle warming converts rhenium dioxide into the heptoxide, the white form of the latter being formed below 150°, and the yellow form above.

[1228] The changes of colour here and with K_2ReOCl_5 (p. 1305) should be compared with those of the *en* compound $[ReO_2(en)_2]Cl$ (almost the only known rhenium ammine) given by V. V. Lebedinski and B. N. Ivanov-Emin, *J. Gen. Chem. Russ.* 1943, **13**, 253.

[1229] NN., p. 63.

Concentrated hydrogen halides and their salts dissolve ReO_2 easily to give the complex halides M_2ReX_6. Alkalies dissolve it slowly to form the rhenites M_2ReO_3; nitric acid, hydrogen peroxide, chlorine water, etc., oxidize it to the perrhenate.

In general the chemical behaviour of ReO_2 is like that of MnO_2; like the latter it acts as a base and as an acid, but it is stronger as an acid than as a base.

Rhenites, M_2ReO_3

These are formed[1230-1] when ReO_2 is fused with metallic oxides in the absence of air. They are brown microcrystalline solids, insoluble in water and alkaline hydroxide solutions, and decomposed by water and acids with precipitation of the dioxide; nitric acid, hydrogen peroxide, and (slowly) air oxidize them to perrhenates.

Very few rhenites have been isolated. Na_2ReO_3 is made by fusing ReO_2 with excess of sodium hydroxide in an atmosphere of nitrogen, and washing out the excess of alkali with water. It forms brown crystals. The potassium salt is similar. These compounds are insoluble and diamagnetic, which suggests that the anions are not simple.

Rhenium Disulphide, ReS_2

This is made[1232-3] by fusing the elements together; by the action of heat on the heptasulphide Re_2S_7; or by the action of H_2S on a solution of a tetravalent rhenium compound.

The anhydrous sulphide ReS_2 made in the dry way is a soft black substance with a layer-lattice like that of MoS_2 or CdI_2. It is volatile at 1,000° with some decomposition. The vapour contains no lower sulphides: on the other hand, Briscoe has found[1233] that if the dry heptasulphide Re_2S_7 is heated on a spring balance in nitrogen at 250° it loses sulphur quite steadily and regularly until the residue has a composition very near to ReS_2. We may therefore conclude that the only stable sulphides of rhenium are Re_2S_7 and ReS_2.

When the sulphide is made in the wet way it is obtained in a very fine state of division. It is insoluble in alkaline hydroxide or sulphide solution, in HCl, and in H_2SO_4; it can be oxidized to perrhenic acid. It can be used (like metallic rhenium) as a catalyst to dehydrogenate alcohols to aldehydes or ketones.[1234]

Rhenium Diselenide, $ReSe_2$

This is made[1233] by heating the heptaselenide Re_2Se_7 to 300–25° *in vacuo*. It is stable in air, and is only attacked by strong oxidizing agents.

[1230] Ib., p. 64.
[1231] I. and W. Noddack, *Z. anorg. Chem.* 1933, **215**, 129.
[1232] NN., p. 64.
[1233] H. V. A. Briscoe, P. L. Robinson, and E. M. Stoddart, *J.C.S.* 1931, 1439.
[1234] M. S. Platonov, *J. Gen. Chem. Russ.* 1941, **11**, 683.

Rhenium Tetrafluoride, ReF_4

This compound[1235] is formed in small quantity from the elements, but it is best made by passing the vapour of ReF_6 along with hydrogen or sulphur dioxide through a hot platinum tube (at 200° with hydrogen or 400° with SO_2). The tetrafluoride being almost non-volatile stays behind.

Rhenium tetrafluoride ReF_4 melts at 124·5° C.: both the solid and the liquid are dark green. Its vapour pressure is not perceptible at the ordinary temperature. It attacks quartz at 80°, but in a platinum tube it can be sublimed without change in a current of SO_2 at 500°.

Rhenium tetrachloride, $ReCl_4$, probably does not exist,[1221-2] though very stable complexes are derived from it. If it is liberated (as by heating the salt Ag_2ReCl_6) it at once changes to a mixture of $ReCl_5$ and $ReCl_3$.

$ReBr_4$ and ReI_4 may be among the products of the action of these halogens on rhenium, but they have not been isolated in the pure state.

No simple oxyhalides of tetravalent rhenium are known, although complexes derived from them exist, and Ruff and Kwasnik[1235] have shown that it is almost certain that an oxyfluoride $ReOF_2$ exists, although they were not able to isolate it.

Complex Halides of Tetravalent Rhenium

This is a remarkably stable group of compounds, formed by all four halogens, and it is the only considerable series of complex rhenium compounds known. The corresponding manganese complexes occur, but they are much less stable, and they do not include any bromides or iodides; this is probably due to the fact that the tetravalent manganese oxidizes the bromine and iodine anions, while tetravalent rhenium is practically devoid of oxidizing power.

Complex Fluorides, $M_2[ReF_6]$

These salts are most conveniently made[1235] by reducing $KReO_4$ in HF solution with KI:

$$2\, KReO_4 + 6\, KI + 16\, HF = 2\, K_2ReF_6 + 4\, KF + 3\, I_2 + 8H_2O.$$

K_2ReF_6 forms green crystals, giving a green solution. The acid H_2ReF_6 (which has not been isolated) must be relatively strong, because the salt is hydrolysed by water only on warming.

The behaviour of these fluorides is very like that of the complex chlorides described below, but the fluorides seem to be rather less stable.

A solution of K_2ReF_6 in HF reacts slowly with silicon dioxide to give K_2SiF_6 together with what is apparently a mixture of the two oxy-fluorides $Re^{vii}O_3F$ and $Re^{iv}OF_2$.

Complex Chlorides, $M_2[ReCl_6]$

If rhenium tetrachloride (or the mixture of $ReCl_5$ and $ReCl_3$) is dissolved in concentrated hydrochloric acid, or if ReO_2 is boiled in this acid,

[1235] O. Ruff and W. Kwasnik, *Z. anorg. Chem.* 1934, **219**, 76.

or $KReO_4$ dissolved in it and reduced with KI and the iodine removed, a green solution is obtained, which no doubt contains H_2ReCl_6, and from this a variety of salts (of K, Rb, Cs, NH_4, $N(CH_3)_4$, Ag, Tl′, Hg′, etc.) have been made. The exceptional stability of this $ReCl_6''$ complex is shown by the facts already mentioned that it is produced (1) with evolution of chlorine when KCl is heated with $ReCl_5$, and (2) with separation of metallic rhenium when it is heated with $ReCl_3$. The alkaline salts are all green when pure, and give yellow-green solutions; K_2ReCl_6 gives a 0·063 molar (30 g./litre) solution in 10 per cent. HCl at 20°. The silver (orange) mercurous and thallous (yellow) salts are only slightly soluble. The salts of the alkylammoniums, and of the very large organic bases such as cinchonine, are very soluble: those of the aromatic bases like *p*-toluidine, pyridine, and quinoline are relatively insoluble and can be isolated and purified.[1236] The 2-oxy-quinoline salt is practically insoluble, and will detect 1 mg. of K_2ReCl_6 in 20 c.c. of water.[1237]

If the silver salt is heated *in vacuo* to 300° it gives off a brown vapour, and silver chloride is left behind; this might be supposed to yield the tetrachloride $ReCl_4$, but nothing could be isolated from the distillate except $ReCl_5$ and $ReCl_3$.[1222]

In aqueous solution the alkaline salts are stable, and only precipitate ReO_2 after long standing or on boiling. Before precipitation begins the solution turns olive-green, owing probably[1236] to the production of an oxychloride ion such as $[Re(OH)Cl_5]''$ in equilibrium with the normal $[ReCl_6]''$; $K_2[PtCl_6]$ behaves in solution in this way.[1238]

In presence of alkalies the hexachlororhenates undergo a complicated series of disproportionations. In the cold an unstable Re^{iv} oxychloride, perhaps $ReOCl_2$, is formed, which changes over to $Re^{iii} + Re^v$; the latter soon changes further to $Re^{iv} + Re^{vii}$, so that the final result is:

$$4\,Re^{iv} = 3\,Re^{iii} + Re^{vii}.$$

If the solution is boiled with alkali two further changes occur:

1. $Re^{iii} = 2\,Re^{ii} + Re^v$
2. $3\,Re^v = 2\,Re^{iv} + Re^{vii}.$

Adding all these together we get:

$$5\,Re^{iv} = 3\,Re^{ii} + 2\,Re^{vii}.$$

Complex Bromides[1231]

The free acid, presumably H_2ReBr_6, aq., must be present in the deep yellow solution of ReO_2 in HBr; on dilution this is hydrolysed in the same way as the chloride, with precipitation of the hydrated dioxide. The acid can also be made by reducing perrhenic acid (even at 20°) with HBr.

[1236] H. Schmid, ib. 1933, **212**, 187.
[1237] H. Hölemann, ib. **211**, 195.
[1238] A. Hantzsch, *Z. physikal. Chem.* 1910, **72**, 362.

From this solution the K, Rb, and Cs salts can be obtained in brick-red crystals.

Complex Iodides

The potassium salt K_2ReI_6 was obtained[1239] by reducing $KReO_4$ with KI in HI solution; it is a black crystalline solid, and gives a deep violet solution in water and in acetone; this is readily hydrolysed.

Its behaviour on acidification is peculiar.[1240] If the solution of the potassium salt in 20 per cent., H_2SO_4 is shaken with ether, all the rhenium and 5/6 of the iodine (but none of the K) go over into the ether; the reaction must therefore be

$$K_2ReI_6 + H_2SO_4 = K_2SO_4 + HI + HReI_5.$$

It was proved that the rhenium was still tetravalent, and had not been oxidized or reduced. This reaction is specific for the hexaiodide: the bromide and chloride do not give it.

This apparent difference of structure between the acid and its salt is very peculiar; but it must be remembered that though the composition of the salt has been shown to be K_2ReI_6, there is so far no evidence, either from X-ray analysis or even from isomorphism, that the complex ion really is $[ReI_6]$; the salt might be a crystal aggregate of $K[ReI_5]$ and $K[I]$.

Oxyhalide Complexes

These complexes are formed[1241] when $KReO_4$ is reduced by HI in HCl solution. The following reactions then occur:

(1) $Re^{vii} + I^- = Re^{vi} + \quad I$

(2) $3\, Re^{vi} \qquad = Re^{iv} + 2\, Re^{vii}.$

The perrhenate formed in this last reaction then undergoes reduction according to (1), so that in all:

$$2\, Re^{vii} + 6\, I^- = 2\, Re^{iv} + 3\, I_2.$$

It is remarkable that the oxyhalide complexes of tetravalent rhenium formed in this way contain two atoms of rhenium in the molecule, the potassium salt being $K_4[Re_2^{iv}OCl_{10}]$; this forms small brown crystals, and is isomorphous with its ruthenium analogue $K_4[Ru_2OCl_{10}]$. In water it gives a yellow solution, which easily hydrolyses. Its relation to K_2ReCl_6 is obviously very close; it is converted into it by boiling with 6 per cent. HCl; on treatment with alkalies it disproportionates in exactly the same way, and—most remarkable of all—it forms mixed crystals with K_2ReCl_6 whose colour varies from yellow to orange as the amount of oxychloride increases. But no explanation in terms of structure has been suggested.

[1239] H. V. A. Briscoe, P. L. Robinson, and A. J. Rudge, *J.C.S.* 1931, 3218.

[1240] W. Biltz, F. W. Wrigge, E. Prange, and G. Lange, *Z. anorg. Chem.* 1937, **234**, 142.

[1241] NN., p. 68.

Similar oxyhalide complexes are probably formed when rhenium dioxide dissolves in hydrobromic or hydriodic acid, but they have not been isolated.

COMPOUNDS OF TRIVALENT RHENIUM

These are very imperfectly known. Trivalent rhenium can be obtained from tetravalent by disproportionation, or by reduction with metallic rhenium.

With manganese the acidic properties have entirely disappeared at the trivalent stage, and at the same time the trivalent cation is so easily oxidized (to Mn^{iv}) that it can scarcely exist; we are therefore confined with manganese to the covalent compounds such as the trihalides and their complexes, and even these are unstable from the ease with which they form the divalent cations.

With rhenium we should expect this trivalent stage to be rather more stable; the rise of atomic number has increased the stability of the trivalent as compared with the divalent state, and also diminished the tendency of these lower valencies to ionize, so that two causes of weakness are absent.

On the whole this is so. There is no sign of the formation of an Re^{+++} cation; but the stability of the compounds is much limited by the ease with which they are oxidized to the higher valencies, especially to Re^{iv} and Re^{vii}; it is only in acid solution, where a complex ion ReX_4' is produced, or in the trihalides, where the 4-covalent octets of the rhenium are secured by polymerization, that this tendency to oxidation is suppressed, and the compounds show a reasonable stability. The complexes are all of the $MReX_4$ type, and those of higher covalencies, such as $[ReX_6]$ (which occur with Re^{iv}, Re^v, and probably Re^{vi}) are not found.

Rhenium Sesquioxide, Re_2O_3

A hydrate of this can be got as a black precipitate when a solution of trivalent rhenium is treated with an alkaline hydroxide. It is extraordinarily easily oxidized,[1242] for example, by 10 minutes shaking with oxygen in the cold, to the perrhenate. This oxidation is much more rapid than that of the hydrated dioxide ReO_2, and is in sharp contrast to the marked resistance to oxidation offered by rhenium trichloride in acid solution.

The original precipitate of hydrated sesquioxide always contains more oxygen than corresponds to Re_2O_3, even when the greatest care has been taken to exclude oxygen during its preparation, and it has been shown[1242] that $ReCl_3$ will decompose water at $100°$ with evolution of hydrogen, even in presence of 1 per cent. H_2SO_4, and much more readily in alkaline solution. Salts of trivalent tungsten, and ferrous hydroxide, behave in the same way.

[1242] W. Geilmann and F. W. Wrigge, *Z. anorg. Chem.* 1933, **214**, 239.

If the sesquioxide is boiled in alkaline solution, we have the usual series of disproportionations

$$(1)\quad 3\,Re^{iii} \longrightarrow 2\,Re^{ii} + Re^{v}$$

$$(2)\quad 3\,Re^{v} \longrightarrow 2\,Re^{iv} + Re^{vii}$$

or in all

$$9\,Re^{iii} \longrightarrow 6\,Re^{ii} + 2\,Re^{iv} + Re^{vii}.$$

A series of alkylates of Re^{iii}, $Re(OAlk)_3$ have been described[1243]; they are brown solids soluble in alcohol and hydrolysed by water, and resemble the corresponding Mn^{iii} compounds.

There is no evidence that the trivalent rhenium oxide has any acidic properties: no alkaline salts of the type of M_3ReO_3 or $MReO_2$ are known (the same is true of manganese).

Trihalides of Rhenium

No trifluoride is known, possibly because of the great stability of the higher fluorides. The chloride and bromide have been prepared, but all attempts to make the tri-iodide have been unsuccessful.

Rhenium Trichloride

This compound[1222,1244-5] is formed when we might expect to get $ReCl_4$ (for example, by heating Ag_2ReCl_6), the actual product being a mixture of the penta and trichloride $ReCl_5$ and $ReCl_3$, from which the pentachloride can be distilled off, leaving the trichloride behind. It can also be made by heating $ReCl_5$ with metallic rhenium to 500°.

Rhenium trichloride forms reddish-black crystals, which give a deep red solution in acetone, in water, and in aqueous HCl. It is reduced by hydrogen at 250–300° to HCl and metallic rhenium; X-ray examination of the partially reduced material gave no indication of any solid phase other than $ReCl_3$ and the metal.[1222]

Rhenium trichloride does not in any way behave as a salt. The freshly made aqueous solution gives no precipitate with silver nitrate, and so can contain no chloride ions. At 25° the conductivity is found nearly to reach its maximum in half an hour. In a moist atmosphere the solid takes up water to form the hydrate $ReCl_3,2\,H_2O$, but this water can be removed again in a desiccator, leaving the rhenium trichloride undecomposed, but in a very fine state of division, which is unusually active, and dissolves more easily than the ordinary form. The molecular weight in glacial acetic acid is that of Re_2Cl_6,[1245] the structure no doubt being like that of Al_2Cl_6 and Fe_2Cl_6:

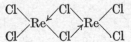

[1243] J. G. F. Druce, *J.C.S.* 1937, 1407.
[1244] W. Biltz, W. Geilmann, and F. W. Wrigge, *Ann.* 1934, **511**, 301.
[1245] F. W. Wrigge and W. Biltz, *Z. anorg. Chem.* 1936, **228**, 372.

A solution of trivalent rhenium is very easily oxidized by air (mainly to Re^{iv}) if it is alkaline, and fairly easily if it is neutral; but in acid, and especially in strongly acid solution, where no doubt complexes are formed, rhenium trichloride is very resistent to oxidation, even by hydrogen peroxide or chlorine water; blowing air through a solution in 2-normal H_2SO_4 for 90 minutes had no effect.[1244] If, however, the dry solid rhenium trichloride is heated in air or oxygen, it catches fire at 400°, and burns with the evolution of a dark green vapour, from which it is possible to isolate ReO_3Cl and $ReOCl_4$.

Rhenium Tribromide

This can be made by the action of hydrobromic acid on the hydrated sesquioxide, or by heating the metal with bromine; the bromine may be passed over the metal in a stream of nitrogen at 450°.[1246] Another method[1247] is to heat silver hexabromorhenate Ag_2ReBr_6 to a moderate temperature in a high vacuum, when it decomposes thus:

$$2\ Ag_2ReBr_6 = 4\ AgBr + 2\ ReBr_3 + Br_2.$$

The bromine passes away; the rhenium tribromide distils over and can be purified by resublimation.

Rhenium tribromide is a greenish-black (otherwise described as dark red) solid, which in general resembles the trichloride. It is extraordinarily stable, and can be sublimed at 500° either in nitrogen or in a vacuum; the vapour is dark greenish-yellow. If there is any oxygen in the nitrogen used in its preparation, a dark blue sublimate is produced, which is probably an oxybromide.

No tri-iodide of rhenium is known. Biltz[1240] tried to make it from K_2ReI_6 by heating, as $ReBr_3$ can be made from K_2ReBr_6. But the salt began to evolve iodine at 240°; no rhenium came over, and no compound of rhenium and iodine could be obtained.

Complex Halides of Trivalent Rhenium

These are all of the type $M[ReX_4]$. No fluoride complexes have been made: the simple ReF_3 is of course unknown. But the behaviour of rhenium trichloride in concentrated hydrochloric acid indicates that a complex acid is formed, and by the addition of alkaline halides the alkaline salts $M[ReCl_4]$ can be obtained. They are red solids, giving red to yellow solutions. The pyridine salt $(pyH)\cdot[ReCl_4]$, which is dark red, is only slightly soluble in water.

The alkaline salts are readily soluble in aqueous hydrochloric acid; but the rubidium and caesium salts are only slightly soluble in presence of a large excess of the alkaline halide,[1248] so that they can be used for the microchemical detection of rhenium trichloride. $RbReCl_4$ is a bright red

[1246] H. Hagen and A. Sieverts, ib. 1933, **215**, 111.
[1247] W. Schüth and W. Klemm, ib. 1934, **220**, 193.
[1248] W. Geilmann and F. W. Wrigge, ib. 1935, **223**, 144.

powder, easily soluble in water and dilute hydrochloric acid; like the potassium salt it is converted on heating (at 550–600°) into

$$Rb_2ReCl_6 + ReCl_3 + Re.$$

The caesium salt is much less soluble in water and dilute acid, but otherwise behaves like the rubidium salt. $KReCl_4$ is much more soluble, as usual with a strong acid.

Complex bromides of the similar type $M[ReBr_4]$ are made in the same way, and show a similar behaviour. The pyridine salt has been isolated.

DIVALENT RHENIUM

Though this certainly exists in solution, none of its compounds have been isolated, at any rate in a state approaching purity.

Solutions containing divalent rhenium are formed, as we have seen, by the disproportionation of complex chlorides of tetravalent rhenium:

$$5\ Re^{iv} \longrightarrow 3\ Re^{ii} + 2\ Re^{vii},$$

or by boiling hydrated rhenium sesquioxide with sodium hydroxide:

$$9\ Re^{iii} \longrightarrow 6\ Re^{ii} + 2\ Re^{iv} + Re^{vii}.$$

Further, rhenium trichloride can be reduced[1249] with zinc and sulphuric acid to give a blue-violet strongly reducing solution, which evolves hydrogen on heating.

The only further evidence for the existence of divalent and even of monovalent rhenium is a claim by Young and Irvine,[1250] that by the reduction of potassium perrhenate in sulphuric acid, a black solid is formed, from which rhenium dioxide can be dissolved out with 12-normal HCl, leaving an insoluble residue containing divalent and monovalent rhenium. This cannot be accepted without confirmation, especially as their products did not evolve hydrogen when heated with alkali, while Manchot[1249] has shown that a solution of divalent rhenium evolves hydrogen on boiling.

Apart from this, there is no evidence that rhenium can exist in the monovalent form (except in certain carbonyls) even in solution, and none that either monovalent or divalent rhenium compounds can be isolated. For evidence of Re' in solution, see references [1251-2].

Rhenium Carbonyl Compounds

These were recently discovered by Hieber and his co-workers, by his method of direct synthesis from carbon monoxide under pressure (see Cobalt, VIII. 1422). The simple carbonyl $[Re(CO)_5]_2$ (the E.A.N. of the Re in $Re(CO)_5$ is 85, so this complies with the rule) cannot be made from the metal, or from the halides $Re(CO)_5X$ by removal of the halogen,

[1249] W. Manchot and J. Düsing, *Ann.* 1934, **509**, 228.
[1250] R. C. Young and J. W. Irvine, *J.A.C.S.* 1937, **59**, 2648.
[1251] G. E. F. Lundell and H. B. Knowles, *Bur. Standards J. Res.* 1937, **18**, 629.
[1252] J. J. Lingane, *J.A.C.S.* 1942, **64**, 2182.

as they are too stable. It can, however, be made from the oxides: thus the reaction

$$Re_2O_7 + 17\ CO = [Re(CO)_5]_2 + 7\ CO_2$$

goes quantitatively at 250° under 200 atm. CO [1253]; $KReO_4$ reacts in the same way, but less easily; Re_2S_7 also gives the carbonyl with difficulty, along with a little of a very volatile rhenium compound, no doubt the hydride, which should have the formula $Re(CO)_4COH$. The carbonyl is very insoluble, but it is dimeric (± 10 per cent.) by the freezing-point in camphene and in cyclopentanone. $[Re(CO)_5]_2$ forms small crystals without colour or smell, which are unaffected by dilute acid or alkali, but are attacked by hot concentrated nitric or sulphuric acid; it melts at 177° in a sealed tube, and above this decomposes slowly, separating rhenium. It sublimes easily at 140°, and combines with the halogens (with chlorine only with difficulty, but with bromine and iodine readily at 120°) to form the carbonyl halides $Re(CO)_5X$. In hexane and in dioxane it has a strong absorption band at 3,100 A,[1254] obviously due to the link that holds the two parts of the dimer together.

The *carbonyl halides*, $Re(CO)_5X$, were the first rhenium carbonyl compounds made,[1255-6] the high pressure method being used. With rhenium (as with iron, cobalt, and nickel, but not with molybdenum or tungsten) the bromide and iodide are more easily made than the chloride,[1257] being formed at 200° under 1 atm.; they are thus more easily formed than the carbonyl halides of cobalt and nickel, but not than those of the platinum metals. All three are without smell, the iodide pale yellow and the rest colourless; they are stable in air (stabler than chromium carbonyl), and sublime undecomposed in an atmosphere of carbon monoxide, the iodide at 90° and the chloride at 140°, both fairly fast; they are soluble in benzene and ligroin, the iodide most. This order of volatility and solubility is also found with the iron compounds $Fe(CO)_4X_2$, but practically nowhere else. On heating they do not decompose below 400°.

Amines react with rhenium carbonyl as they do with chromium carbonyl, displacing CO groups, usually 2 from each Rh.[1258] The reaction goes slowly, and only on heating (like $M(CO)_6$, but unlike the iron and cobalt compounds) both with the carbonyl and with its halides. Thus the chloride on boiling with pyridine gives $Re(CO)_3py_2Cl$; the simple carbonyl only forms $Re(CO)_3py_2$ at 200°. *o*-Phenanthroline (phn) reacts in benzene at 120° to give $Re(CO)_3phn$ and $Re(CO)_3(phn)X$, yellow compounds which crystallize well.

All these compounds are remarkably stable. Even concentrated hydrochloric acid does not affect the ammines, which are only broken down by concentrated nitric or sulphuric acid on warming.

[1253] W. Hieber and H. Fuchs, *Z. anorg. Chem.* 1941, **248**, 256.
[1254] R. Schuh, ib. 1942, **248**, 276.   [1255] H. Schulten, ib. 1939, **243**, 145.
[1256] Id., ib. 164.
[1257] W. Hieber, R. Schuh, and H. Fuchs, ib. 1941, **248**, 243.
[1258] W. Hieber and H. Fuchs, ib. 1942, **248**, 269.

GROUP VIII

26 Iron	27 Cobalt	28 Nickel
44 Ruthenium	45 Rhodium	46 Palladium
76 Osmium	77 Iridium	78 Platinum

THE eighth group of Mendeleeff's Table consists of three triads Fe, Co, Ni:Ru, Rh, Pd:Os, Ir, Pt. The combining of these into a single group is really a departure from the method adopted earlier in the Table, where the elements of a group are distinguished by being the same distance from the nearest inert gas (with appropriate modification for the elements following the rare earth metals). In each triad of the so-called eighth group we have three elements which, with this modification, have respectively 8, 9, and 10 electrons more than the preceding inert gas, and so it would be more accurate to divide the group vertically into three which should be called Groups VIII, IX, and X; but the convention of including them all in one group is too well established to be changed. We must recognize that the true division of this group is a vertical one, into what we may call VIII. 1, VIII. 2, and VIII. 3.

Mendeleeff's method of collecting each set of three consecutive elements into a triad (which enables the 10 elements of the half-period to be fitted into 8 places) has over-emphasized the resemblance of the elements of a triad to one another, a resemblance which is not much closer than that between any three consecutive elements of different transitional groups, especially if we remember that usually the most characteristic valency of a group is the group valency, and that none of these elements show this except ruthenium in a single compound and osmium in a small number. The average difference in atomic weight between two consecutive elements in Group VIII is 2·2, in the platinum metals 2·5, and over the whole Periodic Table 2·6. The chemical differences between cobalt and nickel were sufficient to convince the nineteenth-century chemists that cobalt must come next after iron and before nickel in spite of its greater atomic weight.

At the same time there is a marked difference between the members of the iron triad as a whole and the platinum metals. This is largely due to the fact that the first three all form simple cations, which the elements of the first platinum triad scarcely do, and those of the second triad not at all. There is also a very marked increase in the stability of the higher valencies when we pass to the platinum metals. These are examples of tendencies which are quite general in any transitional subgroup: as the atomic number increases the stability of the higher as compared with the lower valencies increases also, while in any given valency the tendency to ionization grows less.*

* The objection that thorium salts are more fully ionized than those of tetravalent titanium or hafnium is only apparent: an element in the group valency (as these

It will therefore be convenient to discuss the elements of the first (iron) triad separately, and then to consider the platinum metals under the sub-groups ruthenium and osmium: rhodium and iridium: palladium and platinum.

The elements of Group VIII are all greyish-white metals with high melting-points and very high boiling-points; they all absorb hydrogen, and have marked catalytic power. The affinity for oxygen falls off in each triad from left to right; there is always a strong affinity for sulphur. All the elements form complexes readily, and some of them (for example, cobalt and platinum) extremely readily. Their distribution in the earth's crust is peculiar, being roughly in the proportion iron:cobalt and nickel: platinum metals = $10^7 : 10^4 : 1$.

The radii of these elements, and especially of the platinum metals, are small as compared with their atomic weights; they fall on the lowest parts of Lothar Meyer's atomic volume curves. The relevant values are given in the following table; those of the Group IV B elements in the same Periods are added for comparison.

	26 Iron	*27 Cobalt*	*28 Nickel*	*32 Germanium*
At. radius .	1·27	1·25	1·24	1·22
Density . .	7·85	8·8	8·8	5·40
At. vol. . .	7·11	6·70	6·67	13·4
M. pt. . .	1,530°	1,490°	1,455°	959°
Abundance* .	51,000	40	100	. .
	44 Ruthenium	*45 Rhodium*	*46 Palladium*	*50 Tin*
At. radius .	1·32	1·34	1·37	1·51
Density . .	12·3	12·1	11·5	5·62
At. vol. . .	8·30	8·50	9·28	21·1
M. pt. . .	>1,950°	1,966°	1,557°	232°
Abundance* .	0·001	0·001	0·01	. .
	76 Osmium	*77 Iridium*	*78 Platinum*	*82 Lead*
At. radius .	1·34	1·35	1·38	1·75
Density . .	22·5	22·4	21·4	11·34
At. vol. . .	8·45	8·62	9·12	18·3
M. pt. . .	2,500°	2,454°	1,774°	327°
Abundance* .	0·001	0·001	0·005	. .

* Parts per million (g./ton) in the earth's crust.

Before we come to the separate sections of the group it may be useful to give a brief table indicating the relative importances of the various valencies for each element ($\underline{N}$ = commonest: N = next most stable: N = definite but few: (N) = doubtful); monatomic ions only occur in the

are) is not in the transitional state; its ion has the inert gas number, and so it obeys the simple Fajans rules, which require the ionization to increase with the atomic number. A second objection, that tetravalent uranium ionizes well, while tetravalent molybdenum and tungsten do not, has lost its force now that we realize that uranium is an actinide or uranide element.

first triad. Peculiar valencies confined to carbonyl and nitrosyl compounds are omitted.

Iron			*Cobalt*			*Nickel*		
(1) 2̲ ion	3 ion		2̲ ion	3 ion	(4)	0	1	2̲ (3)
2 covt.	3̲ covt.	6 covt.	2̲ covt.	3̲ covt.				
Ruthenium			*Rhodium*			*Palladium*		
2	3̲	4 5 6 7 8	(2)	3̲	4 or 5	(1)	2̲ 3	4̲
Osmium			*Iridium*			*Platinum*		
2	3	4̲ 6̲ 8̲	(1) 2	3̲	4̲ 5 6	(1)	2̲ 3	4̲ (6)

The formulae of the various binary fluorides of this group (given by Ruff) show clearly how the stable valencies rise as we go from right to left and as we pass in any section from the lighter to the heavier elements.

FeF_3	CoF_3	
FeF_2	CoF_2	NiF_2
RuF_5	RhF_{4-5}	
	RhF_3	PdF_3
		PdF_2
OsF_8		
OsF_6	IrF_6	
OsF_4	IrF_4	PtF_4
		PtF_2 ?

ALL these elements, like their predecessors in this period, chromium and manganese, are metallic in character, and give a series of definite salts in their lower valencies, especially in the divalent state, which is reasonably stable with all three elements, and becomes more so as we go from left to right: with iron the divalent state is more stable in the ionized form, with cobalt it is far more stable except in the complexes: with nickel the trivalent form is very rare. Valencies higher than 3 are relatively unstable with all three elements. The chief properties of these three elements in their various valency states may be briefly summarized as follows.

Iron

Valency = 0. $Fe(CO)_5$: (not in the other carbonyls).

Valency = 1. Uncertain: may exist in solution.

Valency = 2. $Fe(OH)_2$ colourless, basic. Salts many, pale green, usually soluble in water. More stable than the trivalent state when ionized, less when covalent. Hydroxide a strong reducing agent; in presence of platinum it reduces water at 200°. Ferrous fluoride insoluble, other halides, as also nitrate and sulphate, soluble.

Complexes. Co ordination number usually 6 for the cations, rarely 6 for the anions, except in the ferrocyanides. Ammines (co-ordination numbers 6 and 2) rather unstable; complex halides formed with F_3 and F_4 : Cl_3 and Cl_4 (one Cl_6): no bromides or iodides. Cyanogen complexes are very stable; they all have the co-ordination number 6, and are of two types, $M_4[Fe(CN)_6]$ and $M_x[Fe(CN)_5X]$: the former, though covalent ferrous compounds, are only slowly oxidized by air in presence of acid. In the latter series X may be H_2O, NH_3, SO_3, NO_2, CO, NO: the last gives the nitroprussides $M_2[Fe(CN)_5NO]$, in which the iron is really divalent.

Valency = 3. $Fe(OH)_3$ is basic and slightly acidic, giving ferrites $M[FeO_2]$. The trivalent state is more stable when covalent. The Fe''' ion is reduced to ferrous by hydrogen in presence of a platinum catalyst. The salts are numerous, usually soluble in water, and much less hydrolysed than the ferrites (i.e. $Fe(OH)_3$ is much weaker as an acid than as a base). Fluoride very slightly soluble. Chloride soluble, bromide doubtful, no iodide. Ferric nitrate and sulphate soluble.

Complexes are nearly all anions. Stability of the halides is in the order F,Cl > Br: no iodides. Co-ordination numbers of these are F_4, F_5 (the commonest, usually with H_2O), F_6: Cl_4, Cl_5 (H_2O), Cl_6, few Cl_7: Br few, 4, and 5. $M_3[Fe(CN)_6]$ not quite so stable as the ferrous. Pentacyanoform with the ion $[Fe'''(CN)_5X]$ occurs: X can be OH_2, NH_3, or NO_2, but not SO_3, CO, or NO. Oxalato-complexes, 4 and 6-covalent, occur.

Valency = 4. Only in $Fe_2(CO)_9$.

Valency = 6. This occurs in the ferrates $M_2[FeO_4]$ made by oxidizing iron with potassium nitrate, or ferric hydroxide with chlorine or bromine, but only in alkaline solution. Red: isomorphous with M_2SO_4, etc.: strong oxidizing agent: acids convert it into the ferric state with liberation of ozone.

H h

Cobalt

Valency = 1. $Co(CO)_3NO$.

Valency = 2. This is the stable state for the simple ion when not co-ordinated to anything but water. Forms the oxide CoO; $Co(OH)_2$ has some acidic character, giving cobaltites, probably of the type M_2CoO_2. CoS and CoF_2 slightly soluble, most other salts halides, nitrate, sulphate, formate, acetate, etc., soluble.

Complexes. These are relatively speaking few and unstable. Ammines of co-ordination numbers 6, 4, and 2 are known: they are not very stable, being decomposed by water (except the 'en' complexes) and oxidized by air. Among the complex halides the co-ordination number of 4 is the commonest, but 3, 5, and rarely 6 occur. The chlorides are the most numerous, then the bromides, and there are a few fluorides. The cobaltous cyanides $M_4[Co(CN)_6]$ are very unstable, and are oxidized by air to cobaltic. Other unstable complexes are $M_2[Co(NO_2)_4]$, $M_2[Co(SO_4)_2]$, and $M_2[Co(C_2O_4)_2]$.

Valency = 3. The simple trivalent cobaltic ion is excessively unstable; almost the only apparently simple salts that are known are the fluoride, sulphate, and acetate, and these are probably really complex. The oxide and sulphide occur. The trifluoride CoF_3 forms various hydrates; it evolves fluorine in the dry state at 250°, and gives off oxygen briskly from cold water; no trichloride has been isolated. The sulphate $Co_2(SO_4)_3$, 18 H_2O soon evolves oxygen in water; it forms alums, which also are decomposed by water. The acetate is trimeric in acetic acid, is stable in water, but evolves chlorine with hydrochloric acid.

Complexes. The complexes of trivalent cobalt are as numerous as those of any element, even trivalent chromium or tetravalent platinum. The co-ordination number is always 6. The structures are subject to curious limitations. The ammines can have up to 3 of the 6 amine groups (but no more) replaced by water, giving the trivalent cations

$$[Co(NH_3)_6] : [Co(NH_3)_5OH_2] : [Co(NH_3)_4(OH_2)_2] : [Co(NH_3)_3(OH_2)_3] :$$

the stability diminishes as the amount of water increases. In these ammines up to three of the NH_3 groups can be replaced by OH, F, Cl, Br, I, —N=O, nitrosyl, NO_2, NO_3, CN, CO_3, SO_3, SO_4, S_2O_3, oxalato- and other radicals.

But it is remarkable that trivalent cobalt, unlike all other trivalent metals, and even unlike divalent cobalt, forms no pure complex halides such as $M[CoX_4]$ or $M_3[CoX_6]$; there are never more than three of the NH_3 groups replaced by halogens, so that the halide complex is always either cationic or neutral. The behaviour of the cyanide group is the exact opposite. The hexacyanide $M_3[Co(CN)_6]$ is very stable; the pentacyanide ion $[Co(CN)_5X]$ probably occurs also, but no cyanide complexes are known with less than 5 CN groups. The hexacyanides $M_3[Co(CN)_6]$ are more stable than the corresponding salts of trivalent chromium, manganese, or iron: thus like ferrocyanides but unlike ferricyanides the calcium salt is not poisonous.

The SO_4 group is like the halogens: only one will enter the complex: the carbonato-group behaves in the same way. On the other hand, the SO_3 and oxalato-groups give the pure types $M_3[Co(SO_3)_3]$ and $M_3[Co(C_2O_4)_3]$.

Valency = 4. Nearly all the supposed compounds of this kind are doubtful or have been shown not to exist. But there is one class of compounds which Werner supposes to contain tetravalent cobalt. These are the dark green peroxides of the formula $[(NH_3)_5Co—O_2Co(NH_3)_5]X_5$.

Nickel

Valency = 0. This occurs in nickel carbonyl $Ni(CO)_4$, in the nitrosyl compound $K_2[Ni(CN)_3NO]$, and in $K_4[Ni(CN)_4]$.

Valency = 1. This only occurs in the complex salts $M_2[Ni(CN)_3]$, and perhaps in the simple cyanide NiCN. This forms red flocks which dissolve in potassium cyanide to form the above complex. A solution of $M_2Ni(CN)_4$ when reduced by sodium amalgam in an atmosphere of hydrogen gives a red solution of the complex salt, which is intensely coloured; it evolves hydrogen slowly in the cold and also precipitates metallic nickel.

Valency = 2. This is by far the commonest valency of nickel. All the simple salts are of this valency, the oxide, sulphide, all four halides, cyanide, carbonate, nitrate, sulphate, etc.

Complexes. They are about as stable as those of divalent iron, cobalt, or copper, but much less than those of trivalent cobalt. The ammines are very various, but mainly 6-covalent. They are slowly hydrolysed by water, but the ethylene diamine compounds are not, and are much more stable. Of the complex halides, the fluorides are mainly F_4, but some F_3: the chlorides are mainly Cl_3, but some Cl_4; complex bromides and iodides are formed, but they have not been isolated.

The NO_2 complexes are all 6: the cyanides all 4. These cyanides $M_2[Ni(CN)_4]$ are especially stable, and have been shown to be planar. Their solutions give no reactions for nickel, not even with sodium sulphide.

There are various very stable dichelate complexes, linked through two nitrogens, or an oxygen and a nitrogen; the best known is the dimethyl-glyoxime compound, used for the estimation of nickel, of which a litre of water will only dissolve 0·2 mg. when cold and 1·2 when hot.

Valency = 3. The occurrence of this valency with nickel is uncertain; if it occurs anywhere it is in the oxide Ni_2O_3 and its hydrates, which resemble Co_2O_3 and its hydrates in many ways.

IRON

IRON is the fourth most abundant element in the earth's crust, coming after oxygen, silicon, and aluminium; it amounts to 5·1 per cent. (V. M. Goldschmidt).

Its great technical importance has led to an immense amount of investigation, especially of the methods of preparation of the metal, and of its most mechanically valuable alloys, including those with carbon. Most of this work does not concern us here, but some of the main points may be briefly mentioned.

The chief native ores of iron are the oxides (magnetite Fe_3O_4, haematite Fe_2O_3, etc.), the carbonate (siderite $FeCO_3$), and the sulphides, especially pyrites FeS_2. The methods of preparing the metal from the ore always involve its reduction by carbon. The properties of the metal so obtained depend (1) on its previous treatment, which determines the size and in some cases the nature of the crystals present, (2) on the carbon content, and (3) on the other elements present.

In its compounds iron is nearly always either divalent or trivalent. The hydroxides $Fe(OH)_2$ and $Fe(OH)_3$ are basic in character, but the latter is also feebly acidic, and with alkalies can form the unstable ferrites $M[FeO_2]$. Scheele was the first man to realize that iron can form two distinct series of salts, the ferrous and the ferric, and Lavoisier in 1782 recognized that the corresponding oxides contain different proportions of oxygen.

Both ferrous and ferric salts are as a rule readily soluble in water, exceptions being ferrous fluoride FeF_2, and the oxides, hydroxides, sulphides, carbonates, and phosphates. Both series, but especially, as we should expect, the ferric, give numerous complexes.

The salts of iron have a remarkable power (shared to some extent by other elements, especially of the eighth group) of combining directly with carbon monoxide and with nitric oxide.

Iron has also, like the transitional elements in general, but in an exceptionally high degree, the power of acting as a catalyst, both homogeneous and heterogeneous; this is especially true with oxidations, for example, of arsenites, phosphites, or sulphites, or of hydrogen peroxide (to oxygen and water); iron salts hasten the oxidizing action of hydrogen peroxide, of nitric acid, of dichromates or permanganates: they promote the synthesis of ammonia from its elements, its oxidation to nitric acid, and that of sulphur dioxide to the trioxide. A full account of these and many other reactions which are promoted by iron compounds is given in Abegg's *Handbuch*.[1]

Compounds of iron are of fundamental importance to living organisms,[2] vegetable as well as animal, being required mainly but not solely to promote oxidation.

The human body contains about 0·005 per cent. (3–4 g.) of iron, about

[1] Abegg, *Eisen*, B. 675–754 (1935).
[2] See A. Reid in Abegg, ib. 755–65 (1935).

three-quarters of it in the form of haemoglobin, which transports the oxygen of the air to the tissues; about a decigram of iron is excreted by a man every day, and this quantity must be made up from the food, or deficiency diseases, mainly anaemia, will set in. The lower animals, and also nearly all plants, contain iron in about the same proportion; its presence is necessary to the production of chlorophyll, though it does not seem to be a constituent of it.

Most of the iron is contained in the porphyrins, which are essentially built up of four pyrrol residues joined into a ring by four CH groups; the (ferrous) iron is attached to the nitrogen, usually in the form

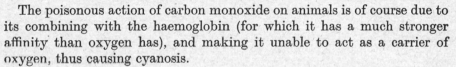

The poisonous action of carbon monoxide on animals is of course due to its combining with the haemoglobin (for which it has a much stronger affinity than oxygen has), and making it unable to act as a carrier of oxygen, thus causing cyanosis.

It is remarkable that various fermentations are arrested by carbon monoxide, and alcoholic fermentations by nitric oxide, both gases which combine readily with iron; in these fermentations the presence of porphyrin-bound iron has been shown to be essential.

Metallic Iron

Pure iron is a rather soft metal, softer than any other metal of the whole group except nickel and platinum. It occurs in four different solid forms, the transition points being:

$$\alpha \xrightarrow{770°} \beta \xrightarrow{928°} \gamma \xrightarrow{1,411°} \delta \xrightarrow{1,530°} \text{liquid} \xrightarrow{3,235°} \text{gas}_{760\,mm.}$$

The relations of the solid forms (which are known as ferrites) are very peculiar. α, β, and δ all have the same crystal lattice; α is ferromagnetic; when it is transformed into β the ferromagnetism disappears, but the lattice remains unchanged; hence, this is not, properly speaking, a phase change at all, and accordingly the α and β forms are both commonly included under the name of α-ferrite. The change of β to γ (or of α-ferrite to γ-ferrite) at 928° involves a change of lattice and is a true phase change; so is that of γ to δ at 1,411°, but the crystal lattice of the δ-form is the same as that of the α and β.

Iron forms a series of alloys, which are of more importance to human life than those of any other metal, as is shown by the name of Iron Age given to the latest stage of prehistoric development. Of these the alloys with carbon (steel, cast iron) are the most important, and are briefly discussed in the next section. Chemically, iron is a very active metal, being readily attacked by a variety of substances, especially oxygen and oxidizing agents.

Iron and Carbon Alloys

The phase-rule diagram for the system iron—carbon has been worked out on the iron side in great detail.[3-5]

Pure iron (i.e. δ-ferrite) melts at 1,530°, but the liquid will dissolve carbon, and the melting-point is thereby depressed down to a eutectic at 1,125°, where the liquid is in contact with the two solids, austenite, which is a solution of 1·8 per cent. of carbon in γ-ferrite, and cementite Fe_3C, the only carbide of iron that can be isolated; this has a very complicated crystal structure.[4,5] Each C atom is at the centre of a distorted trigonal prism, with the Fe—C distances varying from 1·89 to 2·15 A.

On further cooling the austenite separates out some cementite and becomes poorer in carbon, and then at about 700° it breaks up into a eutectic mixture of α-ferrite (i.e. pure iron in the α-form, which dissolves no carbon) and cementite; this eutectic mixture is known as pearlite. All the forms of iron and steel are made up of these materials, their mechanical properties depending not only on the nature and the proportions of the phases, but also on the size of the crystals of which the solid is composed.

Other Alloys of Iron

The properties, and especially the mechanical properties, of iron are greatly affected by the presence of small quantities of other substances. The most important of these, as we have seen, is carbon, of which all ordinary technical forms of iron contain a certain amount. Wrought iron or malleable iron is the purest (and hence the least fusible) form, and usually has less than half a per cent. of carbon; cast iron, which is the richest in carbon and the most fusible, and is brittle when cold, contains up to 4·5 per cent. of carbon, partly in the form of enclosures of separated graphite.

Besides these fundamental forms there are numerous alloys of steel with other elements which are used for special purposes; these may contain, in addition to carbon, any of the elements manganese, nickel, chromium, tungsten, silicon, vanadium, molybdenum, and cobalt. Thus the steel which is used for springs may have from 1 to 2·5 per cent. of silicon; manganese steels (up to 10 per cent. Mn or more) are very elastic and very durable, and are used for railway axles; invar, which has only a very small expansion with heat, and is used for the pendulums of clocks, has a large proportion (up to 36 per cent.) of nickel; steel containing 45 per cent. of nickel has the same coefficient of expansion as glass, and can be sealed into it like platinum. 'High-speed tool steel', containing about 4 per cent. of chromium with some tungsten and vanadium, retains its

[3] See, for example, Findlay, *Phase Rule*, ed. 7, 1931, p. 138.
[4] H. Lipson and N. J. Petch, *J. Iron and Steel Inst.* 1940, **142**, 95.
[5] Wells, *S.I.C.*, p. 568.

hardness up to high temperatures; with tools made of this material it is possible to cut metal at a high speed without fear of the tool being softened by the heat evolved. Stainless steel usually has a high chromium content (up to 18 per cent.), and some nickel.

Iron and Hydrogen

Iron, like all the metals of Gp. VIII, has the power of absorbing hydrogen, as was discovered by Deville and Troost in 1863. Ordinary commercial iron may contain from one-tenth of its volume to its own volume of the gas. The solubility of hydrogen in pure iron at equilibrium, in c.c. of the gas at N.T.P. per c.c. of iron, is[6] 0·1 at 600° C., 0·4 at 1,000°, and at the melting-point (1,530°) about 1·0 in the solid and 2·0 in the liquid: the heat of solution in the liquid is 13·3 k.cals./H. Atomic hydrogen, produced in the gas by a glowing tungsten spiral, readily diffuses through an iron sheet at room temperature.[7] It is possible electrolytically to get a metastable concentration of hydrogen in iron that is much higher than this, from an acid solution as much as 35 c.c. per c.c. of iron (this corresponds to a formula $Fe_{45}H$).

Weichselfelder[8] claims to have obtained, by the action of phenyl magnesium bromide on ferrous and ferric chloride, a black powder FeH_2 and a black oil FeH_6, both unstable; but this has not been confirmed.

Iron and Carbon

Iron carbide has already been discussed (p. 1324). Iron forms no alkyls or aryls, but ferrous chloride gives with phenyl magnesium bromide a nearly quantitative yield of diphenyl, which may be due to the intermediate formation of an unstable iron phenyl.[9] The only other Fe—C compounds are the large series of cyano-derivatives, which are discussed later (ferrous, p. 1335; ferric, p. 1358), and the carbonyls (p. 1369).

Iron and Nitrogen[10]

Metallic iron will absorb nitrogen, but only at high temperatures (above 800°, and especially above its melting-point) and in small quantities; the amount depending on the condition, and especially the carbon content, of the iron.

On the other hand, ammonia reacts very readily with iron on heating, and causes it to take up as much as 11·1 per cent. of nitrogen, corresponding to the formula Fe_2N.

[6] See especially A. Sieverts and W. Krumbhaar, *Ber.* 1910, **43**, 893; A. Sieverts, *Z. Elektrochem.* 1910, **16**, 707; M. H. Armbruster, *J.A.C.S.* 1943, **65**, 1043.

[7] J. H. de Boer and J. D. Fast, *Rec. Trav.* 1939, **58**, 984.

[8] T. Weichselfelder and B. Thiede, *Ann.* 1926, **447**, 64.

[9] H. Gilman and M. Lichtenwalter, *J.A.C.S.* 1939, **61**, 957.

[10] Gmelin, *Eisen*, B. 137–56 (1929).

Of the various nitrides of iron described in the literature, the only two which may be considered definite compounds are Fe_2N and Fe_4N.

Fe_2N (11·1 per cent. of nitrogen)[11-12] is made by passing ammonia at 400° to 500° over iron or its chlorides or oxides. It is a grey substance looking not unlike powdered iron; it forms hexagonal crystals. Its individuality has been established by X-ray analysis.[13-14]

If it is heated in a vacuum to temperatures not above 600° it loses half its nitrogen to give the lower nitride Fe_4N (see below), the decomposition beginning about 440°. Above 600° the dissociation goes farther, and at 800° only about 0·28 per cent. of nitrogen remains.[15] The nitride is oxidized by air at about 200°, catches fire in chlorine, and dissolves in dilute hydrochloric acid to give ferrous and ammonium chlorides, with evolution of hydrogen. Water has little effect on it even at 100°, where there is a very slight evolution of hydrogen.

The lower nitride Fe_4N (5·9 per cent. nitrogen) remains behind when Fe_2N is heated *in vacuo* to 440–550°.[16-17] It is shown by its X-ray pattern[13-14,18-19] to be a definite individual. By 800° it loses nearly all its nitrogen. In its general properties it resembles Fe_2N.

The X-ray results show clearly that these are two definite chemical individuals, but they do not throw much light on the nature of the linkages which they contain.

The formation of these nitrides is of technical importance owing to the use of oxides of iron as catalysts in the synthesis of ammonia from its elements; the oxides are no doubt reduced by the hydrogen and converted into nitrides. In practice the oxides must be 'activated' by admixture, usually with other less reducible oxides such as alumina. Under these conditions it has been shown[20] that the nitrides (which contained 5–11 per cent. of nitrogen, i.e. from Fe_4N to Fe_2N) decomposed at temperatures up to 600° with a heat of activation of about 10 k.cals. The alumina did not alter the activation energy, but it increased the effective surface 5 times, apparently by preventing the recrystallization of the iron into larger particles, which otherwise happens at 400–500°. This conclusion was confirmed by an X-ray examination of the materials,[21] and is in agreement with the results of previous workers.[22]

[11] G. J. Fowler, *J.C.S.* 1901, **79**, 285.

[12] G. J. Fowler and P. J. Hartog, ib. 299.

[13] A. Osawa and S. Iwaizumi, *Z. Krist.* 1929, **69**, 30.

[14] G. Hägg, *Nature*, 1928, **122**, 962.

[15] N. Tschischewski, *J. Iron Inst.* 1915, **92**, 58.

[16] G. Charpy and S. Bonnerot, *C.R.* 1914, **158**, 996.

[17] A. Fry, *Stahl u. Eisen*, 1923, **43**, 1272.

[18] G. Hägg, *Nature*, 1928, **121**, 826.

[19] R. Brill, *Naturwiss.* 1928, **16**, 593; *Z. Krist.* 1928, **68**, 379.

[20] N. I. Kobosev, B. W. Jerofejev, and S. I. Sluchowsky, *Z. Elektrochem.* 1935, **41**, 274.

[21] G. L. Natanson, *Z. Elektrochem.* 1935, **41**, 284.

[22] R. Wyckoff and E. Crittenden, *J.A.C.S.* 1925, **47**, 2866; A. Mittasch and E. Keunecke, *Z. Elektrochem.* 1932, **38**, 666; R. Brill, ib., 669.

Iron and Phosphorus[23]

With a tin-iron alloy phosphorus under pressure forms an unstable black compound of the composition $FeP_{2.57}$; X-ray diagrams give no signs of compounds FeP_2 or FeP_3.

Monovalent Iron

This has never been isolated, except in certain nitrosyl compounds (p. 1372): but Treadwell and Huber[24] say that after cyanide complexes containing Fe″, Co″, and Ni″ had been reduced electrolytically in the presence of potassium cyanide, electrometric titration of the product with $K_3[Fe(CN)_6]$ showed a 95–7 per cent. yield of the monovalent Fe, Co, and Ni.

FERROUS COMPOUNDS

THE great majority of the compounds of iron are either ferrous, with an atomic core of effective atomic number $24 = 2.8.14$, or ferric, with a core of $23 = 2.8.13$. The ferrous compounds are more stable (especially in air) in the ionized state and the ferric in the covalent.

Ferrous compounds are formed either from the metal or by the reduction of the ferric. Acids, even reducible acids like nitric or perchloric, if they are dilute, dissolve iron without being reduced by it, and form ferrous salts. In its direct combination with other elements iron sometimes (for example, with iodine, sulphur, selenium, etc.) stops at the ferrous stage, but with other more active elements like fluorine and chlorine it goes on to the ferric: with these last the ferrous salt can be made by treating the metal with the halogen hydride such as HCl or HF.

The ferrous ion in solution is pale green, almost colourless, and most of the hydrated salts have the same colour; the ion has, however, a strong absorption in the infra-red at about 10,000 A. The salts are often isomorphous with those of other divalent elements, and resemble them in their solubilities, the halides, nitrate, sulphate, and thiosulphate being soluble, and the hydroxide, sulphide, phosphate, and oxalate relatively insoluble.

The E.M.F. of a platinum electrode in a solution containing equal amounts of ferrous and ferric ions is 0·75 volt higher than that of the normal hydrogen electrode, showing that the ferric ion is reduced by hydrogen to the ferrous; this reduction is, however, found in practice not to be complete except in the presence of colloidal platinum as a catalyst.[25]

The conditions of interconversion of ferrous and ferric compounds are discussed in more detail later (p. 1348).

Ferrous Oxide, FeO

The oxide scale formed on iron that has been heated to a high temperature in air consists of three layers, ferrous oxide, FeO; magnetic oxide,

[23] M. Heimbrecht and W. Biltz, *Z. anorg. Chem.* 1939, **242**, 233.

[24] W. D. Treadwell and D. Huber, *Helv. Chim. Acta.* 1943, **26**, 10.

[25] C. Fredenhagen, *Z. anorg. Chem.* 1902, **29**, 405.

Fe_3O_4; and ferric oxide, Fe_2O_3. Ferrous oxide is not produced below 575°; but above that temperature it can be made the sole product if the pressure of oxygen is kept low enough.[26,27] The oxide can also be made by heating ferrous oxalate; it is then obtained as a fine black powder, which is pyrophoric and decomposes water; on strong heating this loses its reactivity, being converted into a less finely divided form.

Some contradictory statements have been made about ferrous oxide, because it is not a stable substance,[28] but changes slowly into a mixture of the magnetic oxide Fe_3O_4 and metallic iron. Hence the oxide FeO can only be made by heating iron under the right pressure of oxygen to a temperature above 575°, and then chilling it to a temperature at which this change is practically stopped. Wyckoff,[29] who examined the crystal structure, made the ferrous oxide by saturating the fused magnetic oxide Fe_3O_4 with iron, powdering the mass, and then separating the ferrous oxide magnetically from the excess of iron.

Ferrous oxide FeO is a black substance melting about 1,360°. It is not magnetic when pure, and it has a sodium chloride lattice, suggesting that the solid is ionized.

Ferrous Hydroxide, $Fe(OH)_2$

This is obtained as a white precipitate when a solution of a ferrous salt in air-free water is treated with alkali, but the precipitate is only white if oxygen is absolutely excluded.[30] It very readily absorbs oxygen from the air, and becomes first a dirty green, then black, and finally is converted into the reddish-brown ferric hydroxide $Fe(OH)_3$. In presence of excess of alkali the oxidation stops at an intermediate stage, with the production of a black substance containing both ferrous and ferric iron, which may well be ferrous ferrite $Fe''[Fe'''O_2]_2$.[31] That an intermediate oxide should be darker in colour than either of the extreme forms is a common experience (compare cerium).

Ferrous hydroxide, like the oxide, is an unstable substance, and changes slowly, even in the cold, to Fe_3O_4, water, and hydrogen.[32-3]

Ferrous hydroxide is a fairly strong diacid base. Its acidic properties are very weak: its tendency to form the 'ferroates' $M_2Fe^{ii}O_2$ is very small, but in the anodic oxidation of iron in presence of concentrated alkali a

[26] T. Iimori, *Nature*, 1937, **140**, 278.

[27] L. S. Darken and R. W. Gurry, *J.A.C.S.* 1946, **68**, 798.

[28] H. Forestier, *Ann. Chim.* 1928, [10] **9**, 316.

[29] R. W. G. Wyckoff and E. Crittenden, *J.A.C.S.* 1925, **47**, 2876; *Z. Krist.* 1926, **63**, 144.

[30] O. Baudisch, *Ber.* 1938, **71**, 992, gives directions for preparing perfectly white ferrous hydroxide by precipitating a solution of ferrous hydrogen carbonate $Fe(HCO_3)_2$, made from iron powder and carbon dioxide solution, with guanidine carbonate in presence of potassium nitrate free from nitrite.

[31] A. Krause, *Z. anorg. Chem.* 1928, **174**, 145.

[32] R. Fricke and S. Rihl, *Naturwiss.* 1943, **31**, 326.

[33] Id., *Z. anorg. Chem.* 1943, **251**, 414.

green solution can be obtained, which may probably contain a salt of this kind.[34]

In contrast to the relatively stable ferrous ion, the hydroxide is a strong reducing agent; it is not quite strong enough to reduce water at the ordinary temperature, but if it is heated with water to 200° in presence of palladium as a catalyst it decomposes it with evolution of hydrogen.

If ammonia is added to a solution of a ferrous salt the hydroxide is only incompletely precipitated, and in presence of an ammonium salt it is not precipitated at all. The conclusion that ferrous hydroxide, like magnesium hydroxide, has a relatively high solubility product is not quite true: for $Fe(OH)_2$ it is 3×10^{-14}, which is 1/300 of that of $Mg(OH)_2$ (10^{-11}); a saturated solution of ferrous hydroxide in pure water contains about 6 mg. to the litre at 20°. The imperfect precipitation of the hydroxide by ammonia is at least in part due to the formation of ammines of the ferrous ion: if a ferrous solution containing excess of an ammonium salt is treated in complete absence of air with gaseous ammonia, the first few bubbles produce a white (or usually a greenish-white) precipitate of the hydroxide, which redissolves (like a precipitate of cupric hydroxide) when more ammonia is passed in.[35]

Ferrous Sulphide, FeS[36]

The only solid phases found in the investigation of the system iron-sulphur were iron, FeS, FeS_2, and sulphur.

Ferrous sulphide can be made by fusing the elements together, when they combine with the evolution of enough heat to melt the iron. This method is used on the large scale in making ferrous sulphide for the production of hydrogen sulphide. The product so obtained generally contains an excess of one or other constituent, both of which form solid solutions with it; to prepare the pure sulphide a slight excess of sulphur is used, and this excess is then distilled off; the pure compound may also be made[37] by passing a mixture of hydrogen sulphide with excess of hydrogen over ferric oxide at 950–1,050°.

Ferrous sulphide is ordinarily a dark grey or brown solid, but when quite pure it forms colourless crystals, melting at 1,193°.[38] It is trimorphic,[39] with transition points at 135° and 325°. It is identical with the mineral pyrrhotite, which, however, usually is deficient in iron. It has the nickel arsenide lattice.[40]

Ferrous sulphide can also be made in the wet way by the action of ammonium or alkaline sulphide on a ferrous solution (hydrogen sulphide only precipitates it very imperfectly if at all) when it comes down as a

[34] G. Grube and H. Gmelin, *Z. Elektrochem.* 1920, **26**, 459.

[35] E. Weitz and H. Müller, *Ber.* 1925, **58**, 363.

[36] See Abegg, *Eisen*, A. 644, 649 (1938); Gmelin, ib. B. 345 (1930).

[37] J. V. Kariakin, *J. Appl. Chem. Russ.* 1938, **11**, 1575.

[38] R. Loebe and E. Becker, *Z. anorg. Chem.* 1912, **77**, 305.

[39] H. Haraldsen, *Z. Elektrochem.* 1939, **45**, 370.

[40] V. M. Goldschmidt, *Ber.* 1927, **60**, 1285; *Trans. Far. Soc.* 1929, **25**, 274.

black precipitate which on prolonged washing goes over into the colloidal form.

Ferrous sulphide is almost insoluble in water, with a solubility product of about 4×10^{-19} at $20°^{41}$ (about 6×10^{-5} mg. per litre).

When heated in a vacuum ferrous sulphide dissociates into iron and sulphur, the dissociation beginning at 1,100° and being complete at 1,600°. It is very readily oxidized when moist by air with the separation of elementary sulphur and the liberation of much heat, the iron being converted into Fe_3O_4 or at a red heat into ferric oxide. It may even catch fire when ground in a mortar. It reacts with water on boiling to give hydrogen and sulphuric acid. It is readily soluble in dilute mineral acids, with the evolution of hydrogen sulphide and the production of a ferrous salt.

Iron Pyrites, Marcasite, FeS_2

Owing to its high sulphur content this is commonly discussed among the ferric compounds, but it is really ferrous, the salt of the anion $[S_2]^{--}$.

It occurs in nature as marcasite (rhombic) and pyrites (regular); pyrites is at all temperatures the more stable. It is found especially in SW. Spain, and is an important source of sulphur as well as iron; about 7 million tons are used per annum.

Pyrites was one of the first crystals whose structure was examined by the Braggs by means of X-rays.[42] The lattice is not unlike that of sodium chloride, the sodium atoms being replaced by iron, and the chlorine by pairs of sulphur atoms 2·10 A.U. apart (theory S—S 2·08 A).[43] The marcasite lattice is on the whole very similar: the S—S distance is 2·21 A.U., and the Fe—S 2·24.[44] The repulsion of the negatively charged sulphur atoms in $[S—S]^{--}$ may be expected to drive them farther apart.

In a vacuum pyrites begins to give off sulphur at about 600°. The behaviour of the system iron—sulphur from the composition FeS to FeS_2[45-6] indicates no definite molecular species between FeS and FeS_2 (certainly not Fe_2S_3), but each of these two has a limited solid solubility in the other.

Chemically, pyrites is extremely inactive at the ordinary temperature, and is scarcely attacked by anything, but on heating it reacts with many substances. It burns in air to ferric oxide and sulphur dioxide; hence its use for making sulphuric acid.

Marcasite is rather more reactive than pyrites, owing to its greater energy content; it changes into pyrites on heating.

[41] L. Bruner and J. Zawadski, *Z. anorg. Chem.* 1909, **65**, 143; 1910, **67**, 454.

[42] W. H. and W. L. Bragg, *Proc. Roy. Soc.* 1913, **88**, 428; **89**, 468. For later work see W. L. Bragg, *Phil. Mag.* 1920, [6] **40**, 169; H. M. Parker and W. J. Whitehouse, ib. 1932, [7] **14**, 939.

[43] L. Pauling and L. O. Brockway, *J.A.C.S.* 1937, **59**, 1234.

[44] M. J. Buerger, *Z. Krist.* 1937, **97**, 504.

[45] F. de Rudder, *Bull. Soc.* 1930, [iv] **47**, 1225.

[46] R. Juza and W. Biltz, *Z. anorg. Chem.* 1932, **205**, 273.

FERROUS HALIDES
Ferrous Fluoride, FeF$_2$

The direct action of fluorine on iron gives rise to the ferric compound. Anhydrous ferrous fluoride can be made[47] by reducing the trifluoride with hydrogen, by the action of hydrogen fluoride on iron at a high temperature, or by treating anhydrous ferrous chloride with fluorine in the cold. The hydrated form (at first supposed to be an octohydrate, but more probably a tetrahydrate)[48] can be made by dissolving iron in aqueous hydrofluoric acid; the hydrate, which like the anhydrous salt is only slightly soluble in water, can be dehydrated by heating in a stream of hydrogen fluoride.

Anhydrous ferrous fluoride FeF$_2$ consists of white tetragonal crystals with a rutile lattice; it boils at about 1,100°, and melts very little below this temperature. It is only slightly soluble in water, and is insoluble in alcohol, ether, and benzene. It gives no visible reaction with bromine, iodine, or sulphur, but reacts with great violence when heated with such metals as sodium, magnesium, aluminium, or zinc. With hydrogen it is stable up to 400°, at which temperature it can be produced by passing a stream of hydrogen over ferric fluoride FeF$_3$, but at a red-heat hydrogen reduces it to metallic iron.

It forms a series of complex salts (see later, p. 1348).

Ferrous Chloride, FeCl$_2$

The anhydrous salt can be made by the action of hydrogen chloride on iron at temperatures not above a red heat, or by reducing ferric chloride with hydrogen, or by the dehydration of the hydrate.

Anhydrous ferrous chloride forms colourless rhombohedral crystals with the same crystal lattice[49] as the dichlorides of magnesium, manganese, cobalt, and nickel. It melts at 672° and boils at 1,030°; the heat of evaporation is 32·1 k.cals. per mole,[50] involving a Trouton constant of 23·2. The vapour density just above the boiling-point indicates that it is a mixture of FeCl$_2$ and Fe$_2$Cl$_4$ molecules,[51] but at higher temperatures, from 1,300° to 1,500°, Nilson and Pettersson[52] found almost the theoretical value for FeCl$_2$.

Ferrous chloride is excessively hygroscopic and very soluble in water. It forms a series of hydrates, whose transition points, so far as they are known, are as follows[53-4]:

$$0\ H_2O \longrightarrow 1 \longrightarrow 2 \underset{76\cdot5°}{\longrightarrow} 4 \underset{12\cdot3°}{\longrightarrow} 6\ H_2O.$$

[47] O. Ruff and E. Ascher, *ib.* 1929, **183**, 196.
[48] C. Poulenc, *C.R.* 1892, **115**, 941; *Ann. Chim. Phys.* 1894, [7] **2**, 5.
[49] G. Bruni and A. Ferrari, *Z. physikal. Chem.* 1927, **130**, 488.
[50] C. G. Maier, *U.S. Bur. Mines Techn. Papers*, 1925, No. 360.
[51] V. Meyer, *Ber.* 1884, **17**, 1335.
[52] L. F. Nilson and O. Pettersson, *Z. physikal. Chem.* 1888, **2**, 671.
[53] G. Agde and F. Schimmel, *Z. anorg. Chem.* 1928, **173**, 111.
[54] F. Schimmel, *ib.* **176**, 285.

The saturated solution at 20° contains 68·5 g. of $FeCl_2$ in 100 g. of water, and at the boiling-point (117·5°) 101·8 g. The aqueous solution is very slightly hydrolysed.

Ferrous chloride forms a series of complexes (p. 1348).

Ferrous Bromide, $FeBr_2$

Unlike chlorine, bromine vapour acts on the heated metal to produce the ferrous and not the ferric compound. This can also be made from its hydrate, which is formed by dissolving the metal in aqueous hydrobromic acid. The anhydrous substance forms yellow or brown crystals with a layer lattice of the cadmium iodide type.[55] In air it is stable in the cold, but at 310° it is slowly converted into ferric oxide and bromine. It is very soluble in water, and forms a series of pale green hydrates; the system $FeBr_2$—H_2O gives the following hydrates[56] and transition points:

$$9\,H_2O \xrightarrow[-29\cdot3°]{} 6\,H_2O \xrightarrow[+49\cdot0°]{} 4\,H_2O \xrightarrow[+83°]{} 2\,H_2O.$$

At the cryohydric point of −43·6° the solution contains 42·3 per cent. of $FeBr_2$, and at the boiling-point 70·2 per cent. The hexahydrate has the sol^y 117/21°.

Ferrous Iodide, FeI_2

This also is formed by the direct action of the halogen on the metal, and it is easier to get in the free state than the other halides, because no ferric iodide exists. It can be made in solution by dissolving iron in a suspension of iodine in water.

The properties of the anhydrous salt have been much disputed; according to Ferrari and Giorgi[57] it forms dark red hexagonal crystals with the cadmium iodide lattice; it melts at 177°.

With water it forms a series of hydrates of which the only certain ones are a tetrahydrate (green) and a hexahydrate (yellow). On warming even at 50°, the hydrates and their aqueous solution turn black, but they recover their original colour on cooling (like cupric bromide).

Some double salts are known, such as $FeI_2, 2\,HgI_2, 6\,H_2O$; but there is no evidence that they contain complex ferrous anions.

Ferrous Cyanide, $Fe(CN)_2$

Though the ferrocyanide complexes are so stable, the simple cyanide $Fe(CN)_2$ cannot be obtained from solution. If, however, ammonium ferrocyanide $(NH_4)_4[Fe(CN)_6]$ is heated *in vacuo* it begins at 110° to evolve ammonium cyanide, and at 320° pure ferrous cyanide $Fe(CN)_2$ is left behind as pale-green transparent crystals, which on further heating decom-

---

[55] A. Ferrari and F. Giorgi, *Atti R.* 1929, [6] **9**, 1134.
[56] F. Schimmel, *Ber.* 1929, **62**, 963.
[57] A. Ferrari and F. Giorgi, *Atti R.* 1929, [6] **10**, 522.

pose above $430°$.[58-9] Their crystal structure[60-1] may be that of a ferrous ferrocyanide, $Fe_2[Fe(CN)_6]$.

Ferrous Thiocyanate, $Fe(CNS)_2$

This can be obtained as a trihydrate $Fe(CNS)_2, 3 H_2O$, by dissolving iron in thiocyanic acid in the absence of air. It forms green prisms, which are very soluble in water, and very easily oxidized.

Ferrous Carbonate, $FeCO_3$

Ferrous solutions, when treated with alkaline carbonate, give a white precipitate of the normal carbonate $FeCO_3$, but this rapidly darkens through oxidation by the air. The solid[62] begins to dissociate into carbon dioxide and ferrous oxide at $200°$; at $490°$ the dissociation tension is 1 atm. ($MgCO_3$ at $540°$, $CaCO_3$ at $900°$), but at this temperature the gas has to some extent reacted with the solid to give carbon monoxide and Fe_3O_4.

The solubility of ferrous carbonate in water is much affected by the presence of carbon dioxide, partly because this represses hydrolysis, and partly because the ferrous ion (like calcium) forms a soluble acid carbonate $Fe(HCO_3)_2$. In water saturated with carbon dioxide at atmospheric pressure the solubility at $20°$ is about 1 g. per litre. In complete absence of oxygen iron powder will dissolve in pure water in a stream of CO_2 to give a solution of $Fe(HCO_3)_2$ containing 1 g. or more of iron per litre, which will remain clear and colourless for months.[63]

The water of many springs contains the acid carbonate, and on exposure to the air this loses carbon dioxide and is oxidized with precipitation of hydrated ferric oxide.

Ferrous Nitrate, $Fe(NO_3)_2$

This salt can be made from ferrous sulphate and lead nitrate, or by dissolving iron in cold dilute nitric acid:

$$4 Fe + 10 HNO_3 = 4 Fe(NO_3)_2 + NH_4NO_3 + 3 H_2O.$$

The salt is known only in the form of two hydrates, at the ordinary temperature a hexahydrate, and at temperatures below $-12°$ an ennea-hydrate $Fe(NO_3)_2, 9 H_2O$.

The hexahydrate forms green crystals, sol^y $81.8/20°$. On warming, especially with acids, the solution decomposes to give ferric ion and nitric oxide (Tiemann and Schulze's method of estimating nitrates).

Ferrous nitrite cannot be prepared; it decomposes at once on formation to give ferric ion and nitric oxide.

[58] A. Mittasch, E. Kuss, and O. Emert, *Z. anorg. Chem.* 1928, **170**, 193.
[59] Id., *Z. Elektrochem.* 1928, **34**, 159.
[60] W. Brill and H. Mark, *Z. physikal. Chem.* 1928, **133**, 443.
[61] See also K. A. Hofmann, H. Arnoldi, and H. Hiendlmaier, *Ann.* 1907, **352**, 54.
[62] For its crystal structure see R. W. G. Wyckoff, *Amer. J. Sci.* 1920, [4] **50**, 317.
[63] O. Baudisch, *Ber.* 1938, **71**, 992.

Ferrous Sulphate, $FeSO_4$

This is the most important and the longest known of ferrous salts; the heptahydrate 'green vitriol' was described by Albertus Magnus in the thirteenth century. The only certain hydrates are those with 1, 4, and 7 H_2O, the transition points being:

$$0 \xrightarrow[(>90°)]{} 1 \xrightarrow[65·0°]{} 4 \xrightarrow[56·6°]{} 7\ H_2O.$$

The heptahydrate ordinarily forms green crystals, but according to Abegg[64] this is due to the presence of basic salt; when it is quite free from this it is bluish-white, and it is then quite stable in air, whilst the ordinary green salt slowly oxidizes in air, with the formation of a yellow-brown layer of basic ferric sulphate.

On heating, the heptahydrate loses 6 H_2O to form the monohydrate, which gives up the last molecule of water only at a much higher temperature to form a white powder of the anhydrous salt, which on heating to a still higher temperature breaks up to give sulphur dioxide, basic ferric sulphate, and other products. At 20° 100 g. of water will dissolve 26·6 g. of the anhydrous salt in the form of the heptahydrate.

The heptahydrate is monoclinic, and forms mixed crystals with the corresponding salts (vitriols) of other divalent metals, such as magnesium, manganese, cobalt, nickel, and copper. It also forms a series of double sulphates of the general formula M_2SO_4, $FeSO_4$, 6 H_2O, where M may be K, Rb, Cs, NH_4, Tl′; all the corresponding double selenates have also been made.

The ammonium salt $(NH_4)_2SO_4$, $FeSO_4$, 12 H_2O has been used for producing very low temperatures by the magnetic method of Debye and Giauque. Its temperature can be reduced by demagnetization from 8·5° K to 0·36° or 0·15° K. by using magnetic fields of 29 or 42 kilogauss.[65]

Solutions of ferrous sulphate, even in pure water, are only very slowly oxidized by air. On passing air through the decinormal solution at 25° Ennos[66] found that only 0·03 per cent. was oxidized per hour. In alkaline solution the oxidation proceeds much more rapidly, and it does so too in presence of alkaline tartrates or citrates, which no doubt form covalent ferrous complexes; it also goes quicker in alcohol.[67]

Ferrous Salts of Oxy-halide Acids

The perchlorate $Fe(ClO_4)_2$, 6 H_2O is a colourless salt, sol^y 68·7/25°, which is stable up to 100°. This is a sign of the exceptional stability of the perchlorate ion; usually the oxy-halide ions are easily able to oxidize the ferrous ion: thus the bromate goes over as soon as it is made into the basic ferric salt, and the iodate $Fe(IO_3)_2$ is converted into a ferric compound with separation of iodine.

[64] *Eisen*, B. 52.   [65] N. Kürti, P. Lainé, and F. Simon, *C.R.* 1939, **208**, 173.
[66] F. R. Ennos, *Proc. Camb. Philos. Soc.* 1913, **17**, 182.
[67] H. Wieland and W. Franke, *Ann.* 1928, **464**, 101.

Ferrous Salts of Organic Acids

When the acids are monobasic, the salts seem (unlike the corresponding ferric salts) to be simple; thus there is a slightly soluble green formate ($2 H_2O$) and a very soluble colourless acetate ($4 H_2O$). This last is very easily oxidized, because owing to the weakness of the acid it is highly hydrolysed (1·76 per cent. in normal solution in the cold).[68]

Ferrous salts of dibasic acids like oxalic are clearly auto-complex, and as such are discussed below among the 'ato' complexes.

Complex Ferrous Compounds

In general ferrous complexes are less stable than ferric, as we should expect. For example, by using radio-active iron as a tracer it has been shown[69] that slow radioactive exchange occurs with chelate ferrous complexes of o-phenanthroline and dipyridyl, but not with ferric complexes such as ferri-haemoglobin and ferri-phaeophytin. Some, however, of the ferrous complexes are very stable, especially the cyanides.

FERROUS CARBON COMPLEXES

THESE are confined to the cyanides, which are of two kinds, the ferro-cyanides $M_4[Fe(CN)_6]$, and the pentacyano-compounds $M_x[Fe(CN)_5X]$.

FERROCYANIDES

Stable complex cyanides are particularly common among the elements in this neighbourhood, such as manganese and cobalt, and the platinum metals; they are, however, especially numerous with iron: Abegg[70] devotes over 200 pages, with 1,360 references, to the discussion of this group of complexes.

Attention was very early directed to compounds of this class by the discovery of the valuable dye Prussian blue (ferrous ferricyanide), which was made accidentally by a colour-maker named Diesbach in Berlin in 1704–10.[71] It was then found by Macquer in 1753 that this dye when treated with alkali gives, and can in turn be made from, the 'yellow Blutlaugensalz' (yellow prussiate of potash, i.e. potassium ferrocyanide) which could be got by fusing animal residues with iron and potassium carbonate. The chemistry of the group was thoroughly investigated by Scheele in 1783; he showed that Prussian blue on distillation with sulphuric acid gave a peculiar new acid which was therefore called prussic acid, and from this he was able to make the prussiate and Prussian blue itself.

The ferrocyanide complex is exceptionally stable; the salts are not poisonous, and give none of the ordinary reactions for iron. Hence this was one of the first complexes whose complexity was recognized.

[68] N. Löfman, *Z. anorg. Chem.* 1919, **107**, 241.

[69] S. Ruben, M. D. Kamen, M. B. Allen, and P. Nahinsky, *J.A.C.S.* 1942, **64**, 2297.

[70] *Eisen*, B. 465–674 (1935).

[71] J. Brown, *Phil. Trans.* 1724, **33**, 17 (given in facsimile in Abegg, B. 465).

The ferrocyanides were formerly made by heating crude potashes (K_2CO_3) with iron filings and nitrogenous animal matter such as horn, feathers, and dried blood. They are now made from the residues of the purification of coal gas; the crude gas contains prussic acid, and when this is removed by passing it over ferric oxide, Prussian blue is formed. This product is heated with lime, which converts it into the soluble calcium ferrocyanide, and when this is treated with potassium chloride, the potassium salt $K_4Fe(CN)_6$, 3 H_2O crystallizes out.

The idea that the alkaline ferro- and ferricyanides occur in isomeric forms has been disproved for both,[72-5] though isomerism certainly occurs in the ferrocyanic esters (see below); $K_4[Fe(CN)_6]$ 3 H_2O may be dimorphic.[75]

Ferrocyanic Acid, $H_4Fe(CN)_6$

This can be obtained in solution by precipitating the lead salt with hydrogen sulphide or sulphuric acid, and from this solution the solid acid can be got by evaporation. It is more easily made by adding to a solution of a salt, hydrogen chloride and ether, when a crystalline etherate of the acid separates, from which the ether can be removed by heating in a stream of hydrogen to 80–90°, or by leaving it over sulphuric acid at 50°.

The free acid forms colourless crystals, or a white powder. It is curious that there is a doubt[76] whether the acid contains water or not; one would have supposed that as a strong acid it would have the hydrogen ions hydrated, but apparently some complex acids, especially of this type, can have the hydrogen covalently attached to the anion; examples (see later) are the carbonyl-prusso-acid $H_3[Fe(CN)_5CO], H_2O$, and the nitroprusside acid $H_2[Fe(CN)_5NO]$, 1 or 0 H_2O. Ferrocyanic acid is easily soluble in water (sol^y 15/14°); the solid is stable in dry air.

Of the four (classical) dissociation constants[77-8] only the first two are definitely those of a strong acid, the third being much weaker (about 10^{-3}), and the fourth only 5×10^{-5} (about one-third of that of monochloracetic acid).

Free ferrocyanic acid forms crystalline addition compounds with a large number of organic nitrogen and oxygen compounds, containing from one to four molecules of the organic component to one of the acid. Where the organic component is a base, these are obviously substituted ammonium salts, for example, with $4 R \cdot NH_2$, $(R \cdot NH_3)_4[Fe(CN)_6]$. The complexes with organic oxygen compounds[79-81] are formed by alcohols, ethers, aldehydes, and ketones. They resemble the amine compounds very closely: they are

[72] S. H. C. Briggs, *J.C.S.* 1920, **117**, 1026.
[73] Id., *J. Phys. Chem.* 1928, **32**, 1422.
[74] S. Iimori, *Z. anorg. Chem.* 1927, **167**, 145.
[75] R. H. Vallance, *J.C.S.* 1927, 1328. [76] Abegg, B. 481.
[77] I. M. Kolthoff, *Z. anorg. Chem.* 1920, **110**, 143.
[78] B. V. Nekrassov and G. V. Zotov, *J Appl. Chem. Russ.* 1941, **14**, 264.
[79] M. Freund, *Ber.* 1888, **21**, 931.
[80] A. v. Baeyer and V. Villiger, ib. 1902, **35**, 1202.
[81] P. Duprat, *Bull. Inst. Pin*, 1933, **37**, 17.

formed by direct addition, and dissociate into their components very readily; the only general difference is that while the number of amine molecules added to one of acid is usually four, the number of the oxygen compounds is often less than this. As Baeyer and Villiger said, these must be oxonium salts, for example, $(CH_3 \cdot OH_2)_2 H_2[Fe(CN)_6]$. Oxonium is a weaker base than ammonium, and so cannot always saturate all the hydrogen atoms of the acid. But the number of these compounds, and the ease of their formation, is remarkable. Platinocyanic acid forms a similar compound with alcohol, of the composition $H_2Pt(CN)_4, 2 C_2H_5OH$.

Salts of Ferrocyanic Acid

These are very numerous. The alkaline and alkaline earth salts, which are yellow, or when anhydrous nearly white, are readily soluble in water, and are considerably hydrated, as the following figures show:

Metal .	Li	Na	K	NH$_4$	Rb	Cs	Mg	Ca	Sr	Ba	Tl′
Hydration	6, 9	10	3	3	2	3	10(12)	11	8, 15	6	2

The hydration of some of these salts (as Rb, Cs, NH$_4$) is unusual; since the anion does not seem likely to be hydrated, it may be due to the large size of the anion as compared with the cation. The solubility increases from lithium to caesium, and from calcium to barium. This would normally be taken to indicate that the acid is weak, but it is very doubtful whether this rule, which is based on the behaviour of mono- and dibasic acids, can be applied to tetrabasic.

The other salts are nearly all insoluble. The ferrocyanides form an enormous number of double salts of such types as

$$Ag_3KFe(CN)_6, CaK_2Fe(CN)_6, \text{ etc.};$$

there is no sign that these are anything more than ordinary double salts or that they contain any larger complexes than the $Fe(CN)_6$ ions. The supposed 8-covalent salt $M_6[Fe(CN)_6Cl_2]$ does not exist.[82]

The rare earth salts[83] may be useful for separations. If a rare earth salt is added to a solution of potassium ferrocyanide, a relatively insoluble salt is precipitated, of the composition $M'M'''[Fe(CN)_6]$ aq., where M' may be Na or K, and M''' practically any rare earth metal. These salts are almost insoluble in water, but are more soluble (1·5–3·5 g. $M_2'''O_3$ per litre in the cold) in decinormal hydrochloric acid.

The solubilities of some of the simpler ferrocyanides are as follows (Abegg), in g. of anhydrous salt to 100 g. of water; Li, 6 H_2O, very large; Na, 10 H_2O, 20·8; K, 3 H_2O, 32·6 at 25° (falling to about 6 in 2-normal potassium hydroxide); Rb, *ca.* 100 at the ordinary temperature; Ag, H_2O, about as soluble as silver bromide; Mg, 10 H_2O, 25 at the ordinary temperature; Ca, 11 H_2O, 57·2 at 25°; Ba, 6 H_2O, 0·1 at 15°; and 1·0 at 75°.

[82] H. Irving and G. W. Cherry, *J.C.S.* 1941, 25.
[83] W. Prandtl and S. Mohr, *Z. anorg. Chem.* 1938, **236**, 243; **237**, 160.

The ferrocyanides of the alkalies and the alkaline earths are no doubt simple salts of the ferrocyanide ion. But most of the heavy metal derivatives give signs of greater complexity, with several iron atoms in the complex.[84]

The copper and iron derivatives are of special interest. Cupric ferrocyanide has the property that a film of it is permeable to water but not to certain solutes.[85] This was discovered by Moritz Traube in 1867, and became of practical importance 10 years later, when Pfeffer showed[86] that the membrane could be supported in the pores of a clay cell, and in this form could be used to measure comparatively high osmotic pressures; it was on these measurements that van 't Hoff based his theory of osmotic pressure 10 years later. The most singular fact is that this compound is not only the best but practically the only one which it has ever been found possible to use for this purpose; this imposes a serious limitation on the possible range of direct osmotic pressure measurements, as we are confined to aqueous solutions, and to solutes that do not react with cupric ferrocyanide. The mechanism of the action is uncertain, but the material used is a colloidal gel containing water: if the water is removed from it, either by drying or by immersing it in a non-aqueous solvent, the membrane breaks down. Hence it is at least probable that the passage of water through it is not merely mechanical, but involves the combination of the water with the colloid and its subsequent dissociation. It is permeable to many solutes, especially acids (which, however, may react with it) and many salts of the uni-univalent type; but for many salts with polyvalent ions, and for large organic molecules like those of the sugars, though not for small ones like the alcohols, it is almost, if not quite, impermeable.

The ferro- and ferricyanides of iron itself are of interest because they include the remarkable and important substance (or substances) Prussian blue. In discussing this group of compounds it is difficult to distinguish between the ferro- and the ferricyanides, in many of them each iron atom plays both parts. We may therefore anticipate somewhat and treat the ferro- and ferricyanides of iron together.[87]

When the iron is entirely ferrous, we get ferrous ferrocyanide $Fe_2[Fe(CN)_6]$ aq., and also a series of compounds in which the ferrous cation is partly replaced by hydrogen or by alkali metals, as in FeH_2, FeK_2, etc. These substances can be made by adding a ferrous solution to a ferrocyanide, and when they are precipitated in the absence of air they are white, pale yellow, or green substances, which oxidize in air with very different degrees of ease according to the method of preparation and the nature of the cation.

At the other end of the scale we have the wholly ferric compounds,

[84] H. Reihlen and U. v. Kummer, *Ann.* 1929, **469**, 30 (lead): H. Reihlen and W. Zimmermann, ib. **475**, 101 (cadmium).

[85] See Abegg, B. 581, 632.

[86] *Osmotische Untersuchungen*, Leipzig, 1877.

[87] See Abegg, *Eisen*, B. 557–78.

made from a ferric salt and a ferricyanide. These are but little known; they are usually dark coloured solids, and are mostly colloidal. They include the so-called 'Berlin green' which has been shown[88] to be the simple ferric ferricyanide $Fe[Fe(CN)_6]$, but this is not a dye, and it is at least probable that the green colour is due to the presence of impurities of the Prussian blue type.

The brilliant colours which we associate with these cyanide compounds of iron are only found when the substance contains both ferrous and ferric iron. The most obvious form of molecule to meet this requirement would be ferric ferrocyanide $Fe_4'''[Fe''(CN)_6]_3$, or ferrous ferricyanide $Fe_3''[Fe'''(CN)_6]_2$, but there must be (and are) compounds in which the cation is composed of hydrogen or alkali metals as well as iron. There is in fact a whole series of these dyes, differing in method of preparation, in composition, and in properties, some of them soluble but most of them insoluble. The discussion of the structures of compounds of this kind is of little use unless the crystal lattice has been determined. This has been done for some members of the Prussian blue group by Keggin and Miles.[88] This remarkable work showed that many compounds of this group have almost identical lattices. The structure is cubic. At every corner of the cube is an iron atom, joined to the next iron atom by the linear $Fe—C{\equiv}N—Fe$ group lying along the edge of the cube. Each Fe is attached to 6 CN, each CN to 2 Fe, giving for the cube $FeFe(CN)_6$; to these are added in the various ($Fe''Fe''$, $Fe''Fe'''$, $Fe'''Fe'''$) compounds 2, 1, or 0 alkaline cations per Fe_2. The white ferrous ferrocyanide is $M_2Fe''(Fe''CN)_6$): there is an alkaline ion at the centre of each cube. The Prussian blues in the crystalline form have the composition $MFe'''(Fe''(CN)_6)$; they have the same cubic lattice, the iron atoms being alternately ferrous and ferric, and the M cations being at the centres of alternate cubes. 'Ruthenium purple' $FeMRu(CN)_6$ is the same, except that alternate (ferrous) iron atoms are replaced by divalent ruthenium. Finally, 'Berlin green' $Fe'''Fe'''(CN)_6$ has again the same lattice, but now all the iron atoms are ferric, and there are no alkaline cations.

When the iron or ruthenium atoms are alternatively divalent and trivalent there is a possibility of resonance between two structures in which the two valencies change places: this causes an intense and very selective absorption of light; but when both the iron atoms are divalent, or both trivalent, this cannot happen, and so the brilliant colour disappears. (For the crystal structure, see further, reference [89], and for the magnetism reference [90]).

Reactions of the Ferrocyanides

In the solid state the alkaline ferrocyanides are very stable to heat, but at a red heat they begin to decompose with the formation of potassium cyanide, while cyanogen and nitrogen are evolved, and a mixture of iron,

[88] J. F. Keggin and F. D. Miles, *Nature*, 1936, **137**, 577.

[89] H. B. Weiser, W. O. Milligan, and J. B. Bates, *J. Phys. Chem.* 1942, **46**, 99.

[90] J. Richardson and N. Elliott, *J.A.C.S.* 1940, **62**, 3182.

iron carbide, and carbon is left. On heating with dilute sulphuric acid they give off prussic acid (as Scheele showed), while concentrated sulphuric acid gives the decomposition product of prussic acid, carbon monoxide.

In water the alkaline and alkaline earth ferrocyanides are strong electrolytes with the very stable $Fe(CN)_6''''$ anion. They give a series of characteristic precipitates with heavy metal salts,[91] for example, white with lead or zinc, reddish-brown with a cupric and bright blue with a ferric salt. The complex is so stable that it gives scarcely any reactions for the ferrous or the cyanide ion; there must, however, be a minute dissociation of the complex, for it is found[92] that if a stream of carbon dioxide is blown through the hot solution of a ferrocyanide there is a very slow but far-reaching evolution of hydrogen cyanide.

At the ordinary temperature neutral ferrocyanide solutions are only very slowly oxidized by air. In the presence of normal potassium hydroxide they are practically not oxidized at all, but in decinormal acetic acid the oxidation (to the ferricyanide) is complete.[93]

In practice the oxidation to the ferricyanide is effected by a number of reagents, such as the halogens, iodates, and electrolytic oxidation.

Ferrocyanic Esters

A series of alkyl derivatives of ferrocyanic acid, of the composition $R_4Fe(CN)_6$ (where R = methyl, ethyl, or propyl), has been prepared, of which the methyl compounds are peculiarly interesting from their occurrence in isomeric forms.[94–106]

It has been pointed out by Meyer[106] that of the eight known types of anion of the form $[A(CN)_6]$, only four give the free acids, and it is only two of these last, and moreover the two which give the most stable hydrogen compounds, of which the esters can be prepared. The whole list of these compounds is given in the following table, in which S stands for salt, A for acid, and E for ester; N is the number of unshared electrons in the third quantum group; it will be seen that the only two that form esters are the only two in which the E.A.N. of the metal is 36.

[91] For a full list see Abegg, B. 619.

[92] W. Autenrieth, *Chem. Ztg.* 1898, **22**, 866; J. Matuschek, ib. 1901, **25**, 815.

[93] C. Fredenhagen, *Z. anorg. Chem.* 1902, **29**, 396.

[94] H. L. Buff, *Ann.* 1854, **91**, 253.

[95] M. Freund, *Ber.* 1888, **21**, 931.

[96] E. G. J. Hartley, *J.C.S.* 1910, **97**, 1066.

[97] Id., ib. 1911, **99**, 1549.   [98] Id., ib. 1912, **101**, 705.

[99] Id., ib. 1913, **103**, 1196.

[100] F. Hölzl, *Mon.* 1927, **136**, 41.

[101] S. Glasstone, *J.C.S.* 1930, 321.

[102] Lord Berkeley and E. G. J. Hartley, *Proc. Roy. Soc.* 1916, **92**, 480.

[103] G. Buchböck, *Z. physikal. Chem.* 1897, **23**, 157.

[104] E. G. J. Hartley and H. M. Powell, *J.C.S.* 1933, 101.

[105] G. Spacu, *Z. Elektrochem.* 1934, **40**, 125.

[106] J. Meyer, H. Domann, and W. Müller, *Z. anorg. Chem.* 1937, **230**, 336.

$$
\begin{array}{llll}
N = 12 & H_4[Cr''Cy_6] & S \\
11 & H_3[Cr'''Cy_6] & S \\
13 & H_4[Mn''Cy_6] & S \\
12 & H_3[Mn'''Cy_6] & S \\
14 & H_4[Fe''Cy_6] & S & A & E \\
13 & H_3[Fe'''Cy_6] & S & A \\
15 & H_4[Co''Cy_6] & S & A \\
14 & H_3[Co'''Cy_6] & S & A & E
\end{array}
$$

Our first real knowledge of these compounds is due to the work of Hartley,[96-9] beginning in 1910. He showed that if dry potassium ferrocyanide is treated with methyl sulphate the salts (sulphate, acid sulphate, and methyl-sulphate) of a base of the composition $[(CH_3)_6FeCy_6]X_2$ can be formed, and that the chloride of this base when it is heated to 140° loses two molecules of methyl chloride to give a mixture of two isomeric (α and β-) forms of the substance $(CH_3)_4FeCy_6$, which is formally at least the methyl ester of ferrocyanic acid. In addition Hölzl[100] has got a third (γ) isomer,[104,106] and J. Meyer[106] a fourth (Meyer's a), formed together with Hartley's α by the action of diazo-methane on the acid in the cold. There are thus five methyl derivatives of ferrocyanic acid:

1. The salts $[(CH_3)_6Fe(CN)_6]X_2$ (apart from the ionization these formulae are intended only to express the composition); formed from methyl halide and silver ferrocyanide.

2. Hartley's α-ester (Meyer's b) $(CH_3)_4Fe(CN)_6$; made along with (3) by heating the salt (1) to 140°, or from methyl iodide and silver ferrocyanide,[38] or by treating the etherate of ferrocyanic acid with diazomethane.[106] This is a solid easily soluble in water, alcohol, or chloroform; it separates from the last in large transparent lemon-yellow crystals, with 4 molecules of $CHCl_3$ of crystallization,[106] which are easily removed. It is monomeric by osmotic pressure measurements in water[102]; it is evidently covalent since it has a very low electric conductivity, and silver nitrate precipitates no silver cyanide.

3. Hartley's β; made together with the α as above, and obtained from the mother liquor after extraction with chloroform; it is less soluble than (2) in water and alcohol, and almost insoluble in chloroform; it is monomeric by the osmotic pressure. In its general behaviour it is very like (2).

4. Hölzl's γ: got[100] among the products of heating $(CH_3)_6Fe(CN)_6Cl_2$; it behaves as a salt, conducts in water, and with silver nitrate precipitates two CN groups.

5. Meyer's a,[106] got by treating the acid with diazomethane; it has not yet been obtained pure, so its composition is uncertain; it is hygroscopic. It is a salt, and with silver nitrate precipitates at least one CN; at 140° it goes over to (2) and (3).

The ethyl[95] and propyl[100] esters are known only in one form each, which behaves like Hartley's α-form (2).

Structures. It is clear that in all these compounds the methyl groups are attached to the CN and not to the iron, and moreover to the N and not the C of the CN, for they have a strong isonitrile smell, and when they are decomposed by alkali they give methyl isocyanide and not acetonitrile. We have already seen that in the complex cyanides it is the carbon of the CN that is joined to the metal.

The structure of the salt (1) must thus be $[(CH_3—N≡C→)_6Fe]X_2$, and this has been confirmed by Powell and Bartindale.[108] (2) and (3) are non-ionized and covalent, and must be $(CH_3—N≡C→)_4Fe(CN)_2$; they are true isomers and not merely dimorphic[104]; they combine with equal readiness with methyl iodide in presence of mercuric iodide to give the same salt $[(CH_3·NC)_6Fe](HgI_3)_2$.[104] They are evidently *cis* and *trans* octahedral forms; this has been confirmed by X-ray analysis,[107] which shows that the β-form is the *trans*, and that the group $H_3C—N—C—Fe$ is linear, as the above structure requires.

A detailed X-ray examination of the hydrate $[Fe(CN·CH_3)_6]Cl_2, 3 H_2O$[108] gives an octahedral structure, with the distances $Fe—C$ 1·85, $C—N$ 1·18 (theory 2·04, 1·15 A), suggesting about 50 per cent. double-bond character in the $Fe—C$ link. The carbon atom in $Fe—C—N—CH_3$ is bent 7° from the straight line.

The salt (4) is presumably the 4-covalent compound

$$(CH_3—N≡C→)_4Fe[CN]_2.$$

(5) is still uncertain, but it may well be, as Meyer suggests, the penta-cyano-compound $[(CH_3—N≡C→)_4Fe(OH_2)CN](CN)$.

PENTACYANO-COMPOUNDS[109]

Iron forms a series of complexes, both ferrous and ferric, in which one (but not more than one) of the six cyanide groups is replaced by another group, which may either be another radical such as NO_2, or a neutral molecule like water or ammonia, so that the 6-fold co-ordination is maintained. Of these compounds the ferrous are, on the whole, the more numerous. These compounds are somewhat less stable than the hexa-cyanides, but they resemble them in their reactions, and can all be converted into them by treatment with excess of cyanide ion.

Following K. A. Hofmann we may call the ferrous pentacyano-compounds (which alone concern us here) 'prusso' and the ferric 'prussi'.

In these the anion is always $FeCy_5X$, with a valency varying according to the nature of the group X, which can be water, ammonia, an amine, $—SO_3^-$, NO_2, CO, or NO, the latter occurring in the nitroprussides, which are commonly assumed to be ferric, but really are ferrous, as is shown below.

I. *Aquo-prusso-compounds*, $M_3[FeCy_5(OH_2)]$. These can be made by the hydrolysis of the ferro-cyanides in presence of light, heat, and dilute acids,[110–12] or by the action of either oxidizing or reducing agents on the

[107] H. M. Powell and G. B. Stanger, *J.C.S.* 1939, 1105.

[108] H. M. Powell and G. W. R. Bartindale, ib. 1945, 799.

[109] See Abegg, *Eisen*, B. 584–618 (1932).

[110] S. Iimori, *Z. anorg. Chem.* 1927, **167**, 145.

[111] R. Schwarz and K. Tede, *Ber.* 1927, **60**, 69.   [112] O. Baudisch, ib. 1929, **62**, 2706.

nitrito-prusso-compounds, that is, on the nitro-prussides in alkaline solution.[113-14]

II. *The ammonia-prusso-compounds* $M_3[FeCy_5NH_3]$. These are formed by the action of concentrated aqueous ammonia on the aquo-compounds,[115] or by the reduction of the nitroprussides with sodium amalgam.[116] Amines react with the aquo-compounds in the same way as ammonia, primary amines violently, secondary less so, and tertiary only slowly.[117]

III. *The sulphito-compounds*, $M_5[FeCy_5SO_3]$, are formed when almost any pentacyano-compound is treated with sodium sulphite; with sodium nitrite they reform the nitroprussides.

IV. *The nitrito-compounds*, $M_4[FeCy_5NO_2]$, are formed by the action of alkalies on the nitro-prussides:

$$M_2[FeCy_5NO] + 2 MOH = M_4[FeCy_5NO_2] + H_2O.$$

The mechanism of this peculiar reaction is discussed later, under the nitroprussides.

V. *The carbonyl compounds*, which are numerous, are all derived from the type $M_3[FeCy_5CO]$. In this, as in nearly all carbonyl compounds, the central atom has the E.A.N. of the next inert gas, here 36 ($26+3+5+2$); the ferric compound would be $M_2[FeCy_5CO]$ with an E.A.N. one less ($26+2+5+2 = 35$), and this prussi-carbonyl compound does not exist.

The carbonyl compounds are produced by the action of carbon monoxide on a hot solution of potassium ferrocyanide, or on the ammonia-prusso-compounds.[118-24] They are very like the ferro-cyanides in behaviour, but are much less easily oxidized (as oxidation would destroy the inert gas number of the iron, which is not important in the hexacyanides). Unlike the other prusso-compounds mentioned above, the carbonyl derivatives give a free acid $H_3[FeCy_5CO]$, H_2O, made by treating a suspension of the cupric salt in water with hydrogen sulphide, and evaporating the filtrate.[123] It forms colourless or pale yellow crystals readily soluble in water with a strong acid reaction, sol^y 51.7/16°. This acid, like ferrocyanic, does not contain enough water to solvate all the acidic hydrogen.

VI. The most remarkable of the prusso-compounds are the *nitroprussides* $M_2[FeCy_5NO]$. There are two distinct classes of pentacyano-compounds with NO groups, the nitroprussides $M_2[FeCy_5NO]$, and a much smaller and less stable class of nitroso-compounds $M_3[FeCy_5NO]$—the

[113] K. A. Hofmann, *Ann.* 1900, **312**, 1.
[114] A. Ungarelli, *Gaz.* 1925, **55**, 118.
[115] K. A. Hofmann, *Z. anorg. Chem.* 1896, **12**, 146.
[116] Id., ib. 1895, **10**, 262.
[117] W. Manchot and P. Woringer, *Ber.* 1913, **46**, 3514.
[118] J. A. Müller, *C.R.* 1887, **104**, 992.
[119] Id., ib. 1898, **126**, 1421.   [120] Id., *Bull. Soc.* 1899, [3] **21**, 472.
[121] M. Stoecker, *J. Gasbel.* 1904, **47**, 338.
[122] J. A. Müller, *Ann. Chim. Phys.* 1900, [7] **20**, 377.
[123] Id., *Bull. Soc.* 1914, [4] **15**, 491.   [124] F. Hölzl, *Mon.* 1930, **139**, 349.

anion having the same composition in both, but a different valency. The latter class have been regarded as ferrous compounds, and the nitro-prussides as ferric; but in fact the reverse is true: the nitroprussides are ferrous compounds; the nitroso- are ferric, and will therefore be dealt with later, among the ferric prussi-compounds.

The *nitroprussides* $M_2[FeCy_5NO]$ were the first pentacyano-compounds to be discovered. They were made by Playfair in 1849 by the action of 30 per cent. nitric acid on a ferro- or a ferricyanide, a violent and compli-cated reaction still used for their preparation. There are several other ways of making them. Thus the nitrite ion acts on a ferrocyanide to give two successive reversible reactions:[125]

$$\text{(I)} \quad [FeCy_6]''' + NO_2^- \rightleftharpoons [FeCy_5NO_2]''' + CN^- ;$$
$$\text{(II)} \quad [FeCy_5NO_2]''' + H_2O \rightleftharpoons [FeCy_5NO]'' + 2\ OH^-.$$

The reaction can be carried to completion if the cyanide and hydroxyl ions are removed; for example, if the prussic acid is driven out by a stream of inert gas and the hydroxyl ions removed by the addition of acid. Ferri-cyanides react in the same way, being reduced to ferrocyanides by the nitrite ion. The salts can also be made by the action of sodium nitrite on the prusso-compounds.

The nitroprussides are mostly hydrated; Na, 2 H_2O; K, 1; NH_4, 1; Ca, 4 and 1; Ba, 6 and 3 (some of these values are unusual, especially the last). Conductivities show that the alkaline salts are tri-ionic, so that the formula should not be doubled, which rules out the hyponitrite structure, and probably the nitroso-structure as well.

The nitroprussides are obviously nitrosyl compounds, and if we assume the constitution $\overset{=}{A}-\overset{+}{N}\equiv\overset{+}{O}$ assigned to this grouping (V. 686), then in $M_2[FeCy_5NO]$ the iron will have an E.A.N. of $26+2+5+3 = 36$ (the same as in the carbonyl prusso-complexes $M_3[FeCy_5CO]$) and a valency of 2. This conclusion that the iron in the nitroprussides is ferrous is supported by the whole of their behaviour, and in particular by the fact that they are diamagnetic,[126] like all the ferrous cyanide complexes, whereas the ferric are paramagnetic.

The free acid of the nitroprussides can be obtained from the silver salt with hydrochloric acid, or from the barium salt with sulphuric acid, and on evaporation separates out in dark red crystals, which are said to have 1 molecule of water, and are also said to be anhydrous.[127] It is easily soluble in water, alcohol, and ether. The electrical conductivity[127] shows its first dissociation constant to be that of a strong acid; this agrees with its having one molecule of water of crystallization.

The nitroprussides are relatively stable substances, which resist oxida-tion in neutral and in acid solution. In alkaline solution they are oxidized

[125] V. Schwarzkopf, *Lotos*, Prag, 1911, **3**, 1.
[126] L. A. Welo, *Phil. Mag.* 1928, [7] **6**, 481.
[127] G. J. Burrows and E. E. Turner, *J.C.S.* 1921, **119**, 1450.

by permanganate, but alkali alone will convert the nitroprusside into a nitrito- (really nitro-) prusso-compound, according to the reversible equation

$$[FeCy_5NO]'' + 2\ OH^- \rightleftharpoons [FeCy_5NO_2]'''' + H_2O.$$

The equilibrium has been determined colorimetrically,[128] and was found to be at 15°

$$K = \frac{[FeCy_5NO]'' \cdot [OH^-]^2}{[FeCy_5NO_2]''''} = 1 \cdot 35 \times 10^4,$$

so that in a $n/10$ alkaline solution 13·2 per cent. of the nitrito-compound is converted into nitroprussides.

This is a very unusual kind of reaction, but it is a natural result of the high positive charge on the NO group, which attracts the negative hydroxyl ions:

$$\overset{=}{Fe}\!-\!\overset{+}{N}\!\!=\!\!\overset{+}{O} \atop +\ OH^- + OH^- \quad = \quad \overset{=}{Fe}\!-\!N\!\!\underset{\diagdown OH}{\overset{\diagup O}{\underset{}{\overset{}{-}OH}}} = \overset{=}{Fe}\!-\!N\!\!\underset{\diagdown O}{\overset{\diagup O}{\Big\langle}} + H_2O.$$

The nitroprussides also give remarkable colour reactions. In 1850 Playfair found that a solution of a nitroprusside will give with sulphide ion, but not with hydrogen sulphide itself, a transient reddish-violet coloration; this is sufficiently intense to detect a concentration of 0·02 mg. of sodium sulphide per c.c.[129] A bright blue compound also may be formed. Electrometric titration showed[130] that a large drop in E.M.F. occurs when one mole of nitroprusside has been added to one mole of sodium sulphide, indicating that the reaction is

$$[FeCyNO]'' + S'' = [FeCy_5NOS]'''',$$

like that with alkali:

$$[FeCy_5NO]'' \quad \begin{array}{l} +\ 2\ OH^- = [FeCy_5NO_2]'''' + H_2O \\ +\ 2\ SH^- = [FeCy_5NOS]'''' + H_2S. \end{array}$$

By working in methyl alcoholic solution the sodium and potassium salts $M_4[FeCy_5NOS]$ were isolated, both blue-violet and very soluble in water. The aqueous solution decomposes with loss of colour, forming not, as we might have expected, a pentacyano-compound, but the ferro-cyanide and ferrous oxide.

Another remarkable colour reaction is with compounds containing a mobile methylene group.[131] A nitroprusside solution gives with acetone and alkali a red colour which on addition of acetic acid goes green (the 'Legal' reaction). This reaction occurs with all organic molecules containing a mobile methylene group, and is due to the nitroprusside forming deep red unstable complexes with them, which with dilute acids breaks up into the aquo-prusso-compounds and the isonitroso-derivatives of the organic

[128] L. Cambi and L. Szegö, *Gaz.* 1928, **58**, 64, 71.

[129] J. Fages y Virgili, *Z. anal. Chem.* 1906, **45**, 409.

[130] G. Scagliarini and P. Pratesi, *Atti R.* 1928, [6] **8**, ii. 75; 1930, **11**, i. 193; 1931, **13**, i. 199.

[131] L. Cambi and T. Ricci, *Atti R.* 1930, **11**, i. 443: Cambi, *Gaz.* 1931, **61**, i. 3.

compound. The essence of the reaction is the oximation of the CH_2 by the nitrosyl group:

$$M\text{---}NO + H_2C\diagup{R}\diagdown{R_1} + OH^- = \bar{M}\leftarrow OH_2 + HON\text{=}C\diagup{R}\diagdown{R_1}.$$

COMPLEX FERROUS THIOCYANATES

Ferrous iron forms complex salts with the thiocyanate radical, of the type $M_4[Fe(CNS)_6]$,[132] made by dissolving ferrous hydroxide in thiocyanic acid solution, and adding the alkaline thiocyanate. They are colourless when pure, but are usually tinged with red from slight oxidation by air to the deeply coloured ferric thiocyanates. The alkaline salts (Na, 12 H_2O; K, 4 H_2O; NH_4, anhydrous) are all readily soluble in water.

The complex is not very stable; ammonia gives a precipitate of ferrous oxide.

FERROUS NITROGEN COMPLEXES

Ammines of the ferrous ion can be made by treating anhydrous ferrous salts with ammonia, and may contain up to 10 NH_3 per Fe^{++}. These last dissociate very readily, but the hexammine $[Fe(NH_3)_6]Cl_2$ has a dissociation tension of only 6 mm. at 20°, and the diammine of 121 mm. at 230°. Many other ammines and substituted ammines of ferrous salts are known,[133] including the very stable $Fe\,py_4\,Cl_2$,[134] which is a convenient source for the preparation of pure ferrous compounds. It is to be noticed that 6-co-ordinated ferrous cations are frequent, while complex 6-covalent ferrous anions (except in the cyanides) are very rare.

The chelate complexes include a series of cyclic ammines[135-40] which have been made[138-9] with ethylene diamine and trimethylene diamine; they are mostly of the type $[Fe(en)_3]Cl_2$, and in spite of the chelation are not very stable, losing amine in the air. It is interesting to compare the stability constants[141] of the complexes $[A(en)_3]^{++}$:

Mn	.	.	.	$4{\cdot}6 \times 10^5$	Co	.	.	.	$6{\cdot}6 \times 10^{13}$
Fe	.	.	.	$3{\cdot}3 \times 10^9$	Ni	.	.	.	$4{\cdot}1 \times 10^{18}$

Similar derivatives, also trichelate, of dipyridyl and phenanthroline are known,[69,137,140] for example, $[Fe(dipy)_3]Cl_2, 7\,H_2O$, which forms dark red crystals. These are used as redox indicators.

Complex Nitrites (really nitro-compounds). A series of the type $M'_2M''[Fe(NO_2)_6]$ have been made,[142] where $M' = K$, NH_4, and Tl': and

[132] A. Rosenheim and R. Cohn, *Z. anorg. Chem.* 1901, **27**, 280.
[133] See Abegg, *Eisen*, B. 92–7.　　[134] *Inorganic Syntheses*, vol. i, p. 184.
[135] B. Emmert and R. Jarcyznski, *Ber.* 1931, **64**, 1072.
[136] B. Emmert and H. Gsottschneider, ib. 1933, **66**, 1871.
[137] R. Kuhn and A. Wassermann, *Ann.* 1933, **503**, 203.
[138] R. E. Breuil, *C.R.* 1933, **196**, 2009.　　[139] Id., ib. 1934, **199**, 298.
[140] F. M. Jaeger and J. A. van Dijk, *Proc. Akad. Amst.* 1934, **37**, 333.
[141] J. Bjerrum, *Metal Ammine Formation*, Copenhagen, 1941.
[142] L. Cambi and A. Ferrari, *Gaz.* 1935, **65**, 1162.

$M'' = $ Ca, Sr, Ba, Cd, Hg, and Pb. They seem to be the only known hexa-acido-complexes of ferrous iron.

Among the *N, O chelate complexes* are those formed by *o*-nitrosophenol[143]; these are green and can be used colorimetrically for the estimation of ferrous iron, and will detect 1/2000 mg. Fe'' in 50 c.c. For the *N, S thiazol complexes*, see reference [144].

FERROUS OXYGEN COMPLEXES

Ferrous chloride forms complexes with alcohols and esters, mostly having one or two, but sometimes as many as four organic molecules to one Fe''.[145]

Chelate derivatives of diketones, ketonic esters, salicylaldehyde, etc., are readily made[135-6] from a ferrous salt solution and the diketone, etc., in presence of a base such as pyridine or trialkylamine, which neutralizes the liberated acid and may also co-ordinate with the iron. These complexes have only two chelate rings, but the covalency is often raised by amines to 6, as in

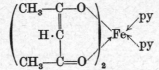

the acetylacetone compound. Piperidine and trialkylamines often do not co-ordinate, but the hydrate FeA_2, $1 \cdot 5 H_2O$ is formed instead. These are mostly dark red or brown solids, easily dehydrated to an orange-red FeA_2, which is volatile at very low pressures, and so presumably polymerized. These complexes are stable when dry, but easily oxidized if moist.

The 'ato' compounds of ferrous iron are relatively few, and practically always only 4-covalent. There are numerous double sulphates, especially of the type $M_2SO_4, FeSO_4, 6 H_2O$ (the normal vitriol double salts), but there is little evidence of their being true complexes. A more probably complex compound is the acid sulphate $H_2[Fe(SO_4)_2]$, with 6, 5, and 3 H_2O.

Ferrous carbonate is more soluble in concentrated alkaline hydroxide solution than in pure water, presumably forming a complex carbonate, and a potassium salt of the composition $K_2[Fe(CO_3)_2]$, 4 H_2O has been obtained.

Oxalato complexes also exist, including ferrous oxalate itself, as is shown by its lemon yellow colour, and by the fact that the molecular conductivity at $V = 30,000$ is only $0 \cdot 65$ of the calculated value for infinite dilution, which suggests that its true formula is $Fe[Fe(C_2O_4)_2]$.[146]

Rather unstable double oxalates of the type $M_2[FeOx_2]$, aq. are also known.

[143] G. Cronheim and W. Wink, *Ind. Eng. Chem. [Anal.]* 1942, **14**, 447.
[144] H. Erlenmeyer and H. Ueberwasser, *Helv. Chim. Acta*, 1940, **23**, 1268.
[145] D. R. Chesterman, *J.C.S.* 1935, 906.
[146] R. Scholder, *Ber.* 1927, **60**, 1510, 1525.

COMPLEX FERROUS HALIDES

These are formed with fluorine and chlorine, but not with bromine or iodine.

COMPLEX FLUORIDES

These are few in number and of two types, $M[FeF_3]$ and $M_2[FeF_4]$; they have been but little investigated.[147]

COMPLEX FERROUS CHLORIDES

These are rather better known. They are of three types, $M[FeCl_3]$, which is the commonest, $M_2[FeCl_4]$, and (in one example) $M_4[FeCl_6]$. No complex acid has been isolated, nor does one seem to be formed in solution.[148]

Abegg[149] mentions the following salts of each type:

$M[FeCl_3]$	$M_2[FeCl_4]$	$M_4[FeCl_6]$
Li, 3 H_2O	Rb_2, 2 H_2O	K_3Na, anhydr.
(No Na)	Cs_2, 2 H_2O	
K, Rb, Cs, all		
with 2 H_2O		

The hexachloride is found in nature as the mineral Rinneite in potash deposits. Ammonium chloride forms mixed crystals with ferrous chloride, but no double salt.[150-1]

No true complex ferrous bromides or iodides are known.[152]

FERRIC COMPOUNDS

THE ferric compounds, in which the core of the iron atom is reduced to $23 = 2, 8, 13$, are made by the oxidation of ferrous compounds, into which they can be converted by reduction. For the ions this can be expressed by the equation

$$Fe^{++} \rightleftharpoons Fe^{+++} + \text{Electron}.$$

In general, the ferrous ion is about as stable as the ferric, but in the covalent state the ferric is more stable than the ferrous: in particular, ferrous salts are fairly stable in presence of air in acid solution, but are readily oxidized by it on addition of alkali and precipitation of the hydroxide. The reason is given by the potential changes involved in the oxidation.[153]

These are expressed by the equation

$$E = E_0 + 0 \cdot 058 \log \frac{[Fe''']}{[Fe'']},$$

where E_0 is the value of the E.M.F. when the concentrations of ferrous

---

[147] R. Wagner, *Ber.* 1886, **19**, 896.

[148] S. R. Carter and N. J. L. Megson, *J.C.S.* 1927, 2023.

[149] *Eisen*, B. 32.　　　　　[150] F. W. J. Clendinnen, *J.C.S.* 1922, **121**, 801.

[151] A. C. D. Rivett and F. W. J. Clendinnen, ib. 1923, **123**, 1634.

[152] Abegg, *Eisen*, B. 37, 39.　　　　　[153] Id., ib. 8 (1930).

and ferric ions are the same: this is found to be 0·771 v.[154-5] Hence if the concentration of the ferrous ion is increased or that of the ferric diminished, the second term becomes negative, and the ferrous ion becomes a more powerful reducing agent than it was before. If now to the mixed ferrous-ferric solution we add alkali until the hydroxyl concentration becomes normal, this will precipitate ferrous and ferric hydroxides. The solubility products of these hydroxides are approximately: $Fe(OH)_2$, 10^{-14}, $Fe(OH)_3$, 10^{-36}. When the hydroxyl concentration is unity, these figures will be the concentrations of the ferrous and ferric ions in the solution, so that $Fe^{+++}/Fe^{++} = 10^{-36}/10^{-14} = 10^{-22}$. Hence for this solution

$$E = E_0 - 0 \cdot 058 \log 10^{-22} = E_0 - 1 \cdot 28 \text{ volt.}$$
$$= -0 \cdot 50 \text{ volt.}$$

Hence the ferrous ion, though its concentration is so minute, has enormously increased its reducing power[156]; it will in fact reduce the nitrate and the nitrite ions, and hydroxylamine, to ammonia,[157-8] and will even, in the presence of palladous chloride, decompose water.[159] Another example of this effect is that ferric salts will oxidize copper and cuprous compounds to cupric, but in presence of ammonia ferrous salts will reduce cupric salts to cuprous, and in presence of alkali to metallic copper.

This argument from the solubility of the hydroxides to their stability must apply in some degree to every change in the valency of a cation.

The kinetics of a variety of oxidations of ferrous to ferric are discussed in Abegg, *Eisen*, B. 8120 (1930). Other references are given below.[160-3]

As a base ferric hydroxide is, as we should expect, much weaker than ferrous, and accordingly the salts are much more highly hydrolysed; the solutions, unless they are strongly acid, contain the ions $FeOH^{++}$ and $Fe(OH)_2^+$, and as soon as the concentration of $Fe(OH)_3$ exceeds 0·00022 mg. per litre it begins to separate out in a colloidal form.[164] It has a much stronger tendency to form complexes. Almost the only ferric salts which are not complex are those of the strong oxy-acids such as nitric, perchloric, sulphuric, and benzene-sulphonic, and even with these there may be some complex formation. The tendency of ferric iron to form complexes is almost as strong as that of trivalent chromium, but each element has its own preferences; the ferric ion gives much more stable complexes than the chromic with cyanides, and the chromic with ammonia and amines.

[154] W. C. Bray and A. V. Hershey, *J.A.C.S.* 1934, **56**, 1889.
[155] W. C. Schumb, M. S. Sherrill, and S. B. Sweetser, ib. 1937, **59**, 2360.
[156] E. Müller, *Z. Elektrochem.* 1908, **14**, 76.
[157] A. Klemenc, *Ber.* 1925, **58**, 492.
[158] A. Kurtenacker and F. Werner, *Z. anorg. Chem.* 1927, **160**, 333.
[159] W. Traube and W. Lange, *Ber.* 1925, **58**, 2773.
[160] H. M. Dawson and E. Spivey, *J.C.S.* 1932, 1838 (iodine).
[161] W. Manchot and W. Pflaum, *Z. anorg. Chem.* 1933, **211**, 1 ($H_2O_2 + KI$).
[162] M. H. Gorin, *J.A.C.S.* 1936, **58**, 1787 (tin perchlorate).
[163] W. C. Schumb and S. B. Sweetser, *J.A.C.S.* 1935, **57**, 871 (silver salts).
[164] A. B. Lamb and A. G. Jaques, ib. 1938, **60**, 977, 1215.

The solubilities of ferric salts are in general much the same as those of ferrous. The anhydrous salts are usually white, yellow, or brown. The yellow-brown colour of the ordinary ferric solutions is due to colloidal ferric hydroxide; with excess of acid the hydrolysis is repressed, and at the same time complexes are formed, which are often colourless, but sometimes have characteristic colours: thus the ferric fluoride complex is pink, and the ferric chloride complex yellow.

The pure hydrated ferric salts are violet or amethyst coloured, but when crystallized from a slightly hydrolysed solution their small content of the yellow colloidal hydroxide may suppress the violet and make them colourless; thus ferric nitrate is colourless if it is crystallized from water, but from concentrated nitric acid it is violet. The same effect has been found with ferric ammonium alum. The suggestion that the violet colour is due to traces of manganese has been experimentally disproved.[165]

[*Ferric Cyanide*, $Fe(CN)_3$

Though the complex ferric cyanides are numerous and stable, the simple compound $Fe(CN)_3$ cannot be made.][166]

Ferric Thiocyanate

The remarkable blood-red colour produced when a thiocyanate is added to a ferric solution, and the coloured substance extracted with ether, are familiar facts in qualitative analysis. But the precise nature of the coloured substance is still uncertain.

Ferric thiocyanate $Fe(CNS)_3$ can be made by dissolving ferric hydroxide in thiocyanic acid, by extracting a solution of ferric salts and potassium thiocyanate with ether and evaporating off the ether, or by the action of excess of thiocyanogen on iron.[167] It consists of dark violet crystals which are very soluble in water and crystallize from it as a dark red trihydrate $Fe(CNS)_3, 3 H_2O$; it is also very soluble in ether.

The nature of this substance, with its solubility in ether, is obscure. Hantzsch[168-9] found that the partition between water and ether (C_{water}/C_{ether}) rose from 0·53 at 0° to 4·32 at 35°, suggesting an etherate which dissociates on heating. Schlesinger and van Valkenburgh[170] showed that the compound was dimeric $(Fe_2(CNS)_6)$ both in ether and in benzene, and claimed that the red colour (which was the same in water and in ether) migrated on electrolysis to the anode; they concluded that the colour is due to the $[Fe(CNS)_6]$ group, and that the ethereal solution contains $Fe[Fe(CNS)_6]$; they do not, however, suggest a structure for this molecule in benzene, where it must be covalent.

[165] J. Bonell and E. P. Perman, *J.C.S.* 1921, **119**, 1994.
[166] A. Hantzsch and C. H. Desch, *Ann.* 1902, **323**, 25.
[167] E. Söderbäck, *Ann.* 1919, **419**, 217.
[168] A. Hantzsch and F. Sebaldt, *Z. physikal. Chem.* 1899, **30**, 286.
[169] A. Hantzsch and A. Vagt, ib. 1901, **38**, 732.
[170] H. I. Schlesinger and H. B. van Valkenburgh, *J.A.C.S.* 1931, **53**, 1212.

More recently Bent and French[171] measured the relation of the colour intensity to the concentrations of $[Fe]^{+++}$ and $[CNS]^-$, and found that this gives no evidence of a complex ion $[Fe(CNS)_6]^{---}$; they consider that the colour is due to a complex cation $[FeCNS]^{++}$; they also claim to show that on electrolysis the colour migrates to the cathode. This has been confirmed by light-absorption measurements of the equilibrium of Fe^{+++} and CNS^- ions in perchloric acid solution.[172]

Ferric Azide, $Fe[N_3]_3$[173]

This is a very soluble salt, considerably hydrolysed in solution; it has a dark red colour, especially in presence of excess of ferric ions. This resemblance in colour to the thiocyanate is remarkable: the CNS and azide ions are both linear.

Ferric Oxide, Fe_2O_3

Both ferric oxide and its hydrate Fe_2O_3, H_2O or $FeO \cdot OH$ occur in two forms α and γ, which form distinct series of compounds[174 5]; this view is supported by the X-ray measurements.[176-8] Of the oxides the α-form is paramagnetic and the γ- ferromagnetic.[179] The α-form occurs in nature as haematite, and can be made by heating the α-form of the hydrated oxide, or the nitrate or oxalate. It melts at about $1,550°$.[180]

The γ-form of Fe_2O_3 is made by the oxidation of Fe_3O_4, or from any ferrous compound if it is oxidized so slowly that Fe_3O_4 is first formed. It changes reversibly into the α-form at about $600°$. Its crystal structure is remarkable.[181] While the α-form has the corundum lattice, like Al_2O_3 or Cr_2O_3, the lattice of the γ-oxide is that of a spinel $M''M_2'''O_4$, and hence is identical with that of the magnetic oxide Fe_3O_4, which almost certainly (see later) is ferrous ferrite, $Fe(FeO_2)_2$. It is very remarkable that the lattice should persist when the Fe_3O_4 is oxidized to Fe_2O_3; the only change during oxidation is a slight contraction of the unit cube whose side changes from $8 \cdot 380$ to $8 \cdot 322$ A.U.[182] This retention of the spinel lattice is due[182] to the presence of empty places where the magnetic oxide has iron atoms: in the fully oxidized ferric oxide one-ninth of these places are empty, whereby instead of $Fe_9O_{12} = 3 Fe_3O_4$, we have $Fc_8O_{12} = 4 Fe_2O_3$.

[171] H. R. Bent and C. L. French, ib. 1941, **63**, 568.

[172] H. S. Frank and R. L. Oswalt, ib. 1947, **69**, 1321.

[173] L. Wöhler and F. Martin, *Ber.* 1917, **50**, 594.

[174] E. Posnjak and H. E. Merwin, *Amer. J. Sci.* 1919, **47**, 311; *J.A.C.S.* 1922, **44**, 1965.

[175] N. S. Kurnakow and E. I. Rode, *Z. anorg. Chem.* 1928, **169**, 57.

[176] J. Bohm, *Z. Krist.* 1928, **68**, 567.

[177] G. F. Hüttig and A. Zörner, *Z. Elektrochem.* 1930, **36**, 259.

[178] R. Fricke, T. Schoon, and W. Schröder, *Z. physikal. Chem.* 1941, B **50**, 13.

[179] H. Albrecht and E. Wedekind, *Z. anorg. Chem.* 1931, **202**, 209.

[180] For its crystal structure see W. H. Zachariasen, *Vid. Akad. Oslo*, 1928, **4**, 1. He finds the Fe—O distance to be $1 \cdot 985$ A.U., and the O$\cdots$O $2 \cdot 545$.

[181] L. A. Welo and O. Baudisch, *Phys. Rev.* 1925, **25**, 587; *Phil. Mag.* 1925, [6] **50**, 399.

[182] G. Hägg, *Z. physikal. Chem.* 1935, B **29**, 95.

The energy content of either form of the oxide, as measured by the heat of solution in acids, may vary by several k.cals. per mol. according to the exact method of preparation, owing probably to a difference in the size of the particles; the determination of the surface by the adsorption of a radioactive indicator such as radiothorium supports this conclusion.[183-4]

Ferric Hydroxides

The fully hydrated ferric hydroxide $Fe(OH)_3$ has not been isolated; the only known hydrated oxides have the composition Fe_2O_3, H_2O or $FeO \cdot OH$, of which, as of the oxide, there are two different forms.[174-5] The α-form, also known as ortho-ferric hydroxide, is reddish-brown. The γ-form (the meta oxide of Krause) is yellow, and apparently the more acidic. For further details on these crystalline forms, see references [187-9].

The hydroxide $FeO \cdot OH$ occurs as the mineral limonite. When it is precipitated from a solution of a ferric salt by hydrolysis or by the addition of alkali, it soon aggregates to form a gel of variable particle-size, which is shown by X-ray examination to be really amorphous. There has been much investigation of the properties of colloidal ferric hydroxide,[185] which has been prepared in an exceptionally pure and salt-free form by such methods as the hydrolysis of the ethylate (see next section) or by the action of hydrogen peroxide on a solution of the pentacarbonyl in ether.[186]

Ferric Alkylates

Ferric ethylate $Fe(O \cdot C_2H_5)_3$ has been made in (1) by the action of sodium ethylate on anhydrous ferric chloride in absolute alcohol,[190] and (2) by treating ferric chloride with magnesium bromo-ethylate MgBrOEt, which is itself made by the action of alcohol on ethyl magnesium bromide $C_2H_5 \cdot MgBr$.[191] It forms dark brown crystals, which can be freed from enclosed salt by recrystallization from absolute alcohol.[192] It is readily soluble in alcohol (sol^y 33/20°) and monomeric in the solution by the boiling-point. It is very easily hydrolysed, giving the salt-free colloidal hydroxide.

Ferrites, $M[FeO_2]$, etc.

Ferric hydroxide $Fe(OH)_3$ is amphoteric, but it is much weaker as an acid than as a base, and while its salts with acids are only moderately hydrolysed in water, its salts with bases, the ferrites, are only stable in the presence of a considerable concentration of hydroxyl ion.

[183] R. Fricke, *Ber.* 1937, **70**, 138.
[184] R. Fricke and O. Glemser, *Z. physikal. Chem.* 1937, B **36**, 27.
[185] Abegg, B. 239–54.
[186] W. H. Albrecht and E. Wedekind, *Z. anorg. Chem.* 1931, **202**, 205.
[187] R. Fricke, F. Blaschke, and C. Schmitt, *Ber.* 1938, **71**, 1731.
[188] Id., ib. 1738.
[189] O. Kratky and H. Nowotny, *Z. Krist.* 1938, **100**, 356.
[190] P. A. Thiessen and O. Koerner, *Z. anorg. Chem.* 1929, **180**, 65.
[191] R. Sutra, *Bull. Soc.* 1930, [iv] **47**, 68.
[192] P. A. Thiessen and O. Koerner, *Z. anorg. Chem.* 1930, **191**, 74.

The alkaline ferrites $M[FeO_2]$ can be made by dissolving hydrated ferric oxide (best the γ-form)[193] by heat in a concentrated alkaline solution, when the ferrite separates on cooling, but only in small quantity owing to its slight solubility. A better method is to decompose a ferrate by boiling it with water:

$$4\,Na_2FeO_4 + 2\,H_2O = 4\,NaFeO_2 + 4\,NaOH + 3\,O_2.$$

The ferrite then crystallizes out in quantity.

The alkaline ferrites such as $KFeO_2$, which is green, and $NaFeO_2$, which appears to occur in various forms, colourless, green, and red, are decomposed by water slowly, or in presence of carbon dioxide at once. The lithium salt $Li[FeO_2]$ has a rock-salt structure.[194] Silver seems[193,195] to form not only a normal salt $AgFeO_2$ but also an acid salt $Ag_3H[FeO_2]_4$, both, curiously, with the same crystal lattice.

The ferrites of divalent metals can be made by precipitating a mixed solution of a salt of the divalent metal and a ferric salt with alkali, or by heating the divalent oxide with ferric oxide to a high temperature; thus[196] ferric oxide forms $Zn[FeO_2]_2$ with zinc oxide above $600°$, and $Ba[FeO_2]_2$ with barium carbonate at $720°$. These divalent ferrites have the spinel structure.

A variety of more complicated ferrites, with more than one Fe_2O_3 to each $M_2'O$ or (more often) $M''O$, are known, in particular a series

$$M''Fe_4O_7 = M''[FeO_2]_2, Fe_2O_3$$

which seem to have the same crystal lattice as Fe_2O_3, since they can take up as much as $6\,Fe_2O_3$ per molecule to form a solid solution, without any change occurring in the lattice.[197] Similar compounds are formed by monovalent bases, and it has been found that when these contain as much as $5\,Fe_2O_3$ mols. to one M_2O the crystal lattice is actually identical with that of α ferric oxide.[198]

Ammonia reduces ferric oxide at $420°$ to the nitride Fe_2N, and it has been shown[198] that with these higher ferrites all but one of the Fe_2O_3 groups per $2\,Na$ are reduced in the same way, the product being

$$Na_2O, Fe_2O_3 + xFe_2N.$$

Ferrosoferric Oxide, Fe_3O_4

This is the most important of the ferrites, and may be written $Fe[FeO_2]_2$. It is the only certain compound of, or intermediate between, ferrous and ferric oxide.[199] It is clearly ferrous ferrite $Fe''[Fe'''O_2]_2$ and has the spinel

[193] A. Krause and K. Pilawski, *ib.* 1931, **197**, 301.

[194] A. Hoffmann, *Naturwiss.* 1938, **26**, 431.

[195] A. Krause, Z. Ernst, S. Gawrych, and W. Kocay, *Z. anorg. Chem.* 1936, **228**, 352.

[196] J. Guillissen and P. J. van Rysselberge, *Trans. Amer. Electrochem. Soc.* 1931, **59**.

[197] S. Hilpert and A. Lindner, *Z. physikal. Chem.* 1933, B **22**, 395.

[198] R. S. Hilpert, A. Hoffmann, and F. H. Huch, *Ber.* 1939, **72**, 848.

[199] O. Baudisch and L. A. Welo, *Phil. Mag.* 1927, [7] **3**, 396.

lattice common to all the ferrites of divalent metals.[200] It can be made either from a mixture of ferric oxide with ferrous oxide or metallic iron, or by the partial oxidation of ferrous compounds, or by burning iron filings in a suitably limited supply of air. It is a black substance melting at 1,538°, insoluble in water and in acids. It is ferromagnetic: it occurs in nature as magnetic iron ore, and is the material of which lodestones are formed. It is a fairly good conductor of electricity. It also occurs in a hydrated form, which loses its water below 100°.

If it is heated in air it can be oxidized further to ferric oxide Fe_2O_3.

Ferric Sulphide, Fe_2S_3

This can be obtained as a black precipitate by the action of a sulphide on a solution of a ferric salt. It is very unstable; it is insoluble in water, but soluble in acids; it is readily oxidized in moist air to hydrated ferric oxide and free sulphur, and if heated in the absence of air it is converted into a mixture of FeS and FeS_2; Biltz and others (see ref. [46], p. 1330) have shown that this sulphide is really always metastable with respect to the $FeS+FeS_2$ mixture.

[Pyrites, FeS_2 is really a ferrous compound Fe[S—S], and as such is described above, p. 1330.]

Ferric Halides

Iron forms ferric halides with all four halogens, but their stability falls off as the atomic weight increases, owing to a growing tendency of the halogen ion to reduce the cation, until the iodide is only stable in presence of a large excess of ferrous salt. There is also a tendency with the lighter halogens to auto-complex formation, which, however, falls off rapidly as the atomic weight increases.

Ferric Fluoride, FeF_3

This can be made[201] in the anhydrous state by the action of fluorine on metallic iron or on ferrous or ferric chloride, or by heating the hydrated fluoride in a stream of hydrogen fluoride. It is greenish, and can be sublimed in hydrogen fluoride above 1,000°. It forms two pale pink hydrates, with 3 and 4·5 molecules of water.[202]

100 c.c. of water will dissolve only 0·091 g. at 25°. When heated in hydrogen it is reduced first to ferrous fluoride FeF_2 and then to the metal. If heated in air or in steam it is converted into ferric oxide.

The aqueous solution has a very small conductivity and a low depression of the freezing-point[203]; calcium salts give practically no precipitate of calcium fluoride, and potassium ferrocyanide and thiocyanate give no

[200] R. W. G. Wyckoff and E. D. Crittenden, *J.A.C.S.* 1925, **47**, 2866; the Fe‴—O distance is 1·80 and the Fe″—O distance 2·08 A.U.

[201] See O. Ruff and E. Ascher, *Z. anorg. Chem.* 1929, **183**, 193.

[202] E. Deussen, *Mon.* 1929, **138**, 75.

[203] R. Peters, *Z. physikal. Chem.* 1898, **26**, 195, 219.

reactions for iron until the solution has been acidified; moreover, the hydrolysis is very slight, in spite of the weakness of hydrogen fluoride as an acid, and on addition of potassium iodide scarcely any iodine is liberated. These facts show that ferric fluoride is not a normal ferric salt or a normal fluoride, and like the chloride it might form a complex anion $[FeF_4]^-$, giving the salt $Fe[FeF_4]_3$. This, however, would not explain the absence of the reactions for the ferric ion, which seems to indicate that the solution contains a unionized complex such as

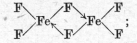

this, however, implies that fluorine is able to co-ordinate, of which there is no certain proof.

Ferric Chloride, $FeCl_3$

The anhydrous compound can be made by heating iron in dry chlorine; it forms dark red crystals with a greenish reflex, which melt at 300° and sublime at the same temperature, the boiling-point being probably about 310°; it can be purified by sublimation in a current of chlorine.[204]

In a vacuum it begins above 500° to dissociate into ferrous chloride and chlorine. Its vapour density at 400° is that of Fe_2Cl_6; at 750°, with excess of chlorine to depress decomposition, it is that of $FeCl_3$.

Ferric chloride is very soluble in water and in a variety of inorganic solvents, such as phosphorus oxychloride, phosphorus tribromide, and sulphur dioxide, but it does not dissolve in phosphorus trichloride, carbon disulphide, or stannic chloride. It is very soluble in many organic solvents: 100 g. of cold acetone will dissolve 63 g. ferric chloride, and the same weight of methyl alcohol 143. It can even be removed from water quantitatively by continuous extraction with di-isopropyl ether. This must be done in the dark, or the ferric iron is reduced to ferrous. Diethyl ether is less efficient.[205]

The selectivity of these solubilities indicates that the natural solubility is low (as the melting-point suggests), and that in many solvents the solubility is greatly promoted by solvation: indeed a series of solvates such as $FeCl_3, 2 C_2H_5OH$, and $FeCl_3, (C_2H_5)_2O$ are known. Accordingly we find that the molecular weight in donor solvents is usually that of $FeCl_3$: it has this value by the boiling-point in alcohol, ether, pyridine, and acetone, and by the freezing-point in phosphorus oxychloride; in benzophenone by the freezing-point it is about half $FeCl_3$ and half Fe_2Cl_6; in ethyl acetate it appears from the boiling-point to be wholly Fe_2Cl_6, and here its colour is very like that of the vapour, and quite unlike that of the solution in alcohol. The electrical conductivity in most of these (non-aqueous) solvents is small.

[204] O. Hönigschmid, L. Birkenbach, and R. Zeiss, *Ber.* 1923, **56**, 1473.
[205] S. E. Q. Ashley and W. M. Murray, *J. Ind. Eng. Chem. Anal. Ed.*, 1938, **10**, 367.

It is obvious that ferric chloride is in some way complex, owing, no doubt, to the instability of the shared sextet in

The suggested structure $Fe[FeCl_6]$ is negatived by the light absorption of the solution, which is quite different from that of the salts M_3FeCl_6 which undoubtedly contain this anion. In the vapour state, and in those solvents in which it is dimeric, it must have a structure

$$\underset{Cl}{\overset{Cl}{>}}Fe\underset{Cl}{\overset{Cl}{<}}Fe\underset{Cl}{\overset{Cl}{<}}$$

like that of aluminium bromide. This has been shown by electron diffraction, the Fe-Cl distance[206] being 2·17 A, theory 2·21. In this connexion it is interesting to notice that ferric chloride can be used in many Friedel-Crafts reactions in place of aluminium chloride.[207-9]

Ferric chloride is extremely hygroscopic, and very soluble in water: the cryohydric point is −55°, and the saturated solution at 20° contains 47·9 per cent. $FeCl_3$. It forms with water a series of hydrates which were examined in detail by Roozeboom[210]: it is almost unique among salts in giving four hydrates all of which have congruent melting-points: they are $Fe_2Cl_6, 12 H_2O$ (m. pt. 37°); $Fe_2Cl_6, 7 H_2O$ (32·5°); $Fe_2Cl_6, 5 H_2O$ (56°), and $Fe_2Cl_6, 4 H_2O$ (73·5°); the formula is doubled so as to make the number of water molecules integral. The solution is highly hydrolysed, according to Bjerrum[211] 47 per cent. at the ordinary temperature at $V = 160$, giving for K_h $24·8 \times 10^{-4}$ (K_h for chromic chloride $0·89 \times 10^{-4}$, for aluminium chloride $0·14 \times 10^{-4}$). The ferric hydroxide produced gradually becomes colloidal, and so the hydrolysis, the colour, and the conductivity all slowly rise.[212]

Ferric chloride is capable of forming complex ions of the type $[FeCl_4]^-$ and $[FeCl_6]^{---}$, and these (or some of them) are undoubtedly produced when hydrochloric acid is added to the solution (see later, under complexes).

Ferric Bromide, FeBr₃

Anhydrous ferric bromide can be made by heating iron or ferrous bromide with bromine to 170–200°. It is extremely soluble in water, and also in alcohol, ether, and acetic acid. It forms a hexahydrate $FeBr_3, 6 H_2O$ (like $FeCl_3, 6 H_2O$), which is dark green, melts at 27°, and is very soluble in water.

[206] O. Hassel and H. Viervol, *Tids. Kjemi, Bergwesen*, 1943, **3**, No. 8, 97.
[207] E. Wertyporoch, I. Kowaski, and A. Roeske, *Ber.* 1933, **66**, 1232.
[208] W. M. Potts and R. J. Dodson, *J.A.C.S.* 1939, **61**, 2553.
[209] D. Nightingale, R. G. Taylor, and H. W. Smelser, ib. 1941, **63**, 258.
[210] H. W. B. Roozeboom, *Z. physikal. Chem.* 1892, **10**, 477.
[211] N. Bjerrum, ib. 1907, **59**, 349.
[212] A. B. Lamb and A. G. Jaques, *J.A.C.S.* 1938, **60**, 907.

Ferric bromide is less stable than the chloride, and loses halogen more easily, as we should expect from the stronger reducing power of the bromine ion; if its aqueous solution is boiled, it breaks up into ferrous bromide and free bromine. It has the same tendency to complex formation as the chloride. The absorption spectrum of the aqueous solution indicates the presence of complexes, which seem to break down when the solution is diluted, but the addition of hydrobromic acid to the solution, while it makes the absorption more intense, does not shift its position in the spectrum as hydrochloric acid does with ferric chloride, which suggests that the bromide is already mainly in the complex form in the neutral solution.

Ferric Iodide, FeI_3

Ferric iodide cannot be isolated. It is not formed from the elements, which only give ferrous iodide, nor by dissolving ferric oxide in hydriodic acid, which reduces it to the ferrous state, a reaction which can be used in analysis. Ferric iodide can only occur, if at all, in presence of a large excess of ferrous salt.

[Ferric Carbonate

No simple carbonate can be isolated, though complexes are known.]

Ferric Salts of Organic Acids

The base being weak, all simple carboxylic salts will be too highly hydrolysed to be isolated, and so all the known ferric salts of these acids are complex.

Ferric Nitrate, $Fe(NO_3)_3$

This can be made by dissolving the metal in nitric acid; the acid must not be too weak (specific gravity not less than 1·115), or the ferrous salt is produced: it must not be too strong, or the metal becomes passive. The nitrate is not known in the anhydrous state; it forms two hydrates, with 9 and 6 H_2O. The enneahydrate $Fe(NO_3)_3, 9 H_2O$ forms pale amethyst crystals when crystallized from nitric acid, but from water it is colourless, owing to a slight inclusion of the brown hydrolytic product ferric hydroxide; for the same reason the aqueous solution is brown. The enneahydrate forms mixed crystals with $Al(NO_3)_3, 9 H_2O$[213]; it melts at 47° to a red liquid; its solubility in water is 87·3/25°. The hexahydrate has a (probably congruent) melting-point at about 35°. No definite basic nitrates have been obtained.

No complex or double ferric nitrates are known. Malquori[214] found in the 3-component systems formed by water and ferric nitrate with either nitric acid, potassium nitrate, or (?) aluminium nitrate, no sign of double or mixed crystals. In the same way Brönsted[215] in his work on hydrolysis salts showed that while the chloride forms complexes, the nitrate does not.

[213] A. I. Saslavski and J. A. Ravdin, *J. Gen. Chem. Russ.* 1939, **9**, 1473.
[214] G. Malquori, *Gaz.* 1927, **57**, 663; *Atti R.* 1927, [6] **5**, i. 801, 1000.
[215] J. N. Brönsted and K. Volqvartz, *Z. physikal. Chem.* 1928, **134**, 97.

Ferric Sulphate, $Fe_2(SO_4)_3$

Ferric sulphate can be made in solution in the usual way and forms a series of hydrates. From these by careful heating the anhydrous salt can be got as a white powder, which dissolves only slowly in water, but does so quickly in presence of a trace of ferrous sulphate (compare the behaviour of anhydrous chromic chloride). The anhydrous sulphate is dimorphic, one form being rhombic and the other rhombohedral.[216]

On heating it decomposes to give ferric oxide and sulphur trioxide.

It forms hydrates,[217] with 12, 10, 9, 7, 6, and 3 H_2O; the decahydrate and the enneahydrate are the minerals quenstedtite and coquimbrite. In solution the salt is much hydrolysed, especially on standing (owing to the separation of the colloidal ferric hydroxide).

FERRIC COMPLEXES

THE tendency to form complexes is naturally stronger with ferric than with ferrous iron.

Ferric Cyanide Complexes

These are very similar, in type and in stability, to those of ferrous iron. They consist like them of the hexacyanides, with the anion $Fe(CN)_6$, now tri- instead of tetravalent, and of the pentacyano- or prussi-compounds, in which one of these six CN groups is replaced by a molecule or radical.

The ferricyanides, the salts of the acid $H_3[Fe(CN)_6]$, are almost but not quite as stable as the ferrocyanides. They are not formed directly by the action of a cyanide on a ferric salt, but by the oxidation of the ferro-cyanides: this is effected by a variety of oxidizing agents, electrolytic oxidation, halogens, iodates, &c.; even atmospheric air will oxidize potassium ferrocyanide completely to ferricyanide in presence of decinormal acetic acid, though not in presence of alkali.

The free acid $H_3[FeCy_6]$, unlike its ferrous analogue, cannot be isolated in the pure state. If concentrated hydrochloric acid is added to the potassium salt, crystals of the impure acid will separate; many of its properties are uncertain,[218-19] but it has been shown[220] that all three dissociation constants, K_1, K_2, K_3, are those of strong acids. Like ferro-cyanic acid it forms addition compounds with numerous organic nitrogen and oxygen compounds, such as amines, aldehydes, alcohols, ethers, etc., which are no doubt ammonium and oxonium salts. No ferricyanic esters are known.

The salts are usually dark red when anhydrous, yellow or brown when hydrated, and give yellow solutions in water. The following are the degrees of hydration of some of them: Li, 4; Na, 2; K, 0; NH_4, 3; Rb, 0; Cs, 0; Mg, 7·5 and 10; Ca, 10, 12; Sr, 14; Ba, 20; Zn, Cd, Mn, Co″, Cu″,

[216] E. Posniak and H. E. Merwin, *J.A.C.S.* 1922, **44**, 1965.

[217] F. Wirth and B. Bakke, *Z. anorg. Chem.* 1914, **87**, 13.

[218] A. v. Baeyer and V. Villiger, *Ber.* 1901, **34**, 2679.

[219] W. M. Cumming and D. G. Brown, *J.S.C.I. Trans.* 1925, **44**, 110.

[220] B. V. Nekrassov and G. V. Zotov, *J. Appl. Chem. Russ.* 1941, **14**, 264.

Ni, Fe″, all 8. Though there are 4 alkaline or 2 alkaline earth cations in the molecule, the hydration is high, and the increasing values from calcium to barium (to which there is a parallel in the nitroprussides) are remarkable.

The most familiar of these salts is that of potassium, 'red prussiate of potash', which was discovered by Gmelin in 1822; it forms dark red prisms[221]; the crystal structure has been examined by Gottfried and Nagelschmidt[222]: it has the six CN groups arranged octahedrally round the iron. The potassium and caesium salts are isomorphous with the mangani-cyanide K_3MnCy_6 and the chromicyanide K_3CrCy_6.

Van Bever[223] has examined the crystal structures of a series of divalent ferricyanides $M_3''[Fe(CN)_6]_2$, $8 H_2O$ where M″ = Zn, Cd, Mn″, Co″, Cu″, Ni, and Fe″, and finds that when on further drying the water is reduced to $2 H_2O$, the intensity ratios of the X-ray lines, and the cell dimensions, do not change. It is suggested that the water is entangled in the crystals, and does not form part of the lattice.

The alkaline and alkaline earth ferricyanides are easily soluble in water (sol^y of K salt 50/25°). The silver salt is very insoluble, only 0·066 mg. dissolving in a litre at 20°. The heavy metal salts are usually insoluble. The ferrous and ferric salts have already been discussed among the ferrocyanides.

The ferricyanides are less stable than the ferrocyanides, as is shown by their being poisonous, which the ferrocyanides are not. In alkaline solution they are strong oxidizing agents; otherwise they behave chemically like the ferrocyanides. Like them, they form pentacyano-derivatives ('prussi-compounds', see next section).

Pentacyano-ferric Complexes, Prussi-compounds

The following list shows how far the ferric pentacyano-complexes differ from the ferrous. The first column gives the composition of the anion, and the other two give for the ferro- and ferri-compounds the valency of the anion (number of alkaline cations); + indicates that the compound exists.

Anion	*Ferrous*		*Ferric*	
$[FeCy_5(OH_2)]$	M_3	+	M_2	+
$[FeCy_5(NH_3)]$	M_3	+	M_2	+
$[FeCy_5(SO_3)]$	M_5	+	..	
$[FeCy_5NO_2]$	M_4	+	M_3	+
$[FeCy_5CO]$	M_3	+	..	
$[FeCy_5NO]$ Nitroprusside	M_2	+	..	
$[FeCy_5NO]$ Nitroso-	..		M_3	+

[221] For its magnetic properties see J. B. Howard, *J. Chem. Phys.* 1935, **3**, 813, and L. C. Jackson, *Proc. Phys. Soc.* 1938, **50**, 797, who measures its paramagnetism down to 14·2° K.

[222] C. Gottfried and J. G. Nagelschmidt, *Z. Krist.* 1930, **73**, 357.

[223] A. K. van Bever, *Rec. Trav.* 1938, **57**, 1259.

The correspondence is very close, except that in the ferric series there are no carbonyl compounds (the E.A.N. of the iron in the ferric series being necessarily 35 instead of 36) and no nitroprussides; the isomeric $FeCy_5NO$ ion here has a different structure, which is discussed below, and which does not appear in the ferrous series.

1. *Aquo-prussi-compounds* $M_2[FeCy_5(OH_2)]$. These can be made like the ferrous compounds by the hydrolysis of the ferricyanides under the influence of light, heat, or acids: by oxidation of the ferrocyanides: or best by the oxidation of the aquo-prusso-compounds with bromine water, nitrous acid, or permanganate and acetic acid. They form deep violet crystals, and the alkaline salts are soluble in methyl alcohol as well as in water.

2. The *ammonia-prussi-compounds* $M_2[FeCy_5(NH_3)]$ are made by oxidizing the ammonia-prusso-series with nitrous acid and acetic acid. The sodium salt $Na_2[FeCy_5(NH_3)], 2 H_2O$ is a dark yellow powder, easily soluble in water to give a brownish-red solution.[224]

3. The *nitrito-salts* $M_3[FeCy_5NO_2]$ can be made by oxidizing the nitro-prussides with alkaline permanganate at $0°$. They are dark red, and differ from the nitroprussides in being insoluble in methyl and ethyl alcohols.

4. The *nitroso-prussi-compounds.* These curious substances probably have the composition $M_3[FeCy_5NO]$: the anion is isomeric with that of the nitroprussides, but is trivalent instead of divalent. They have been assumed to be nitrosyl compounds; if so, on the nitrosyl structure we have adopted, the iron must be univalent, which is very rare, and its E.A.N. 37, which is unknown in true nitrosyls. They are more likely to be true nitroso-compounds with the grouping $Fe—N{=}O$: such a compound should exist in a dimeric colourless state and a blue or green monomeric one, and the peculiar colours which these compounds show—they are dark yellow in neutral solution, and violet in presence of acid—support this view.

They are made[225-7] by the action of nitric oxide on an aqueous solution of the aquo-prusso-compound,[225] or on an ammonia-prusso-compound.[226] Their composition is assumed to be $M_3[FeCy_5NO]$, but it is not certain. They are sharply distinguished from the nitro-prussides by their colour; they cannot be derivatives of hyponitrous acid $HON{=}NOH$ since the aquo-prusso-compound does not react with sodium hyponitrite.[227]

Ferric Thiocyanate Complexes[228]

These are all of the type $M_3[Fe(CNS)_6]$, corresponding to the ferro-cyanides and the complex ferrous thiocyanates.[229] They are made by dissolving freshly precipitated ferric hydroxide in aqueous thiocyanic acid,

[224] K. A. Hofmann, *Ann.* 1900, **312**, 1.
[225] Id., *Z. anorg. Chem.* 1896, **12**, 146.
[226] W. Manchot, E. Merry, and P. Woringer, *Ber.* 1912, **45**, 2869.
[227] L. Cambi and T. Ricci, *Atti R.* 1930, [6] **11**, i. 443.
[228] Abegg, B. 217.
[229] A. Rosenheim and R. Cohn, *Z. anorg. Chem.* 1901, **27**, 280.

adding an alkaline thiocyanate, and evaporating in a desiccator. They are bright red salts, very soluble in water, but not very stable, and considerably broken up in solution, except in presence of excess of CNS ion: from the aqueous solution ether will extract ferric thiocyanate $Fe(CNS)_3$. Transport experiments show, however, that the complex ion exists in solution. The sodium salt $Na_3[Fe(CNS)_6]$, $12 H_2O$ gives a permanganate-coloured solution in absolute alcohol, from which it can be recrystallized. Other salts are K, $4 H_2O$; NH_4, $4 H_2O$; Cs, $2 H_2O$; the last two are very hygroscopic.

Ferric Nitrogen Complexes: Ammines[230]

The affinity of ferric iron for nitrogen is very small; the ferric ammines are less stable than the ferrous, which is most unusual. The ferric complexes of organic amines, especially pyridine and quinoline, are more stable than those of ammonia, and unlike the latter are stable to water.

The simple ammines of ferric salts can be made only from the dry salts and ammonia gas; they are at once decomposed by water with the separation of ferric hydroxide. Thus the hexammine of ferric chloride $FeCl_3$, $6 NH_3$[231] has a dissociation tension of 324 mm. at $49°$ C.; the bromide $FeBr_3$, $6 NH_3$[232] is less stable, 661 mm. at $49°$; the sulphate is also known.[233]

A series of urea derivatives of the type $[Fe(CO(NH_2)_2)_6]X_3$[233] are known, but these are perhaps co-ordinated through oxygen and not through nitrogen.

Numerous complexes with pyridine and quinoline[234-9] and with antipyrine[236,239-40] have been prepared, but little is known of their constitution; they are mostly dark red or brown substances, which are more stable than the simple ammines, and can be prepared in water.

There are also several chelate nitrogen complexes, for example, with dipyridyl and o-phenanthroline.[241-2]

Ferric Oxygen Complexes

Ferric iron has a great affinity for oxygen, and hence a strong tendency to react with alcoholic hydroxyl groups to form compounds which are especially stable when they contain chelate rings, but also occur when they

[230] See Abegg, *Eisen*, 1930, B. 390–4.
[231] W. Biltz and E. Birk, *Z. anorg. Chem.* 1923, **134**, 125.
[232] F. Ephraim and S. Millmann, *Ber.* 1917, **50**, 529.
[233] F. Ephraim, ib. 1926, **59**, 1219.
[234] G. A. Barbieri and G. Pampanini, *Atti R.* 1910, [5] **19**, 591.
[235] G. A. Barbieri, ib. 1913, [5] **22**, i. 867.
[236] F. Calzolari, *Boll. Chim. Farm.* 1911, **50**, 763.
[237] G. Spacu, *Ann. Sci. Univ. Jassy*, 1914–16.
[238] R. F. Weinland and A. Kissling, *Z. anorg. Chem.* 1922, **120**, 209.
[239] R. F. Weinland and O. Schmid, *Arch. Phar.* 1923, **261**, 4.
[240] G. Spacu, *Bul. Soc. Stiinte Cluj*, 1927, **3**, 285.
[241] F. Blau, *Mon.* 1898, **107**, 767.
[242] A. Gaines, L. P. Hammett, and G. H. Walden, *J.A.C.S.* 1936, **58**, 1669.

do not (as with phenols); in the same way ferric chloride forms addition compounds with alcohols and ethers. The colour reactions of ferric chloride with phenols, aromatic amines, diketones, etc., have long been familiar, and were of great service in the discovery by Wilhelm Wislicenus and others of the cause of the tautomerism of keto-enols. These coloured substances are ferric substitution and not oxidation products of the organic oxy-compounds[243]; Hantzsch and Desch[244] pointed out that the products cannot be ferric salts. Acetylacetone, for example, has a dissociation constant of only $4 \cdot 7 \times 10^{-6}$,[245] and yet it can set free a considerable amount of hydrochloric acid from a solution of ferric chloride, forming FeA_3 (HA = acetylacetone) which is practically a non-electrolyte in water. Similarly a considerable amount of hydrochloric acid is needed to destroy the colour of a solution of one of these ferric compounds.

The great majority of these organic ferric compounds are chelate, which is always a source of stability; they include derivatives of β-diketones, and of compounds like salicylic acid, with three chelate groups in the molecule, as well as 'ato' compounds.

Ferric acetylacetonate can be made[244] by the action of acetylacetone on

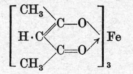

an aqueous solution of ferric chloride and sodium acetate, or on an alcoholic solution of ferric ethylate. It crystallizes from alcohol or ether in garnet-red prisms, melting at 179°. It is readily soluble in alcohol, ether, chloroform, and benzene, but less so in water; its aqueous solution has practically no electric conductivity, and is completely decomposed on boiling or on treatment with alkalies with separation of colloidal ferric hydroxide.

It is, however, extremely stable to acids; only a large excess of hydrochloric acid will destroy the colour of the solution, and even then only after some hours.

With phenyl hydrazine[246] the iron in this compound is reduced to the ferrous state with the loss of one diketone ring, which, however, is replaced by the co-ordination of two molecules of phenyl hydrazine:

$$Fe'''A_3 \longrightarrow A_2Fe'' \underset{NH_2 \cdot NH\Phi}{\overset{NH_2 \cdot NH\Phi}{\Big\langle}}$$

On the other hand, ferrous acetylacetonate is oxidized by air in alcohol to the ferric state,[247-8] the third valency of the iron being satisfied by an

[243] A. W. Bishop, L. Claisen, and W. Sinclair, *Ann.* 1894, **281**, 340.
[244] A. Hantzsch and C. H. Desch, ib. 1902, **323**, 1.
[245] R. v. Schilling and D. Vörlander, ib. 1899, **308**, 184.
[246] B. Emmert and O. Schneider, *Ber.* 1936, **69**, 1316.
[247] B. Emmert and E. Jacob, ib. 1934, **67**, 286.
[248] B. Emmert and W. Seebode, ib. 1938, **71**, 242.

alkoxy-group in $A_2Fe'''\cdot O\cdot Alk$. In the salicylic acid derivative Hantzsch showed that the hydrogen comes not from the acidic but from the phenolic hydroxyl, since the methyl ester forms a coloured compound with ferric iron, but the methyl ether does not. This is because the stability of the compound is due to its having a relatively unstrained 6-ring:

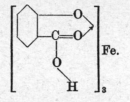

In the same way a number of derivatives of catechol

are known. They form two series of complex salts, one violet, of the type (catechol $=$ H_2cat) $M[Fe(cat)_2]$, and the other red and trichelate, $M_3[Fe(cat)_3]$.[249-50]

The tendency of ferric iron to link through oxygen is very strong; a whole series of poly-alcohols and hydroxy-acids, such as the sugars and their oxidation and reduction products, have been shown to form ferric compounds.[251]

FERRIC ATO-COMPLEXES
Carboxylato-compounds[252]

The ferric derivatives of monobasic carboxylic acids like acetic can be seen from their blood-red colour to be complex. The structure and even the composition of these complexes are uncertain; they are highly complex, usually having three iron atoms in the molecule, and they often form colloidal precipitates. These polynuclear complexes (i.e. with several iron atoms) are formed by the monobasic acids like acetic as opposed to the dibasic like oxalic, clearly because the two oxygen atoms of one carboxyl group are too near together to attach themselves to one iron atom (which would give a 4-ring), but two or more carboxyls can be joined through two ferric atoms with the production of an unstrained ring as in

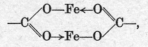

or in other ways.

The so-called simple ferric carboxylates are themselves complexes,

[249] R. Weinland and H. Seuffert, *Arch. Pharm.* 1928, **266**, 455.

[250] E. Sellés, *Anal. Fis. Quim.* 1929, **27**, 569.

[251] W. Traube, F. Kuhbier, and H. Härting, *Ber.* 1933, **66**, 1545.

[252] Abegg, B. 362–73.

which usually have an unexpected formula, and when they have not, as in the acetate of the composition $Fe(O \cdot CO \cdot CH_3)_3$ [= $FeAc_3$], the structure can be shown to be $[Fe_3Ac_6]Ac_3$, by the replacement of the ionized groups without disturbance of the complex ion.[253] It is only in the chelate form that the carboxyl group could give a stable compound with so weak a base as the ferric.

According to Weinland[254] the cations produced by the monobasic carboxylic acids are mainly of three kinds:

$$[Fe_3Ac_6]^{+++}: \quad [Fe_3Ac_6(OH)]^{++}: \quad [Fe_3Ac_6(OH)_2]^+,$$

of which the last are the most stable, several of their salts, including the acetate, having been isolated. The existence of cationic complexes of this kind has been confirmed by potentiometric measurements.[255-6]

All the other 'ato' complexes are derived from diabasic acids, where each covalency involves the replacement of a hydrogen atom, and accordingly they are anionic.

Carbonato-complexes

The red precipitate formed on adding ammonium carbonate to a ferric solution is soluble in excess of the carbonate to give a blood-red solution,[257] which must contain a fairly stable complex, since potassium ferrocyanide gives no reaction for the ferric ion; but no complex could be isolated.

Ferric Oxalato-complexes

These are numerous and stable. The tendency to form them is so great that calcium oxalate will dissolve in ferric chloride solution. Ferric oxalate itself is complex.

The complex oxalato-salts belong to two series, the dioxalato, which are greenish-yellow, and the trioxalato, which are emerald green, and much the more stable.

Ferric oxalate is difficult to prepare, owing to the tendency of the anion to reduce the cation, but it can be made[258] by dissolving ferric nitrate $Fe(NO_3)_3 \, 9 \, H_2O$ and oxalic acid in much concentrated nitric acid, and evaporating in a desiccator. It is a canary-yellow microcrystalline powder of the composition $Fe_2(C_2O_4)_3, 5 \, H_2O$. It dissolves in water only slowly, forming a yellow solution of acid reaction, which gives no test for the oxalate ion, and only a weak reaction for ferric ion with potassium iodide or thiocyanate; it has the conductivity of at least a di-ionic salt. The structure is probably $Fe[FeOx_3]$, but the weak reaction for ferric ion is remarkable.

[253] A. Krauss, *Z. anorg. Chem.* 1928, **169**, 273.
[254] R. Weinland and H. Holtmeier, ib. **173**, 49.
[255] W. Treadwell and W. Fisch, *Helv. Chim. Acta*, 1930, **13**, 1209, 1219.
[256] W. Treadwell and E. Wettstein, ib. 1935, **18**, 200.
[257] O. Hauser, *Ber.* 1905, **38**, 2707.
[258] R. Weinland and K. Rein, *Z. anorg. Chem.* 1929, **178**, 219.

Of the complex oxalates[259] the trioxalato are formed by the alkalies: their hydration is Li, 4, 5 H_2O; Na, x H_2O; K, 3; Rb, 3; NH_4, 3; Tl', 3. Some at least of the water must be attached to the oxalato group. The salts are emerald green, both in the solid state and in solution; they are sensitive to light, which reduces the ferric atom at the expense of the oxalato-group, with the production of carbon dioxide. They give the ordinary reactions for the ferric ion (the test with potassium thiocyanate only after acidification); they give a precipitate of calcium oxalate with calcium chloride. At the same time the freezing-points of the solutions show that the amount of dissociation of the complex is small. The concentration of the free oxalate ion with potassium ferrioxalate K_3FeOx_3 was found[260] to be at the ordinary temperature $12 \cdot 6 \times 10^{-4}$ at $V = 10$, and $4 \cdot 77 \times 10^{-4}$ at $V = 80$ (3·8 per cent.); it is thus a little more stable than the chromi-oxalate, for which the oxalate concentration at $V = 10$ is $23 \cdot 2 \times 10^{-4}$ but much less so than the cobaltioxalate ($1 \cdot 04 \times 10^{-4}$ at $V = 10$). The per-centage present as free oxalate ion in N/10 solution is thus Fe 1·25, Cr 2·3, Co 0·1.

The trioxalato-ion is asymmetric, and resolution into the optical anti-mers was effected for the chromioxalates by Werner,[261] and later for the cobaltioxalates[262] and the ferrioxalates.[263] The ferrioxalate racemizes the most easily of the three, in less than an hour at the ordinary temperature. The cobaltioxalate is much more stable to racemization, and the chromi-oxalate rather less so.

The dioxalato compounds[254] M[FeOx$_2$], with probably 2 H_2O in the anion, are greenish-yellow. They are difficult to crystallize: the only alkaline salt known is K[FeOx$_2$], 2·5 H_2O, but a pyridine and a quinoline salt, (pyH), 2 and 2·5 H_2O, and (quin. H), 3 H_2O, have been prepared.

There are also[259,264] a certain number of mixed oxalato-salts which are 4-covalent, containing one oxalato ring with two halogens or one sulphato group, for example, (pyH)[FeOxF$_2$].

Tartrato-complexes[265] are also known.

A number of ferric *double sulphates* are known, including the alums of K, Rb, Cs, NH_4, and methylammonium; there are also others, such as $KFe(SO_4)_2$, 4 H_2O, and $(NH_4)Fe(SO_4)_2$[266]; but there is no evidence for their complexity; the alums we know are not complex. A more probable complex is the 'acid sulphate' $FeH(SO_4)_2$, of which two hydrates, with 2 and 8 H_2O, have been isolated.[267]

[259] R. Weinland and F. W. Sierp, ib. 1921, **117**, 64.

[260] W. Thomas and R. Frazer, *J.C.S.* 1923, **123**, 2973.

[261] A. Werner, *Ber.* 1912, **45**, 3061.

[262] F. M. Jaeger and W. Thomas, *K. Akad. Wet. Amst.* 1919, **21**, 673.

[263] W. Thomas, *J.C.S.* 1921, **119**, 1140.

[264] R. Weinland and W. Hübner, *Z. anorg. Chem.* 1929, **178**, 275.

[265] Abegg, B. 385.

[266] N. Schischkin, E. A. Bachrak, A. W. Smirnowa, and T. S. Badeeva, *Z. anorg. Chem.* 1940, **245**, 226.

[267] R. Scharizer, *Z. Krist.* 1902, **35**, 345; 1921, **56**, 353.

Complex Ferric Halides

These are numerous; their stability falls off as the atomic number of the halogen increases, and there are no complex iodides.

Complex Fluorides

The large heat of reaction of ferric fluoride with hydrofluoric acid is a sign of complex formation, and the E.M.F. and freezing-points of such solutions support this conclusion.[268] There must be complex ferric anions in solution since in the electrolysis of a solution of the double salt Na_3FeF_6 the iron goes to the anode.[268]

A free complex acid has not been isolated, but many complex salts have been prepared, of the types $MFeF_4$, M_2FeF_5, and M_3FeF_6. Rémy and Busch[269] find that of the salts described up to 1933 there are 3 $MFeF_4$, 14 M_2FeF_5, and 6 M_3FeF_6. The alkaline ferrifluorides are mostly anhydrous, except those of the pentafluoro-type (Na_2FeF_5, $\frac{1}{2}H_2O$; K_2, $\frac{1}{2}$, 1; $(NH_4)_2$, 0; Tl_2, 3; Ag_2, 2 H_2O). The divalent metals cadmium, ferrous iron, cobalt, and nickel give a series of penta-salts of the type $M''[FeF_5]$, 7 H_2O, suggesting that there is one molecule of water in the anion of the pentafluoro-salts, giving the 6-covalent complex $M_2[FeF_5(OH_2)]$.

Complex Chlorides

Ferric chloride is more than 1,000 times as soluble at 25° as the fluoride (sol^y FeF_3 0·091, $FeCl_3$ 96), and this more than offsets the smaller intrinsic stability of the chlorides, making them much easier to prepare.

If hydrochloric acid is added to a solution of ferric chloride in water, the colour is first weakened by the removal of colloidal ferric hydroxide; with more acid it becomes yellow from the production of the complex chloride.[270] The phase equilibrium in the system $FeCl_3$, HCl, H_2O was worked out by Roozeboom,[271] who found the three solid ternary compounds $HFeCl_4$, 2 H_2O (m. pt. 45·7°), $HFeCl_4$, 4 H_2O (m. pt. −3°), and $HFeCl_4$, 6 H_2O (m. pt. −6°, metastable).

The colour of the aqueous solution indicates an equilibrium between the two complex acids $HFeCl_4$ and H_3FeCl_6 (or the anions). These acids (or one of them) are soluble in ether. If a solution of ferric chloride in water is shaken with ether, practically none of the salt is removed from the water, but on addition of hydrochloric acid, as soon as the acid is more than twice normal in the water, some of the iron is found in the ether; the partition ether/water reaches 140 for ethyl ether at 6·2 normal acid, and 1,440 for isopropyl ether at 8-normal acid.[272] It is evident that the hydrogen of the complex acid can be solvated both by water and by ether. The

[268] R. Peters, *Z. physikal. Chem.* 1898, **26**, 195, 219.

[269] H. Rémy and H. Busch, *Ber.* 1933, **66**, 961.

[270] See further, E. Rabinovitch and W. H. Stockmayer, *J.A.C.S.* 1942, **64**, 335.

[271] H. W. B. Roozeboom and F. A. Schreinemakers, *Z. physikal. Chem.* 1894, **15**, 588.

[272] R. W. Dodson, G. J. Forney, and E. H. Swift, *J.A.C.S.* 1936, **58**, 2573.

solvation by the ether changes the colour: the ethereal solution has quite a different absorption from the aqueous, especially in the ultra-violet, and the intensity follows Beer's law, indicating that the iron is present in the ether entirely in one form, probably as H_3FeCl_6.

A large number of complex ferrichlorides have been made, of all types from $MFeCl_4$ to M_4FeCl_7. The commonest type (as with the fluorides) is M_2FeCl_5, and as the salts of this type almost invariably have a molecule of water (K_2, Rb_2, Cs_2, $(NH_4)_2$, Be″, Mg″ all have 1 H_2O), we may suppose that this forms part of the anion. This has been proved for

$$(NH_4)_2[FeCl_5, H_2O]$$

by X-ray examination, which shows it to have octahedral anions of this composition.[273] Ferrichlorides of sodium have not been isolated,[274] presumably because they are too soluble.

If gaseous nitrosyl chloride is passed over sublimed anhydrous ferric chloride at the ordinary temperature, a dark-red liquid is produced,[275] from which, after evaporating off the excess of nitrosyl chloride, a bright-yellow powder is obtained, of the composition $FeCl_3$, NOCl. It is very hygroscopic, forming a dark-red liquid in moist air, and melts in a sealed tube at about 128°. It is obviously the salt $[NO] \cdot [FeCl_4]$. It is so readily formed that if nitrosyl chloride is added to ferrous chloride at $-20°$, there is a violent evolution of nitric oxide and the ferric compound is produced[276]:

$$FeCl_2 + 2\,NOCl = [NO] \cdot [FeCl_4] + NO.$$

The ferrichlorides of organic bases are formed with unusual ease.[277] All of them are anhydrous, and most are of the type $(BH)[FeCl_4]$. In the same way ferrichlorides, practically always of the $M[FeCl_4]$ type, are formed by a large number of oxygen bases, such as the pyrones, and are frequently used in organic chemistry for separating and identifying these bases; they are as a rule brilliantly coloured.

While with the salts of monatomic metallic cations like the alkali metals and alkaline earths the type $M_2[FeCl_5]$, or more probably $M_2[FeCl_5(OH_2)]$ is much commoner than $M[FeCl_4]$, the reverse holds good with the salts of organic bases, which are nearly all of the tetrachloride type. This is presumably on account of the much larger size of the organic cation, which only leaves room for one cation to each ferric complex.

Complex Bromides

These are evidently less stable than the chlorides: no free acids have been isolated, the number of known salts is small, and they cannot be recrystallized without decomposition.

[273] I. Lindqvist, *Arkiv. Kemi, Min., Geol.* 1947, **24**, A, No. 1.

[274] H. F. Johnstone, H. C. Weingartner, and W. E. Winsche, *J.A.C.S.* 1942, **64**, 241.

[275] H. Rheinboldt and R. Wasserfuhr, *Ber.* 1927, **60**, 732.

[276] H. Gall and H. Mengdehl, ib. 1927, **60**, 86.

[277] Abegg, *Eisen*, B. 211.

They are all green, or almost black, in colour, and are of two types, $MFeBr_4$ and M_2FeBr_5. A series of mixed chlorobromides have been made,[278] including the rubidium and caesium salts $M_2[FeCl_2Br_3(OH_2)]$ and $M_2[FeCl_3Br_2(OH_2)]$, and the organic salts $(BH)[FeClBr_3]$ and $(BH)[FeCl_3Br]$, where B = triethylamine or pyridine. The characteristically distinct types of the organic and inorganic salts are maintained here too, as is also the hydration of the pentahalides, as in the pentachlorides and pentafluorides.

No *complex iodides* have been prepared, presumably because the iodide ion reduces the ferric atom (as in cupric iodide).

Hexavalent Iron: The Ferrates

Apart from certain abnormal valencies of the iron in the carbonyl, and more especially in the nitrosyl compounds (where the valencies have rather a different meaning from what they have elsewhere), the only valency other than 2 or 3 which we find in isolable compounds of iron is 6, and that only in the ferrates.[279]

The ferrates can be made both in the wet and in the dry way. If iron filings are fused with nitre, the mixture glows, and on treatment with water gives a bright reddish-violet solution, from which barium chloride precipitates a carmine-red solid of the composition $BaFeO_4$, $2 H_2O$. The salts can also be made by oxidizing a suspension of freshly precipitated ferric hydroxide in concentrated alkali, either electrolytically, or by treatment with chlorine or bromine; but it is only if the oxidation takes place in alkaline solution that the ferrates are formed.

The potassium salt K_2FeO_4, which is deep red, is more soluble than the barium salt; it is isomorphous with the salts of the type K_2XO_4, where X = sulphur, selenium, chromium, and molybdenum but not tellurium. The structure of the FeO_4'' ion must be the same as that of the others, with the 4 oxygen atoms co-ordinated tetrahedrally to the iron which is hexavalent like the sulphur in a sulphate.

The ferrates range from violet-red to dark-red; the alkaline salts, and those of magnesium, calcium, and zinc are easily soluble in water; the strontium salt is less so, and the barium salt still less. They are insoluble in alcohol. Examples of the hydration are: Ca, 2; Sr, 2; Ba, 2; Ag_2, 0; Cu'', 1; Pb, Zn, Co, Ni all 0.

Potassium ferrate K_2FeO_4 is fairly stable if it is kept in sealed vessels. At 250° it decomposes to form a ferrite $M[Fe^{III}O_2]$ with evolution of oxygen mixed with ozone.[280] The aqueous solution of a ferrate is a stronger oxidizing agent than potassium permanganate; it will oxidize ammonia to nitrogen in the cold. If the solution is acidified, oxygen is at once evolved, and the iron passes from the hexavalent to the trivalent state:

$$4 FeO_4^{--} + 20 H^+ = 4 Fe^{+++} + 3 O_2 + 10 H_2O.$$

[278] F. Kraus and T. v. Heidlberg, *J. prakt. Chem.* 1929, [ii] **121**, 364.

[279] For possible other valencies see Abegg, B. 423.

[280] L. Moeser, *J. prakt. Chem.* 1897, [2] **56**, 425.

Iron Carbonyls[281]

As we have seen (carbonyls, IV. 547; nitrosyls, V. 685) the valencies of an element in its carbonyl and nitrosyl compounds have little relation to those which it shows in other compounds. Hence these complexes are treated separately from the rest.

Iron forms three 'pure' carbonyl compounds, $Fe(CO)_5$, $Fe_2(CO)_9$, and $Fe_3(CO)_{12}$; their compositions all follow the general rule for carbonyls (IV. 548). The second and third are made from the first.

Iron pentacarbonyl $Fe(CO)_5$ is made[282] by the action of carbon monoxide on iron powder, especially under pressure (commercially at 100–200° under 200 atm.). It commonly occurs in coal gas and is liable to cause blocks in pipes; it is sometimes used as an anti-knock in petrol, but is less effective than lead tetra-ethyl. It is a pale-yellow liquid melting at −20° and boiling at 102·7°; the Trouton constant is 23·7.[283] The structure has been determined by electron diffraction[284]; the Fe—C—O groups are linear, and the arrangement is that of a trigonal bipyramid (as usual with a shared decet, e.g. in PF_5, $MoCl_5$, etc.). It has a very low electric conductivity.[285] It is stable in air in the dark, but is decomposed by light or heat, losing carbon monoxide to form the enneacarbonyl, and ultimately going to $Fe+CO$[286]; this decomposition absorbs 54·4 k.cals./Fe.[287] In alcoholic solution it is decomposed by acids.

On exposure to light alone[283] or in acetic acid solution[288] the penta-carbonyl gives the enneacarbonyl $Fe_2(CO)_9$, which forms yellow non-volatile crystals almost insoluble in water, ether, or benzene, more soluble in alcohol and acetone. When pure it is not acted on by air. On heating it goes over to a mixture of the pentacarbonyl and the dodecacarbonyl (or trimeric tetra-carbonyl) $Fe_3(CO)_{12}$.

The structure of the enneacarbonyl was determined by X-ray analysis by Powell and Ewens[289] with unexpected results. Each iron atom carries

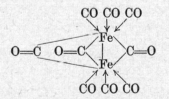

three CO groups, and in addition the two iron atoms are joined through the carbon atoms of the three remaining CO groups, which are acting more

[281] See J. S. Anderson, *Quarterly Reviews of Chem. Soc.* 1948, **1**, No. 4.

[282] L. Mond and C. Langer, *J.C.S.* 1891, **59**, 1090.

[283] J. Dewar and H. O. Jones, *Proc. Roy. Soc.* 1905, **76**, 564.

[284] R. V. G. Ewens and M. W. Lister, *Trans. Far. Soc.* 1939, **35**, 681.

[285] M. T. Harrington, *Iowa State Coll. J. Sci.* 1942, **17**, 74.

[286] D. Beischer, *Z. Elektrochem.* 1939, **45**, 310.

[287] W. A. Roth, *Angew. Chem.* 1929, **42**, 982.

[288] E. Speyer and H. Wolf, *Ber.* 1927, **60**, 1424.

[289] H. M. Powell and R. V. G. Ewens, *J.C.S.* 1939, 286.

like ketones than metallic carbonyl groups. Also, as Pauling[290] points out, the two iron atoms must be directly linked, because (1) the compound is diamagnetic, and (2) the Fe··Fe distance is that of a covalent link (found 2·46, theory Fe—Fe 2·52). This leads to the remarkable results (*a*) that the iron is 7-covalent, an exception to the rule that the maximum covalency of iron is 6; (*b*) that the iron is tetravalent, which is not found elsewhere $(26+6+3+1 = 36 = (22)\underline{14})$, and (*c*) that the E.A.N. of the iron in this compound is still 36.

The structure suggested by Jensen and Asmussen[292] requires a resonance between $\overset{+}{Fe}^{iv}\cdots\overset{-}{Fe}^{ii}$ and $\overset{-}{Fe}^{ii}\cdots\overset{+}{Fe}^{iv}$, and so should involve an intense colour, whereas the enneacarbonyl is only yellow.

Analogous structures must occur in the enneacarbonyls of ruthenium and osmium, in dimeric cobalt tetracarbonyl (p.1422), and probably also in Roussin's salts (p. 1373).

If the enneacarbonyl is heated to 60° with any of a variety of organic solvents—ether, toluene, benzene, bromobenzene—it is converted without loss of carbon monoxide into the pentacarbonyl and the *trimeric tetra-carbonyl* $Fe_3(CO)_{12}$, which is also formed by the action of alkali on the pentacarbonyl followed by oxidation with MnO_2.[291] This forms dark-green prisms and is diamagnetic.[293-4] It decomposes on heating above 100° to carbon monoxide and iron, but is volatile in steam without decomposition. It is soluble in organic solvents. Its molecular weight was found by the freezing-point in $Fe(CO)_5$ solution to be that of the triple polymer,[295] as the rule requires. Its structure is unknown.

The carbonyl groups in iron tetra- and pentacarbonyl can be partly replaced by amines to give complexes with CO:Fe ratios of 2, $2\frac{1}{2}$, and 3. Thus with pyridine alone $Fe(CO)_5$ yields $Fe_2(CO)_4py_3$, and in the presence of pyridine it gives $Fe_2(CO)_5en_2$ with ethylene diamine, $Fe(CO)_3(NH_3)_2$ with ammonia,[296] and $Fe(CO)_3phen$ with orthophenanthroline.[297]

The tetracarbonyl reacts even more readily and gives $Fe(CO)_3py$, $Fe(CO)_3en$ as well as others of greater complexity,[295] including $Fe_2(CO)_4en_3$ and $Fe_4(CO)_{12}en_3$.[298]

The structures of some of these may resemble those of the pure carbonyls, but the reactions usually throw little light on the constitution. Thus decomposition with acid frequently produces ferrous salt, iron carbonyl hydride, and other products; sometimes $Fe(CO)_5$ or $Fe_3(CO)_{12}$ is formed. The interpretation is made more difficult by the widespread

[290] *Chem. Bond*, ed. 2, p. 254.
[291] W. Hieber, *Z. anorg. Chem.* 1932, **204**, 165.
[292] K. A. Jensen and R. W. Asmussen, ib. 1944, **252**, 234.
[293] H. Freundlich and E. J. Cuy, *Ber.* 1923, **56**, 2265.
[294] H. G. Cutforth and P. W. Selwood, *J.A.C.S.* 1943, **65**, 2414.
[295] W. Hieber and E. Becker, *Ber.* 1930, **63**, 1405.
[296] W. Hieber, F. Sonnekalb, and E. Becker, ib. 973.
[297] W. Hieber and F. Mühlbauer, ib. 1932, **65**, 1082.
[298] W. Hieber and F. Leutert, ib. 1931, **64**, 2832.

occurrence of disproportionation or carbonyl exchange. The behaviour of $Fe_2(CO)_4en_3$ is of interest. It decomposes quantitatively according to the equation[298]

$$Fe_2(CO)_4en_3 + 2\,H^+ = Fe^{++} + Fe(CO)_4H_2 + 3en,$$

suggesting that the structure is $[Fe(en)_3]\cdot[Fe(CO)_4]$[299] although the salt cannot be prepared synthetically from these ions.[301]

Iron Carbonyl Hydride

When iron pentacarbonyl is treated with alkali it loses one CO and gains two hydrogen atoms[300]:

$$Fe(CO)_5 + 2\,OH^- = H_2Fe(CO)_4 + CO_3^{--}.$$

The product is a volatile unstable yellow liquid, melting at $-68°$, and forming a series of derivatives in which the hydrogen can be replaced either by halogens ($-Cl_2$, $-Br_2$, $-I_2$) or by metals, with which it forms both ionized and covalent derivatives. The hydride (and its ammonium salt) can also be made by dissolving the pentacarbonyl in concentrated ammonia. From this solution a series of salts of the ammines of divalent metals (for example $[Ni''(NH_3)_6]^{++}$) have been made[301]; they include 'acid' salts such as $[Co(NH_3)_6]\cdot[Fe(CO)_3COH]_2$. An analogous cobalt hydride $H\cdot Co(CO)_4$ is also known (p. 1422).

Electron diffraction has shown[284] that both the cobalt and the iron hydride have the four CO groups arranged tetrahedrally round the central atom as in nickel carbonyl $Ni(CO)_4$. Hence the hydrogen must be attached to the CO and not to the metal, and the structure must be $\overset{=}{A}\!-\!\overset{+}{C}\!\!=\!\!\overset{+}{O}\!-\!H$, like that of the nitrosyl group $\overset{=}{A}\!-\!\overset{+}{N}\!\!\equiv\!\!\overset{+}{O}$; NO can in fact replace COH in both compounds, giving $Fe(CO)_2(NO)_2$ and $Co(CO)_3NO$. The ion in the salts must have the grouping $[\overset{=}{A}\!-\!\overset{+}{C}\!\!\equiv\!\!O]$.

Among the metallic derivatives of iron carbonyl hydride are a series of mercuric compounds,[302-5] which are largely covalent. They are of two types $(X\cdot Hg)_2Fe(CO)_4$ and the compound $HgFe(CO)_4$. Thus mercuric chloride reacts with $Fe(CO)_5$ in acetone to give $(Cl\cdot Hg)_2Fe(CO)_4$ and carbon dioxide[303-5]; with mercury alkyls other than the methyl, $HgFe(CO)_4$ is produced, along with ketones of the alkyls.[302] Compounds of the first type are often salts, and some, such as $[SO_4]Hg_2Fe(CO)_4$, are fairly soluble in water. $HgFe(CO)_4$ is a dark-yellow solid, practically insoluble in all solvents. It is obvious from the structure of $Fe(CO)_2(COH)_2$ that though it can form salts, it cannot, for steric reasons, have the two hydrogens

[299] F. Feigl and P. Krumholz, *Z. anorg. Chem.* 1933, **215**, 242.

[300] W. Hieber and F. Leutert, *Naturwiss.* 1931, **19**, 360.

[301] W. Hieber and E. Fack, *Z. anorg. Chem.* 1938, **236**, 83.

[302] F. Hein and H. Pobloth, ib. 1941, **248**, 84.

[303] H. Hock and H. Stuhlmann, *Ber.* 1928, **61**, 2097.

[304] Id., ib. 1929, **62**, 431. [305] Id., ib. 2690.

replaced by a single mercury atom. The carbonyls must be covalently linked through the mercury atoms to large molecules; hence the infusibility and insolubility of the products: this also explains why Hieber found[307] these metallic derivatives to be commoner with $Co(CO)_3COH$ than with $Fe(CO)_2(COH)_2$. On the other hand, no such polymerization is necessary with the compound $(CH_3 \cdot Hg)_2Fe(CO)_4$—really

$$
\begin{array}{l}
CH_3 \cdot Hg\text{---}O\!\!=\!\!C \diagdown \qquad \diagup C\!\!\equiv\!\!O \\
\qquad\qquad\qquad\quad Fe \\
CH_3 \cdot Hg\text{---}O\!\!=\!\!C \diagup \qquad \diagdown C\!\!\equiv\!\!O
\end{array}
$$

which melts at 101° and is soluble in organic solvents though not in water.[306]

More complicated derivatives, whose structures are uncertain, have also been described.[303,305]

Iron Carbonyl Halides

A series of these is known, with compositions $Fe(CO)_2X_2$, $Fe(CO)_4X_2$, and $Fe(CO)_5X_2$; the structures of the first and last of these are obscure, but the second no doubt is $(OC\!\!\rightarrow\!)_4Fe\!\!\diagup^{X}_{\diagdown X}$, with the E.A.N. 36, and divalent iron. They can be made[308] by the action of the halogen on $HgFe(CO)_4$, or on $Fe(CO)_5$ the first product then being[310] $Fe(CO)_5X_2$. The iodide can also be made[309] by passing carbon monoxide at 110 atm. for 10 hours into cold FeI_2. They are yellow or brown powders, which are monomeric in ethylene dibromide and in nitrobenzene. The stability increases markedly from the chloride to the iodide; the chloride loses carbon monoxide slowly even at $+10°$.[308] The ease of formation increases in the same order,[312-13] and so do the volatility and solubility.[311]

Another series of iron carbonyl derivatives are the prusso-compounds $M_3[Fe(CN)_5CO]$, very stable salts of which the free acid has been prepared (p. 1343), the iron here is divalent, and its E.A.N. 36.

Iron Nitrosyls

A pure nitrosyl derivative is iron tetranitrosyl $Fe(NO)_4$.[314-15] This is made by letting nitric oxide act on iron pentacarbonyl under pressure, at temperatures not above 45°. It forms black crystals, which have no appreciable vapour pressure at 0°, and slowly decompose above that temperature. It is very reactive, and can be converted into a series of nitrosyl

[306] F. Hein and E. Heuser, *Z. anorg. Chem.* 1942, **249**, 293.

[307] W. Hieber and U. Teller, ib. 58.

[308] W. Hieber and G. Bader, *Ber.* 1928, **61**, 1720.

[309] W. Hieber and H. Lagally, *Z. anorg. Chem.* 1940, **245**, 295.

[310] W. Hieber and A. Wirsching, ib. 35.

[311] W. Hieber and H. Lagally, ib. 305.

[312] W. Hieber, H. Behrens, and U. Teller, ib. 1942, **249**, 26.

[313] W. Hieber and U. Teller, ib. 58.

[314] W. Manchot and H. Gall, *Ann.* 1929, **470**, 271.

[315] W. Manchot and E. Enk, ib. 275.

compounds of such compositions as $Fe(NO)$, $Fe(NO)_2$, and perhaps $(NH_4)[Fe(NO)_3]$. It may be supposed to be a nitrosyl salt $[NO]^+[Fe(NO)_3]$; if so, the iron has the required E.A.N. of $26+9+1 = 36$. This would also account for the salt $NH_4[Fe(NO)_3]$.

The mixed carbonyl-nitrosyl $Fe(CO)_2(NO)_2$ can be made by the action of nitric oxide on $Fe_2(CO)_9$[316] or better $Fe_3(CO)_{12}$[317] at 85° (it does not act on $Fe(CO)_5$ any more than on nickel tetracarbonyl or chromium, molybdenum or tungsten hexacarbonyls). It forms deep-red crystals, m. pt. $+18°$, b. pt. 110°, Trouton constant 24·0.[317] Electron diffraction[318] shows the molecule to be tetrahedral, like $Ni(CO)_4$; for distances see under cobalt, p. 1424. $Fe(CO)_2(NO)_2$ is soluble in organic solvents but not in water; it is quickly oxidized by air. On treatment with amines like pyridine and phenanthroline (phthr) or with iodine, the CO groups are displaced, but not the NO (which would disturb the E.A.N.), giving $Fe(NO)_2$ (phthr) and $Fe(NO)_2I$.[319]

Iron nitrosyl halides are also known. Ferrous halides (like the other divalent halides of the iron group[320]) take up nitric oxide, ferrous iodide the most readily, reacting in the cold with evolution of heat and losing iodine, to form $Fe(NO)_2I$; the bromide reacts in the same way on warming, the chloride scarcely at all. The products are blackish-brown, very sensitive to air and water, and sublime on heating.[321] Their structure is discussed under cobalt (p. 1425); it is presumably

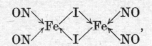

and if so the E.A.N. of the iron is 35, and the valency 1; if, however, there is a direct link between the iron atoms (as in $Fe_2(CO)_9$), the E.A.N. is 36 as we should expect, and the valency 0.

A new type of halide $Fe(NO)_3Cl$ was made[322] from ferrous chloride and nitric oxide. It is very unstable and evolves nitric oxide at once; it is also very volatile (it should be monomeric, as the E.A.N. of the iron is 36; valency 2).

By the action of nitric oxide on ferrous salts in the presence of sulphides the curious Roussin's Black Salt $M[Fe_4(NO)_7S_3]$ is produced, which is converted by alkalies into the less stable Red Salt $M_2[Fe_2(NO)_4S_2]$[326] Esters of

[316] R. L. Mond and A. E. Wallis, *J.C.S.* 1922, **121**, 32.

[317] J. S. Anderson, *Z. anorg. Chem.* 1932, **208**, 238.

[318] L. O. Brockway and J. S. Anderson, *Trans. Far. Soc.* 1937, **33**, 1233.

[319] W. Hieber and J. S. Anderson, *Z. anorg. Chem.* 1933, **211**, 132.

[320] W. Hieber and R. Marin, ib. 1939, **240**, 242.

[321] W. Manchot and H. Fischer, vide H. Fischer, Diss. Munich Techn. Hochschule, 1937.

[322] W. Hieber and R. Nast, *Z. anorg. Chem.* 1940, **244**, 23.

[323] W. Manchot, ib. 1924, **140**, 22.

[324] W. Manchot and E. Linckh, ib. 41.

[325] W. Manchot and F. Huttner, *Ann.* 1910, **372**, 172.

[326] Gmelin, *Eisen*, B, pp. 471–7.

the red salt are formed if thiols (mercaptans) are used instead of sulphides.[327-8] A corresponding thiosulphate is also known.[329]

These compounds may be formulated similarly to the enneacarbonyls.[330] The red salt and its derivatives are all of the type $Fe(NO)_2X$, where X may be —S[K] (the red salt), —Cl, —I,[319] —S·C_2H_5, —S·C_6H_5, or —S·$SO_3[K]$ (the thiosulphate). Of these, the chloride and the ethyl and phenyl esters have been shown to be dimeric; the red salt itself[331] and the thiosulphate[332] are diamagnetic; so that we may assume that they are all dimeric and diamagnetic. They presumably all have the structure

$$(ON)_2Fe \underset{X}{\overset{X}{\rightleftarrows}} Fe(NO)_2$$

in which each NO group contributes as usual three electrons to the metallic atom. In addition each iron atom gains three electrons from the bridging groups and one from the Fe—Fe link, giving it the effective atomic number of $26+2\times3+3+1 = 36$. The more complicated black salt can be explained on similar lines.

Other ferrous salts, especially the sulphate, absorb nitric oxide to give the familiar dark solution. With the sulphate 1 mol. of NO is taken up for every Fe.[323-4] A rather unstable red crystalline compound of the composition $FeSO_4$, NO has been isolated from the solution.[325]

The nitroprussides, with the formula $M_2[Fe(CN)_5NO]$, have already been discussed (p. 1343).

Valencies of Iron in Carbonyls and Nitrosyls

The following are the technical valencies of the iron in some of its best known carbonyl and nitrosyl derivatives:

Carbonyls: Val. 0:$Fe(CO)_5$.

2:$Fe(CO)_2(COH)_2$:$Fe(CO)_4(hal)_2$:$M_3[Fe(CN)_5CO]$.

4:$Fe_2(CO)_9$.

Nitrosyls: Val. 1:$Fe_2(NO)_4I_2$.

2:$Fe(CO)_2(NO)_2$:$Fe(NO)_3Cl$:$M_2[Fe(CN)_5NO]$.

4: ? [NO]·[$Fe(NO)_3$].

[327] K. A. Hofmann and O. F. Wiede, *Z. anorg. Chem.* 1895, **9**, 301.
[328] W. Manchot and H. Gall, *Ber.* 1927, **60**, 2318.
[329] W. Manchot and S. Davidson, ib. 1929, **62**, 681.
[330] R. V. G. Ewens, *Nature*, 1948, **161**, 530.
[331] L. Cambi and L. Szego, *Atti R.* 1931, vi. **13**, 168.
[332] D. M. Bose, *Z. Phys.* 1930, **65**, 677.

COBALT

In practically all its compounds cobalt has a valency of either 2 or 3, the divalent being the more stable form in the simple salts and the trivalent in the complexes; this is a common phenomenon, but it is seldom so marked as it is with cobalt, where the simple trivalent ion will decompose water with evolution of oxygen, and some of the divalent complexes will do the same with evolution of hydrogen.

The cobaltous salts are derived from a strong base, and so are little hydrolysed. They are remarkable for their brilliant colours, being in solution often pink when cold or dilute, and blue when hot or concentrated. The causes of these colour changes are still obscure (see later, p. 1390).

The cobaltous ion can form complexes, but not very stable ones. The cobaltic complexes, on the other hand, are very numerous and stable, particularly the ammines, and the great majority of cobaltic salts are known only in the complex form; the simple cobaltic ion (standing between the stable ferric and the non-existent trivalent nickel ions) is so unstable that it nearly always oxidizes its surroundings.

Cobalt is the least abundant of the three metals of the triad, being rather less than half as common as nickel. In minerals it usually occurs along with nickel, often as arsenide; its chief source is in Ontario, on Lake Temiskaming; the next most abundant source is at Katanga in the Belgian Congo.

Metallic Cobalt

Cobalt is a very hard metal (harder than steel), and resembles iron closely; it has a now familiar bluish-white tinge. Its physical properties are given on p. 1317; the density is $8\cdot8$. It is ferromagnetic up to above $1{,}000°$, coming between iron and nickel.

When the oxide CoO is reduced by hydrogen below a red heat it gives a pyrophoric powder, which catches fire in air, but is not attacked by water; in the compact form the metal is very resistant. It is less readily attacked by dilute mineral acids than iron, as we should expect since the normal potential to the hydrogen electrode is $-0\cdot26$ volt, while that of iron in contact with a ferrous solution is $0\cdot44$ volt.

The blue pigment smalt is made by fusing the oxide with sand and potash, and is a double silicate of potassium and cobalt.

Cobalt and Hydrogen[333]

The absorption of hydrogen by metallic cobalt is small; it scarcely begins below $700°$, and the amount absorbed varies greatly with the temperature of reduction, and the impurities.

When the product of the action of cobaltous chloride on phenyl magnesium bromide is treated with hydrogen in the complete absence of air and water, a brown powder is obtained of the composition CoH_2.[334] Similar compounds FeH_2 and FeH_6 (p. 1325), NiH_2 (p. 1428), and (?) CrH_3

[333] Gmelin, *Kobalt*, A. 221 (1932).
[334] T. Weichselfelder and B. Thiede, *Ann.* 1926, **447**, 64.

(VI. 1001) were prepared in the same way. The preparation of this cobalt hydride was repeated by Hieber *et al.*[335]; the hydride separated as a black powder very sensitive to air and moisture. On exposure for 24 hours at 180° to a pressure of 240 atm. of carbon monoxide this gave a considerable yield of the hydride $Co(CO)_3COH$—a larger yield than cobalt powder under the same conditions.

This CoH_2 seems to belong to the same class of compounds as copper hydride (I. 111).

Cobalt and Carbon[336]

Above 1,300° carbon dissolves in cobalt, much as it does in iron. The carbides Co_3C, Co_2C, and CoC_2 have been described, of which the first two seem to be fairly definite. Their structures are unknown.

Cobalt and Nitrogen

Apart from cobaltous azide $Co(N_3)_2$ and one or two double azides, no definite nitride of cobalt seems to be known.

Cobalt and Phosphorus

Examination of the system Co—P showed[337] the compounds Co_2P, CoP, and CoP_3 to be formed.

MONOVALENT COBALT

Apart from the nitrosyls and $Co(CO)_3COH$, no compound of monovalent cobalt seems to have been isolated; the supposed Co_2O has been shown[338-9] to be a mixture of the metal and the oxide CoO. They may, however, occur in solution. Treadwell[340] claims to have reduced cyanide complexes of Co″ electrolytically in presence of KCN; electrometric titration of the product with $K_3Fe(CN)_6$ showed the presence of 95–97 per cent. of monovalent cobalt (similar Fe′ and Ni′ compounds were described).

DIVALENT COBALT

The cobaltous salts are derived from the strong base $Co(OH)_2$; they are numerous, stable, and all strong electrolytes. The ion has a relatively small tendency to form complexes; it is usually pink in the more, and blue in the less, hydrated state (see p. 1390).

Cobaltous Oxide, CoO

Cobaltous oxide can be made by heating the metal in air, or by heating the hydroxide or carbonate. It is also formed reversibly when the metal is heated in steam[341]:

$$Co + H_2O = CoO + H_2.$$

[335] W. Hieber, H. Schulten, and R. Marin, *Z. anorg. Chem.* 1939, **240**, 272.
[336] Gmelin, A. 345.
[337] W. Biltz and M. Heimbrecht, *Z. anorg. Chem.* 1939, **241**, 349.
[338] L. Wöhler and O. Balz, *Z. Elektrochem.* 1921, **27**, 413.
[339] G. Natta and M. Strada, *Gaz.* 1928, **58**, 433.
[340] W. D. Treadwell and D. Huber, *Helv. Chim. Acta*, 1943, **26**, 10.
[341] P. H. Emmett and J. F. Shultz, *J.A.C.S.* 1929, **51**, 3251.

The ratio H_2O/H_2 in the gas assumes a constant value, which has been shown to be 67 at 450° and 50·5 at 470°.

The most reactive form of cobaltous oxide is made by[342] heating the carbonate *in vacuo* at 350°: it then forms a very fine powder.

As ordinarily made cobaltous oxide is an olive-green powder. It has a sodium chloride lattice, and so is presumably ionic in the crystal. It melts at 1,935°[343]; on further heating it begins to lose oxygen at 2,800°: at about 3,150° the dissociation tension is 1 atm.[344] On the other hand, it is able to take up more oxygen. In the finely divided form made from the carbonate it can absorb oxygen even at 18°[342] up to a composition of Co_3O_4 and beyond, but the X-ray pattern is not thereby altered, showing that the oxygen is only superficially adsorbed. When this oxygenated material is heated, the lattice changes over to that of Co_3O_4, as is shown by the X-ray pattern. This again adds on oxygen up to a composition of Co_2O_3 and beyond, but now no further lattice change occurs on heating: it seems that cobaltic oxide Co_2O_3 does not exist[342] and that the only anhydrous oxides of cobalt that can exist are CoO and Co_3O_4 (see p. 1393).

Cobaltous Hydroxide, $Co(OH)_2$

This compound can be precipitated in a more or less hydrated form by adding alkali to the solution of a cobaltous salt. It is remarkable for occurring in two forms, one blue and the other pink.[345] The blue form, which is the less stable, is got by adding the alkali slowly to the cobaltous solution at 0°. On standing or warming it changes over to the pink, which can also be obtained directly if the cobaltous solution is added to the alkali. If air is bubbled through a suspension of blue $Co(OH)_2$ in water, some of this is oxidized to $CoO \cdot OH$, while some goes to the pink $Co(OH)_2$. A mixed hydroxide of the composition 4 $Co(OH)_2$, $CoO \cdot OH$ (green) is first formed, and this is then oxidized to $CoO \cdot OH$.[346] On drying, each form without change of colour gives a compound of the composition CoO, H_2O, or $Co(OH)_2$; these forms are practically identical both in their dissociation tensions and in their X-ray patterns, so that the difference in colour can only be ascribed to a difference in particle-size, which is smaller for the blue form. The X-ray diagram is quite different from that of CoO, and shows the lattice of the hydroxide to be that of brucite $Mg(OH)_2$.

Like ferrous hydroxide, though less readily, cobaltous hydroxide is oxidized by air to a hydrated form of cobaltic oxide Co_2O_3, H_2O; this is more rapidly produced by strong oxidizing agents such as sodium hypochlorite, bromine, or hydrogen peroxide, which will carry the oxidation farther to give the hydrated dioxide CoO_2, aq.

Cobaltous hydroxide has some amphoteric character, and will dissolve

[342] M. le Blanc and E. Möbius, *Z. physikal. Chem.* 1929, **142**, 151.
[343] H. v. Wartenberg and W. Gurr, *Z. anorg. Chem.* 1931, **196**, 377.
[344] W. Biltz, *Z. physikal. Chem.* 1909, **67**, 571.
[345] G. F. Hüttig and R. Kassler, *Z. anorg. Chem.* 1930, **187**, 17.
[346] W. Feitknecht and W. Bedert, *Helv. Chim. Acta*, 1941, **24**, 676.

in excess of alkali, especially on warming, to give a deep-blue solution, which must almost certainly contain a cobaltous salt M_2CoO_2, though nothing can be isolated from the solution but $Co(OH)_2$. See reference [347].

Cobaltous Sulphide, CoS

Anhydrous cobaltous sulphide is a reddish solid melting above 1,100°. When a cobaltous solution is treated with sodium sulphide it is formed as a black precipitate, which is insoluble in water, but when freshly precipitated dissolves in acids; on standing it changes over into an insoluble form.

Two other sulphides also exist, probably both cobaltous. CoS_2 has been shown to have a pyrites structure.[348] In Co_3S_4 each cobalt atom is linked tetrahedrally to 4 sulphur atoms at 2·19 A[349] (theory for Co—S 2·29). At about 680° it breaks up into 2 $CoS + CoS_2$.[350]

Cobalt and Selenium

X-ray powder photographs show[351] that in $CoSe_2$ the interatomic distances are Co—Se 2·43 (theory Co—Se 2·42) and Se—Se 2·49 (theory 2·34); so this must be a pyrites structure, like that of CoS_2.

Cobaltous Halides

Cobaltous salts of all four halogens are known; these salts form a certain number of not very stable complexes, which are described later.

Cobaltous Fluoride CoF_2

Fluorine acts on metallic cobalt to give a mixture of cobaltous and cobaltic fluorides CoF_2 and CoF_3.[352] The difluoride can also be made by the action of hydrogen fluoride gas on cobaltous chloride at the ordinary temperature, or by dehydrating the tetrahydrate, which is formed by dissolving the hydroxide in hydrofluoric acid.

Anhydrous cobaltous fluoride is a pink crystalline solid with a rutile lattice. The anhydrous compound will not react at all with ammonia,[353-4] apparently because the lattice is too compact (GaF_3 and InF_3 behave in the same way). But ammines can be made from the hydrate: they contain a molecule of water, and have the composition CoF_2, $H_2O + 5$, 1, and $\frac{1}{2}NH_3$.

Cobaltous fluoride is only moderately soluble in water (sol^y 1·42/25°).[355] It forms two tetrahydrates and is said also to give a di- and a trihydrate.

[347] Gmelin, A. 408.
[348] W. F. de Jong and H. W. V. Willems, *Z. anorg. Chem.* 1927, **160**, 185.
[349] D. Lundqvist and A. Westgren, ib. 1938, **239**, 85.
[350] M. Heimbrecht and W. Biltz, ib. 1939, **242**, 229.
[351] B. Lewis and N. Elliott, *J.A.C.S.* 1940, **62**, 3180.
[352] O. Ruff and E. Ascher, *Z. anorg. Chem.* 1929, **183**, 194.
[353] E. Birk and W. Biltz, ib. 1926, **153**, 122.
[354] W. Biltz and E. Rahlfs, ib. 1927, **166**, 351.
[355] R. H. Carter, *J. Ind. Eng. Chem.* 1928, **20**, 1195.

It is stable to water at the ordinary temperature, but at a red heat it reacts with it to form cobaltous oxide and hydrogen fluoride.

Cobaltous Chloride, $CoCl_2$

The anhydrous salt can be made from the elements, or by the dehydration of the hydrate. It is a pale-blue solid, which has the same crystal lattice as magnesium chloride[356]—a typical ionic lattice with 6 chlorines at the points of a regular octahedron round each cobalt. It melts at 735°[357] ($MgCl_2$ at 718°), and boils at 1,049°. It forms a series of hydrates with water of which the best known (with their transition points) are

$$6\,H_2O \xrightarrow[52\cdot25°]{} 2\,H_2O \xrightarrow[90°]{} 1\,H_2O.$$

Hydrates with 1·5 and with 4 H_2O are also described. The lower hydrates are blue-violet, the tetra- and hexahydrate pink, the last going blue on gentle warming.

The salt is readily soluble in water (sol^y 34·4/25°). It is also very soluble in alcohol (56·2/20°), acetone (8·62/25°), methyl acetate (0·37/18°), acetonitrile (4·08/18°), pyridine (0·58/25°), etc. (values from Seidell). The aqueous solution is pink, but it goes blue on warming, or on addition of hydrochloric or sulphuric acid, or of soluble chlorides. (For further discussion of these colour changes see below, p. 1390).

Cobaltous chloride has been used as a 'sympathetic ink': on pink paper the writing is invisible when cold, but turns blue on warming.

Cobaltous Bromide, $CoBr_2$

This is in general similar to the chloride. The anhydrous salt is bright green, and melts at 678°. Its molecular weight by the boiling-point in pyridine and in quinoline[358] is that of $CoBr_2$, which is remarkable, as one would expect it to dissolve in these solvents as the ionized bromide of a solvated cation.

It is very soluble in water, and both the anhydrous salt and the hexahydrate are hygroscopic, forming a red liquid in moist air. The anhydrous salt being green, the dihydrate is purplish-blue, and the hexahydrate red. Solubility in water is 200/60°; it is very soluble in many organic solvents, especially in the alcohols, but it also dissolves readily in acetone (65·0/25°) and even in methyl acetate (10·3/18°).

A green basic bromide is also known, of which the crystal structure has been determined.[359]

Cobaltous Iodide, CoI_2

This compound occurs in two isomeric anhydrous forms. The ordinary α-form, made in any of the usual ways (most conveniently by heating the

[356] L. Pauling, *Proc. Nat. Acad.* 1929, **15**, 709.
[357] H. Bassett and W. L. Bedwell, *J.C.S.* 1931, 2479.
[358] E. Beckmann, *Z. anorg. Chem.* 1906, **51**, 242.
[359] W. Feitknecht and W. Lotmar, *Z. Krist.* 1935, **91**, 136.

finely divided metal got from the oxalate in a stream of hydrogen iodide at 400–450°[360]), is a black hygroscopic crystalline mass and forms the usual pink solution in water. If it is heated in a high vacuum[361] it melts undecomposed at 515–520°, begins to give off iodine at 540°, and at 570° boils with some decomposition into iodine and metallic cobalt; it sublimes mainly as the black α-form, but to a small extent (not more than 1 per cent.) condenses as an ochre-yellow β-modification, which can be freed from an admixture of free iodine by heating it *in vacuo* to 100°. This new form differs from the α-form not merely in the solid state, but also in its solution in water, which instead of being pink (like the α-) is a pale yellow, and if the remaining traces of iodine are removed by extraction with chloroform is practically colourless, and remains so for months in the cold, though it turns pink on warming. Its electrical conductivity is identical with that of the α-form; the molecular conductivity is 57 at $V = 37$, much less than that of barium iodide, but rather more than that of cadmium iodide. If the β-form is heated to 400° instead of 100° in removing iodine it turns black, but does not seem to have undergone any serious change, as it still gives a practically colourless solution in water.

The cause of this isomerism is unknown. There is, however, a similar case in mercuric iodide.

Cobaltous iodide forms a series of hydrates; perhaps $9\,H_2O: 6\,H_2O$, dark-red hygroscopic: $4\,H_2O$, separating from a hot solution, green: $2\,H_2O$, separating above 100°, also green. The concentrated aqueous solution below 20° is dark red, while above 35° it is bright green.

The salt is soluble in many organic solvents, the solutions often being blue.

Cobaltous Cyanide, $Co(CN)_2$

This occurs in the anhydrous state, and also as a trihydrate and probably a dihydrate. When an equivalent of potassium cyanide is added to a cobaltous solution, an insoluble precipitate of the trihydrate is formed, which can be dehydrated in a stream of nitrogen at 250°.[362] It then forms a blue crystalline powder which very readily takes up water. It is insoluble in water, but easily dissolves in a solution of potassium cyanide, ammonia, etc.; with potassium cyanide it forms in the cold a cobalto-cyanide K_4CoCy_6, but on warming this is oxidized by the water to the cobalticyanide K_3CoCy_6, with evolution of hydrogen.

Cobaltous Thiocyanate, $Co(CNS)_2$

This occurs with $\frac{1}{2}$, 3, and 4 molecules of water. The tetrahydrate forms deep red-violet very hygroscopic crystals, dissolving in water to form a dark-blue solution, which turns red on dilution. The change of colour seems to be due to the complex formation.[363]

[360] W. Biltz and E. Birk, *Z. anorg. Chem.* 1923, **127**, 34.

[361] E. Birk and W. Biltz, ib. 1923, **128**, 45.

[362] W. Biltz, W. Eschweiler, and A. Bodensiek, ib. 1928, **170**, 161.

[363] A. v. Kiss and P. Csokan, *Z. physikal. Chem.* 1941, **188**, 27.

The electrical conductivity is small, and indicates that $i = 2$ in 1·5 per cent. solution, and 2·5 in 0·8 per cent. solution. This suggests the formation of autocomplexes such as $[Co(OH_2)_5CNS]CNS$.[364]

Cobaltous thiocyanate is soluble in many organic solvents, these solutions being always dark blue, whatever the temperature or concentration.

Cobaltous Carbonate, $CoCO_3$

This is found almost pure in the mineral cobalt spar, and also often in isomorphous mixtures with magnesium and ferrous carbonates.

The precipitate formed when an alkaline carbonate is added to a cobaltous solution is ordinarily a basic carbonate, owing to hydrolysis; but in presence of an atmosphere pressure of carbon dioxide the neutral carbonate is precipitated as the violet-red hexahydrate $CoCO_3$, $6 H_2O$. If this is heated in a sealed tube at 140° it is converted into the anhydrous carbonate, a pale red powder. The precipitated hydrated carbonate tends[342] (like cobaltous oxide) to be oxidized by air, and is pure only if it is precipitated in an oxygen-free atmosphere. At 350° in a high vacuum cobaltous carbonate is completely converted into cobaltous oxide.

The solubility of the carbonate in water is small, 2·73 mg./15°.

Cobaltous Formate, $Co(O \cdot CHO)_2$

The dihydrate is a pink salt which can be dehydrated at 140°[365]; sol^y in water 4·06/20°.[366] The solution is pink.

Cobaltous Acetate, $Co(O \cdot CO \cdot CH_3)_2$

The anhydrous salt is pink[365]; the tetrahydrate is deep red, and is isomorphous with the acetates of magnesium, manganese, nickel, and zinc. It is easily soluble in water, giving a red solution; sol^y in glacial acetic acid 16·8/25°.

Cobaltous Oxalate, $Co[C_2O_4]_2$

The ordinary form is the dihydrate, which is pink; a yellowish-pink tetrahydrate also occurs, and the anhydrous salt can be made. Cobaltous oxalate is almost insoluble in water (2·1 mg./18°); this is perhaps a sign that it is not complex. It is readily soluble in strong ammonia solution, or in ammonium carbonate, with the formation of complexes.

Cobaltous Nitrate, $Co[NO_3]_2$

At low temperatures this salt forms an enneahydrate ($+9 H_2O$), going over at 21° to the ordinary hexahydrate, red hygroscopic crystals; this changes at 55·5° into a trihydrate which melts at 91° and decomposes at higher temperatures[367]; the hexahydrate forms mixed crystals with the corresponding nickel salt. Sol^y in water 103/25°.

[364] A. Hantzsch and F. Schlegel, *Z. anorg. Chem.* 1927, **159**, 295.
[365] F. Ephraim and E. Rosenberg, *Ber.* 1918, **51**, 134.
[366] W. Lossen and G. Voss, *Ann.* 1891, **266**, 45.
[367] R. Funk, *Ber.* 1899, **32**, 96; *Z. anorg. Chem.* 1899, **20**, 408.

The aqueous solution is always pink, and has no tendency to turn blue, which is taken to show that the nitrate forms no complexes; true complex nitrates are very rare. Copper nitrate behaves in the same way.[368]

Cobaltous nitrate is easily soluble in many organic solvents such as alcohols, acetone, and methyl acetate; sol^y in the last $16·4/15°$.

[*Cobaltous Nitrite*

This can be made in solution, but it has never been isolated, although complex cobalto-nitrites are known.]

Cobaltous Sulphate, $Co[SO_4]$

The heptahydrate, which occurs as the mineral bieberite, is carmine, and is isomorphous with $FeSO_4, 7 H_2O$; it is in fact a vitriol. At $41·5°$ it goes over to the hexahydrate, and at $71°$ this changes to the monohydrate, which is isomorphous with kieserite, $MgSO_4, H_2O$.[369] All these three hydrates are monoclinic. Tetra- and dihydrates have been described, but seem to be doubtful.[370] The hexa- and monohydrates are isomorphous with the corresponding nickel salts, and form mixed crystals with them.[371]

The sol^y in water is $39·3/25°$. It rises with the temperature up to about $100°$, and then falls off, as happens with many sulphates (compare Na_2SO_4), being less at $145°$ than at $15°$.

A basic sulphate $CoSO_4, 3 Co(OH)_2$ can be prepared, the lattice of which has been shown to contain alternate layers of sulphate and hydroxide ions.[372]

Cobaltous Sulphite

The pentahydrate $CoSO_3, 5 H_2O$ is a reddish salt, only slightly soluble in water. It readily forms double salts.

Cobaltous Sulphoxylate $Co[O—S—O]$

This compound,[373] which is remarkable as being the only certain salt of sulphoxylic acid, has already been described under that acid (VI. 905). It is formed along with ammonium sulphite when sodium hyposulphite $Na_2S_2O_4$ is treated with cobaltous acetate and ammonia:

$$CoS_2O_4 + 2 NH_4OH = CoSO_2 + (NH_4)SO_3 + H_2O.$$

The reaction can be represented as a hydrolysis of the free acid thus:

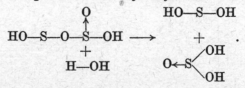

[368] N. V. Sidgwick and H. T. Tizard, *J.C.S.* 1908, **93**, 187.

[369] A. Benrath, *Z. anorg. Chem.* 1931, **202**, 168.

[370] N. Demassieux and B. Fedoroff, *C.R.* 1939, **208**, 1223.

[371] A. Benrath and W. Thiemann, *Z. anorg. Chem.* 1934, **217**, 347.

[372] W. Feitknecht and G. Fischer, *Helv. Chim. Acta*, 1935, **18**, 40.

[373] R. Scholder and G. Denk, *Z. anorg. Chem.* 1935, **222**, 17.

The salt is very unstable, and decomposes when attempts are made to convert it into the sulphoxylates of other metals.

Cobaltous Chlorate, $Co(ClO_3)_2$

This salt[374] forms three hydrates, with the following colours and transition points:

$$6 \text{ H}_2\text{O (dark red)} \xrightarrow{18\cdot6°} 4 \text{ H}_2\text{O (dark red)} \xrightarrow{62°} 2 \text{ H}_2\text{O (pale red)}.$$

It is relatively unstable; it decomposes below 100° and probably at 61°; the dihydrate is made by dehydrating the tetrahydrate over phosphorus pentoxide. It is extremely soluble in water, 180·8/21°.

Cobaltous Iodate, $Co(IO_3)_2$

This forms a metastable red tetrahydrate and a blue dihydrate which at 65° goes over into the blue anhydrous salt; the changes are very sluggish. The salt is only slightly soluble in water, 0·52/30°.

Cobaltous Perchlorate, $Co(ClO_4)_2$

The anhydrous salt cannot be prepared, but hydrates are known with 9, 7, 6, and 5 molecules of water; these are all red or dark red (the aqueous solution of cobaltic perchlorate $Co(ClO_4)_3$ is blue).

The salt is extremely soluble in water, sol^y 254·5/26°.

COMPLEX COMPOUNDS OF DIVALENT COBALT

The divalent cobalt atom has a certain tendency to form complexes, though nothing like so much as the trivalent; thus Gmelin's *Handbuch* gives to the cobaltous ammines 37 pages, and to the cobaltic 335. The difference is to be expected, but it is unusually marked with cobalt, the trivalent atom being one of the most powerful of complex builders,* along with trivalent chromium and di- and tetravalent platinum, while divalent cobalt does not stand very high in this respect among the divalent elements. Its affinity in these complexes is greatest for nitrogen and next greatest for oxygen; but complex cyanides, thiocyanates, and halides are also formed. In its divalent complexes the covalency of the cobalt is usually 4, but sometimes 6, and other values are found (in cobaltic complexes it is always 6).

Complex Cobaltous Cyanides

Cobalt, like iron, forms two series of hexacyano-complexes, in one of which it is divalent, and in the other trivalent, the formulae being M_4CoCy_6 and M_3CoCy_6. But while the latter are very stable, more so than the

---

* The element with the greatest power of complex formation is in a sense trivalent gold, since it forms no compounds which are not complex; but the range of its complexes is limited.

[374] A. Meusser, *Ber.* 1902, **35**, 1418.

corresponding compounds of trivalent chromium, manganese, iron, etc., the cobaltocyanides are very unstable,[375] not that the CN groups are loosely attached, but that the salts are very readily oxidized to cobalticyanides. The potassium salt, K_4CoCy_6, will crystallize from mixed solutions of its components at low temperatures; it is violet, and gives a deep red solution[376-7]; the sodium salt is similar. The aqueous solutions of these salts are very readily oxidized by air to the cobalticyanides, and in the absence of air they will even decompose the water with evolution of hydrogen.[378-9]

Complex Cobaltous Cyanates

A rather unstable potassium salt $K_2[Co(CNO)_4]$ has been made.[380-1]

Complex Cobaltous Thiocyanates[382]

While the complex ferrous thiocyanates (which are few) are all of the type $M_4Fe(CNS)_6$, the cobaltous thiocyanates are all of the 4-covalent form $M_2[Co(CNS)_4]$.

The salts are moderately stable, and can be recrystallized unchanged from water. The solids are blue; the aqueous solution is also blue when it is concentrated, but on dilution it turns pink; this is presumably due to a breakdown of the complex, a conclusion which is supported by the measurements of the transport numbers,[383-4] and by the fact that an alkaline hydroxide will precipitate cobaltous hydroxide from the solution.

These salts, like many simple thiocyanates, are readily soluble in organic solvents; thus the sodium salt $Na_2Co(CNS)_4$, $8 H_2O$ gives deep blue solutions of considerable concentrations in methyl, ethyl, and amyl alcohols, in acetone, and in aqueous ether[383,385]; indeed the ammonium and potassium salts can be extracted from the aqueous solution with amyl alcohol.[386-7] The salts of the alkalies, alkaline earths, and amines are mostly soluble, and contain rather large amounts of water of crystallization, perhaps on account of the large size of the anion; thus we have Na, $8 H_2O$[385]; Ba, $8 H_2O$[388]; K, $4 H_2O$[385]; NH_4, $4 H_2O$[383]

The mercuric salt $HgCo(CNS)_4$, which is anhydrous and extremely

[375] W. Biltz, W. Eschweiler, and A. Bodensiek, *Z. anorg. Chem.* 1928, **170**, 172.
[376] A. Descamps, *Bull. Soc. Chim.* 1879, [2] **31**, 52.
[377] A. Rosenheim and I. Koppel, *Z. anorg. Chem.* 1898, **17**, 67.
[378] R. Peters, *Z. physikal. Chem.* 1898, **26**, 217.
[379] W. Nernst and A. Lessing, *Gött. Nachr.* 1902, 158.
[380] J. Sand, *Ber.* 1903, **36**, 1441.
[381] R. Ripan, *Bul. Soc. Stiinte Cluj*, 1929, **4**, 146.
[382] On the very obscure question of the structure of the complex thiocyanates see J. W. Jeffery, *Nature*, 1947, **159**, 610.
[383] A. Rosenheim and R. Cohn, *Z. anorg. Chem.* 1901, **27**, 289.
[384] A. Hantzsch and Y. Shibata, ib. 1912, **73**, 317.
[385] A. de Sweemer, *Natuurwet. Tijds.* 1933, **15**, 14.
[386] A. Grossmann, *Z. anorg. Chem.* 1908, **58**, 269.
[387] F. P. Treadwell and E. Vogt, ib. 1901, **26**, 109.
[388] V. Cuvelier, *Natuurwet. Tijds.* 1933, **15**, 177.

insoluble, will detect 0·10, 0·12, and 0·58 mg. respectively of mercuric, cobaltous, and thiocyanate ions.[389]

Cobaltous Ammines[390]

The great majority of cobaltous salts will take up ammonia. If we disregard those in which the ammonia tension is very great, we find that the number of ammonia molecules taken up does not exceed 6, and often falls below it, the usual numbers being 6, 4, and 2. Substituted amines, alkylamines, and substituted alkylamines,[391-2] pyridine and quinoline, and even arylamines and oximes can replace ammonia, but usually form less stable complexes, and with lower co-ordination numbers. Certain diamines, especially ethylene diamine, form cyclic (chelate) complexes of considerable stability.

The cobaltous ammines are not in any case of great stability, often less stable than the nickelous,[393] and they are usually decomposed by water; but with the more tenacious ethylene diamine molecule this does not happen, and cobaltous hydroxide will dissolve in an aqueous solution of the diamine, no doubt to form the ion $[Co(en)_x]^{++}$, though as no compound could be isolated we do not know the value of x.[394]

The hexammines are presumably fully ionized salts of the type

$$[Co(NH_3)_6]X_2;$$

the diammines, on the other hand, appear to be non-ionized compounds of the general form

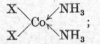

the structure of the tetrammines is not certain, and probably varies. These suggestions are supported by the behaviour of the compounds in question, and especially by their stereochemistry. The hexammines of cobaltous chloride and iodide have been shown by X-ray analysis to have the 6 NH$_3$ groups arranged round the cobalt at the points of a regular octahedron,[395] which is the arrangement to be expected for an ion $[Co(NH_3)_6]$; they are all paramagnetic.[396] The diammines, on the other hand, exhibit an isomerism (see below) which can best be explained by supposing that the four covalencies of the cobalt lie in a plane, admitting of *cis* and *trans* isomers:

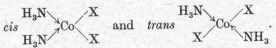

[389] S. Augusti, *Gaz.* 1934, **64**, 33. [390] Gmelin, *Kobalt*, B. 9–45 (1930).

[391] A. Tettamanzi and B. Carli, *Gaz.* 1934, **64**, 315 (N(CH$_2$·CH$_2$OH)$_3$).

[392] W. Hieber and E. Levy, *Z. anorg. Chem.* 1934, **219**, 225 (N(CH$_2$·CH$_2$OH)$_3$ and (C$_2$H$_5$)$_2$N·CH$_2$·CH$_2$OH).

[393] T. L. Davis and A. V. Logan, *J.A.C.S.* 1940, **62**, 1276.

[394] W. Traube and B. Loewe, *Ber.* 1914, **47**, 1911.

[395] P. Stoll, *Diss. Zurich*, 1926.

[396] D. P. Mellor and R. J. Goldacre, *Proc. Roy. Soc. N.S. Wales*, 1940, **73**, 233.

The idea that the hexammines are ionized completely and the diammines not at all is supported by the observation[397-8] that the order of stability in the hexammines is $Cl < Br < I$, and in the diammines $Cl > Br > I$; this would be natural if in the former the halogen atoms are ionized, while in the latter they form part of the complex.

The evidence for the planar structure of these diammines $X_2Co(NR_3)_2$[399] is much the same as that given by Werner for the platinous analogues. Many of them occur in pairs of isomers differing in colour (one blue and the other violet or pink) even in solution. They are usually monotropic, and the stable form, which may be either the blue or the violet, is obtained by any slow method of preparation, but by sudden precipitation from solution or rapid breaking down of the hexammine at a higher temperature, the metastable form is produced. In $CoCl_2py_2$ the change from one form to the other is easy[400]; both give the same colour and the same (monomeric) freezing-point depression in bromoform; in water and in methyl alcohol both give the same highly conducting solution, from which silver nitrate precipitates all the chlorine, so that in these solvents they are clearly ionized.

The observation that the solid form obtained depends on the solvent (the stable violet form separates from chloroform on slow evaporation, but the blue form is precipitated on adding ligroin) has been made with other isomers as well. It is obvious that the same solid form must be stable in contact with any solvent, and the explanation evidently is that in a particular solvent the metastable form may be present in excess, and if it is suddenly precipitated will come out as such, whereas if it is given time it will go over into the stable one. This explanation has been shown to be true in other cases.[401]

Hantzsch gives a list of these isomeric cobaltic diammines and similar compounds, with their reactive stabilities. This list, slightly enlarged, is as follows:

Compound	$CoCl_2(NH_3)_2$[a]	$CoCl_2py_2$	$CoBr_2(NH_3)_2$[a]	$CoBr_2py_2$
Blue	Stable	Metastable	Metastable	Stable
Violet	Metastable (pink)	Stable	Stable	[Not isolated]
Compound	$CoI_2(NH_3)_2$[a]	$Co(SCN)_2py_2$	$CoCl_2(H_2O)_2$[b]	$CoCl_2(CH_3OH)_2$
Blue	Stable	Only in soln.	? Unstable ?	Stable
Violet	Metastable	Stable	Stable	[Not isolated]

$a = $ [397]; $b = $ [402]

The more recent evidence that many of the later transitional elements can have this planar arrangement has greatly strengthened Hantzsch's

[397] W. Biltz and B. Fetkenheuer, *Z. anorg. Chem.* 1914, **89**, 97.

[398] F. Ephraim, *Ber.* 1915, 48, 628.

[399] A. Hantzsch, *Z. anorg. Chem.* 1927, **159**, 278.

[400] D. P. Mellor and B. S. Morris, *Proc. Roy. Soc. N.S. Wales*, 1938, **71**, 536.

[401] See, for example, the formaldehyde phenylhydrazones: N. V. Sidgwick and E. K. Ewbank, *J.C.S.* 1921, **119**, 486.

conclusion. The two forms of $CoCl_2py_2$ have recently[403] been shown to differ considerably in their magnetic moments, that of the stable violet form being 5·34, and that of the blue 4·60, at 20°. This is not easy to explain.

Nitro-complexes

These are also far less stable in the cobalto- than in the cobalti-series. A few are known,[404-5] mostly of the type $M_2Co(NO_2)_4$: they are relatively insoluble. Thus we have $K_2[Co(NO_2)_4]$, H_2O, insoluble in cold water, soluble in hot to give a pink solution; $Tl'_2[Co(NO_2)_4]$, orange crystals, slightly soluble in water, and readily oxidized to the cobaltic state.

Oxygen Complexes

The non-chelate oxygen complexes of divalent cobalt are weak. Cobaltous salts are usually hydrated, and also solvated by organic solvents such as the alcohols; the hydrates in most cases contain 6 and the alcoholates 2 or 3 molecules of solvent.

A double cobaltous *nitrate* $(pyH)_3[Co(NO_3)_5]$ has been made[407]; it is red and stable in air; there is no evidence that it is truly complex.

A double *formate* $Ba_2[Co(HCO·O)_6]$, $4H_2O$ has been described[408]; it is reddish-violet, not very soluble in water, and isomorphous with the corresponding $BaCu''$, BaNi, and BaZn salts.

'Ato' compounds—double salts of dibasic oxyacids—are numerous; they are formed by sulphates, sulphites, carbonates, oxalates, etc., as well as by β-diketones. These, being chelate, are naturally more stable, and many of them give evidence of complexity.

Carbonato-Compounds

These are made by the action of an alkaline carbonate or bicarbonate solution on a cobaltous salt[409-10]; they are all dichelate (cobalt 4-covalent). They are usually red salts with $4H_2O$. The potassium salt

$$K_2[Co(CO_3)_2], 4H_2O$$

loses all its water in a stream of carbon dioxide at 100–20°, and then turns violet.

These salts are decomposed by water, but can be recrystallized from alkaline carbonate or bicarbonate solutions; their solubility in such solutions indicates the formation of true carbonato-complexes, but they do not seem to be very stable.

[402] J. Bersch, *Ber. Wien. Akad.* 1867, **56**, ii. 724.
[403] E. D. P. Barkworth and S. Sugden, *Nature*, 1937, **139**, 374.
[404] V. Cuttica and G. Carobbi, *Gaz.* 1922, **52**, ii. 277.
[405] V. Cuttica and M. Paoletti, ib. 279.
[407] L. Pincussohn, *Z. anorg. Chem.* 1897, **14**, 390.
[408] W. Lossen and G. Voss, *Ann.* 1891, **266**, 45.
[409] M. P. Applebey and K. W. Lane, *J.C.S.* 1918, **113**, 611.
[410] F. de Carli, *Atti R.* 1929, [vi] **9**, 417.

Oxalato-complexes

Cobaltous oxalate, which is almost insoluble in water, readily dissolves in a solution of an alkaline oxalate, and double salts can be made in this way. There is thus no doubt that true complexes are formed, but transport measurements show that they are considerably broken down in solution.[411] The known salts are nearly all of the type $M_2CoOx_2, x\,H_2O$ (no Li salt; Na, $4\,H_2O$[412]; K, $6\,H_2O$[413]; NH_4, $6\,H_2O$[414]). Ephraim has obtained one salt of the 6-covalent type $(NH_4)_4CoOx_3, 6\,H_2O$. It forms pink crystals and can be recrystallized from water; the concentrated aqueous solution is dark violet.

Some obscure *double sulphites* and some *double sulphates* with no signs of complexity have been prepared.

Chelate β-diketone Compounds

Cobalt forms several types of derivatives of acetylacetone ($C_5H_8O_2 = HA$), the simple cobaltous and cobaltic compounds CoA_2 and CoA_3, and also a salt derived from the former, in which the divalent cobalt atom is able to acquire the stable trichelate grouping as a monovalent anion $M[CoA_3]$.

Cobaltous acetylacetonate $Co(C_5H_7O_2)_2$ can be made[415] by the action of the diketone on cobaltous hydroxide. It forms ruby-red crystals which sublime without melting, and give a red vapour, whose density corresponds to the simple formula. It is soluble in water and in most organic solvents. The 4-covalent cobalt atom is evidently co-ordinately unsaturated, and so ready for further co-ordination; thus it crystallizes from alcohol or acetone with one molecule of solvent of crystallization, and it forms diammines with ammonia and pyridine. The formation of the trichelate compound described in the next section is further evidence of this.

Sodium Cobaltous Acetylacetonate

If a cobaltinitrite $M_3[Co(NO_2)_6]$ is treated with sodium acetylacetonate it gives the cobaltic salt $Na[CoA_2(NO_2)_2]$, and when this is further treated with excess of sodium acetylacetonate the trivalent cobalt is reduced, and the complex cobaltous acetylacetonate $Na[Co''A_3]$ is formed. This consists of pale pink needles: it differs sharply from the simple CoA_2 in being insoluble in water and alcohol, the co-ordinately unsaturated 4-covalent atom having been converted into a saturated 6-covalent one.[416]

Other β-diketones appear to behave in the same way.

It is to be noticed that divalent atoms of the non-transitional elements like the alkaline earths (II A) and zinc cadmium and mercury (II B) do not behave in this way, in II A probably because they have less tendency

---

[411] J. Vranek, *Z. Elektrochem.* 1917, **23**, 337.

[412] J. W. Dodgson, *Proc. Chem. Soc.* 1911, **27**, 261.

[413] S. Deakin, M. Scott, and B. D. Steele, *Z. physikal. Chem.* 1909, **69**, 129.

[414] F. Ephraim, *Ber.* 1909, **42**, 3855.

[415] F. Gach, *Mon.* 1900, **21**, 106.

[416] A. Rosenheim and A. Garfunkel, *Ber.* 1911, **44**, 1873.

to covalency formation (owing to the large size and inert gas number of the cation) and in II B because for some reason these elements have a very slight tendency to increase the covalency from 4 to 6.

Complex Cobaltous Halides

Double (presumably complex) cobaltous halides are known with all four halogens, the chlorides being by far the most numerous. They are almost confined to the alkalies and the nitrogenous organic bases, such as ammonia and the amines; they are not formed by beryllium, nor, with the exception of one double magnesium chloride, by the alkaline earths. They are of all types from $MCoX_3$ to M_4CoX_6, but the commonest is M_2CoX_4. A fairly complete list of the known salts[417-19] gives the following numbers of each type:

	$MCoX_3$	M_2CoX_4	M_3CoX_5	M_4CoX_6
X = F	2	2	..	..
Cl	3	7	1	3
Br	..	6	1	2
I	..	3	..	1
Total	5	18	2	6

A list of the salts with their colours and degree of hydration follows:

Fluorides. $MCoF_3$: Na, H_2O, pink; K, H_2O, red.
  M_2CoF_4: K, 0, pink; NH_4, 2 H_2O, red; 0, blue.
Chlorides. $MCoCl_3$: Li, ? 5 H_2O, blue; Cs, anhy. blue; 2 H_2O, violet; Rb, 2 H_2O.
  M_2CoCl_4: NH_4, 2 H_2O, enH$_2$ 0, blue; 6 H_2O, pale green; pyH 0 H_2O, blue; quinH 0 H_2O, blue; 1 H_2O, blue; 2 H_2O, green; Rb, 0 H_2O, blue; 2 H_2O, lilac; Cs 0, blue; Mg, 8 H_2O, dark blue.
  M_3CoCl_5: Cs, 0, blue.
  M_4CoCl_6: Li, 10 H_2O; $(NH_4)_2(pyH)_2$, 3 H_2O, pale blue; enH$_2$, 0, blue.
Bromides. M_2CoBr_4: pyH, blue; quinaldineH, enH$_2$, 2 H_2O, blue; pyH, 0 and 2 H_2O, both greenish-blue; quinH 0, dark blue; 2 H_2O blue-green; Cs, green.
  M_3CoBr_5: Cs, 0, green.
  M_4CoBr_6. Li, 12 H_2O, blue; enH$_2$, 0, blue.
Iodides. M_2CoI_4: quinH, 0, green; py. H, 0, blue; Cs, green.
  M_4CoI_6: ? enH$_2$, not got pure.

The salt Cs_3CoCl_5, apparently of the rare 5-covalent type, has been shown[420] to contain not the complex $CoCl_5$ but $CoCl_4$, the fifth chlorine being at a distance: it may be written $Cs_3[CoCl_4]Cl$.

The 6-covalent complexes are very few, which is remarkable because compounds in which a cobaltous atom is co-ordinated with 6 molecules of

[417] See Gmelin, A. 398–461. [418] H. W. Foote, *Am. J. Sci.* 1927, **13**, 158.
[419] E. G. V. Percival and W. Wardlaw, *J.C.S.* 1929, 1505.
[420] H. M. Powell and A. F. Wells, ib. 1935, 359.

water, ammonia, methylamine, or pyridine, or with 6 CN groups, are known;* but it appears that these hexahalides are very soluble, and can only be induced to crystallize out if the monovalent halide is very soluble too: of the alkaline halides it appears that only lithium halides are sufficiently soluble, the other known hexahalides being all formed by organic bases.[421]

The double chloride of cobalt and ammonium has a peculiar behaviour. No definite double salt can be isolated; the two chlorides separate from water as a continuous series of solid solutions, but the positions of the solid-liquid tie-lines suggest the occurrence of a double salt of the composition $(NH_4)_2[CoCl_4]$, $2 H_2O$, forming a continuous series of solid solutions with both its component salts.[422-4] Something of the same kind seems to happen in the system LiCl, $CoCl_2$.[425]

Colour and Constitution of Cobaltous Compounds

The sharp change of colour of cobaltous salts both in the solid state and in solution, from pink to blue and vice versa, has long been known and has been much discussed.[426-42]

The colours of cobaltous compounds range from pink or red to pure blue, and though all intermediate tints can be found, there is a strong tendency for the extremes of colour to occur. It is found that in the pink state the positions of the absorption bands are practically always the same, the strongest being at 5,100 A, while in the blue state they vary somewhat, the wave-lengths increasing a little with the molecular weight of the complex.[441] The blue colour is much more intense (nearly 90 times)[434] than the pink, so that a very small amount of it can entirely mask the pink to the

---

* It is not uncommon for the co-ordination number of an atom to be higher in ammines than in acidic compounds, or in the cyanides than in the halides.

[421] J. Meyer and K. Hoehne, *Z. anorg. Chem.* 1935, **222**, 161.

[422] F. W. J. Clendinnen, *J.C.S.* 1922, **121**, 801.

[423] A. C. D. Rivett and F. W. J. Clendinnen, ib. 1923, **123**, 1634.

[424] A. Benrath, *Z. anorg. Chem.* 1927, **163**, 396.

[425] A. Ferrari and A. Baroni, *Atti. R.* 1928, [vi] **7**, 848.

[426] See Gmelin, *Kobalt*, A. 490–502 (1932) for an account of the work done up to that date.

[427] R. Hill and O. R. Howell, *Phil. Mag.* 1924, **48**, 833. [This is discussed by R. W. James, J. West, and A. J. Bradley in *Ann. Rep. Chem. Soc.* 1927, **24**, 288.]

[428] O. R. Howell, *J.C.S.* 1927, 158.

[429] Id., ib. 2039.   [430] Id., ib. 2843.   [431] Id., ib. 1929, 162.

[432] O. R. Howell and A. Jackson, *Proc. Roy. Soc.* 1933, **142**, 587.

[433] Id., ib. 1936, **155**, 33.   [434] Id., *J.C.S.* 1936, 1268.

[435] Id., ib. 1937, 621.   [436] Id., ib. 973.

[437] I. Rohde and E. Vogt, *Z. physikal. Chem.* 1932, B. **15**, 353.

[438] R. J. Macwalter and S. Barratt, *J.C.S.* 1934, 517.

[439] H. Grime and J. A. Santos, *Z. Krist.* 1934, **88**, 136.

[440] H. Dirking, *Z. anorg. Chem.* 1937, **233**, 321.

[441] A. v. Kiss and M. Richter, *Z. physikal. Chem.* 1940, **187**, 211.

[442] M. L. Schultz and E. F. Lilek, *J.A.C.S.* 1942, **64**, 2748.

eye. Thus Rohde found[437] that in a solution of cobaltous chloride in pyridine at 50°, which looks pure blue, spectroscopic measurements showed only a tenth of the cobalt to be present in the blue form. These differences of colour occur in the solid state, and in solutions in water and other solvents.

In solution the pink form is favoured by dilution, by using water as the solvent, by the absence of other salts (e.g. of alkalies), and by a low temperature; the opposite conditions favour the blue form. It is remarkable that while the addition of potassium or hydrogen chloride to the pink aqueous solution of cobaltous chloride will turn it blue, the addition of zinc or mercuric chloride to the blue alcoholic solution of the same cobaltous salt will turn it pink. The change from pink to blue occurs much less readily with the salts of oxy-acids (such as the nitrate or sulphate), than with the halides or the thiocyanate (in all these points cupric compounds behave very similarly).

In 1902 Donnan and Bassett showed[443] that in the blue solution of the chloride in water the blue colour migrated on electrolysis to the anode, and so must have a negative charge; they assumed it to be $[CoCl_3]^-$ or $[CoCl_4]^{--}$. Hantzsch[448] considered that the blue compound was less hydrated, and was not dissociated, the two compounds being $[Co(H_2O)_6]Cl_2$ (pink), and $[Co(H_2O)_2Cl_2]°$ (blue). These two views agree in supposing that the blue is due to a halide complex, while the pink is the colour of the simple ion in which the cobalt is attached only to water, an undoubtedly weaker link. They differ only as to whether the complex is ionized or not. All the conditions that promote the blue colour would favour the formation of such complexes. Further, if the alcoholic solution of cobaltous chloride, which is blue, and so must be supposed to contain a large proportion of the complex cobaltous anion, is treated with the chloride of mercury or zinc, which have a stronger tendency to form complex halides than divalent cobalt, they will remove the chlorine ions, and we shall have present the salt of the simple Co'' cation and the complex mercuric or zinc anion; hence the colour should change to pink, as in fact it is found to do. This conclusion was supported by the transport measurements of Kohlschütter[444] and Denham,[445] and by the electrical and optical measurements of Gróh.[446-7]

Much further work has been done on the absorption and other physical properties of the solutions (see, for example, Howell,[427-36] and refs. [438,442]), but no definite conclusion has been reached.

The solid phases of the complex halides are usually pink when highly solvated, and blue when less so, which agrees with the above ideas. On

[443] F. G. Donnan and H. Bassett, *J.C.S.* 1902, **81**, 939.
[444] V. Kohlschütter, *Ber.* 1904, **37**, 1153.
[445] H. G. Denham, *Z. physikal. Chem.* 1908, **65**, 641.
[446] J. Gróh, *Z. anorg. Chem.* 1925, **146**, 305.
[447] J. Gróh and R. Schmid, ib. 1927, **162**, 321.
[448] A. Hantzsch, *Z. anorg. Chem.* 1927, **159**, 273.

Donnan and Bassett's theory all the complex halides should be blue (of the simple anhydrous halides the colours are CoF_2 pink, $CoCl_2$ pale blue, $CoBr_2$ green, and CoI_2 in its two forms yellow and black); the following list, taken from Meyer and Hoehne,[449] with a few additions, shows that this is nearly always so:

Colours in the Solid State

$[Co(H_2O)_4]F_2$ . . . red	$Cs[CoCl_3]$ . . . pale blue	
$[Co(H_2O)_2]F_2$ . . . red	$Rb_2[CoCl_4]$ . . . green-blue	
$[Co(H_2O)_6]Cl_2$ . . . pink	$Cs_3[CoCl_5]$ . . . blue	
$[Co(H_2O)_6]Br_2$ . . . red	$Li_4[CoCl_6]$ . . . dark blue	
$[Co(H_2O)_6]I_2$ . . . red	$(enH_2)_2[CoCl_6]$ . . blue	
$[Co(NH_3)_5H_2O]F_2$ . . red	$(NH_4)_2(pyH)_2[CoCl_6], 6\ H_2O$ blue	
$[Co(NH_3)_6]Cl_2$ . . red		
$[Co(NH_3)_6]Br_2$ . . pink	$Li_4[CoBr_6], 12\ H_2O$ . . blue	
$[Co(NH_3)_6]I_2$ . . . deep pink	$(enH_2)_2[CoBr_6]$ . . deep blue	
$[Co(H_2O)_x]^{++}$ ion . . pink		

The fact that all the hexahalides are blue and the hexammines pink certainly suggests that it is the electrical condition rather than the co-ordination number which determines the colour.

Howell[427,430] examined the colours of a series of pigments, that is, coloured insoluble crystalline compounds of cobalt; some of these are red and others blue, and the positions of the absorption bands in the two classes are the same as in the red and blue solutions respectively. He showed that whenever the cobalt had four nearest neighbours the pigment was blue, and when it had six it was red; in this way he predicted some structures which have since been confirmed by X-ray analysis.[450-1] Anhydrous cobaltous chloride is, however, anomalous; the cobalt has six nearest neighbours, and so it should be red, whereas it is pale blue. On cooling with liquid air it turns red, but there is no corresponding change in the crystal lattice.

The problem is obviously by no means solved; perhaps the most probable suggestion is that of Donnan and Bassett that divalent cobalt is pink in a cation and blue in an anion, but a number of difficulties still remain.

COBALTIC COMPOUNDS

THE trivalent state of cobalt is excessively unstable in the simple ion and its salts, but in the complexes it is more stable than the divalent. The simple cobaltic salts are produced from the cobaltous only by the action of the strongest oxidizing agents, such as electrolytic oxidation,[452] or treatment in solution with fluorine,[453] ozone,[454] or such reagents as sodium bismuthate.[455] They are very unstable and are readily decomposed

[449] J. Meyer and K. Hoehne, *Z. anorg. Chem.* 1935, **222**, 161.

[450] W. H. Zachariasen, *Norsk. Geol. Tidskrift*, 1926, **9**, 65.

[451] W. L. Bragg and G. B. Brown, *Z. Krist.* 1926, **63**, 538.

[452] A. A. Noyes and T. J. Deahl, *J.A.C.S.* 1937, **59**, 1337.

[453] F. Fichter and H. Wolfmann, *Helv. Chim. Acta*, 1926, **9**, 1093.

[454] E. Brunner, ib. 1929, **12**, 208.

[455] S. Kitashima, *Bull. Inst. Phys.-Chem. Res. Japan*, 1928, **7**, 1035.

by water even in the cold with evolution of hydrogen and formation of the cobaltous salt. The apparently simple salts are almost confined to the fluoride, sulphate, and acetate, which probably owe their existence to the fact that they are really complex, though it is not certain what their structures are.

In the more definitely complex compounds such as the cobaltinitrites, the cobalticyanides, and above all the cobaltammines, the trivalent state of the cobalt is so completely stabilized that it is formed from the divalent by the action of air, and even under some circumstances of water.

The co-ordination number of trivalent cobalt in its complexes is always 6.

Cobaltic Oxide, Co_2O_3

It is very doubtful whether this compound exists at all, though a hydrated form Co_2O_3, H_2O is known; the only definite compounds of cobalt and oxygen appear to be CoO and Co_3O_4.[456] Cobaltic hydroxide $Co(OH)_3$ cannot be isolated, although it presumably exists. The lower hydrate Co_2O_3, H_2O, or $HO \cdot CoO$ can be made as a brown or black powder by oxidizing CoO or Co_3O_4 with a variety of oxidizing agents, such as air, peroxides, halogens, permanganate, &c., or by precipitating a cobaltic salt with alkali. The precipitate is readily dried at 150° to the monohydrate, but more water can only be removed by heating it to 300°, and at this temperature it begins to lose oxygen.[456]

The solubility of the hydroxide in cold water has been found by means of a radioactive isotope to be 0·01046 mg. per litre.[457]

Cobalto-cobaltic Oxide, Co_3O_4

This is quite a definite compound, which can be made by heating the hydrated sesquioxide. It is a black crystalline substance, which is isomorphous with magnetite Fe_3O_4 and like it has a spinelle lattice. On strong heating it loses more oxygen, and at 900° it is converted into cobaltous oxide CoO. It has a remarkable power of taking up more oxygen, apparently by surface adsorption, but without forming the sesquioxide. It can take up water, but no definite hydrate has been isolated. It dissolves in fused sodium hydroxide, or in boiling aqueous soda to give a blue solution.

A *dioxide* CoO_2 has been described, but it probably does not exist.

Cobaltic Sulphide, Co_2S_3

Cobalt and sulphur form three compounds, CoS and the stable pyrites CoS_2, which are cobaltous and have already been described, and a metastable cobaltic sulphide Co_2S_3.

A solid of the composition Co_2S_3 can be made by fusing a cobaltous compound with sulphur and potassium carbonate. It is grey, crystalline,

[456] G. F. Hüttig and R. Kassler, *Z. anorg. Chem.* 1929, **184**, 284.
[457] B. N. Cacciapuotti and F. Ferla, *Atti R.* 1938, [vi] **28**, 385.

insoluble in water, and only slowly attacked even by strong acids. Its chemical identity is not quite certain. If, however, a solution of a cobaltic ammine is precipitated with hydrogen sulphide or sodium sulphide under exactly the right conditions,[458] a precipitate of Co_2S_3 is obtained. This, however, is not stable, and on heating goes over even at 450° into a mixture of the monosulphide and the disulphide.[459]

Cobaltic Fluoride, CoF_3

This trihalide exists in the anhydrous and also in the hydrated state. The hydrate $CoF_3, 3\cdot5\ H_2O$ or $Co_2F_6, 7\ H_2O$ can be made[460-1] by electrolysing a saturated solution of cobaltous fluoride in 40 per cent. hydrofluoric acid, when it separates out as a green powder.

Fluorine combines with metallic cobalt to form a mixture of the di- and trifluorides, but not below 450°, where fluorine attacks both silica and platinum. The anhydrous fluoride was made by Ruff[462] by treating anhydrous cobaltous chloride with fluorine, in the cold, or more conveniently at 150°.

Anhydrous cobaltic fluoride CoF_3[462] is a pale brown crystalline powder which turns much darker in the presence of even minute traces of water. In a stream of carbon dioxide it begins to lose fluorine at 250–300°, and at 350° only cobaltous fluoride CoF_2 is left. It is insoluble in alcohol, ether, and benzene. With water it gives a lively evolution of oxygen even in the cold, and with hydrochloric acid it liberates chlorine, the cobaltous salt being of course produced. It reacts with many elements (bromine, iodine, sulphur, phosphorus, arsenic, carbon, silicon), fluorinating them and being itself reduced to cobaltous fluoride.

Its crystal structure does not seem to be quite certain,[462-3] but it closely resembles that of ferric and chromic fluorides. In the same way CoF_3, $3\cdot5\ H_2O$, whose composition suggests that the formula should be doubled, as $Co_2F_6, 7\ H_2O$, has a green chromic analogue, which has been shown by Werner[464] to be $Cr_2F_6, 7\ H_2O$; so that in all probability the cobaltic compound should have a doubled formula also, and be written Co_2F_6, 0 and $7\ H_2O$. The assumption that these net formulae should be expanded to $Co'''[CoF_6]$ and for the hydrate to $[Co(H_2O)_6]\cdot[CoF_6],H_2O$, and that this will account for the relative stability of the compound[461,465] (which certainly needs explanation) is, however, not satisfactory. These formulae still leave half the cobalt in the form of the simple cobaltic ion, so that the instability should persist, especially in the hydrated form. The anhydrous fluoride by itself can show instability only by losing fluorine, which it does

[458] E. Birk, *Habilitationsschrift*, Hannover, 1928.

[459] O. Hülsmann and W. Biltz, *Z. anorg. Chem.* 1935, **224**, 73.

[460] G. Barbieri and F. Calzolari, *Atti R.* 1905, [v] **14**, i. 464.

[461] E. Birk, *Z. anorg. Chem.* 1927, **166**, 284.

[462] O. Ruff and E. Ascher, ib. 1929, **183**, 193.

[463] F. Ebert, ib. 1931, **196**, 395.

[464] A. Werner and N. Costaschescu, *Ber.* 1908, **41**, 4244.

[465] W. Biltz, *Z. anorg. Chem.* 1927, **166**, 275.

on heating; if it can pass on one of its fluorines to another element it does so, as we have seen. But the existence of the heptahydrate, though it decomposes in water, suggests that it must have the whole of its cobalt, and not only half of it, in some more stable complex form. What this is, only X-rays can tell us.

Cobaltic Chloride, $CoCl_3$

This is doubtful. It cannot be made by dissolving the hydrated sesquioxide in hydrochloric acid, as the chlorine ion is at once oxidized to the element, with the production of cobaltous chloride. It is said to be formed by treating the hydrated sesquioxide with hydrogen chloride gas in presence of ether at $-5°$ in the dark,[466] as a green solid which becomes pale yellow below $-60°$. The ethereal solution on treatment with ammonia gives the hexammine $[Co(NH_3)_6]Cl_3$.

Cobaltic Acetate

A solution of this salt can be obtained by oxidizing a cobaltous salt in acetic acid. The solid salt is best prepared by the electrolytic oxidation of cobaltous acetate in glacial acetic acid containing 2 per cent. of water, as the salt is less soluble in this solvent.[467]

It forms apple-green octahedra, which decompose at $100°$. It is trimeric by the freezing-point in acetic acid, and on the analogy of the similar ferric acetate may be supposed to have the formula

$$[Co_3(O\cdot CO\cdot CH_3)_6](O\cdot CO\cdot CH_3)_3,$$

and to be only ionized in the acid. In water it is green, and only oxidizes the water slowly, but it will oxidize hydrochloric acid to chlorine, ferrous to ferric ion, iodide ion to the free halogen, etc.

Cobaltic Carbonate, $Co_2(CO_3)_3$

This can be got in solution by oxidizing a cobaltous salt in presence of sodium bicarbonate with hydrogen peroxide, bromine, etc. The solution is green. It is said[468] that if hydrogen peroxide is used the compound can be made to separate as a green powder which is stable when dry.

Cobaltic Oxalate, $Co_2(C_2O_4)_3$

A green aqueous solution can be made by electrolysing an oxalic acid solution with a cobalt anode. The solution decomposes with evolution of carbon dioxide, and no definite solid cobaltic oxalates have been isolated, though double salts are known.

Cobaltic Nitrate, $Co(NO_3)_3$

This is known only in solution, and changes rapidly into the cobaltous salt.

[466] D. Hibert and C. Duval, *C.R.* 1937, **204**, 780.
[467] C. Schall and C. Thieme-Wiedtmarckter, *Z. Elektrochem.* 1929, **35**, 337.
[468] C. Duval, *C.R.* 1930, **191**, 615.

Cobaltic Sulphate

The hydrated salt $Co_2(SO_4)_3$, $18 H_2O$ can be made by the oxidation, electrolytically or with ozone or fluorine, of a solution of cobaltous sulphate in 8-normal sulphuric acid. It forms blue crystals; if it is perfectly dry it can be kept without decomposition, but if it is moist it soon changes, especially on warming, into oxygen and cobaltous sulphate. It gives a stable solution in dilute sulphuric acid, but pure water decomposes it with evolution of oxygen.

The cobaltic alums of the general formula $MCo(SO_4)_2$, $12 H_2O$ have been made, where $M = K$, Rb, Cs, and NH_4. They are all dark blue, and the potassium salt, as usual, is the most soluble. It is diamagnetic.[469-70] They are decomposed by water with evolution of oxygen.

Cobaltic Perchlorate

This again can only be got in solution, by the oxidation of cobaltous perchlorate, either electrolytically, or with fluorine.[471] The solution, which is blue, is unstable, and the salt, which must be very soluble, cannot be made to crystallize out.

COBALTIC COMPLEXES

Trivalent cobalt has as strong a tendency as any other element, even platinum or chromium, to form complexes, in which it can be the 'central atom' of a cation, a neutral molecule, or an anion, and in which its co-ordination or covalency number is always 6.[472]

The chief donor atoms attached to trivalent cobalt in these complexes are (in order of diminishing strength of the link) nitrogen, carbon in the cyanides, oxygen, sulphur (a few), and the halogens. The great majority of the compounds are ammines in the sense that the complex has one or more amine (including ammonia) molecules attached to the cobalt.

Cyano-complexes

A cyanide group and a halogen atom often behave similarly, but in the cobaltic complexes they are in striking contrast to one another. With the halogens, more than three cannot be made to combine with a trivalent cobalt atom, and the pure complex halides are not formed. The behaviour of the cyanide group is the exact reverse; the 6-covalent cobalticyanides are very stable, even the free acid being known: pentacyano-compounds also probably occur: but of the cobaltic complexes with less than 5 CN groups only one appears to have been made, the monocyano-tetrammine

[469] R. W. Asmussen, *Nordiske Kemikermode*, 1939, 196.

[470] H. Bommer, *Z. anorg. Chem.* 1941, **246**, 275.

[471] F. Fichter and A. Goldach, *Helv. Chim. Acta*, 1930, **13**, 717.

[472] The elucidation of the structures of these complexes is primarily due to Werner, *Beiträge zur Theorie der Affinität und Valenz*, 1891; *Z. anorg. Chem.* 1893, **3**, 267. For later developments see his *Neuere Anschauungen*, 1st ed. 1905, 3rd (the last in his lifetime) 1913, 5th (revised by P. Pfeiffer) 1925.

$[Co(NH_3)_4(OH_2)CN]Cl_2$,[473] a reddish-yellow crystalline substance, which is sufficiently stable for silver nitrate not to precipitate any silver cyanide from its solution.

Cobalticyanides, $M_3[Co(CN)_6]$

These are more stable than the hexacyano-complexes of trivalent chromium, manganese, or iron, as is shown by the fact that (like the ferro- but unlike the ferricyanides) neither the salts nor the free acid are poisonous. The salts are formed by the oxidation of the cobaltocyanides, a reaction which occurs so readily that a cobaltocyanide will even decompose water with evolution of hydrogen.

Free cobalticyanic acid H_3CoCy_6 can be got by the evaporation of its aqueous solution as colourless very hygroscopic needles, with more or less water of crystallization, which can be removed at 100°, but only with a break up of the crystals. If the acid is recrystallized from alcohol it forms 'alkyloxonium' salts, in which some or all of the hydrogens are replaced by $[Alk \cdot OH_2]^+$ groups, as in $(EtOH_2)_3[CoCy_6]$.[474] These are crystalline compounds which are readily soluble in and hydrolysed by water. They will give the anhydrous acid if they are warmed *in vacuo*. The acid also forms an oxonium salt with cineol, which has been used for its preparation.[475]

The salts are numerous, those of the alkalies being as a rule readily soluble in water, and those of the heavy metals insoluble. For example we have Li, $6 H_2O$,[476] excessively soluble in water and soluble in alcohol; Na, $2 H_2O$, easily soluble in water, insoluble in alcohol: K, anhydrous,[477] almost colourless, isomorphous with potassium ferricyanide, easily soluble in water, especially hot: Rb, and Cs[476] are anhydrous and similar.

A variety of substituted ammonium salts are known, which are all readily soluble in water.[478]

Cobalticyanic acid, like ferrocyanic but unlike ferricyanic,* can be esterified in various ways. If the acid (or its alcohol compound) is heated in a sealed tube at 100° with alcohol, a partial replacement of the acidic hydrogens by alkyl radicals takes place,[479] giving, for example,

$$(C_2H_5)H_2[CoCy_6],$$

or as it undoubtedly should be written $H_2[Co(CN)_5(CN \cdot C_2H_5)]$. By the

---

* It should be noticed that the E.A.N. of the cobaltic atom is the same as that of the ferrous in any given state of covalency: the cores being Fe″ 24; Fe‴ 23; Co″ 25; Co‴ 24.

[473] K. A. Hofmann and S. Reinsch, *Z. anorg. Chem.* 1898, **16**, 379.

[474] F. Hölzl, T. Meier-Mohar, and F. Viditz, *Mon.* 1929, **138**, 241; F. Hölzl and A. Sallmann, ib. 1931, **140**, 29; F. Hölzl and G. Schinko, ib. 249: F. Hölzl, E. W. Brell, and G. Schinko, ib. 1933, **142**, 155.

[475] A. v. Baeyer and V. Villiger, *Ber.* 1901, **34**, 2688; 1902, **35**, 1206.

[476] J. Meyer and P. Chao, *Z. anorg. Chem.* 1937, **232**, 238.

[477] A. Benedetti-Pitchler, *Z. anal. Chem.* 1927, **70**, 258.

[478] Gmelin, A. 446.

[479] F. Hölzl, T. Meier-Mohar, and F. Viditz, *Mon.* 1929, **53/4**, 237; F. Hölzl, W. Brell, and G. Schinko, ib. 1933, **62**, 349.

continued action of methyl iodide on the silver salt a second[480] and a third[481] hydrogen atom can be replaced, giving $[Co(CN)_3(CN \cdot CH_3)_3]$. In this way a mixture of about equal parts of the two isomers of the trimethyl ester was obtained. Both are colourless, and decompose above 100°; the solubilities are in water at 7·5° α- 0·16, β- 0·44; in alcohol at 78° α- 0·05, β- 1·18. They both give off their alkyls as isocyanides, and so must be the *cis* and *trans* isomers of $[Co(CN \cdot CH_3)_3(CN)_3]°$. The resemblance to Hartley's isomeric tetramethyl ferrocyanides (p. 1341) is very close in every way.

Pentacyano-compounds

Very few compounds with five cyanide groups attached to trivalent cobalt have been isolated. There is evidence for the existence in solution of an aquo-ion $[Co(CN)_5(OH_2)]^{--}$,[482-3] and perhaps a nitro-pentacyano-compound,[484-5] but only one type of pentacyano-compound has been obtained for certain in the solid state. This is the carbonyl compound $M_2[Co(CN)_5(CO)]$,[486] in which the CO is obviously co-ordinated as in nickel carbonyl, the E.A.N. of the cobalt being 36 (as it is in all cobaltic complexes of a covalency of 6). The potassium salt is made by treating a solution of cobaltous acetate and potassium acetate with gaseous carbon-monoxide in the complete absence of air. It is yellow,[487] and gives a yellow solution in water.

Isothiocyanato-complexes

In all the cobaltic thiocyanate complexes it can be shown that the NCS is attached to the cobalt through the nitrogen; in these compounds it behaves like a halogen and not like a cyanide group, in that a few (here only one or two) of these groups can be introduced into an ammine, but no pure thiocyanates such as $M_3[Co(NCS)_6]$ are known.

The ammine thiocyanates are mostly of the types of $[Co(NH_3)_5NCS]X_2$ and $[Co(NH_3)_4(NCS)_2]X$.

The first (pentammine) series can be made by the action of potassium thiocyanate on the aquo-salts; they form yellow-red crystals, not very soluble in water (sol^y of the sulphate 0·97/20°).[488]

They have the peculiarity of adding on silver nitrate to form brown compounds such as $[Co(NH_3)_5NCS](NO_3)_2, AgNO_3$, which are so stable that the silver is not precipitated by hydrochloric acid. Werner has suggested[489]

[480] C. E. Bolser and L. B. Richardson, *J.A.C.S.* 1913, **35**, 377.

[481] E. G. J. Hartley, *J.C.S.* 1914, **105**, 521.

[482] E. Müller and H. Lauterbach, *Z. anal. Chem.* 1923, **62**, 25; E. Müller and W. Schluttig, *Z. anorg. Chem.* 1924, **134**, 333.

[483] H. Bassett and A. S. Corbet, *J.C.S.* 1924, **125**, 1365.

[484] C. L. Jackson and A. M. Comey, *Ber.* 1896, **29**, 1020; *Am. Chem. J.* 1897, **19**, 271.

[485] A. Rosenheim and I. Koppel, *Z. anorg. Chem.* 1898, **17**, 63.

[486] W. Manchot and H. Gall, *Ber.* 1926, **59**, 1056.

[487] W. Hieber, K. Ries, and G. Bader, *Z. anorg. Chem.* 1930, **190**, 219.

[488] J. N. Brönsted and A. Petersen, *J.A.C.S.* 1921, **43**, 2269.

[489] A. Werner, *Ann.* 1912, **386**, 50.

that the silver is attached to the sulphur of the NCS, the AgSCN group being co-ordinated to the cobalt like an ammonia, as

$$[(NH_3)_5Co \leftarrow N\equiv C-S-Ag](NO_3)_3.$$

These compounds are oxidized by hydrogen peroxide or by chlorine, with replacement of the NCS by NH_3, which is evidence that it is the nitrogen which joins the NCS to the cobalt; oxidation with nitric acid eliminates the NCS altogether, and evaporation with hydrochloric acid replaces it by chlorine.

The di-isothiocyanato-compounds, such as [Co en$_2$(NCS)$_2$]X, were first obtained by Werner in 1900[490]; they occur in two series, which have been shown[491] both to be isothiocyanates, and to be *cis* and *trans* isomers.

The *cis* salts are yellow-red, while the *trans* are dark red. They can be made, for example, by treating the dichloro-compounds with potassium thiocyanate. Complexes in which one of the two CNS groups is replaced by nitrito, chlorine, or bromine are also known.

In all these diacyl derivatives, as in the pentammine-mono-thio-cyanato-complexes, the thiocyanato-group is replaced by ammonia on oxidation with hydrogen peroxide.

*Cobaltic Ammines**

The affinity of trivalent cobalt for nitrogen is very strong, much stronger than for oxygen, as is shown by the readiness with which the ammines are produced in aqueous solution, in spite of the competition of the much more numerous water molecules. The complexes can contain one cobaltic atom or several joined through covalent 'bridges' of atoms; for the latter see p. 1415. The ammonia groups can be replaced partly or wholly by other amines (including diamines and triamines), and partly by water and by a large number of mono- and divalent acid radicals such as those of prussic,

thiocyanic (as $-N-C-S$), nitrous (both $-N\!\!\begin{smallmatrix}\nearrow O\\\searrow O\end{smallmatrix}$ and $-O-N=O$), and

oxalic acids, as well as the halogens.

The ammines can have any number of amine groups from 6 down to 2 (not to 1); the stability falls off as the number of amine groups diminishes, especially in the tri-electrovalent series of cations where this is replaced by water (from [Co(NH$_3$)$_6$]X$_3$ to [Co(NH$_3$)$_3$(OH$_2$)$_3$]X$_3$).

Anderson *et al.*[491] find that [Co(NH$_3$)$_6$]Cl$_3$ and [Co en$_3$]Cl$_3$ containing heavy hydrogen exchange with ordinary water at a rate = k/[H$^+$], with activation energies 28·4 and 28·1 k.cals.; they suggest that Co—NH$_3$ ionizes to [Co—NH$_2$]$^-$+H$^+$.

---

* For a full account of the cobaltammines up to 1930 see Gmelin, *Kobalt*, B., pp. 46–375; he enumerates some 1,500 compounds. References to this are given in the text as (Gm. B. *X*), where *X* is the page. For a list of the solubilities in water of a very large number of cobaltammine salts see F. Ephraim, *Ber.* 1923, **56**, 1530.

[490] A. Werner and F. Bräunlich, *Z. anorg. Chem.* 1900, **22**, 95.
[491] J. S. Anderson, H. V. A. Briscoe, and N. L. Spoor, *J.C.S.* 1943, 361.

The various groups which go to make up these almost innumerable compounds are of four kinds: (1) the amines, ammonia and its substitution products; (2) water: other oxygen compounds might act as donors in the same way, but no such compounds appear to be known; (3) acid radicals, i.e. covalently attached groups which in other compounds can behave as ions; (4) the other ions (for example, a halogen ion or a sodium ion) which with the complex form the neutral salt molecule.

Of the amines the simplest and most important is ammonia, but a very large number of substituted ammonias can take its place. The principles determining the stability of ammines in general, which apply also to those of trivalent cobalt, are, on the one hand, that the replacement of hydrogen in ammonia by hydrocarbon groups diminishes the strength of the link, and on the other, that the formation of chelate rings by molecules which have two amine groups in a position to form an unstrained ring (β or γ) greatly increases it; the second effect is stronger than the first, so that ethylene diamine with two primary amine groups gives more stable compounds than ammonia itself.

Among the monamines that have actually been used are ethylamine, allylamine, benzylamine, aniline, toluidine, pyridine, and also hydroxylamine (the cobaltic complexes containing oximes are discussed later). Among the diamines are ethylene diamine, propylene diamine

$$CH_3 \cdot CH(NH_2) \cdot CH_2 \cdot NH_2,$$

its diphenyl derivative $\Phi NH \cdot CH_2 \cdot CH_2 \cdot NH\Phi$,[492] β, δ-diaminobutane[494] butylene diamine $CH_3 \cdot CH(NH_2) \cdot CH(NH_2) \cdot CH_3$, trimethylene diamine $H_2N \cdot CH_2 \cdot CH_2 \cdot CH_2 \cdot NH_2$,[493] diaminocyclopentane, and *o*-phenylene diamine.[495-8] Another polyamine of great interest from the stereochemical point of view is α, α', β-triaminopropane

$$H_2N \cdot CH_2 \cdot CH(NH_2) \cdot CH_2 \cdot NH_2.^{499,500-1}$$

The acid radicals which can be attached to the cobalt in these complexes include those of almost all known monobasic and many polybasic acids; the more important are: OH, F, Cl, Br, I, NO (true nitroso-, Co—N=O), NO_2

(in two forms, the true nitro Co—N$\overset{\nearrow O}{\underset{\searrow O}{}}$ and the much less stable nitrito-

[492] J. Frejka and L. Zahlova, *Coll. Czech. Chem. Comm.* 1930, **2**, 639.

[493] E. N. Gapon, *Bull. Soc.* 1930, [4] **47**, 343.

[494] C. J. Dippell and F. M. Jaeger, *Rec. Trav.* 1931, **50**, 547.

[495] F. M. Jaeger and H. B. Blumendal, *Z. anorg. Chem.* 1928, **175**, 161.

[496] F. M. Jaeger and L. Bijkerk, ib. 1937, **233**, 97.

[497] F. M. Jaeger, *Proc. Akad. Amst.* 1937, **40**, 108.

[498] F. M. Jaeger and L. Bijkerk, ib. **40**, 246, 316.

[499] See, for example, P. Terpstra and J. ter Berg, *Proc. K. Akad. Amst.* 1937, **40**, 602.

[500] F. G. Mann, *J.C.S.* 1929, 409.

[501] P. Job and J. Brigando, *C.R.* 1940, **210**, 438.

Co—O—N=O), NO_3, CN, CNS, acetate and similar carboxylic radicals; also a variety of radicals of dibasic acids which can fill either one co-ordination place on the cobalt or two, as with the CO_3, C_2O_4, SO_3, SO_4, S_2O_3, malonato, etc., radicals.

The general strength of the links of trivalent cobalt to other atoms is in the order given above (especially $N > O >$ halogen), but it varies to some extent not only with the nature of the donor atom, but also with that of the whole group of which this is a part, and further that of the other groups attached to the same cobalt atom. As usual divalent chelate groups are much more firmly attached than monovalent amine molecules or acyl radicals. Thus the complexes $[Co(NH_3)_4(H_2O)_2]X_3$ (Gm. B. 113, 118) and $[Co(NH_3)_2py_2(H_2O)_2]X_3$ (ib. 121) do not give *cis-trans* isomers, as the groups are not sufficiently firmly fixed; but the chelate complexes $[Co\,en_2(H_2O)_2]X_3$ do so (Gm. B. 121: en = ethylene diamine). The en group seems to be peculiarly firmly attached, more so than its methyl homologue $CH_3 \cdot CH \cdot NH_2$ (pn), since the *cis-trans* changes are much quicker with
$\quad\quad |$
$\quad CH_2NH_2$
$[Co\,pn_2Cl_2]X$ than with $[Co\,en_2Cl_2]X$ (Gm. B. 243). The 6-ring complexes of trimethylene diamine $[Co\,tn_2Cl_2]X$ ($tn = H_2N \cdot CH_2 \cdot CH_2 \cdot CH_2 \cdot NH_2$) may occur in one form, so this ring must be still less stable. Similar effects are shown among the oxygen complexes in the very stable oxalato (5-ring) complexes, and the rather less stable malonato (6-ring).

All these complexes form numerous salts; the individual properties of most of these are not very important, but the free bases (hydroxy-compounds, $[CoA_6](OH)_3$) are interesting, particularly in their relation to the aquo-complexes (with $Co\leftarrow OH_2$) and the hydroxy- (with Co—OH).

These complex ammine cations practically always form strong bases. If a solution of the halide is ground with silver oxide, a strongly alkaline solution is obtained, which absorbs carbon dioxide from the air to form a carbonate; the hydroxides themselves are usually too soluble to be isolated, but where this can be done, as with $[Co(en)_3](OH)_3$,[502] they are deliquescent solids. The conductivities of many of them in water[503] show them to be strong electrolytes. Since the covalency of 6 which trivalent cobalt always shows is its maximum, it is evident that unless some rearrangement occurs the base must be wholly ionized: the cobalt atom cannot form an additional link with a hydroxyl. Sometimes, however, when the base is formed the complex cation reacts with its own hydroxyl ion. This may hydrolyse acid radicals attached to the cobalt, and when these are halogen atoms it always appears to do so[504]; thus attempts to prepare the base of the 'bromopurpureo' salts $[Co(NH_3)_5Br](OH)_2$ leads only to decomposition products.[505] In the true nitro-compounds, however,

[502] S. M. Jörgensen, *J. prakt. Chem.* 1889, [2] **39**, 12.
[503] A. B. Lamb and V. Yngve, *J.A.C.S.* 1921, **43**, 2357.
[504] See B. Adell, *Z. anorg. Chem.* 1941, **246**, 303.
[505] S. M. Jörgensen, *J. prakt. Chem.* 1879, [2] **19**, 54.

the strong Co—N link is not easily broken in this way, and a series of nitro-ammine bases such as $[Co(NH_3)_4(NO_2)_2]OH$ and $[Co(NH_3)_3(OH_2)(NO_2)_2]OH$ has been made.

The hydroxyl ion in these bases can react with a water molecule in the cation:

$$[Co{\leftarrow}OH_2]OH \longrightarrow [Co{-}OH] + H_2O,$$

the hydroxyl expelling (or taking a hydrogen ion from) a water molecule. Where the cation only contains amines together with one or two water molecules the reaction seems always to go to completion, for example:

$$[Co(NH_3)_5(OH_2)](OH)_3 \longrightarrow [Co(NH_3)_5OH](OH)_2$$

$$[Co(NH_3)_4(OH_2)_2](OH)_3 \longrightarrow [Co(NH_3)_4(OH)_2]OH.$$

The possibility of this reaction was recognized by Werner, and is supported by the work of Job,[506] Lamb,[503] and King.[507]

When, however, the cation contains acid radicals, and its positive charge is thereby reduced, this reaction is much less easy. Thus the dinitro-aquo-triammine salts should, if they behave like the others, on treatment with silver oxide, give the neutral covalent hydroxide:

$$[Co(NH_3)_3(OH_2)(NO_2)_2]OH \longrightarrow [Co(NH_3)_3(OH)(NO_2)_2]^\circ.$$

The resulting solution, however, has a considerable conductivity,[504] showing that some ionized base is present, but the amount of dissociation is much less than with the pure aquo-ammines.

In the language of the acid-base theory of Brönsted this reaction of the co-ordinated water with the hydroxyl ion may be written

$$[Co(NH_3)_5(OH_2)]^{+++} \rightleftharpoons [Co(NH_3)_5(OH)]^{++} + H^+$$
$$\text{Acid} \qquad\qquad\qquad \text{Base}$$

as the dissociation of an acid. Brönsted has shown[508-9] that the dissociation constant, which measures the extent to which the trivalent ion loses a hydrogen ion, increases rapidly as the NH_3 molecules are replaced by water. To a certain extent this is a statistical necessity: the probability of the reaction occurring is greater the more water molecules there are in the cation which can undergo it. But even when allowance is made for this, the 'chemical factors' remaining are still in the same order, having for the various ions $[Co(NH_3)_{6-x}(OH_2)_x]^{+++}$, the relative values

for $x =$	1	2	3	4
Rel. $K =$	1	1·5	3·3	50

indicating that in cobaltic hydroxide or the hexa-aquo-ion $[Co(OH_2)_6]^{+++}$ the reaction will go very far indeed.

[506] P. Job and G. Urbain, *C.R.* 1920, **170**, 843; 1922, **174**, 613.
[507] H. J. S. King, *J.C.S.* 1932, 1275.
[508] J. N. Brönsted and C. V. King, *Z. physikal. Chem.* 1927, **130**, 699.
[509] J. N. Brönsted and K. Volqvartz, ib. 1928, **134**, 97.

The chelate ethylene diamine ('en') derivatives were the compounds through which Werner was first able to prove his octahedral theory; in 1911 he resolved [Co en$_2$(NH$_3$)Cl]X$_2$,[510] [Co en$_2$(NO$_2$)Cl]X[511] and [Co en$_3$]X$_3$[512] into their optical antimers.

Many other complexes with chelate rings attached through nitrogen are known. They include, for example, the glyoxime derivatives, with a chelate ring of the form

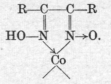

They are mainly dichelate, such as [Co(DH)$_2$(NH$_3$)$_2$]Br (glyoxime = DH$_2$). They can be made from the cobaltous derivatives by the action of air in the presence of excess of glyoxime.[513] They are green in colour.

Among the complexes in which the links are through nitrogen and oxygen (N—M—O) are the derivatives of the *o*-hydroxy-azo-compounds, which are known to be mordant dyes; if these are treated in alcoholic solution with cobaltous acetate in presence of hydrogen peroxide,[514] dark brown or black substances are precipitated, which are insoluble in water and soluble in organic solvents, and are of the type (co = ⅓ of Co)

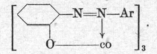

Of the other complexes with the cobaltic atom attached to nitrogen the nitrosyls and their isomeric nitroso-derivatives are discussed later (p. 1423); the nitro-compounds Co—N$\diagup^O_{\diagdown O}$ will now be dealt with; their isomers, the nitrito-complexes Co—O—N=O, though really oxygen complexes (and hence less stable), may be discussed along with them.

Nitrito-compounds

Complexes containing the NO$_2$ group occur in two isomeric forms, the nitrito Co—O—N=O and nitro Co—N$\diagup^O_{\diagdown O}$; the nitrito-compounds are far more readily decomposed, and also isomerize easily to the nitro.

These facts were discovered by Jörgensen.[516] He prepared a red salt

[510] A. Werner, *Ber.* 1911, **44**, 1887. [511] Id., ib. 2445, 3272, 3279.
[512] Id., ib. 1912, **45**, 121.
[513] L. Cambi and C. Coriselli, *Gaz.* 1936, **66**, 81.
[514] M. Elkins and L. Hunter, *J.C.S.* 1935, 1598.
[515] B. Adell, *Z. anorg. Chem.* 1944, **252**, 272.
[516] S. M. Jörgensen, ib. 1894, **5**, 168; **7**, 294; 1898, **17**, 463; 1899, **19**, 149.

$[Co(NH_3)_5NO_2]Cl_2$ isomeric with the already known yellow 'xantho-chloride' and going over into it on standing; he suggested that the new salt was the nitrito- and the xantho-salt the nitro-compound. The dynamics of the change of the nitrito-pentammine chloride to the nitro- (a unimolecular reaction with a half-life of about 11 hours at 20°) has been examined by Adell.[515]

The nitrito-salt is the less soluble in water (0·5/15°), and cannot be recrystallized from it; the solution is at first red and gives red precipitates of nitrito-salts with ammonium nitrate, potassium chloroplatinite and platinate, etc., but it soon turns yellow and then contains the nitro-compound only.

The salts of $[Co\ en_2(CNS)ONO]X$ are similar[517]; they are red, but change slowly on standing and at once on heating to 70–80° into the isomeric nitro-compounds.

The *cis* and *trans* dinitrito-salts in the series $[Co\ en_2(ONO)_2]X$ can be made by the action of nitrous acid on the corresponding *cis* and *trans* diaquo-di-en salts.[518-19] They show the characteristic instability of the nitrito-compounds; they are stable in acetic acid but are decomposed by mineral acid, reforming the diaquo-compounds with evolution of the oxides of nitrogen. In the solid state they soon change over into the dinitro (*cis* = flavo; *trans* = croceo) salts.

The diammino-dipyridino-salts $[Co(NH_3)_2py_2(ONO)_2]X$ are similar.[518]

The nitrito-compounds are usually made by the action of nitrous acid on aquo-compounds; the replacement of ammonia requires more drastic treatment, and generally leads at once to the nitro-compound.

The nitrito-compounds are easily distinguished from the nitro (1) by losing the ONO for H_2O with dilute HCl, the nitro-group reacting only with concentrated HCl, and then being replaced by Cl; (2) by their instability, as they go over in the solid state into the nitro-isomers on standing. (See A. Werner, loc. cit.,[519] pp. 24, 157, 163, 174, 194, 217, etc.)

Nitro-compounds

These are among the stablest and most numerous of the cobaltic complexes; the pentammino-nitro-salts were discovered by Wolcott Gibbs in 1852. They occur in all series from the pentammine type $[Co(NH_3)_5NO_2]X_2$ to the familiar cobaltinitrites $M_3[Co(NO_2)_6]$, with the sole exception of the pentanitro-type $M_2[Co(NH_3)(NO_2)_5]$, which, like all the monammines, is unknown.

The mono-nitro-derivatives $[Co(NH_3)_5NO_2]X_2$ are yellow, and were called the xantho-compounds, the isomeric nitrito-salts being known as iso-xantho.

The dinitro-salts of the type of $[Co(NH_3)_4(NO_2)_2]X$ can exist in two

[517] A. Werner, *Ann.* 1912, **386**, 162.
[518] Id., *Ber.* 1907, **40**, 769.
[519] Id., *Ann.* 1912, **386**, 24, 247.

series, both of which are known (*cis*, flavo; *trans*, croceo). The *cis* dinitro-salts with two chelate en rings [Co en$_2$(NO$_2$)$_2$]X[520] are asymmetric and were resolved by Werner[521] into their optical antimers.

The tri-nitro-series, such as [Co(NH$_3$)$_3$(NO$_2$)$_3$]°, are necessarily non-ionic, but they are fairly soluble in water, and the solution is practically non-conducting even after standing, which is evidence of their stability.

In the tetranitro-series the complex is of course an anion, giving such salts as M[Co(NH$_3$)$_2$(NO$_2$)$_4$]. The structure obviously allows of *cis* and *trans* isomers; but only one series has yet been found, long regarded as the *cis*, but recently proved to be the *trans* by Wells,[522] who showed Ag[Co(NH$_3$)$_2$(NO$_2$)$_4$], to have an octahedral crystal structure of the *trans* form, with the distances Co—N 1·92 and N—O 1·25 A (theory Co—N 2·02, N—O 1·36, N=O 1·15).

The potassium salt K[Co(NH$_3$)$_2$(NO$_2$)$_4$][523] forms yellow-brown crystals with sol^y 1·76/16·5°. The dark yellow solution is not decomposed by alkali or ammonium carbonate in the cold, but if it is warmed with alkali to 60° cobaltic hydroxide is slowly precipitated.

The absence of pentanitro-compounds is noticeable because it seems to be a general rule that though the penta-ammino-compounds are relatively stable, the penta-ato-compounds, with 5 acid radicals in the ion, do not occur, even where, as with these nitro-salts, the hexa-derivatives, M$_3$[CoR$_6$], are stable.

The hexanitro-cobaltic salts or cobaltinitrites M$_3$[Co(NO$_2$)$_6$] are familiar from their use in separating cobalt from nickel. The lithium salt[524] Li$_3$[Co(NO$_2$)$_6$], 8 H$_2$O forms large yellow crystals, which are hygroscopic and very soluble in water. The sodium salt[525-6] can be made by passing a stream of air through a solution of cobaltous nitrate and sodium nitrite in 50 per cent. acetic acid. Conductivity measurements show it to be a strong 4-ionic electrolyte. The dilute aqueous solution slowly decomposes. The potassium salt ('Fischer's salt')[527] forms pale yellow or greenish-yellow crystals, sol^y 0·089/17°[528]; in presence of potassium salts the solubility is much less. The aqueous solution is stable in the cold, but decomposes on boiling with the formation of a cobaltous salt. Potassium cobaltinitrite has been much used for the quantitative separation of cobalt from nickel. This salt (to which there is no nickel analogue) is precipitated, washed with potassium acetate solution, and then with 80 per cent. alcohol, and dried at 100°. The salt has also been used for the quantitative

[520] Id., *Ber*. 1901, **34**, 1706.

[521] Ib. 1911, **44**, 2450.

[522] A. F. Wells, *Z. Krist*. 1936, **95**, 74.

[523] G. F. Hüttig and R. Kassler, *Z. anorg. Chem*. 1929, **184**, 281.

[524] S. Kikuchi, *C.R.* 1934, **199**, 1414.

[525] E. Biilmann, *Z. anal. Chem*. 1900, **39**, 286.

[526] M. Cunningham and F. M. Perkin, *J.C.S.* 1909, **95**, 1568.

[527] A. Duflos and N. W. Fischer, *Pogg. Ann*. 1847, **72**, 477; N. W. Fischer, ib. 1848, **74**, 124.

[528] T. Rosenbladt, *Ber*. 1886, **19**, 2535.

estimation of potassium.[529] The solubilities of the cobaltinitrites in g. salt to 100 g. water at temperature $t°$ are:

Salt	Li	Na	K	Rb	Cs	Tl′	NH$_4$	Et·NH$_3$
..	v. v. big ord.	very big ord.	0·089	0·0051	0·0050	0·0042	0·88	31·7
Temp.			17°	17°	17°	17°	0°	0°

The lead and barium salts of the type $M_3''[Co(NO_2)_6]_2$ have also been prepared.[530]

Complexes with Donor Oxygen

These are uniformly weaker than the nitrogen complexes. The replacement of ammonia molecules by water can be carried on until 4 H_2O have been introduced, but the complex weakens as this proceeds. The peculiar position of complexes with attached OH (hydroxo-) groups has already been discussed (pp. 1401–2). No doubt other hydroxylic compounds such as the alcohols could replace water in these complexes, but such compounds do not seem to have been prepared. The great majority of the oxygen complexes of trivalent cobalt are formed by acyl groups, mono- or divalent, the latter (ato- or chelate) being the more stable.[531]

Chelate Diketone Derivatives

Cobaltic acetylacetonate CoA_3 ($A = C_5H_7O_2$) was made[532] by acting with acetylacetone on a cobaltous solution that had been oxidized with sodium hypochlorite. It forms dark green crystals, melting at 241°. It is isomorphous with the corresponding compounds of trivalent aluminium, chromium, manganese, and gallium.[533] It is easily soluble in organic solvents including ligroin (unlike cobaltous acetylacetonate). It is monomeric by the freezing-point in benzene.[532]

Ammine derivatives of complexes with acetylacetone and similar β-diketones have been made. Thus by the action of acetylacetone on the compound [Co en$_2$(OH$_2$)(OH)]Br$_2$ Werner[534] obtained the salts [Co en$_2$A]X$_2$, which can be resolved into optically active forms[535]; all these salts are red. Similar derivatives of propionylacetone were made. If sodium acetylacetonate acts on sodium cobaltinitrite, 4 of the 6 NO$_2$ groups are expelled and replaced by 2 acetylacetonyl residues[536]:

$$Na_3[Co(NO_2)_6] \longrightarrow Na[Co(NO_2)_2A_2].$$

Considering the firmness with which NO$_2$ groups are attached to trivalent

[529] M. Wikul, *Z. anal. Chem.* 1929, **72**, 345.

[530] A. Ferrari and L. Coghi, *Gaz.* 1939, **69**, 3.

[531] For the magnetic properties of these complexes see D. P. Mellor and D. P. Craig, *Proc. Roy. Soc. N.S. Wales*, 1940, **74**, 495.

[532] G. Urbain and A. Debierne, *C.R.* 1899, **129**, 304.

[533] W. T. Astbury, *Proc. Roy. Soc.* 1926, **112**, 449.

[534] A. Werner and S. Matissen, *Helv. Chim. Acta*, 1918, **1**, 78.

[535] A. Werner, J. E. Schwyzer, and W. Karrer, ib. 1921, **4**, 115.

[536] A. Rosenheim and A. Garfunkel, *Ber.* 1911, **44**, 1873.

cobalt this is a remarkable proof of the stability of this chelate acetylacetone ring; salts of this complex are Na, anhydrous, red, 5 H_2O, purplish-
red; K, anhydrous, pale brownish-red; NH_4, Rb, and Cs salts similar.
Other diketones and keto-esters such as acetoacetic ester behave in the
same way.

It has been shown, especially by Morgan and his pupils,[537-41] that mordant dyes such as the alizarines, quinone-oximes, etc., which owe their
dyeing power to their capacity for forming chelate compounds (lakes) with
trivalent metals like aluminium, chromium, and iron, can expel NH_3
groups from a hexammine cobaltic salt, and replace them in pairs by the
chelate ring, up to the neutral compound

Nitroso-β-naphthol gives a compound of this type, which has been used
for the quantitative estimation of cobalt.[542]

Similarly, salicylic acid will give the tetrammine

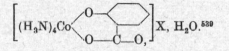

Carbonato-compounds

No pure complex carbonates are known, but several carbonato-ammines
have been prepared, the CO_3 apparently (like SO_3) occupying sometimes
one co-ordination place (CO_3') and sometimes two (CO_2'') (Gm. B. 180, 198,
279). Thus there is a series of blue or brownish-red salts $[Co(NH_3)_5CO_3']X$,
usually with one H_2O. They have an alkaline reaction, and also (owing to
the free valency of the CO_3') form acid salts $[Co(NH_3)_5(CO_3H)]X_2$.

The tetrammines $[Co(NH_3)_4CO_3'']X$ are bluish-red salts made by the
action of sulphuric acid on a suspension of cobaltous carbonate in ammonia
and ammonium carbonate, on oxidation by a current of air. The series
$[Co\,en_2CO_3]X$ (also bluish-red) is similar. If the laevo-form of the *cis*-
dichloro-dien is treated with potassium carbonate,[543 4] the two chlorine
atoms are replaced by CO_3, giving $[Co\,en_2CO_3]X$, and it is the dextro-
carbonato-compound that is formed. The same thing happens if the
dichloro-compound is ground up in water with a small amount of silver
carbonate, but if a large amount of the silver salt is used, the product is
the laevo-form of the carbonato-compound. This is an example of the
occurrence of the Walden transformation among inorganic compounds, the

[537] G. T. Morgan and J. D. Main Smith, *J.C.S.* 1921, **119**, 704.
[538] Id., ib. 1922, **121**, 160.   [539] G. T. Morgan and H. J. S. King, ib. 1723.
[540] G. T. Morgan and J. D. Main Smith, ib. 1956.
[541] Id., ib. 1924, **125**, 1731.
[542] L. Philippot, *Bull. Soc. Chim. Belge*, 1935, **44**, 150.
[543] J. C. Bailar and R. W. Auten, *J.A.C.S.* 1934, **56**, 774.
[544] J. C. Bailar, F. G. Jonelis, and E. H. Huffmann, ib. 1936, **58**, 2224.

transformation taking place probably with the silver salt. Similarly when the laevo-dichloro-dien is treated with ammonia, which replaces the two chlorines by NH_3, giving [Co en$_2$(NH$_3$)$_2$]X$_3$, if the reaction is made to occur below —33° the product is laevorotatory, but if it goes above 25° it is dextrorotatory.[545]

Many other compounds with an acidic hydroxyl group, not only formic and acetic acids, but also di- and trinitrophenol, can replace the hydroxyl group in the pentammines, to give compounds of the type of

$$[Co(NH_3)_5O \cdot CO \cdot CH_3]X_2 \text{ (Gm. B. 186)}.$$

Oxalato-compounds

These occur as 'pure' complexes, in M$_3$[CoOx$_3$], and also in ammines (Gm. B. 186, 199, 202, 291). They can occupy in the complex either two co-ordination places or one, but the tendency to occupy two and so form the chelate 5-ring is very strong with the oxalato-group, and the resulting ring is very stable. The only non-chelate oxalato-compounds are the pentammines [Co(NH$_3$)$_5$Ox]X.[546] These are red salts, whose behaviour is typical of the 1-co-ordinated ato derivatives of dibasic acids; they readily form acid salts [Co(NH$_3$)$_5$(C$_2$O$_4$H)]X$_2$, and the oxalato-group is much less firmly attached than in the compounds in which it forms a ring; after treatment with ammonia in the cold, or after warming, the solution gives a precipitate with calcium chloride.

In all the other compounds, both the ammines and the double oxalates, the oxalato-group forms a chelate ring, and is remarkably stable. Thus in the formation of the oxalato-tetrammines [Co(NH$_3$)$_4$Ox]X and [Co en$_2$Ox]X Schramm[547] has shown that oxalic acid will displace from a tetrammine salt H$_2$O, OH, Cl, Br, NO$_3$, NO$_2$, and the malonato-group (the last two sometimes with great difficulty). The resulting oxalato-salts are not hydrolysed by boiling with ammonia, are stable to dilute acid, and some of them even to cold concentrated hydrochloric or sulphuric acid. These salts are red or carmine.

The triammine-aquo-salts [Co(NH$_3$)$_3$(OH$_2$)Ox]X, bluish-red easily soluble compounds, must have the water molecule in the complex not only because a covalency of 6 is necessary in a cobaltic complex, but also because aqueous ammonia converts them into the corresponding hydroxo-compounds [Co(NH$_3$)$_3$(OH)Ox]°, blue powders which are not salts, are insoluble in water, alcohol, and ether, but readily dissolve in dilute aqueous acids, even acetic, with the re-formation of the aquo-salts.

The diammino-dinitro-salts of the type M[Co(NH$_3$)$_2$(NO$_2$)$_2$Ox] can exist as *cis* and *trans* forms, of which the *cis* but not the *trans* should be separable into optical isomers, and this separation has actually been effected.[548]

[545] J. C. Bailar, J. H. Haslam, and E. M. Jones, *J.A.C.S.* 1936, **58**, 2226.
[546] S. M. Jörgensen, *Z. anorg. Chem.* 1896, **11**, 416.
[547] W. Schramm, ib. 1929, **180**, 161.
[548] W. Thomas, *J.C.S.* 1923, **123**, 617.

Cobaltioxalates

These are all of the type $M_3[CoOx_3]$. The alkaline salts are all dark green, and easily soluble in water: Li, 6 H_2O, extremely soluble and difficult to isolate, isomorphous with the corresponding hexahydrated chromi- and aluminioxalates[549]; Na, 5 (and 4) H_2O, isomorphous with the penta-hydrates of the sodium alumini- chromi- and ferri-oxalates[549]; K, H_2O. This potassium salt is best made by oxidizing a solution of cobaltous oxalate in potassium oxalate solution with lead dioxide. It is produced as a racemate, which crystallizes as such only below 13°; above that temperature the dextro- and laevo-forms separate side by side. The active form racemises in solution much more slowly than the corresponding chromic or ferric compounds.[550-1] The ammonium salt has 3 H_2O, and the rubidium salt 4 H_2O; these high hydration numbers are no doubt due to the tendency of the oxalate group to take up water.

These cobaltioxalates are very fairly stable, as is shown by the slowness with which they racemize; but they seem to be less stable than the oxalato-ammines.

Dithio-oxalato-complexes

H. O. Jones showed[552-3] that if a cobaltous salt and potassium dithio-oxalate $K_2C_2O_2S_2$ are mixed in solution an intense reddish-brown colour is produced, which can be recognized if there is only 1 part of cobalt to 40 million parts of water. Barium chloride precipitates from the solution the salt $BaK[Co(C_2O_2S_2)_3]$, 6 H_2O, from which the K salt, 2 H_2O and the anilinium salt 2 H_2O can be obtained. The freezing-points and conductivities in water are those of a 4-ionic salt. These salts are remarkably stable: the colour is not destroyed by adding potassium cyanide, or by boiling with moderately strong hydrochloric acid.

Malonato-compounds

Pure cobaltimalonates do not seem to occur.[554] The same is true of the succinates and glutarates.[547]

Among the ammines, however, and especially the tetrammines, derivatives of malonic acid and other dibasic acids of that series are found; they can be made by acting with the acid on the carbonato-compound $[Co(NH_3)_4CO_3]X$. Schramm has shown[547] that malonic acid, unlike oxalic, will not expel from a tetrammine such groups as halogens or NO_3, but only the radicals of weak acids like carbonic.

In this way a series of tetrammine (especially di-en) salts have

[549] H. Copaux, *C.R.* 1902, **134**, 1215; *Ann. Chim. Phys.* 1905, [8] **6**, 565.

[550] F. M. Jaeger and W. Thomas, *K. Akad. Amst.* 1918, **27**, 676.

[551] W. Thomas and R. Fraser, *J.C.S.* 1923, **123**, 2973. See also C. H. Johnson and A. Mead, *Trans. Far. Soc.* 1933, **29**, 626.

[552] H. O. Jones and H. S. Tasker, *J.C.S.* 1909, **95**, 1904.

[553] C. S. Robinson and H. O. Jones, ib. 1912, **101**, 62.

[554] R. C. Lord, *J. Phys. Chem.* 1907, **11**, 173.

been made from dimethyl malonic,[555] succinic, and dibromosuccinic acids.[556]

Nitrato-compounds[557]

In general the NO_3 group is very reluctant to attach itself covalently to a metal; double nitrates are not common, and it is doubtful whether any of them are truly complex. True nitrato-cobaltic complexes occur, but only when they are stabilized by the presence of several amine groups, and even then the NO_3 is easily removed.[558-9]

Nitrato-ammines are known with 1, 2, and 3 (but not more) nitrato-groups attached to the cobalt. They are usually made by the action of fairly concentrated nitric acid on the corresponding aquo-salts; the reaction is commonly reversible, the NO_3 groups being hydrolysed in dilute solution and replaced by water molecules as they are also by ammonia on treatment with liquid ammonia:

$$[Co(NH_3)_5(OH_2)]^{+++} + HNO_3 \longrightarrow [Co(NH_3)_5NO_3]^{++} + H^+ + H_2O.$$

The trinitrato-triammine $[Co(NH_3)_3(NO_3)_3]°^{559}$ forms reddish-violet crystals, insoluble in cold water, by which it is slowly hydrolysed to the triaquo-triammine nitrate, $[Co(NH_3)_3(OH_2)_3](NO_3)_3$.

No compounds with a nitrato group attached to a cobalt in an anion are known.

Sulphato-compounds

No cobaltic double sulphates are known except the alums (p. 1396) which are not true complexes. Among the ammines, however, there are a few undoubted sulphato-complexes in some of which certainly, and in most probably, the SO_4 group is only attached to the cobalt atom through one oxygen,

$$Co-O-S \overset{\overset{\displaystyle \bar{O}}{\diagup}}{\underset{\diagdown O}{\rightarrow O}};$$

this must be so in the pentammine $[Co(NH_3)_5SO_4]X$, since the total covalency of the trivalent cobalt is always 6. The other compounds contain 4 and 3 molecules of ammonia, but also water, which is probably part of the complexes, so that these may be written

$$[Co(NH_3)_4(OH_2)SO_4]X$$
$$[Co(NH_3)_3(OH_2)_2SO_4]X$$
$$[Co\ en_2(OH_2)SO_4]X.$$

The salts are prepared by the action of sulphuric acid on the aquo- or carbonato-compounds. They are all bluish or purple. The SO_4 group is not very firmly attached; barium chloride does not give a precipitate with

[555] T. S. Price and J. C. Duff, *J.C.S.* 1920, **117**, 1077.
[556] J. C. Duff, ib. 1921, **119**, 387.
[557] See Gmelin, B. 144, 147, 148, 227, 259 (1930).
[558] See also A. Werner, *Ann.* 1911, **386**, 214, 255.
[559] E. Birk, *Z. anorg. Chem.* 1928, **175**, 409.

the nitrate or chloride in the cold, but it does so on boiling, when the SO_4 is replaced by OH_2. This looseness of attachment of the sulphate group is no doubt partly due to its being linked only by one oxygen, and not forming a ring, and the fact that in none of the other types does it show greater stability than in the pentammines (where it can only be linked through one oxygen) is an indication that in the tetrammine and triammine compounds also there is no sulphato-ring.

Sulphito-complexes

These are more numerous and more stable than the sulphato-compounds, and 'pure' complexes, such as those of the type $M_3[Co(SO_3)_3]$ occur, as well as ammines like $[Co(NH_3)_5SO_3]X$. It is clear that the sulphito-group can occupy either one place in the complex (SO_3') or two (SO_3''); in the pure complex sulphites it is always two: in the ammines it is sometimes one and sometimes two.

Complex Cobaltic Sulphites

The double sulphites are mainly of the type $M_3[Co(SO_3)_3]$. The lithium salt ($4 H_2O$) can be made[560] by warming lithium cobaltinitrite with lithium sulphite solution. It forms red crystals very slightly soluble in water (this small solubility is characteristic of all the salts of this group). It is decomposed slowly by water and at once by alkalies to precipitate the cobaltic hydroxide; acids form the cobaltous salt. The sodium ($4 H_2O$), potassium ($6 H_2O$), and ammonium ($1 H_2O$) salts are all red, and almost insoluble in water.[561] Owing to the presence of the easily oxidizable SO_3 groups the salts are liable to catch fire in air.

Sulphito-cobaltammines[562-5]

Two questions arise about these compounds: (1) whether the SO_3 is attached to the cobalt by two links or one,[562] and (2) whether these links are always through oxygen, or whether a direct Co—S link can occur.

Cobaltic ammines are known with 1, 2, and 3 SO_3 groups to one cobalt. Of the monosulphites the pentammines $[Co(NH_3)_5SO_3]X^{564}$ must clearly have the SO_3 group 1-covalent; this is confirmed by the fact that the chloride is converted by hydrochloric acid into the purpureo-chloride $[Co(NH_3)_5Cl]Cl_2$. These sulphito-pentammines are brown salts soon decomposed by water, which can form acid salts $[Co(NH_3)_5SO_3H]X_2$, owing to the presence of the negatively charged oxygen atom of the SO_3'.

The tetrammine monosulphites may either be $[Co(NH_3)_4(OH_2)SO_3']X$ or $[Co(NH_3)_4SO_3'']X H_2O$. The former is the more probable view since they can have the H_2O replaced by NO_2,[563] to give the non-electrolyte

$$[Co(NH_3)_4(NO_2)(SO_3)]^\circ.$$

[560] G. Jantsch and K. Abresch, *Z. anorg. Chem.* 1929, **179**, 351.

[561] F. L. Hahn, H. A. Meier, and H. Siegert, ib. 1926, **150**, 126.

[562] E. H. Riesenfeld and W. Petrich, ib. 1924, **132**, 99: the theoretical part is by Riesenfeld and the experimental by Petrich.

[563] K. A. Hofmann and S. Reinsch, ib. 1898, **16**, 377.

The tetrammines $M[Co(NH_3)_4(SO_3)_2]$ which occur in *cis* and *trans* modifications[563-5] must obviously have 1-co-ordinated SO_3 groups.

The triammines $M[Co(NH_3)_3(OH_2)(SO_3)_2]$[563,565] must have one mono-covalent SO_3, but the other may be mono- as written above, or di-covalent with the water outside the bracket. They occur in two series, which Hofmann ascribes to *cis-trans* isomerism and not to any change of the structure of the SO_3 groups; this has not been proved, but the di-en salt, where *cis-trans* isomerism is impossible but not the change in the SO_3, could not be got in two forms.[562]

The diammine $(NH_4)[Co(NH_3)_2(SO_3)_2]$[562] is almost certainly dichelate.

The trisulphito-ammines such as $(NH_4)_2[Co(NH_3)_3(SO_3)_3]$ must have 3 SO_3' groups.

The doubt whether the SO_3 is linked to the cobalt through oxygen, as in

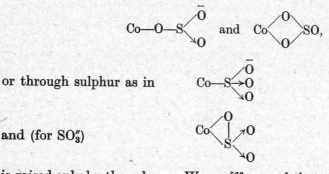

or through sulphur as in

and (for SO_3'')

is raised only by the colours. Werner[566] argued that since $[Co\ en_2(SO_3'')]X$ is brown, it could not have

$$Co\langle\!\!\!\begin{array}{c}O\\[-2pt]\\[-2pt]O\end{array}\!\!\!\rangle SO,$$

which should be red like the diaquo-compound. Duff[567] found that while the sulphato-di-en salts were red, the thiosulphato (which must have

$$Co\langle\!\!\!\begin{array}{c}O\\[-2pt]\\[-2pt]S\end{array}\!\!\!\rangle SO_2,$$

since they were not attacked by silver oxide) were brown. Hence, he says the golden-brown $[Co\ en_2(SO_3'')Br],\ 3\ H_2O$ must have the Co—S link. Further, the sulphito-pentammines are brown, while the complex sulphites $M_3[Co(SO_3)_3]$ are red. We might accept this evidence for the Co—S link where the SO_3 occupies only one co-ordination place, but it does not justify the assumption of a $Co\langle\!\!\!\begin{array}{c}O\\[-2pt]|\\[-2pt]S\end{array}$ 3-ring.

[564] A. Werner and H. Grüger, ib. 1898, **16**, 398.

[565] K. A. Hofmann and A. Jenny, *Ber.* 1901, **34**, 3855.

[566] *Ann.* 1911, **386**, 81. This paper is repeatedly quoted in this section, and because of its length (**386**, pp. 1–272) it is useful to mention the page referred to.

[567] J. C. Duff, *J.C.S.* 1922, **121**, 450.

Halogen-complexes

All four halogen elements can form part of cobaltic ammine complexes; the number of such cations formed by each element, according to Gmelin, is fluorine 4; chlorine 25; bromine 13; iodine 1. As there are obvious reasons why the number of known fluorine complexes should be small, we may take it that the stability falls off as the atomic number of the halogen increases.

The number of halogens united to a cobaltic atom in these complexes is F 1, 2; Cl, Br 1, 2, 3; I 1. No compound with more than three halogen atoms attached to a trivalent cobalt is known: this atom cannot form pure complex halides of such types as $M[CoX_4]$ or $M_3[CoX_6]$. In this it stands alone among trivalent metals, differing even from divalent cobalt, which gives a large number of complex halides of the $M_2[Co(hal)_4]$ type with all four halogens, and a considerable number of $M_4[Co(hal)_6]$ salts with all but fluorine; yet we should expect an atom to form any such complexes more easily when trivalent than when divalent. It is probably a question of the relative affinities of the Co–hal and the Co←OH_2 links.

In these ammine complexes the halogen atoms are less firmly attached than NO_2 groups. The mono-halogen compounds are stable in solution in the cold, but if the solution is boiled, or even warmed to 70°, the halogen is fairly rapidly replaced by H_2O. With the di-halogen compounds the change is still easier, and hydrolysis to the aquo-compound occurs in solution fairly quickly even in the cold, often with a striking change of colour, for example, with the $[Co(NH_3)_4Cl_2]X$ salt from blue to reddish-violet.

The non-ionized trihalogen compounds such as $[Co(NH_3)_3Cl_3]°$ behave in the same way.[568-9]

Note on Cis-trans *Cobaltic Isomers*

The *cis* and *trans* isomers among these complexes differ greatly in ease of transformation; with some, only the stable series can be isolated. The isomers differ in other properties as well, such as colour, solubility, and stability of the complex. Examples are given in Tables I, II, and III below (p. 1414). No differences characteristic of *cis* as opposed to *trans* compounds in general are to be expected, since the groups concerned differ so widely, especially in that some are neutral molecules and some radicals. The differences of stability seem to indicate that in complexes of the types $[CoAm_4(H_2O)_2]X_3$ and $[CoAm_4(H_2O)X']X_2$ (Am = NH_3 or an amine) the *cis* form is usually the more stable, while with $[CoAm_4X'_2]X$ it is the *trans*.

Differences in colour are almost invariable, and in some cases have led to different trivial names: thus in the dinitro-tetrammines

$$[Co(NH_3)_4(NO_2)_2]X$$

the yellow *cis* forms are called flavo and orange *trans* croceo.

[568] E. Birk, *Z anorg. Chem.* 1926, **158**, 111.   [569] Id., ib. 1928, **175**, 412.

In solubility in water the *cis* forms are more soluble (sometimes 10 times as soluble) where the groups other than $4 NH_3$ or 2 *en* are H_2O, NH_3; $2 H_2O$; or $2 NO_2$; they are less soluble when these are 2 NCS; NCS, Cl; NCS, NO_2; Cl, Br. Lists from Gmelin B follow.

Cis-trans *Differences*

I. *Colour*

Gm. B, p.	Formula	Cis	Trans
119	$[Co\ en_2(H_2O)_2]X_3$	Fiery red	Brownish-red
122	$[Co(NH_3)_3(H_2O)_3]Cl_3$	Pale or red-violet	Dark violet
141	$[Co(NH_3)en_2(NO_2)]X_2$	Darker	Paler
143	$[Co\ en_2(H_2O)NO_2]X_2$	Red	Orange
176	$[Co(NH_3)\ en_2Br]X_2$	Red-brown	Blue-violet
183	$[Co(NH_3)en_2(CNS)]X_2$	*Both* form brick-red to brown-red	
205	$[Co(NH_3)_4(NO_2)_2]X$	Yellow (flavo)	Orange (croceo)
254–5	$[Co\ en_2(NCS)_2]X$	Yellow-red	Dark red
265	$[Co\ en_2ClBr]X$	Grey	Green
250	$[Co\ en_2Br_2]X$	Violet	Green
267	$[Co(NH_3)_4(NCS)NO_2]X$	Brown-yellow	Flesh-coloured
269	$[Co\ en_2(NCS)NO_2]X$	Brown-yellow	Dark brown
271	$[Co\ en_2Cl(NCS)]X$	Blue-pink	Violet
275	$[Co\ en_2Br(NCS)]X$	Blue-red	Blue

II. *Solubility*

Gm. B, p.	Formula	Cis	Trans
119	$[Co\ en_2(H_2O)_2]X_3$	*Very* sol. water	Less sol. water
141	$[Co(NH_3)en_2(NO_2)]X_2$	More sol.	Less sol.
205	$[Co(NH_3)_4(NO_2)_2]X$	Much more sol.	Sol^y 1/5–1/10 of *cis*.
255	$[Co\ en_2(NCS)_2]X$	Less sol.	More sol.
265	$[Co\ en_2ClBr]X$	Slightly sol.	Easily sol.
269	$[Co\ en_2(NCS)NO_2]X$	Slightly sol.	Much more sol.
271	$[Co\ en_2Cl(NCS)]X$	Less sol.	Much more sol.

III. Cis-trans *Stability*

Gm. B, p.	Formula	Cis	Trans
119	$[Co\ en_2(H_2O)_2]X_3$	*Cis*+alkali goes to *trans*	
166	$[Co(NH_3)_4(H_2O)Cl]X_2$	Only *cis* occurs	
178	$[Co(NH_3)_4(H_2O)Br]X_2$	Only *cis* occurs	
176	$[Co\ en_2(H_2O)Br]X_2$	Only *cis* occurs	
228	$[Co(NH_3)_4Cl_2]X$	In acid *cis* goes to the (in acid) more stable *trans*	
233	$[Co\ py_4Cl_2]X$	..	Only *trans* known
235	$[Co\ en_2Cl_2]X$	Neutral goes to *cis*, acid sol. to *trans*.	
250	$[Co\ en_2Br_2]X$	The same	The same

Note on Trivial Names of Cobaltammines

Many of these series have trivial names derived from the colours; these were first introduced by E. Frémy in 1851–2, when the constitutions were not understood, and hence some of them do not fit the colours of all the compounds included in the definitions. The following are some of the more important ($Am = NH_3$).

Luteo. $[Co(Am_6)]X_3$.

Roseo. $[Co(Am_5)(H_2O)]X_3$ and $[Co(Am_4)(H_2O)_2]X_3$.

Xantho. $[CoAm_5NO_2]X_2 : [CoAm_4(H_2O)NO_2]X_2$.

Isoxantho. $[CoAm_5(-O-N=O)]X_2$.

Purpureo. $[CoAm_5X']X_2$, where $X' = NO_3$, Cl, Br; also $[CoAM_5SO_4]X$.

Flavo. *cis* $[CoAm_4(NO_2)_2]X$.

Croceo. *trans* ½ en. ½ pn, etc.

Violeo. *cis* $[CoAm_4X_2']X$.

Praseo. *trans* ½ en, etc., and $X' = $ Cl, Br.

Dichro. $[CoAm_3(H_2O)Cl_2]X$.

'Erdmann's salts.' $M[CoAm_2(NO_2)_4]$.

'Vortmann's sulphate' is mainly

$$\left[(NH_3)_4Co \underset{\underset{H_2}{N}}{\overset{\overset{H}{\overset{.}{O}}}{<>}} Co(NH_3)_4 \right] (SO_4)_2,\ 2\ H_2O.$$

Polynuclear Cobaltic Complexes[571]

Among the complexes formed by any element there are always some which contain more than one atom of the element in question in the molecule. These have usually been omitted so far, because the evidence for their structure is as a rule insufficient to establish it with any certainty.

With some elements, however, and especially with those of Group VIII, compounds of this kind, which Werner called polynuclear (*mehrkernig*), have been examined with care, and their structures made reasonably probable. This is especially true of the cobaltic compounds.[570-1] For example, there is a series of bright-blue cobaltic salts of the composition $[Co_2(NH_2)(NH_3)_{10}]X_5$. If these are warmed with a mixture of hydrochloric and sulphuric acids they break up into a mixture of the hexammine and chloropentammine chlorides, which makes their structure clear:

$$[(H_3N)_5Co{-}N{\to}Co(NH_3)_5]X_5 + HCl = [(H_3N)_6Co]Cl_3 + [Co(NH_3)_5Cl]Cl_2.$$
$$\underset{H\ \ \ H}{\wedge}$$

It is evident that the bridge holding the two cobalt atoms together is the NH_2, which is united to one by a normal and to the other by a co-ordinate covalency.

[570] A. Werner, *Ann.* 1910, **375**, 1.

[571] Werner–Pfeiffer, *Neu. Ansch.* 1923, pp. 269–91.

A related series is that known as the Vortmann salts

$$[Co_2(NH_3)_8(OH)(NH_2)]X_4.$$

If these are treated with concentrated nitric acid they add on a molecule of the acid to give a salt $[Co_2(NH_3)_8(OH_2)(NH_2)]X_4(NO_3)$ which is converted by liquid ammonia into the decammine-μ-amino-salt itself. Now the decammine salt has in the molecule 11 co-ordinated groups (including the NH_2) to 2 cobalt atoms: we have seen that probably one of them, the NH_2, forms a bridge and occupies one position on each cobalt, thus raising the co-ordination number to the 6 apiece needed for the stability of the trivalent cobalt. The nitrate made from the Vortmann salt also has 11 such groups, and no doubt the NH_2 is acting as a bridge here too. The closely related Vortmann salt itself has only 10 groups, and it is not an improbable suggestion that there is here a second bridge, formed no doubt by the hydroxyl group, raising the co-ordination number for each cobalt again to 6, thus:

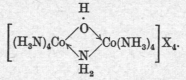

This is confirmed by the observation that the OH in this compound does not behave like an ordinary hydroxo-group: it would normally be convertible by acids with great ease into OH_2, but in this salt it is not. The resemblance of this linkage to that in a trivalent halide such as auric bromide is obvious:

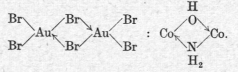

These polynuclear cobalt complexes occur with one, two, or three bridges between cobalt atoms, and there may be one set of such bridges (2 cobalt atoms) or two (3 Co) or three (4 Co). The groups acting as bridges are always attached by normal covalencies to one cobalt atom (as in Co—N→Co) and sometimes to both (Co—N—Co). Practically the only groups which can act as bridges in any of these complexes are NH_2, NH, NO_2, OH, O_2, $O \cdot CO \cdot CH_3$, SO_4, and SeO_4. Where there is only a single bridge this is always either NH_2 or $—O_2—$, the latter very rarely except in the curious complexes with tetravalent cobalt which are discussed later (p. 1420). The doubly bridged compounds have the pairs of bridges NH_2, NH_2; NH_2, NO_2; NH_2, $O \cdot CO \cdot CH_3$; NH_2, SO_4; NH_2, SeO_4; NH, SO_4; NH_2, O_2; NH, O_2; NH_2, OH; OH, OH; OH, O_2; OH, $O \cdot CO \cdot CH_3$. In the triply bridged complexes one bridge is always OH, a second usually OH, but sometimes NH_2 and rarely NO_2; while the third can be NH_2, NO_2, OH, O_2 or $O \cdot CO \cdot CH_3$.

One Bridge

NH_2: see above, p. 1415.

Peroxo, as in $[(NH_3)_5Co—O_2—Co(NH_3)_5]X_4$. These salts[570] are the first products of the action of air on an ammoniacal solution of a cobaltous salt; thus cobaltous nitrate $Co(NO_3)_2$ gives the nitrate of the above cation; it explodes at 200°, and its solution in acid, alkali, or water alone decomposes in the cold. These peroxo-compounds are chiefly remarkable for the ease with which they are oxidized to the $Co'''—Co''''$ complexes (p. 1420).

Two Bridges

(1) NH_2, NH_2. These complexes seem to be very unstable, and have only once been made[572]; by drying the dichloro-tetrammine *cis*

$$[Co(NH_3)_4Cl_2]Cl$$

over phosphorus pentoxide the complex

$$\left[(NH_3)_4Co \underset{H_2N}{\overset{NH_2}{<>}} Co(NH_3)_4 \right] X_4$$

was obtained as an ochre-red salt.

Complexes in which only one of the two bridges is NH_2 are more stable.

(2) NH_2, OH. These have already been described (p. 1416); they are the Vortmann salts.[573-4] Corresponding *en* salts, such as

$$\left[en_2Co \underset{HO}{\overset{NH_2}{<>}} Co\ en_2 \right] X_4$$

are also known.[575]

A very remarkable series of salts are those in which one of the bridges is a nitro-group. Thus by the action of nitrous acid on the amino-ol complexes (NH_2, OH) the amino-nitro-complex can be made: for example the brown salt[576]

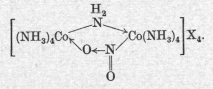

These compounds are extraordinarily stable; the NO_2 group is not split off even by boiling with concentrated hydrochloric acid: this strongly supports the view that the NO_2 forms a bridge. Though they are normally hydrated, the anhydrous salts can be made from them, so that it is not

[572] A. Werner, *Ann.* 1910, **375**, 23, 83.   [573] Id., *Ber.* 1907, **40**, 4612.
[574] Id., *Ann.* 1910, **375**, 16.   [575] Id., ib. 76.
[576] A. Werner, F. Salzer, and M. Pieper, ib. 54.

an HO that forms the bridge. Corresponding aquo-nitro salts, with the

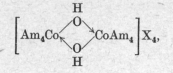

bridge are also known.[577] They are dark violet or dark grey, and are very insoluble in water.

(3) OH, OH.[578] These are Werner's 'diol' complexes, for example[579]

$$\left[Am_4Co \begin{array}{c} H \\ O \\ \diagdown \diagup \\ \diagup \diagdown \\ O \\ H \end{array} CoAm_4 \right] X_4,$$

made by dehydration of the hydroxo-aquo-tetrammine

$$\left[Am_4Co \diagup^{OH}_{\diagdown OH_2} \right] X_2:$$

they are garnet-red salts, which unlike the hydroxo-salts are neutral to litmus. The *en* salts are also known.[580] Anionic diols have likewise been made, such as the oxalato-complex[581-2]

$$K_4 \left[Ox_2Co \diagup^{OH}_{\diagdown HO} CoOx_2 \right].$$

Three Bridges

Examples are

$$\left[(NH_3)_3Co \diagup^{NH_2}_{\diagdown HO}\!\!-OH\!\rightarrow\!Co(NH_3)_3 \right] X_3{}^{583}$$

and the triol complex

$$\left[(NH_3)_3Co\!\leftarrow\!\diagup^{OH}_{\diagdown OH}\!\!HO\!\rightarrow\!Co(NH_3)_3 \right] X_3{}^{584-5},$$

which can be made from the chloro- or bromo-aquo-triammines with aqueous sodium hydroxide. They are red salts. The evidence for the structure, especially of the last-mentioned series, is (1) that hydrochloric acid gives $[Co(NH_3)_3(H_2O)Cl_2]X$, showing that each cobalt atom is attached to 3 ammonia molecules; (2) all the three X groups ionize; (3) the salts are neutral to water, and so cannot be aquo- or hydroxo-salts.

The OH bridges are easily broken. Nitrous acid converts the triol into a nitro-diol,[586] and acetic acid into the acetate-diols.[587]

[577] A. Werner and E. Welti, *Ann.* 1910, **375**, 128.
[578] P. Pfeiffer, *Z. anorg. Chem.* 1901, **29**, 130.
[579] A. Werner, *Ber.* 1907, **40**, 4434.   [580] Id., *Ann.* 1910, **375**, 83.
[581] R. G. Durrant, *J.C.S.* 1905, **87**, 1781.
[582] E. G. V. Percival and W. Wardlaw, ib. 1929, 2628.
[583] A. Werner, *Ann.* 1910, **375**, 91.   [584] Id., *Ber.* 1907, **40**, 4838.
[585] E. Birk, *Z. anorg. Chem.* 1928, **175**, 411.
[586] A. Werner, A. Grün, and E. Bindschedler, *Ann.* 1910, **375**, 123.
[587] A. Werner, ib. 115.

Trinuclear Complexes

These complexes have a series of 3 cobalt atoms united by two bridges. The bridges may be double, as in

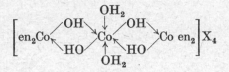

red or brownish-red salts.[588-9] The bridges may also be triple; there are numerous salts known of the complex cation

$$\left[(NH_3)_3Co\!\!\overset{OH}{\underset{OH}{\longleftarrow}}\!\!HO\!\!-\!\!Co\!\!\overset{OH}{\underset{OH}{\longleftarrow}}\!\!HO\!\!-\!\!Co(NH_3)_3 \right] X_3. $$

These are green salts.[590]

Quadrinuclear Complexes

These are almost confined to the salts of the dodecammine hexol ion and of the corresponding hexa-en complex.

The dodecammine compounds were made[591] by the action of alkali or aqueous ammonia on the di-aquo- or the chloro-aquo-tetrammine sulphate in the cold. Their constitution was established by Werner,[592] who showed that when they are treated with cold concentrated hydrochloric acid, enough chlorine is evolved to reduce one cobalt atom out of four from the trivalent to the divalent state (forming cobaltous chloride $CoCl_2$), while the other three atoms appear as the tetrammine cobaltic salt. Later[593] he resolved the bromide

$$\left[Co\!\!\left(\begin{matrix} H \\ O \\ \diagdown \\ \diagup \\ O \\ H \end{matrix} Co(NH_3)_4 \right)_3 \right] Br_6 $$

into its optically active forms, giving a further proof of the correctness of the structure, and also affording the first example of an optically active molecule containing no carbon. The en salts are very similar[592]; the nitrate $(NO_3)_6$ and the bromide, iodide, and thiocyanate all have three molecules of water, but the chloride appears to be anhydrous. The salts decompose slowly in water in the presence of a little alkali to form cobaltic hydroxide Co_2O_3, H_2O, and the green salts $[Co\ en_2(H_2O)OH]X_2$.

[588] A. Werner, ib. 41.
[589] A. Werner and G. Jantsch, *Ber.* 1907, **40**, 4430.
[590] A. Werner, *Ann.* 1910, **375**, 141.
[591] S. M. Jörgensen, *Z. anorg. Chem.* 1898, **16**, 184.
[592] A. Werner, *Ber.* 1907, **40**, 2118.
[593] Id., ib. 1914, **47**, 3090.

TETRAVALENT COBALT

THE evidence for the occurrence of tetravalent cobalt is of a very singular kind. It is entirely confined to one small group of complexes, consisting of some (not all) of the binuclear peroxo-compounds, but in this group it seems to be very strong. As there are no indications of tetravalency in nickel and practically none in iron, its occurrence with cobalt is surprising, and the evidence for it clearly needs careful scrutiny.

As we have seen, normal peroxide compounds of trivalent cobalt occur in which the O_2 group is exerting two valencies to the two cobalt atoms in the molecule as Co—O_2—Co, giving a salt $[(H_3N)_5Co—O_2—Co(NH_3)_5]X_4$. But in addition to these salts, which are brownish-black, another series of deep-green salts can be made by oxidation,[594-5] differing only in having an electrovalency of 5 instead of 4; they still contain the pentammine group, and so must have the structure $[(H_3N)_5Co—O_2—Co(NH_3)_5]X_5$. But if so, the two cobalt atoms are exerting between them 2 covalencies to the oxygen and 5 electrovalencies, or 7 in all, and so must be tri- and tetravalent respectively. The remarkable point is, of course, that a valency of 4 for cobalt is only known in this very peculiar position, in the group $Co'''—O_2—Co^{iv}$, which may be combined with a second and even a third bridge (see later). But in these binuclear peroxides this is the prevalent form; of the five series of peroxo-compounds that have been prepared, three exhibit this abnormal valency.[596]

Werner fully recognized the exceptional nature of these compounds, and he has examined them with such care, both by analysis and by determination of their oxidizing power, that there can be no doubt that the compositions assigned to them are correct; but further work on them by modern methods is much to be desired. There must obviously be resonance between the trivalent and the tetravalent cobalt atoms, and this must be favoured by the presence of the peroxide group. This resonance should have a marked effect on the colour, increasing the sharpness and the intensity of the absorption bands. Unfortunately many of these cobaltic complexes already have such intense colours that the further effect of a possible resonance is difficult to detect. The compounds themselves are enumerated in Werner's *N. Ansch.* (ed. Pfeiffer), 1923, pp. 274–81).

1. The decammine salts $[(H_3N)_5Co—O_2—Co^{iv}(NH_3)_5]X_5$[594-5] as already described are made by the oxidation of the trivalent peroxo-salts; they are bright deep-green, and the peroxide oxygen is much more firmly held than in the trivalent peroxides (perhaps on account of the resonance).

2. The hexammine salts

$$\left[\begin{array}{c} Cl \qquad\qquad Cl_2 \\ HO—Co—O_2—Co \\ (H_3N)_3 \qquad (NH_3)_3 \end{array} \right] X^{597}$$

are less stable than the others.

3. The octammine

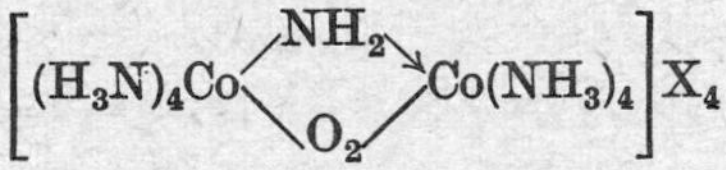

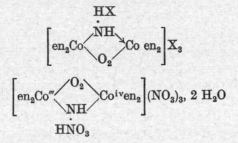

$$\left[(H_3N)_4Co\diagdown^{NH_2}_{O_2}\diagup Co(NH_3)_4\right]X_4$$

is formed along with the trivalent Vortmann salt by oxidizing ammoniacal cobaltous nitrate solution and saturating with sulphuric acid. These salts are intense green; they are rather easily reduced, and on warming with sulphuric acid give off the excess of oxygen quantitatively.[598]

4. The 4 NH_3 groups on each cobalt in the last compound can be replaced by 2 en groups; the 4-en compound produced[598] is deep green.

5. These tetra-en salts will go over into an isomeric red form, which has a trivalent cation and is written by Werner[599]

$$\left[en_2Co\diagdown^{\overset{HX}{\overset{.}{NH}}}_{O_2}\diagup Co\ en_2\right]X_3$$

or, the nitrate

$$\left[en_2Co'''\diagup^{O_2}_{\underset{HNO_3}{\overset{.}{NH}}}\diagdown Co^{iv}en_2\right](NO_3)_3,\ 2\ H_2O$$

6. Another type which can be got from the above, and are intense brown, are

$$\left[en_2Co\diagdown^{NH}_{O_2}\diagup Co\ en_2\right]X_3.$$

7. A hexammine salt

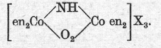

$$\left[(H_3N)_4Co\diagdown^{NH_2}_{O_2}\diagdown Co\diagup^{(NH_3)_2}_{Cl_2}\right]X_3,$$

8. The corresponding dibromide.

9. The salt

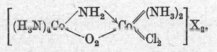

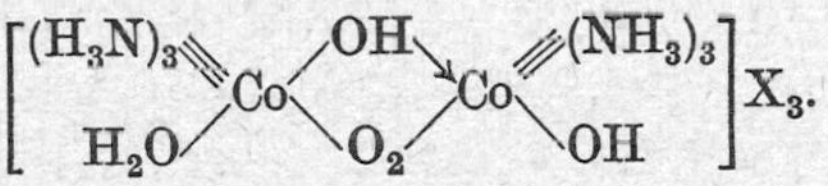

$$\left[{}^{(H_3N)_3}_{H_2O}\diagdown Co\diagdown^{OH}_{O_2}\diagdown Co\diagup^{(NH_3)_3}_{OH}\right]X_3.$$

10. These tetravalent cobalt salts can also occur with three bridges instead of one or two. The so-called melanochloride, which is got by oxidizing an ammoniacal solution of cobaltous chloride, contains the salt

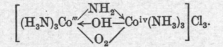

$$\left[(H_3N)_3Co'''{\leftarrow}OH{-}Co^{iv}(NH_3)_3\diagup^{NH_2}_{O_2}\right]Cl_3.$$

[594] G. Vortmann, *Mon.* 1885, **6**, 404.
[595] A. Werner and A. Mylius, *Z. anorg. Chem.* 1898, **16**, 245.
[596] A. Werner, *Ann.* 1910, **375**, 1–141.
[597] Id., ib. 137.
[598] Id., ib. 61, 70.
[599] Id., ib. 72.

These salts are also made by the action of ammonium chloride on the tri-tetravalent octammine salt described under 1. These salts have an intense green colour, and a neutral reaction to litmus.[600]

It has recently been found[601] that both the decammine and the octammine salts (1 and 3 above) have magnetic moments of 1·6 to 1·7 Bohr magnetons.

Cobalt Carbonyl Complexes

The various valencies of the elements in their carbonyl and nitrosyl complexes have so little relation to those in other compounds that these complexes are better discussed separately.

There are two 'pure' carbonyls of cobalt, $Co_2(CO)_8$ and $Co_4(CO)_{12}$, both of which comply with the 'inert gas rule' (IV. 548). Their structures are unknown, but it is possible that the first is similar to $Fe_2(CO)_9$ (p. 1369) but with one of the three linking CO groups absent; if the two cobalt atoms are directly linked, this would make them trivalent and 6-covalent, with the E.A.N. 36.

The 'tetracarbonyl' $Co_2(CO)_8$ can be made by the action of carbon monoxide at 1–200 atm. and at 150–200° on finely powdered cobalt[602]: or in presence of copper (or some other metal that can take up sulphur or halogens) on cobalt sulphide CoS or on a cobaltous halide (best CoI_2).[604,607] This last is the best method. It forms orange crystals which are quickly oxidized by air. Its molecular weight was determined by the freezing-point in benzene[605] in which, as in other organic solvents, it is readily soluble. At 50° or above it loses carbon monoxide to form the 'tricarbonyl' $Co_4(CO)_{12}$,[602] very unstable black crystals easily oxidized by air, and much less soluble than the first compound, though it can be recrystallized from hot benzene; its molecular weight was found by the freezing-point in iron pentacarbonyl.[605]

$Co_2(CO)_8$ forms the volatile hydride $Co(CO)_3COH$ with great ease, for example on treatment with bases:

$$3 Co_2(CO)_8 + 4 H_2O = 4 Co(CO)_3COH + 2 Co(OH)_2 + 8 CO.$$

It is also formed in the preparation of this carbonyl if moisture is present, and it can be made by heating cobalt powder with carbon monoxide and hydrogen, or cobaltous oxide with carbon monoxide.[603] In fact the reaction

$$2 Co(CO)_3COH \rightleftharpoons Co_2(CO)_8 + H_2$$

is reversible. The best way of making the hydride[607] is by saturating a solution of cobaltous nitrate in water at 0° with carbon monoxide in presence of potassium cyanide. This gives a yellow solution of the salt

[600] A. Werner, *Ann.* 1910, **375**, 104.   [601] L. Malatesta, *Gaz.* 1942, **72**, 287.

[602] L. Mond, H. Hirtz, and M. D. Cowap, *J.C.S.* 1910, **97**, 798.

[603] W. Hieber, H. Schulten, and R. Marin, *Z. anorg. Chem.* 1939, **240**, 261.

[604] H. Schulten, ib. 1939, **243**, 145.

[605] W. Hieber, F. Mühlbauer, and E. A. Ehmann, *Ber.* 1932, **65**, 1090.

[606] W. Hieber and H. Schulten, *Z. anorg. Chem.* 1937, **232**, 17.

[607] A. A. Blanchard and P. Gilmont, *J.A.C.S.* 1940, **62**, 1192.

$K[Co(CO)_4]$. On the addition of hydrochloric acid the hydride $Co(CO)_3COH$ is liberated and carried off by the carbon monoxide stream, from which it can be frozen out at —78°.

The hydride[608] forms pale-yellow crystals with an unpleasant smell, boiling-point extrapolated +10°, melting-point —26·2°. The vapour has a deep-yellow colour.[607] It begins to decompose a little above its melting-point. Electron diffraction[609] shows that it has a tetrahedral structure, which proves that like the iron analogue it has the hydrogen attached to the oxygen; the Co—C distances are for three of the carbons 1·75 and for the fourth (in —COH) 1·83 (theory for Co—C 2·09 A).

The hydride forms metallic derivatives like an acid[606,610]; for steric reasons these are more numerous than those of the iron carbonyl hydride (p. 1371); they liberate the hydride when treated with dilute hydrochloric acid. The derivatives of the alkalies (like the compound $K[Co(CO)_4]$ mentioned above) are salts giving yellow solutions.[607] Those of many of the heavy metals are covalent, and can be formed directly; thus if cobaltous bromide or even metallic cobalt is heated with zinc under a high pressure of carbon monoxide, a 100 per cent. yield of the compound $Zn(Co(CO)_4)_2$ is obtained. Cadmium and mercury will do the same, and will combine directly with the tetracarbonyl under 200 atm. at 180°. Gallium, indium, and thallium (which last forms both a thallous and a thallic compound) behave in the same way, but not copper, silver, germanium, or lead. Tin, however, gives pale-yellow crystals of $Sn[Co(CO)_4]_4$, the only known molecule with 16 CO groups.

These so-called 'mixed' carbonyl derivatives are all crystalline, soluble in benzene and ligroin but not in water, and monomeric by the freezing-point in benzene. They are stable up to 70° (though $Co_2(CO)_8$ decomposes at 50°), but liberate the hydride with dilute hydrochloric acid. Nitric oxide converts them into $Co(CO)_3NO$, and halogens into the metallic halide and $Co_2(CO)_8$.

$Co_2(CO)_8$ reacts also with bases like pyridine and phenanthroline, and even with alcohol, displacing some of the CO groups and forming for example $Co_2(CO)_5py_4$ and $Co_2(CO)_5CH_3 \cdot OH$, this last forming black crystals which give a blood-red solution in alcohol, and are almost insoluble in water or organic solvents other than glacial acetic acid, in which they are shown by the freezing-point to be monomeric.[605]

Except for an unstable compound $Co(CO)I_2$ which is an intermediate product in the reaction of cobaltous iodide with carbon monoxide under pressure[607] cobalt (unlike iron) forms no carbonyl halides.

Cobalt Nitrosyls

There are no 'pure' nitrosyls of cobalt, but we have the carbonyl nitrosyl, the nitrosyl halides, and certain nitrosyl ammines.

[608] W. Hieber and H. Schulten, *Z. anorg. Chem.* 1937, **232**, 29.
[609] R. V. G. Ewens and M. W. Lister, *Trans. Far. Soc.* 1939, **35**, 681.
[610] W. Hieber and E. Fack, *Z. anorg. Chem.* 1938, **236**, 83.

Cobalt carbonyl nitrosyl $Co(CO)_3NO$ can be made by the action of nitric oxide on the carbonyl $Co_2(CO)_8$ at 40°[611-12] or better[607,613-14] by passing it through the solution of $K[Co(CO)_4]$ made (p. 1423) by treating a cobalt salt in water with carbon monoxide in presence of potassium cyanide. It is a dark-red mobile liquid, monomeric in the vapour[611]; it is diamagnetic.[615] Electron diffraction[616] shows that the M—C—O and M—N—O groups are linear and tetrahedrally arranged. This compound, $Fe(CO)_2(NO)_2$, and $Ni(CO)_4$ are obviously similar in structure, and are isoelectronic (as they are with the hydrides $Co(CO)_3COH$ and $Fe(CO)_2(COH)_2$). The atomic distances found in these compounds,[616] and their boiling- and melting-points are given below:

	M—C		M—N		C—O	N—O
	Obs.	*Calc.*	*Obs.*	*Calc.*		
$Fe(CO)_2(NO)_2$ . .	1·84	2·00	1·77	1·93	1·15	1·12
$Co(CO)_3NO$ . . .	1·83	2·02	1·76	1·95	1·14	1·10
$Ni(CO)_4$ . . .	1·82	2·19	..	..	1·15	..

Other calculated values:	C—O	C=O	C≡O	N—O	N=O	N≡O
	1·43	1·22	1·10	1·36	1·15	1·05

	$Fe(CO)_2(NO)_2$	$Co(CO)_3NO$	$Ni(CO)_4$
B. pt. . .	110°	78·6°	43°
M. pt. . .	+18°	−1·1°	−23°

The NO groups appear to be more firmly held than the CO, since it is the latter that are replaced by amines: for example, $Co(CO)_3NO$ gives with o-phenanthroline $Co(CO)(NO)$phthr.[615]

There is also a series of nitrosyl pentammines, derived from cobaltous salts. Nitric oxide acts[617-18] very readily in the cold on an ammonical solution of a cobaltous salt to give two isomeric series of salts, one red and the other black, of the composition $[Co(NH_3)_5NO]X_2$. The red salts are probably[618] true nitroso-compounds, with the group Co—N=O: they are not hyponitrite derivatives, since they do not give hyponitrous acid[615]; with hydrochloric acid they do not evolve nitric oxide, but form the chloro-compound $[Co(NH_3)_5Cl]Cl_2$; and they are diamagnetic, like all the ammines of trivalent cobalt. The black isomers, on the other hand, evolve nitric oxide with hydrochloric acid, being converted into cobaltous chloride; and they are paramagnetic. We may conclude that they are

[611] R. L. Mond and A. E. Wallis, *J.C.S.* 1922, **121**, 34.
[612] F. Reiff, *Z. anorg. Chem.* 1931, **202**, 375.
[613] A. A. Blanchard, J. R. Rafter, and W. B. Adams, *J.A.C.S.* 1934, **56**, 16.
[614] G. W. Coleman and A. A. Blanchard, ib. 1936, **58**, 2160.
[615] W. Hieber and J. S. Anderson, *Z. anorg. Chem.* 1933, **211**, 132.
[616] L. O. Brockway and J. S. Anderson, *Trans. Far. Soc.* 1937, **33**, 1233.
[617] J. Sand and O. Genssler, *Ber.* 1903, **36**, 2083.
[618] Id., *Ann.* 1903, **329**, 194.

nitrosyl compounds with the structure $[(NH_3)_5Co-N\equiv O]X_2$, which, however, is unusual in that the E.A.N. of the monovalent cobalt atom is 38.[619,620]

The nitrosyl halides $Co(NO)_2hal$ are formed (as with iron) by the action of nitric oxide on cobaltous halides.[621] They are most readily formed by the iodides, and least by the chlorides; with bromine and chlorine metallic cobalt or zinc must be added to remove part of the halogen. The melting-points are $Co(NO)_2Cl$ 101°, $Co(NO)_2Br$ 116°, $Co(NO)_2I$ 131°. They are stable substances, and sublime unchanged in carbon dioxide, hydrogen, nitric oxide, or even air. They are somewhat soluble, the chlorides most, in water (with some hydrolysis) and in organic solvents, but not enough for their molecular weights to be determined. We may suppose them to be dimeric, like auric chloride or its alkyl derivatives:

This makes the cobalt monovalent and 4-covalent, with the usual E.A.N. for a nitrosyl of 36. When the iodide is treated with pyridine it loses a molecule of nitric oxide and forms a solid of the composition $Co(NO)I,py_6$, which it is almost impossible to formulate; with o-phenanthroline it forms an addition compound $Co(NO)_2I(phthr.)$, which may be written in the monomeric form as the salt

$$\left[\begin{array}{c} \overset{+}{O}=\overset{+}{N} \\ \overset{+}{O}=\overset{+}{N} \end{array} \quad\equiv\quad \overset{>}{\underset{>}{Co}} \begin{array}{c} \overset{+}{N} \\ \overset{+}{N} \end{array} \right]^+ I.$$

where $\overset{+}{N}$ stands for the nitrogen atom of the amine.

In this the cobalt is monovalent, with the E.A.N. 36.

Valencies of Cobalt in the Carbonyls and Nitrosyls

The values of the valencies and the covalencies of the cobalt in the chief types of these complexes are:

	Valency	*Covalency*
$CO_2(CO)_8$ . . .	Prob. 3	Prob. 6
$Co(CO)_3COH$ . .	,, 1	,, 4
$Co(CO)_3NO$ . .	,, 1	,, 4
$[(NH_3)_5Co-N\equiv O]X_2$.	,, 1	,, 6 (E.A.N. 38)
$(Co(NO)_2hal)_2$ . .	,, 1	,, 4

It is to be noticed that with an E.A.N. of 36 the valency of the cobalt is necessarily 1 if it is 4-covalent, and 3 if it is 6-covalent.

[619] J. L. Milward, W. Wardlaw, and W. J. R. Way, *J.C.S.* 1938, 233.
[620] A. Werner and P. Karrer, *Helv. Chim. Acta*, 1918, 1 54.
[621] W. Hieber and R. Marin, *Z. anorg. Chem.* 1939, **240**, 241.

NICKEL has a valency of 2 in nearly all its compounds, and in all its simple salts, but there is a small group of unstable compounds, entirely confined to the complex cyanides $M[NiCy_3]$ and a few of their derivatives, in which it is undoubtedly monovalent. In the carbonyl $Ni(CO)_4$ and in the remarkable cyanide $K_4[Ni(CN)_4]$ it is non-valent. On the other hand, there are certain hydroxides in which the valency may probably be 3, and possibly, but not probably, 4 as well. The general relations of these valency states have already been discussed.

Nickel is rather more than twice as abundant as cobalt in the earth's crust, the proportion being 1 part in 10,000; in the whole mass of the earth the proportion is no doubt greater: nickel is nearly always found in iron meteorites, and there must be a considerable concentration in the central iron core of the earth: Sonder[623] guesses it to be about 3 per cent.; in the sun's atmosphere the ratio Fe/Ni is 17 (in the earth's crust it is 510).

Nickel is found chiefly in combination with sulphur, arsenic, and antimony (millerite, NiS: kupfernickel NiAs); its chief source is an igneous dike of pyrrhotite (Fe_nS_{n+1}) at Sudbury in Ontario, which contains 3–5·5 per cent. of nickel and 0·2–8 per cent. of copper.

The commercial separation of nickel is usually effected by one of two processes. The first (the Mond process) depends on the formation and decomposition of nickel carbonyl; the ore is converted into oxides, and these are reduced by water gas at 250–350°, at which temperature the ferrous oxide and cuprous oxide are not reduced. Carbon monoxide is then passed over the mass at 50°, and the nickel converted into the carbonyl (b. pt. 43°), which is passed through tubes heated at 150–200°, where it is decomposed.

The method now used for the Sudbury nickel is the Orford process, known as 'tops and bottoms smelting' (*Kopfbodenschmelzen*). The ores are fused with nitre cake (sodium hydrogen sulphate) and coke, and so converted into a mixture of sulphides with sodium sulphide. Two layers are formed in the melt; the upper consists of a double salt of sodium sulphide, ferrous sulphide, and cuprous sulphide (with about 3 per cent. of the nickel present) and the lower, of the uncombined nickel sulphide with about 10 per cent. of the copper. After solidification the silvery upper layer is cut off from the black lower layer; for complete separation the process is repeated.

Nickel occurs to a small extent in animals and plants; the amount is from 0·1 to 3 parts per million of dried substance, which is from 1/1,000 to 1/30 of the amount in the rocks, and from 5 to 15 times as much as the cobalt content of these organisms.

Nickel, of which 45,000 tons were produced in 1933, 20,000 of them in

---

[622] In the volume in Abegg's *Handbuch* on nickel, which appeared in 1937 (Bd. iv. 3, 4) the literature of the subject is fully given. This is referred to below as Abegg, p. *x*.

[623] R. A. Sonder, *Z. anorg. Chem.* 1930, **192**, 257.

Canada and the U.S.A., is used for coinage purposes, for various alloys (German silver contains 10–20% of nickel, 40–70% copper, and 5–40% zinc: constantan, which has an abnormally small temperature coefficient of electrical conductivity, 40% nickel and 60% copper: nichrome, used for electrical heating, 60% nickel and 40% chromium); it is also used very largely for electroplating.

Cobalt and nickel were the first observed case in which the chemical order of the elements was not that of the atomic weights; the whole behaviour of the elements shows that the natural order is Fe—Co—Ni: the valency table given above in the summary is sufficient evidence of this; but the order of the atomic weights is Fe 55·84; Ni 58·69; Co 58·94. This inversion was recognized quite early in the history of the Periodic Table, and the original object of Moseley's determination of the wavelengths of the shortest X-rays of the elements was to see whether those of nickel and cobalt would come in the order of the atomic weights or in that of the chemical properties. We now know that the inversion is due to the predominance of the lighter of the two main isotopes of nickel (58, 67·5 per cent.; 60, 26·7 per cent.), while cobalt is practically if not absolutely pure 59.

Metallic Nickel

Nickel is a hard silver-white metal, melting at 1,452° C., with a vapour pressure of $3 \cdot 52 \times 10^{-4}$ mm. at 1,310° C., and a heat of sublimation of 101·64 k.cals. at 0° K.[624]; it can receive a high degree of polish; it is ferromagnetic, but less so than iron.[625] Its electrical conductivity is 13·8 per cent. and its heat conductivity 15 per cent. of those of silver.

In the compact form nickel is very stable to air and water, perhaps because it is covered by a layer of oxide, since the fine powder is pyrophoric.[626-7] Nickel wire will burn in oxygen. Dilute acids dissolve it, but more slowly than iron. The normal potential to the hydrogen electrode of nickel is $-0 \cdot 25$ volt (cobalt $-0 \cdot 26$, iron $-0 \cdot 44$).

Nickel, especially the metal, is a very powerful catalyst; the salts are much less effective. Nickel and platinum are the best known metallic catalysts, and recent experience shows that the third metal of Group VIII C, palladium, comes near them. Nickel is especially useful for the hydrogenation and dehydrogenation of organic compounds, owing perhaps to the considerable solubility of hydrogen in this metal. Our knowledge of this activity is largely due to the work of Sabatier in the years from 1897 onwards. As its efficiency depends on the extent of its surface, the oxide is reduced with hydrogen at the lowest convenient temperature, from 150° to 250°; it is often spread on a carrier such as silica gel, coke, pumice, asbestos, etc. A very finely divided metal made by reducing nickel chloride with the Grignard reagent in ether is also very active. The

[624] H. L. Johnston and A. L. Marshall, *J.A.C.S.* 1940, **62**, 1382.
[625] See G. Le Clerc and A. Michel, *C.R.* 1939, **208**, 1583.
[626] G. Tammann and W. Köster, *Z. anorg. Chem.* 1922, **123**, 196.
[627] R. Fricke and W. Schweckendiek, *Z. Elektrochem.* 1940, **46**, 90.

activity of the metal may be increased by the addition of other metals, and of oxides such as thorium dioxide, alumina, and magnesia. In organic reductions nickel is as effective for removing oxygen as for adding hydrogen. It is very largely used for the hardening of fats, that is, for the conversion of liquid oleic acid and its esters into the solid stearic compounds, in the manufacture of margarine; for this purpose the finely divided oxide is suspended in the oil, and reduced at 180° with hydrogen: or the formate can be used, which is converted into the metal at 250°.[628]

Nickel and Hydrogen

Nickel, like the other two members of Group VIII C, has a considerable power of absorbing hydrogen. Taylor and Burns[629] give the following values of the volume of hydrogen absorbed by one volume of various metals at 25°:

Cu	Fe	Co	Ni	Pd	Pt
0·05	0·05	0·05	4·15	753·3	4·05

At higher temperatures hydrogen has a measurable solubility in the metal, especially in the liquid state. The mean values given by Abegg[630] for the solubility at 1 atm. pressure, in mg. of hydrogen to 100 g. nickel, or in volumes of hydrogen at N.T.P. per volume of nickel (which happen to be numerically the same) are:

at 212° C.	1,400° (solid)	1,465° (liquid)	1,600° C.
0·16	1·54	3·50	3·87

At 400° and 600° C. they are 0·328 and 0·542.[631]

When anhydrous nickel chloride acts on phenyl magnesium bromide in an atmosphere of hydrogen a black powder of the composition NiH_2 is produced, which may be a definite hydride,[632-4] and may be formed from an unstable $Ni(C_6H_5)_2$. It is an active reducing agent. See further references [635-7].

Nickel and Carbon

Molten nickel will dissolve as much as 6·25 per cent. of carbon, but no compound seems to be formed.

Nickel and Nitrogen

The solubility of nitrogen in nickel at 450° is only 0·07 per cent., but a nitride Ni_3N can be made[638] by heating nickel or its fluoride or bromide

[628] For full references see Abegg, p. 412.

[629] H. S. Taylor and R. M. Burns, *J.A.C.S.* 1921, 43, 1275.　　　[630] p. 390.

[631] M. H. Armbruster, *J.A.C.S.* 1943, 65, 1043.

[632] W. Schlenk and T. Weichselfelder, *Ber.* 1923, 56, 2230.

[633] T. Weichselfelder and B. Thiede, *Ann.* 1926, 447, 64.

[634] T. Weichselfelder and M. Kossode, *Ber.* 1929, 62, 769.

[635] A. A. Balandin, B. V. Jerofeev, K. A. Petscherskaja, and M. S. Stacanova, *J. Gen. Chem. Russ.* 1941, 11, 577.

[636] Id., *Acta Phys.-Chem. U.R.S.S.* 1943, 18, 157.　　　[637] Id., ib. 300.

[638] R. Juza and W. Sachsze, *Z. anorg. Chem.* 1943, 251, 201.

in ammonia at 445°; it has a hexagonal close-packed lattice of nickel atoms, with nitrogen atoms in the interstices. It is stable to alkalies, but is attacked by acids.

Nickel and Phosphorus

A tensimetric and X-ray study of the system nickel-phosphorus[639] shows the existence of NiP_3, NiP_2, Ni_3P, and probably Ni_6P_5.

Non-valent Nickel

Nickel is of course non-valent in the carbonyl $Ni(CO)_4$, but another compound has been prepared in which also its valency must be zero. This is the salt $K_4[Ni(CN)_4]$ obtained by reducing the monovalent nickel salt $K_2[Ni(CN)_3]$ with potassium in liquid ammonia.[640] It is a yellow solid, copper-coloured when dry, which blackens at once in air, and decomposes water with evolution of hydrogen. Metallic calcium can be used for making it in place of potassium.[641]

This compound can be regarded as the carbonyl $Ni(CO)_4$ in which the 4 neutral CO groups have been replaced by 4 monovalent cyanogen ions.

MONOVALENT NICKEL

Nickel is unusual among the transitional elements in forming a few isolable compounds in which it is definitely monovalent.

The supposed oxide Ni_2O[642] and sulphide Ni_2S have been shown not to exist. The X-ray diagram given by the former contains no lines except those of nickel and nickelic oxide NiO.[643]

Nickel Monocyanide, NiCN

When the red solution of the salt K_2NiCy_3 (made by reducing the ordinary double cyanide K_2NiCy_4) is acidified, the colour disappears, and the compound NiCN is precipitated in orange flocks.[644-5] It gradually oxidizes in air to give a mixture of the green dicyanide $Ni(CN)_2$ and the oxide NiO. It absorbs carbon monoxide to give a yellow compound which is apparently $(Ni(CN)CO)_x$, and it dissolves in potassium cyanide solution to re-form the red salt K_2NiCy_3.

This salt K_2NiCy_3[644-6] is the best known of these monovalent nickel compounds. It is made by reducing a cold saturated solution of potassium nickelicyanide K_2NiCy_4 with potassium or sodium amalgam in an atmosphere of hydrogen, and precipitating with alcohol; the reduction can also be carried out (in potassium cyanide solution) with zinc, stannous chloride, alkaline hypophosphite, or by electrolysis.[647] The product is a dark-red

[639] W. Biltz and M. Heimbrecht, ib. 1938, **237**, 132.

[640] J. W. Eastes and W. M. Burgess, *J.A.C.S.* 1942, **64**, 1187.

[641] Id., ib. 2715.   [642] F. Glaser, *Z. anorg. Chem.* 1903, **36**, 1.

[643] G. R. Levi and G. Tacchini, *Gaz.* 1925, **55**, 28.

[644] I. Bellucci and R. M. Corelli, *Atti R.* 1913, [5] **22**, ii. 485.

[645] Id., *Z. anorg. Chem.* 1914, **86**, 88.

[646] I. Bellucci, *Gaz.* 1919, **49**, ii. 70.

[647] G. Grube and H. Lieder, *Z. Elektrochem.* 1926, **32**, 561.

oily substance, which rapidly decomposes in air with change of colour. $K_2Ni(CN)_3$ is diamagnetic.[648] This must mean *either* (1) there is no unpaired spin, *or* (2) the unpaired spin exists, but is quenched because of some inter- or intra-atomic interaction. As there is no theoretical reason to think that (2) is true, Mellor and Craig suggest the formula

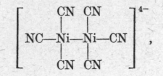

with linked atoms of divalent nickel. It dissolves readily in water to give a red solution, the colour of which is so intense that $\frac{1}{2}$ mg. of nickel can be detected in this way in presence of excess of cobalt. The extinction coefficient e is 10 times as great as that for the nickelicyanide K_2NiCy_4.

The solution is very unstable. It evolves hydrogen slowly in the cold, and rapidly and quantitatively on boiling, to give divalent nickel. The cold solution in absence of air precipitates a fine powder of metallic nickel. If it is shaken with air it rapidly oxidizes to divalent nickel, and at the same time a certain amount of hydrogen peroxide is formed. In alkaline solution and in the absence of air the compound is more stable; if the solution is made up with boiled out water and a layer of ligroin run onto the surface to exclude air, it can be kept unchanged for days.[646]

Potassium nickelocyanide K_2NiCy_3 is of course a very vigorous reducing agent. It will reduce silver nitrate, lead chloride, or mercuric chloride to the metal. The solution readily absorbs both carbon monoxide and nitric oxide, giving carbonyl and nitrosyl derivatives; see below, p. 1451.

DIVALENT NICKEL

This is the predominant valency of nickel, and the valency which it has in all its simple salts.

The hydrated nickelic salts are green, sometimes with a yellow or bluish tinge. Their colour in solution is always green, and it is remarkably little affected by concentration or temperature, especially as compared with the cupric, or still more, the cobaltous salts. It was in connexion with this work that A. Beer discovered in 1852 the law that goes by his name.[649]

The anhydrous salts are mostly yellow, but the iodide NiI_2 is black, and the thiocyanate $Ni(CNS)_2$ chocolate. The ammines are mostly blue. All the simple nickelic salts are paramagnetic.

Nickel Oxide, NiO

Pure nickel oxide cannot be made by heating the metal in oxygen; below 400° the product still contains metallic nickel, and at 400–480° it contains up to 3 per cent. of the sesquioxide Ni_2O_3. The monoxide can,

[648] D. P. Mellor and D. P. Craig, *Proc. Roy. Soc. N. S. Wales,* 1943, **76**, 281.
[649] A. Beer, *Pogg. Ann.* 1852, **86**, 78.

however, be made by heating the hydroxide or carbonate in absence of air to 600°, or the nitrate to 1,000°.

It forms a green powder, and is found in nature as the mineral bunsenite, in dark green opaque crystals. It is isomorphous with cobalt monoxide CoO, and has a sodium chloride lattice.[650-1] It melts at 1,990° C.[652]; its vapour pressure at this temperature is low, but it becomes considerable at 2,350° C.; the dissociation pressure of oxygen is low even at these temperatures.

Nickel oxide is practically insoluble in water, but if it has been prepared at not too high a temperature it is easily soluble in acids; strong ignition converts it into grey octahedra, whose solubility in acids is small.

The finely powdered oxide has the power of taking up more oxygen even in the cold, and turns black in so doing; this behaviour is further discussed later under trivalent nickel (p. 1449).

Nickelic Hydroxide, $Ni(OH)_2$

This separates from a solution of a nickel* salt on addition of alkali as an apple-green precipitate, soluble in acids, ammonia, and ammonium salt solutions. It is very difficult to wash free from salts, especially from anions, and is best made by the action of alkaline hydroxide on the nitrate, or of water on an ammine. It is isomorphous with the cobalt compound $Co(OH)_2$, and its lattice is of the cadmium iodide type. It readily takes up more water, and when it is precipitated may contain as much water as corresponds to $Ni(OH)_2, 1·5 H_2O$; but on heating or in a vacuum this excess is steadily lost until $Ni(OH)_2$ remains, and the Debye X-ray patterns do not indicate the existence of a higher hydrate.[653] On further heating the last molecule of water is slowly lost (at 230° under 10 mm. pressure), but this process is irreversible, and if nickel oxide is treated under any conditions with water the product gives no $Ni(OH)_2$ X-ray lines, but only those of the monoxide.[651]

Nickel hydroxide is almost insoluble in water; the solubility product is about 10^{-18}, which means that the saturated solution is about 10^{-6} normal[654] (about 0·1 mg./litre).

Nickel hydroxide dissolves in aqueous ammonia to give a blue solution; no solid ammine can be isolated from this, but the relation between the NH_3 concentration and the amount of nickel dissolved suggest that the substance formed is the tetrammine $[Ni(NH_3)_4](OH)_2$.[655]

* The phrase 'nickel salt' when not otherwise qualified may be taken always to mean a salt of divalent nickel.

[650] S. B. Hendricks, M. E. Jefferson, and J. F. Shultz, *Z. Krist.* 1930, **73**, 376.
[651] R. W. Cairns and E. Ott, *J.A.C.S.* 1933, **55**, 527.
[652] H. v. Wartenberg and E. Prophet, *Z. anorg. Chem.* 1932, **208**, 369. His earlier value of 2,090° is here corrected.
[653] G. F. Hüttig and A. Peter, ib. 1930, **189**, 183.
[654] K. Murata, *Bull. Chem. Soc. Japan*, 1928, **3**, 267.
[655] W. Bonsdorff, *Z. anorg. Chem.* 1904, **41**, 132.

Nickel Sulphide, NiS

This is precipitated by ammonium sulphide from a nickel solution which is neutral or weakly acidified with acetic acid, but not in presence of hydrochloric acid. It forms a black precipitate, which seems to change over after it has separated into a form insoluble in acids; for though it is not formed in presence of hydrochloric acid, it will not dissolve in hydrochloric acid when once it has been precipitated in neutral solution.

Nickel sulphide occurs in three forms, of which the α- is amorphous and unstable in air: the β- is the form usually prepared synthetically, and seems to be the most stable of the three: the γ-form is rhombic, and is identical with millerite.[656]

The ordinary black form is practically insoluble in water, the solubility product being 1.4×10^{-24}, so that the saturated solution is 1.2×10^{-12} normal.[657] There is another sulphide Ni_3S_2, whose crystal structure gives Ni—S as 2·28 A (theory for Ni—S 2·28).[658]

For indications of possible compounds NiTe and $NiTe_2$ see reference [659].

Dihalides of Nickel

These are formed by all four halogens.

Nickel Difluoride, NiF_2

The anhydrous salt is best made[660] by the action of gaseous hydrogen fluoride on dry nickel chloride, or by heating the double ammonium fluoride $(NH_4)_2[NiF_4]$. It forms brownish-green crystals which have a rutile lattice. It can be sublimed in a stream of hydrogen fluoride above 1,000°. Probably[661] the only stable hydrate is $NiF_2, 4 H_2O$. This forms pale-green crystals which do not lose their water of crystallization even over sulphuric acid. The change of lattice from the anhydrous to the hydrated form is evidently slow, for the solubility of the anhydrous salt in water is 0·02 in the cold, while that of the tetrahydrate at 25° (it is but little affected by temperature) is 2·50[661]; yet the hydrate being the stable form must be less soluble than the anhydrous salt. Anhydrous nickel chloride, manganous fluoride MnF_2, and cadmium fluoride show a similar reluctance to hydrate.[661]

Nickel fluoride NiF_2 is a very stable substance; it is scarcely attacked by concentrated hydrochloric, nitric, or sulphuric acid even on boiling. It reacts on heating with electropositive metals like sodium, but not with electronegative elements like chlorine, bromine, iodine, sulphur, phosphorus, or arsenic.[660]

[656] G. R. Levi and A. Baroni, *Z. Krist.* 1935, **92**, 210.
[657] L. Bruner and J. Zawadski, *Z. anorg. Chem.* 1910, **67**, 454.
[658] A. Westgren, ib. 1938, **239**, 82.
[659] W. Klemm and N. Fratini, ib. 1943, **251**, 222.
[660] O. Ruff and E. Ascher, ib. 1929, **183**, 193.
[661] A. Kurtenacker and W. Finger, ib. 1933, **211**, 83.

Nickel Chloride, $NiCl_2$

This can be made in the anhydrous state by burning nickel in chlorine or by heating the hydrated or the ammoniated salt. It forms yellow crystals which are isomorphous with the dichlorides of Mg, Mn, Co, Fe, Cd, In, Ru, Rh, Pd, Ir, and Pt: it has a cadmium chloride lattice.[662] For its paramagnetism see references [663-4]. It sublimes under 1 atm. pressure at 993°, and melts in a sealed tube at 1,001°.[665] The sublimed anhydrous salt, like the fluoride, dissolves in water extraordinarily slowly.

Nickel chloride forms several hydrates, all of them green, and the lowest yellow-green; according to recent work[666-7] the monohydrate is doubtful, but the compositions and transition points of the others are:

$$7 \xrightarrow[-33\cdot3°]{} 6 \xrightarrow[+28\cdot8°]{} 4 \xrightarrow[64°]{} 2 \xrightarrow[?]{} ?$$

Sol^y 67·8/26°.

Nickel chloride is much less soluble in organic solvents than cobaltous chloride $CoCl_2$.

Nickel chloride acts like cuprous chloride in catalysing the oxidation of hydrogen chloride by air to chlorine (Deacon process).

Nickel Bromide, $NiBr_2$

This is very like the chloride. The anhydrous salt can be made by the action of bromine on metallic nickel at a red heat, or in ethereal solution in the cold, or on a solution of nickel carbonyl in carbon tetrachloride, or by the dehydration of the hydrate. It forms yellow crystals with a cadmium chloride lattice. It can be sublimed at a rather high temperature (in quartz or porcelain vessels, but scarcely in glass).

It forms a series of hydrates: an ennea-hydrate ($9\,H_2O$) going below $-2\cdot5°$ into a hexahydrate, which changes at $+28\cdot5°$ into the trihydrate[668]; sol^y 33/25°.

It also dissolves (0·36 per cent. at 25°) in methyl alcohol, in ethyl alcohol, acetone (0·0081 per cent. at 20°) and quinoline.

Nickel Iodide, NiI_2

This again is similar. It can be made from the elements, or by solution of the hydroxide in hydriodic acid. The anhydrous salt is black, and looks like elementary iodine; it has a cadmium chloride lattice.[669] The only known hydrate is $NiI_2, 6\,H_2O$, sol^y 144/25°.

[662] L. Pauling, *Proc. Nat. Acad.* 1929, **15**, 709.

[663] P. Laurent, *J. Phys. Radium*, 1938, [vii] **9**, 331.

[664] H. R. Nettleton and S. Sugden, *Proc. Roy. Soc.* 1939, **173**, 313.

[665] W. Fischer and R. Gewehr, *Z. anorg. Chem.* 1935, **222**, 303.

[666] H. Benrath, ib. 1932, **205**, 417.

[667] E. Boye, ib. 1933, **216**, 29.

[668] Abegg, p. 513.   [669] J. A. A. Ketelaar, *Z. Krist.* 1934, **88**, 26.

Nickel Cyanide, $Ni(CN)_2$

The anhydrous salt can be made[670-1] from the hydrate; it is brownish-yellow, almost insoluble in water (see below) and quite in methyl acetate, but it dissolves in alkaline cyanide solutions to give complex cyanides (p. 1438). The addition of hydrocyanic acid or potassium cyanide to nickel acetate solution precipitates an amorphous green hydrated cyanide of variable water content[672]; the one certain hydrate is $Ni(CN)_2, 4 H_2O$, which forms bluish plates.[672] The solubility of nickel cyanide in water (from E.M.F. measurements) is $0.059/18°$ (5.35×10^{-4} moles per litre: solubility product 1.53×10^{-10}).[673]

Nickel cyanide forms an ammine of the composition $Ni(CN)_2, NH_3, H_2O$ (the water is easily removed), which has the remarkable property of forming solid compounds with benzene and some other organic substances.[674-5] If the aqueous solution is shaken with benzene bluish-white crystals separate, of the composition $Ni(CN)_2, NH_3, C_6H_6$. This compound is remarkably stable; it can be kept *in vacuo* over sulphuric acid for weeks without change, and treatment with alcohol or ether only removes the benzene very slowly; it is, however, expelled by boiling with water, by alkaline or acid solutions, and by potassium cyanide. This power of a solution of nickel cyanide in dilute ammonia to absorb benzene has been made the basis of a method for the quantitative estimation of benzene in coal gas.[676-8]

Very similar compounds are formed with pyrrol, thiophene, furfurane, and other organic compounds.[679]

Nickel Thiocyanate, $Ni(CNS)_2$

This can be made in a hydrated form by dissolving nickel carbonate in thiocyanic acid, or by the action of barium thiocyanate on nickel sulphate. The anhydrous salt (made from the hydrate at 150°) is a chocolate amorphous powder. It is soluble in water (sol[y] 55.0/25°), from which it separates[680] below 15° as a tetrahydrate (large green crystals), and above 25° as a yellow hemihydrate $Ni(CNS)_2, 0.5 H_2O$.

A number of double nickel thiocyanates have been made from their components, and can be recrystallized from water or sometimes alcohol; examples[681] are $Na_2[Ni(CNS)_4]$, $8 H_2O$, pale green; $K_4[Ni(CNS)_6]$, $4 H_2O$, blue; $(NH_4)_4[Ni(CNS)_6]$, 6 and $4 H_2O$. They are not true complexes.[680-1] Various double salts of organic bases are also known.

[670] W. Biltz, W. Eschweiler, and A. Bodensiek, *Z. anorg. Chem.* 1928, **170**, 163.
[671] E. Hertel, E. Rissel, and F. Riedel, ib. 1929, **178**, 202.
[672] K. A. Hofmann and F. Höchtlen, *Ber.* 1903, **36**, 1149.
[673] K. Masaki, *Bull. Chem. Soc. Japan*, 1931, **6**, 143.
[674] K. A. Hofmann and F. Küspert, *Z. anorg. Chem.* 1897, **15**, 204.
[675] K. A. Hofmann and H. Arnoldi, *Ber.* 1906, **39**, 339.
[676] L. M. Dennis and E. S. McCarthy, *J.A.C.S.* 1908, **30**, 233.
[677] E. S. McCarthy, *J. Gasbel.* 1912, **55**, 891.
[678] E. Stock, *Farben Ztg.* 1930, **35**, 897.
[679] Abegg, p. 680.   [680] A. de Sweemer, *Natuurw. Tijdschr.* 1932, **14**, 231.
[681] A. Rosenheim and R. Cohn, *Z. anorg. Chem.* 1901, **27**, 280; *Ber.* 1901, **33**, 1111.

Nickel Carbonate, $NiCO_3$

If sodium carbonate is added to a nickel chloride solution, the basic salt is always produced, except in an atmosphere of carbon dioxide under pressure.[682] Even then the precipitate is a solid solution of nickel chloride in nickel carbonate, which may contain as much as 33 per cent. of the chloride.[683]

The purest carbonate that has been obtained is a pale green substance insoluble in water, but more soluble in carbon dioxide solution, i.e. as the acid carbonate $NiH_2[CO_3]_2$; from this solution crystals of $NiCO_3$, $6 H_2O$ separate on exposure to the air.[684]

Nickel Formate, $Ni(O \cdot CHO)_2$, $2 H_2O$

This salt begins[685] to decompose below 200° mainly to carbon dioxide, hydrogen, and metallic nickel. It is less soluble in water than the corresponding cobaltous salt, and is insoluble in concentrated formic acid.

Nickel Acetate, $Ni(O \cdot CO \cdot CH_3)_2$

The anhydrous salt is a pale yellow powder[686-7]; the tetrahydrate forms apple-green monoclinic prisms, isomorphous with the cobaltous salt; sol^y in water 17·0/16°, in glacial acetic acid 10/25°, in alcohol 0. The aqueous solution precipitates nickel hydroxide on boiling.

Nickel Oxalate, NiC_2O_4

Metallic nickel does not dissolve in oxalic acid solution, but the hydroxide does, and from this solution, or from the solution of a nickel salt treated with an alkaline oxalate, nickel oxalate separates in greenish-white flocks, which dry at 100° to NiC_2O_4, $2 H_2O$; it loses its water at 150°.

If it is heated *in vacuo* nickel oxalate begins to decompose below 320° into nickel and carbon dioxide, a reaction sometimes used to prepare finely divided nickel for conversion into the carbonyl, or for catalytic purposes.

Nickel oxalate is even less soluble in water than the cobaltous salt; sol^y 0·3 mg./18° ($0·04 \times 10^{-6}$ equivalent normal[688]: the sol^y of cobaltous oxalate is 2·1 mg./18°). The electrical conductivity of the saturated solution at 18° indicates only 39 per cent. ionization, and points to complex formation, perhaps of the salt $Ni[NiOx_2]$.[689-90]

The oxalate is soluble in strong acids (with decomposition), and in ammonia through the formation of an ammine.

[682] A. Ferrari and C. Colla, *Atti R.* 1929, [6] **10**, 594.
[683] J. Krustinsons, *Z. anorg. Chem.* 1933, **212**, 45.
[684] E. Müller and A. Luber, ib. 1930, **187**, 209; **190**, 427.
[685] J. Kendall and H. Adler, *J.A.C.S.* 1921, **43**, 1470.
[686] F. Ephraim, *Ber.* 1913, **46**, 3103.
[687] H. Bassett and W. L. Bedwell, *J.C.S.* 1933, 877.
[688] R. Scholder, E. Gadenne, and H. Niemann, *Ber.* 1927, **60**, 1510.
[689] R. Scholder, ib. 1525.
[690] R. W. Money and C. W. Davies, *Trans. Far. Soc.* 1932, **28**, 609.

Nickel Nitrate, $Ni(NO_3)_2$

Nickel nitrate can be obtained in the anhydrous state (which is by no means always possible with the nitrates of polyvalent metals), but only by heating the hydrate with a mixture of 100 per cent. nitric acid and nitrogen pentoxide.[691] It forms a pale yellow powder, which decomposes at 105° and is very hygroscopic.[692]

Nickel nitrate forms a series of hydrates, of which the transition points are[693]:

$$9 \xrightarrow[-3°]{} 6 \xrightarrow[54°]{} 4 \xrightarrow[85.4°]{} 2 \longrightarrow ?$$

The hexahydrate, which is emerald green, and isomorphous with the cobaltous salt, has the high sol^y of 94·2/25°.

Double Nitrates of Nickel

It is practically certain that these double salts are not really complex, or at least do not contain the nickel in a complex anion; the other metal is always trivalent or tetravalent, so that if any complex nitrate is formed, which is doubtful, it is not the nickel that has formed it.

The two most important series of double nitrates containing nickel are (1) with trivalent metals, of the type $M_3''M_2'''(NO_3)_{12}, 24 H_2O$, in which the nickel can be replaced by Mg, Mn'', Co'' and Zn, and M''' can be Bi, Ce, La, Nd, Pr, Sm, and Gd. The nickel salts of this series are pale green.

(2) There are two double nitrates with tetravalent metals, of the type $NiM''''(NO_3)_6, 8 H_2O$, where M'''' = Th and Ce''''. These salts are olive-green, and form mixed crystals.[694-5]

Nickel nitrite $Ni(NO_2)_2$[696] probably does not exist[697-8]; a basic salt (? $Ni_2O(NO_2)_2$) can be made. The complex double nitrites are discussed on p. 1446.

Nickel Sulphate, $NiSO_4$

The anhydrous salt is greenish-yellow; it appears to be quite insoluble in cold water, and it is only very slowly hydrated by it; this behaviour is common with anhydrous nickel salts (for example NiF_2, $NiCl_2$, and (see below) $Ni(IO_3)_2$), and it is also not uncommon with anhydrous sulphates. The solubilities of anhydrous nickel sulphate in methyl and ethyl alcohols, with which it does not form alcoholates, are 0·061 and 0·017 per cent. respectively at 15°.[699]

With water it forms a series of hydrates whose transition points are

[691] A. Guntz and F. Martin, *Bull. Soc.* 1909, [4] **5**, 1004.

[692] A. Seyewetz and Brissaud, *C.R.* 1930, **190**, 1131.

[693] A. Sieverts and L. Schreiner, *Z. anorg. Chem.* 1934, **219**, 105.

[694] R. J. Meyer and R. Jacoby, ib. 1901, **27**, 359; *Ber.* 1900, **33**, 2135.

[695] V. Cuttica and A. Tocchi, *Gaz.* 1924, **54**, 628.

[696] C. Duval, *C.R.* 1926, **182**, 1156.

[697] L. Le Boucher, *Anal. Soc. Espan. Fis. Quim.* 1929, **27**, 145, 358.

[698] J. J. Errera, ib. 1930, **28**, 358.

[699] G. C. Gibson, J. O'L. Driscoll, and W. J. Jones, *J.C.S.* 1929, 1440.

difficult to determine because the solutions supersaturate with greatest ease; the most probable are[700-2]:

$$7 \xrightarrow[31\cdot5°]{} 6\,\alpha \xrightarrow[53\cdot3°]{} 6\,\beta \xrightarrow[ca.\ 110°]{} 5\ ?\ 4\ ?\ 3\ ?\ 2\ ?\ 1\ H_2O.$$

It is possible[701] that the only stable hydrates are the hepta-, the two hexahydrates, and the monohydrate, and that the rest, with 5, 4, 3, and 2 H_2O, all of which certainly exist, are metastable. For the optical activity of the solid hexahydrate see reference [703], and for the magnetic properties reference [704].

The heptahydrate is a vitriol, and forms unbroken series of mixed crystals with the corresponding salts of Mg, Mn, Fe, Co, and Zn; sol^y 40·5/25°. The two hexahydrates are quite definite, and are enantiotropic: the α- is bluish-green and tetragonal; the β- is green and monoclinic. The β-form is isomorphous with the magnesium salt.

Like the other vitriols, nickel sulphate forms double sulphates of the series $M_2'M''(SO_4)_2, 6\,H_2O$ (schönite series: 'Tutton's salts'), in which $M' = K, Rb, Cs, NH_4, Tl'$ (not Na): $M'' = Mg, Fe, Co, Ni, Cu, Zn, Cd$, etc.; these salts are all isomorphous, and give unbroken series of mixed crystals with one another. The ammonium salt is used for electroplating. The only double salt formed by sodium is $Na_2Ni(SO_4)_2, 4\,H_2O$. The corresponding potassium salt is known both anhydrous and with 6 H_2O; sol^y 6·79/25°.[705]

Nickel Sulphite, Ni(SO₃)

The hexa- and tetrahydrates form greenish crystals which are practically insoluble in water, but dissolve in sulphur dioxide solution.[706] A few dark green insoluble double sulphites are known.[707-8]

Nickel Chlorite, Ni(ClO₂)₂, 2 H₂O

This salt[709] explodes violently even at 100°. It is very soluble in water, and the solution rapidly decomposes on warming, precipitating $Ni(OH)_2$ and evolving oxides of chlorine.

Nickel Chlorate, Ni(ClO₃)₂

This forms a hexa- and a tetrahydrate, with a transition point at 39°. The hexahydrate consists of dark green rhombic crystals, sol^y 131/18°. The

[700] B. D. Steele and F. M. G. Johnson, *ib.* 1904, **85**, 113.

[701] A. Chretien and R. Rohmer, *C.R.* 1934, **198**, 92.

[702] A. Simon and H. Knauer, *Z. anorg. Chem.* 1939, **242**, 375.

[703] N. Underwood, F. G. Slack, and E. B. Nelson, *Phys. Rev.* 1938, ii. **54**, 355.

[704] F. G. Slack, R. T. Lageman, and N. Underwood, *ib.* 358.

[705] Lattey, *Diss.*, Braunschweig, 1923.

[706] H. A. Klasens, W. G. Perdok, and P. Terpstra, *Z. Krist.* 1936, **94**, 1.

[707] F. L. Hahn and H. A. Meier, *Z. anorg. Chem.* 1926, **150**, 126.

[708] G. Canneri, *Gaz.* 1923, **53**, i. 182.

[709] G. R. Levi, *Atti R.* 1923, [5] **32**, i. 165.

hydrates begin to evolve chlorine and oxygen at 140°, but if they are quite dry, or in presence of alkali, they are much more stable.[710]

Nickel Bromate, $Ni(BrO_3)_2$, $6 H_2O$

This forms green octahedra, isomorphous with the corresponding bromates of magnesium, cobalt, and zinc, sol^y 28/ord. temp. They lose nearly all their water at 130°, but above this temperature begin to decompose.

Nickel Iodate, $Ni(IO_3)_2$

This salt, sol^y only 0·55/18°, is peculiar in many ways, and may have a complex structure. The anhydrous salt occurs in two forms, and so does the dihydrate; there is also a tetrahydrate, which is probably metastable. The solid phases supersaturate easily, and only come to equilibrium slowly; thus the anhydrous salt showed no sign of hydration after being 3 months in contact with water.[711]

Nickel Perchlorate, $Ni(ClO_4)_2$

This salt occurs in the anhydrous form, and hydrates with 9, 7, 5, 4, and 2 H_2O are described. Goldblum[712] found only an enneahydrate going over into a pentahydrate somewhere between 0° and $-23°$; the cryohydric point is $-49°$; sol^y 104/18°.[713]

DIVALENT NICKEL COMPLEXES

The tendency of divalent nickel to form complexes, taking the average for all kinds of addenda,[714] is much the same as that of the neighbouring elements iron, cobalt, copper, etc., when in the divalent state, and so is not very strong, nothing like so strong as that of trivalent cobalt. The maximum covalency of 6 is not very often reached, and lower values, especially 4 and sometimes 3, are more common. The chief co-ordination numbers are: in the cyanides 4, in the ammines 4 and 6, in the nitro-compounds 6, and in the fluorides and chlorides 4 and 3.

Complex Nickel Cyanides

These are perhaps the stablest of the nickel complexes; they are all of the same type $M_2[Ni(CN)_4]$ (in sharp contrast to the very widespread $[A(CN)_6]$ type), and the 4 CN groups lie in the same plane with the nickel, at the corners of a square of which it is the centre.

They are made by dissolving nickel cyanide in an alkaline cyanide solution, or by adding excess of an alkaline cyanide to a solution of a

[710] J. Amiel, *C.R.* 1934, **198**, 1033.

[711] A. Meusser, *Ber.* 1901, **24**, 32.

[712] H. Goldblum and F. Terlikowski, *Bull. Soc.* 1912, [4] **11**, 103, 146.

[713] R. Salvadori, *Gaz.* 1912, **42**, i. 458.

[714] For the ammines see H. M. Dawson and J. McCrae, *J.C.S.* 1900, **77**, 1239; H. M. Dawson, ib. 1906, **89**, 1666; H. J. S. King, A. W. Cruse, and F. G. Angell, ib. 1932, 2928.

nickel salt. The stability of the complex (in contrast to the weakness of most nickel complexes) and the fact that it contains 4 CN groups are shown in many ways. When potassium cyanide solution is added to nickel cyanide the evolution of heat is considerable, and it continues until 2 KCN have been added for every Ni; this conclusion is supported by electrometric titration, and by the electrical conductivity. The solution gives none of the reactions for nickel, not even with an alkaline sulphide, though the solubility product of nickel monosulphide NiS is only $6·2 \times 10^{-22}$ at $20°$[715]; the complex is not affected by acetic acid, though it is broken up by strong mineral acids. The solid salts and the solution are diamagnetic, which is a theoretically necessary result (Pauling) of the plane structure of the anion. The association constant of the complex

$$K = \frac{[\text{Ni(CN)}_4^{--}]}{[\text{Ni}^{++}] \cdot [\text{CN}^-]^4}$$

has been found by E.M.F. measurements[716] to be $5·6 \times 10^{13}$ at $25°$ (this means that if the concentration of the complex is normal, that of the free divalent nickel ion Ni^{++} is $2·8 \times 10^{-3}$ normal).

The solid nickelicyanides always form hydrates, and are mostly yellow or reddish-yellow. Their aqueous solutions have the same colour, but the addition of excess of potassium cyanide (at any rate with the potassium salt) turns it a deep red, possibly through the formation of an $[\text{Ni(CN)}_6]^{4-}$ ion, though there is no other evidence for this.

Among the individual nickelicyanides we have $\text{Na}_2[\text{Ni(CN)}_4]$, $3\,\text{H}_2\text{O}$; K, anhydrous (pale yellow) and $1\,\text{H}_2\text{O}$ (large orange prisms), sol^v $69·5/25°$. The ammonium salt readily loses ammonium cyanide. The barium salt $\text{Ba}[\text{Ni(CN)}_4]$, $4\,\text{H}_2\text{O}$ is isomorphous with the corresponding pallado- and platinocyanides,[717] which have also been shown to have a plane structure of the anion.[718-19]

Nickel Ammines

Divalent nickel produces numerous ammines with ammonia and many organic amines and diamines.

The fifty-four ammines (i.e. ammonia compounds) of simple divalent nickel salts given in Abegg[720] are distributed as follows:

$1\,\text{NH}_3$	$2\,\text{NH}_3$	$3\,\text{NH}_3$	$4\,\text{NH}_3$	$5\,\text{NH}_3$	$6\,\text{NH}_3$
3	10	2	9	4	26

The nickel ammines closely resemble those of divalent cobalt. In general the stability of a hexammine molecule $[\text{M(NH}_3)_6](\text{hal})_2$ (as measured by the dissociation tension of ammonia) is greater with nickel than with any other divalent metal. The stability of the ammines to water (the strength of the

[715] L. Moser and M. Behr, *Z. anorg. Chem.* 1924, **134**, 49; I. M. Kolthoff, *J. Phys. Chem.* 1931, **35**, 2720.
[716] K. Masaki, *Bull. Chem. Soc. Japan*, 1931, **6**, 233.
[717] H. Brasseur, A. de Rassenfosse, and J. Piérard, *Z. Krist.* 1934, A 88, 210.
[718] R. G. Dickinson, *J.A.C.S.* 1922, **44**, 774, 2404.
[719] H. Brasseur and A. de Rassenfosse, *Bull. Soc. franc. Min.* 1938, **61**, 129.
[720] pp. 669–96 (1936).

Ni—N as compared with the Ni—O link) is also considerable, and several tetrammines and even some hexammines can be recrystallized from dilute aqueous ammonia.

The question whether this stability is greater with nickel or with divalent copper is not easy to answer; it has been found by King,[721] who measured the degree of dissociation of the complex ion in water by the freezing-point method, that $Ni(NH_3)_6^{++}$ is more stable than $Cu(NH_3)_6^{++}$, although with the hexapyridine ions the difference is in the opposite direction. But the tetrammine seems to be the stable form with copper, and the hexammine with nickel, which makes a direct comparison difficult. The strength of the ammine varies of course with the nature of the co-ordinated groups: the simple ammines (NH_3 compounds) of nickel, though they can be recrystallized from aqueous ammonia, are decomposed by water, but the *en* compounds are not. Measurements of the paramagnetism in 0·1 to 0·4 normal solution indicate[722] that the order of increasing stability is for nickel, pyridine $< NH_3 < en <$ phenanthroline; for copper it is practically the same.

The resemblance between the ammines and the hydrates is obvious, and has been emphasized by Pfeiffer,[723] who, by the use of naphthalene-α-sulphonic acid (HA) prepared the whole series of salts:

[Ni en_3]A_2	reddish-violet
[Ni $en_2(OH_2)_2$]A_2	pale blue-violet
[Ni $en(OH_2)_4$]A_2	pale blue
[Ni$(OH_2)_6$]A_2	pale green

As we have seen, the hexammines are the most frequent of these compounds, and after them the tetrammines and the diammines. Some nickel salts, especially those with large anions,[724-6] can take up more than 6 molecules of ammonia, even as much as 16 or 18: a salt has been prepared which has the composition $Ni[Pt(SCN)_6]$, $18\,NH_3$,[727] although in a vacuum it loses 8 of these 18. Whether these extra ammonia molecules are attached as double or triple NH_3 molecules, or fill up interstices in the crystal lattice like the water in a hetero-poly-salt (VI. 1042), cannot be decided without X-ray analysis.

Wyckoff[728] showed that the salts $[Ni(NH_3)_6]Cl_2$ and $[Ni(NH_3)_6](NO_3)_2$ have lattices just like that of potassium platinichloride.

Anhydrous nickel salts take up ammonia very slowly, as do also cobaltous salts; the presence of a little water makes the reaction go more quickly, presumably by breaking up the lattice.

[721] H. J. S. King, A. W. Cruse, and F. G. Angell, *J.C.S.* 1932, 2928.

[722] C. D. Russell, G. R. Cooper, and W. C. Vosburgh, *J.A.C.S.* 1943, **65**, 1301.

[723] P. Pfeiffer, T. Fleitmann, and T. Inoue, *Z. anorg. Chem.* 1930, **192**, 346.

[724] F. Ephraim and E. Rosenberg, *Ber.* 1918, **51**, 644.

[725] F. Ephraim, F. Moser, and P. Mosimann, ib. 1920, **53**, 548.

[726] G. L. Clark and H. K. Buckner, *J.A.C.S.* 1922, **44**, 230.

[727] W. Peters, *Z. anorg. Chem.* 1912, **77**, 137.

[728] R. W. G. Wyckoff, *J.A.C.S.* 1922, **44**, 1239, 1260.

The stability of the solid hexammines depends greatly on the anion; with twelve hexammines, all $[Ni(NH_3)_6]A_2$, but with different anions, the temperature at which the dissociation tension of the ammonia is 1 atm. ranges from 36° for the formate and 84·5° for the thiocyanate to 245° for the perchlorate.[729]

As regards the influence of the amine, it is found[730] that among the alkyl-amines (apart from the diamines) as the number and size of the alkyl groups increase, the number and stability of the amine groups in the complex diminish.

The chelate ammines formed by ethylene diamine ('*en*') and other diamines, such as α, α'-dipyridyl ('dipy') and *o*-phenanthroline ('phth'), are more stable than the open-chain complexes; the *en* complexes are not decomposed by water, and the attraction of the nickel ion for *en* is so strong that it will take it away from zinc or cadmium salts.[731] The cations are usually trichelate, sometimes di-, and only rarely monochelate. The trichelate compounds have been resolved into their optical antimers in the case of the dipyridyl derivatives $[Ni(dipy)_3]X_2$ by Morgan and Burstall[732]; in water the active salt racemizes spontaneously with a half-life period of about 15 minutes at 17°; the solid salt is more stable and can be kept for days. This slowness of racemization is evidence of the stability of the complex cation, and is supported by freezing-point and conductivity measurements that have been made on many of these chelate salts. The trichelate ethylene diamine compounds could not be resolved,[733] perhaps because the tri*en* complex is rather less stable, and so racemizes too quickly to be resolved.

Further evidence of this stability of tri*en* complexes is given by the fact that they are not attacked at all by potassium cyanide, which converts the simple nickel cations quantitatively into $K_2[Ni(CN)_4]$. The di*en* complexes do react with KCN, but only so far as to rearrange themselves into the tri*en* compound and the nickelicyanide[734]:

$$3 \,[\text{Ni } en_2(\text{OH}_2)_2]^{--} \longrightarrow 2 \,[\text{Ni } en_3]^{--} + [\text{Ni}(\text{CN})_4]^{--} \;.$$

There are other signs that the stability of a chelate group is greater when the nickel has three of them: thus $[\text{Ni } en_2\text{Br}_2]^{\circ}$ changes to

$$[\text{Ni } en_3]\text{Br}_2 + \text{NiBr}_2[735];$$

in the same way the bis-dipyridyl salt disproportionates into a mixture of the tris and the simple nickel salt[736]; the corresponding bis-phenanthroline salt does not, however, do this.

[729] F. Ephraim, *Ber.* 1913, **46**, 3103.

[730] F. Ephraim and R. Linn, ib. 1913, **46**, 3742.

[731] A. A. Grünberg, *Z. anorg. Chem.* 1926, **157**, 201.

[732] G. T. Morgan and F. H. Burstall, *J.C.S.* 1931, 2213.

[733] W. R. Bucknall and W. Wardlaw, ib. 1928, 2739.

[734] A. Werner, J. Pastor, W. Spruck, and W. Mœgerle, *Z. anorg. Chem.* 1899, **21**, 201.

[735] W. Hieber and E. Levy, *Z. Elektrochem.* 1933, **39**, 26.

[736] P. Pfeiffer and F. Tappermann, *Z. anorg. Chem.* 1933, **215**, 273.

Various other diamines, besides ethylene diamine, have been used for making these chelate ammines; the methyl derivative α, β-propylene diamine $CH_3 \cdot CH(NH_2) \cdot CH_2 \cdot NH_2$ (pn) gives complexes very similar to those of *en*,[734,736] but differing very markedly in solubility: thus while [Ni en_3]SO_4 is only slightly soluble in water, [Ni pn_3]SO_4 is so soluble that it is difficult to get it to crystallize out. (This result of introducing an unsymmetrical methyl group may be compared with its effect in changing the melting-point of benzene $+6°$ to that of toluene, $-95°$.)

The dipyridyl and *o*-phenanthroline derivatives[732,736-7] are, as we have seen, very stable. The tri*en* salts are nearly always anhydrous, while the [Ni(dipy)$_3$]X_2 and [Ni(phth)$_3$]X_2 salts always have water of crystallization, often 6 molecules. This may be the result of the large size of the cation. For further ammine derivatives see references [738-9]. The simple *monoximes* are also to some extent capable of co-ordination, though much less than the amines (probably because the unshared electrons on the nitrogen are partly occupied in back-co-ordination to the oxygen). The aldoxime compounds are all of the type [Ni(RCH:NOH)$_4$](hal)$_2$[740]; they are decomposed by water or ammonia. Ketoximes also seem to combine, but no definite compounds could be isolated.[741]

Among the stablest and best known of the N,N-chelate complexes of nickel are those derived from the *dioxime of an* α-*diketone*, the mother substance being glyoxime

the nickel derivatives have the general structure

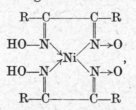

in which it is obvious that the passage of the hydrogen from the OH to the →O involves only a tautomeric change of the easiest kind. The best known of these compounds is the dimethyl glyoxime derivative (R = CH_3).[742] It can be made from dimethyl glyoxime and nickel acetate in alcoholic solution. It forms scarlet or dark red crystals, which on heating do not melt, but sublime above 250°, especially *in vacuo*; it is practically insoluble in water (sol^y about 0·02 mg. cold and 0·12 mg. hot); it is only slightly soluble in organic solvents. It is not affected by acetic

[737] F. M. Jaeger and J. A. Dijk, *Proc. K. Akad. Amst.* 1935, **38**, 972.
[738] H. Glaser and P. Pfeiffer, *J. prakt. Chem.* 1939, ii. **153**, 300.
[739] I. Lifschitz, J. G. Bos, and K. M. Dijkema, *Z. anorg. Chem.* 1939, **242**, 97.
[740] W. Hieber and F. Leutert, *Ber.* 1927, **60**, 2296.   [741] Id., ib. 2310.
[742] L. A. Tschugaev, ib. 1905, **38**, 2520; *Z. anorg. Chem.* 1905, **46**, 144.

acid, ammonia, or hydrogen sulphide, and only slowly by ammonium sulphide (this may be partly due to its insolubility), but mineral acids decompose it back to the nickel salt and the glyoxime, and it is at once and completely converted by potassium cyanide into the glyoxime and the nickelicyanide. Tschugaev made a series of homologues, from methyl-ethyl, methyl-propyl, etc., glyoxime, which are similar in their general properties, but have accessible melting-points (Me—Et 280°, Me—Pr 144°), and are remarkably more soluble than the dimethyl compound, the methyl-ethyl derivative being about 50 times as soluble in alcohol or benzene as the dimethyl.[743]

In the quantitative estimation of nickel by means of this compound, the precipitation is carried out in presence of ammonia or sodium acetate (to neutralize the liberated acid); the precipitate is washed with water and dried to a constant weight at 110–120°. By suitable modifications of the process the precipitation of other metals can be avoided.[744]

Tschugaev originally[745] supposed that in these complexes the nickel is attached to the oxygens of the two oxime groups, giving an (improbable) 7-ring; later he assumed a 6-ring with the N—Ni—O group, and finally,[746] a 5-ring with the nickel linked on all sides to nitrogen, as shown above. This was strongly supported by Pfeiffer,[747] from the behaviour of the monoxime compounds, especially those of benzil. Of the two isomers the α- forms a complex with nickel and with cobalt[748] but not the β-, and it has been shown that the structures are

$$\alpha \quad \begin{array}{ccc} \Phi\cdot C & \!\!\!\!\!\text{———}\!\!\!\!\! & C\cdot\Phi \\ \| & & \| \\ HO\text{—}N & & O \end{array} \qquad \beta \quad \begin{array}{ccc} \Phi\cdot C & \!\!\!\!\!\text{———}\!\!\!\!\! & C\cdot\Phi \\ \| & & \| \\ N\cdot OH & & O \end{array} ,$$

which agrees with the N—Ni—O grouping and the 5-ring, but not the O—Ni—O and the 6. The conclusion is further supported by all the evidence that nickel (and cobalt) co-ordinates with nitrogen more strongly than with oxygen.

Compounds of this type have been of value in establishing two important theoretical points in the behaviour of nickel. It was shown by Pauling in 1931,[749] that the application of wave-mechanics indicates that while the normal arrangement of atoms round a 4-covalent central atom is tetrahedral, with transitional elements, where one or more of the electrons used in the links may belong to the d-subgroup of the incomplete electron group of the atom, the four attached atoms may lie in a plane with the central atom, and where this happens, since the d-electrons are largely responsible for the magnetic moment, this will be altered, and in particular a 4-covalent nickelic atom of this kind will be diamagnetic.

[743] E. G. Cox, E. Sharratt, W. Wardlaw, and K. C. Webster, *J.C.S.* 1936, 129.
[744] Abegg, pp. 442, 444.   [745] L. A. Tschugaev, *Ber.* 1907, **40**, 3498.
[746] Id., *J.C.S.* 1914, **105**, 2187.
[747] P. Pfeiffer and J. Richarz, *Ber.* 1928, **61**, 103.
[748] See L. A. Tschugaev, ib. 1908, **41**, 1678.
[749] L. Pauling, *J.A.C.S.* 1931, **53**, 1367.

To test these conclusions Sugden[750] investigated these nickel glyoxime derivatives. He showed that the benzyl-methyl-glyoxime compound having two rings of the structure

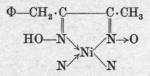

(where we may fairly assume that the interchange of —OH and →O is instantaneous) occurs in two different forms, α-, m. pt. 168°, β- m. pt. 76, which are interconvertible. This is only possible if the two rings lie in the same plane, where there are the alternatives of the phenyl in the upper ring being on the side of the phenyl in the lower, or on the side of the methyl—in other words, of *cis* and *trans* isomerism. The planar structure of the complex (as anticipated by Pauling) was therefore established. It is curious that Tschugaev himself had shown[751] that the nickel compound of monoethyl glyoxime occurs in two interconvertible forms, but he attached no special importance to this.

Finally, Sugden showed that these compounds were diamagnetic, thus confirming the second part of Pauling's prediction.

Later Cavell and Sugden[752] found that the nickel compounds of methyl-*n*-propyl and methyl-*n*-butyl glyoxime both occur in two interconvertible forms, and that these also are diamagnetic. They further showed from the dipole moment that the *p*-chlorophenyl *n*-butyl derivative is planar. For further work on compounds of this type see the references [743,753-4]. The magnetic properties are discussed below (p. 1445).

Nickel can also form addition compounds with the dioximes, analogous to its *en* cations, with rings of the structure

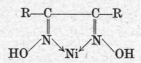

They have either one $(Ni(DH_2)X_2)$ or two $(Ni(DH_2)_2X_2)$ chelate rings, where X may be a halogen, or half of SO_4, $(COO)_2$, etc. The monochelate compounds are pale green when anhydrous and dark green when hydrated; the second type are blue or dark green. They are not very stable—remarkably less so than the corresponding *en* compounds—being decomposed by water, aniline, or alcohol to give the much more stable substitution products $Ni(DH)_2$.[755]

Another compound containing the N—Ni—N group as part of a ring

[750] S. Sugden, *J.C.S.* 1932, 246.
[751] *J. Russ. Phys. Chem. Soc.* 1910, **42**, 1466.
[752] H. J. Cavell and S. Sugden, *J.C.S.* 1935, 621.
[753] G. Ponzio and E. Biglietti, *Gaz.* 1933, **63**, 159.
[754] A. Rosenheim and L. Gerb, *Z. anorg. Chem.* 1933, **210**, 289.
[755] Abegg, pp. 724–6.

is the derivative of phthalocyanine. The molecule of this remarkable blue pigment has at the centre four nitrogen atoms symmetrically (or almost symmetrically) disposed in a plane, and carrying two hydrogen atoms. In the nickel derivative the two hydrogens are replaced by the nickel, which becomes attached to all 4 nitrogens in a way which may be written

A careful study of the crystal structure by Robertson[756] has shown that the whole molecule, including the nickel, is planar, and the compound was found to be diamagnetic.

A series of chelate compounds is known in which the nickel is attached to nitrogen and oxygen; they are less stable than the N,N-complexes, as the co-ordination of nickel is weaker to oxygen than to nitrogen. They include the derivatives of α-diketones such as benzil $\Phi \cdot CO \cdot CO \cdot \Phi$, and even their hydrazones, such as

$$\underset{O \quad N \cdot NH_2}{\Phi \cdot C\!\!=\!\!C \cdot \Phi}{}^{758}$$

Another example is the nickel derivative of salicylaldoxime

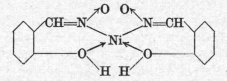

which has been shown[757] to have a plane structure, and also to be dia-magnetic.

A singular reaction for producing chelate compounds of this kind has been discovered by Pfeiffer and his co-workers.[759] They found that *o*-hydroxyaldehydes and ketones will condense in presence of nickel with *en* or *o*-phenylene diamine to give dichelate compounds in which the two chelate rings are also united to one another: thus with *en* and salicylalde-hyde is formed:

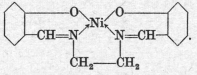

The magnetic properties of some of these dichelate nickelic complexes are peculiar. We have seen that many are planar and diamagnetic, as Pauling's theory suggests. Others, however, are found to be paramagnetic,

[756] J. M. Robertson, *J.C.S.* 1935, 615.
[757] E. G. Cox, F. W. Pinkard, W. Wardlaw, and K. C. Webster, ib. 459.
[758] T. W. J. Taylor, N. H. Callow, and C. R. W. Francis, ib. 1939, 257.
[759] P. Pfeiffer, E. Breith, E. Lübbe, and T. Tsumaki, *Ann.* 1933, **503**, 84.

to about the same extent as the Ni^{++} ion. Quite small differences will determine a compound to belong to one class or the other; it is even stated[764] that the nickel complex of salicylaldehyde methyl-imine $C_6H_4(OH)CH{=}N\cdot CH_2$ occurs in two forms, one dia- and the other paramagnetic. It is a natural assumption commonly made[765] that the paramagnetic compounds are tetrahedral, but in no case has this yet been established. See references [760-6].

Another N—Ni—O ring is that produced by dicyano-diamidine, the so-called Grossmann reagent.[767] This gives with nickel a remarkable insoluble complex of the structure

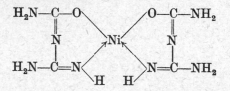

which can be used for the quantitative estimation of nickel.[768]

Complex Nickel Nitrites (*Nitro-complexes*)

Our knowledge of this remarkable group of complexes is largely due to Ferrari and Colla.[769-75]

All these compounds, without exception, contain the group $[Ni(NO_2)_6]^{4-}$; they are all anhydrous, brownish-red, stable in air to temperatures above 100° and sometimes 140°, recrystallizable from water and insoluble in alcohol. There can be no doubt that they are true complex salts,[772] and that they are nitro-compounds, $Ni{-}N{\overset{\nearrow O}{\underset{\searrow O}{}}}$. No isomeric nitrito-compounds Ni—O—N=O are known.

They dissolve readily in water to give greenish solutions, which are decomposed by boiling or by treatment with hydroxyl ion or hydrogen sulphide, this last precipitating the nickel completely, so that the complex must be more dissociated than that of the nickelicyanides $Ni(CN)_4''$. They are formed both by monovalent (Li, Na, K, Tl′) and by divalent (Sr, Ba,

[760] L. Malatesta, *Gaz.* 1938, **68**, 319.

[761] D. P. Mellor and D. P. Craig, *Proc. Roy. Soc. N.S. Wales,* 1940, **74**, 475.

[762] D. P. Mellor, ib. 1941, **75**, 157.

[763] W. Klemm and K. H. Raddatz, *Z. anorg. Chem.* 1942, **250**, 204.

[764] Id., ib. 207.

[765] H. S. French, M. Z. Magee, and E. Sheffield, *J.A.C.S.* 1942, **64**, 1924.

[766] S. Sugden, *J.C.S.* 1943, 332.

[767] H. Grossmann and B. Schück, *Ber.* 1906, **39**, 3356.

[768] P. Fluch, *Z. anal. Chem.* 1926, **69**, 232.

[769] F. Ephraim, *Helv. Chim. Acta,* 1923, **6**, 920.

[770] A. Ferrari and C. Colla, *Atti R.* 1930, [6] **11**, 755.

[771] Id., ib. 1931, [6] **14**, 435.

[772] Id., ib. 511.   [773] A. Ferrari and R. Curti, *Gaz.* 1933, **63**, 499.

[774] A. Ferrari and C. Colla, ib. 1935, **65**, 168.   [775] Id., ib. 809.

Cd, Hg, Pb) metals. The crystal structure of the strontium, barium, and lead salts has been shown to be the same, and to correspond to that of potassium platinichloride K_2PtCl_6, that is, to have the 6 NO_2 groups arranged round the nickel at the points of an octahedron.[773]

A peculiarity of these salts is the readiness with which mixed compounds are formed, of the type $M_2M''[Ni(NO_2)_6]$, where M' = K, Rb, Cs, NH_4, Ti', and M'' = Mg, Ca, Sr, Ba, Zn, Cd, Hg, Pd: these are the so-called 'triple nitrites'.[769-72,775] They are yellow, red, or brown salts, all anhydrous, which are isomorphous with one another, with the corresponding cupri- and cobaltonitrites, and with the simple cobaltinitrite $K_3[Co(NO_2)_6]$.

Nickel-Oxygen Complexes

The co-ordination of nickel to oxygen is weak. Apart from the hydrated Ni^{++} ion there is little evidence of its occurrence except in chelate compounds, and even these are few and usually unstable. The 'ato' complexes, formed with the radicals of dibasic acids, are almost confined to the carbonato- and oxalato-compounds.

Carbonato-Complexes

Precipitated nickel carbonate, although unlike cobalt carbonate it will not dissolve in sodium bicarbonate, dissolves in excess of potassium carbonate, and no doubt carbonato-complexes are present in the solution. Several of these double carbonates have been isolated. They are all of the di-ato type $M_2[Ni(CO_3)_2]$, H_2O. Examples are $Na_2[Ni(CO_3)_2]$, 10 H_2O, and K, 4 H_2O; both of these salts are green. Their stability is small, and they are decomposed by water.

Oxalato-Compounds

Nickel oxalate dissolves somewhat in boiling potassium oxalate solution, and on cooling a pale-green slightly soluble salt $K_2[NiOx_2]$ 6 H_2O (or perhaps 4 H_2O[776]) separates; when this is heated it loses water, giving first a di- and then a monohydrate, and finally at 200° becoming anhydrous: the green colour darkens as the water is lost. This seems to be the only certain double oxalate of nickel.

By polarographic measurements on the solution Sartori[777] estimated the value of the dissociation constant

$$K = \frac{[NiOx_2^{--}]}{[Ni^{++}] \cdot [Ox^{--}]^2}$$

to be 5×10^{13}, almost identical with the value obtained (with the same form of constant) for the cyano-complex.

Dithio-oxalato-Complexes

When potassium dithio-oxalate $K_2C_2O_2S_2$ acts on a solution of a nickel salt, an intense purple colour is produced which is stable on boiling, and

[776] S. R. Brinkley, *J.A.C.S.* 1939, **61**, 965.
[777] G. Sartori, *Gaz.* 1934, **64**, 3.

a purple-black crystalline solid of the composition $K_2Ni(C_2S_2O_2)_2$ can be made to separate out.[778] The colour is so intense that it will detect one part of nickel in 40 million of water. Robinson and Jones[779] showed by freezing-point and conductivity measurements that the potassium salt is a strong ternary electrolyte. The nickel can be precipitated from the solution by alkaline hydroxides and sulphides, but only slowly, though potassium cyanide decomposes it at once.

Cox and his colleagues[780] have shown that this compound and the palladium and platinum analogues all have planar anions, the structure of which must be

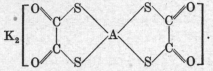

The nickel derivatives of oxy-acids like malic, tartaric, citric, and salicylic[781] are either ill-defined, or show little signs of complexity.

Complex Nickel Halides

The tendency to complex halide formation falls off with nickel in the order $Cl > Br > I$, and presumably even more fluorides than chlorides would be known if an equal amount of attention had been paid to them. The sharp fall in the co-ordination number from 4 with fluorine to nearly always 3 with chlorine is to be noticed.

Complex Fluorides

Only a few of these have been prepared, if we exclude those of the heavy metals, where we are not sure which the co-ordination centre is.

The known complex fluorides of divalent nickel are nearly all of the type M_2NiF_4. Only the potassium and ammonium salts seem to be known. K_2NiF_4 forms green quadratic tables[782]; it dissolves easily in water, only slightly in methyl or ethyl alcohol. While there is no doubt that the anhydrous salt exists, an investigation of the system $KF—NiF_2—H_2O$ showed[783] that no definite double salts occurred as solid phases, but that there is a continuous series of solid solutions containing all three components.

The behaviour of the system $NH_4F—NiF_2—H_2O$[783] shows that $(NH_4)_2NiF_4, 2H_2O$ exists, and the corresponding anhydrous salt can be got by fusing its component salts together.[784]

[778] H. O. Jones and H. S. Tasker, *J.C.S.* 1909, **95**, 1904.

[779] C. S. Robinson and H. O. Jones, ib. 1912, **101**, 62.

[780] E. G. Cox, F. W. Pinkard, W. Wardlaw, and K. C. Webster, ib. 1935, 459.

[781] F. E. Jones and C. R. Bury, *J. phys. Chem.* 1928, **32**, 1272.

[782] For the crystal structure see V. M. Goldschmidt, *Geochem. Vert.* viii. 1927.

[783] A. Kurtenacker, W. Finger, and F. Hey, *Z. anorg. Chem.* 1933, **211**, 281.

[784] C. Poulenc, *C.R.* 1892, **114**, 1426; *Ann. Chim. Phys.* 1894, [7] **2**, 5.

Complex Nickel Chlorides

Unlike the fluorides these are almost all of the tricovalent type $MNiCl_3$. No complex acid has been prepared, and nickel chloride, unlike cobaltous chloride, is much less soluble in water in presence of hydrochloric acid.

With lithium $LiNiCl_3$, 2 and 3 H_2O occur and probably also Li_4NiCl_6, 10 H_2O,[785] which is practically the only known complex halide of divalent nickel of the 6-covalent type. $KNiCl_3$, 5 H_2O, $CsNiCl_3$, and perhaps Cs_2NiCl_4 are known. NH_4NiCl_3 has been made, but ammonium chloride forms a series of mixed crystals with nickel chloride, and this may merely be one of them.

Double chlorides of organic bases (alkyl and arylamines, pyridine, quinoline, etc.) are more frequent; nearly all of these are of the type $(BH)NiCl_3$.[786]

Complex Bromides

Hydrobromic acid turns a nickel bromide solution greenish-yellow, but the only double salt isolated is $CsNiBr_3$, yellow crystals stable in air, but decomposed by water or alcohol. Ammonium bromide forms mixed crystals with nickel bromide,[787] as happens with the chlorides.

Complex Iodides

Nickel iodide forms a blood-red solution in concentrated hydriodic acid, but no salt can be isolated except a very complex compound of unknown constitution containing acetone.[788]

COMPOUNDS OF TRIVALENT NICKEL

There is a small number of nickel compounds in which the valency of the element is almost certainly 3, and possibly, but not probably, more. The only undoubted members of this group are the black hydrated oxides which are formed by the alkaline oxidation of divalent nickel, and are used as strong oxidizing agents, as catalysts, and in the construction of secondary cells. Much recent work seems to have proved that no anhydrous oxide of nickel with more oxygen than NiO exists; but higher oxides certainly occur in the hydrated state, although their constitution, and hence the valency of the nickel in them, is not yet fully determined. Attempts to prepare salts of trivalent nickel, such as a chloride or sulphate[789,790] have all failed.

Higher Oxides and Oxide-Hydrates of Nickel

It has been stated that by heating the oxide, carbonate, or nitrate of divalent nickel to high temperatures in air, higher oxides of nickel, especially the sesquioxide Ni_2O_3 are obtained; and that if nickel salts are oxidized in neutral or alkaline solution, these oxides are produced in the

[785] H. Benrath, *Z. anorg. Chem.* 1932, **205**, 417.   [786] Abegg, p. 508.
[787] G. F. Campbell, *Z. anorg. Chem.* 1895, **8**, 126.
[788] L. Cambi, *Gaz.* 1909, **39**, i. 361.
[789] C. Schall and H. Markgraf, *Trans. Amer. Electrochem. Soc.* 1924, **45**, 119.
[790] C. Schall, *Z. Elektrochem.* 1932, **38**, 27.

hydrated form as black precipitates. Recent work,[791-3] however, has shown that the higher oxides do not exist in the anhydrous state.

The most decisive results are those of Hüttig and Peters,[793] who showed that the behaviour of this oxide is very like that of the hydrated cobalt sesquioxide Co_2O_3, H_2O (see under cobalt, p. 1393). They obtained this sesquioxide (of the composition Ni_2O_3, $4 \cdot 25 H_2O$) by oxidizing a (divalent) nickel salt in solution with alkali and bromine, filtering, and drying the black precipitate over sulphuric acid in the cold. When heated under 10 mm. pressure it loses water down to Ni_2O_3, H_2O at 138°, and at this temperature gives off oxygen and water until the monoxide NiO is left. This is exactly what Co_2O_3, H_2O does at 148–157°. A Debye X-ray diagram showed only the lines of Ni_2O_3, H_3O, and NiO, and mixtures of the two sets for the partially decomposed material.[793,796-7] Hence the substance cannot (as was suggested[794-5]) contain a hydrated dioxide, or an intermediate oxide such as Ni_3O_4.

The K edge of the X-ray absorption[798] of the nickel in these compounds showed the usual increase of the shift (the difference of wave-length from that for the pure metal) with the rise of valency, the shifts for NiO, $Ni(OH)_2$ and Ni_2O_3, H_2O being 0·81, 1·10, and 1·82 X.U. (1,000 X.U. = 1 A.U.).

Finely divided hydroxide $Ni(OH)_2$ will take up oxygen in the cold from sodium hypochlorite as a superficial layer, without affecting the crystal lattice; on heating the oxygen seems to go into the lattice.[799]

Nickel Peroxide-Hydrate

The highly oxidized black precipitates prepared in the ways already mentioned often contain more oxygen than corresponds to Ni_2O_3, and this has been ascribed to the presence of a dioxide NiO_2. The compounds of course always contain water, no anhydrous oxide above NiO being known, and no oxide with an oxygen content as high as that of NiO_2, H_2O.[799-800] Howell found[794] that if the precipitate is heated under the mother liquor there is a fairly rapid loss of oxygen, until the ratio corresponding to Ni_2O_3 is reached, after which the loss is very slow. Clark and his colleagues[801] could get no definite X-ray patterns from these highly oxidized products, and concluded that they were amorphous.

These hydrated oxides of nickel, with an O:Ni ratio equal to, or greater than, 3:2, which undoubtedly exist (they are the depolarizers in 'alkaline' accumulators such as the Edison), might all be formulated as peroxides

[791] G. Lunde, *Z. anorg. Chem.* 1928, **169**, 405.

[792] G. B. Taylor and H. W. Starkweather, *J.A.C.S.* 1930, **52**, 2314.

[793] G. F. Hüttig and A. Peter, *Z. anorg. Chem.* 1930, **189**, 190.

[794] O. R. Howell, *J.C.S.* 1923, **123**, 669, 1772.

[795] I. Bellucci and E. Clavari, *Atti R.* 1905, **14**, ii. 234.

[796] R. W. Cairns and E. Ott, *J.A.C.S.* 1933, **55**, 534.

[797] Id., *Z. Elektrochem.* 1934, **40**, 286.　　　　[798] Id., *J.A.C.S.* 1934, **56**, 1094.

[799] M. C. Boswell and R. K. Iler, ib. 1936, **58**, 924.

[800] I. Bellucci and E. Clavari, *Atti R.* 1905, [v] **14**, ii. 234: 1907, **16**, i. 647.

[801] G. L. Clark, W. G. Asbury, and R. M. Wick, *J.A.C.S.* 1925, **47**, 2661.

without assigning to the nickel any valency greater than 2, and as there are no other compounds of nickel which indicate for it a higher valency than 2, this conclusion is not impossible. It seems, however, more likely that the nickel has a valency of at least 3 in these oxides, and this for two reasons, the shift in the K edge in the X-ray absorption spectrum found by Cairns and Ott, and the very close resemblance found by Hüttig between the behaviour of the hydrated sesquioxides of nickel and cobalt, Ni_2O_3, H_2O and Co_2O_3, H_2O. On the other hand, the existence of tetravalent nickel in the highest oxidation products is very doubtful. It is more likely that the excess of oxygen over that required for Ni_2O_3, so far as it is not merely an absorbed layer on the surface, is held in the form of peroxide links.

Nickel Carbonyl Compounds

The chief of these is nickel tetracarbonyl, $Ni(CO)_4$, the first of the metallic carbonyls to be discovered.[802] It is made by passing carbon monoxide over finely divided metallic nickel at a temperature below 100°. It is a colourless liquid melting at −25° and boiling at +43°. It is miscible with benzene, but almost insoluble in water (sol^y 0·018/10°). On heating it decomposes below 100° into carbon monoxide and nickel, and the benzene solution does the same on boiling, but in the cold the compound is not acted on by dilute acids or alkalies. It is diamagnetic. It is highly poisonous, four parts by volume in 10,000 of air being lethal to animals; the amount of carbon monoxide which it contains is quite insufficient to account for this, and the toxicity must be due to the nickel. The parachor is 259·9, at 8–20°, giving 19·9 as the atomic parachor of nickel.[803]

The decomposition of the vapour at 100–128° is[804] mainly a homogeneous reaction, with a heat of activation of 10·25 k.cals. Alone or in benzene solution the carbonyl reacts with the oxides of nitrogen, and the more readily the more oxygen they contain,[805] giving among other more obscure products the curious compound $Ni(NO)OH, H_2O$ (see p. 1453).

$Ni(CO)_4$ obviously has the 4 CO groups acting as donors in the co-ordination to the nickel giving (mainly) the formula $Ni(\leftarrow C\equiv O)_4$; hence the valency is, strictly speaking, zero. The E.A.N. is 36, that of krypton.

The molecule has been shown by electron diffraction[806] to be tetrahedral, as we should expect since the nickel has a valency octet; the grouping Ni—C—O is linear. This is supported by the infra-red spectrum.[807-8] The conclusion drawn[809] from the Raman spectrum that the molecule is planar has been shown[810] to be incorrect.

[802] L. Mond, C. Langer, and F. Quincke, *J.C.S.* 1890, **57**, 749.
[803] F. W. Laird and M. A. Smith, *J.A.C.S.* 1935, **57**, 266.
[804] C. E. H. Bawn, *Trans. Far. Soc.* 1935, **31**, 440.
[805] J. C. W. Fraser and W. E. Trout, *J.A.C.S.* 1936, **58**, 2201.
[806] L. O. Brockway and P. C. Cross, *J. Chem. Phys.* 1935, **3**, 828.
[807] C. R. Bailey and R. R. Gordon, ib. 1938, **6**, 225.
[808] B. L. Crawford and P. C. Cross, ib. 525.
[809] A. B. F. Duncan and J. W. Murray, ib. 1934, **2**, 636.
[810] E. Bright Wilson, ib. 1935, **3**, 59.

Carbonyl Derivatives of Monovalent Nickel

Divalent nickel compounds do not take up carbon monoxide, but the red solution of the monovalent $K_2Ni(CN)_3$ absorbs the gas (with loss of its red colour) extraordinarily quickly[811-12] (70 c.c. at 0° in less than 30 seconds).[812] The colour changes from deep red to orange yellow. The resulting (like the original) solution has a strong reducing power (for example it will reduce ammoniacal silver solution to the metal) which it soon loses on exposure to the air. With sulphuric acid it gives a grey precipitate which with hydrogen peroxide assumes the greenish colour of nickel dicyanide $Ni(CN)_2$.

This easily oxidized carbon monoxide compound has not yet been isolated, but the carbon monoxide absorbed (at 0° or below) by a solution of known Ni' content, is the average 15·5 litres (70 per cent. of a g. mol.) per gram-atom of nickel[812]; since there is always some oxidation of the nickel by the water with the liberation of hydrogen, we may take it that this shows that the composition of the compound is $K_2Ni(CN)_3CO$. If it is monomeric the E.A.N. of the nickel is 35, so that we should expect it to be dimeric.

The orange nickel monocyanide which is precipitated from the red solution on acidification is also able to take up carbon monoxide on vigorous shaking. The precipitate turns to a yellow colour, and finally to the green of the dicyanide $Ni(CN)_2$: the gas above the liquid was found to contain nickel carbonyl.

In the tetracarbonyl the valency of the nickel is zero; in the other carbonyl compounds (if they are monomeric) it is 1.

Nitrosyl Compounds

Nitric oxide, like carbon monoxide, is absorbed by monovalent but not by divalent nickel.[813] The solution of the potassium salt $K_2Ni(CN)_3$ absorbs nitric oxide with a change of colour from red to deep wine-red, the product probably being of the composition $K_2[Ni(CN)_3NO]$. Further, when potassium thiosulphate acts on a solution of nickel (Ni'') acetate in aqueous alcohol in an atmosphere of nitric oxide, the gas is absorbed, the liquid turns deep blue, and a blue oil separates which solidifies to a bluish-green powder looking rather like chromium sesquioxide, which has the composition $K_3[Ni(S_2O_3)_2(NO)]$, 2 H_2O.[813] This gives in water a blue solution which is slowly oxidized by air; it is decomposed by acids or alkalies at once, but by sodium carbonate solution only on boiling.

A good deal of light has been thrown on these phenomena by the work of Anderson.[814-15] Following up an observation of Reihlen's[816] he showed

[811] A. Job and A. A. Samuel, *C.R.* 1923, **177**, 188.
[812] W. Manchot and H. Gall, *Ber.* 1926, **59**, 1060.
[813] W. Manchot, ib. 1926, **59**, 2445.
[814] J. S. Anderson, *Z. anorg. Chem.* 1936, **229**, 357.
[815] H. Reihlen, ib. 1937, **230**, 223. (This is a criticism of the preceding paper.)
[816] H. Reihlen, A. Grühl, G. v. Hessling, and O. Pfréngl, *Ann.* 1930, **482**, 161.

that nitric oxide acts on a solution of $Ni(CO)_4$ in benzene to give a blue powder of $Ni(NO)OH, x\,H_2O$ ($x = 1\cdot52$); this is volatile in a high vacuum, but decomposes below 90°; it is very soluble in ethyl and methyl alcohol and water to give a blue solution with an alkaline reaction, which decomposes slowly.

This substance (whose molecular weight is of course unknown) is clearly a base, of which Manchot's compounds $K_2Ni(CN)_3NO$ and

$$K_3[Ni(S_2O_3)_2NO], 2\,H_2O$$

can be regarded as complex salts.

The valency of the nickel in all these nitrosyl compounds, if they are monomeric, is zero.

THE PLATINUM METALS

AS already explained, there is a very sharp difference between the first triad of Group VIII and the others, due mainly to the facts that in the second and third triads simple ions practically do not occur, and that the higher valencies become increasingly important. The relation between the remaining two members of each of the vertical series VIII A, VIII B, and VIII C is apparent as soon as we pass the first triad; the second triad differs much less from the third than it does from the first. We shall therefore discuss the six platinum metals in the order ruthenium, osmium: rhodium, iridium: palladium, platinum.

The abundance of these elements in the earth's crust in parts per million (g./ton) is Ru, Os, Rh, Ir about 0·001; Pd 0·01; Pt 0·005.

For the magnetic behaviour of compounds of the platinum metals see Mellor.[817]

[817] D. P. Mellor, *Proc. R.S. N. S. Wales*, 1943, **77**, 145.

GROUP VIII A (8)
RUTHENIUM AND OSMIUM

THESE elements resemble one another in many respects, and especially in their power of assuming a large number of different valencies. Of these ruthenium has 9, all from zero (in the carbonyl) to the group valency of 8 in the tetroxide. Osmium does not go so far as this, but it can have valencies of 0, 2, 3, 4, 6, and 8. The properties of the two elements in each of these various valencies may be briefly compared; they show a close resemblance in many even quite small details, and the usual increase in stability of the higher valencies as we pass from ruthenium to osmium.

Valency = 0

Ruthenium has one compound in which it has this valency, the carbonyl $Ru(CO)_5$: the osmium analogue $Os(CO)_5$ has recently been discovered.

Valency = 1

With ruthenium there is some sign of this valency occurring in solution: with osmium there is none. [The absence of this lowest valency with osmium, while it occurs, or may occur, with the lighter ruthenium, is the usual effect of the rise of atomic number.]

Valency = 2

With ruthenium this is a valency of some importance. No simple compounds have been isolated, but ruthenium compounds, and quite probably the divalent ruthenium ion, must occur in the blue solution got by reducing trivalent ruthenium compounds. They are, however, far less stable than the ferrous ion and its compounds.

The divalent ruthenium complexes are confined to a few types, but all these are fairly stable, and some are very stable, far more so than the weak complexes of ferrous iron; apart from a carbonyl compound $Ru(CO)_2Cl_2$, which is presumably 4-covalent, they are all 6-covalent, which is very unusual for the complexes of a divalent atom.

With the ammines there is a sharp distinction between the chelate diamine derivatives, and the simple monamine compounds. The chelate compounds are all trichelate. The others all have a co-ordination number of 6, which, however, is never made up of 6 amine groups, but only of 5, 4, or 2 (not 3), at least one of the remaining places being filled up by a sulphite residue, $(SO_3)''$, $(SO_3H)'$, or $(SO_2)°$, as in the compound
$$[Ru(NH_3)_4(SO_3H)_2]°.$$

The anionic complexes are either cyanides, or nitrosyl compounds, or both. The pure cyanides are all of the ferrocyanide type $M_4[Ru(CN)_6]$; they are very stable, and as with the ferrocyanides the acid can be isolated. The nitrosyl compounds (discussed later, p. 1484) are peculiarly numerous with ruthenium: there are over eighty enumerated in Gmelin. They all have only one nitrosyl group; properly interpreted they all contain divalent ruthenium. They include a fairly stable group of the type $Ru(NO)(hal)_3$ (hal = Cl, Br, I); and many complexes. The ammines have 1, 2, 3, or 4 but never 5 amine groups; the anions include such complexes as $M_2[Ru''(NO)Cl_5]$, $M_2[Ru''(NO)Ox_2Cl]$, and the cyanides, which are all of the nitroprusside type $M_2[Ru''(NO)(CN)_5]$.

The divalent osmium compounds are rather fewer. The binary compound $OsCl_2$ can be isolated; it must be highly complex: it is a brown solid unaffected by boiling with water. There is also a compound $Os(CO)_3Cl_2$, almost but not quite corresponding to $Ru(CO)_2Cl_2$; the complexes are almost confined to the three types $M_4[Os(CN)_6]$, very stable: $M_2[Os''(NO)X_5]$ the only nitrosyl compound formed by osmium (hal = Cl, Br, I): and $M_4[Os(SO_3)_3]$. These complex sulphito-compounds, the one class of divalent osmium complexes to which ruthenium has no exact analogue, are especially common with osmium, occurring in the valencies 2, 4, and 6.

Valency = 3

With ruthenium this is the most important of the valencies. The 'simple' compounds, such as the chloride $RuCl_3$ and the cyanide $Ru(CN)_3$, are no doubt really complex. The complex salts include ammines, nearly all with a co-ordination number of 6, of the types

$$[RuAm_6]X_3, \ [RuAm_5R]X_2, \ [RuAm_4R_2]X, \ and \ [RuAm_3R_3]°;$$

R is always a radical, and not H_2O. The complex halides are formed by chlorine and bromine, not by fluorine or iodine. All types occur from $M[RuX_4]$ to $M_4[RuX_7]$ (structure unknown); they are not very stable, and the bromides less so than the chlorides. There are also complex nitro-salts $M_2[Ru(NO_2)_5]$, which are stable enough to be recrystallized from water.

This state is less stable with osmium, and the compounds are very limited in number. There is one binary compound $OsCl_3$, subliming at $350°$, and changing at $560°$ to $OsCl_2+OsCl_4$. It dissolves in water but only ionizes slowly. There are two types of complexes, the halides $M_3[OsCl_6]$ and $M_3[OsBr_6]$, which decompose easily, and the nitro-compounds $M_2[Os(NO_2)_5]$, of the same odd type as with ruthenium.

Valency = 4

The ruthenium compounds of this valency are few but stable. The simple compounds include the very stable dioxide RuO_2, and of the halides only the tetrachloride $RuCl_4$ and an oxy-halide $RuCl_3OH$, made by the reduction of ruthenium tetroxide with hydrochloric acid. There is also a sulphate.

Of the complexes the ammines are few and uncertain, probably all having the co-ordination number of 6. The complex halides are numerous and definite; they are only formed by chlorine and bromine, and are all either $M_2[Ru(hal)_6]$ or $M_2[Ru(hal)_5OH]$; they are fairly stable.

With osmium tetravalency is much the most stable state, as trivalency is with ruthenium. The binary compounds include the tetrafluoride OsF_4, black, non-volatile, soluble in water: $OsCl_4$, which only dissolves in water as it hydrolyses: a hydroxy-chloride $OsCl_3OH$.

There is a tetraiodide, and a dioxide (the disulphide, diselenide, and ditelluride have a pyrites structure, and so contain divalent ruthenium). The complex salts are also numerous, though they are all anionic, and there are practically no ammines; they are all 6-covalent and are usually quite stable. The hexahalides $M_2[Os(hal)_6]$ occur both pure and mixed, with $(hal)_6$ represented by F_6, Cl_6, Br_6, I_6, Cl_5Br, Cl_3Br_3, Cl_5OH, Br_5OH, and Cl_5NH_2. There are also sulphito-compounds.

Valency = 5

With ruthenium this is only found in the fluoride RuF_5, boiling-point 273°, which is hydrolysed by water.

Osmium forms no pentavalent compounds at all.

Valency = 6

With ruthenium this valency only occurs in the ruthenates M_2RuO_4 and their derivatives, which correspond to the ferrates. The ruthenates are made by oxidizing ruthenium with potassium permanganate or nitrate; the corresponding chloro-ruthenates $M_2[RuO_2Cl_4]$ by the action of hydrochloric acid on ruthenium tetroxide. The chlorine in the latter compound is easily hydrolysed.

For osmium the valency of 6 is the next most important valency after that of 4. There is a hexafluoride OsF_6 (b. pt. 204°, hydrolysed by water at once), and a phosphide OsP_2; all the other hexavalent compounds are complexes. They include the osmates M_2OsO_4, which can be made by the alkaline oxidation of metallic osmium, or the alkaline reduction of osmium tetroxide; they are red or brown salts, easily soluble in water, stable when dry but decomposing when wet. They give two series of so-called osmyl derivatives, the 'osmyl' salts, of the type $M_2[OsO_2X_4]$ (like the ruthenium compounds) where $X = Cl$, Br, CN, NO_2, $\frac{1}{2}Ox$, $\frac{1}{2}SO_3$: and the 'osmyl-oxy' salts $M_2[OsO_2 \cdot O \cdot X_2]$, where $X = Cl$, Br, NO_2, and $\frac{1}{2}Ox$. All these salts are stable when dry, but decompose in solution. It should be noticed that there is no real analogy between the osmyl group and the uranyl group except the formal one that both are XO_2; the osmyl group is always a constituent of a complex anion, whereas the uranyl group is itself a cation.

There are also the very curious 'nitrilo-halides' $M[OsNBr_4]$, $M_2[OsNCl_5]$ and $M_2[OsNBr_5]$ which are made by the reduction of the osmiamates (octovalent osmium derivatives) $M[OsO_3N]$ with halogen hydride.

Valency = 7

With ruthenium this is entirely confined to the perruthenates $M[RuO_4]$, corresponding to the permanganates; they are stable in air when dry, but the green aqueous solution changes on standing to the orange ruthenate $M_2[RuO_4]$, with precipitation of the dioxide RuO_2 and evolution of oxygen.

Osmium forms no heptavalent compounds at all.

Valency = 8

This is the group valency.

With ruthenium this is found only in the tetroxide RuO_4, made by the oxidation of the metal, or of a ruthenate M_2RuO_4 with chlorine. It melts at 27°, sublimes easily, and is somewhat soluble in water. It is an unstable substance, readily reduced (usually to a trivalent or tetravalent ruthenium compound, or to a ruthenate) by light, hydrochloric acid, or heat.

There are a fair number of octovalent osmium compounds. There is the tetroxide OsO_4, melting at 40° and boiling at 130°. It behaves in water as the anhydride of a very weak acid, such as $H_2[OsO_4(OH)_2]$; it is much less easily reduced than ruthenium tetroxide. There is an octofluoride OsF_8 (the only known compound AB_8), melting at 34·4° and boiling at 47·5°; very reactive, and hydrolysed by water.

There are several complex acids derived from the tetroxide, such as $M[OsO_4(OH)]$, and $M_2[OsO_4F_2]$. There are also the curious osmiamates $M[OsO_3N]$, easily formed from the tetroxide with ammonia in concentrated alkali; they are derived from OsO_4 by replacing one oxygen atom by an NH group, the hydrogen of which is acidic.

RUTHENIUM

RUTHENIUM is usually regarded as the rarest of the platinum metals, and this is true of the proportions in the platinum ores, but in the earth's crust ruthenium is no rarer than rhodium, osmium, or iridium.

The chemistry of ruthenium is peculiarly obscure; it is so rare that only small quantities are available, and it occurs in nine valency states, often going very readily from one to another. The atomic weight is among the least certain,[818] since no really suitable compounds for its determination are known.

Metallic Ruthenium

Ruthenium is a hard white metal, melting at about 2,500° and boiling at about 3,700°. It occurs in four modifications, with the following transition points:[819]

$$\alpha \xrightarrow[1030-1040°]{} \beta \xrightarrow[1200°]{} \gamma \xrightarrow[ca.\,1500°]{} \delta.$$

Its specific resistance is $7 \cdot 46 \times 10^{-6}$ at 0°; it is not a superconductor.

Though it is not oxidized by air in the cold, ruthenium combines with oxygen on heating more readily than any other platinum metal except osmium. The powdered metal is converted by ignition in air into the dioxide RuO_2. The metal is insoluble in acids, even in aqua regia, but if potassium chlorate is added to the solution it is oxidized explosively. It is dissolved by fused potash to give the ruthenate K_2RuO_4, and is converted by chlorine into the trichloride $RuCl_3$.

The metal is a powerful catalyst, especially for oxidations, and is sometimes used technically for this purpose, in spite of its high price.

Ruthenium and Hydrogen

Compact ruthenium takes up no hydrogen, but as a fine powder it absorbs a large amount, which is not removed in a vacuum in the cold, and is presumably held on the surface in the atomised condition.[820]

Ruthenium and Carbon

Carbon dissolves in molten ruthenium. According to Moissan[821] the carbon crystallizes out again on cooling, but if the solution is kept for an hour at 2,500° a purple crystalline carbide is said to be formed; it was not analysed.[822]

Ruthenium and Nitrogen

It is very doubtful if any nitride exists.[823]

[818] K. Gleu and K. Rehm, Z. anorg. Chem. 1938, 235, 352.

[819] F. M. Jaeger and E. Rosenbohm, Proc. Acad. Amst. 1931, 34, 812; Rec. Trav. 1932, 51, 37; F. M. Jaeger, Z. anorg. Chem. 1931, 203, 98.

[820] E. Müller and K. Schwabe, Z. physikal. Chem. 1931, 154, 143; Z. Elektrochem. 1929, 35, 181.

[821] H. Moissan, C.R. 1906, 142, 191.

[822] J. C. McLennan, J. F. Allen, and J. O. Wilhelm, Trans. Roy. Soc. Canada, 1931, [3] 25, iii. 15.

[823] See W. Manchot and W. J. Manchot, Z. anorg. Chem. 1936, 226, 411.

Ruthenium and Phosphorus

The phosphide RuP is stable in contact with phosphorus vapour under 1 atmosphere between 900° and 1,100°; it is black, very resistant to alkalies, and scarcely attacked even by aqua regia.[824]

Monovalent Ruthenium

Apart from certain carbonyls and nitrosyls all attempts to isolate mono-valent ruthenium compounds especially the monohalides[825-6] have failed. Monovalent ruthenium may, however, exist in solution. The blue solution obtained by reducing a solution of trivalent ruthenium[827-8] is now generally admitted to contain the divalent form (see next section). But Manchot claims[829-30] that if a ruthenium dihalide or trihalide is treated in solution with a hypophosphite, a colourless or pale yellow solution is obtained, which evolves hydrogen, and has a very high reducing power. He concludes that this contains monovalent ruthenium. This has, how-ever, been denied.[831]

DIVALENT RUTHENIUM

SCARCELY any simple compounds of divalent ruthenium are known, but there are a variety of complexes, and the divalent atom can undoubtedly exist in solution, though whether as a simple or a complex ion is not certain.

If the solution of a compound of trivalent ruthenium, say the trihalide, is reduced electrolytically or in other ways, the reddish-brown liquid becomes pure blue. This blue colour was observed by Fourcroy and Vauquelin as early as 1804, and was at first attributed to osmium. The nature of the blue substance which this solution contains has been much disputed, but there can be little doubt that it is some form of divalent ruthenium. The evidence for this is the quantitative determination of the amount of reducing agent needed to convert the trivalent ruthenium into the blue form, which has been carried out with a variety of reducing agents: with sodium amalgam,[832-4] with hydrogen and platinum black,[835-6] with a chromous solution,[837-8] and by cathodic reduction.[839] This is sup-

[824] W. Biltz, H. J. Ehrhorn, and K. Meisel, *Z. anorg. Chem.* 1939, **240**, 117.
[825] H. Rémy and M. Köhn, ib. 1924, **137**, 369.
[826] L. Wöhler and P. Balz, ib. **139**, 412.
[827] H. Rémy, ib. 1920, **113**, 229.
[828] E. Zintl and P. Zaimis, *Ber.* 1927, **60**, 842.
[829] W. Manchot and H. Schmid, ib. 1931, **64**, 2673.
[830] W. Manchot and J. Düsing, *Z. anorg. Chem.* 1933, **212**, 29.
[831] G. Grube and H. Nann, *Z. Elektrochem.* 1939, **45**, 871.
[832] H. Rémy and A. Lührs, *Ber.* 1928, **61**, 919.
[833] H. Rémy and T. Wagner, ib. 1927, **60**, 494.
[834] H. Rémy, ib. 1928, **61**, 2109.
[835] H. Gall and G. Lehmann, ib. 1926, **59**, 2858.
[836] Id., ib. 1927, **60**, 2492.   [837] E. Zintl and P. Zaimis, ib. 1927, **60**, 842.
[838] W. R. Crowell and D. M. Jost, *J.A.C.S.* 1928, **50**, 377.
[839] W. Manchot and H. Schmid, *Z. anorg. Chem.* 1933, **216**, 104.

ported by a determination of the amount of potassium permanganate needed to convert the ruthenium in the blue solution into the ruthenate.[840]

The exact nature of the blue compounds is uncertain, but in a hydrochloric acid solution there is no doubt a complex chloride present, which may be $H[RuCl_3]$ or $H_2[RuCl_4]$; in any case it is evidently not very stable, since the ruthenium can be precipitated slowly by various anions such as those of the alkalies, hydrogen sulphide, and hydrogen peroxide; potassium permanganate oxidizes the compound at once. As often, the oxidation is much more rapid in alkaline than in acid solution; the precipitated dihydroxide $Ru(OH)_2$ is oxidized by oxygen almost immediately. The blue solution is not colloidal: it does not give the Tyndall effect, and it is not precipitated by salts.

The simple compounds of divalent ruthenium are few. The supposed oxide RuO has been shown[841-2] not to exist.

The hydroxide is undoubtedly produced (probably hydrated) as a brown precipitate darkening in the air through oxidation to $Ru(OH)_3$, when the blue solution is treated with alkaline hydroxide; but it has not been obtained in the pure state.[842-5]

The monosulphide RuS does not exist, but the compounds RuS_2, $RuSe_2$, and $RuTe_2$, which do, have been shown to have pyrites lattices (with S—S ions), and so to contain divalent ruthenium.

Ruthenium Disulphide, RuS_2

Tensimetric and X-ray examination shows[846] that the disulphide is the lowest and the only certain sulphide of ruthenium; the supposed higher sulphides are probably mixtures of the disulphide with free sulphur. It can be made from the trichloride and sulphur at 400°,[847] or by the action of hydrogen sulphide on the trichloride either wet or dry, or from the elements at 1,200°.[846] It forms grey-blue crystals, which are shown by X-ray analysis[847] to have a pyrites lattice, with a Ru—S distance of 2·31 A. It begins to decompose into its elements about 1,000°; it is easily oxidized by air on warming, or by nitric acid.

The selenide $RuSe_2$ and the telluride $RuTe_2$ are shown by X-ray measurements[848] to be the only compounds formed by the elements in question. They have a pyrites lattice, and are very similar in every way to the disulphide.[849]

The *dihalides* must undoubtedly occur in the blue solutions, and the

[840] H. Gall and G. Lehmann, *Ber.* 1928, **61**, 1575.
[841] A. Gutbier and F. Ransohoff, *Z. anorg. Chem.* 1905, **45**, 245.
[842] L. Wöhler, P. Balz, and L. Metz, ib. 1924, **139**, 205.
[843] H. Rémy, ib. 1923, **126**, 185.
[844] F. Krauss and E. Bruchhaus, ib. 1930, **189**, 64.
[845] W. Manchot and H. Schmid, ib. 1933, **216**, 107.
[846] R. Juza and W. Meyer, ib. 1933, **213**, 273.
[847] W. F. de Jong and A. Hoog, *Rec. Trav.* 1927, **46**, 173.
[848] L. Thomassen, *Z. physikal. Chem.* 1929, B **2**, 360.
[849] L. Wöhler, K. Ewald, and H. G. Krall, *Ber.* 1933, **66**, 1638.

dichloride and dibromide have been separated, though not in the pure state. If the blue solution in hydrochloric acid is evaporated down, a dark blue or blue-black solid of intermediate composition is left behind, but this has usually been found to give the vapour pressure of the trihalide.

Gall and Lehmann, however,[835] by the reduction of the chloride obtained a dark blue substance which on analysis gave the ratio Ru:Cl as 1:2·1, and formed an intensely blue solution in water and in alcohol. In the same way by the reduction of ruthenium tribromide in absolute alcohol with hydrogen and platinum black they obtained a black crystalline substance in which the ratio Ru:Br was 1:2·04. With the tri-iodide RuI_3 a blue solution was formed, but no solid could be separated from it.

Ruthenium dicyanide, $Ru(CN)_2$. If potassium cyanide is added to the blue $RuCl_2$ solution a grey-green precipitate is formed, which is easily soluble in excess of potassium cyanide, and may be the dicyanide.[850]

A dithionate RuS_2O_6 is said[851] to be formed by the action of sulphur dioxide on a solution of the divalent sulphate $RuSO_4$. It is a yellow powder, easily soluble in water, and begins to give off sulphur dioxide at 80°. It needs further investigation.

These are the only simple compounds of divalent ruthenium that are known, but the complexes, especially the cyanides, ammines, and nitrosyl-derivatives (p. 1484), are numerous.

COMPLEXES OF DIVALENT RUTHENIUM

THESE complexes are reasonably stable, and some of them very stable; they nearly all have the co-ordination number of 6. On theoretical grounds we should expect that 6-covalent complexes of divalent ruthenium would be diamagnetic like the ferrocyanides, and those of trivalent paramagnetic like the ferricyanides, and so far as the compounds have been examined this is so. But these divalent complexes are limited in extent in a very peculiar way. They comprise complex ammines, with 6 nitrogen atoms attached to the ruthenium when they are chelate, but never more than 5 when they are not: the cyanides, of the type $M_4[Ru(CN)_6]$, like the ferro-cyanides: and an extensive series of nitrosyl derivatives, never having more than one NO in the molecule, which are discussed in a later section (p. 1484).

Complex Cyanides of Divalent Ruthenium

These compounds are all of the type $M_4[Ru(CN)_6]$, corresponding to the ferrocyanides; they can be made (1) by converting ruthenium into the ruthenate by fusion with potassium hydroxide and nitrate, and treating the product in boiling aqueous solution with potassium cyanide,[852] or (2) by evaporating ruthenium trichloride in a water bath with excess of

[850] H. Rémy, *Z. anorg. Chem.* 1920, **113**, 250.
[851] U. Antony and A. Lucchesi, *Gaz.* 1898, **28**, ii. 139; 1900, **30**, ii. 75.
[852] J. L. Howe, *J.A.C.S.* 1896, **18**, 981.

potassium cyanide until it becomes colourless.[855] In either case the excess of potassium cyanide acts as a reducing agent.

Ruthenocyanic acid, $H_4[Ru(CN)_6]$.[854] The complex is so stable that it is possible to isolate the free acid, which is precipitated by ether from an acidified solution of the potassium salt: colourless plates, stable when dry, easily soluble in water and alcohol.

The sodium salt $Na_4[Ru(CN)_6]$, 0 and $3\,H_2O$ is made[855] from sodium ruthenate and sodium cyanide: it is colourless. The potassium salt has $3\,H_2O$ which it loses *in vacuo* at 110°. The aqueous solution is decomposed by mineral acids with evolution of prussic acid.

Various other salts are known, such as Ca_2A,[853] very soluble in water: Sr_2A, $15\,H_2O$: Ba_2A, $6\,H_2O$, moderately soluble in water.

The ferric-potassium salt $Fe'''K[Ru(CN)_6]$ is 'ruthenium purple', which can be used as a pigment. It is in fact Prussian Blue $Fe'''K[Fe''(CN)_6]$ in which the ferrous atom is replaced by divalent ruthenium[856] (see above, p. 1339).

AMMINES OF DIVALENT RUTHENIUM

Hexammines

The hexammines are all trichelate, and are only known in the derivatives of dipyridyl and tripyridyl, examined by Morgan and Burstall.

The dipyridyl salts are made[857] by the direct action of α, α'-(2,2'-) dipyridyl on ruthenium trichloride or a complex of trivalent ruthenium such as ruthenium red (a chloro-ammine) or a complex halide like $M[RuCl_4]$, at a high temperature (250°) in the absence of a solvent, or more slowly in aqueous or alcoholic solution. The ruthenium is reduced to the divalent state by part of the dipyridyl:

$$2\,RuCl_3 + 8\,C_{10}H_8N_2 = 2\,[Ru(C_{10}H_8N_2)_3]Cl_2 + C_{20}H_{14}N_4 + 2\,HCl$$

$C_{10}H_8N_2$ is dipyridyl: the product $C_{20}H_{14}N_4$ is a new tetramine, whose constitution is not yet known. The ready occurrence of this unusual reduction suggests that the tri-dipyridyl complex is exceptionally stable with divalent rather than trivalent ruthenium. These salts are remarkably stable; the chloride is not affected by heating to 300° or by boiling with concentrated hydrochloric acid or 50 per cent. potassium hydroxide, and the optically active bromide (see below) does not racemize in solution at all in the cold, and only slowly at 90°.

The free base $[Ru(dipy)_3](OH)_2$, $8\,H_2O$ consists of red hygroscopic crystals, very soluble in water; it is strong enough to expel ammonia from its salts and absorb carbon dioxide from the air to form a solid carbonate. The salts, which are all red, contain a large amount of water of crystallization, presumably because of the large size of the cation: thus we have

[853] J. L. Howe and E. D. Campbell, ib. 1898, **20**, 32.
[854] F. Krauss and G. Schrader, *Z. anorg. Chem.* 1927, **165**, 70.
[855] W. Manchot and J. Düsing, ib. 1933, **212**, 109.
[856] J. F. Keggin and F. D. Miles, *Nature*, 1936, **137**, 577.
[857] F. H. Burstall, *J.C.S.* 1936, 173.

[Ru(dipy)$_3$]Cl$_2$, Br$_2$, I$_2$, (ClO$_4$)$_2$, (NO$_3$)$_2$, all with 6 H$_2$O : (OH)$_2$, 8 H$_2$O : CO$_3$, 10 H$_2$O : tartrate, 6 H$_2$O. They retain their water of crystallization rather firmly: the chloride loses it only at 200°, and the carbonate goes *in vacuo* to the hexahydrate. The perchlorate, in spite of its large water-content, is only slightly soluble in water.

The tartrate was resolved by Burstall by fractional crystallization into its optical antimers, and the activity persisted after conversion into the bromide: it has the high value usual among such compounds, [M] being 7,205°. The aqueous solution of the bromide is quite stable in the cold, and only racemizes slowly at 90°.

The tripyridyl complex of divalent ruthenium was made[858] by heating the base with ruthenium trichloride, metallic ruthenium being present as well to act as a reducing agent. The chloride [Ru(tripy)$_2$]Cl$_2$, 4 H$_2$O (again a hydrate) is a red soluble salt, not affected by treatment with concentrated hydrochloric acid or concentrated alkaline hydroxide. Attempts to resolve it through the tartrate were not successful.

Lower Ammines: Ammonia Compounds

The ammonia complexes of divalent ruthenium also form a remarkable series. They are known to us only through the work of Gleu and Breuel.[859-60] Although their co-ordination number is always 6 they never have 6 NH$_3$ groups but 5, 4, or 2,* and of the remaining places in the sixfold complex at least one is always occupied by a sulphite radical of one kind or another.

When sodium bisulphite acts on the 'purpureo' salts of trivalent ruthenium [Ru(NH$_3$)$_5$Cl]X$_2$, the ruthenium is reduced to the divalent state, and one NH$_3$ is expelled giving a mixture of two colourless products, an almost insoluble tetrammine [Ru″(NH$_3$)$_4$(SO$_3$H)$_2$], and a readily soluble diammine Na$_4$[Ru″(NH$_3$)$_2$(SO$_3$)$_2$(SO$_3$H)$_2$]. If the first of these is heated with dilute acid it undergoes a remarkable change:

$$[Ru''(NH_3)_4(SO_3H)_2] + 2\,HCl = [Ru''(NH_3)_4(SO_2)Cl]Cl + SO_2 + 2\,H_2O.$$

The chlorine in this last complex is not very firmly held: it is to some extent replaced by H$_2$O in aqueous solution, and if the solid is treated with aqueous ammonia it is replaced by NH$_3$, with the formation of the pentammine complex Ru″(NH$_3$)$_5$SO$_3$.[860]

The behaviour of the sulphurous residues in these complexes is peculiar. They can occur in three forms, [SO$_2$]°, [SO$_3$H]⁻, and [SO$_3$]⁼, all three of which can occupy one co-ordination place (SO$_3$ as M—O—S$\overset{\displaystyle O}{\underset{\displaystyle O}{\diagdown}}$), and the

---

* The triammine (NH$_3$)$_3$ form seems to be as unstable here as it is found (see pp. 1471, 1487) to be in the nitrosyl ammines.

[858] G. T. Morgan and F. H. Burstall, *J.C.S.* 1937, 1654.

[859] K. Gleu, W. Breuel, and K. Rehm, *Z. anorg. Chem.* 1938, **235**, 201.

[860] K. Gleu and W. Breuel, ib. 211.

last also two, as $M{<}^{O}_{O}{>}S{\rightarrow}O$. The last two of these groups are familiar in complexes, but the first, SO_2, has never been found in any complexes but these. Gleu and Breuel point out that the occurrence of SO_2 as a group replacing H_2O or NH_3 in complexes is to be expected, especially in view of the similarity of SO_2 and H_2O as solvents[861] (VI. 898) (i.e. of the strong donor properties of sulphur dioxide), and they suggest an analogy to carbon monoxide in the carbonyls. This analogy goes far, since not only is ruthenium among the elements which readily form carbonyls, but in these sulphito-compounds, as in all its divalent 6-covalent complexes, it has the E.A.N. of 54 (krypton).

The colours of these compounds should be noticed:

A. Hexammines: all red.

B. Pentammines[860]:

$[Ru(NH_3)_5SO_3]$, $2 H_2O$: colourless.

$[Ru(NH_3)_5SO_2]Cl_2$, Br_2, $(NO_3)_2$, S_2O_6, SO_4, $2 H_2O$: all red.

C. Tetrammines.[859]

$[Ru(NH_3)_4SO_3H)_2]$: colourless insoluble.

$[Ru(NH_3)_4SO_2Cl]Cl$, red: $]SO_4H$ red: $—Br]Br$, brown, very slightly soluble: $—(OH_2)](NO_3)_2$, yellow: $—(OH_2)]S_2O_6$, pale yellow.

D. Diammines.[859]

$Na_4[Ru(NH_3)_2(SO_3)_2(SO_3H)_2]$, $6 H_2O$, colourless, slightly soluble.

Ammonium salt, $4 H_2O$, colourless, readily soluble.

TRIVALENT RUTHENIUM

This is on the whole the stablest state of ruthenium, but even here the simple salts scarcely exist. The trihalides, other than the trifluoride, can be got in a more or less pure state, and there is also a cyanide. For the redox potentials of the ruthenous ion see reference [862].

The complexes are numerous, comprising ammines of co-ordination number 6, with from 2 to 6 amine groups attached to the ruthenium: complex halides of every type from $MRuX_4$ to M_4RuX_7, and a few nitro- and oxalato-compounds. The complete absence of complex cyanides of trivalent ruthenium is remarkable, in view of the stability of the divalent cyanides, of the ferricyanides, and of the simple tricyanide.

Ruthenium Sesquioxide, Ru_2O_3

Recent work has shown that this does not exist: see under RuO (p. 1461) and RuO_2 (p. 1475).

Ruthenium Trihydroxide, $Ru(OH)_3$

This is certainly contained in the black precipitate formed by the action of alkalies on a solution of ruthenium trichloride. It is very difficult to

[861] G. Jander and K. Wickert, *Z. physikal. Chem.* 1936, A **178**, 57.

[862] F. P. Dwyer, J. E. Humpoletz, and R. S. Nyholm, *Proc. R.S. New S. Wales*, 1946, **80**, 212.

wash it free from alkali, and the substance is very unstable, being easily oxidized by the air to the tetravalent state and reduced by hydrogen below 40°.[863-6]

Ruthenium Trihalides

Attempts to prepare the trifluoride RuF_3 have all failed.[867] The other trihalides are known.

Ruthenium Trichloride, $RuCl_3$

This substance, which is the easiest simple compound of trivalent ruthenium to obtain in the pure state, is used as a standard for the determination of the valency of ruthenium in other compounds.

It can be made by the action of chlorine on the metal at 450°, a reaction which is catalysed by the presence of carbon monoxide, apparently through the formation of an intermediate carbonyl compound[868]; at 600° it is deposited on the sides of the tube in crystals. It can also be made from ruthenium tetroxide by the combined action of chlorine and carbon monoxide, or by heating it in hydrochloric acid to 110°: from the trihydroxide $Ru(OH)_3$ and hydrochloric acid: by the reduction of the tetrachloride $RuCl_4$: or by the oxidation of the blue $RuCl_2$ solution. The best method is either by the action of chlorine (containing some carbon monoxide) on the metal at 700–800°, or by evaporating a solution of ruthenium tetroxide in hydrochloric acid in a current of hydrochloric acid gas.

It forms black opaque leaflets, which have a layer-lattice (V. M. Goldschmidt). On heating it volatizes with considerable decomposition; the dissociation pressure of chlorine at 450° is 24 mm. When it is prepared from the elements at a high temperature the chloride is almost completely insoluble in water, but the trihydrate which is made from the tetroxide and hydrochloric acid is hygroscopic, and gives brown or reddish solutions in water, which at first contain no ionized chlorine.[831] This latter form is the 'water-soluble' trichloride of Rémy,[869] which is used as a standard in the determination of the valency of ruthenium in its compounds.

The aqueous solution of ruthenium trichloride readily hydrolyses, especially on warming, precipitating the black hydroxide $Ru(OH)_3$.

Ruthenium Tribromide, $RuBr_3$

Hydrobromic acid acts on ruthenium tetroxide in the same complicated way as hydrochloric, giving a variety of products which include the tribromide and the tetrabromide and their complexes. Ruthenium tribromide free from these other substances can be made[867,870-1] by dissolv-

[863] A. Gutbier, G. A. Leuchs, and H. Wiessmann, *Z. anorg. Chem.* 1916, **95**, 185.
[864] F. Krauss and H. Kükenthal, ib. 1924, **132**, 316.   [865] Id., ib. **136**, 70.
[866] W. N. Ipatiev and O. E. Swjaginzev, *Ber.* 1929, **62**, 708.
[867] F. Krauss and H. Kükenthal, *Z. anorg. Chem.* 1924, **137**, 36.
[868] H. Rémy and T. Wagner, ib. 1926, **157**, 344.
[869] H. Rémy and A. Lührs, *Ber.* 1928, **61**, 918.
[870] A. Gutbier and C. Trenkner, *Z. anorg. Chem.* 1905, **45**, 178.
[871] A. Gutbier, ib. 1919, **109**, 207.

ing the trihydroxide $Ru(OH)_3$ in hydrobromic acid and evaporating the solution. It forms dark hygroscopic crystals, but it has never been got in the pure state. It dissolves in water and in aqueous hydrobromic acid to form a brown solution: the acid solution goes red on standing, probably owing to the formation of the complex ion $[RuBr_5]^=$. The aqueous solution readily hydrolyses. On addition of alkaline bromides it gives complex bromides (p. 1473).

Ruthenium Tri-iodide, RuI_3

This is made by treating ruthenium trichloride with potassium iodide, or by adding potassium iodide to the solution of ruthenium tetroxide in hydrochloric acid, or directly from the tetroxide and hydriodic acid solution, which is perhaps the best method of preparation.[867,872]

It is a black substance,[870] not hygroscopic, and not more than slightly soluble in any solvent. It is easily oxidized with the separation of iodine.

Ruthenium Tricyanide, $Ru(CN)_3$, $5\,H_2O$

If chlorine is passed into the colourless solution of potassium ruthenocyanide $K_4[Ru(CN)_6]$, this turns yellow and then reddish-brown, and the addition of sulphuric acid to the solution precipitates a blackish-green substance which after drying has the composition $Ru(CN)_3$, $5\,H_2O$. It is stable and does not decompose in a vacuum below $250°$; it is insoluble in water, and with ammonia gives an (also insoluble) diammine

$$[Ru(NH_3)_2(CN)_3(H_2O)]°.[873]$$

No ruthenicyanides (of trivalent ruthenium) are known.

? Ruthenium Sulphite, $Ru_2(SO_3)_3$

When the pale red solution of tetravalent ruthenium sulphate $Ru(SO_4)_2$ is reduced with sulphur dioxide and alcohol added, a blue precipitate separates from the blue liquid, which after drying at $80°$ has the composition $Ru_2(SO_3)_3$.[874] The solution seems to be colloidal, as it is precipitated by the addition of any salts.

This substance is obscure. The blue colour strongly suggests that the ruthenium is divalent.

COMPLEXES OF TRIVALENT RUTHENIUM

THESE are numerous, but somewhat limited in their types. They are especially common among the ammines, and also, though in a less degree, among the complex halides (no complex halides of divalent ruthenium are known). There are also some nitro- and oxalato-salts, and a few derivatives of β-diketones. There are no complex cyanides.

[872] O. Ruff and E. Vidic, ib. 1924, **136**, 57.
[873] F. Krauss and G. Schrader, ib. 1928, **173**, 65.
[874] U. Antony and A. Lucchesi, *Gaz.* 1900, **30**, ii. 71.

Ammines

With the exception of the curious compounds $2\,RuX_3, 7\,NH_3$ (X = Cl, Br, I), whose constitution is not understood, these are all hexa-, penta-, tetra-, or triammines, and all these classes are of about the same stability. They all seem to have a co-ordination number of 6. No chelate ammines have been made except of the tetrammine class, but this may be only an accident.

Hexammines

These are known as 'Luteo' salts, the name being taken over from the chromic and cobaltic salts of the analogous composition, to which it was given on account of their yellow colour. The ruthenium salts are colourless, which illustrates the danger of using these significant trivial names for elements other than those for which they were invented.

The hexammines[875] are all of the type $[Ru(NH_3)_6]X_3$, and are the final products of the action of ammonia on the ruthenium trihalides. They are all colourless, and in this differ from their chromium and cobalt analogues, but resemble those of rhodium.[875]

The salts are extremely stable; they have a neutral reaction in water, and are very resistant to acids, showing that they hold the NH_3 groups with great firmness. Even concentrated mineral acids have no action in the cold; boiling concentrated hydrochloric acid removes only one NH_3, forming the pentammine, and fuming sulphuric acid dissolves the salt, but does not break up the complex except on heating.

On the other hand, these hexammines are very sensitive to alkalies, and react with them to give coloured products which are not yet understood. With sodium hydroxide the solution evolves ammonia and turns yellow, and then on the addition of hydrochloric acid (but not of hydrobromic or sulphuric) bright blue; this suggests divalent ruthenium, but a blue colour is also given by nitric acid. Neither of these blue colours is formed by the pentammines.

A delicate colour test is the formation of 'ruthenium red' (below, p. 1472) on continued boiling of the ammine with alkali; this is given by the pentammine as well.

Solutions of these luteo-salts are precipitated by nearly the same anions as the hexammines of trivalent chromium and cobalt (I, C_2O_4, CrO_4, Cr_2O_7, $Fe(CN)_6'''$, $Fe(CN)_6''''$, ClO_4).

An example is the sulphate $[Ru(NH_3)_6]_2\,(SO_4)_3$, which crystallizes from dilute sulphuric acid as the acid salt $[Ru(NH_3)_6]SO_4, HSO_4$ in large yellow crystals. Both the normal and the acid sulphate are exactly parallel to the salts of the hexammines of trivalent cobalt, rhodium, etc.

Pentammines

These are of the forms $[Ru(NH_3)_5(OH_2)]X_3$ (scarcely known) and $[Ru(NH_3)_5R]X_2$, where R may be any monovalent radical such as hydroxyl

---

[875] K. Gleu and K. Rehm, *Z. anorg. Chem.* 1936, **227**, 237.

(only in solution), chlorine, or NO_3. They are known as purpureo-salts, but the chloro- (R = Cl) compounds are intensely yellow, and the bromo-compounds orange-red.

The chloro-salts are formed[875] almost quantitatively by boiling the luteo-sulphate with concentrated hydrochloric acid. The chloro-chloride ($—Cl]Cl_2$) thus obtained forms deep yellow crystals which are easily soluble in hot water.[876] The bromo-compound is less easily formed, and is less soluble in water.

The pentammines like the hexammines are stable to acids, but they are decomposed by alkalies with loss of ammonia, though the resulting solution gives no trace of a blue colour on treatment with concentrated hydrochloric acid. The chloro- or bromo-salts will dissolve in ammonia solution on warming, no doubt with the formation of hydroxo-salts

$$[Ru(NH_3)_5OH]X_2,$$

which, however, are much too soluble to be isolated. On careful acidification in the cold, colourless, very soluble salts which must belong to the 'roseo' (aquo) series of the type $[Ru(NH_3)_5(H_2O)]X_3$ will separate.

A weak alkaline solution of the purpureo-salts gives on warming the intense red of ruthenium red, but a much weaker alkali can be used (even an equivalent of ammonia) and the reaction is much more rapid, than with the hexammines.

All the three compounds

$$[Ru(NH_3)_6]_2(SO_4)_3,\ 5\ H_2O,\ [Ru(NH_3)_6](SO_4)SO_4H,\ and\ [Ru(NH_3)_5Cl]Cl_2$$

were found to be paramagnetic, with moments of 2·0–2·1 Bohr magnetons[875]; the theoretical value, allowing for electron spin alone, is 1·73. (The 6-covalent ammines of divalent ruthenium are diamagnetic.)

Tetrammines

Tetrammines of trivalent ruthenium[877-80] are formed by ammonia, ethylamine, pyridine, and ethylene diamine, the last being the only *en* compound of trivalent ruthenium yet described. The most convenient method of preparation[878] is by the oxidation of the sulphito-tetrammine of divalent ruthenium $[Ru(NH_3)_4(SO_2)Br]Br$ (see above, p. 1464) with bromine, which gives the bromide $[Ru(NH_3)_4Br_2]Br, H_2O$, from which the other salts can be prepared. These form the so-called praseo-series, the bromine atoms in the cation being, as will be shown later, in the *trans* positions. They are very stable to acids, and can be boiled with hydrobromic acid without change; the two bromine atoms in the ion are not removed by silver nitrate, which excludes the possibility of an aquo-structure $[Ru(NH_3)_4(H_2O)_2]Br_3$. Unlike the praseo-salts of cobalt they are not hydrolysed to aquo-salts by boiling with water. Like the hexammines

[876] Id., ib. 1938, **235**, 352.
[877] G. T. Morgan and F. H. Burstall, *J.C.S.* 1936, 41.
[878] K. Gleu and W. Breuel, *Z. anorg. Chem.* 1938, **237**, 326.
[879] Id., ib. 335.　　　　　　　　　　　　　　　[880] Id., ib. 350.

and pentammines these salts are paramagnetic, with a moment of about 2 Bohr magnetons. The evidence that they are *trans* (praseo) and not *cis* (violeo) compounds is given below, p. 1471.

[Ru(NH$_3$)$_4$Br$_2$]Br, H$_2$O: brilliant violet-red prisms, more soluble in water than the purpureo but less than the luteo-salts. Other salts of this dibromo-cation are [M]Cl, H$_2$O, red octahedra: [M]Br$_3$, dark brown, very slightly soluble; [M]NO$_3$, brownish-red; [M]SO$_4$H easily soluble in water, a monobasic acid; [M]$_2$SO$_4$, pale red, neutral, less soluble; [M]$_2$S$_2$O$_6$, brownish-orange, slightly soluble. The corresponding praseo-cobaltic salts are but little known.[881]

The bromides are darker than the dichlorides, and there are some small differences in behaviour, but in general the resemblance is very close.

Of the dichloro-compounds [Ru(NH$_3$)$_4$Cl$_2$]X[879] the *trans* series can be made like the dibromo-salts from the sulphito-tetrammines of divalent ruthenium with hydrochloric acid and chlorine. The *cis* are made by treating the hydroxo-pentammines with oxalic acid, the (obviously *cis*) oxalato-tetrammine so formed being decomposed by boiling for a short time with excess of concentrated hydrochloric acid.

$$[Ru(NH_3)_5OH]'' \longrightarrow [Ru(NH_3)_4Ox]' \longrightarrow [Ru(NH_3)_4Cl_2]'$$

This preparation is a conclusive proof of the *cis* structure. These *cis* salts are entirely different from the previously described *trans* series in solubility, crystalline form, water of crystallization, and chemical reactions.

It is curious that the chelate oxalato-group, when once it has become attached, is more firmly fixed to cobalt than to the other elements; treatment with hydrochloric acid will split it off from ruthenium and chromium, but not from cobalt. In the same way the conversion of the hexammine into the pentammine by hydrochloric acid occurs with ruthenium and chromium, but not with cobalt. In both these reactions the ruthenium salt reacts less easily than the chromium, and so in a sense it comes between chromium and cobalt, but nearer to chromium.

The 3/4 H$_2$O of the chloride is reduced on heating to 2/3 H$_2$O, which is held very firmly; this water, however, is not constitutional, since the nitrate and dithionate are anhydrous. The two chlorine atoms in the complex are removed fairly easily by silver nitrate (no doubt with the formation of a di-aquo-salt), and there is no sign that this replacement goes in two stages, as there is with chromium and cobalt.

The salts are paramagnetic, with a moment of about 2 Bohr magnetons.

Comparison of the Cis *and* Trans *Dichlorides*

The two series are not interconvertible. With ruthenium both are orange and practically identical in colour (with cobalt there is a distinct though not very great difference). Stability to acids and to oxidation is the same for both; but the chlorine in the complex is held much more

---

[881] A. Werner and A. Wolberg, *Ber.* 1905, **38**, 991.

firmly in the *trans* compound, which scarcely gives it up to silver nitrate on boiling, than in the *cis*, which reacts in the cold; a similar difference is found elsewhere, as in the *cis* and *trans* forms of the platinous diammine [Pt″(NH₃)₂Cl₂].[882] The solubility is on the whole greater with the *cis*.

In the *cis* compounds ruthenium holds the chlorine much more firmly than cobalt; it is in accordance with this that the *cis* cobaltic salts go quite easily over into the *trans*, while the *cis* ruthenium salts will not go over at all, not even when the solution is boiled, or the dry salt heated to 140°. Trivalent rhodium gives no tetrammines, but trivalent iridium does, and as these closely resemble the violeo-ruthenium salts, they also must be *cis*.

Violeo (cis) *Dibromo-tetrammines*[880]

The *cis*-dibromo-tetrammines are difficult to make with any metal. With cobalt they are known only in the di-*en* complexes. The *cis* dibromides of ruthenium can be made, like the chlorides, through the oxalato-compounds. The bromine in the complex is removed by silver nitrate in the cold, though only slowly. The salt is quite stable to acids, and can be heated to boiling with concentrated hydrobromic acid without change, though on long boiling it seems to be converted into the triammine [Ru(NH₃)₃Br₃]°.

Like the dichlorides, the *cis* and *trans* dibromides are not interconvertible. Both series are reddish, and the colours are scarcely distinguishable in solution, but in the solid state the *trans* is more violet, and the *cis* more brown. The stability to acids is about the same in both, but the *trans* hold their halogens more firmly. The *cis* halides and nitrate are more soluble than the *trans*, but the *trans* sulphate is more soluble than the *cis*.

As compared with the dichloro-compounds the dibromides are darker, but otherwise there is very little difference between the two series, and in particular very little in the firmness with which the complex halogen is held.

Triammines[879]

The triammines, which are all of the type [Ru(NH₃)₃hal₃]°, were first obtained by Gleu and Breuel,[879] who showed that the violeo-chloride, [Ru(NH₃)₄Cl₂]Cl, is decomposed by prolonged heating with concentrated hydrochloric acid up to the boiling-point, with the separation of a red precipitate of the triammine [Ru(NH₃)₃Cl₃]°; this forms red crystals which can be recrystallized from much dilute hydrochloric acid, but as it is not a salt it is far less soluble than most of these ammines. As it is much easier to make from the *cis* dichloro-compounds than from the *trans*, it probably is itself a *cis* compound. The corresponding bromide is much less easily made.[880]

These seem to be the only two known triammines of trivalent ruthenium. They are examples of the instability so common among triammines.

[882] H. D. K. Drew and F. W. Chattaway, *J.C.S.* 1938, 198.

Ruthenium Red

It was discovered by Joly in 1892[883] that if ruthenium trichloride is treated with ammonia, the product forms an intensely red solution which will dye animal fibres red: he called it 'ruthenium red'. Gleu and Hubold[884] found that it had very remarkable properties as a redox indicator: the brilliantly red solution is stable to acids and alkalies, but in acid solution the colour is turned yellow by even weak oxidizing agents such as ferric chloride, and restored by strong reducing agents like titanous chloride; the reaction is so delicate that it will detect one drop of $n/1,000$ ceric sulphate solution in 100 c.c.; the colour of ruthenium red itself can be detected in solutions more dilute than one in a million.[877]

The structure and even the composition of this substance are doubtful; every formula proposed is open to attack,[877,880] and all that we can be sure of is that the molecule must contain two ruthenium atoms.

Ammines of the Trihalides

These again are substances of uncertain structure. All the three trihalides of ruthenium when treated in the dry state with ammonia take this up with the production of highly coloured red or violet solids, which have been said[883,885] to have the composition $2\,RuX_3, 7\,NH_3$, but at least the first two are more probably $RuCl_3, 3\,NH_3$, and $RuBr_3, 3\,NH_3$.[877,886] They dissolve in water, the first being converted into ruthenium red, and the other two giving very similar substances. They are not very stable and seem on treatment with acid to lose the ammonia and be converted into oxides.

It is difficult to see how they can be formulated, as they are certainly not identical with the insoluble triammines $[Ru(NH_3)_3X_3]$ already described.

Nitro-complexes

These are of the type $M_2[Ru(NO_2)_5]$; they are prepared[887] by treating ruthenium trichloride with excess of the alkaline nitrite; they are reddish-orange. The sodium and potassium salts are very soluble in water, and stable enough to be recrystallized from it unchanged.

Oxygen Complexes

These seem to be confined to β-diketone derivatives and oxalato-compounds.

The *acetylacetonate* RuA_3 is made[888] by warming ruthenium trichloride with acetylacetone in potassium bicarbonate solution. The liquid turns red, and the RuA_3 is precipitated as a blood-red powder. It is insoluble in

[883] A. Joly, *C.R.* 1892, **114**, 291; **115**, 1299.
[884] K. Gleu and R. Hubold, *Z. anorg. Chem.* 1935, **223**, 312.
[885] A. Gutbier and C. Trenkner, ib. 1905, **45**, 182.
[886] W. Peters, ib. 1917, **77**, 147, 165.
[887] A. Joly and E. Leidié, *C.R.* 1894, **118**, 469.
[888] G. A. Barbieri, *Atti R.* 1914, [5] **23**, 336.

water but soluble in nearly all organic solvents giving red solutions, and it can be recrystallized from benzene or chloroform. Cryoscopic determinations in bromoform solution give the simple molecular weight of RuA_3. It sublimes on heating, and gives a red vapour which burns in air. It is decomposed by concentrated hydrochloric acid. It forms mixed crystals with the aluminium analogue AlA_3, which separate from a solution of the two substances in benzene.

The *oxalato-salts* are of the type $M_3[RuOx_3]$. The potassium salt is made by the action of potassium oxalate on the pentachlororuthenate $K_2[RuCl_5(H_2O)]$, and the others are prepared from this or in a similar way.

The free acid must be present in the solution obtained by boiling ruthenium trihydroxide $Ru(OH)_3$ with oxalic acid, since this has the characteristic green colour of the ion; but it has not been isolated. The sodium (5 H_2O), potassium (5, 1, $\frac{1}{2}$ H_2O), and ammonium (3 H_2O) salts are very similar[889]; the water in the last two is no doubt attached to the oxalato-groups.

Complex Halides of Trivalent Ruthenium

These are formed by the chlorides and rather less easily by the bromides, but they are not known with the fluorides (there is no RuF_3) or iodides.

With many of them there is a doubt whether the water they contain is to be taken as part of the complex or not. This must be decided on the evidence in each case (and ultimately by X-ray analysis), which generally is in favour of assigning to the complex a covalency of 6 if possible (e.g. $[RuX_4(OH_2)_2]$ and $[RuX_5(OH_2)]$). They are, however, most conveniently classified by the halogen:ruthenium ratio, which is not in doubt. On this basis they are of four different types, from $MRuX_4$ to M_4RuX_7; the last of these is confined to the salts of certain organic amines.

Tetrahalides, $M[Ru(hal)_4]$, x H_2O

The free acid of the chloro-series, $H[RuCl_4]$, 2 H_2O, can be made[890] by boiling ruthenium tetrachloride solution with alcohol and evaporating down. It is remarkable for occurring in two forms, which differ even in solution. As first prepared it forms very hygroscopic reddish needles, giving a red solution. Repeated treatment with alcohol converts this into a green form, also very soluble, which gives a green solution. If this is warmed with hydrochloric acid it is reconverted into the red form. The suggestion that the green form is a mixture of ruthenium compounds in different valency states has been disproved by mixing solutions of ruthenium di-, tri-, and tetrachlorides, without its being produced. The isomers are no doubt the *cis* and *trans* forms of the diaquo-complex $H[RuCl_4(OH_2)_2]$.

The salts of the tetrachloro-series[891] are made from the ammonium salt, which is itself prepared by reducing ammonium ruthenate with stannous

[889] R. Charonnat, *Ann. Chim.* 1931, [10] **16**, 133.
[890] Id, *C.R.* 1925, **181**, 867; *Ann. Chim.* 1931, [10] **16**, 72.
[891] M. Buividaite, *Z. anorg. Chem.* 1935, **222**, 281.

chloride in hydrochloric acid solution. They are all red or reddish-brown salts, with at least two molecules of water of crystallization, which can never be removed without decomposition, and so must form part of the complex anion, as in $M[RuCl_4(OH_2)_2]$. None of these salts have been found to occur in two forms like the acid. The complex does not seem to be very stable, since, at least in the ammonium salt, the chlorine is fairly rapidly removed by silver nitrate.

The corresponding bromides[892] are similar, but less stable.

Pentahalides

The properties of the pentachlororuthenates (Deville, 1859) have been much disputed.[893-5] Gutbier and Niemann[896] find that there are two potassium salts, $K_2[RuCl_5(OH_2)]$ and $K_2[RuCl_5]$. The aquo-salt is formed by the reduction of ruthenium tetrachloride solutions with alcohol, stannous chloride, etc., in presence of potassium chloride; it forms red crystals, which dissolve in water to form a red solution. If this aquo-salt is heated to 180–200° it loses water and is converted into the anhydrous salt $K_2[RuCl_5]$. This consists of black prisms which readily dissolve in water to give a stable yellow solution. This salt changes only slowly into the red aquo-compound if its solution in dilute hydrochloric acid is boiled, or if the solid is allowed to stand in hydrochloric acid for hours.

Rubidium and caesium give similar aquo-salts, but their anhydrous salts are not known.

The aquo-bromides $M_2[RuBr_5(OH_2)]$ are known of potassium, rubidium, and caesium; they are brown or red-brown. The anhydrous bromides $M_2[RuBr_5]$ have probably[897] never been made.

Hexahalides

These are only known with the chlorides.

Sodium hexachlororuthenate $Na_3[RuCl_6]$, 12 H_2O is made[890] by reducing ruthenium tetrachloride with alcohol in presence of sodium chloride; it forms large deep red crystals, which readily lose 10 H_2O in air in the cold, and the last 2 H_2O at 130°. It is extraordinarily like the corresponding rhodium compound in colour, crystalline form, and behaviour.[890] The

[892] M. Buivadaite, *Z. anorg. Chem.* 1937, **230**, 286.
[893] J. L. Howe, *J.A.C.S.* 1901, **23**, 775; 1904, **26**, 543.
[894] A. Gutbier, F. Falco, and T. Vogt, *Z. anorg. Chem.* 1921, **115**, 225.
[895] S. Aoyama, ib. 1924, **138**, 249.
[896] A. Gutbier and W. Niemann, ib. 1924, **141**, 312.
[897] J. L. Howe, *J.A.C.S.* 1927, **49**, 2389.
[898] A. Gutbier and H. Zwicker, *Ber.* 1907, **40**, 691.
[899] A. Gutbier and G. A. Leuchs, ib. 1911, **44**, 306.
[900] A. Gutbier and F. Krauss, *J. prakt. Chem.* 1915, [2] **91**, 103.
[901] Id., *Ber.* 1921, **54**, 2835.   [902] A. Gutbier, ib. 1923, **56**, 1008.
[903] Id., *Z. anorg. Chem.* 1923, **129**, 83.
[904] F. G. Mann and W. J. Pope, *Proc. Roy. Soc.* 1925, **109**, 453.
[905] R. Charonnat, *Ann. Chim.* 1931, [10] **16**, 98.
[906] G. T. Morgan, *J.C.S.* 1935, 569.   [907] Gmelin, pp. 110–15 (1938).

potassium and ammonium salts both have 1 H_2O and are red; they are made by saturating the aquo-pentachloride $M_2[RuCl_5(H_2O)]$ with hydrogen chloride gas at 0°.[890]

Heptahalides

These are only known among the numerous ruthenihalides of organic bases, perhaps on account of the large size of the cation. These salts[898-906] are of all types from $M_2[RuX_5]$ to $M_4[RuX_7]$, but there are no tetrahalides $M[RuX_4]$.

These salts are all brown, reddish, or black, the bromides being on the whole darker than the chlorides. Their structure is not known. According to Gmelin[907] the number of salts obtained from 29 bases were (X = Cl and Br) $M_2[RuX_5]$ 47, $M_3[RuX_6]$ 38, $M_4[RuX_7]$ 20.

TETRAVALENT RUTHENIUM

THIS state of the ruthenium atom is evidently very stable in a limited number of molecules; the compounds in which it occurs are quite definite, but there are fewer of them than of trivalent or even probably of divalent ruthenium. They include some binary compounds, as an oxide, sulphide, and chloride (no other halide), and the salts of one or two oxyacids such as sulphuric. The complexes again are quite definite but not numerous. They include one or perhaps two ammines, complex halides (bromides as well as chlorides), and a few ato-compounds.

Ruthenium Dioxide, RuO_2

X-ray investigations have shown[908] that the only oxide of ruthenium produced by heating the metal in oxygen, or by dehydrating the hydroxide, is the dioxide RuO_2; it is in fact the only oxide other than the volatile tetroxide RuO_4 that exists.

It can be made by roasting ruthenium disulphide in air, or heating the metal in pure oxygen at 1,000°; by heating ruthenium trichloride in oxygen to 600–700°[909]; by precipitating the trihydroxide $Ru(OH)_3$ with alkali from solution of ruthenium trichloride, and after exposure to air completing the oxidation with hydrogen peroxide[910]; or by igniting the tetravalent sulphate $Ru(SO_4)_2$.[911]

It is stable up to a red heat, and forms beautiful blue apparently homogeneous crystals; but analyses show that the composition is seldom exactly that of the dioxide, and the blue colour certainly suggests the presence of some lower valency of ruthenium, probably 3. At higher temperatures the dioxide breaks up into its elements, the dissociation pressure of oxygen being about 50 mm. at 950°.

Acids have no action on the dioxide in the cold, but it is reduced on heating with hydrogen or carbon monoxide.

[908] G. Lunde, *Z. anorg. Chem.* 1927, **163**, 345.
[909] L. Wöhler, P. Balz, and L. Metz, ib. 1924, **139**, 213.
[910] E. Müller and K. Schwabe, *Z. Elektrochem.* 1929, **35**, 171.
[911] A. Gutbier and F. Ransohoff, *Z. anorg. Chem.* 1905, **45**, 252.

Ruthenium Tetra-hydroxide, Ru(OH)$_4$

There is no doubt that hydrated ruthenium dioxide exists, though its composition is not quite certain. Wöhler[909] obtained a hydroxide of the composition Ru(OH)$_4$ by reducing a solution of the tetroxide in water with mercury light or with hydrogen peroxide, or by decomposing a ruthenate M$_2$RuO$_4$ with alcohol or nitric acid or carbon dioxide. Charonnat[912] claims to have got solid Ru(OH)$_4$ by air-oxidation of Ru(OH)$_3$. It may be doubted whether the hydroxide M(OH)$_4$ of any element has ever been got pure.

Chlorides of Tetravalent Ruthenium

Tetravalent ruthenium is almost unique in forming no binary halide except with chlorine. Even so, the anhydrous halide is not known, but only the pentahydrate RuCl$_4$, 5 H$_2$O, and a hydroxy-chloride Ru(OH)Cl$_3$. These are among the various products of the decomposition of ruthenium tetroxide by aqueous hydrochloric acid. This is a very complicated process, which is probably[913-17] expressed by the following reactions:

$$\text{I.}\quad RuO_4 \quad + 6\,HCl \longrightarrow H_2RuO_2Cl_4 + Cl_2 + 2\,H_2O$$
$$\text{II.}\quad H_2RuO_2Cl_4 + 2\,HCl \longrightarrow RuCl_4 \quad + Cl_2 + 2\,H_2O$$
$$\text{III } a.\quad RuCl_4 \quad + H_2O \longrightarrow Ru(OH)Cl_3 + HCl$$
$$\text{III } b.\quad RuCl_4 \quad \longrightarrow RuCl_3 \quad + 1/2\,Cl_2$$

To prepare the hydrate RuCl$_4$, 5 H$_2$O, a solution of the complex oxychloride H$_2$RuO$_2$Cl$_4$ in hydrochloric acid is heated with a stream of chlorine passing through it, and then evaporated over phosphorus pentoxide. The hydrate forms large red crystals, excessively hygroscopic, and gives off most of its water in a stream of chlorine at 100°. It is hydrolysed in dilute aqueous solution, with precipitation of the hydroxide.

The hydroxychloride Ru(OH)Cl$_3$ is made by evaporating the solution of the tetroxide in concentrated hydrochloric acid to dryness; it is dark red and very soluble in water.[917-18] In solution it is reduced by stannous chloride or by heating with alcohol to the trichloride RuCl$_3$.

The work of Ruff and Vidic[919] throws some light on the absence of the other tetrahalides. They consider that when ruthenium tetroxide is heated to boiling with a halogen hydride the tetrahalide is the first product in every case; this is certainly so with chloride, where the change to the trihalide is very slow: with bromine, though no tetrabromide was isolated, it probably occurs, but the change to RuBr$_3$ is much quicker. With hydriodic acid the tri-iodide is formed at once, and there is no sign that a tetraiodide RuI$_4$ really exists.

[912] R. Charonnat, *Ann. Chim. Phys.* 1931, [10] **16**, 13.
[913] S. Aoyama, *Z. anorg. Chem.* 1926, **153**, 248.
[914] J. L. Howe, *J.A.C.S.* 1901, **23**, 778.
[915] F. Krauss, *Z. anorg. Chem.* 1921, **117**, 111.   [916] Id., ib. 1924, **136**, 64.
[917] H. Rémy and A. Lührs, *Ber.* 1928, **61**, 924; 1929, **62**, 200.
[918] E. Zintl and P. Zaimis, ib. 1928, **61**, 2110.
[919] O. Ruff and E. Vidic, *Z. anorg. Chem.* 1924, **136**, 49.

Tetravalent Ruthenium Sulphate, $Ru(SO_4)_2$

This salt is contained in the bright red solution produced[920] by the action of concentrated sulphuric acid on barium ruthenate. It is also formed[923] by the oxidation of the pyrosulphite (next section) $Ru(S_2O_5)_2$. It is not affected by dilution with water, but the whole of the ruthenium is precipitated as disulphide RuS_2 by hydrogen sulphide.

Tetravalent Ruthenium Pyrosulphite, $Ru(S_2O_5)_2$

This compound is made[921] by the action of air on the so-called hexa-sulphide RuS_6 (probably a mixture of the disulphide RuS_2 and sulphur) which is precipitated by hydrogen sulphide from a solution of a tetra-valent ruthenium salt.

It is a reddish-violet powder which turns black and metallic-looking at 110°. When freshly prepared it dissolves in water as a reversible colloid, but after it has been heated it is black and insoluble.

COMPLEXES OF TETRAVALENT RUTHENIUM

These are almost confined to the complex halides, though a few ammines and an oxalato-compound are known. The ruthenium has a covalency of 6 in all of them.

Ammines

Apart from a few doubtful examples mentioned in a dissertation in 1904[922] and not confirmed since,[923] the only ammine of tetravalent ruthenium that has been described is the (covalent) pyridine compound $[Ru(py)_2Cl_4]°$ obtained[924] by oxidizing a ruthenium trichloride solution with hydrogen peroxide and then adding pyridine hydrochloride. It separates from an acid solution of pyridine hydrochloride in yellow crystals, very slightly soluble in water (as it is not a salt), and insoluble in chloroform; it is easily soluble in concentrated hydrochloric acid to give a pale red solution, which turns deep green on heating.

Oxalato-compound

The only compound known is the trichelate salt $K_2[Ru''''(C_2O_4)_3]$, made by oxidizing the trivalent $K_3[Ru'''(C_2O_4)_3]$ with air or hydrogen peroxide.[925] It forms black crystals, and is black in concentrated aqueous solution, but on dilution changes colour owing to hydrolysis.

Complex Halides of Tetravalent Ruthenium

These compounds are quite definite and fairly numerous. They are formed by chlorine and bromine with about equal ease, but not by fluorine or iodine. Unlike the complex halides of trivalent ruthenium they

[920] U. Antony and A. Lucchesi, *Gaz.* 1899, **29**, ii, 314.
[921] F. M. Jaeger and J. H. de Boer, *Rec. Trav.* 1921, **40**, 163.
[922] K. Trenkner, Diss., Erlangen 1904; see Gmelin, pp. 33, 60, 67, 71.
[923] A. Gutbier and C. Trenkner, *Z. anorg. Chem.* 1905, **45**, 166.
[924] R. Charonnat, *Ann. Chim. Phys.* 1931, [10] **16**, 118.   [925] Id., ib. 173.

all have the co-ordination number of 6; they are of only two types $M_2[RuX_6]$ and $M_2[RuX_5OH]$, and are usually anhydrous.

Hexahalides, $M_2[RuX_6]$

Potassium hexachlororuthenate $K_2[RuCl_6]$ can be made by fusing ruthenium with potassium chlorate, and adding excess of potassium chloride to the dissolved product[920]: or by passing chlorine through a solution of the trivalent ruthenium salt $K_2[RuCl_5(OH_2)]$.[926] On heating it loses chlorine at 520° to give the trivalent salt K_2RuCl_5. It consists of small dark brown crystals, forming mixed crystals with potassium chloroplatinate, and it is isomorphous with the corresponding osmium, iridium, palladium, and platinum salts.[927] It dissolves readily in water to give a yellow solution which soon turns black owing to hydrolysis. The other alkaline hexachlorides are similar, but become less soluble as the atomic weight of the alkali metal increases, until the caesium salt $Cs_2[RuCl_6]$[914] (dark purple crystals) is almost insoluble in cold water: it is decomposed by hot.

The hexabromides are similar, but they are darker in colour, and rather more easily hydrolysed.

Hydroxo-pentahalides, $M_2[RuX_5(OH)]$

The potassium chloro-salt of this series has been disputed, but it was shown by Charonnat[928] that however it is made it always has the composition $K_2[RuCl_5(OH)]$, and contains tetravalent ruthenium.[929] It is best made by the action of hydrochloric acid on ruthenium tetroxide, or by reducing potassium ruthenate with alcohol and hydrochloric acid.[930-2]

It forms red-brown crystals fairly soluble in hot water to give an orange or red-brown solution, which decomposes easily, especially on warming, and forms a black precipitate; it is more stable in presence of hydrochloric acid. If it is dissolved in concentrated hydrochloric acid, the hexachloride K_2RuCl_6 crystallizes out. It is not liable to oxidation, but it is readily reduced, for example by potassium iodide to the tri-iodide RuI_3.

The other hydroxo-pentachlorides are similar, and so are the bromine compounds $M_2[RuBr_5(OH)]$.

PENTAVALENT RUTHENIUM: RuF_5

PENTAVALENT ruthenium is found so far as we know only in one compound, the pentafluoride RuF_5[933]; this is the more remarkable since this

[920] J. L. Howe, *J.A.C.S.* 1904, **26**, 544; J. L. Howe and L. P. Haynes, ib. 1925, **47**, 2924.

[927] R. Weinland, *Komplexverbindungen*, Enke, Stuttgart, 1919, p. 146.

[928] R. Charonnat, *C.R.* 1925, **180**, 1272; *Ann. Chim. Phys.* 1931, [10] **16**, 37.

[929] See also J. L. Howe, *J.A.C.S.* 1927, **49**, 2383.

[930] A. Gutbier, F. Falco, and T. Vogt, *Z. anorg. Chem.* 1921, **115**, 226.

[931] S. H. C. Briggs, *J.C.S.* 1925, **127**, 1044.

[932] H. Rémy and T. Wagner, *Z. anorg. Chem.* 1928, **168**, 6.

[933] O. Ruff and E. Vidic, ib. 1925, **143**, 171.

is the only binary compound of ruthenium and fluorine known, and almost the only known compound containing both ruthenium and fluorine. Ruff[933] considers that when fluorine acts on metallic ruthenium a small quantity of a lower fluoride may be formed, but he did not isolate it.

Ruthenium pentafluoride is very difficult to prepare; it attacks glass, even when quite dry, so that platinum vessels must be used, and at the temperature (290°) at which the ruthenium reacts, the platinum does so too, forming the tetrafluoride PtF_4 which contaminates the ruthenium pentafluoride. These difficulties were, however, overcome, the pentafluoride being finally purified by distillation in a stream of nitrogen at 260°.

Ruthenium pentafluoride forms a dark green transparent mass, which is excessively sensitive to moisture; it fumes in air, and quickly decomposes even over phosphorus pentoxide in a vacuum. It melts at 101°, and boils under 1 atm. pressure at 270–5°.

It is decomposed by moisture, and on treatment with water forms hydrofluoric acid and ruthenium tetroxide (easily detected by its smell), while a black precipitate of a lower oxide of ruthenium is produced. Organic solvents act on it only superficially.

Ruthenium pentoxide, Ru_2O_5, has been shown not to exist; the tetroxide on reduction goes at once to the dioxide.[909,911,934]

HEXAVALENT RUTHENIUM

THE compounds of hexavalent ruthenium are nearly all derivatives of ruthenic acid $H_2[RuO_4]$, and consist of the salts, one or two ammine derivatives, and an acid chloride. There is also a phosphide RuP_2.

Ruthenates, $M_2[RuO_4]$

The potassium salt is made by fusing metallic ruthenium or a compound with potassium hydroxide and either the nitrate[936] or the permanganate.[935] It forms hygroscopic black crystals with a green reflex. It is easily soluble in water to give a deep orange solution, which is very unstable, and often decomposes of itself within 15 minutes of its preparation; the salt is decomposed by acids and reduced by most organic compounds. While the potassium salt has a molecule of water of crystallization, the sodium salt[937] is anhydrous; otherwise this salt, and those of rubidium and caesium,[936] behave very like the potassium salt. The salts of the alkaline earths are also similar.

When the potassium salt is treated with ammonia a substance is obtained with the composition of an ammonium ruthenate $(NH_4)_2[RuO_4]$, but with quite different properties. On the addition of ammonia the red colour changes to yellow, or in higher concentrations to greenish-brown, and the

[934] A. Gutbier, G. A. Leuchs, H. Wiesmann, and O. Maisch, ib. 1916, **96**, 182.
[935] O. Ruff and E. Vidic, ib. 1924, **136**, 49.
[936] F. Krauss, ib. 1924, **132**, 309.
[937] R. Juza and W. Meyer, ib. 1933, **213**, 274.

solution is no longer decomposed by heating or by acids. Also the 'ammonium sa't' which is isolated in this way is quite unlike the alkaline ruthenates: it consists of small black crystals which are scarcely soluble in water and only slightly in concentrated sulphuric or nitric acid, though they dissolve readily in concentrated hydrochloric acid. If triethylamine is used instead of ammonia, a solid of the corresponding composition $(Et_3NH)_2[RuO_4]$ is obtained, which is exactly like the ammonia product in appearance and behaviour. It is clear that these are not true ruthenates, and they are probably not salts at all; they may well have the constitution $[RuO_2(NH_3)_2(OH)_2]°$. This conclusion is supported by the fact[936] that if the ammonia compound is dissolved in excess of concentrated hydrochloric acid and evaporated, a soluble brown mass is obtained of the composition $RuO_2(NH_3)_2Cl_2, 2 H_2O$, which is reconverted into the original 'salt' by warming with ammonia. The chloride (which retains its water of crystallization up to 120° when it decomposes) gives in water a brown solution with a strong acid reaction, from which silver nitrate precipitates all the chlorine, suggesting that the structure is $[RuO_2(NH_3)_2(H_2O)_2]Cl_2$.

Tetrachlororuthenates

These compounds are the acid $H_2[RuO_2Cl_4]$ and its salts. The free acid $(+3 H_2O)$ can be made[938] by the action of chlorine and hydrochloric acid on ruthenium tetroxide. It forms brown very hygroscopic crystals, very soluble in water and in alcohol. It loses most of its water in a stream of hydrogen at 100°; it melts at 120° and decomposes above that temperature. The solution has an acid reaction; it is stable if it is concentrated or if it is acidified, but in dilute solution it is hydrolysed. Concentrated hydrochloric acid converts it into the hexachlororuthenate $H_2[RuCl_6]$, and ammonia reduces it to compounds of trivalent ruthenium.

The rubidium salt $Rb_2[RuO_2Cl_4]$ is made[939] by the action of rubidium chloride on a solution of ruthenium tetroxide in hydrochloric acid, the ruthenium being reduced by the acid from the octovalent to the hexavalent state. It consists of dark purple crystals, which are at once decomposed by water. The caesium salt is similar.

Ruthenium Diphosphide, RuP_2

This is formed from its elements at temperatures above 650°, and is stable in presence of 1 atm. of phosphorus vapour up to 900°.[940]

HEPTAVALENT RUTHENIUM

THIS occurs only in the perruthenates. The analogy between the ruthenates and the manganates and rhenates, and between the perruthenates and the permanganates and perrhenates, is obvious, the anions having the same relations of valency and structure, but a difference in the

[938] S. Aoyama, *Z. anorg. Chem.* 1924, **138**, 252.
[939] J. L. Howe, *J.A.C.S.* 1901, **23**, 779.
[940] W. Biltz and H. Ehrhorn, *Z. anorg. Chem.* 1939, **240**, 117.

size of the core of the central atom, the number of unshared valency electrons being:

	M_2XO_4	MXO_4
X = Mn, Re . .	9	8
X = Ru . . .	10	9

This is in accordance with the general tendency of the elements of the second long period in the table as compared with those in the first (and third), to attract more electrons from the outermost into the penultimate group, i.e. into the outermost group of the core; this appears too in the structure of the isolated atoms, the two outermost electronic groups being in iron 14, 2 and in ruthenium 15, 1.

Potassium perruthenate $K[RuO_4]$ is the primary product of the fusion of metallic ruthenium with potassium nitrate and excess of potassium hydroxide[941-2]; it is also formed slowly along with the dioxide when a solution of the ruthenate K_2RuO_4 is diluted, and rapidly if it is acidified.[941] It is best made by passing chlorine into a concentrated alkaline solution of potassium ruthenate until the orange solution turns green.

$KRuO_4$ forms black crystals which are not isomorphous with potassium permanganate.[943] They are stable in air, but in a vacuum at 440° they are converted into $K_2RuO_4 + RuO_2 + O_2$. The aqueous solution, which is dark green, is unstable, and soon decomposes with formation of the orange ruthenate and precipitation of ruthenium dioxide. If alkali is added to the solution, oxygen is at once evolved, and the ruthenate formed.

OCTOVALENT RUTHENIUM

THIS valency is only found in the tetroxide RuO_4; attempts to make an octofluoride RuF_8 corresponding to the osmium compound OsF_8 have failed, although it may possibly be formed.[933]

Ruthenium tetroxide was first prepared by Claus[944] in 1860, by passing chlorine into a solution of potassium ruthenate, when the volatile ruthenium tetroxide distilled over. It can be freed from chlorine by washing with water. Special care must be taken to prevent any trace of the vapour from escaping into the air, as it is excessively poisonous. It can also be made[935] by fusing ruthenium powder with potassium hydroxide and permanganate, and decomposing the powdered product (which contains ruthenate, manganite, and manganate) with sulphuric acid in a stream of carbon dioxide, which carries the tetroxide over. The reaction is:

$$3 K_2RuO_4 + 2 KMnO_4 + 4 H_2SO_4$$
$$\longrightarrow 3 RuO_4 + 4 K_2SO_4 + 2 MnO_2 H_2O + 4 H_2O.$$

[941] H. Debray and A. Joly, *C.R.* 1888, **106**, 1499.
[942] R. Charonnat, *Ann. Chim. Phys.* 1931, [10] **16**, 9.
[943] H. Dufet, *Bull. Soc. Min.* 1888, **11**, 216.
[944] C. Claus, *J. prakt. Chem.* 1860, **79**, 43.

Ruthenium tetroxide occurs in two forms, one yellow and the other brown or orange. The tetroxide comes over as a yellow vapour, from which long yellow needles of the unstable form separate. This form melts at 25·5°, to a brown liquid, from which the brown form, m. pt. 27°,[941,944] solidifies. If this is heated it sublimes, condensing again in the original yellow form.

Ruthenium tetroxide has a strong smell like that of concentrated ozone; it is extremely poisonous, but it does not attack the eyes so violently as osmium tetroxide.

It begins to volatilize at 7°, and it readily sublimes,* but if it is heated above 100° it is liable to explode violently, leaving a residue of the dioxide RuO_2; in contact with oxidizable organic substances like alcohol it may explode at a lower temperature. In the cold it is stable when dry. It dissolves in water to give a golden yellow solution, which begins in a few hours to decompose with the formation of a lower oxide of ruthenium; the solution can, however, be kept unchanged for years (it has been kept for 5 years) if a few drops of chlorine water are added to it; with this stabilized solution it has been shown that the solubility is 2·21/25° and 2·28/75°.[945]

Ruthenium tetroxide is in general an unstable substance. It is decomposed by sunlight: it is reduced as we have seen by hydrochloric acid, mainly to chlorides of tetravalent and trivalent ruthenium, and by hydrogen peroxide to ruthenium dioxide; the addition of alkaline halides to its solution in aqueous hydrogen halide gives rise to complex halides. Alkalies dissolve it with the formation of a ruthenate M_2RuO_4, or if the tetroxide is in excess of a perruthenate $MRuO_4$ (presumably with the liberation of oxygen); in all these reactions the valency of the ruthenium is reduced.

The links in RuO_4 (which is monomeric in the vapour) are presumably in resonance between $Ru{\rightarrow}O$ and $Ru{=}O$; but the observed shortness of the Os—O links in the obviously analogous OsO_4 (p. 1504) suggest that the doubly linked state predominates.

RUTHENIUM CARBONYLS

Ruthenium Pentacarbonyl, $Ru(CO)_5$, is made[946] by heating finely divided ruthenium with carbon monoxide under 200 atm. pressure at 180°, or more easily by the action of carbon monoxide on ruthenium tri-iodide RuI_3 at 170° under 1 atm.

It is a liquid freezing at −22° to colourless crystals, and having a vapour pressure of 50 mm. at 18°. It dissolves readily to form a colourless solution in organic solvents such as alcohol, benzene, chloroform, etc., but it is insoluble in water. On standing the liquid soon turns yellow, evolves

---

* Its boiling-point seems to be unknown.

945 H. Remy, *Z. angew. Chem.* 1926, **39**, 1061.
946 W. Manchot and W. J. Manchot, *Z. anorg. Chem.* 1936, **226**, 388.

carbon monoxide, and deposits orange crystals of the enneacarbonyl $Ru_2(CO)_9$, especially in sunlight, or on warming to 50°. It reacts with halogens with evolution of carbon monoxide to form carbonyl halides such as $Ru(CO)Br$.

The volatility of this compound shows that it is monomeric, and it no doubt has the same structure as its iron analogue $Fe(CO)_5$ (p. 1369), with the five groups arranged in a trigonal bipyramid. The valency of the ruthenium is zero, and the E.A.N. $44 + 10 = 54$ (krypton).

Ruthenium Ennea-carbonyl, $Ru_2(CO)_9$, is formed[946] by the loss of carbon monoxide from the pentacarbonyl at any temperature above its melting-point ($-22°$) and rapidly at 50°. It is best made by warming the benzene solution.

It forms yellow-green crystals, very like iron ennea-carbonyl (p. 1369) in appearance. In air it is stable in the cold, but it decomposes at 150°; it can be sublimed in carbon dioxide. It is soluble in organic solvents; it reacts with iodine to give $Ru(CO)_2I_2$, and nitric oxide expels the carbon monoxide to form the peculiar compound ruthenium pentanitrosyl $Ru(NO)_5$, of unknown structure.

The structure of the enneacarbonyl is no doubt the same as that of the iron compound, and has three CO groups on each Ru, while the two ruthenium atoms themselves are joined by 3 more, with the grouping

This makes the ruthenium tetravalent and 7-covalent, with the krypton E.A.N. of 54.

Ruthenium Tetracarbonyl, $Ru(CO)_4$? The nature and even the composition of this substance are doubtful. It separates in small quantities as a by-product when the enneacarbonyl is formed from the pentacarbonyl,[946-7] and also when the ennea- is treated with alkali. It is insoluble in benzene and ether, soluble in alcohol and acetic acid. It dissolves in aqueous acids, the solution in hydrochloric acid being yellow, and that in hydrobromic acid first green and then bluish-red.

It is a very obscure substance, but it has some resemblances to iron tetracarbonyl (p. 1370).

Ruthenium Carbonyl Halides

Apart from one compound of uncertain composition, these are of two types, $Ru(CO)hal$ and $Ru(CO)_2(hal)_2$.

Ruthenium Monocarbonyl Bromide, $Ru(CO)Br$, which is the only compound of the type known, and appears to contain monovalent ruthenium, is made[947] by the action of carbon monoxide on ruthenium tribromide under 350 atm. at 180°. It forms colourless crystals which decompose at

[947] W. Manchot and E. Enk, *Ber.* 1930, **63**, 1635.

200° to give $Ru(CO)_2Br_2$ with separation of the metal. It is insoluble in all solvents except aqueous acids, which decompose it. It is presumably polymerized, but we do not know how, or how much.

Ruthenium Dicarbonyl Dichloride, $Ru(CO)_2Cl_2$, is made by heating ruthenium trichloride in carbon monoxide above 210°,[948] some phosgene being formed at the same time,[949] or by treating the dichloride $RuCl_2$ with carbon monoxide at the same temperature.[950] It is a yellow fairly volatile product, insoluble in water; it reduces ammoniacal silver. Nitric oxide expels CO from it, presumably to form the compound $Ru(NO)Cl_2$.[951]

Ruthenium Dicarbonyl Dibromide, $Ru(CO)_2Br_2$, is very similar to the dichloride. When ruthenium tribromide is heated in carbon monoxide, best at 280°,[948,951] this compound is formed as a pale orange sublimate. It is insoluble in water and in all the other solvents that were tried. Nitric oxide expels carbon monoxide from it reversibly to give $Ru(NO)Br_2$.

Ruthenium Dicarbonyl Di-iodide, $Ru(CO)_2I_2$. This is made[952] in the same way as the last, by heating up to 250° either the tri-iodide RuI_3 in carbon monoxide or the ennea-carbonyl with iodine. It is insoluble in water and organic solvents; it burns in oxygen to carbon dioxide, iodine, and ruthenium dioxide. If it is heated in carbon monoxide it is converted into the pentacarbonyl $Ru(CO)_5$. Concentrated hydrochloric acid has hardly any action upon it, but nitric oxide at 180° converts it into $Ru(NO)I_2$. It reduces ammoniacal silver solution.

In these compounds the carbonyl group is no doubt attached as usual to the metal by a co-ordinate link as in $Ru{\leftarrow}C{\equiv}O$, and the halogen atoms covalently linked. The monomeric structure would thus be

(I) $Br-Ru{\leftarrow}C{\equiv}O$ (II)

Ru monovalent.   Ru divalent.
E.A.N. of Ru 47.   E.A.N. of Ru 50.

They are probably polymerized, but presumably by the formation of links in which the ruthenium acts as acceptor, so that its valency is not altered, and is 1 in type I and 2 in type II. If so, $Ru(CO)Br$ is perhaps the only isolated compound of monovalent ruthenium.

The dihalogen compounds (type II) must be co-ordination compounds of the binary dihalides of ruthenium, all of which except the difluoride exist.

RUTHENIUM NITROSYL COMPOUNDS

RUTHENIUM forms more nitrosyl compounds than any other element (more than 80 are given in Gmelin). With the exception of the one 'pure' nitrosyl described below, none of them has more than one NO in the molecule.

[948] W. Manchot and J. König, *Ber.* 1924, **57**, 2131.
[949] W. Manchot and G. Lehmann, ib. 1930, **63**, 1224.
[950] H. Gall and G. Lehmann, ib. 1926, **59**, 2895.
[951] W. Manchot and H. Schmid, *Z. anorg. Chem.* 1934, **216**, 102.
[952] W. Manchot and W. J. Manchot, ib. 1936, **226**, 389.

Ruthenium ? Pentanitrosyl, $Ru(NO)_5$. This compound[953] is made by the action of nitric oxide under pressure on ruthenium ennea-carbonyl $Ru_2(CO)_9$, the best yield being got by heating under 320 atm. for 50 hours, at temperatures rising from 100° to 190°. It forms red cubic crystals, insoluble in water, ether, or benzene, but slightly soluble in alcohol. It slowly loses nitric oxide in the air, especially if it is moist, and it decomposes on warming. It is reduced by hydrogen at 220° to metallic ruthenium and ammonia.

It is very difficult to purify, and though the percentage of metal is that required by Manchot's formula (calcd. for $Ru(NO)_5$ 40·40 per cent., for $Ru(NO)_4$ 45·87, found 40·60), the nitrogen found was for some reason less than half the theoretical amount. It is therefore possible that the compound is not $Ru(NO)_5$ (which seems impossible to formulate), but $Ru(NO)_4$ corresponding to $Fe(NO)_4$ (p. 1372), and like this a salt $(NO)^+[Ru(NO)_3]$, with the E.A.N. of 54.

The other ruthenium nitrosyl compounds contain only one NO group in the molecule, and are of two kinds, the 'simple' compounds $Ru(NO)X_2$ and $Ru(NO)X_3$ (X being a halogen or other acid radical) and the 6-covalent complexes derived from the complex cyanides, ammines, or halides by replacing one group (never more) by NO.

Ruthenium Nitrosyl Halides

These compounds are closely analogous to the carbonyls (p. 1483), the replacement of a CO by an NO involving the addition of a halogen atom to maintain the valency:

Monovalent ruthenium	Divalent ruthenium
$Ru(CO)hal.$	$Ru(CO)_2hal_2.$
$Ru(NO)hal_2.$	$Ru(NO)hal_3$

Dihalides

$Ru(NO)Br_2$ is made from the corresponding carbonyl compound $Ru(CO)_2Br_2$ by heating it in a stream of nitric oxide at 230° for 40 hours. The reaction is reversible.

It is a dark brown powder insoluble in water and organic solvents. It is very resistant even to concentrated sulphuric acid; on heating it decomposes with evolution of nitric oxide and bromine.[954] No chloride of this type is known.

$Ru(NO)I_2$ is made in the same way as the bromide[954] by heating $Ru(CO)_2I_2$ for 30–40 hours at 230° in nitric oxide, the reaction, as with the bromide, being reversible. It is a velvet black powder, insoluble in water, methyl and ethyl alcohol, and acetone, slightly soluble in chloroform. It is rather less stable to sulphuric acid than the bromide: it resists the dilute acid, but is rapidly decomposed by the concentrated acid with evolution of nitric oxide.

[953] Id., ib. 410.   [954] W. Manchot and H. Schmidt, ib. 1934, **216**, 101.

These two compounds seem to be the only nitrosyl derivatives of mono-valent ruthenium.

Trihalides

The *trichloride* $Ru(NO)Cl_3, 5 H_2O$ is present in the characteristic red solution got by fusing ruthenium with potassium hydroxide and nitrate, and treating the product with hydrochloric acid. It is also formed by evaporating a solution of ruthenium tetroxide in hydrochloric acid with a large excess of nitric acid,[955] or by the action of liquid nitrogen tetroxide on a ruthenium trichloride solution at 0°, or from the double salt $Na_2[Ru(NO)Cl_5]$ by dissolving it in alcohol and letting the sodium chloride crystallize out.

It forms monoclinic crystals, red in transmitted and black in reflected light. In a vacuum, or in air at 100°, the pentahydrate gives off $2 H_2O$, and at 120–150° it loses two more, leaving $Ru(NO)Cl_3,H_2O$, a brick-red substance which only dissolves very slowly in water; the last molecule of water is only lost with partial decomposition at 360°. At 440° the compound decomposes with violence.

It is easily soluble in water to give a raspberry-coloured solution which forms the complex salts $M_2[Ru(NO)Cl_5]$ with alkaline chlorides. Alkaline hydroxides and carbonates on heating precipitate from the solution the gelatinous trihydroxide $Ru(NO)(OH)_3$.

The *bromide* $Ru(NO)Br_3, 5 H_2O$ is very similar to the chloride, and isomorphous with it.[956-7]

The *iodide* $Ru(NO)I_3$[956] is made by warming the chloride with hydriodic acid; it is a black powder, slightly soluble in water, and forms no hydrate. Chlorine expels the iodine to give the trichloride.

$Ru(NO)(NO_3)_3$

This substance has not been isolated, but it is presumably present in the brilliant red solution produced when ruthenium nitrosyl trichloride is heated with excess of concentrated nitric acid, or the hydroxide $Ru(NO)(OH)_3$ (see below) is dissolved in this acid.[955,958] Dilute hydrochloric acid on boiling converts it into the chloride $Ru(NO)Cl_3$.

? Ruthenium Nitrosyl-hydroxide, $Ru(NO)(OH)_3$

When alkali acts on the chloride $Ru(NO)Cl_3$[955] or on the tetrammine $[Ru(NH_3)_4(NO)(OH)]Cl$[959] a very unstable brownish-yellow powder is deposited, which is easily decomposed by heat, and gives in concentrated nitric acid a red solution, presumably of the trinitrate. This precipitate is assumed to be the trihydroxide, the base of the trihalides.

[955] A. Joly, *C.R.* 1889, **108**, 854.
[956] Id., in M. Fremy's *Encycl. de Chim.* 1900, III, **17**, i. 189.
[957] H. Dufet, *Bull. Soc. Min.* 1889, **12**, 471.
[958] A. Werner, *Ber.* 1907, **40**, 2620.
[959] A. Joly, *C.R.* 1890, **111**, 972.

Complex Nitrosyl Cyanides, $M_2[Ru(CN)_5(NO)]$

These salts are the ruthenium analogues of the nitroprussides.[960] The sodium salt is made by heating the rutheno-cyanide $Na_2[Ru(CN)_6]$ with fairly strong nitric acid and evaporating to dryness. A very insoluble dark reddish-brown solid remains, which can only be purified by washing with water. It has two molecules of water of crystallization, which are lost over phosphorus pentoxide. Ammonium or alkaline sulphides give a red or reddish-blue coloration, which is destroyed by excess of the reagent. The potassium salt $K_2[Ru(CN)_5(NO)]$, $2 H_2O$ is similar. The resemblance to potassium nitroprusside, also with $2 H_2O$, giving the same colour reaction with sulphides, discharged in the same way by excess of sulphide, is obvious.[961]

Ruthenium Nitrosyl Ammines

These complexes have one NO group and from one to four but never five amine groups attached to the ruthenium. They can be classified by the number of amine groups present. The approximate number of known compounds in each class, according to Gmelin, is

Tetrammine	Triammine	Diammine	Monammine
36	1	8	5

Tetrammine Nitrosyl Compounds

The tetrammine salts of the type of $[Ru(NH_3)_4(NO)(OH)]X_2$ are made[962-3] by treating the complex nitrosyl chlorides $M_2[Ru(NO)Cl_5]$ with ammonia. The corresponding aquo-compounds $[Ru(NH_3)_4(NO)(OH_2)]X_3$ are evidently very unstable. They are only known with the tetrammines, not with the *en* compounds, and they decompose with the greatest ease, even on solution in water, going into the hydroxo-compounds:

$$[Ru(NH_2)_4(NO)(OH_2)]X_3 \longrightarrow [Ru(NH_3)_4(NO)(OH)]X_2 + HX.$$

The aquo-cobaltic compounds behave in the same way.

These hydroxo-compounds are yellow and are of neutral reaction in solution.

The tetrammines are essentially of two types, $[RuAm_4(NO)(H_2O)]X_3$ and $[RuAm_4(NO)R]X_2$. Am is usually NH_3, sometimes $\frac{1}{2}$ *en*, and rarely anything else. R can be OH, Cl, Br, I, NO_3, $\frac{1}{2} SO_4$ (for references see Gmelin, pp. 35, 52–3, 64, 68–9, 70, 75–7, 83–4).

The tetrammine compounds in general are stable to alkaline hydroxides, but the ruthenium is precipitated as sulphide by alkaline sulphides. The *en* compounds as usual tend to be more stable than those of ammonia, and the NH_3 group is readily replaced by *en*.[964]

The only *triammine* is the salt $[Ru(C_{15}H_{11}N_3)(NO)Cl_2]Cl$[965] of the

[960] W. Manchot and J. Düsing, *Z. anorg. Chem.* 1933, **212**, 111.
[961] Id., *Ber.* 1930, **63**, 1226. [962] A. Joly, *C.R.* 1888, **107**, 994.
[963] A. Werner, *Ber.* 1907, **40**, 2614.
[964] A. Werner and A. P. Smirnoff, *Helv. Chim. Acta*, 1920, **3**, 737.
[965] G. T. Morgan, *J.C.S.* 1935, 569.

'tridentate' α, α', α''-tripyridyl molecule: this clearly makes the unstable triammine type possible. The salt is soluble and has 4 and 1 H_2O.

The *diammines* nearly always have either ethylene diamine or dipyridyl. They do not occur in the aquo form: they are all of the type $[RuAm_2(NO)R_3]$, and accordingly are all non-electrolytes.* Not being ionized they are very slightly soluble in water, and silver nitrate does not remove the halogen. They show, however, a readiness to undergo a reversible replacement of one halogen by another which is in general characteristic of halogen atoms covalently attached to ruthenium.

The *monammines* are very few, and all contain a pyridine molecule as the amine, and all but one (a very unstable salt) have two oxalato-groups for the four R radicals. Here again no aquo-compounds are known, so they are all monovalent anions $M[Ru\ py(NO)R_4]$.

The chloride $K[Ru\ py(NO)Cl_4]$, which is yellowish-red, is very unstable,[966] and is decomposed by water with the separation of potassium chloride. The dioxalato-salts, which are red, are much more stable[967]; the ammonium salt has been resolved into its optical antimers.[966]

Complex Nitrosyl Halides

These are all derived from the trihalides, and all have a co-ordination number of 6. The simple type is $M_2[Ru(NO)hal_5]$, but there are one or two in which two halogens are replaced by an oxalato-group. The simple type is formed by all three halogens chlorine, bromine, and iodine. It will be remembered that no complex halides of divalent ruthenium are known.

The *complex chlorides* $M_2[Ru(NO)Cl_5]$ are dark red salts, giving reddish-violet solutions in water. The best known is the potassium salt, which was prepared by Claus in 1847, and possibly by Berzelius in 1828. It can be got by fusing ruthenium with potassium hydroxide and nitrate, and dissolving the product in hydrochloric acid, or by mixing very concentrated solutions of potassium chloride and ruthenium nitrosyl trichloride $Ru(NO)Cl_3$[968]: or by the action of potassium nitrite on ruthenium trichloride solution. It forms dark red almost black crystals. It is a remarkably stable substance especially to heat; sol^y 12·0/25°. Its conductivity in water is that of a strong tri-ionic electrolyte; on electrolysis the coloured ion which contains the ruthenium migrates to the anode.[966] The compound is not easily reduced, but hot concentrated alkaline hydroxide precipitates the oxide. The sodium salt readily dissolves in absolute alcohol, sodium chloride crystallizing out while the nitrosyl trichloride $Ru(NO)Cl_3$ remains in solution.

The potassium rubidium and caesium salts are isomorphous. The sodium

---

* For references see Gmelin: $[Ru\ en(NO)Cl_3]°$, p. 57; $[Ru\ en(NO)I_3]°$, p. 71. $[Ru\ dipy(NO)Br_3]°$, p. 67; $[Ru(py)_2(NO)Cl,C_2O_4]°$ (oxalato-), p. 84.

[966] R. Charonnat, *Ann. Chim.* 1931, [10] **16**, 201.
[967] Id., *C.R.* 1924, **178**, 1423.
[968] J. L. Howe, *J.A.C.S.* 1894, **16**, 389.

salt forms a trihydrate; the others (K, NH_4, Rb, and Cs) form dihydrates, in which the water is presumably attached to the anion as

$$[Ru(NO)Cl_5(OH_2)_2]''$$

(the covalency maximum of ruthenium is 8).

The complex bromides $M_2[Ru(NO)Br_5]$ and iodides $M_2[Ru(NO)I_5]$ are similar.

The *potassium oxalato-chloride*, $K_2[Ru(NO)Ox_2Cl],H_2O$, is prepared by treating the chloride $K_2[Ru(NO)Cl_5]$ with potassium oxalate and heating. It forms dark red very soluble crystals, sol[y] 47/20°. On heating with hydrochloric acid it is converted into the pentachloride: the ruthenium is precipitated by hydrogen sulphide but not by potassium hydroxide.

Silver nitrate or lead acetate give pale red precipitates of the corresponding complex salts, which only slowly go over into silver or lead chloride.[966]

The *potassium oxalato-iodide*, $K_2[Ru(NO)OxI_3]$, aq. This is made by adding potassium oxalate solution slowly to a boiling solution of the pentaiodide $K_2[Ru(NO)I_5]$. It forms black crystals stable in air, which lose their water of crystallization at 100°, and are easily soluble in water.

OSMIUM

OSMIUM resembles its predecessor in Group VIII A, ruthenium, in many respects, and especially in its power of assuming a large number of valency states. Ruthenium has 9; osmium has 6: 0, 2, 3, 4, 6, and 8. The two elements show a close resemblance in many respects, even in small details, but there is a tendency for the stability to pass from lower to higher valencies as we go from ruthenium to osmium (see above, p. 1455).

Metallic Osmium

Like ruthenium, osmium is a very hard and infusible metal, not attacked by acids unless they are oxidizing agents. It is bluish-white in colour; it has a density of 22·5, and so is the heaviest of known solids. It has the highest melting-point of any of the platinum metals, 2,700°.

Its most remarkable quality is its tendency (much stronger than that of ruthenium) to combine with oxygen to form the volatile tetroxide. The massive metal is stable in air in the cold, but the powder is slowly oxidized by air even at the ordinary temperature, and has a perceptible smell of the tetroxide; any dust or grease in the vessel containing the powder becomes covered with a black deposit of osmium dioxide formed by the reduction of the tetroxide. (Ruthenium is not acted on by air until it is heated, and then only forms the dioxide; the production of the tetroxide requires a stronger oxidizing agent than elementary oxygen.)

Osmium and its compounds are excellent catalysts, often more effective than platinum, especially for hydrogenation.

Finely powdered osmium, such as is obtained by reducing the dioxide at low temperatures, absorbs a large amount of hydrogen; in the compact form, however, the metal absorbs none, so that the action appears to be superficial.[969]

DIVALENT OSMIUM

THE compounds of divalent osmium are few and nearly all complex. The monoxide OsO has been described, but it does not really exist. On the other hand, osmium (like ruthenium, p. 1461) forms a disulphide OsS_2, a diselenide $OsSe_2$, and a ditelluride $OsTe_2$, which have the pyrites structure, and so must contain divalent osmium.

Osmium Disulphide, OsS_2[970-4]

Numerous sulphides of osmium have been described, but the only one that certainly exists is the disulphide OsS_2. The elements combine at temperatures above 600° with the evolution of much heat, and if excess of sulphur is used and the excess removed by solvents, the disulphide remains.[970] The vapour tensions indicate no other compound.[971]

[969] See E. Müller and K. Schwabe, Z. physikal. Chem. 1931, **154**, 143; Z. Elektro-chem. 1929, **35**, 181.

[970] L. Wöhler, K. Ewald, and H. G. Krall, Ber. 1933, **66**, 1639.

[971] R. Juza, Z. anorg. Chem. 1934, **219**, 130.

[972] I. Oftedal, Z. physikal. Chem. 1928, **135**, 293.

Osmium disulphide is a black solid, or if prepared above 1,000° it is dark blue-grey.[971] It forms cubic crystals, which have a pyrites structure.[972-3] On heating it dissociates into its elements, the dissociation tension being 490 mm. at 1,094°.[971] It is insoluble in alkaline hydroxide or sulphide solutions, and in acids other than nitric, which dissolves it even in the cold, and when the liquid is boiled osmium tetroxide distills over.

Osmium Diselenide and Ditelluride

These substances $OsSe_2$ and $OsTe_2$ also appear to be the only compounds of their respective elements.[970] They are oxidized by air or nitric acid to osmium tetroxide, but other acids, and alkaline solutions, have no action on them. Like the disulphide they have a pyrites structure.[974]

Divalent Halides

The *dichloride* $OsCl_2$ is made by heating the trichloride *in vacuo* to 500°[975]; the remaining solid is purified by boiling with dilute hydrochloric acid and then with water, which do not act on the dichloride. It is dark brown and insoluble in water; it is not acted on by hydrochloric or sulphuric acid, but nitric acid or aqua regia slowly converts it into the tetroxide.

No dibromide has been prepared in anything like purity, and the supposed di-iodide has not been confirmed.

Complex Salts of Divalent Osmium

These are relatively few; they comprise a very stable group of osmocyanides, and a sulphito-complex (and some mono-nitrosyl complex halides discussed later, p. 1510).

Complex Cyanides

These are all of the type $M_4[Os(CN)_6]$, and so belong to the group of the ferrocyanides and the ruthenocyanides.

The free acid is said to be precipitated from a solution of the potassium salt by hydrochloric acid in presence of ether (Claus, 1854; Martius).[976] The salts are numerous; the potassium salt[977] $K_4[Os(CN)_6], 3 H_2O$ can be made by fusing the complex chloride $(NH_4)_2[Os^{iv}Cl_6]$ with potassium cyanide, or by evaporating potassium osmate K_2OsO_4 with potassium cyanide solution and igniting the residue. It forms colourless quadratic tables, which on heating first lose water and then decompose. Various other salts have been prepared.[976-7]

[973] A. K. Meisel, *Z. anorg. Chem.* 1934, **219**, 141.
[974] L. Thomassen, *Z. physikal. Chem.* 1929, B **2**, 349.
[975] O. Ruff and E. Bornemann, *Z. anorg. Chem.* 1910, **65**, 454.
[976] A. Martius, *Ann.* 1861, **117**, 361.
[977] F. Krauss and G. Schrader, *J. prakt. Chem.* 1928, [ii] **119**, 279.

Sulphito-complexes

A sulphito-compound $Na_4[Os(SO_3)_3]$, $6\,H_2O$ has been prepared[978] by treating the ester of osmic acid (see later, p. 1500) with sodium sulphite in dilute alcohol. It is blackish-brown in colour. The formation of complex sulphito-compounds is characteristic of osmium in various states of valency (divalent, tetravalent, hexavalent), and is not shared by ruthenium to anything like the same extent.

TRIVALENT OSMIUM

In the very small number of trivalent derivatives it forms, osmium is in strong contrast to ruthenium, of which the trivalent state is the most important and the richest in compounds. The derivatives are nearly all complex, and as with divalent osmium the only binary compound is the chloride $OsCl_3$; there are only two kinds of complex salts, the halides (few, and nearly, if not quite, all 6-covalent) and a well-marked series of nitro-salts, all of the 5-covalent type $M_2[Os(NO_2)_5]$.

Osmium Trichloride, $OsCl_3$

This is formed (along with the tetrachloride) by chlorinating osmium at a very high temperature, and is best made[979] by decomposing the tetra-valent salt $(NH_4)_2[OsCl_6]$ in a stream of chlorine at 350°. It is a brown hygroscopic powder, which sublimes above 350°, and at 560–600° decomposes into $OsCl_4$ which volatilizes away, and the dichloride $OsCl_2$ which remains behind. It is easily soluble in water and alcohol. The dark brown aqueous solution has a faint acid reaction, but with silver nitrate it gives at first a scarcely visible turbidity, which increases slowly on standing, and rapidly on heating, so that evidently the compound dissolves in water in the first instance without ionization of the chlorine. The aqueous solution is stable even on boiling (as is also the alcoholic) and is not attacked by weak reducing agents such as ferrous sulphate, sulphur dioxide, or formaldehyde. Alkalies and ammonia precipitate an oxide only on boiling. Boiling with concentrated nitric acid converts the trichloride into the tetroxide.

Complex Nitro-salts, $M_2[Os(NO_2)_5]$[980]

The potassium salt can be made by treating K_2OsCl_6 with excess of potassium nitrite. Other salts are known; they are orange, most of them easily soluble in water, and the aqueous solution stable for some time in the cold. The silver salt forms rather insoluble golden yellow crystals. There is a strong but not universal tendency to hydration:

Cation	Na	K	NH$_4$	Ag	Mg	Ca	Sr	Ba	Zn
Mols. of H$_2$O	2	0	2	2	4	4	2	4, 1	1/2

[978] R. Criegee, *Ann.* 1936, **522**, 81.

[979] O. Ruff and F. Bornemann, *Z. anorg. Chem.* 1910, **65**, 454.

[980] L. Wintrebert, *C.R.* 1905, **140**, 586.

Complex Halides of Trivalent Osmium

The only certain type of these is $M_3[OsX_6]$, and only the chloride has been obtained in the pure state. $K_3[OsCl_6]$, 0 and 3 H_2O can be made[981] by the action of chlorine on a mixture of osmium and potassium chloride at temperatures higher than those which form K_2OsCl_6: or from potassium osmiamate $K[OsO_3N]$ in solution in hydrochloric acid. It is a red-brown solid, very soluble in water and alcohol, and giving in water a cherry-red solution which very easily decomposes.

The bromide K_3OsBr_6 has been made, at least in solution,[982] by the electrolytic reduction of K_2OsBr_6 in hydrobromic acid solution in an atmosphere of carbon dioxide. Titration of the resulting yellow-brown solution showed that all the osmium is reduced to the trivalent state. On evaporation dark red-brown octahedra separate.

TETRAVALENT OSMIUM

THIS is the valency in which osmium gives the largest number of compounds, and of the most diverse kinds: in this respect it corresponds to the trivalent state of ruthenium. The general characteristics of tetravalent osmium have already been described (p. 1456). For the redox potentials of Os^{iii}—Os^{iv} see references [983, 4].

Osmium Dioxide, OsO_2

This is the lowest oxide of osmium that has been shown to exist.[985-8] It is not easy to obtain it in the pure state, because in presence of water it readily goes over into a highly absorbent colloidal form. It can be made[985] by the moderated reduction of osmium tetroxide, or by treating $K_2[OsCl_6]$ with sodium carbonate, or probably better by heating the metal in nitric oxide, or in a stream of osmium tetroxide vapour.[986]

Osmium dioxide varies considerably in properties according to the method of preparation, but probably does not occur in different modifications.[987] When it is made by removing water from the hydrate at a low temperature, it is a black pyrophoric powder; if at a high temperature it forms dark brown crystals, which are much less reactive. The crystal structure is the same as that of ruthenium dioxide (p. 1475). It is easily reduced by hydrogen to the metal, and (unlike RuO_2) is oxidized to the

[981] C. Claus and Jacoby, *Bull. Acad. Petersb.* 1863, [iii] **6**, 158; *J. prakt. Chem.* 1863, **90**, 78.

[982] W. R. Crowell, R. K. Brinton, and R. F. Evenson, *J.A.C.S.* 1938, **60**, 1105.

[983] F. P. Dwyer, H. A. McKenzie, and R. S. Nyholm, *Proc. R.S. New S. Wales,* 1947, **80**, 183.

[984] F. P. Dwyer, J. E. Humpoletz, and R. S. Nyholm, ib. 242.

[985] O. Ruff and H. Rathsburg, *Ber.* 1917, **50**, 484.

[986] L. Wöhler and L. Metz, *Z. anorg. Chem.* 1925, **149**, 301.

[987] F. Krauss and G. Schrader, ib. 1928, **176**, 394.

[988] O. Ruff and F. W. Tschirch, *Ber.* 1913, **46**, 946.

tetroxide by heating in air. It is converted by hydrochloric acid into the corresponding (tetravalent) chloride, but the reaction

$$OsO_2 + 6\,HCl = H_2OsCl_6 + 2\,H_2O$$

seems to be reversible.

Osmium dioxide forms a dihydrate $OsO_2, 2\,H_2O$.[985,988] This can be made by reducing a solution of the tetroxide, or by precipitating K_2OsCl_6 with alkali. It occurs as a brown powder or as blue-black crystals, but it very easily assumes the colloidal form, and then is very difficult to purify from adsorbed salts. A monohydrate also occurs.[985]

Halides of Tetravalent Osmium

The binary halides OsF_4, $OsCl_4$, and OsI_4 have been made, though not the tetrabromide; an oxychloride which is probably $Os(OH)Cl_3$ is also known.

Osmium Tetrafluoride, OsF_4

This compound is formed[989] by the combination of metallic osmium with a defective supply of fluorine in a platinum apparatus at 300°. The tetra- hexa- and octofluorides are all formed, and the last two can then be distilled off in a current of nitrogen, leaving the tetrafluoride OsF_4 behind.

Osmium tetrafluoride is a black non-volatile substance. It dissolves readily in water with a certain amount of hydrolysis, accompanied presumably by the formation of some of the hexafluoro-acid H_2OsF_6, the sodium salt of which can be obtained by adding hydrofluoric acid and sodium fluoride to the solution and evaporating.

Osmium Tetrachloride, $OsCl_4$

This is made[990] by the action of chlorine on metallic osmium at 650–700°. It forms black crusts which on heating in a vacuum or in chlorine sublime away without residue. It is apparently insoluble in all ordinary solvents, except oxidizing acids like nitric. With water it only dissolves slowly as it reacts; the products of the reaction are obscure, but they certainly do not include hypochlorous acid, which is formed under these conditions by iridium tetrachloride; the ultimate product is the dioxide OsO_2.

Osmium Tetraiodide, OsI_4

This compound is made[991-2] by evaporating a solution of the hydrated dioxide in hydriodic acid. It forms violet-black octahedra with a metallic glance. It is very hygroscopic, and gives with water a brown solution, which is stable in the cold, but evolves hydrogen iodide on warming. It is remarkable that the tetrafluoride and tetraiodide are very soluble in water, while the tetrachloride is practically insoluble.

[989] O. Ruff and F. W. Tschirch, *Ber.* 1913, **46**, 929.
[990] O. Ruff and F. Bornemann, *Z. anorg. Chem.* 1910, **65**, 446.
[991] H. Moraht and C. Wischin, ib. 1893, **3**, 174.
[992] A. Rosenheim and E. Sasserath, ib. 1899, **21**, 122.

Oxychloride of Tetravalent Osmium, Os(OH)Cl₃[993-4]

The vapour of osmium tetroxide is passed into hydrochloric acid of density 1·17: on evaporation and cooling a very deliquescent mass of brown needles is obtained. These could not be purified for analysis, but it was shown that the osmium was tetravalent, that the ratio Os:Cl was approximately 1:3, and that the crystals on heating give off water. Hence the formula is very probable, especially as the compound with alkaline chlorides or bromides gives $M_2[Os(OH)Cl_5]$ or —Br_5], and with HCl or HBr, H_2OsCl_6 or H_2OsBr_6 and their salts.

COMPLEXES OF TETRAVALENT OSMIUM
Hexammines

Nearly all the numerous complex salts of osmium in all its valencies have the osmium in the anion: the element has a much stronger tendency to combine in its complexes with acid radicals like the halogens than with neutral molecules like ammonia. Complexes with osmium in the cation include a series of tetrammine derivatives of hexavalent osmium of the curious type $[OsO_2(NH_3)_4]X_2$, and one or two compounds of the tetravalent element. Also a thiourea derivative of the composition

$$[Os(CS(NH_2)_2)_6]Cl_4, 4 H_2O$$

can be made by heating a solution of $Na_2[OsCl_6]$ with thiourea: the solution turns brilliant red, and after cooling and adding hydrochloric acid and an alkaline chloride this compound separates in brown tables. They are readily soluble in water, giving a solution of so deep a red that it will detect osmium tetroxide or tetrachloride in a dilution of 1 in 100,000.

The formulation of this compound as the chloride of a tetravalent base is supported by the high conductivity of the aqueous solution, and the fact that its freezing-points indicate a value of 3·6 to 4·0 for the van 't Hoff factor i.[995]

Complex Acids of Tetravalent Osmium

These are very numerous. The complex ions are all divalent, probably all 6-covalent, and all have as their chief acidic constituent either sulphito-groups, or halogen atoms, or both. As with ruthenium (p. 1464) the SO_3 groups can occupy either one place on the osmium (open-chain) as

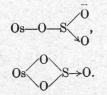

or two (chelate) as

In these salts the covalency is probably 6, but it may be 8; in the absence

993 H. Rémy, *J. prakt. Chem.* 1921, [2] **101**, 341.
994 F. Krauss and D. Wilken, *Z. anorg. Chem.* 1924, **137**, 352.
995 L. Tschugaev, ib. 1925, **148**, 65.

of X-ray data we cannot distinguish between the two, or say, for example, whether the osmium in $M_6Os(SO_3)_5$ has a covalency of 6, with one chelate and 4 open-chain SO_3 groups, or of 8, with 3 and 2.

Type $M_8[Os(SO_3)_6]$[1002]

The sodium salt, with 8 and 3 H_2O, is made by allowing the osmyl compound $Na_6[OsO_2(SO_3)_4], 5 H_2O$ to stand with sodium bisulphite solution for weeks. It forms brown crystals, very slightly soluble in water, which decompose on boiling with concentrated hydrochloric acid. The potassium salt, which is strictly an acid salt, $K_6H_2[Os(SO_3)_6], 2 H_2O$, is similar.

Type $M_6[Os(SO_3)_5]$[1002]

The sodium salt, $Na_6[Os(SO_3)_5], 5 H_2O$, is made in the same way, but by prolonged heating; the potassium salt (also with 5 H_2O, perhaps one H_2O to each SO_3) has been made by heating K_2OsCl_6 with potassium sulphite. It is a colourless powder (the sulphite complexes of osmium seem to be usually colourless, and the halides deeply coloured) which is decomposed by HCl.

Type $M_7[OsCl(SO_3)_5]$[1002]

The sodium salt (6 H_2O) is made from Na_2OsCl_6 and sodium sulphite in water at 60°. It is pale violet: its solution decomposes on boiling.

Type $M_6[OsCl_2(SO_3)_4]$[1013]

The sodium salt (10 H_2O) is made in the same way, but at a lower temperature and more slowly; it is brownish purple.

Type $M_8[OsCl_4(SO_3)_4]$[1013]

The potassium salt is made in the same way as the sodium salts described above, but with potassium hydrogen sulphite, and at the ordinary tempera-

[996] J. D. McCullough, *Z. Krist.* 1936, **94**, 143.
[997] F. Puche, *C.R.* 1936, **202**, 1285.
[998] R. Gilchrist, *Bur. Stand. J. Res.* 1932, **9**, 282.
[999] O. Ruff and F. W. Tschirch, *Ber.* 1913, **46**, 932.
[1000] L. Wintrebert, *Ann. Chim. Phys.* 1903, [vii] **28**, 58.
[1001] F. Krauss and D. Wilken, *Z. anorg. Chem.* 1924, **137**, 360.
[1002] A. Rosenheim and E. A. Sasserath, ib. 1899, **21**, 132.
[1003] A. Gutbier and K. Maisch, *Ber.* 1910, **43**, 3235.
[1004] A. Gutbier and P. Walbinger, ib. 1911, **44**, 309.
[1005] A. Gutbier and L. Mehler, *Z. anorg. Chem.* 1914, **89**, 333.
[1006] A. Gutbier and K. Maisch, *Ber.* 1909, **42**, 4240.
[1007] A. Gutbier, N. Pfanner, and O. Edelhäuser, ib. 1913, **46**, 2098.
[1008] W. R. Cromwell and H. L. Baumbach, *J.A.C.S.* 1935, **57**, 2607.
[1009] A. Gutbier, L. Mehler, N. Pfanner, and O. Edelhäuser, *Z. anorg. Chem.* 1914, **89**, 313.
[1010] L. Wintrebert, *Ann. Chim. Phys.* 1903, [vii] **28**, 133.
[1011] H. Dählmann, Diss., Braunschweig, 1932, p. 22.
[1012] L. Brizard, *C.R.* 1896, **123**, 182; *Ann. Chim. Phys.* 1900, [vii] **21**, 375.
[1013] A. Rosenheim, *Z. anorg. Chem.* 1900, **24**, 420.

ture. On heating with hydrochloric acid it is reconverted into K_2OsCl_6. It is clear that these chloro-sulphites are the successive products of the replacement of chlorine in the hexachlorides by SO_3; this might be used as evidence in favour of the open-chain position of the SO_3.

COMPLEX HALIDES

These are especially numerous: they include the types $M_2[OsF_6]$, $M_2[OsCl_6]$, $M_2[OsBr_6]$, $M_2[OsI_6]$, $M_2[OsCl_5Br]$, $M_2[OsCl_3Br_3]$, $M_2[Os(OH)Cl_5]$, $M_2[Os(OH)Cl_3Br_2]$, $M_2[Os(NH_2)Cl_5]$.

Hexafluorides, $M_2[OsF_6]$

The potassium salt can be made[999] by the careful evaporation of a solution of osmium tetrafluoride in hydrofluoric acid which has been neutralized by potassium hydroxide. It forms yellow regular crystals.

Hexachlorides, $M_2[OsCl_6]$[1003-6,1008]

The free acid $H_2[OsCl_6]$, aq. no doubt occurs in solution, and has probably been got in the solid state. Gilchrist[998] found that when the pale yellow solution of osmium tetrachloride in 20 per cent. hydrochloric acid is boiled, it first turns brown and then red. On evaporation a crystalline mass remains which is probably (though it was not analysed) the free acid. On treatment with ammonium chloride it gives the ammonium salt $(NH_4)_2[OsCl_6]$.

A variety of salts of the acid are known. The potassium salt can be made[1000-1] by heating a mixture of osmium and potassium chloride in chlorine, or by adding potassium chloride and alcohol (as a reducing agent) to a solution of osmium tetroxide. It is a red salt, stable in air; on heating it begins to lose chlorine at 600°, the dissociation tension reaching one atmosphere at 855°; the ultimate products are chlorine, metallic osmium, and potassium chloride. The anhydrous sodium salt[1002] is dark red, but it forms an orange dihydrate. The ammonium salt (dried at 140–150° in a stream of nitrogen) has been used for determining the atomic weight of osmium.[998] In general the salts are all brownish-red, and give orange solutions in water.[997] The caesium salt is the least soluble of the alkaline salts [salt of strong acid].

Hexabromides, $M_2[OsBr_6]$[1007,1009,1022]

Gilchrist[998] has obtained a crystalline mass which appears to be the free acid by the method used for the chloride. The salts are numerous, and

[1014] O. Ruff and F. W. Tschirch, *Ber.* 1913, **46**, 929.
[1015] W. Biltz and H. Ehrhorn, *Z. anorg. Chem.* 1939, **240**, 117.
[1016] W. Gibbs, *Am. Chem. J.* 1881, **3**, 238.
[1017] A. Rosenheim and E. A. Sasserath, *Z. anorg. Chem.* 1899, **21**, 139.
[1018] A. Werner and K. Dinklage, *Ber.* 1901, **34**, 2702.
[1019] L. Wintrebert, *Ann. Chim. Phys.* 1903, [vii] **28**, 54, 86.
[1020] Id., ib. pp. 76, 114.
[1021] A. Werner and K. Dinklage, *Ber.* 1906, **39**, 500.
[1022] A. Gutbier, ib. 1913, **46**, 2101.

exactly similar to the chlorides except in colour: the bromides are darker, the solids being usually black and the aqueous solutions dark purple.

The hexachlorides and hexabromides have the same crystal structure as the corresponding platinichlorides with which they are isomorphous.[996]

Hexa-iodides, $M_2[OsI_6]$

The potassium salt of the acid was obtained[1010] by the action of hydriodic acid on $K_2[OsO_3(NO_2)_2]$, a reaction which involves reduction as well as substitution. It forms blackish-violet octahedra, rather slightly soluble in water, but more so than the hexachloride or hexabromide. The solution is violet, and soon decomposes on warming, even if it contains excess of hydriodic acid. The ammonium salt (blue-black octahedra) is similar.

The mixed halide types $M_2[OsCl_5Br]$[1001] and $M_2[OsCl_3Br_3]$[1001,1011] are also similar.

Hydroxy- and Amino-halides

These complex acids can have one (but only one) of the six halogens replaced by a hydroxyl, or by an NH_2 group. The products seem little if at all less stable than the hexahalides, but fewer salts are known. (The corresponding ruthenium compounds $M_2[Ru(OH)Cl_5]$ and $M_2[Ru(OH)Br_5]$ are known (p. 1478).)

Hydroxy-chlorides, $M_2[Os(OH)Cl_5]$

These salts are made[1001] by adding the alkaline chloride to a feebly acid solution of the oxychloride $Os(OH)Cl_3$; they are red in colour. They are not very stable, and usually cannot be recrystallized from water without decomposition. The salts include a silver salt[1011] which forms greenish-black insoluble crystals.

Hydroxy-bromides, $M_2[Os(OH)Br_5]$

The only known example[1001] is the salt $(CH_3 \cdot NH_3)_2[Os(OH)Br_5]$, made from methyl-ammonium bromide and the oxybromide $Os(OH)Br_3$; it forms pale brown needles.

Hydroxy-chlorobromides, $M_2[Os(OH)Cl_3Br_2]$

The methylammonium salt of this mixed oxyacid was made by Krauss[1001] by treating the oxychloride $Os(OH)Cl_3$ with methylammonium bromide. It forms pale pink plates, which are easily soluble in water, and slightly soluble in alcohol.

Aminochloride, $K_2[Os(NH_2)Cl_5]$

This, the only known salt, is made[1012] by reducing potassium osmiamate $K[OsO_3N]$ with stannous chloride at 60°; deep yellow octahedra, stable up to 110°, and moderately soluble in water to give a greenish-brown solution, which slowly hydrolyses.

HEXAVALENT OSMIUM

THIS is the next most important valency of osmium after that of 4 (see p. 1457). There are two binary compounds, the hexafluoride and the diphosphide, and a considerable number of complex salts, all of which are in some sense derivatives of osmic acid H_2OsO_4.

Osmium Hexafluoride, OsF_6

This is made along with the tetra- and octofluorides by the combination of its elements at about 250°.[1014] (For details see the octofluoride, p. 1505.) If the resulting solid is distilled in dry nitrogen at 50° and 20 mm., the octofluoride evaporates away, and the hexafluoride is just able to sublime a short distance, while the tetrafluoride remains behind.

Osmium hexafluoride is a pale green crystalline substance, which melts between 50° and 120° (all transparent vessels are attacked by it), and boils at 202–205°. It is very hygroscopic, and is at once decomposed by water into osmium dioxide, osmium tetroxide, and hydrogen fluoride.

Osmium Diphosphide, OsP_2[1015]

The study of the system osmium–phosphorus at temperatures from 500° to 1,000° shows that the elements begin to combine above 500°, and that the diphosphide OsP_2 is the only compound formed.

Osmium diphosphide is a grey-black powder, which decomposes into its elements *in vacuo* at 1,000°. It is stable to air and to aqueous acid or alkaline solutions, but it dissolves in alkali on fusion. Its structure, and hence the valency of the osmium in it, are unknown.

Complexes of Hexavalent Osmium

These include the osmates M_2OsO_4 (if we call these complex) and the chloro-osmates $M_2[OsO_2Cl_4]$ to both of which there are ruthenium analogues; but the rest of the rather numerous hexavalent osmium complexes belong to types that are peculiar to osmium: they are not formed by hexavalent ruthenium, and hexavalent iridium forms no complexes, while hexavalent rhodium does not exist at all. The hexavalent osmium com plexes are of four types:

1. Osmic acid and the osmates M_2OsO_4.
2. The osmyl (OsO_2) complexes: these include the ammines
$$[OsO_2(NH_3)_4]X_2,$$
the cyanides $M_2[OsO_2(CN)_4]$, and the substituted osmates $M_2[OsO_2X_4]$, where X = Cl, Br, NO_2, $\frac{1}{2}Ox$, SO_3Na.
3. The oxy-osmyl (OsO_3) salts $M_2[OsO_3X_2]$, where X = Cl, Br, NO_2, $\frac{1}{2}Ox$.
4. The nitrilohalides $M[OsN(hal)_4]$ and $M_2[OsN(hal)_5]$.

Osmates, $M_2[OsO_4]$

These salts can be made[1023] by fusing osmium with potassium hydroxide (best with the addition of potassium nitrate), or by reducing osmium

[1023] E. Müller, *Z. Elektrochem.* 1922, **28**, 307.

tetroxide in alkaline solution with alcohol or potassium nitrite. The alkaline salts are red or brown, and are easily soluble in water to give a red solution, but insoluble in alcohol or ether. The dry salts are stable in the cold, but when heated in air they form osmium tetroxide; when wet or in solution they decompose. The aqueous solution slowly absorbs oxygen from the air, no doubt to give osmium tetroxide or a derivative. The osmates are less stable than the corresponding ruthenates, mainly on account of the greater stability of the octovalent state with osmium.

Werner suggested[1024] that the dihydrate of the potassium salt should be written $K_2H_4[OsO_6]$, on the analogy of telluric acid $H_6[TeO_6]$, but according to Patry[1028] X-ray analysis shows that the crystal lattices of the salts $K_2OsO_4, 2 H_2O$ and $K_2TeO_4, 2 H_2O$ are different.

Cyclic osmic esters of the form

$$R_2C{-}O \diagdown \atop R_2C{-}O \diagup OsO_2,$$

and even dicyclic esters like

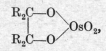

can be made[1029-30] by the action of osmium tetroxide in ethereal solution on unsaturated hydrocarbons such as indene (brown crystals) and dihydronaphthalene (olive-green crystals). When these compounds are warmed with sodium chlorate they are hydrolysed to the corresponding diols (glycols) with the re-formation of the osmium tetroxide. This would appear to be the explanation of the effect of a small quantity of the tetroxide in causing the conversion of unsaturated hydrocarbons into diols by sodium chlorate.[1031,1036,1045] There must, however, be a more

[1024] A. Werner, *Neuere Ansch.* 1923, p. 110.

[1025] F. Krauss and G. Schrader, *J. prakt. Chem.* 1928, [2] **120**, 36.

[1026] J. Verhulst, *Bull. Soc. Chim. Belge,* 1933, **42**, 359. See also *Strukturbericht,* Bd. III, 1933/5, p. 507.

[1027] J. L. Hoard and J. D. Grenko, *Z. Krist.* 1934, **87**, 100.

[1028] M. Patry, *C.R.* 1936, **202**, 1517.

[1029] R. Criegee, *Ann.* 1936, **522**, 75.

[1030] Id., *Z. angew. Chem.* 1938, **51**, 519.

[1031] K. A. Hofmann, *Ber.* 1912, **45**, 3329; K. A. Hofmann, O. Ehrhardt, and O. Schneider, ib. 1913, **46**, 1657.

[1032] R. Criegee, B. Marchand, and H. Wannovius, *Ann.* 1942, **550**, 99.

[1033] P. Walden, *Z. anorg. Chem.* 1910, **68**, 315.

[1034] K. A. Hofmann, *Ber.* 1912, **45**, 3329.

[1035] K. A. Hofmann, O. Ehrhardt, and O. Schneider, ib. 1913, **46**, 1657.

[1036] J. Boeseken, *Rec. Trav.* 1922, **41**, 201.

[1037] H. v. Wartenberg, *Ann.* 1924, **440**, 102.

[1038] F. Krauss and D. Wilken, *Z. anorg. Chem.* 1925, **145**, 151.

[1039] E. Fritzmann, ib. 1927, **163**, 165.

[1040] D. M. Yost and R. J. White, *J.A.C.S.* 1928, **50**, 81.

[1041] E. Ogawa, *Bull. Soc. Japan,* 1931, **6**, 320.

general cause than this, since the oxidation potential of a potassium chlorate solution is definitely raised by adding a trace of osmium tetroxide.[1031,1034-5] Recently it has been shown[1032] that the tetroxide reacts with potassium or caesium hydroxide in methyl alcohol to give the tetramethyl osmate $(MO)_2Os^{vi}(O \cdot CH_3)_4$, which is converted by warm acetic acid into the acetate $MO \cdot Os^{vi}O(O \cdot CO \cdot CH_3)_3$.

Osmyl Complexes

These all contain the osmyl group OsO_2. Apart from one remarkable tetrammine (below) they all have this group in a complex anion, nearly always of the type $M_2[OsO_2X_4]$.

Cyano-osmyl Salts, $M_2[OsO_2(CN)_4]$[1025]

The potassium salt is made by the action of potassium cyanide on osmium tetroxide. The complex is remarkably stable: it is not decomposed by hydrochloric or sulphuric acid, even on boiling; the excess of potassium cyanide is decomposed by this treatment, but the complex ion remains unchanged.

Nitro-osmyl Salts, $M_2[OsO_2(NO_2)_4]$[1025]

The potassium salt can be got by passing nitric oxide into a solution of osmium tetroxide and potassium nitrite, or by the action of the nitrite on potassium osmate. It forms orange prisms, which are unstable; the solution soon decomposes, and even the dry salt blackens in a few days.[1019]

Tetrammines $[OsO_2(NH_3)_4]X_2$

The oxalate of this tetrammine is formed[1016,1020] by the action of ammonium oxalate on potassium osmate. It forms yellow-orange crystals, moderately soluble in water.

Sulphito-osmyl Salts, $M_6[OsO_2(SO_3)_4]$

These salts[1017,1022] appear at first sight to be different in type from the rest, but they can be written in the same form as $M_2[OsO_2(SO_3M)_4]$, which is only a way of expressing that the sulphite groups are attached to the central atom by one valency only. The sodium salt $(+5 H_2O)$ can be got by the action of sulphur dioxide on osmium tetroxide in alkaline solution. It forms brownish crystals, fairly soluble in water at $50°$; they cannot, however, be recrystallized from water as the solution at once begins to decompose.

Oxalato-osmyl Salts, $M_2[OsO_2Ox_2]$[1020]

Numerous salts of this type have been made. In the dry state they are stable up to $170°$ or above, but in water they soon decompose. The sodium

[1042] H. D. Kirschmann and W. R. Crowell, *J.A.C.S.* 1933, **55**, 488.
[1043] A. Langseth and B. Qviller, *Z. physikal. Chem.* 1934, B **27**, 79.
[1044] L. O. Brockway, *Rev. Mod. Phys.* 1936, **8**, 260.
[1045] R. Criegee, *Ann.* 1936, **522**, 75.

salt is made by heating a solution of osmium tetroxide in sodium oxalate for 40 hours under reflux; it forms greenish-red dichroic crystals, sol^y 7 at ordinary temperature. The potassium salt is similar but less soluble, sol^y 0·75/15°. The salts of the alkaline earths seem to be especially unstable in solution. The silver salt is stable when dry, and can be heated alone or in hydrogen to 160° without decomposition.

Chloro-osmyl Salts, $M_2[OsO_2Cl_4]$[1019,1027]

The potassium salt (2 and 0 H_2O) is made by the action of hydrochloric acid on osmyl or oxy-osmyl salts, or on potassium osmate.[1019] It forms garnet-coloured crystals easily soluble in water and fairly stable when dry. The ammonium salt is obtained from this, and is isomorphous with it, but is rather less soluble.

It has been shown[1027] that the crystal lattice of the potassium salt closely resembles that of potassium chloroplatinate, so that presumably the osmium in the anion is 6-covalent and octahedral.

The potassium and ammonium *bromo-osmyl* salts $M_2[OsO_2Br_4]$[1019] are similar, but are difficult to prepare. If too little hydrobromic acid is used the oxy-osmyl bromide $M_2[OsO_3Br_2]$ is formed, and if too much, the hexabromide $M_2[OsBr_6]$.

Oxy-osmyl Complexes[1020]

These are derived from the osmyl salts by replacing two acid radicals by one oxygen, and so are of the general type $M_2[OsO_2 \cdot O \cdot X_2]$, where X can be chlorine, bromine, NO_2, or half an oxalate radical. Only a few of these salts have been prepared[1020]; their structure is unknown. The halides are made from the nitro-compounds by treatment with hydrogen halide; with more of this the osmyl tetrahalide $M_2[OsO_2(hal)_4]$ is formed.

The ammonium salt of the chloro-acid $(NH_4)_2[OsO_2 \cdot O \cdot Cl_2]$ is a yellow powder, stable up to 150°, which is very slightly soluble in water; the bromo-salt is similar. The nitro-salts seem to be the most stable members of this group; the potassium salt $K_2[OsO_2 \cdot O(NO_2)_2]$, 3 and 0 H_2O, can be made by the action of potassium nitrite on a solution of osmium tetroxide, or from the tetranitro-osmyl salt $K_2[OsO_2(NO_2)_4]$ and potassium osmate. It forms brown slightly soluble crystals, and decomposes slowly in solution. Hydrochloric acid converts it successively into

$$K_2[OsO_2 \cdot O \cdot Cl_2], \ K_2[OsO_2Cl_4], \text{ and } K_2[OsCl_6];$$

hydrobromic acid behaves in the same way. The other salts, which are yellow or brown, are very similar. They hydrate strongly: K, 3 H_2O; Sr 3 H_2O; Ba 4 H_2O; Ag H_2O.

The oxalato-derivative $K_2[OsO_2 \cdot O \cdot C_2O_4]$, 2 H_2O was made by letting the tetroxide stand in potassium oxalate solution for months in the cold. It decomposes at 125° and is very slightly soluble in water.[1020]

Nitrilo-halides

These singular compounds were discovered by Werner.[1018,1021] They are of two types, $M[OsN(hal)_4]$ and $M_2[OsN(hal)_5]$. They are thus the complex halides derived from the unknown compound $OsN(hal)_3$, which must be supposed to contain hexavalent osmium. They are made by treating the octovalent osmiamate $M[OsO_3N]$ with hydrogen halide, which both substitutes and reduces, the free halogen being evolved.

The only known tetrahalide salt $K[OsNBr_4], 2 H_2O$[1018] separates in ruby-red crystals when $K[OsO_3N]$ is treated with hydrobromic acid in the cold, bromine being evolved. It is excessively soluble in water to give a cherry-red solution, which rapidly decomposes by itself, but is quite stable in presence of excess of hydrobromic acid. When it is boiled with an alkaline hydroxide no ammonia is evolved.

The *nitrilo-pentachlorides* are better known. Werner and Dinklage showed[1018] that the red crystalline solid produced with evolution of chlorine when an osmiamate is treated with hydrochloric acid has the composition $M_2[OsNCl_5]$; they called it nitrilopentachloro-osmate. The yield is increased by adding potassium chloride, as required by the equation

$$K[OsO_3N] + KCl + 6 HCl = 3 H_2O + Cl_2 + K_2[OsNCl_5].$$

The other salts were obtained from this. They are red crystalline substances, and are fairly stable when dry; in water they give red solutions which soon decompose, especially if they are warmed, with the separation of a black precipitate, but they do not evolve ammonia even when boiled with sodium hydroxide. They are more stable in presence of acid; the crystal lattice is of the C_{2v}^{12} type.[1026] The structure may be

$$K_2 \left[N \mathrel{\overset{\leftarrow}{=}} Os \begin{matrix} Cl \\ | \\ \nearrow Cl \\ \leftarrow Cl \\ \searrow Cl \\ | \\ Cl \end{matrix} \right].$$

Pentabromo-nitrilo-salts

These salts, $M_2[OsNBr_5]$, were made[1021] by adding the alkaline bromide in suitable excess to the mother liquor from the formation of the tetrabromo-potassium salt in the reaction described above. An ammonium salt ($+1 H_2O$), a rubidium salt (anhydrous), and an acid caesium salt $Cs_3H[OsNBr_5]_2$ were prepared. They are all red or brown solids, giving red solutions in water which soon decompose.

OCTOVALENT OSMIUM

FOR the general characteristics of this, the group valency, see p. 1458; its greater stability in osmium than in ruthenium is very marked.

Osmium Tetroxide, OsO_4

Osmium tetroxide, OsO_4, is the usual product of the oxidation of metallic osmium and many of its compounds by atmospheric air and other oxidizing agents; the ease with which it sublimes from the osmium-iridium alloy when that is heated in air is very important for the isolation of osmium. It is most easily prepared by heating metallic osmium to redness in air.

It is a colourless or yellow solid, melting at about 40° and boiling at about 130°; the best values seem to be

				M. pt.	B. pt.
v. Wartenberg[a]	.	.	.	40·6°	129°
Krauss[b]	.	.	.	39·5°	134°
Ogawa[c]	.	.	.	40·6°	131·2°

$$a = {}^{1037}, b = {}^{1038}, c = {}^{1041}.$$

The critical temperature is 404·8°[1037,1041]: the Trouton constant 21·5[1041]: the parachor 157·7.[1041] The substance has been said[1038] to occur (like ruthenium tetroxide) in two modifications, but this is improbable.[1041] The vapour has a characteristic and penetrating smell (which has given its name to the element) and attacks the lungs and throat.

Osmium tetroxide has a normal molecular weight in the vapour at 246° and 286° (Deville), and in solution in phosphorus oxychloride from the freezing-point (Walden).[1033] In benzene solution the dipole moment is practically zero,[1043] as the volatility would lead us to expect. Electron diffraction measurements[1044] showed that the 4 oxygen atoms are tetrahedrally arranged round the osmium, which is supported by the absorption spectrum and the Raman spectrum,[1043] and that the Os—O distance is 1·66±0·05 A. This distance is remarkably short. The theory for Os—O is about 2·04; the observed length is about that to be expected for a triple Os≡O link, but as we saw with ruthenium tetroxide there is no reason to expect the occurence of more than double links in these tetroxides. Osmium tetroxide is diamagnetic (Faraday) and its electrical conductivity in the liquid state is less than 10^{-11}.

It behaves as a normal non-associated substance (or nearly so) in solution both in water and in carbon tetrachloride; the partition between these two solvents does not vary more than 50 per cent. for large changes in concentration.[1040,1046] It is very soluble, especially in non-associated solvents; at 25° the sol[y] is in water 7·24 and in carbon tetrachloride 375.[1046] Its solubilities are like those of an organic hydroxy-compound such as phenol, and it can be salted out of its aqueous solution by inorganic salts. The vapour pressure of the carbon tetrachloride solution does not indicate any serious degree of association.

The aqueous solution[1039] is neutral to litmus, but the oxide in it certainly behaves as an acid, though a very weak one. This is shown by the electrical conductivity, which is perceptible, though not much greater than that of water, and also by the effect of alkalies upon the solution. The value[1040] of the partition coefficient CCl_4/water is cut down from 12 in pure water to 3·8 in 0·028 normal alkali, and to 2·12 in 0·06-normal. This shows that it

[1046] L. H. Anderson and D. M. Yost, *J.A.C.S.* 1938, **60**, 1822.

is being held back by the alkali, and indicates that if we assume the acid to be H_2OsO_5, its first dissociation constant must be 8×10^{-13}, much smaller even than the second dissociation constant of carbonic acid, which is 6×10^{-11}, so that it is not surprising that the acidic character of the solution was at first overlooked; this constant implies that a salt $NaHOsO_5$ would be some 30 per cent. hydrolysed in decinormal solution. Strong alkalies should be able to form definite salts with the solution, and it has been found that when alkali is added to the solution it turns yellow, and if it is concentrated enough salts such as $K_2[OsO_4(OH)_2]$ (p. 1509) can be isolated.

Osmium tetroxide is a strong but not violent oxidizing agent. It oxidizes hydrochloric acid of a density greater than 1·6, with the formation of chlorine and $H_2[OsCl_6]$, the osmyl halides being intermediate products; but a more dilute hydrochloric acid does not reduce it though it reduces ruthenium tetroxide, showing that the osmium compound is the more stable, as we should expect. The reaction is reversible. Hydrobromic acid behaves in the same way; see references [1041-2,1045].

Osmium tetroxide will also oxidize organic substances, being itself reduced to the dioxide OsO_2, aq., or even to the metal; hence its use in biology as a stain. In organic oxidations it has the advantage that it does not cause substitutions, as nitric acid and the halogens are liable to do.

Osmium Octofluoride, OsF_8

This is produced[1047-8] along with the tetra- and hexafluorides, by the action of fluorine gas on heated osmium, the apparatus being made of platinum. With an active osmium powder and plenty of fluorine at 250°, the only products are the hexa- and the octofluoride[1048]; the latter (about 35 per cent.) is then distilled off and condensed in solid carbon dioxide and alcohol, or in liquid air.

Osmium octofluoride forms fine yellow needles, which melt at 34·4° to a yellowish-red liquid boiling at 47·5°[1047]; the density of the solid at $-183°$ is 3·87, giving a molecular volume of 88·7[1048]; the Trouton constant is 22·1. The vapour density at 100° is that of OsF_8 within 3 per cent. The vapour begins to decompose into fluorine and a lower fluoride above 225°, but no considerable decomposition occurs below 400°.

The vapour is colourless, has a peculiar and characteristic smell, fumes in air, and attacks the eyes and nose violently. It has no action on platinum, gold, silver, or copper except on heating; with most metals it reacts in the cold, for example with magnesium, aluminium, chromium, manganese, iron, nickel, zinc, and mercury, and still more readily with phosphorus, arsenic, antimony, and lead; it also attacks warm glass with evolution of silicon tetrafluoride. In water it gives a colourless solution, which, however, has lost the octofluoride smell, and only smells of the tetroxide, so that presumably it is more or less completely hydrolysed. In sodium hydroxide solution osmium octofluoride gives the characteristic yellow-red colour of the 'perosmates', such as $M_2[OsO_4(OH)_2]$ (see later, p. 1509).

Osmium octofluoride has a very remarkable reaction with alkaline fluorides[1047]; they combine with it with unusual ease to form a salt-like addition product which can also be obtained by passing fluorine over a heated mixture of osmium powder and the alkaline fluoride. This addition compound is so stable that in the preparation of the octofluoride the product must be kept out of contact with alkaline fluorides, which would hold it back; it is also much less easily reduced by alcohol or hydrazine hydrate than the octofluoride itself. The sodium compound is a white substance which when treated with sodium hydroxide solution evolves ozone and forms a greenish-yellow solution. Unfortunately these addition compounds have not been analysed.[1047]

[*Osmium Tetrasulphide*, OsS_4

Berzelius and others claimed that this is formed by the action of hydrogen sulphide on osmium tetroxide. But recent work[1049] indicates that the product is of uncertain composition, and contains oxygen.]

Structures of Osmium Tetroxide and Octofluoride

The tetroxide is shown by electron diffraction to have a tetrahedral structure with remarkably short links from the osmium to the oxygen. These links might be either single co-ordinate links or double links: if they are all of one kind we have the two alternative structures

$$\begin{array}{cc}
O & O \\
\uparrow & \parallel \\
O{\leftarrow}Os{\rightarrow}O \qquad & O{=}Os{=}O \\
\downarrow & \parallel \\
O & O
\end{array}$$

Atomic structure
of Os $\qquad$ $2.8.18.32.8.\underline{8}$ $\qquad$ $2.8.18.32.8.\underline{16}$

The absence of a volatile tetroxide of iron might be used to support the second formula, on the ground that ruthenium and osmium, but not iron, can have covalencies of 8; more probably, however, the absence of FeO_4 is due to the instability of this highest valency with the lighter element, and the tetroxide is a resonance hybrid of the two forms, the shortness of the link indicating, as with ruthenium (p. 1482), that the doubly bonded form predominates.

In either case the core is the same, having a pseudo-inert-gas form like that of the central atom in all the XO_4 ions of A elements in their group valency, such as the zirconates, tantalates, tungstates, permanganates, and perrhenates; the electrovalency, which is always equal to 8 minus the

[1047] O. Ruff and F. W. Tschirch, *Ber.* 1913, **46**, 929.
[1048] P. Henkel and W. Klemm, *Z. anorg. Chem.* 1935, **222**, 67.
[1049] R. Juza, *Z. anorg. Chem.* 1934, **219**, 137.

group number, has fallen to zero, and the RuO_4 and OsO_4 molecules are uncharged, giving us the series

Group	4	5	6	7	8
	ZrO_4'''	TaO_4'''	WO_4''	MnO_4'	$RuO_4°$
				ReO_4'	$OsO_4°$

With the octofluoride the question is whether the osmium is covalently saturated. The covalency rule gives 8 as the maximum covalency for elements after the end of the first long period; but there always is a possibility that a further increase to 10 takes place somewhere lower down in the Table. If the maximum for osmium is 8, then in the octofluoride the osmium is covalently saturated, and in that case we should certainly expect the compound to show the same kind of inactivity that we find in carbon tetrafluoride and in sulphur and selenium hexafluorides. In fact, however, its behaviour is quite different, and it is as reactive—for example, with water, alkalies, or lead—as a covalently unsaturated halide such as, say, silicon tetrachloride or tellurium hexafluoride. This suggests that the osmium is not exerting its maximum covalency in the octofluoride, and so is able to form co-ordinate links as an acceptor, giving, for example, with water, $F_8Os{\leftarrow}OH_2$.

This conclusion, which is admittedly very uncertain, is supported by the behaviour of the octofluoride with alkaline fluorides like sodium fluoride. Though the products have not been analysed, it can scarcely be doubted that they are addition compounds of a composition such as NaF, OsF_8, or $2 NaF, OsF_8$. We cannot suppose that the fluorine atoms are attached to one another, and so the only probable structure for the compound would seem to be $Na[OsF_9]$ or $Na_2[OsF_{10}]$, which would imply that a covalency of 10 is possible for osmium. It is very unsatisfactory to have to base an argument for an extension of the covalency limits on un-analysed compounds such as these, and it is to be hoped that they will be examined in more detail.

Complexes of Octovalent Osmium

The complex salts derived from osmium tetroxide are the osmiamates, in which one of the oxygen atoms in OsO_4 is replaced by the NH group or its ion, and a few rather unstable so-called 'osmenates', formed by the addition of the tetroxide to alkaline hydroxides and fluorides.

Osmiamates, $M[OsO_3N]$

The constitution of the osmiamates, which are very readily formed by the action of concentrated ammonia on a strong solution of osmium tetroxide in alkali,[1050,1052] was finally established by Werner in 1901.[1053] He pointed out that the suggested structure

$$O{=}Os{\Big\langle}{\begin{matrix}NO\\O\ [M]\end{matrix}}$$

was improbable (1) on account of the ease with which they are formed (rapidly on slight warming of the tetroxide with aqueous ammonia); (2) because they give off nitrogen when heated alone[1051]; potassium osmiamate evolves nitrogen *in vacuo* above 200°, giving a mixture or compound of potassium osmate and osmium dioxide:

$$2\,K[OsO_3N] = N_2 + K_2OsO_4 + OsO_2.$$

(3) Thirdly, and most conclusively, the osmiamates when treated with hydrochloric or hydrobromic acid are converted with the loss of all the oxygen but not the nitrogen into nitrilo-halides such as $M_2[OsNCl_5]$; we cannot suppose that the acid reduces the NO group to nitrogen. All these facts go to show that the nitrogen is combined only with the osmium. If one oxygen atom on the osmium is replaced by an NH group we shall get an acid of the required composition $H[OsO_3N]$, which could give a mono-valent ion OsO_3N^-

We should expect the three oxygen atoms and the nitrogen to occupy the points of a distorted tetrahedron: the crystal structure of the potassium salt $KOsO_3N$ was examined by Jaeger,[1055] who found that these four atoms are at the corners of a tetragonal bisphenoid.

Free osmiamic acid is known only in solution, which is yellow and keeps for days if it is dilute. It is a strong acid. If a concentrated solution of osmium tetroxide in strong caustic potash is treated with strong ammonia solution at 50°, the brown colour of the solution soon disappears, and yellow crystals of the potassium salt separate out:

$$OsO_4 + KOH + NH_3 = K[OsO_3N] + 2\,H_2O.$$

On heating in air the solid darkens at 140° and then explodes gently; concentrated hydrochloric acid converts it into the nitrilo-chloride $K_2[OsNCl_5]$. It is remarkable that the aqueous solution can be heated with potassium hydroxide up to its boiling-point without decomposition, and without liberation of ammonia.[1052,1054]

The sodium salt is so soluble that it cannot be made in this way, but must be prepared from the silver salt. The other salts are similar; the rubidium and caesium salts are increasingly insoluble (strong acid salts), and those of barium and zinc very soluble.

[1050] J. Fritsche and H. Struve, *J. prakt. Chem.* 1847, **41**, 97.
[1051] A. Joly, *C.R.* 1891, **112**, 1443.
[1052] L. Brizard, *Ann. Chim. Phys.* 1900, [vii] **21**, 373.
[1053] A. Werner and K. Dinklage, *Ber.* 1901, **34**, 2698.
[1054] L. Tschugaev and F. Butkewitsch, *Z. anorg. Chem.* 1928, **172**, 232.
[1055] F. M. Jaeger and J. E. Zanstra, *Proc. Acad. Amst.* 1932, **35**, 610.

Per-osmates or Osmenates[1056-7]

These salts are all of the compositions $2\,MOH, OsO_4$, or $2\,MF, OsO_4$. They are undoubtedly complex salts, and are clearly of the type $M_2[OsO_4X_2]$, where $X = OH$ or F. The covalency we ascribe to the osmium in them depends on the view we take of the Os—O links: if these are single the covalency is 6: if they are double it is 10. (It is at least probable that the unanalysed compound of osmium octofluoride with alkaline fluorides[1047] has the corresponding structure $M_2[OsF_{10}]$.)

The salts are got by adding freshly made solid osmium tetroxide to a saturated solution of alkaline hydroxide or fluoride at $-10°$. The salts are very soluble in water (the caesium less so than the potassium salt) and in alkalies, and are decomposed by acids. The solid salts are stable under the mother liquor, but when they are exposed to the air they lose osmium tetroxide. They are yellow or brown. They could not be purified or analysed in the ordinary way, but the valency of the osmium and the ratio osmium: alkali metal were determined. These results make their composition (apart from water of crystallization) certain.

OSMIUM CARBONYLS

OSMIUM forms two 'simple' carbonyls, several kinds of carbonyl halides, and probably a carbonyl hydride. All three types are formed together[1059-60] when carbon monoxide acts under pressure on osmium halides (iodide most, chloride least easily) in presence of metallic copper or silver to take up the halogen.

Osmium pentacarbonyl, $Os(CO)_5$, is a volatile liquid of m. pt. $-15°$; it is monomeric.[1060]

Osmium enneacarbonyl, $Os_2(CO)_9$, is the chief product of the reaction; it forms yellow crystals melting at $224°$ and subliming above $130°$. It is soluble in indifferent solvents (the ruthenium compound is also volatile, fusible, and soluble, but the iron analogue is not). No compound $[Os(CO)_4]_3$ (as with iron and ruthenium) could be obtained.

The *hydride* is no doubt the volatile substance formed in small quantities in the above reaction. It does not seem to have been analysed, but it is presumably $Os(CO)_2(COH)_2$.

Several types of *carbonyl halides* have been described. Manchot[1058] obtained as the chief product of the reaction of carbon monoxide on osmium dichloride in the absence of a metal a compound $Os(CO)_3Cl_2$, obviously polymerized (we should expect a trimer): colourless, m. pt. $269-273°$, decomposing at $280°$; it is insoluble in water and most acids. When heated with oxygen or copper it gives osmium tetroxide.

[1056] L. Tschugaev, *C.R.* 1918, **167**, 162.
[1057] F. Krauss and D. Wilken, *Z. anorg. Chem.* 1925, **145**, 151.
[1058] W. Manchot and J. König, *Ber.* 1925, **58**, 229.
[1059] W. Hieber and H. Fuchs, *Z. anorg. Chem.* 1941, **248**, 256.
[1060] W. Hieber and H. Stallmann, *Z. Elektrochem.* 1943, **49**, 288.

Hieber and Stallmann[1060], in presence of copper or silver, got two other types of halide, $Os(CO)_4X_2$ (perhaps the same as Manchot's compound) and a dimeric $[Os(CO)_4X]_2$. They also obtained the tricarbonyl halides $Os(CO)_3X_2$; the chloride, bromide, and iodide were made.[1061]

The valency of the osmium is zero in the penta-carbonyl and in the hydride if this is $Os(CO)_2(COH)_2$; in the enneacarbonyl, if it has the same structure as the iron analogue, it is 4; the E.A.N. of the osmium in all these compounds is 86.

OSMIUM NITROSYLS

THE only nitrosyls of osmium are the complex halides $M_2[Os(NO)X_5]$, where $X = Cl$, Br, I.[1062] This is in striking contrast to ruthenium, which gives a very numerous series of nitrosyl derivatives. The potassium salts of this type are made[1062] by prolonged heating of the trivalent osmium salt $K_2[Os(NO_2)_5]$ with a solution of the halogen hydride. The chloride $K_2[Os(NO)Cl_5]$ is a very dark red crystalline substance, giving a red solution in water, which is very stable and only slowly oxidized by nitric acid. The bromide and iodide are similar but black. The three potassium salts are isomorphous with one another and with the ruthenium salt $K_2[Ru(NO)Cl_5]$. In these complexes the osmium has the E.A.N. of 86, and it is divalent, as ruthenium is in nearly all its nitrosyl derivatives.

[1061] W. Hieber and H. Stallmann, *Ber.* 1942, **75**, 1472.
[1062] L. Wintrebert, *Ann. Chim. Phys.* 1903, [vii] **28**, 129.

GROUP VIII B (9)

RHODIUM AND IRIDIUM

RHODIUM is in sharp contrast to the preceding pair of elements, with their many valencies, since in nearly all its compounds it is trivalent. This is far less true of iridium: its trivalent compounds are still the most important group, but it also has valencies of 1, 2, 4, and 6.

Valency = 1

Rhodium has none.

Iridium has only one type of monovalent compounds, the monohalides, which are made by heating the higher halides: IrCl, IrBr, and IrI are known. These are non-volatile solids not attacked even by concentrated sulphuric acid.

Valency = 2

There probably are no simple compounds of divalent rhodium, though the oxide RhO and the sulphide RhS have been described. Certain ammines and arsine derivatives are said to occur.

Divalent iridium forms a few compounds. The solid dihalides $IrCl_2$, $IrBr_2$, and IrI_2 have been made, like the monohalides, by heating the trihalides, and there is a monosulphide IrS; there are also a few ammines and a series of complex cyanides of the ferrocyanide type $M_4[Ir(CN)_6]$.

Valency = 3

This is the chief valency both for rhodium and for iridium (as it is for cobalt in the covalent state).

With rhodium it is the valency of the element in all its compounds with only a few exceptions. As is usual with the platinum metals, the apparently simple compounds are no doubt really complex, which explains why so many of them (the hydroxide, chloride, and sulphate) occur in isomeric forms. We have a sesquioxide Rh_2O_3, a hydroxide $Rh(OH)_3$, occurring in a soluble and an insoluble form, a fluoride RhF_3 which is a red powder, a non-volatile trichloride in several forms, a cyanide, hydrated and obviously complex, decomposed only by strong alkali, and several salts, including a sulphate, which are probably auto-complexes.

The recognized complexes are practically confined to the ammines, halides, and cyanides.

The ammines all have a co-ordination number of 6; every type occurs from the hexammines $[RhAm_6]X_3$ to the monammines $M_2[RhAmR_5]$. The great diversity of amines, diamines, oximes, etc., which form these compounds, and the stability of the products, recall the corresponding complexes of trivalent cobalt.

The complex halides are formed by all the halogens except fluorine, but the bromides are less stable than the chlorides, and very few iodides are known.

The complex cyanides are all of the type of the ferricyanides,

$$M_3[Rh(CN)_6],$$

and are extraordinarily stable, not being affected even by boiling with concentrated sulphuric acid. They can be made by fusing metallic rhodium with potassium ferrocyanide, but they are not formed by the action of potassium cyanide on rhodium tricyanide, or on a solution of the trichloride $RhCl_3$. Complex oxalato-salts are also known.

With iridium again this is the most stable valency, though it is not so exclusively stable as it is with rhodium. The apparently simple salts are like those of trivalent rhodium: there is an oxide Ir_2O_3, a sulphide Ir_2S_3, a trichloride and a tribromide (the last two occurring in anhydrous and in hydrated forms, of which only the hydrated are soluble in water, probably being complex acids), and a few salts such as the sulphate.

The complexes are again similar to those of trivalent rhodium. The ammines are less various than those of rhodium, but there are more types of complex anions (there are signs that in each pair, and indeed in each vertical triad of Gp. VIII, as the atomic weight increases the cations become less stable and the anions more stable).

The anions are all of the type $M_3[IrX_6]$, where $X = Cl$, Br, I, NO_2, CN, $\frac{1}{2}SO_3$, $\frac{1}{2}SO_4$. The range of types given by trivalent rhodium in its complex halides is replaced by the uniformly 6-fold anionic complexes of trivalent iridium.

Valency = 4

There is only one rhodium compound which may be of this valency, and its composition is uncertain. This is a fluoride, which is undoubtedly higher than the trifluoride, and must be either RhF_4 or RhF_5.

With iridium there are a few tetravalent compounds, but only a few. There is a dioxide and a disulphide: tetrahalides are given probably by all four halogens, and all of them are solids except the tetrafluoride IrF_4, which is an easily hydrolysed oil; the other halides are insoluble except in the hydrated forms which are probably complex acids (like the halides of trivalent iridium). There are also a few complex salts, a few tetrammines of the type of $[IrAm_4Cl_2]X_2$, and a few hexahalide salts $M_2[IrCl_6]$.

Valency = 5

Here again there is only one possible rhodium compound, the higher fluoride mentioned above, which may be the pentafluoride RhF_5.

Iridium has no pentafluoride compound. The supposed pentafluoride has been shown to be an oxyfluoride of hexavalent iridium.

Valency = 6

There are no hexavalent rhodium compounds.

Iridium has very few compounds in this valency; there is a hexafluoride IrF_6, an oxyfluoride IrF_4O derived from it, and possibly an oxide IrO_3 and a sulphide IrS_3.

RHODIUM

RHODIUM, like ruthenium, is one of the rarest of elements, occurring to the extent of about 1 part in 10^9 in the earth's crust, but it is rather more abundant than ruthenium in platinum ores, where, however, it seldom reaches 5 per cent. It was discovered along with palladium by Wollaston in 1803[1063]; he gave it the name from the rosy colour of many of its salts.

Rhodium is trivalent in nearly all its compounds and in all its numerous complexes; there are, however, signs of the existence of divalent rhodium, and also of higher valencies than 3, though it is not certain what these are. The resemblance of rhodium to cobalt is close, and the differences are what we should expect. Cobalt is nearly always trivalent in its covalent compounds: the rhodium compounds are practically all covalent, and so rhodium is almost confined to a valency of 3.

Trivalent rhodium has the strong power of complex formation that is common in trivalent transitional elements, not so strong perhaps as that of chromium and cobalt, but no weaker than that of ruthenium in this valency. It forms all the usual kinds of complexes, ammines, halides, cyanides, ato-compounds: its co-ordination number in the cations is always, and in the anions usually, 6.

Metallic Rhodium

Rhodium is a white ductile metal melting at 1,966°.[1064-5] It absorbs oxygen when melted, and on solidification expels it with 'spitting', like silver.[1066] At a red heat it is slowly oxidized by air or oxygen to the sesquioxide Rh_2O_3, which at a much higher temperature breaks up again into its elements. Chlorine at a red heat converts it into the trichloride, but it is extremely resistent to fluorine (see under RhF_3, p. 1517).

Compact rhodium is insoluble in all acids, even aqua regia, but in fine division (as sponge or as black) it dissolves. If it is fused with potassium bisulphate it dissolves to form the sulphate $Rh_2(SO_4)_3$. Metallic rhodium can be obtained from any of its compounds by ignition in hydrogen, but it must be allowed to cool in a stream of carbon dioxide or the adsorbed hydrogen will catch fire on exposure to air.

Rhodium is used as an alloy with platinum (generally containing 10 per cent. of rhodium) along with pure platinum in thermocouples.[1067-8] It is also used for making crucibles and similar vessels.[1069] Recently it has been found possible to deposit electrolytically on silver a very thin film of rhodium which does not affect the appearance (not only because of its thinness, but also because the colour of rhodium is very like that of silver),

[1063] Published a year later: *Phil. Trans.* 1804, **94**, 419.

[1064] W. F. Roeser and H. T. Wensel, *Bur. Stand. J. Res.* 1934, **12**, 519.

[1065] C. R. Barber and F. H. Schofield, *Proc. Roy. Soc.* 1939, **173**, 117.

[1066] W. H. Swanger, *Bur. Stand. J. Res.* 1929, **3**, 1029.

[1067] F. R. Caldwell, ib. 1933, **10**, 373.

[1068] J. S. Acken, ib. 1934, **12**, 249.

[1069] See, for example, G. Trömel and F. Wever, *Naturwiss.* 1931, **19**, 519.

but stops it from tarnishing through the formation of a black layer of silver sulphide.[1070]

Rhodium, like palladium and platinum, has a strong catalytic power, especially in forms which have a large surface, such as the sponge or black, made by the reduction of trivalent rhodium salts* with ammonium formate: or still more in the colloidal form, which is made by reducing the chloride (usually as the complex salt Na_3RhCl_6) with hydrazine hydrate,[1071] or with titanous chloride and alkali,[1072] especially in the presence of a protective colloid like gum arabic. The colloidal metal has a strong bactericidal action even in quantities much too small to be poisonous to man. It absorbs in the cold up to 2,900 times its volume of hydrogen, and it is particularly remarkable that it absorbs 346 volumes of carbon monoxide at 13° and 1,820 at 60° (if the density of the metal is taken as 12·1, this is 0·7 mol. of CO to 1 Rh), which suggests a definite chemical reaction with the carbon monoxide.[1073] Kahl and Biesalski[1074] have compared the catalytic activity of colloidal rhodium with that of colloidal palladium and platinum, and find that the order varies with the reaction: thus for the combination of hydrogen and oxygen, or the reduction of ethylene, it is Pd > Pt > Rh; for that of a solution of sodium chlorate Pt > Rh > Pd; and for that of potassium nitrite Rh > Pt > Pd. It is curious that the stability of the colloidal solution is not increased by dilution but rather diminished, and concentrations up to 2 and even 10 per cent. can be obtained.[1071]

Rhodium sponge and rhodium black in the same way behave like platinum black; they catalyse the combination of hydrogen and oxygen, the oxidation of alcohol to acetic acid, the conversion of chlorine water into hydrochloric acid and oxygen, and the decomposition of formic acid into hydrogen and carbon dioxide at the ordinary temperature. It is singular that their activity is not destroyed by the presence of sulphur, but may even be increased by it (Bredig).[1075]

Rhodium and Hydrogen

Hydrogen is not perceptibly absorbed by compact rhodium at any temperature between 400° and 1,000°; its adsorption by colloidal rhodium has already been mentioned. In this way rhodium behaves to hydrogen much more like platinum than like palladium.[1076-7]

* When the valency of rhodium in its compounds is not specified, it may be assumed to be 3.

[1070] The colour and the methods of its electrolytic deposition are discussed by G. Grube and E. Kesting, *Z. Elektrochem.* 1933, **39**, 948.

[1071] A. Gutbier and E. Leutheusser, *Z. anorg. Chem.* 1925, **149**, 181.

[1072] Id., ib. 1927, **164**, 287.

[1073] C. Zenghelis and B. Papaconstantinou, *C.R.* 1920, **170**, 1058.

[1074] G. Kahl and E. Biesalski, *Z. anorg. Chem.* 1936, **230**, 88.

[1075] See also T. Blackadder, *Z. physikal. Chem.* 1912, **81**, 385.

[1076] A. Gutbier and O. Maisch, *Ber.* 1919, **52**, 2275.

[1077] I. E. Adadurov and N. I. Pevni, *J. Phys. Chem. Soc. Russ.* 1937, **9**, 592.

Rhodium and Carbon

Fused rhodium dissolves up to 1·8 per cent. of carbon, but this separates as graphite on solidification.[1066]

Rhodium and Nitrogen

Nitrogen is not perceptibly absorbed by rhodium at any temperature from 400° to 1,000°.

DIVALENT RHODIUM

THE evidence for divalent rhodium depends entirely on the existence of some of the following compounds: the monoxide, monosulphide, and dichloride and certain complex sulphito-salts. Unfortunately with all these compounds there is some doubt about the composition or the constitution, or both.

Rhodium Monoxide, RhO

This is said[1078] to be formed from the sesquioxide at 1,113–1,121° (above which it loses oxygen), but its existence is very doubtful.[1079] See further, p. 1516.

Rhodium Monosulphide, RhS

Here again recent confirmation is lacking. Rhodium monosulphide is said to be formed by heating the metal with sulphur, or by igniting the precipitate of $Rh(SH)_3$ which is formed when hydrogen sulphide acts on a solution of a trivalent rhodium compound; and to be a bluish-white mass with a metallic lustre, which burns when heated in air, leaving a spongy mass of rhodium behind. This may, however, be a mixture of the metal with a higher sulphide.

Rhodium Dichloride, $RhCl_2$

Wöhler and Müller[1078] claim to have shown that when rhodium trichloride is decomposed by heat, lower chlorides $RhCl_2$ and $RhCl$ are formed, just as they say that the lower oxides RhO and Rh_2O are formed in the thermal dissociation of rhodium sesquioxide. The product of the partial decomposition of the trichloride they ground up and separated into fractions by washing with benzene. When the decomposition had taken place at 950–955° the heaviest fraction was found to have the composition of the dichloride $RhCl_2$, and when at 965–970°, of RhCl. The dissociation tensions of these fractions showed that this reached one atmosphere for the trichloride at 948°, for the dichloride at 958°, and for the monochloride at 964°. Here, as with the oxides, the existence of the lower compounds seems very doubtful in view of the absence of X-ray or any other evidence of homogeneity, and of the very small differences (of the order of 1 per cent.) in the dissociation temperatures.

Sulphito-compounds. When sodium sulphite is added to a solution of

[1078] L. Wöhler and W. Müller, *Z. anorg. Chem.* 1925, **149**, 125.
[1079] A. Gutbier, A. Hüttlinger, and O. Maisch, ib. 1916, **95**, 225.

rhodium trichloride yellow quite insoluble precipitates are formed,[1080] with the compositions of mixtures of such salts as $Na_2[Rh''(SO_3)_2]$ and $Na_4[Rh''(SO_3)_2SO_4]$; they are not oxidized by iodine, which is very remarkable if they contain divalent rhodium. As they cannot be purified they do not much strengthen the evidence for divalent rhodium.

There is better evidence in a series of complexes of divalent rhodium with amines[1081] and arsines.[1082] The ammines mostly contain pyridine, as $[Rh py_6](hal)_2$. The arsine complexes are of the 6-covalent type $Rh(AsR_3)_4Cl_2$; they are very soluble, even in petrol ether, and in alcohol give no precipitate with silver nitrate in the cold.

TRIVALENT RHODIUM

THIS is the most stable state of the element, and that from which the great majority of its compounds are derived. The strong tendency which both the second and the third triads (the platinum metals) have, as compared with the first, to assume a covalent or complex form, is very evident here. The simple salts can rarely be isolated in a pure state, and clearly are very ready to form auto-complexes; this is probably why so many of them occur in different isomeric modifications, for example, the hydroxide, chloride, and sulphate; the recognized complexes, on the other hand, are relatively stable and easily prepared.

In solution the simple trivalent rhodium salts are usually red, and they have a peculiar and characteristic bitter taste.

Rhodium Sesquioxide, Rh_2O_3

This is the product, and probably the only product, of heating the metal or its nitrate or chloride in air or oxygen to 600–1,000°. For the details of the system $Rh+O$ up to 1,050° see Schenck.[1083] It is a grey crystalline mass, insoluble in acids. According to Gutbier,[1079] if it is heated it is completely broken up into its elements at temperatures above 1,150°. The view of Wöhler and Müller[1078] that the breakdown occurs in two stages, with the intermediate formation of RhO and Rh_2O, is improbable. A further objection is that the heats of formation of the three oxides[1084] when calculated per gram-atom of oxygen, give Rh_2O_3, 22·8; RhO, 21·7; Rh_2O, 22·7 k.-cals., which suggests that they are mixtures of the sesquioxide with the metal.

Rhodium Tri-hydroxide, $Rh(OH)_3$

This seems to occur in two different forms or states. If excess of alkali is added to a solution of the rhodichloride Na_3RhCl_6 it is precipitated as a black probably amorphous mass, said by some to be insoluble in acids,

[1080] H. Riehlen and W. Hühn, ib. 1933, **214**, 189.

[1081] F. P. Dwyer and R. S. Nyholm, *Proc. Roy. Soc. N.S. Wales*, 1942, **76**, 275.

[1082] Id., ib. 1942, **76**, 133.

[1083] R. Schenck and F. Finkener, *Ber.* 1942, **75**, 1962.

[1084] L. Wöhler and N. Jochum, *Z. physikal. Chem.* 1933, **167**, 169.

though others[1085] have no difficulty in getting it to dissolve. If the potassium hydroxide is slowly added in defect, yellow crystals separate of the composition $Rh(OH)_3, H_2O$. This form is soluble in acids, and also in caustic potash, in which it forms a yellow solution, which on treatment with chlorine turns blue, probably owing to the formation of a rhodate $K_2Rh^{vi}O_4$.

The hydroxide readily adsorbs alkali. If it is precipitated in the cold from the rhodium trichloride solution with baryta, the base is much more easily removed.[1085]

Rhodium Sulphides

The best investigation of the sulphides of rhodium is that of Biltz and his co-workers,[1086] made by phase-rule methods, by the measurement of dissociation tension, and by X-ray analysis, of the system rhodium–sulphur. The results apply, of course, to the compounds which are produced by the direct combination of the elements at high temperatures (up to 1,100°); other compounds may be obtainable at lower temperatures from solution. These authors conclude that the only compounds so formed are Rh_2S_5, Rh_2S_3, Rh_3S_4, and Rh_9S_8, and that these do not form solid solutions with one another. [The strong tendency of sulphur, in contrast to oxygen, to form long chains must be remembered.] In particular they get definite evidence, both tensimetric and from X-ray diagrams, that no RhS is formed, and no RhS_2, and nothing with a true pyrites structure such as $Rh''S_2$ should have, although Rh_2S_3 has a pseudo-pyrites structure.

It has also been shown that the highest selenide[1087] and telluride[1088] of rhodium have the compositions Rh_2Se_5 and Rh_2Te_5, corresponding to the pentasulphide Rh_2S_5.

The *hydrosulphide* $Rh(SH)_3$ is said to be produced by passing excess of hydrogen sulphide into a solution of a trivalent rhodium salt at 100°; it is a black precipitate, insoluble in ammonium sulphide $(NH_4)_2S$.

Trihalides of Rhodium

All four of these are known, although our information about some of them is scanty. They show signs of auto-complex formation, which certainly occurs in the chloride.

Rhodium Trifluoride, RhF_3[1089]

Fluorine is remarkably slow to react with metallic rhodium or with rhodium trichloride; the reaction does not occur at all below 400°, and to get anything like complete fluorination it must be carried out at 500–600°,

[1085] F. Krauss and H. Umbach, *Z. anorg. Chem.* 1929, **180**, 42.

[1086] R. Juza, O. Hülsmann, K. Meisel, and W. Biltz, ib. 1935, **225**, 369.

[1087] L. Wöhler, K. Ewald, and H. G. Krall, *Ber.* 1933, **66**, 1638 (corrected with respect to the telluride by the next reference).

[1088] W. Biltz, *Z. anorg. Chem.* 1937, **233**, 282.

[1089] O. Ruff and E. Ascher, ib. 1929, **183**, 193.

and even then the product has a slight excess of rhodium. At these temperatures vessels made of fluor spar must be used. The formation of the non-volatile trifluoride is accompanied by that of a small quantity of a higher fluoride, which is volatile and must be a tetra- or a pentafluoride RhF_4 or RhF_5 (see later, p. 1527).

Rhodium trifluoride is a red powder, which is not at all hygroscopic, and keeps without change for an indefinite time if it is dry. Above 600° it volatilizes to some extent, but this seems to be due to the formation of the higher fluoride. It is isomorphous with the trifluorides of aluminium, iron, cobalt, and palladium, all of which form layer lattices.[1091] It forms a hydrate RhF_3, $6 H_2O$.[1090] It is very stable to water, acids, and bases, more so than cobalt trifluoride, though rather less than ferric fluoride. It is practically insoluble at their boiling-points in water or concentrated hydrochloric, nitric, sulphuric, or hydrofluoric acids, or in 33 per cent. sodium hydroxide. Fusion with sodium carbonate converts it into rhodium sesquioxide and sodium fluoride. It is attacked by hydrogen at 70°, and by water (with hydrolysis) at 250°. It gives no visible reaction with iodine, sulphur, or carbon, but it burns if it is heated with metals.

Rhodium Trichloride, $RhCl_3$

Chlorine begins to combine with rhodium at 250° (150° lower than fluorine) with the formation of the trichloride. This compound has[1092] a peculiar behaviour, which indicates that it can occur in several forms, some of them certainly complex. As obtained from its elements it is a red powder, insoluble in water and acids; by dissolving the hydroxide in hydrochloric acid and evaporating, a hydrate $RhCl_3$, 4 or 3 H_2O (perhaps both) is got, which is very soluble in water. This hydrate loses its water of crystallization in a stream of hydrogen chloride gas at 180°, but the anhydrous product so formed is still very soluble in water, and so is different from that which is prepared directly from the elements. If, however, this soluble anhydrous chloride is heated to a higher temperature it becomes insoluble. This, however, is not all. Meyer has shown[1093-4] that the dark red hydrated chloride $RhCl_3$, 3 H_2O when dissolved in water gives a brown solution which is quite stable in the cold, and gives with silver nitrate only a slight turbidity (E.M.F. measurements confirm the absence of chlorine ion). But if this brown solution is heated nearly to boiling it suddenly becomes yellow, and now silver nitrate will precipitate the whole of the chlorine. This loss of colour does not occur with concentrated solutions, and there may be an equilibrium between the two forms,

[1090] J. Meyer and H. Kienitz, *Z. anorg. Chem.* 1939, **242**, 281.

[1091] J. A. A. Ketelaar, *Nature*, 1931, **128**, 303.

[1092] B. Cabrera and A. Duperier (*Proc. Phys. Soc.* 1939, **51**, 845) measure the magnetic susceptibility of $RhCl_3$, as well as of $OsCl_2$, $IrCl_3$, and $PtCl_2$, and discuss the results.

[1093] J. Meyer and M. Kawczyk, *Z. anorg. Chem.* 1936, **228**, 297.

[1094] J. Meyer and H. Kienitz, ib. 1939, **242**, 281.

the (brown) form which gives no chlorine ions being favoured by a higher concentration, and so presumably more condensed. Attempts to isolate the yellow form have failed; if the yellow solution is evaporated down it is the original brown-red modification which separates, probably because the equilibrium goes over to this side as the concentration increases.

The change in colour of the solution is, however, accompanied by a marked increase in the electrical conductivity, which (at N/1,000) is about doubled. This is like the behaviour of the sulphate $Rh_2(SO_4)_3$ (below).

Rhodium Tribromide, $RhBr_3$

This is very difficult to isolate, either by direct synthesis[1095] or by the action of hydrogen bromide on the chloride.[1093]

Rhodium Tri-iodide, RhI_3

This is similar to the other halides, but it is very insoluble, even when it is prepared in aqueous solution. One way of separating rhodium from iridium depends on this.[1096] If a solution of the mixed chlorides is boiled for some time with hydriodic acid, the rhodium salt alone is precipitated.

Rhodium Cyanide, $Rh(CN)_3, 3 H_2O$

This can be made[1097] by decomposing $K_3[Rh(CN)_6]$ with concentrated sulphuric acid at 100°. It loses $1 H_2O$ at 145°, and then decomposes. Strong ammonia replaces half the water, giving $4 Rh(CN)_3, 7 NH_3, 7 H_2O$. The cyanide will not dissolve in potassium cyanide to give a complex cyanide; strong potassium hydroxide solution dissolves it, but only with decomposition.

Oxy-salts of Trivalent Rhodium

These are often, but not always, auto-complexes.

Rhodium Sulphates

The 'simple' sulphate $Rh_2(SO_4)_3$ aq. exists in[1098] two forms, a yellow and a red, of which the red is certainly complex, and the yellow probably not; they are related in the same way as the yellow and red trichlorides mentioned above. Both of these form double salts.

If rhodium tri-hydroxide $Rh(OH)_3$ is dissolved in cold sulphuric acid, and the solution precipitated with alcohol, a yellow salt $Rh_2(SO_4)_3, 15 H_2O$ is obtained; this holds the last three molecules of water zeolitically (i.e. in solid solution), but it gives definite hydrates with 12, 9, and $6 H_2O$, the last again losing its 6 molecules gradually like a zeolite. From the aqueous solution of this salt barium chloride precipitates all the SO_4 at once, and potassium hydroxide the rhodium, so there is no evidence of complexity here. If the solution is boiled down, a new red-brown form

[1095] A. Gutbier and A. Hüttlinger, ib. 1916, **95**, 247.

[1096] V. V. Lebedinski, *Ann. Inst. Platine*, 1927, **5**, 364.

[1097] F. Krauss and H. Umbach, *Z. anorg. Chem.* 1929, **179**, 359.

[1098] Id., ib. **180**, 42.

$Rh_2(SO_4)_3$, $4 H_2O$ (in which all the water is zeolitic) separates; this is formed at once if the trihydroxide is dissolved in hot sulphuric acid. This red form is evidently complex; the freshly made solution gives no precipitate with barium chloride or potassium hydroxide, and the conductivity is low, but about doubles itself in the course of 12 hours or so. This increase corresponds to the reaction $Rh[Rh(SO_4)_3] \longrightarrow Rh_2[SO_4]_3$ if we assume that the equivalent mobility of these ions is about constant. Hence the red modification must be complex and the yellow simple. At the same time such a formula for the complex salt as $[Rh''']\cdot[Rh'''(SO_4)_3]$ while it accounts for the absence of reaction for SO_4 does not explain why there is no reaction for Rh'''; there may, however, be an error here, since the hydroxide $Rh(OH)_3$ precipitated by alkali is soluble in excess. Chromic sulphate behaves in precisely the same way.[1099] Of the alums[1100] the caesium salt $CsRh(SO_4)_2$, $12 H_2O$ was prepared by the action of caesium sulphate on a cold saturated solution of yellow rhodium sulphate. It had all the characteristics of an alum; it gave the reactions of trivalent rhodium and of SO_4, and gave no sign of complexity. On dehydration hydrates with 6, 3, and 0 H_2O were formed, all of which also behaved as simple and not as complex salts. On the other hand, when caesium sulphate was added to a cold solution of the red rhodium sulphate at the same concentrations as before, no alum was formed. It is to be noticed that though these double sulphates are certainly not complex in the ordinary sense, they become less soluble in water as the amount of water of crystallization gets less. At complete equilibrium it is obvious that the anhydrous salt must be more soluble than any stable hydrate; hence these double sulphates, though they are not complex, must be slow to reach equilibrium with the solution, a phenomenon which is common with sulphates, especially those of cations of high valency.

True complex rhodium sulphates also occur. Krauss found that if the solution of the alum is boiled and evaporated down, a new double sulphate of the composition $CsRh(SO_4)_2$, $4 H_2O$ separates as a dark yellow powder: the water is zeolitically attached. This substance is shown to be complex by the fact that barium chloride precipitates no barium sulphate, but in very concentrated solution gives a yellow precipitate of the complex barium rhodio-sulphate.

He has also obtained an acid of the composition $H[Rh(SO_4)_2]$, $8 H_2O$, by allowing a cold saturated solution of the alum to evaporate with sulphuric acid; but there is no sign that this is complex.

A trivalent rhodium sulphite and nitrate have been obtained, but not in the pure state.

COMPLEXES OF TRIVALENT RHODIUM

TRIVALENT rhodium has a strong tendency to form complexes like other trivalent transitional elements. These are formed especially with ammonia

[1099] F. Krauss, H. Querengässer, and P. Meyer, *Z. anorg. Chem.* 1929, **179**, 413.
[1100] F. Krauss and H. Umbach, ib. **182**, 411.

and the amines, and with the halogens chlorine and bromine, and to some extent iodine. The covalency is almost invariably 6, the ammines always having this value, and the halides usually, but sometimes 5, and sometimes apparently (but probably not really) 7. Other complexes are the chelate derivatives of α-dioximes (glyoxime compounds) and a certain number of ato-derivatives, including cyanides, and nitro- oxalato- and malonato-complexes.

Complex Rhodium Cyanides

Though the trivalent hexacyano-complex $[Rh(CN)_6]'''$ is of quite exceptional stability, very few of its salts have been prepared. The potassium salt $K_3[Rh(CN)_6]$ can be made[1097] by fusing metallic rhodium with potassium ferrocyanide, or better by fusing the pentammine

$$[Rh(NH_3)_5Cl]Cl_2$$

with potassium cyanide, but it cannot be made by the action of potassium cyanide either on the (insoluble) simple cyanide $Rh(CN)_3$, aq., or on a solution of rhodium trichloride. On the other hand, the complex, when it has once been formed, is extraordinarily stable. The solution is not affected by acids, not even if it is boiled after the addition of concentrated sulphuric acid; the complex can only be decomposed by heating the dry salt above 100° with concentrated sulphuric acid, when a yellow solution is formed, from which the cyanide $Rh(CN)_3$, aq. separates as a yellow-brown (not red) mass.

For more salts of this acid see reference [1101].

Complex Thiocyanates

These seem to be certainly complex. They all have a 6-co-ordinated rhodium atom. Potassium thiocyanate reacts[1101] with the rhodiochloride $K_3[RhCl_6]$ to give the very stable $K_3[Rh(CNS)_6]$; from its solution sulphuric acid liberates the free acid $H_3[Rh(CNS)_6]$ (apparently anhydrous), which can be extracted with amyl alcohol. A silver salt and a hexammine cobaltic salt were also made.

Ammines of Trivalent Rhodium

These all have the co-ordination number 6, but they are of every type from $[RhAm_6]X_3$ to $M_2[RhAmR_5]$, the series being completed by the pure complex halides $M_3[RhR_6]$ (Am = amino-group; R = halogen or other monovalent radical). As usual ammonia forms more stable compounds than its substitution products, except when these are diamines which can form stable chelate rings.

Hexammines

The simplest of the hexammines are the compounds $[Rh(NH_3)_6]X_3$, the so-called luteo salts, which here are colourless.

[1101] G. A. Barbieri, *Atti R.* 1931, [vi] **13**, 433.

Many chelate derivatives are known, made with ethylene diamine[1102,1105] 1,2-diamino-cyclopentane[1103] and the corresponding cyclohexane compound,[1105-8] dipyridyl,[1104] and in a few examples triaminopropane.[1109] All these amines form trichelate complexes of the [Rh en_3]X_3 type, and the stability of this form is so great that the mono- and dichelate compounds do not seem to be formed at all. With the chelate sulphamide molecule $O_2S\diagup^{NH_2}_{\diagdown NH_2}$, on the other hand, where the co-ordinating power of the NH_2 is no doubt weakened by the presence of the SO_2, the dichelate form is produced, still with a co-ordination number of 6, as a di-aquo-complex,[1110] but not the trichelate.

The trichelate ethylene diamine compounds of trivalent rhodium were among the first 6-covalent complexes to be resolved into their optical antimers; this was effected by Werner[1102] in 1912 by means of the camphor-nitronate and the tartrate. Other trichelate compounds of trivalent rhodium have since been resolved, such as the diamino-cyclopentane[1103] and the diamino-cyclohexane[1106] derivatives, and also the oxalato- and malonato-compounds to be described later.

Pentammines

A few aquo-pentammines [Rh$(NH_3)_5(H_2O)$]X_3 (roseo-compounds) have been made by the action of silver oxide on the chloro-pentammines. The hydroxo-compounds [Rh$(NH_3)_5OH$]X_2 can be made[1111] by the action of concentrated ammonia on the aquo-pentammines. They are fairly stable and closely resemble the corresponding iridium compounds, but like many hydroxy-compounds they readily revert to the aquo-form.

The chloro-compounds, such as [Rh$(NH_3)_5Cl$]Cl_2, can be made[1112] by the action of ammonia on a hot solution of ammonium chloride and rhodium trichloride. The salt is rather slightly soluble in water, and almost insoluble in strong hydrochloric acid; sol^y at 25° 0·83 in water, 0·086 in 2·6 per cent. and 0·007 in 10·6 per cent. HCl.[1113] It can thus be used to separate rhodium from its mixture with palladium, iridium, and platinum.[1114]

[1102] A. Werner, *Ber.* 1912, **45**, 1228.
[1103] F. M. Jaeger and H. B. Blumendal, *Z. anorg. Chem.* 1928, **175**, 161.
[1104] F. M. Jaeger and J. A. van Dijk, *Proc. K. Akad. Amst.* 1934, **37**, 284.
[1105] Id., ib. 1937, **40**, 2.
[1106] F. M. Jaeger and L. Bijkerk, ib. 116.
[1107] F. M. Jaeger, *Bull. Soc. Chim.* 1937, [v] **4**, 1201.
[1108] F. M. Jaeger and L. Bijkerk, *Z. anorg. Chem.* 1937, **233**, 97.
[1109] P. Terpstra and J. ter Berg, *Proc. K. Akad. Amst.* 1937, **40**, 602.
[1110] F. G. Mann, *J.C.S.* 1933, 412.
[1111] B. E. Dixon, ib. 1935, 779.
[1112] V. V. Lebedinski, *Ann. Inst. Platine*, 1936, **13**, 9.
[1113] S. F. Shemtschushni, ib. 1927, **5**, 364.
[1114] V. V. Lebedinski, ib. 1936, **13**, 73.

A. B. Lamb[1115] has measured by conductivity the rate of the reversible change

$$[Rh(NH_3)_5X]X_2 \rightleftharpoons [Rh(NH_3)_5OH_2]X_3$$

where X = Cl or Br. At equilibrium at 84° the fraction aquo/(aquo+halo) is 20 per cent. for chlorine and 12 per cent. for bromine.

Tetrammines

Among these are the sulphamide compounds of Mann[1110] already referred to. Sulphamide $O_2S{\Large\langle}{}^{NH_2}_{NH_2}$, owing to the presence of the SO_2 group, is a distinctly acidic substance, and its hydrogen atoms are easily replaceable. With a solution of trivalent rhodium it gives a diaquo-compound of the formula

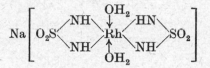

(if we call the sulphamide sH_2 this salt would be written $Na[Rh(H_2O)_2(s)_2]$). It could occur in two stereomeric forms, a *trans* which is symmetrical, and a *cis* which would be resolvable. Mann was able to resolve his product through the α-phenyl-ethylamine salt, and this showed that it is the *cis*-form. It is found to be quite reasonably stable: in solution the active salt does not racemize in the cold, and even at 100° only does so to about 30 per cent. in an hour. Though a *cis* compound, this will not take up a third chelate sulphamide group (as an *en* complex would), which shows that the sulphamide forms a less stable chelate group than the *en*, presumably on account of the influence of the SO_2. The replacement of the hydrogen in this complex is unusual (compare the glyoxime compound); it gives the complex a negative instead of a positive charge.

Triammines

Two simple triacido-triammines are known which are not ionized. The compound $[Rh(py)_3Cl_3]^\circ$ is made[1116] by treating sodium rhodio-chloride Na_3RhCl_6 with pyridine. As a non-salt it is soluble in chloroform, and separates from it with a molecule of chloroform of crystallization.

The Triammino-tribromide

$[Rh(NH_3)_3Br_3]^\circ$ is made[1117] by heating the bromopentammine bromide to 210°, when the change

$$[Rh(NH_3)_5Br]Br_2 \longrightarrow [Rh(NH_3)_3Br_3]^\circ + 2\,NH_3$$

goes quantitatively. This compound is insoluble in water, acids, and alkalies.

[1115] *J.A.C.S.* 1939, **61**, 699.
[1116] M. Delépine, *Bull. Soc.* 1929, [iv] **45**, 235.

Diammines

Some di-pyridine complexes have been prepared by Delépine.[1116] The chloro-compound $M[Rh(py)_2Cl_4]$, like the corresponding iridium compound, occurs in a *cis* and a *trans* form, the *cis* being orange and moderately soluble in water, and the *trans* red and only sparingly soluble. Other dipyridine compounds were made, one of which contains a nitrato-group, $M[Rh(py)_2Cl_3NO_3]$.

Monammines

A certain number of these are known, such as $(NH_4)_2[Rh(NH_3)Cl_5]$, which is made by treating sodium rhodiochloride solution Na_3RhCl_6 with ammonium chloride and ammonium acetate; the potassium salt is also known. They are not very stable, and the halogen atoms are easily hydrolysed.[1118]

Complex Nitro-salts

These, so far as they are known, are all of the type $M_3[Rh(NO_2)_6]$.[1119] The sodium and potassium salts have been made, and are remarkable for being colourless when pure. For their crystal structure see reference [1120].

Oxime Complexes of Trivalent Rhodium

The oxime group normally has far less co-ordinating power than an NH_2, but the dioximes of α-diketones form chelate complexes of great stability. Thus dimethyl glyoxime

$$CH_3—\underset{\underset{NOH}{\|}}{C}——\underset{\underset{NOH}{\|}}{C}—CH_3 \quad (DH_2)$$

will combine with trivalent rhodium[1121] much as it does with trivalent cobalt, forming dichelate complexes with the two remaining places in the 6-fold complex occupied either by ammonia or by chlorine, giving $[Rh(DH)_2(NH_3)_2]X$ and $M[Rh(DH)_2Cl_2]$. With the oxime as with the sulphonamide the products are only dichelate, and in both classes there is replacement of the hydrogen atoms (here only one H per ring). The products are more stable than the corresponding cobalt compounds, but less than those of palladium; if a solution containing the chlorides of palladium and rhodium is treated with the glyoxime, the palladium is precipitated, but the rhodium remains dissolved. This reaction can be used to separate rhodium from palladium.[1122]

[1117] E. Birk and H. Kamm, *Siebert Festschrift*, 1931, 19.
[1118] V. V. Lebedinski, *Ann. Inst. Platine*, 1933, **11**, 5.
[1119] E. Leidié, *C.R.* 1890, **111**, 106.
[1120] G. B. Boki and L. A. Popova, *Bull. Acad. Sci. U.R.S.S.* 1945, 89.
[1121] L. Tschugaev and W. Lebedinski, *Z. anorg. Chem.* 1913, **83**, 1.
[1122] M. Wünder and V. Thuringer, *Z. anal. Chem.* 1913, **52**, 660.

Oxalato-Salts

These are stable and well defined, and both the dichelate (but 6-covalent) and trichelate types are known. Leidié[1123] obtained the salts $Na_3[Rh(C_2O_4)_3], 6 H_2O : K, 4 \cdot 5 H_2O$, and $NH_4, 4 \cdot 5 H_2O$. They were resolved into their optical antimers by Werner in 1914[1124] through the strychnine salts. From the product he obtained the active forms of the salts of sodium (4 H_2O), potassium (H_2O), rubidium (H_2O), and barium, 3 and 0 H_2O. These salts are all red or orange-red. They are very stable in solution, and racemize much more slowly than the corresponding chromi-oxalates; they can be warmed in solution on the water-bath without sensible change in rotatory power. For the crystallography of these and the silver salt see Jaeger.[1125]

The dichelate oxalato-compounds were made by Delépine[1126] from potassium oxalate and the aquo-pentachloro-salt $K_2[RhCl_5(H_2O)]$, which gave the dichelate salt $K_3[Rh(C_2O_4)_2Cl_2]$ in the *cis* form (1 H_2O, dark green), from which the *trans* form (4 H_2O, yellow, like the iridium compound) can be obtained by boiling in solution with dilute hydrochloric acid.

The *malonato*-salts are similar[1125]; the salt $K_3[Rh(mal)_3], 5 H_2O$ was resolved.[1127]

Sulphur Complexes

Complexes with ethyl sulphide, such as $Rh(SEt_2)_3X_3$, can be made by heating the trihalides with ethyl sulphide in alcohol; they have the m. pts. $X_3 = Cl_3$ 126°, Br_3 107°, I_3 98°.[1128]

Complex Halides

Complex halides are formed by trivalent rhodium with all the halogens; the fluorides have only recently been discovered; the bromides seem rather less stable than the chlorides, and iodides are scarcely known at all. As commonly happens the halides are more variable in type than the ammines, and three mononuclear forms are known: (1) $M_2[RhX_5]$ (no compounds of the type $M[RhX_4]$) usually containing one or more molecules of H_2O, one of which may be assumed to complete the 6-fold co-ordination of the complex, though some of the pentachlorides are anhydrous; (2) $M_3[RhX_6]$; (3) $M_4[RhX_7]$ (structure unknown); there are also several polynuclear compounds described, most of which are of uncertain individuality, but one of them (4) is well marked, $M_3[Rh_2X_9]$.

All the fluorides so far prepared (K, Rb, and Cs[1129]) are of the same type, $M_3[RhF_6]$. Among the chlorides $M_3[RhX_6]$ is much the commonest

[1123] E. Leidié, *Ann. Chim.* 1889, [vi] **17**, 309.
[1124] A. Werner, *Ber.* 1914, **47**, 1954.
[1125] F. M. Jaeger, *Proc. K. Akad. Amst.* 1917, **20**, 263.
[1126] M. Delépine, *Anal. Fis. Quim.* 1929, **27**, 485.
[1127] F. M. Jaeger, *Rec. Trav.* 1919, **38**, 300.
[1128] F. P. Dwyer and R. S. Nyholm, *Proc. R.S. New S. Wales*, 1944, **78**, 67.
[1129] J. Meyer and H. Kienitz, *Z. anorg. Chem.* 1939, **242**, 281.

type, and $M_2[RhX_5]$ the next commonest; $M_4[RhX_7]$ and $M_3[Rh_2X_9]$ are confined to a small number of salts of organic bases. Thus we have the pentachlorides $K_2[RhCl_6]$, with 0, 1, and 3 H_2O[1130]; the ammonium, rubidium, and caesium salts all crystallize with one molecule of water, no doubt as aquo-salts.[1131]   Among the hexachlorides $M_3[RhCl_6]$ the best known is the sodium salt $Na_3[RhCl_6]$, usually with 9 H_2O, but it can be got with 12[1131]; this salt is easily crystallized from water or dilute acid, and is often employed in place of rhodium trichloride as a source of trivalent rhodium compounds. *In vacuo* over sulphuric acid this dries sharply to a di-hydrate.[1132]   Other hexachlorides are the lithium salt, with 12 H_2O: the potassium rubidium and ammonium salts, all with one H_2O: alkaline-earth salts are also known, such as $Ba_3[RhCl_6]_2$, 7 H_2O.[1133]

A large number of complex rhodium halides of organic bases have been made,[1134-5] using primary, secondary, tertiary, and quaternary alkyl-ammoniums, as well as other bases such as pyridine and its homologues. Among the chlorides the great majority were of the type $M_3[RhCl_6]$. These salts are usually anhydrous; they are all red or reddish-brown in colour, fairly easily soluble in water, and readily recrystallizable from dilute hydrochloric acid without decomposition.

The heptachlorides appear to include a curious ethylene diamine salt of the composition $RhCl_3(en, 2\,HCl)_2$,[1134] of which there is a bromine analogue.[1136]   This has been shown[1137] to be probably a crystal aggregate of the *en* hydrochloride and the non-ionized form of the trichloride; if this last (the brown form) is added to a solution of the *en* hydrochloride the conductivity is not increased.

There is further the binuclear type $M_3[Rh_2Cl_9]$, of which the tetramethyl and tetraethyl ammonium salts have been made.[1135]   Several bromides of this type are known[1136]: there is also a corresponding chloro-bismuthate $M_3[Bi_2Cl_9]$.[1138]   The structure of these salts is unknown.

The *complex bromides* are on the whole similar to the chlorides, but there are certain definite differences in the particular types that are favoured, especially in the fact that the type $M_3[RhX_6]$, which is the commonest among the chlorides, is relatively rare among the bromides, while the binuclear type $M_3[Rh_2X_9]$ is much more frequent with the bromides, occurring even with inorganic cations. See further, references [1136-7,1139-40].

[1130] O. T. Christensen, *J. prakt. Chem.* 1887, [2] **35**, 164, 179; K. Seubert and K. Kobbe, *Ber.* 1890, **23**, 2557.

[1131] M. Delépine, *Bull. Soc. Chim. Belge*, 1927, **36**, 108.

[1132] F. G. Mann, *J.C.S.* 1933, 417.

[1133] F. M. Jaeger and J. A. van Dijk, *Proc. K. Akad. Amst.* 1934, **37**, 284.

[1134] O. v. Fraenkel, *Mon.* 1914, **35**, 119.

[1135] A. Gutbier and H. Bertsch, *Z. anorg. Chem.* 1923, **129**, 67.

[1136] J. Meyer and K. Hoehne, ib. 1937, **231**, 372.

[1137] J. Meyer, M. Kawkzyk, and K. Hoehne, ib. **232**, 410.

[1138] A. Gutbier and M. Müller, ib. 1923, **128**, 137.

[1139] P. Poulenc, *C.R.* 1930, **190**, 639.

[1140] Id., *Ann. Chim.* 1935, [xi] **4**, 567.

RHODIUM WITH VALENCIES OF 4 OR MORE

THE general conclusion on this obscure question is that it is fairly certain that in its compounds with fluorine and with oxygen, but in no others, rhodium can have a valency greater than 3, though we do not know what this is; the indications are that it is probably 4, and possibly 6 as well.

The evidence for these states of valency is of three kinds: (1) the higher fluorides; (2) rhodium dioxide and its hydrates; (3) the existence of tetra- and hexavalent rhodium in electrolytically oxidized solutions, and of a hexavalent 'rhodiate' $M_2[RhO_4]$ in certain alkaline solutions.

Higher Fluorides of Rhodium

Ruff and Ascher[1141] found that when rhodium is fluorinated at 500–600° though the main product rhodium trifluoride is not volatile, a small quantity of a sublimate is formed. By special arrangements some 50–100 mg. of a red-brown sublimate were collected, and this was found to be volatile enough to go surprisingly far through the apparatus. It was shown to contain rhodium and fluorine; it gave blue-violet solutions in water and liberated chlorine from aqueous hydrochloric acid. The product was almost impossible to analyse (partly because the calcium fluoride tube which must be used is attacked), but the results, though not constant, were enough to show definitely that if rhodium or its trifluoride or trichloride is heated in fluorine at 500° a fluoride higher than RhF_3 is produced, presumably either RhF_4 or RhF_5.

Rhodium Dioxide and its Hydrates

The supposed formation of a dioxide RhO_2 by the oxidation of the metal or in other ways has been disproved[1142]; no pure oxide of rhodium with more oxygen than the sesquioxide Rh_2O_3 can be made. A hydrated oxide with more oxygen than corresponds to Rh_2O_3 can be prepared, but when this is dehydrated it loses oxygen along with the water, and the sesquioxide remains. The occurrence of the higher oxide of a metal in the hydrated, but not in the anhydrous form is not uncommon: compare palladium[1143] and platinum.[1144]

The hydrated dioxide RhO_2, 1–2 H_2O is formed (along with a large excess of oxychloride) by the action of chlorine on a solution of the hydroxide $Rh(OH)_3$ in excess of alkali. But it can only be obtained in any quantity by the electrolytic oxidation of this alkaline solution, when a blue solution is formed, from which a precipitate separates, which always contains more oxygen than corresponds to the formula Rh_2O_3, aq., but never quite as much as is required for RhO_2, aq. After prolonged washing to remove the alkali, a dark olive-green powder remains, which when dried has the composition RhO_2, 1–2 H_2O. Even when the water in this

[1141] O. Ruff and E. Ascher, *Z. anorg. Chem.* 1929, **183**, 206.
[1142] L. Wöhler and K. F. A. Ewald, ib. 1931, **201**, 145.
[1143] L. Wöhler and J. König, ib. 1905, **46**, 323.
[1144] L. Wöhler, ib., 1904, **40**, 449.

was removed over phosphorus pentoxide in a vacuum at the ordinary temperature, the whole of the extra oxygen was lost with the water, and only the sesquioxide Rh_2O_3 remained.

Higher Rhodium Valencies in Solution

When a solution of trivalent rhodium is exposed to oxidizing agents its colour changes from green to blue (Claus, 1860). This happens, for example, when chlorine acts on an alkaline solution of $Rh(OH)_3$[1145] or sodium hypochlorite on the salt $Na_3[RhCl_6]$.[1146]

Grube[1147-8] has found that on electrolytic oxidation a trivalent rhodium solution, which is originally yellow, turns green and finally blue, and by measuring the amount of oxygen given off as compared with the current passed he proved that oxidation takes place in the solution. A solution of trivalent rhodium sulphate can be oxidized electrolytically[1148] to a valency (as found by analysis) of about 4·5; with rhodium perchlorate the valency was found to be as high as 5·8. From a solution in which the valency of the rhodium is about 6, alkalies precipitate a blue substance, which redissolves in excess of the alkali to form a blue solution; when the rhodium is about 4-valent, the precipitate is green, and so is its solution in excess of alkali. Even by purely chemical oxidation with chlorine or sodium hypochlorite he was able to reach a valency of nearly 6.

Preliminary measurements of the E.M.F. gave the results:

$$Rh''' + \oplus \longrightarrow Rh^{iv} \text{ at } + 1\cdot40 \text{ volts}$$
$$Rh^{iv} + 2\oplus \longrightarrow Rh^{vi} \text{ at } + 1\cdot46 \text{ volts.}$$

These results suggest that in acid solution tetravalent rhodium must be largely converted into trivalent and hexavalent.

Taking all the evidence together, we have good reason to think that 3 is not the highest valency possible for rhodium, but very little idea what the higher valencies may be.

RHODIUM CARBONYLS

RHODIUM has lately been shown[1149] to form 2 or 3 'simple' carbonyls, as well as a hydride and the halides $[Rh(CO)_2X]_2$.

If the anhydrous binary halide is heated with carbon monoxide under pressure in presence of copper or silver, three carbonyls and a hydride are formed. The carbonyls are $[Rh(CO)_4]_n$, $[Rh(CO)_3]_n$, and $[Rh_4(CO)_{11}]_n$; their molecular weights are unknown; we should expect the first, m. pt. 76°, to be dimeric, and the second, decomposing at 150°, to be tetrameric. The formula of the third, which decomposes at 220°, is very strange. The volatile hydride, m. pt. $-11°$, has the expected composition $Rh(CO)_4H$.

[1145] E. P. Alvarez, *C.R.* 1905, **140**, 1341.
[1146] E. Demarçay, ib. 1885, **101**, 951.
[1147] G. Grube and E. Kesting, *Z. Elektrochem.* 1933, **39**, 948.
[1148] G. Grube and B. Gu, ib. 1937, **43**, 397.
[1149] W. Hieber and H. Lagally, *Z. anorg. Chem.* 1943, **251**, 96.

The carbonyl halides are formed when the binary halide is heated with carbon monoxide under pressure but with no metal added; the chloride was first made (but wrongly formulated) by Manchot.[1150] All three halides are typical covalent compounds, soluble in organic solvents, and sublime easily. The chloride was shown by the freezing-point to be dimeric in solution (the E.A.N. for $Rh(CO)_2Cl$ would be 50, so that the rule would require it to be pentameric).

$Rh(CO)_2Cl$ is orange-yellow; m. pt. 123°.

$Rh(CO)_2Br$ is red-brown, m. pt. 118°.

$Rh(CO)_2I$ is ruby-red, m. pt. 114°.

[1150] W. Manchot and J. König, *Ber.* 1925, **58**, 2173.

IRIDIUM

IRIDIUM was discovered along with osmium by Tennant in 1804, and was so called from ἰρίδιος (rainbow-coloured) owing to the brilliant colours of many of its compounds. It is always found in nature in the metallic state, usually as a natural alloy with osmium ('osmiridium'), but sometimes also in native gold.

In its compounds it has a series of valencies, 1, 2, 3, 4, probably 5 and 6, but it is only in the valencies of 3 and 4 that it forms more than a few compounds (see summary above, p. 1511). Like its neighbours it does not seem to ionize at all, and its apparently simple compounds are no doubt really complex.

Metallic Iridium

Iridium is a silver-white metal, very hard, with the highest melting-point (2,450°)[1151] of all the platinum metals except osmium, and the smallest compressibility of any known metal.[1152] It has been recommended as superior to platinum for making crucibles[1153]; its hardness makes it less liable to mechanical injury; it is not attacked at any temperature by carbon, sulphur, lead, nickel, or gold; it is not acted on by aqua regia, nor by fused alkalies. It is oxidized on heating, but the massive metal only superficially. Iridium is readily attacked by chlorine at a red heat, and by potassium sulphate or a mixture of the hydroxide and nitrate on fusion. The powdered metal is oxidized by air or oxygen at a red heat to the dioxide IrO_2, which on further heating dissociates again into its elements at 1,140°.

If it is fused with zinc and the alloy extracted with hydrochloric acid, the resulting powder is explosive (Bunsen), apparently owing to occluded hydrogen or oxygen. Rhodium and platinum behave in the same way, but not palladium or osmium.[1154]

Iridium and Hydrogen

Iridium foil normally absorbs hydrogen only on the surface; but if it is disintegrated by prolonged heating it can take up as much as 800 times its volume of hydrogen in the cold. If it is used as a cathode the hydrogen gradually enters into the metal.[1155] There is, however, no reason to think that any definite compound is formed.

Iridium and Phosphorus

X-ray and tensimetric studies of the system Ir—P show no compounds except IrP_2 and Ir_2P; the latter melts at about 1,350°.[1156]

[1151] F. Henning and H. T. Wensel, *Bur. Stand. J. Res* 1933, **10**, 809.
[1152] E. Gruneisen, *Ann. Phys.* 1908, [4] **26**, 394.
[1153] W. Crookes, *Proc. Roy. Soc.* 1908, **80**, 535.
[1154] E. Cohen and T. Strengers, *Z. physikal. Chem.* 1907, **61**, 698.
[1155] F. Rother, *Ber. K. Sächs, Ges. Wiss.* 1912, **64**, 5.
[1156] K. H. Söffge, M. Heimbrecht, and W. Biltz, *Z. anorg. Chem.* 1940, **243**, 297.

MONOVALENT IRIDIUM

THE only compounds in which it can be maintained that iridium is monovalent are the mono-halides. The evidence for the individuality of these compounds is not very satisfactory, and in particular no examination of their crystal structures has been made, but on the whole it seems probable that they exist. The mono-fluoride probably occurs, but is the least certain of them (see below under iridium tetrafluoride, p. 1543). The monochloride IrCl is made[1157] by heating the trichloride, when it loses chlorine to give the dichloride IrCl$_2$, the monochloride, and finally metallic iridium. In a stream of chlorine at atmospheric pressure (i.e. at 1 atm. dissociation pressure of chlorine) the monochloride is stable from 773° to 798° (as with the lower chlorides and oxides of rhodium these temperature ranges are rather small). It forms copper-red crystals of specific gravity 10·18; like the dichloride and the trichloride it is insoluble in acids, even in concentrated sulphuric acid, and in alkaline solutions. It sublimes in chlorine at 790°, and above 798° breaks up into chlorine and metallic iridium.

The corresponding bromide and iodide are also known.[1158] Iridium monobromide IrBr is made like the monochloride by heating the dibromide to 485°; it is a dark brown substance, which is stable in the cold, and very slightly soluble in water, acids, or alkalies. Iridium monoiodide, made in the same way from the di-iodide at 355°, is a black substance closely resembling the bromide in its properties.

There are no other substances in which iridium can be supposed to be monovalent.

DIVALENT IRIDIUM

THERE are several compounds in which iridium is divalent: a monosulphide, three if not four dihalides, and a small number of complexes, including cyanides, ammines, and sulphito-compounds.

Iridium Monosulphide, IrS

This is formed when the metal burns in sulphur. It looks like galena.

A curious sulphur derivative of divalent iridium is the mercaptide Ir(S·Et)$_2$[1159]; it consists of orange crystals which are formed with evolution of heat and of hydrogen chloride when iridium trichloride comes in contact with ethyl mercaptan. Palladium and platinum behave in the same way.

Iridium Difluoride

This is the least certain of the dihalides, but there is little doubt that it is among the lower halides formed by heating the tetrafluoride (see IrF$_4$, p. 1543).

[1157] L. Wöhler and S. Streicher, *Ber.* 1913, **46**, 1577.
[1158] F. Krauss and H. Gerlach, *Z. anorg. Chem.* 1925, **147**, 265.
[1159] K. A. Hofmann and W. O. Rabe, ib. 1897, **14**, 293.

Iridium Dichloride

This is made in the same way as the monochloride, by heating the trichloride.[1157] Under 1 atm. pressure of chlorine it is stable only between 763° and 773°. It closely resembles the monochloride; it forms brown crystals which are insoluble in water, acids, and alkalies.

Iridium Dibromide[1158]

This is made by heating the hydrated tribromide $IrBr_3,H_2O$, or by the action of hydrogen bromide on the tetrahydroxide $Ir(OH)_4$ at 440°. It is brownish-red, stable in the cold, and very slightly soluble in water.

Iridium Di-iodide[1158]

It is made by heating the tri-iodide at 330°. It is black, very slightly soluble in water or acids; it is soluble in alkalies on boiling.

COMPLEXES OF DIVALENT IRIDIUM

These comprise a few cyanides, ammines, and sulphito-compounds.

Complex Cyanides

These salts[1160] are of the type $M_4[Ir(CN)_6]$ and are colourless; they are made by the gentle ignition of potassium ferrocyanide with iridium.

Ammines

A few diammines and tetrammines, such as $[Ir(NH_3)_2]SO_4$ and $[Ir(NH_3)_4]Cl_2$ have been described, but there is no recent confirmation of their existence.

Complex Sulphito-compounds[1161]

When iridium trichloride is treated with sodium hydrosulphite in neutral solution, the iridium is reduced to the divalent state, and the complex sulphite $Na_6[Ir(SO_3)_4]$, $10\,H_2O$ is produced, as a bright yellow crystalline substance. Another sulphite $Na_6H_2[Ir(SO_3)_5]\,4\,H_2O$, has also been described. In these compounds it is to be presumed that most of the SO_3 groups are only attached to the iridium by a single link.

TRIVALENT IRIDIUM

THIS is the chief valency of iridium, and it provides numerous compounds, both 'simple' and complex. The standard redox potential for $Ir'' \rightleftharpoons Ir'''$ is 1·017 v. at 20°.[1162]

Iridium Sesquioxide, Ir_2O_3[1163]

This oxide can be made by igniting the iridichloride K_2IrCl_6 with sodium carbonate, when carbon dioxide and oxygen are evolved, or in the

[1160] Martius, *Ann.* 1861, **117**, 357.

[1161] G. Sailer, *Z. anorg. Chem.* 1921, **116**, 209.

[1162] F. P. Dwyer and R. S. Nyholm, *Proc. R.S. New S. Wales*, 1944, **78**, 266.

[1163] L. Wöhler and W. Witzmann, *Z. anorg. Chem.* 1907, **57**, 323.

hydrated form as $Ir(OH)_3$ by adding potassium hydroxide solution to the iridochloride K_3IrCl_6 in a carbon dioxide atmosphere. This hydrated oxide forms a yellow-green or blue-black precipitate, soluble in alkali, which on heating loses water and turns black. It very readily assumes the colloidal form, which probably explains the change of colour. It cannot be got quite pure. If it is made in the dry way some alkali is retained, while the hydrated form begins at 400°, before all the water has been removed, to lose oxygen, forming a mixture of iridium dioxide IrO_2 and the metal. At 1,139° it (or this resulting mixture) decomposes into the metal and oxygen.

Iridium Sesquisulphide, Ir_2S_3

This is precipitated by hydrogen sulphide from a solution of the sesquioxide in acids, as a brown substance, somewhat soluble in water. It can also be made[1164] by heating the disulphide IrS_2 to a suitable temperature and pressure, the dissociation pressure of the sesquisulphide in contact with metallic iridium being 1·5 mm. at 944°. On further heating the sesquisulphide goes over directly to the metal and sulphur, without any intermediate formation of a monosulphide.[1164]

Iridium Sesquiselenide, Ir_2Se_3[1165]

This can be made from the elements by fusion at a red heat, or more conveniently by passing hydrogen selenide into a hot iridium trichloride solution, when the sesquiselenide is precipitated as an amorphous black solid, which is very resistant to attack; ordinary nitric acid has no action on it: aqua regia slowly dissolves it, and so does fuming nitric acid at 250°. The compound prepared in the dry way is a crystalline mass, which is even more resistant than the amorphous form.

Iridium Trihalides

All the trihalides except the trifluoride* are known, both in the anhydrous state and in a series of compounds with the composition of hydrates, $Ir(hal)_3, x\,H_2O$, which are almost certainly complex acids, though little is known of their salts. The chlorides and bromides (but not the iodides) also form oxyhalides of the type of $Ir(hal)_2OH, x\,H_2O$, which again are presumably complex acids.

Iridium Trichloride

This can be made by treating sodium iridiochloride Na_3IrCl_6 with sulphuric acid and heating the product,[1171] but it is then impure[1166-7]; it

* Indications of the probable existence of a trifluoride have been obtained. See below under iridium tetrafluoride, p. 1543.

1164 W. Biltz, J. Laar, P. Ehrlich, and K. Meisel, ib. 1937, **233**, 257.
1165 C. Chabrié and A. Bouchonnet, *C.R.* 1903, **137**, 1059.
1166 M. Delépine, ib. 1911, **153**, 60.   1167 Id., ib. 1914, **158**, 264.
1168 L. Wöhler and S. Streicher, *Ber.* 1913, **46**, 1577.   1169 Id., ib. 1720.
1170 F. Krauss and H. Gerlach, *Z. anorg. Chem.* 1925, **147**, 265.
1171 E. Leidié, *C.R.* 1899, **129**, 1249.

is more conveniently prepared either by the action of chlorine on iridium powder at 600–620°,[1168,1170] or from the tetrahydroxide $Ir(OH)_4$ by the action of chlorine at 600°, or hydrogen chloride at 310°.[1170] It has a large range of stability; it is formed from its elements at temperatures below 100°, and it does not decompose until 760°.[1168] The rate of chlorination of the metal is greater in presence of sunlight or ultra-violet light; the addition of a trace of carbon monoxide diminishes the rate of reaction in the dark, but increases it in ultra-violet light.[1170]

Anhydrous iridium trichloride varies in colour according to its state of division, the fine powder (from a finely powdered metal at a lower temperature) being olive-green, and the colour changing as the material gets coarser to brown or even blue-black; the colour thus depends on the fineness of the original metallic powder, and the temperature to which the chloride has been heated. The dissociation tension varies in the same way, owing presumably to the change in surface tension, and reaches 1 atm. at temperatures varying from 670° to 763°, the value for the sintered material. This conclusion has been supported by measurements of the grain size by means of the sedimentation and the absorptive power for methylene blue.[1169]

Iridium trichloride forms a hydrate $IrCl_3, 3 H_2O$ (dark-green) which is made by heating the oxychloride (see below) in hydrogen chloride gas.[1170] Another hydrate $IrCl_3, 1·5 H_2O$, has also been described.

The oxychloride $IrCl_2(OH)$, aq.[1170] is made by the action of hydrogen chloride on iridium tetrahydroxide $Ir(OH)_4$. At ordinary temperatures the product is the trihydrate $IrCl_2(OH), 3 H_2O$, a dark green hygroscopic solid, very soluble in water. If this is heated in a stream of hydrogen chloride to 210° it is converted into a similar monohydrate.

These hydrates, when dissolved in water, give a dark green solution of acid reaction, which presumably contains the acid $H[IrCl_2(OH)_2]$, aq.

Iridium Tribromide

When the tri-hydroxide $Ir(OH)_3$ is dissolved in aqueous hydrobromic acid, a blue solution is produced from which an olive-green compound $IrBr_3, 4 H_2O$ separates. The water is readily lost at 100°. A monohydrate $IrBr_3, H_2O$ also occurs, which can be made by heating the oxybromide in hydrogen bromide to 100°. The anhydrous compound can be made by dehydration of the hydrates, or by heating iridium dibromide $IrBr_2$ with bromine at 100° under pressure.[1170]

An oxybromide $IrBr_2(OH)$, 3 and 1 H_2O is also known; it is just like the oxychloride.

Iridium Tri-iodide[1170]

When the trihydroxide $Ir(OH)_3$ is treated with hydriodic acid it is converted into $IrI_3, 3 H_2O$. At 120° this goes over into the monohydrate, and this again *in vacuo* at 200–250° into the anhydrous iodide IrI_3. Dark brown crystals, very slightly soluble in water and acids, soluble in alkalies on boiling.

Trivalent Iridium Sulphites

If $Ir(OH)_3$ is treated with sulphur dioxide in water, the sulphite $Ir_2(SO_3)_3, 6 H_2O$ crystallizes out as a yellow precipitate which is scarcely soluble in water, but dissolves in dilute acids.

Trivalent Iridium Sulphates

By treating the trihydroxide $Ir(OH)_3$ with sulphuric acid in the absence of air a sulphate $Ir_2(SO_4)_3$, aq. can be prepared. From this a series of alums $MIr(SO_4)_2, 12 H_2O$, where $M = K$, Rb, Cs, NH_4 Tl', were made[1172-3]; they are all yellow. Other double sulphates of complicated and obscure composition were described by Delépine.[1174]

COMPLEXES OF TRIVALENT IRIDIUM

In the trivalent state iridium, like rhodium and cobalt, forms a very large number of complexes, both cationic and anionic. In all of them it has the co-ordination number 6.

Iridicyanides, $M_3[Ir(CN)_6]$[1175]

The free acid has been made from the barium salt with sulphuric acid; it is a colourless crystalline compound, very soluble in water. The potassium salt $K_3[Ir(CN_6)]$ is got by fusing $(NH_4)_2IrCl_6$ with potassium cyanide; it is colourless, stable, and not attacked by chlorine.

Nitrilo-complex

Acetonitrile acts on a boiling solution of $(NH_4)_3[IrCl_6]$ in aqueous ammonium chloride to give the salt $(NH_4)_2[IrCl_5(CH_3 \cdot CN)]H_2O$. The corresponding potassium salt has $2 H_2O$.[1176]

Ammines

There is a complete series of ammines having from 0 to 1 molecules of ammonia or an equivalent base attached to the iridium; the bases most examined are ammonia, ethylene diamine, and pyridine. Of acid radicals we have chlorine and bromine, NO_2, and the oxalato-group.

The ammines of trivalent iridium are remarkably stable, much more so than the corresponding cobaltic compounds; in fact they are among the stablest metal-ammine compounds known (Werner[1189]); they can be boiled

[1172] L. Marino, *Gaz.* 1903, **32**, ii. 511.
[1173] Id., *Z. anorg. Chem.* 1904, **42**, 213.
[1174] M. Delépine, *C.R.* 1906, **142**, 1525; 1909, **148**, 557; **149**, 785; *Bull. Soc.* 1909, [4] **5**, 1084: *C.R.* 1910, **151**, 878.
[1175] Martius, *Ann.* 1861, **117**, 357.
[1176] V. V. Lebedinski and P. V. Simanovski, *Ann. Sect. Platine*, 1939, no. 16, 53.
[1177] W. Palmaer, *Ber.* 1889, **22**, 15.   [1178] Id., ib. 1890, **23**, 3810.
[1179] Id., ib. 1891, **24**, 2090.   [1180] Id., *Z. anorg. Chem.* 1895, **10**, 320.
[1181] Id., ib. 1897, **13**, 211.   [1182] E. Leidié, *C.R.* 1902, **134**, 1582.
[1183] A. Miolati and G. Gialdini, *Atti R.* 1902, [v] **11**, ii. 151.
[1184] K. A. Hofmann and F. Höchtlen, *Ber.* 1904, **37**, 245.
[1185] M. Delépine, *Bull. Soc.* 1908, [4] **3**, 901.

with potassium hydroxide without decomposition. They resemble the cobaltic compounds in composition, but not in colour; thus of the nitro-ammines the cobaltic compounds are deep yellow to brown, while those of iridium are colourless. But the complexes which have chlorine attached to the iridium are all coloured, and the colour is deeper the more halogen atoms the complex contains, passing from yellow to orange and then to green as the amount of halogens increases.

Hexammines

These compounds, for example $[Ir(NH_3)_6]Cl_3$, can be made[1180] by treating the chloropentammines with ammonia under pressure at 140°; the trichloride and tribromide are colourless: the tri-iodide is yellow. The hydroxide, which can only be got in solution, is a strong base.

Of the chelate ethylene diamine compounds two series were prepared by Werner and Smirnoff,[1201] and resolved into their optical antimers. They are $[Ir(en)_2(NO_2)_2]X$ and $[Ir(en)_3]X_3$. They are colourless (the iodide is yellowish-pink)[1208] and extremely stable.

Pentammines, $[IrAm_5R]X_n$

In these compounds one of the six ammine groups is replaced by a neutral or acidic group.

The *aquopentammines*, $[IrAm_5(H_2O)]X_3$, are made[1179] by the action of boiling potassium hydroxide on the chloropentammines $[IrAm_5Cl]X_2$. The chloride $[Ir(NH_3)_5(H_2O)]Cl_3$ when heated to 100° loses its water and goes over into the chloro-compound $[Ir(NH_3)_5Cl]Cl_2$.

The *chloropentammines*, $[IrAm_5Cl]X_2$, are the best known pentammine series. They can be made,[1177,1210] along with the di-chloro- and the trichloro-compounds, by the action of hot ammonia solution on iridium

[1186] W. Strecker and M. Schurigin, *Ber.* 1908, **42**, 1767.
[1187] C. Gialdini, *Atti R.* 1907, [v] **16**, ii. 551.   [1188] Id., ib. 648.
[1189] A. Werner and O. de Vries, *Ann.* 1908, **364**, 77.
[1190] M. Vezes and A. Duffour, *Bull. Soc.* 1909, [4] **5**, 869.
[1191] A. Duffour, ib. 872.
[1192] M. Vezes and A. Duffour, ib. 1910, [4] **7**, 507.
[1193] A. Duffour, ib. 512.   [1194] M. Delépine, ib. 1911, [4] **9**, 710.
[1195] Id., *C.R.* 1911, **152**, 1390.   [1196] A. Duffour, ib. 1393.
[1197] Id., *Ann. Chim. Phys.* 1913, [viii] **30**, 169.
[1198] M. Delépine, *Bull. Soc.* 1911, [4] **9**, 771.
[1199] Id., ib. 1917, [4] **21**, 157.
[1200] F. M. Jaeger, *K. Akad. Wet. Amst.* 1918, **21**, 203.
[1201] A. Werner and A. P. Smirnoff, *Helv. Chim. Acta*, 1920, **3**, 472.
[1202] M. Delépine, *Rev. Gen. Sci. pur. appl.* 1921, **32**, 607.
[1203] Id., *C.R.* 1922, **175**, 1408.   [1204] Id., ib. 1923, **176**, 445.
[1205] Id., *Ann. Chim. Phys.* 1923, [9] **19**, 145.
[1206] M. Guillot, *Bull. Soc.* 1926, [4] **39**, 852.
[1207] L. A. Tschugaev, *Ann. Inst. Platine*, 1926, **4**, 52.
[1208] V. V. Iebedinski, ib., p. 235.
[1209] M. Delépine, *Z. physikal. Chem.* 1927, **130**, 222.
[1210] M. Delépine and J. Pineau, *Bull. Soc.* 1929, [4] **45**, 228.

trichloride or on the complex halides M_3IrCl_6 and M_2IrCl_6. The chloride $[Ir(NH_3)_5Cl]Cl_2$ forms red crystals, fairly soluble in water. A series of salts (Cl_2, Br_2, $(NO_2)_2$, SO_4, etc.) have been prepared[1178]; the chlorine in the cation is not precipitated by silver nitrate. They resemble the corresponding compounds of trivalent chromium, cobalt and rhodium, but they are decomposed by chlorine, which the rhodium complex is not. The chloride gives with moist silver oxide a hydroxide

$$[Ir(NH_3)_5Cl](OH)_2, H_2O,^{1178,1212}$$

buff-coloured crystals, very stable, losing its water of crystallization only slowly in a vacuum at 140°; it is a strong base.

The corresponding bromo-compounds are also known.

Nitro-pentammines, $[IrAm_5(NO_2)]X_2$[1189]

They can be made from the chloropentammines through the aquo-complexes, the chloride of which gives with silver nitrite the nitrite $[Ir(NH_3)_5H_2O](NO_2)_3$, and this on heating (like the chloro-compound above) loses water and forms the nitro-salt $[Ir(NH_3)_5NO_2](NO_2)_2$ from which the other salts can be made. With hydrochloric acid, for example, this gives the chloride $[B]Cl_2$, a colourless salt easily soluble in water; like the other nitro-complexes of trivalent iridium it is very stable; in solution it is not attacked by 15 per cent. hydrochloric acid, concentrated nitric acid, or aqua regia, all at their boiling-points, or by cold strong sulphuric acid. Sol^{ies} $[B]Cl_2$ 7·9/25°; $[B]I_2$ (colourless) 3·45/16°; $[B](NO_3)_2$ 20/14°. The sulphate $[B]SO_4$ is rather slightly soluble in water, and forms an acid sulphate.

Tetrammines, $[IrAm_4R_2]X_n$

In the complexes R always seems to be an acid radical, and so n is 1.

Dichloro-tetrammines $[IrAm_4Cl_2]X$. They are formed when an ammonia solution acts on iridium trichloride or its complexes at the boiling-point,[1177] or when concentrated hydrochloric acid acts on the dinitro-compound in a sealed tube at 130–135°.[1189] They could of course occur in two forms, *cis* and *trans*, but the properties of Palmaer's substances[1177] and Werner's[1189] are near enough to show that they were dealing with the same isomers. No example of isomerism in this group has yet been detected.

The dichloride $[Ir(NH_3)_4Cl_2]Cl$ forms yellow crystals; it is not affected by boiling with concentrated hydrochloric acid, and silver nitrate precipitates the ionized chlorine at once, but the chlorine of the complex only very slowly. The corresponding monobromide and monoiodide are also yellow; sol^y chloride 5·73/25°[1187]; bromide 3·85/23°; iodide 1·25/18°.

A similar pyridine derivative[1209] is $[Ir(NH_3)py_3Cl_2]X$. See further, reference [1206].

The corresponding *en* compounds $[Ir (en)_2(NO_2)_2]X$, already mentioned,

1211 I. K. Pschenitsin and S. E. Krasikov, *Ann. Inst. Platine*, 1933, **11**, 13.
1212 B. E. Dixon, *J.C.S.* 1934, 34.

are very stable, and the NO_2 groups can only be removed by some hours' heating with concentrated sulphuric acid; they have been resolved into their optical antimers,[1201] and so must be *cis* complexes.

Triammines

All the known triammines of trivalent iridium contain three acid radicals, and accordingly are non-electrolytes.

The trichloride $[Ir(NH_3)_3Cl_3]°$ is one of the products of the action of hot ammonia solution on iridium trichloride or its complexes.[1177,1181] It is yellow or orange, insoluble in water, and hard to purify.[1189] The pyridine derivative $[Ir py_3Cl_3]°$[1202,1205] is also yellow; it occurs in two forms (*cis* and *trans*), both of which are insoluble in water but soluble in chloroform.

The trinitro-compound $[Ir(NH_3)_3(NO_2)_3]°$[1189] is a pale yellow substance, sol^y 0·389/25°: even at the boiling-point the solubility is small. It can be boiled with 1:1 hydrochloric acid, or 1:5 sulphuric, or even concentrated nitric acid without decomposition. The molecular conductivity of the solution at $V = 1,000$ is only 9·4 even after 15 minutes' heating at 60°.

This complex is much more stable than its cobalt analogue; for example, it is not affected by long boiling with water, which at once decomposes the cobalt compound, nor even by heating to the boiling-point with potassium hydroxide solution or concentrated hydrochloric acid, which react with the cobalt compound in the cold.

Diammines

All the known diammines contain either pyridine or picoline, but never ammonia.

One of them $[Ir py_2(H_2O)Cl_3]°$ is of the non-salt type. It is peculiar in separating from water as a trihydrate, which behaves as an acid, being soluble in alkalies, and probably is really the complex acid

$$H[Ir py_2(OH)Cl_3], 3 H_2O.^{1204}$$

At 140–145° it loses its water and becomes insoluble; it is evident that the hydrogen ion recombines with the hydroxyl group as soon as the water molecules which solvate it in the hydrate are removed. The remaining diammines all contain 4 acid radicals, and so are monovalent anions. The tetrachloro-diammines $M[Ir py_2Cl_4]$ are made by the action of pyridine on the iridiochloride $M_3[IrCl_6]$; they occur in *cis* and *trans* forms, which are yellow and orange respectively.[1202,1215-16] The corresponding bromine compounds are also known.[1214]

Monammines

$M_2[Ir(NH_3)Cl_5]$ can be made by boiling $(NH_4)_2[IrCl_6]$ with ammonium acetate solution.[1217] The pyridine series $M_2[Ir pyCl_5]$ is made from the

[1213] Mme M. Delépine-Tard, *Ann. Chim. Phys.* 1935, [10] **4**, 282.
[1214] Id., *C.R.* 1935, **200**, 1477.   [1215] M. Delépine, ib., p. 1373.
[1216] Id., *Rec. Trav.* 1940, **59**, 486.
[1217] V. V. Lebedinski and N. A. Balitzkaja, *Ann. Inst. Platine*, 1938, **15**, 13.

aquo-compound $M_2[Ir(H_2O)Cl_5]$ with pyridine.[1194-5,1202] They are yellow or orange salts, and of considerable stability; the free acid, though it cannot be isolated, can be extracted from its aqueous solution with amyl alcohol, to which it communicates a beautiful violet colour, like that of a solution of iodine in carbon disulphide. An analogous hydrazine derivative $M[Ir(N_2H_3)Cl_5]$ has been obtained.[1207]

Dimethyl-glyoxime-compounds

Dimethyl-glyoxime

$$CH_3\!-\!\underset{NOH}{\overset{\|}{C}}\!-\!-\!-\!\underset{NOH}{\overset{\|}{C}}\!-\!CH_3 \quad (= DH_2)$$

acting as a monovalent chelate group DH forms with the iridiochloride $(NH_3)_4[IrCl_6]$ the di-chelate free acid $H[Ir(DH)_2Cl_2]$, which has not been isolated, but of which the potassium (2 H_2O) ammonium (1 H_2O), guanidine, and platino-tetrammine $[Pt(NH_3)_4]$ salts have been prepared.[1218]

Hexanitro-iridates

These are formed[1182] by the continuous treatment of a tri- or tetravalent iridium solution with potassium nitrite; the salt $K_3[Ir(NO_2)_6]$ is colourless and only slightly soluble.

Phosphorus Trihalide Complexes

Iridium powder reacts with phosphorus pentachloride to give iridium trichloride, and if excess of phosphorus trichloride is added to the product the compound $IrCl_3(PCl_3)_3$ is formed[1186]; a corresponding bromide $IrBr_3(PBr_3)_3$ can be made in the same way. These compounds are insoluble in water, and on boiling are slowly dissolved by it with decomposition. Their structures have not yet been determined.

Thiourea Complexes

Thiourea $CS(NH_2)_2$ (= T) reacts directly with sodium iridiochloride Na_3IrCl_6 to give a series of compounds $[IrT_3Cl_3]^\circ:[IrT_4Cl_2]Cl:[IrT_5Cl]X_2$ (X = Cl, ClO_4, $\frac{1}{2}Ox$, $\frac{1}{2}PtCl_4''$), and finally, $[IrT_6]Cl_3$.[1219]

Complex Polysulphides[1182,1184]

By saturating ammonium sulphide solution with sulphur, adding this to a solution of iridium trichloride, and leaving this to stand for some months, brown crystals of the composition $(NH_4)_3IrS_{15}$ are got. There is a corresponding $(NH_4)_2PtS_{15}, 2 H_2O$. It is assumed that the iridium is trivalent, and that the sulphur forms three divalent S_5 groups: the change of valency on replacing iridium by platinum supports this.

[1218] V. V. Lebedinski and I. A. Fedorov, *Ann. Sect. Platine*, 1938, **15**, 27.

[1219] I. I. Lebedinski, E. S. Schapiro, and N. P. Kasatkina, *Ann. Inst. Platine*, 1935 **12**, 93.

Trioxalato-salts, $M_3[IrOx_3]$

These can be made by the action of an oxalate solution on a dichloro-oxalato-salt, or by boiling hydrated iridium dioxide with a solution of oxalic acid.[1187-8] The free acid, $H_3[IrOx_3]$, $n\,H_2O$, is an easily soluble solid; the potassium salt ($4\,H_2O$ yellow, slightly soluble in cold water, easily in hot), silver ($3\,H_2O$), and barium ($5\,H_2O$) are known.[1197] The complex has been resolved through the strychnine salt[1199,1200]; it does not racemize even at 120°, but does so considerably on standing for 2 years in the cold. The rotatory power is enormous, and highly dependent on wave-length; the molecular rotation for the potassium salt at 6,800 A is 1,530°, and at 4,790 A it is 16,340°.[1200]

Hexahalide Complexes

The 'chloroiridates' or iridiochlorides $M_3[Ir(hal)_6]$ are prepared[1185,1198] by reducing the tetravalent iridates, most conveniently with an oxalate:

$$2\,M_2[IrCl_6] + M_2C_2O_4 = 2\,M_3[IrCl_6] + 2\,CO_2.$$

The dry crystals are olive-green. The sodium salt has 12 molecules of water. Solubilities of the other salts at 20° are: NH_4 9·5; Rb 110; Cs 200.

The corresponding bromides $M_3[IrBr_6]$ can also be made,[1213] and are remarkable for the extent of their hydration: K, $4\,H_2O$; Rb, H_2O; Cs,H_2O.

Pentahalide Complexes

These are all of the aquo-type $M_2[Ir(H_2O)(hal)_5]$. The chloro-salts $M_2[Ir(H_2O)Cl_5]$ are got from the mother liquor of the preparation of the hexachloro-compounds by reduction of the hexachloro-iridates, as described above. They are strongly coloured; their sol[ies] at 19° are[1185]: K, 9·2; NH_4, 15·4; Rb, 1·05; Cs, 0·83.

The pentabromo-salts have also been made.[1213]

Tetrahalide Complexes

The only known types contain 4 chlorine atoms along with 2 NO_2 groups or an oxalato.

Dinitro-tetrachloro-salts. These are formed by the action of potassium nitrite[1182] or nitrous fumes[1183] on the hexachlorides; they are yellow; the potassium salt is easily, and the caesium salt only slightly, soluble in water.[1183]

Oxalato-tetrachloro-salts.[1196] The sodium salt $Na_3[IrCl_4Ox]$ can be made by the action of sodium oxalate on the hexachloride Na_3IrCl_6. It is dark red. The free acid $H_3[IrCl_4Ox]$ crystallizes out from its solution on evaporation *in vacuo*, but it is too unstable to be recrystallized.

The further action of the oxalate converts the salt into the dioxalato-dichloride $M_3[IrCl_2Ox_2]$.

Trihalide Complexes

The only example of this class seems to be the mixed oxalato-complex $M_3[IrCl_3(NO_2)Ox]$.[1211]

Dihalide Complexes

These again contain chlorine atoms, NO_2 groups, and oxalato-groups mixed in various proportions.

The dichloro-tetranitro-compounds, of the type $M_3[IrCl_2(NO_2)_4]$[1189] are made by warming the tetravalent Na_2IrCl_6, $6 H_2O$ with sodium nitrite. The sodium salt forms yellow crystals with 3 and 2 H_2O; sol^y 100/25°. The potassium salt is anhydrous, yellow, sol^y 5/20°. The cupric salt is soluble, the lead salt insoluble. The potassium salts of the chloro-nitro-acids form a series, with a continuous change of colour and solubility:

$K_3[IrCl_6]$, $3 H_2O$.	$K_3[IrCl_4(NO_2)_2]$	$K_3[IrCl_2(NO_2)_4]$	$K_3[Ir(NO_2)_6]$
Yellow-green	Golden yellow	Pale yellow	White
Very sol. water.	Easily sol. water.	Fairly sol. water.	Very slightly sol.

Dichloro-dinitro-oxalato-type, $M_3[IrCl_2(NO_2)_2Ox]$.[1192-3] The potassium salt (1 H_2O) can be made by the action of concentrated potassium nitrite solution on $K_3[IrCl_2Ox_2]$; it is an orange-yellow salt stable to boiling water. It loses its water of crystallization at 120°, and decomposes at 150°. The silver salt (pale yellow) gives with hydrochloric acid an orange-yellow solution of the free acid, which liberates carbon dioxide from carbonates, but decomposes on evaporation. Other salts are: Li, 2 H_2O, very deliquescent; NH_4 (2 H_2O), Rb, Cs anhydrous.

Dichlorodioxalato-complexes, $M_3[IrCl_2Ox_2]$

These can be made[1190-1] by the action of potassium oxalate on an iridi- or irido-hexachloride M_3 or $M_2[IrCl_6]$, or on the tetrachloro-compound $M_3[IrCl_4Ox]$.[1197] The complex is very stable, being unaffected by boiling with water, and giving no tests for chloride or oxalate ions. From the silver salt, on the addition of hydrochloric acid and evaporation, the free acid $H_3[IrCl_2Ox_2]$, $4 H_2O$ can be got in red hygroscopic crystals. Other salts[1191] are Li, 8 H_2O: Na, 8 H_2O, very soluble; NH_4, H_2O: Rb, 4 and 1 H_2O,[1197] bright red, less soluble than the potassium salt; Cs, H_2O: Ag, 3 H_2O.

This complex occurs in two forms, *cis* and *trans*; the *cis* form is asymmetric, and has been resolved.[1203] The *cis* and *trans* forms are produced together: the *cis* goes over into the *trans* on heating for an hour in potassium chloride solution at 130°. The two forms have the same ruby-red colour, but that of the *cis* form is twice as intense as that of the *trans*.[1205]

TETRAVALENT IRIDIUM

THIS is for iridium the most stable valency after 3, and the compounds are as a rule easily obtained by the oxidation of the trivalent series. The reduction potential of trivalent $IrCl_6$ at 25°, referred to a normal hydrogen electrode, is 1·021 volt.,[1220] and the heat of reaction −30·4 k.cals. It follows that the oxidation of $IrCl_6'''$ to $IrCl_6''''$ by chlorine at 1 atm. pressure is practically complete.

[1220] S. C. Woo, *J.A.C.S.* 1931, **53**, 469.

The 'simple' compounds of tetravalent iridium are the dioxide and its hydrate, the disulphide, the four tetrahalides (or some of them), and probably a sulphate.

Iridium Dioxide, IrO_2

This can be made in the anhydrous and in the hydrated form by a variety of methods, as by heating powdered iridium in air or oxygen: or by heating a solution of M_2IrCl_6 or M_3IrCl_6 with alkali, air or oxygen being blown through the liquid in the latter case.[1221] It is very difficult to get it in the pure condition; when made by oxidation of iridium it is liable to contain free metal, and when made in the wet way it cannot be completely freed from the alkali used to precipitate it (which is probably adsorbed and not combined). The pure dioxide and its hydrate were made[1222] by adding alkali drop by drop to the boiling (and considerably hydrolysed) iridium tetrachloride solution until the brown solution just turned blue; thus there was no excess of alkali to be adsorbed by the blue flocculent precipitate. In a vacuum this dries to a blue-black powder of the composition $IrO_2, 2H_2O$, or $Ir(OH)_4$. In dry nitrogen at 350° it loses all its water, and a black powder of IrO_2 remains.

The dissociation tension of oxygen in the system iridium–oxygen indicates[1223] the formation of IrO_2 and a higher oxide, perhaps IrO_3, but no lower oxide: there is no sign of either Ir_2O_3 or IrO being formed, though (p. 1532) the former (but not the latter) of these can be made by indirect methods.

Iridium dioxide has a rutile lattice, like the dioxides of ruthenium and osmium. It does not begin to lose oxygen below 650°.[1224] The hydroxide is a blue-black amorphous powder, insoluble in sulphuric acid but dissolving in hydrochloric acid to form H_2IrCl_6; it is almost insoluble in alkali. It readily forms a violet or blue colloidal solution.

Iridium Disulphide, IrS_2

Tensimetric measurements of the system iridium–sulphur show[1225] that the only sulphides there produced are Ir_2S_3, IrS_2, and Ir_3S_8, although the trisulphide IrS_3 can probably be made by the action of excess of sulphur on iridium trichloride (see p. 1547). This is supported by Debye-Scherrer diagrams, which indicate a pseudo-pyrites structure for Ir_3S_8 which is not found with IrS_2.

The production of the disulphide by the action of hydrogen sulphide on a tetravalent iridium solution was denied by Claus; but Antony[1226] got in this way from K_2IrCl_6 a brown precipitate of the composition

[1221] L. Wöhler and W. Witzmann, *Z. anorg. Chem.* 1908, **57**, 323.
[1222] F. Krauss and H. Gerlach, ib. 1925, **143**, 125.
[1223] L. Wöhler and W. Witzmann, *Z. Elektrochem.* 1908, **14**, 97.
[1224] S. Pastorello, *Atti R.* 1928, [vi] **7**, 754.
[1225] W. Biltz, J. Laar, P. Erhlich, and K. Meisel, *Z. anorg. Chem.* 1937, **233**, 257.
[1226] U. Antony, *Gaz* 1893, **23**, i. 184.

2 IrS_2,Ir_2S_3. That some reduction of the iridium had occurred was shown by the presence of sulphuric acid in the solution.

Iridium Diselenide and Ditelluride have been prepared[1227] by the reduction of the tri-compounds $IrSe_3$ and $IrTe_3$ with hydrogen at 600°; the diselenide is also formed when the trichloride is heated with excess of selenium in a stream of carbon dioxide or nitrogen at 600° until it ceases to lose weight.

These are greyish crystalline substances, which are stable to acids.

Iridium Tetrahalides

Though there are numerous complex salts derived from all the tetra-halides except the iodide, it is not certain how many of the binary tetra-halides of iridium have been isolated, and probably none of them have been got in a really pure state.

Iridium Tetrafluoride

This is a by-product in many of the reactions of iridium hexafluoride; it is made (along with chlorine fluoride) by treating the hexafluoride with chlorine, or better by heating it with the necessary amount of metallic iridium in a quartz tube to 150°.[1228] The volatile hexafluoride disappears, and a scarcely volatile viscous yellow oil with a choking smell is produced, which is the tetrafluoride. It is very sensitive to moisture, and soon decomposes in air; it is instantly hydrolysed by water to the tetra-hydroxide $Ir(OH)_4$ and hydrogen fluoride. By careful heating it can be sublimed unchanged. On stronger heating it gives off fluorine, and a variety of dark or metallic-looking products are formed. These are also formed when iridium hexafluoride is heated with excess of the metal, and they are all converted into the tetrafluoride by heating with the hexa-fluoride. It seems probable that they are the lower fluorides IrF_3, IrF_2, and IrF (or some of them), corresponding to the lower chlorides.

Iridium Tetrachloride

A hydrated form of this, probably a hydroxo-acid (like the hydrates of the iridium trihalides), can be got by the action of chlorine or aqua regia on the ammonium salt $(NH_4)_2[IrCl_6]$.[1229] It loses water on heating, but still retains some of it at 100°, at which temperature, even in a stream of chlorine, it loses chlorine.[1230-1] Hence the dissociation tension of chlorine over partly hydrated tetrachloride at 100° is more than an atmosphere. Anhydrous iridium trichloride enclosed with liquid chlorine in a sealed tube and heated to 60° (i.e. under 20 atm. pressure) combines with it slowly,[1231] but no pure product could be obtained. The tetrachloride may

[1227] L. Wöhler, K. Ewald, and H. G. Krall, *Ber.* 1933, **66**, 1638.
[1228] O. Ruff and J. Fischer, *Z. anorg. Chem.* 1929, **179**, 161.
[1229] A. Gutbier, *Z. physikal. Chem.* 1910, **69**, 304.
[1230] M. Delépine, *Bull. Soc.* 1911, [4] **9**, 829.
[1231] L. Wöhler and S. Streicher, *Ber.* 1913, **46**, 1577.

be formed[1232] when chlorine acts on the tetrahydroxide $Ir(OH)_4$, but it was not isolated.

The impure tetrachloride is a deep brown hygroscopic mass, deliquescing in the air to a brown liquid that looks like bromine.

Iridium tetrabromide, $IrBr_4$, probably does not exist.[1233] A solution of the acid H_2IrBr_6 decomposes on evaporation, even in the cold.

Iridium tetraiodide IrI_4 has probably never been isolated.

Iridium Sulphate, $Ir(SO_4)_2$

Berzelius obtained a yellowish-brown compound of this composition by oxidizing the sulphide IrS_2 with nitric acid. His work was confirmed by Rimbach and Korten.[1234] They considered the product to be a true tetravalent derivative of this structure, but they say that on treatment with alkalies it gives compounds containing trivalent iridium.

COMPLEXES OF TETRAVALENT IRIDIUM

The complexes of tetravalent iridium are not very numerous; they include a few ammines, certain oxalato-derivatives, and a good many hexahalides (the chlorides the most stable, the bromides rather less so, and only one or two fluorides known).

Ammines

Tetravalent iridium seems to be much more stable in co-ordination with oxygen or the halogens than with nitrogen, and so in complex anions than in complex cations. Very few cationic ammine complexes of it are known. The tetrammine $[Ir(NH_3)_4Cl_2](NO_3)_2$ can be made by treating $Ir(NH_3)_2Cl_2$ with concentrated nitric acid. It is soluble in water, and with hydrochloric acid gives the chloride $[Ir(NH_3)_4Cl_2]Cl_2$, from which silver nitrate precipitates only half the chlorine. The other ammine compounds are either neutral or negatively charged, and seem to be formed only by organic bases like pyridine or quinoline, not by ammonia.

Neutral Compounds. If iridium tetrachloride is treated with pyridine in alcoholic solution it forms a brown substance $Ir(py)_2Cl_4$.[1240] Similar picoline and quinoline derivatives can be made. $Ir(py)_2Cl_4$ can occur in two different forms,[1245] obtainable respectively from the orange and the

[1232] F. Krauss and H. Gerlach, *Z. anorg. Chem.* 1925, **147**, 265.

[1233] A. Gutbier and M. Riess, *Ber.* 1909, **42**, 3905.

[1234] E. Rimbach and F. Korten, *Z. anorg. Chem.* 1907, **52**, 406.

[1235] M. Delépine, *Bull. Soc.* 1908, [4] **3**, 901.

[1236] A. Gutbier, *Z. physikal. Chem.* 1910, **69**, 304.

[1237] A. Gutbier and M. Riess, *Ber.* 1909, **42**, 3905.

[1238] M. Delépine, *C.R.* 1911, **152**, 1390.   [1239] Id., ib. 1589.

[1240] A. Gutbier and D. Hoyermann, *Z. anorg. Chem.* 1914, **89**, 340.

[1241] M. Delépine, *Ann. Chim. Phys.* 1917, [9] **7**, 277.

[1242] Id., *Bull. Soc.* 1917, [4] **21**, 157.

[1243] A. Gutbier and B. Ottenstein, *Z. anorg. Chem.* 1914, **89**, 344.

[1244] E. H. Archibald and J. W. Kern, *Trans. Roy. Soc. Canada*, 1917/18, iii. **11**, 7.

[1245] M. Delépine, *C.R.* 1922, **175**, 1211.

red form of the trivalent iridium salt $M[Ir(py)_2Cl_4]$; they presumably are the *cis* and *trans* isomers.

The *anionic* pentachloro-pyridine derivative $M[IrCl_5py]$ can be made[1238-9] by oxidizing the corresponding trivalent salts $M_2[IrCl_5py]$ with chlorine, nitric acid, or aqua regia, but not with other oxidizing agents such as hydrogen peroxide or chromium trioxide. The salts are dark red. The sodium salt is hydrated; the other salts prepared were anhydrous, and their sol[ies] at 15–20° are: NH_4, 0·61; K, 0·69; Rb, 0·083; Cs, 0·030. They are very stable to acids; the pyridine can only be removed by heating in a sealed tube with concentrated hydrochloric acid to 150–160°.

Oxalato-complexes[1242]

The trioxalato-compound $K_2[Ir(C_2O_4)_3], 4H_2O$ is made by heating the hexachloride $K_2[IrCl_6]$ with potassium oxalate. It has been resolved through its strychnine salt.[1242]

Hexahalides, $M_2[Ir(hal)_6]$

These are the most important class of derivatives of tetravalent iridium.

Hexafluorides, $M_2[IrF_6]$[1247]

By heating powdered iridium with potassium plumbifluoride K_3HPbF_8 the crystalline salts K_2IrF_6 and $PbIrF_6$ were obtained. Their absorption spectra were measured. There seem to be no other records of hexafluorides of this type.

Hexachlorides, $M_2[IrCl_6]$

These can be made by mixing potassium or sodium chloride with iridium powder, and heating in chlorine, or by adding the alkaline chloride to a solution of iridium tetrachloride, or of iridium tetrahydroxide in hydrochloric acid.[1236,1241] They form dark red crystals with a green reflex, or a deep red powder. They are slightly soluble in cold water, readily in hot; they are slowly hydrolysed by water, and are best recrystallized from 10 per cent. hydrochloric acid. The concentrated aqueous solution is brownish-red, the dilute solution yellow. The solubilities of some of these at 19° are[1234-5,1244]: Na, large; K, 1·25; NH_4, 0·69; Rb, 0·0556; Cs, 0·0111. Many salts of organic bases[1236,1243] and of the complex ammines bases of trivalent chromium and cobalt[1246] have been made.

Hexabromides, $M_2[IrBr_6]$

These can be made[1237] from the bright blue solution obtained by dissolving the tetra-hydroxide $Ir(OH)_4$ in hydrobromic acid. On standing, this solution, which no doubt contains the free acid H_2IrBr_6, turns green and evolves bromine. The acid solution can also be made by treating iridium tetrachloride with hydrobromic acid and bromine.

[1246] A. Benrath, W. Bücher, and H. Eckstein, *Z. anorg. Chem.* 1922, **121**, 347.
[1247] H. I. Schlesinger and M. W. Tapley, *J.A.C.S.* 1924, **46**, 276.

The salts are all deep blue-black crystals, forming a dark blue powder, and giving a bright blue solution, which decomposes on standing, with evolution of bromine: it is more stable in presence of hydrobromic acid, and still more if a small quantity of bromine is added; the salts can be recrystallized from this last solvent. The hexabromides are in general more soluble than the hexachlorides. Thus the ammonium salt is easily soluble in cold water, the rubidium and caesium salts slightly, the potassium salt more so. The salts of the chromammine and cobaltammine bases have also been made.[1248] The fact that the bromides are less stable than the corresponding chlorides is clearly shown by their greater tendency to evolve halogen, for example, on standing in solution. The hexaiodides M_2IrI_6 have never been prepared.

[PENTAVALENT IRIDIUM

Now that the supposed IrF_5 has been shown[1249] to be the hexavalent oxyfluoride IrF_4O (see p. 1548) there is no evidence for the existence of pentavalent iridium.]

HEXAVALENT IRIDIUM

IRIDIUM forms a trioxide, a trisulphide, a triselenide, and a tritelluride, IrO_3, IrS_3, $IrSe_3$, $IrTe_3$, in which it may have a valency of 6; but as we do not know the crystal structure, some of these may really be compounds of tetravalent iridium, containing the groups O–O, S–S, etc. There are, however, two other compounds in which iridium must have a valency of 6, the hexafluoride IrF_6, and an oxyfluoride which presumably has the formula IrF_4O, and which has been shown to contain the iridium in the hexavalent state.

Iridium Trioxide, IrO_3

This compound can be made[1250] by igniting iridium with potassium hydroxide and nitrate; by fusing iridium with sodium peroxide; by heating iridium dioxide containing caustic potash in oxygen; or by the anodic oxidation of a blue strongly alkaline iridium dioxide solution at 20°. It can never be obtained free from alkali, and it never contains more than 17·7 per cent. of oxygen, the theoretical percentage being 19·9 (Ir_3O_8, which would correspond to Ir_3S_8, the highest sulphide obtained by Biltz from the elements, would have 18·1 per cent. oxygen). It is a very strong oxidizing agent, which may be due to the instability of the valency 6 for iridium, or to the presence of —O—O— groups; it immediately evolves oxygen with sulphuric acid, and it oxidizes boiling alcohol or [presumably impure] acetic acid.

[1248] A. Benrath, W. Bücher, A. Wolber, and J. Zeutzius, *Z. anorg. Chem.* 1924, **135**, 233.

[1249] O. Ruff and J. Fischer, ib. 1929, **179**, 161.

[1250] L. Wöhler and W. Witzmann, ib. 1908, **57**, 323.

Iridium Trisulphide, IrS_3[1251]

Iridium trichloride and excess of sulphur are heated in an evacuated sealed tube to 600°; the excess of sulphur is removed by extraction first with carbon disulphide and then (to remove the amorphous sulphur) with sodium sulphide. The residue is iridium trisulphide, a grey-black powder, stable to all acids including aqua regia.

Iridium Triselenide, $IrSe_3$[1251-2]

If iridium trichloride is heated with selenium in carbon dioxide or nitrogen at 400° until its weight is constant, it is converted into the diselenide $IrSe_2$; but if this is further heated in a sealed tube with more selenium, and the excess removed with potassium cyanide solution, the triselenide $IrSe_3$ is formed. It is a grey-white crystalline powder, stable even to concentrated acids, and only slowly attacked even by boiling aqua regia.

The *tritelluride* $IrTe_3$[1251-2] is made in the same way, but at 700°, the excess of tellurium being removed with nitric acid. It is dark grey, and is slowly attacked by aqua regia. Like the selenide it is reduced by hydrogen at 600° to the ditelluride $IrTe_2$.

Iridium Hexafluoride, IrF_6

This substance is very difficult to prepare[1253]: it can only be made by the combination of the elements, and they only combine at a temperature at which the fluorine attacks platinum, and indeed any other material of which the apparatus can be made except fluor spar. Ruff has, however, succeeded in making tubes and boats of ground fluor spar, moulded and burnt like pottery at about 1,250°. In an apparatus of this material iridium powder was fluorinated at 260°, when in presence of excess of fluorine the only product was the volatile hexafluoride IrF_6, which came over and was condensed in liquid air. For its investigation silica vessels can be used, as these are not attacked by the hexafluoride below 200°.

Iridium hexafluoride IrF_6 is a pale yellow solid at —180°, and bright yellow at —15°; it melts at +44° to a brownish-yellow liquid which boils at 53° to give a bright yellow vapour. The solid seems to be dimorphic. The heat of evaporation is 8·5 k.cals., giving the high Trouton constant of 26·1; the heat of formation from the elements in their normal states is 130 k.cals.

The hexafluoride is extremely reactive. Owing to its high vapour pressure at the ordinary temperature it gives out thick white clouds in air, being hydrolysed by the moisture to hydrogen fluoride, the oxyfluoride IrF_4O, and the lower fluorides. With water in excess it is at once converted into hydrogen fluoride and $Ir(OH)_4$, with evolution of oxygen mixed with ozone.

[1251] L. Wöhler, K. Ewald, and H. G. Krall, *Ber.* 1933, **66**, 1638.
[1252] W. Biltz, *Z. anorg. Chem.* 1937, **233**, 282.
[1253] O. Ruff and J. Fischer, ib. 1929, **179**, 161.

It is very readily reduced to a lower fluoride; chlorine converts it into the tetrafluoride with the production of chlorine fluoride ClF, and bromine and iodine have a similar action. By hydrogen it is reduced to the metal.

Iridium hexafluoride shows no signs of any tendency to complex formation.

Iridium Oxyfluoride, IrF_4O[1253]

When the hexafluoride was manipulated in glass vessels a greyish-white solid product was obtained, but with silica vessels scarcely any of this was formed, so that it must have been due to the action of the hexafluoride on the glass. It was at first thought that this substance was a pentafluoride, but iodometric determinations proved that it contains hexavalent and not pentavalent iridium. The quantity obtained was so small, and it is so sensitive to moisture, that it could not be analysed, but as it is produced whenever a small quantity of water comes in contact with iridium hexafluoride, we may presume that it is a hydrolytic product, an oxyfluoride, probably IrF_4O. It forms whitish needles, stable in silica vessels in the cold, but decomposing when heated; in water it behaves like the hexafluoride, being hydrolysed with evolution of oxygen.

IRIDIUM CARBONYLS

THE 'simple' carbonyls and their halides can be made by heating the trihalide at 100–140° with carbon monoxide under 200 atm. In copper vessels[1254] (where the copper takes up the halogen) 100 per cent. of the tricarbonyl $Ir(CO)_3$ is obtained; in presence of powdered metal the main product is the tetracarbonyl $Ir(CO)_4$. These two carbonyls are obviously polymerized: we should expect $[Ir(CO)_3]_4$ and $[Ir(CO)_4]_2$: but they are too insoluble for their molecular weights to be determined.

$Ir(CO)_3$ is canary yellow; it is extraordinarily stable (far more so than the tetracarbonyl); it is not affected by acids (even concentrated nitric acid) or alkalies, or even by halogens in the cold, although it is decomposed by aqua regia. It does not sublime below 200°, but does so in carbon monoxide at 210°.

$Ir(CO)_4$ is greenish-yellow; it is readily converted into the tricarbonyl by heat, acid, or alkali. The heavier elements of a group always favour carbonyls with the highest ratio of metal atoms to CO groups: thus unlike iron, ruthenium and osmium scarcely form any penta-carbonyl, but readily go to the ennea; cobalt tetracarbonyl goes to the tricarbonyl at 53°, but the iridium compound undergoes this change in the cold.

The tetracarbonyl can be separated from the tri by sublimation, as it is the more volatile, or by its greater solubility in chloroform (sol^y of the tri in chloroform 6·2 mg./ord. temp.).[1254]

If the materials used in the preparation of these compounds are not quite dry, a very volatile iridium compound is formed, which no doubt is the hydride $Ir(CO)_3(COH)$.

[1254] W. Hieber and H. Lagally, *Z. anorg. Chem.* 1940, **245**, 321.

The *carbonyl halides*,[1255-6] $Ir(CO)_3X$ and $Ir(CO)_2X_2$, can be made by heating the trihalide hydrate IrX_3, H_2O to 150° in carbon monoxide at 1 atm., when a mixture of the two carbonyl halides with some tricarbonyl comes off; the extra halogen separates as COX_2, or if it is iodine as such. The ease of removal of the halogen here is in the order $Cl > Br > I$, the opposite of that for the formation of the simple carbonyl with a metal. In these compounds the volatility falls off as the CO content rises, the approximate sublimation temperature being for $Ir(CO)_3X$ [theoretical polymerization factor 3] 115°, for $Ir(CO)_2X_2$[4] 150°, for $Ir(CO)_3$ [4] 200°.

$Ir(CO)_2X_2$ loses carbon monoxide on exposure to air; $Ir(CO)_3X$ is far more stable, though the chloride is slowly decomposed by water to give iridium and carbon monoxide.

The colours of these halides are:

	$Ir(CO)_2X_2$	$Ir(CO)_3X$
X = Cl	Colourless	Pale brown
Br	Very pale yellow	Chocolate
I	Pale yellow	Dark brown

[1255] W. Manchot and H. Gall, *Ber.* 1925, **58**, 232.
[1256] W. Hieber, H. Lagally, and A. Mayr, *Z. anorg. Chem.* 1941, **246**, 138.

GROUP VIII C (10)

PALLADIUM AND PLATINUM

THESE two elements resemble one another more closely than any other pair in the group. There is the usual increase of stability of higher valencies with rise of atomic weight. Both elements are almost only divalent and tetravalent, but with palladium the tetravalency is much less stable than the divalency, while with platinum it is at least equally stable. Palladium has a remarkable power of absorbing hydrogen, more than any other metal of the group; platinum comes next, but far behind it, and nickel also has some power of doing this. The exact character of the compound of palladium and hydrogen is still obscure, but it is probably metallic.

Valency = 1

No monovalent palladium compounds have been isolated; a solution of the palladocyanide $K_2Pd(CN)_4$ on treatment with sodium amalgam gives a reducing solution, perhaps containing the monovalent salt $K_2[Pd(CN)_3]$, corresponding to $K_2[Ni(CN)_3]$. But this may well contain the non-valent palladium compound $K_4[Pd(CN)_4]$ (p. 1557).

With platinum a solution of the same reducing properties can be got in the same way, which may contain monovalent or non-valent platinum. In addition, by heating platinous chloride to the right temperature a yellow-green solid can be got, with a composition very near PtCl; its stability range is, however, very small.

Valency = 2

This is much the most important valency of palladium (as it is of nickel), but not so markedly of platinum. A large number of binary compounds are known, such as the oxide PdO, the hydroxide $Pd(OH)_2$, the sulphide PdS: all four dihalides, $Pd(NO_3)_2$, $PdSO_4$, etc., and a variety of salts or salt-like compounds, which are mostly soluble in water and easily hydrolysed.

The *complexes* of divalent palladium are nearly if not quite all 4-covalent (6-covalent platinous complexes have been described, but probably in error). They are more stable than those of divalent nickel, but less than those of divalent platinum. Apart from a few trihalides $(BH)PdCl_3$ obtained from organic bases, they are all 4-covalent. The ammines are of four types: (I) $[PdAm_4]X_2$; (II) $[PdAm_3R]X$; (III) $[PdAm_2R_2]°$; (IV) a peculiar type really 4-covalent $[(Pd(NH_3)Cl_2)_2]°$. Of these, (I) are stable enough to give a strongly alkaline hydroxide; (III) occur as *cis-trans* isomers; (IV) can be shown to have the planar structure

$$\text{H}_3\text{N} \diagdown \text{Pd} \diagup^{\text{Cl}} \diagdown \text{Pd} \diagup^{\text{NH}_3}_{\text{Cl}}$$

Trialkyl phosphines and arsines can replace ammonia.

The anionic complexes are all of the type $M_2[PdR_4]$, where R can be CN, NO_2, Cl, Br, or I (not F).

With platinum again this is a very stable valency, probably as stable as with palladium, though probably less stable than that of tetravalent platinum. The divalent compounds are almost identical with those of divalent palladium and are as stable in themselves, though they are more easily oxidized to the tetravalent state; they include the oxide, hydroxide, sulphide, all four dihalides, and a dicyanide $Pt(CN)_2$, yellow and insoluble.

Complexes. These again are very like those of palladium. The ammines all have the co-ordination number of 4, and are of five types (all represented with palladium except No. IV): (I) $[PtAm_4]X_2$; (II) $[PtAm_3R]X$; (III) $[PtAm_2R_2]°$; (IV) $M[PtAmR_3]$; (V) $[(PtAmCl_2)_2]$, with the same structure as that given above for the palladium analogue.

The complex halides also all have the co-ordination number 4. The dichloride dissolves in hydrochloric acid to form the acid H_2PtCl_4: the potassium salt of this is made by the reduction of the platinichloride K_2PtCl_6. The bromide K_2PtBr_4 forms black crystals. Similar acido-complexes are formed with NO_2 and CN: $K_2[Pt(NO_2)_4]$ is got from the platino-chloride K_2PtCl_4 and potassium nitrite: it is soluble in water, and the solution gives no precipitate with potassium hydroxide or hydrogen sulphide. $K_2[Pt(CN)_4]$ is also stable up to 140°, and is not decomposed by hydrogen sulphide.

Valency = 3

This only occurs in a few palladium compounds such as Pd_2O_3 and the trifluoride PdF_3, which curiously is the most stable fluoride of palladium: it is a black powder decomposed by water. There are also complex halides $M_2[PdCl_5]$ which are stable at low temperatures but go over into a mixture of the di- and tetravalent halides M_2PdCl_4 and M_2PdCl_6 on warming.

The trivalent platinum compounds are similar. The trichloride, got by heating $PtCl_4$, is a dark green solid, slowly dissolved by water, and converted by hot hydrochloric acid into the di- and tetrachlorides; the tribromide and tri-iodide are similar, and there is a yellow insoluble tricyanide $Pt(CN)_3$. These compounds are no doubt truly trivalent. But the complexes, such as $[PtAm_4Cl]X_2$ and $M_2[PtCl_5]$, all appear to be 5-covalent and are clearly in fact dimeric and 6-covalent with one di- and one tetravalent platinum atom, as their brilliant colour suggests.

Valency = 4

Tetravalent palladium is more stable than trivalent, but much less than divalent, or than tetravalent platinum. It only occurs in PdO_2, PdS_2, and in a few complex sulphides, halides, and ammines (covalencies 4 and 6). There are no compounds of tetravalent palladium containing fluorine. The thiopalladates $M_2[PdS_3]$ are decomposed by water. Complex halides are formed by chlorine and bromine: the commonest type is $M_2[PdCl_6]$ (as with Pt); there are a few diammines $[PdAm_2Cl_2]Cl_2$. All these halides lose halogen easily on warming.

With platinum this is perhaps the stablest valency: anyhow, it is very near to divalency in stability. Platinum forms an oxide PtO_2 and a hydroxide $Pt(OH)_4$, made by the action of potassium hydroxide on the tetrachloride; they are converted by alkalies into the platinates $M_2[Pt(OH)_6]$, which are isomorphous with the stannates. There is a disulphide PtS_2 and there are 4 tetrahalides.

A remarkable series of compounds are the alkyls, otherwise almost unknown in this group. The trialkyls Alk_3PtX have long been known, and Gilman has recently described $Pt(Alk)_4$ and $Pt_2(Alk)_6$, obtained by the use of sodium alkyl. They are high-melting soluble solids.

The complexes all have the co-ordination number of 6. Tetravalent platinum gives as least as many and as diverse kinds of ammines as divalent, but fewer acido-complexes. The ammines have all the forms from $[PtAm_6]X_4$ to M_2PtR_6. Of the halides $M_2[PtX_6]$ the fluorides are doubtful, the chlorides numerous; the bromides are red, the iodides brown and very unstable, losing iodine with ease. Every stage of replacement of halogen by hydroxyl is known from $M_2[Pt(hal)_6]$ to $M_2[Pt(OH)_6]$.

No pure cyanides, nitro-compounds, or oxalato-derivatives are known, but only mixed salts such as $M_2[Pt(hal)_2(CN)_4]$.

Valency = 6

No hexavalent palladium compounds are known.

Platinum has apparently hexavalent compounds in PtO_3, got by electrolytic oxidation, $PtSe_3$, and also PtP_2 and $PtAs_2$, made from the elements. In none of these are we sure that the platinum is hexavalent, but the trioxide gives no signs of having a peroxide (—O—O—) structure.

PALLADIUM

PALLADIUM was discovered by Wollaston in 1803, and named by him after the recently discovered minor planet Pallas. It is the most abundant of the platinum metals in the earth's crust as a whole, forming about 1 part in 10^8, which is about twice as much as platinum; in the ordinary platinum ores it does not amount as a rule to more than a few per cent., although a certain number are known of which it is a large or even the chief constituent. One of the most peculiar is the small hard crystalline nuggets found in some parts of British Guiana, which contain about 60 per cent. of mercury, the rest being palladium, with traces of rhodium, platinum, and gold.[1257]

The atomic structure of palladium is remarkable. The atomic number of 46 is that of a 'pseudo-inert-gas' 2.8.18.18, like those of nickel and platinum. In nickel the final 18-electron group breaks down, one or perhaps two of its electrons going into the next higher quantum group to give instead of 18 the configuration (17) 1 or (16) 2, or perhaps a mixture of the two. In platinum the structure is (16) 2. The elements of the second transitional series always tend to have fewer electrons in their outermost group than those of the first and third (for example, we have Co, —(15)2; Rh—(16)1; Ir—(15)2), and this effect is shown in a very marked way by palladium, where the spectroscopic data and the absence of a magnetic moment[1258] indicate that in the isolated atom all the 18 electrons are in the fourth quantum group.

We should expect an element with such an atomic structure not to be a metal at all, but to resemble an inert gas, and the fact that elementary palladium is a solid with the conductivity and other properties of a metal shows that this electronic group of 18 breaks down and loses some of its electrons as soon as the atoms come together.

Palladium appears, like platinum, to be diamagnetic in all its compounds,[1259] though many of the analogous nickel compounds are paramagnetic. This is presumably the result of the larger atomic number.

In its general behaviour palladium resembles platinum very closely. The comparison of the elements in this subgroup, nickel, palladium, and platinum, gives a good illustration of the two main ways in which the properties change as we descend the series, the higher valencies becoming more important as compared with the lower, and the tendency in any given valency to dissociation becoming less.

Metallic Palladium

Metallic palladium resembles platinum closely in many ways; it has the lowest m. pt. (1,557°) of any of the platinum metals, and platinum has the next lowest (1,773·5°); it is also the lightest metal in its triad (Ru, 12·3; Rh, 12·1; Pd, 11·5) as platinum is in its triad (Os, 22·5; Ir, 22·4; Pt, 21·4).

[1257] J. B. Harrison and C. L. C. Bourne, *Off. Gaz. Brit. Guiana*, 1925, **27**, ii. 19.
[1258] A. N. Guthrie and M. J. Copley, *Phys. Rev.* 1931, [ii] **38**, 360.
[1259] R. B. Janes, *J.A.C.S.* 1935, **57**, 471.

Its main uses are for artificial teeth and for the mounting of jewellery, and of late years as a catalyst for organic reactions.

Palladium is more readily attacked by various reagents than the other members of the family. At a red heat it is converted by air into the monoxide PdO, and by fluorine and chlorine into the dihalides; it is soluble in nitric and sulphuric acids. Unlike all the other metals of the group it becomes passive in the presence of chlorine ions.[1260] It has the power of absorbing hydrogen reversibly (up to 900 volumes), far more than any other metal. It is also a powerful catalyst, especially in those forms in which it has a large surface, such as palladium black (which has been shown to be actually crystalline), and particularly in the various colloidal forms.

Colloidal palladium can be made[1261-3] by the reduction of palladous chloride solutions with various reducing agents such as formaldehyde, hydrazine hydrate, or carbon monoxide (a specific reducing agent for palladium),[1266] in presence of a protective colloid like sodium protalbate; if titanous chloride is used as the reducing agent, the hydrated titanium dioxide itself acts as the protective colloid.[1264] As a catalyst it is much used for reduction in organic chemistry; it is particularly effective in reducing the triple carbon link to the double in hydrocarbons, acids, and alcohols; the subsequent reduction of the double to the single link is slower.[1265] Like palladium black, colloidal palladium with hydrogen reduces aliphatic double links, and nitro-compounds, but not aromatic rings, ketones, or aldehydes, except when the carbonyl group is immediately next to a benzene ring, when the aldehyde or ketone is reduced to the corresponding hydrocarbon.[1266] It has also been shown[1267] that colloidal palladium is more effective than platinum in the reduction of oxygen or ethylene, but less so in that of potassium nitrite or sodium chlorate.

Palladium and Hydrogen

The enormous power that palladium has of absorbing hydrogen was first noticed by Graham in 1866. Since then there has been a constant series of investigations into the phenomenon, which cannot be said even now to have led to a thoroughly satisfactory explanation, probably because this has been sought along the lines of ordinary molecular chemistry, while the problem is essentially bound up with the peculiarities of metallic structure. All that can be done here is to give an outline of the facts and the more probable theories, with some of the more important references.

[1260] F. Müller, *Z. Elektrochem.* 1928, **34**, 744.

[1261] J. Donau, *Mon.* 1906, **27**, 71.

[1262] W. Traube and W. Lange, *Ber.* 1925, **58**, 2773.

[1263] H. S. Taylor and P. V. McKinney, *J.A.C.S.* 1931, **53**, 3604.

[1264] A. Gutbier and H. Weithase, *Z. anorg. Chem.* 1928, **169**, 264.

[1265] M. Bourguel, *Bull. Soc.* 1927, [4] **41**, 1443.

[1266] For more details see O. Neunhöffer and W. Pelz, *Ber.* 1939, **72**, 433.

[1267] G. Kahl and E. Biesalski, *Z. anorg. Chem.* 1936, **230**, 88.

Palladium in the colloidal, powdered, or compact state will absorb anything up to 900 times its own volume of hydrogen (about Pd_4H_3) at any temperature from zero to a red heat and beyond. As the temperature rises the amount absorbed falls steadily up to 600°, and more slowly above that. The absorption is accompanied by an expansion of the solid, and the lattice constant may increase by as much as 5 per cent.,[1268-9] while the conductivity falls by as much as 35 per cent.[1270] The whole of this hydrogen can be removed from the palladium in a vacuum at 100°. The adsorption isotherm at any temperature between 50° and 200° consists of three parts: (1) a rapid rise of pressure for amount adsorbed up to about $PdH_{0.05}$; (2) a very slow rise of pressure for the increase of hydrogen content up to $PdH_{0.4}$ to $PdH_{0.5}$; and (3) a rapid rise after that. But its course is different according as the gas is being put in or taken out—as the pressure is rising or falling. For a rising pressure there is a considerable increase over the middle section of the curve: for a falling pressure this is very small, and may be practically zero, i.e. the pressure may remain constant for a considerable drop in hydrogen concentration.[1271] As the temperature rises, the second and fairly flat part of the curve gets shorter, beginning a little later (i.e. at a rather higher concentration) and stopping much sooner, until at about 310°[1272] it has vanished altogether; the general shape of the curves is thus like that of the Andrews carbon dioxide diagram. The occurrence of hysteresis shows that either with rising or falling pressure (or both) equilibrium is not reached, and this needs explanation before the results can be interpreted. It has been pointed out by Tammann[1273] and by Smith and Derge[1274] that the behaviour of the palladium, and especially the rate of adsorption of the hydrogen, depend largely on the mechanical state and previous history of the metal, and on the extent to which it has been heated or worked. It seems probable that the hydrogen, having covered the surface, penetrates along the slip planes of the metal, and as it does so causes an expansion, which blocks the way for more hydrogen to enter, so that with rising pressure the attainment of equilibrium will be retarded, while when the pressure is falling the removal of part of the hydrogen will facilitate it. If so, the isotherms at falling pressure will be those which indicate the true equilibrium of the system. These, as we have seen, are nearly horizontal, which should mean that over this range there are two solid phases present, one with more hydrogen than the other. According to simple phase-rule principles, the beginning of the flat part should give the composition of the more dilute solution and the end that of the stronger. Since for temperatures near 100° the

[1268] J. D. Hanawalt, *Proc. Nat. Acad. Sci.* 1928, **14**, 953; *Phys. Rev.* 1929, ii. **33**, 444.

[1269] O. Linde and G. Boerelius, *Ann. Phys.* 1927, [iv] **84**, 747.

[1270] H. Brüning and A. Sieverts, *Z. physikal. Chem.* 1933, **163**, 409.

[1271] B. Lambert and S. F. Gates, *Proc. Roy. Soc.* 1925, **108**, 456.

[1272] H. Brüning and A. Sieverts, *Z. physikal. Chem.* 1933, **163**, 430.

[1273] G. Tammann and J. Schneider, *Z. anorg. Chem.* 1928, **172**, 43.

[1274] D. P. Smith and G. J. Derge, *J.A.C.S.* 1934, **56**, 2513.

end comes near the composition Pd_2H, it has often been assumed that a compound of this composition is formed. There are two objections to this view: (1) The middle parts of the isotherms are not quite flat but almost always show a definite though small rise of pressure. (2) The end is at about Pd_2H for a temperature of 75° or so, but the amount of hydrogen at this end-point gets less as the temperature rises. The answer to (2) probably is that the more concentrated phase is not a compound at all, especially as it is difficult to give Pd_2H a probable structure, but a solution, whose concentration would naturally vary with temperature. The first difficulty, that the isotherms are not strictly horizontal, is less easy to overcome; the suggestion that it is due to the complication of the results by surface action cannot be maintained. The answer is most probably to be found in the peculiar properties of metals, which it does not as yet seem possible to express in simple language. An attack on the problem from this point of view, by the methods of statistical mechanics, has been made by Lacher,[1275] who starts with the assumption that the hydrogen atoms occupy holes in the palladium lattice, and does not suppose that any compound with the metal is formed; on this basis he is able to obtain results agreeing very fairly with observation, and in particular to show that two solid solutions can be formed, with an upper critical solution temperature. This is confirmed by X-ray examination[1276-7]; with a palladium strip dipping into sulphuric acid and charged electrolytically with hydrogen, X-rays will show the migration of the boundary between the two phases.

An interesting point is the relation between the solubility in palladium of hydrogen and that of deuterium. Sieverts[1278-80] showed that the two isotopes behave similarly, but that deuterium is always less soluble than hydrogen. At low temperatures there is little difference (D/H = 0·96 at 30°) but by 200° D/H has fallen to 0·60, though it then rises again to 0·91 at 1,000° (the normal phenomenon of course is that deuterium and hydrogen differ much more at low temperatures than at high). The point where the isotherm begins to be flat is at higher concentrations with deuterium. It is therefore possible to find pressures and temperatures at which hydrogen is present only in the weaker (α) phase, while with deuterium the stronger (β) solution is present, and the solubility ratio D/H is then very small, and may be as low as 0·03; these are the conditions under which palladium may be used to separate the isotopes. The 'critical solution temperature' must be lower with deuterium than with hydrogen, but it has not been measured.

As a result of this power of dissolving in palladium, hydrogen is able to

[1275] J. R. Lacher, *Proc. Roy. Soc.* 1937, **161**, 525.
[1276] E. A. Owen and J. I. Jones, *Proc. Phys. Soc.* 1937, **49**, 587, 603.
[1277] D. P. Smith and C. S. Barrett, *J.A.C.S.* 1940, **62**, 2565.
[1278] A. Sieverts and G. Zapf, *Z. physikal. Chem.* 1935, **174**, 359.
[1279] A. Sieverts and W. Danz, ib. 1936, B **34**, 158.
[1280] Id., ib. 1937, B **38**, 46, 61.

diffuse through the solid when it is warmed. This is strictly specific for hydrogen and deuterium; helium, for example, has no such power.[1281] It is made use of in order to purify hydrogen for spectroscopic or atomic weight purposes, the gas being 'filtered' through a small palladium tube, which is usually heated electrically. The mechanism of this diffusion has recently been examined by Farkas[1282]; he measured the rate of diffusion through a palladium plate, and also the rate of atomization of the hydrogen on both surfaces by means of their efficiency in promoting the ortho/para equilibrium of hydrogen. He was thus able to show that the process of diffusion consists in the atomization of the hydrogen on one surface, the passage of the hydrogen atoms through the foil, and their recombination to hydrogen molecules on the other surface. This explains why the penetration is so rapid when the hydrogen is produced electrolytically; it is then already in the atomic state when it reaches the palladium, and so the heat of activation required by the molecules in order to break the H—H bond is no longer needed. See further, reference [1283].

NON-VALENT PALLADIUM[1284]

A COMPOUND $K_4[Pd(CN)_4]$ in which the metal is non-valent can be made in exactly the same way as its very similar nickel analogue (p. 1429) by the action of potassium on the double cyanide $K_2[Pd(CN)_4]$ in liquid ammonia. It is a yellowish solid, stable in ammonia or *in vacuo* up to 150°, but excessively reactive, even more so than the nickel compound. It will reduce azobenzene to hydrazo, and silver and mercuric ions to the metals. It evolves hydrogen with water. There was no sign of the formation of a compound $K_2[Pd(CN)_3]$.

MONOVALENT PALLADIUM

No compounds of this valency have been isolated; the supposed oxide Pd_2O has been shown[1285-6] to be a mixture of the monoxide PdO and metallic palladium, and the existence of the sulphide Pd_2S has not been confirmed.

Manchot[1287] has shown that if a 2 per cent. aqueous solution of the palladocyanide $K_2Pd(CN)_4$ is reduced with sodium amalgam, a clear yellow solution is obtained, which contains free cyanide ions (which the original solution does not) and has a strong reducing power, separating silver from an ammoniacal silver oxide solution, and mercury from corrosive sublimate; it absorbs oxygen with formation of hydrogen peroxide,

[1281] F. Paneth and K. Peters, ib. 1928, B **1**, 253.
[1282] A. Farkas, *Trans. Far. Soc.* 1936, **32**, 1667.
[1283] W. Jost and A. Widmann, *Z. physikal. Chem.* 1940, B **45**, 285.
[1284] J. J. Burbage and W. C. Fernelius, *J.A.C.S.* 1943, **65**, 1484.
[1285] L. Wöhler and J. König, *Z. anorg. Chem.* 1905, **46**, 323.
[1286] G. R. Levi and C. Fontana, *Gaz.* 1926, **56**, 388.
[1287] W. Manchot and H. Schmid, *Ber.* 1930, **63**, 2782.

and on standing in the absence of air it slowly evolves hydrogen and gives a mixture of the palladous salt and metallic palladium. This cannot be due to colloidal palladium: the solution is too concentrated, is too pale, and separates no gel with excess of potassium chloride. Its reducing power corresponds quantitatively to the conversion of mono- to divalent palladium. Apart from this last statement we should infer from the existence of $K_2[Pd(CN)_4]$, but not of $K_2[Pd(CN)_3]$, that Manchot's reduced solution contained non-valent palladium, and if so there would be no evidence for monovalent palladium whatever.

DIVALENT PALLADIUM

THIS is by far the most important valency of palladium, which in this respect resembles nickel and differs from platinum, where the tetravalent state is as important. The divalent palladium compounds are green, red, or brown, and have an astringent but not metallic taste.

Palladous Oxide, PdO

THIS is made by heating the metal in oxygen,[1288] or better by fusing palladous chloride with sodium nitrate at 600°.[1289] It is a black powder; its crystal structure has been examined by Moore and Pauling,[1290] who find that the metallic atom forms a coplanar rectangular co-ordination group. On further heating it dissociates into the metal and oxygen, the dissociation tension of the oxygen being 1 atm. at 875°.[1288]

It is a strong oxidizing agent; it glows on coming into contact with hydrogen at the ordinary temperature; it oxidizes carbon monoxide to the dioxide, but unlike most oxides of this kind it reacts with carbon monoxide less readily than with hydrogen, and only at temperatures near 100°.[1263,1291-2] At the same time palladous oxide is a powerful catalyst for the reduction by hydrogen, especially of organic compounds such as alkylenes[1293] and aldehydes,[1289] the CHO group being reduced with PdO to CH_3, but with platinum monoxide only to CH_2OH.

The hydroxide $Pd(OH)_2$ or PdO, H_2O can be made by the hydrolysis of the nitrate $Pd(NO_3)_2$. It is soluble in acids, unlike the oxide, which does not dissolve even in aqua regia. It loses its water slowly on heating, but does not lose the whole of it even at 500–600°, where it begins to give off oxygen.

Palladous Sulphide, PdS

This can be made by the action of hydrogen sulphide on a solution of a palladous salt, or by heating the metal with sulphur. When made in the

[1288] L. Wöhler, *Z. Elektrochem.* 1905, **11**, 836.
[1289] R. L. Shriner and R. Adams, *J.A.C.S.* 1924, **46**, 1683.
[1290] W. J. Moore and L. Pauling, ib. 1941, **63**, 1392.
[1291] P. V. McKinney, ib. 1932, **54**, 4498.
[1292] Id., ib. 1933, **55**, 3626.
[1293] J. W. Kern, R. L. Shriner, and R. Adams, *J.A.C.S.* 1925, **47**, 1147.

wet way it is a brown powder, insoluble in dilute hydrochloric acid; when made in the dry way[1294] it forms bluish insoluble crystals.

The system palladium-sulphur has been investigated by Biltz and Laar,[1295-6] who showed that near the ordinary temperature a compound Pd_4S is formed, which at higher temperatures is converted into the mono-sulphide PdS, m. pt. 970°; this will combine with excess of sulphur to give the disulphide PdS_2. Since the structure of Pd_4S is unknown, so is the valency of the palladium in it.

Palladous Selenide, PdSe[1297]

This is a dark brown solid, which can be made by adding palladous chloride solution drop by drop to a saturated solution of hydrogen selenide.

Palladous Halides

All four of these are known, but only the dichloride in any detail.

Palladous Fluoride, PdF_2

According to Berzelius this is precipitated as a brown powder, very slightly soluble in water or hydrofluoric acid, when hydrofluoric acid is added to a concentrated solution of the nitrate $Pd(NO_3)_2$. Ruff and Ascher[1298] have prepared the difluoride by the reduction of the more stable trifluoride PdF_3. This can be done in various ways, for example by hydrogen, or sulphur dioxide, or iodine vapour. The difluoride PdF_2 could not be obtained in the pure state, but if the trifluoride is heated with the necessary amount of palladium powder, the mixture glows, and a violet powder is formed which seems to be nearly pure palladium difluoride, since it dissolves in hydrochloric acid leaving only a small residue of metallic palladium. This product also gives a characteristic X-ray powder diagram, indicating that it forms tetragonal crystals of the rutile type, like the difluorides of iron, cobalt, and nickel. Ebert[1299] confirms the tetragonal structure, and finds the Pd—F distance to be 2·15 A.U. (theory 2·01).

If palladous chloride is heated in hydrogen fluoride gas, or fused with ammonium acid fluoride NH_4F_2H, brown crusts of impure PdF_2 are formed.

Palladous Chloride, $PdCl_2$

This can be made from its elements at a red heat; it forms red crystals which are very hygroscopic and readily soluble in water, from which they crystallize in dark red hygroscopic crystals of the dihydrate $PdCl_2, 2 H_2O$.

[1294] L. Wöhler, K. Ewald, and H. G. Krall, *Ber.* 1933, **66**, 1638.
[1295] F. Weibke and J. Laar, *Z. anorg. Chem.* 1935, **224**, 49.
[1296] W. Biltz and J. Laar, ib. 1936, **228**, 257.
[1297] L. Moser and K. Atynski, *Mon.* 1925, **45**, 235.
[1298] O. Ruff and E. Ascher, *Z. anorg. Chem.* 1929, **183**, 211.
[1299] F. Ebert, ib. 1931, **196**, 395.

The anhydrous crystals have been shown[1300] to consist of a continuous flat chain of atoms of the form

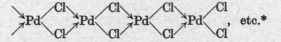

, etc.*

(distance Pd—Cl 2·31 A, theory 2·36).

On heating, palladous chloride begins at about 600° to sublime, and also to dissociate into its elements. The m. pt. is 936°; the dissociation pressure of chlorine is 1 atm. at 738°.[1301]

Palladous chloride is very readily reduced in solution to the metal; hydrogen effects this fairly rapidly in the cold[1303]; ethylene precipitates the metal on warming, and this reaction is specific for palladium, and enables it to be almost quantitatively separated from the other platinum metals.[1304] Many hydroaromatic compounds such as cyclohexane and cyclohexanol, or still better hydroquinolines and hydrocarbazoles, are converted into aromatic by boiling with a 2 per cent. aqueous solution of palladous chloride in dilute hydrochloric acid, with separation of the metal.[1302] It is also reduced by carbon monoxide. It forms a series of complexes $M_2[PdCl_4]$ (see below, p. 1568).

Palladous Bromide, $PdBr_2$, can be made from the elements in presence of nitric acid; it forms a brown mass which is soluble in hydrobromic acid but not in water.

Palladous Iodide, PdI_2, is made[1305] by precipitating palladous chloride solutions with potassium iodide. It forms a dark red or black precipitate, which is very insoluble in water, and can be used for the quantitative estimation of palladium.[1306] It begins to lose iodine at 100°, and at 330° to 360° is completely decomposed. It is slightly soluble in excess of potassium iodide to give a red solution, from which complex iodides such as K_2PdI_4 can be obtained.

---

* This formula is identical with

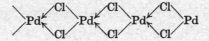

and no resonance is possible between them; this can be seen by writing them in the equivalent form

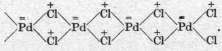

1300 A. F. Wells, *Z. Krist.* 1938, **100**, 189.

1301 J. Krustinsons, *Z. Elektrochem.* 1938, **44**, 537.

1302 G. W. Cooke and J. M. Gulland, *J.C.S.* 1939, 872.

1303 V. V. Ipatiev and V. G. Troner, *J. Gen. Chem. Russ.* 1935, **5**, 643; *C.R. Acad. U.R.R.S.* 1935, **1**, 622.

1304 S. C. Ogburn and W. C. Brastow, *J.A.C.S.* 1933, **55**, 1307.

1305 E. Müller and W. Stein, *Z. Elektrochem.* 1934, **40**, 133.

1306 L. W. Winkler, *Z. angew. Chem.* 1918, **1**, 101.

Other palladous salts:

Palladous cyanide, $Pd(CN)_2$, is got as a yellow precipitate when mercuric cyanide is added to a solution of a palladous salt quite free from acid. It gives complex salts with alkaline cyanides.

Palladous thiocyanate, $Pd(CNS)_2$, is described as a reddish precipitate.

Palladous nitrate, $Pd(NO_3)_2$, forms yellow-brown crystals, deliquescent and readily hydrolysed.

Palladous sulphate. The dihydrate $PdSO_4, 2H_2O$ is reddish-brown, the monohydrate olive-green; both are deliquescent and easily hydrolysed by water, forming palladous hydroxide and basic sulphates.

Palladous selenate, $PdSeO_4$. This can be made[1307] by dissolving palladium powder in a mixture of selenic and nitric acids. Small dark brownish hygroscopic prisms, reduced to selenium dioxide by hot concentrated hydrochloric acid. Forms double salts with ammonium sulphate and with ammonium selenate.

COMPLEX PALLADOUS COMPOUNDS

DIVALENT palladium forms numerous and fairly stable complexes, in nearly all of which it has a co-ordination number of 4, though there are a few which are 3, and a few which may be 6-covalent. The stability of the complexes is greater than with nickel, but definitely less than with platinum. This is the usual trend of stability of covalent links in a periodic subgroup. (For the cyanides, thiocyanates, and nitro-compounds, see p. 1566.)

Tricovalent Palladous Complexes

These seem to be confined to certain complex chlorides and bromides of organic bases, of the type $(BH)[Pd(hal)_3]$. They were prepared by Gutbier and Fellner,[1318] who found that while these components in concentrated solution gave the usual tetrahalides $(BH)_2[Pd(hal)_4]$, if the solution was more dilute dark coloured salts slowly crystallized out which were the trihalides. They were all dark brown or red, could be recrystallized from the halogen acid, and were often quite stable on keeping. Examples are the $(BH)[Pd(hal)_3]$ salts of tripropylamine (dark brown), dibutylamine (dark brown), and benzylethylamine (red).

4-Covalent Palladous Complexes

These are far more numerous; they are very similar to those of divalent platinum, and usually isomorphous with them. They are nearly all of

[1307] K. Hradecky, *Mon.* 1915, **36**, 289.
[1308] A. Cahours and Gal, *C.R.* 1870, **70**, 897.
[1309] I. Bellucci, *Atti R.* 1904, [5] **13**, ii. 386.
[1310] A. Gutbier, *Ber.* 1905, **38**, 2107.
[1311] A. Gutbier and A. Krell, ib. 3869.
[1312] A. Gutbier, A. Krell, and R. L. Janssen, *Z. anorg. Chem.* 1905, **47**, 23.
[1313] A. Gutbier and A. Krell, *Ber.* 1906, **39**, 616.
[1314] Id., ib. 1292.   [1315] A. Gutbier and M. Woernle, ib. 2716.
[1316] G. A. Barbieri, *Atti R.* 1914, [5] **23**, i. 334.   [1317] Id., ib. 880.
[1318] A. Gutbier and C. Fellner, *Z. anorg. Chem.* 1916, **95**, 129.

four types: (I) [PdAm$_4$]Cl$_2$; (II) [PdAm$_2$Cl$_2$]°; (III) [(PdAmCl$_2$)$_2$]°;
(IV) (NH$_4$)$_2$[PdCl$_4$], in which Am represents ammonia, an amine, or half
a diamine, and the chlorine atoms can be replaced by other acidic groups.
The NH$_3$ can also be replaced by the sulphur or selenium of the thio- or
seleno-ethers, or by oxygen.

We have evidence of the weaker attachment of the groups to palladium than to platinum in the facts that the conversion of type I to II by
acid is easy with palladium but difficult with platinum; that isomerism
(*cis-trans*) of compounds of type II is rare and has only recently been
discovered with palladium, while with platinum it has long been known;
and that compounds of the types of [Pd(NH$_3$)$_3$X]X and M[Pd(NH$_3$)X$_3$]
are almost unknown,* though their platinum analogues can be prepared.[1320]

There is abundant evidence (see refs. [1319,1333,1339–40,1345,1347,1351,1354–5]) that

* Mann and Purdie[1349] have made the salt [Bu$_3$P→Pd enCl]Cl.

[1319] R. G. Dickinson, *J.A.C.S.* 1922, **44**, 2404.
[1320] E. Fritzmann, *Z. anorg. Chem.* 1924, **133**, 119.
[1321] Id., ib. 133.   [1322] L. Tschugaev, ib. **134**, 277.
[1323] L. Tschugaev and C. Ivanov, ib. **135**, 153.
[1324] L. Tschugaev, *Arbeiten über Komplexverbindungen des Pt und Pd mit orga-nischen Sulfiden*, published after his death in 1924 by E. Fritzmann in Petrograd.
[1325] G. Landesen, *Z. anorg. Chem.* 1926, **154**, 429.
[1326] F. G. Mann and W. J. Pope, *J.C.S.* 1926, 482.
[1327] G. T. Morgan and J. D. Main Smith, ib. 912.
[1328] F. Krauss and F. Brodkorb, *Z. anorg. Chem.* 1927, **165**, 73.
[1329] F. Krauss and K. Mählmann, *Siebert Festschrift*, 1931, 215.
[1330] H. Reihlen and W. Hühn, *Ann.* 1931, **489**, 42.
[1331] H. Reihlen, E. Weinbrenner, and G. v. Hessling, ib. 1932, **494**, 143.
[1332] H. D. K. Drew, F. W. Pinkard, G. H. Preston, and W. Wardlaw, *J.C.S.* 1932, 1895.
[1333] E. G. Cox and G. H. Preston, ib. 1933, 1089.
[1334] H. D. K. Drew, G. H. Preston, W. Wardlaw, and G. H. Wyatt, ib. 1294.
[1335] A. A. Grünberg and V. M. Schulman, *C.R. Acad. Sci. U.R.S.S.* 1933, 218.
[1336] H. Holzer, *Z. anal. Chem.* 1933, **95**, 392.
[1337] A. Rosenheim and L. Gerb, *Z. anorg. Chem.* 1933, **210**, 289.
[1338] H. D. K. Drew and G. H. Wyatt, *J.C.S.* 1934, 56.
[1339] E. G. Cox, H. Saenger, and W. Wardlaw, ib. 182.
[1340] F. W. Pinkard, E. Sharratt, W. Wardlaw, and E. G. Cox, ib. 1012.
[1341] F. P. Dwyer and D. P. Mellor, *J.A.C.S.* 1934, **56**, 1551.
[1342] K. A. Jensen, *Z. anorg. Chem.* 1934, **221**, 6.
[1343] E. G. Cox, F. W. Pinkard, W. Wardlaw, and K. C. Webster, *J.C.S.* 1935, 459.
[1344] J. S. Jennings, E. Sharratt, and W. Wardlaw, ib. 818.
[1345] E. G. Cox, W. Wardlaw, and K. C. Webster, ib. 1475.
[1346] F. G. Mann and D. Purdie, ib. 1549.
[1347] F. G. Mann, D. Crowfoot, D. C. Gattiker, and N. Wooster, ib. 1642.
[1348] F. P. Dwyer and D. P. Mellor, *J.A.C.S.* 1935, **57**, 605.
[1349] F. G. Mann and D. Purdie, ib. 1936, 873.
[1350] H. Reihlen and E. Flohr, *Ber.* 1936, **69**, 325.
[1351] W. Theilacker, *Z. anorg. Chem.* 1937, **234**, 161.
[1352] J. Chatt and F. G. Mann, *J.C.S.* 1938, 1949.
[1353] M. S. Kharasch, R. C. Seyler, and F. R. Mayo, *J.A.C.S.* 1938, **60**, 882.
[1354] F. G. Mann and A. F. Wells, *J.C.S.* 1938, 702.
[1355] A. F. Wells, *Proc. Roy. Soc.* 1938, **167**, 169.

the four valencies of the divalent palladium in these compounds lie in a plane, with the angles all equal to 90° (when the four attached groups are the same) and the links of the same length. Attempts to dispute this, involving the assumption of small departures from equality of the lengths or angles of the valencies in AB_4 ions, or of the asymmetry of such ions deduced from the rotatory power of their compounds with other ions known to be active (Reihlen[1330-1,1337,1350]) have been well answered by Jensen[1356] and are generally abandoned. A final proof has been given by Mills[1357] by resolving a 4-covalent palladous complex of the same type as that obtained by Mills and Quibell (below, p. 1592) for platinum.

The very various palladous complexes are most satisfactorily classified according to the nature of the atoms attached to the palladium, which are always four in number, the more important being nitrogen, phosphorus, arsenic, oxygen, sulphur, and the halogens.

The peculiar apparently tri-covalent type of the monammines and the like, such as $(R_3P)PdCl_2$, which are really dimeric and 4-covalent, are discussed later (p. 1569.)

Tetrammines

The simple tetrammines, such as $[Pd(NH_3)_4]Cl_2$, are made by the direct combination of their components, and form colourless crystals. The free base $[Pd(NH_3)_4](OH)_2$, got from the sulphate with baryta, forms colourless crystals with a strong alkaline reaction, which precipitate the hydroxides of copper, iron, aluminium, etc. (but not silver), from solutions of their salts. A series of tetrammine salts have recently been made, with ammonia, pyridine, ethylene diamine, etc.[1332]; they are all colourless. Among the chelate tetrammines are the derivatives of 3-methyl-2-aminomethyl-4-ethyl-quinoline ('quen'), of the type $[Pd(quen)_2]Cl_2$.[1330]

The interchange of deuterium between water and $[Pd(NH_3)_4]Cl_2$ has been found[1358] to go more easily than with platinum, and still more easily than with cobalt, in agreement with the general order of stabilities of these complexes.

Of considerable stereochemical significance is the derivative of the 'quadridentate' base β, β', β''-triamino-triethylamine, $N(CH_2 \cdot CH_2 \cdot NH_2)_3$ ('tren'); the iodide $[Pd(tren)]I_2$ was made by Mann and Pope[1326]; it is a cream-coloured salt, only slightly soluble in water.

A curious series of compounds of this type are the triazene or diazo-amino-complexes, derived from the diazoamino-compounds

$$Ar-NH-N=N-Ar';$$

these, which are no doubt chelate, and of the type

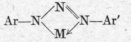

[1356] K. A. Jensen, *Z. anorg. Chem.* 1939, **241**, 126.
[1357] A. G. Lidstone and W. H. Mills, *J.C.S.* 1939, 1754.
[1358] J. S. Anderson, H. V. A. Briscoe, L. H. Cobb, and N. L. Spoor, ib. 1943, 367.

occur only in one form[1359] owing evidently to resonance. The palladium compound $Pd(Ar \cdot N = N - N \cdot Ar)_2$ must have this rather unusual structure

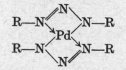

with two 4-rings. Its great stability supports the idea of resonance. It will take on another molecule of diazo-amino-compound by direct addition, giving a presumably trichelate complex, almost the only known 6-covalent complex of divalent palladium.

Glyoxime Compounds

These N_4 complexes are derived from glyoxime $R_2C_2N_2O_2H_2$ ($= DH_2$) containing the chelate ring

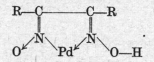

They are dichelate, and of the type $Pd(DH)_2$; they can be made by the action of the oxime on palladous chloride in hydrochloric acid solution (i.e. on the chloropalladite).

They are very slightly soluble in water, and can be used for the separation and estimation of palladium. Palladium is precipitated quantitatively from a solution of palladous chloride in hydrochloric acid by dimethyl glyoxime ($R = CH_3$), by benzoyl methyl glyoxime

$$R = C_6H_5CO, CH_3,$$

and by salicylaldoxime (p. 1566), none of which will precipitate platinum under these conditions.[1336] The benzoyl-methyl-glyoxime derivative $Pd(DH)_2$ occurs in two forms,[1341,1348] α, pale yellow, m. pt. 175°, and β-, dark yellow, m. pt. 207°; the α readily goes over into the β on boiling for a few minutes in xylene. These are no doubt the *cis* and *trans* modifications of the planar dichelate compound.

Diammines, etc.

The diammines $[PdAm_2R_2]°$, which are not ionized, have been made in great variety, by the action of the base on the chloropalladite M_2PdCl_4, or of acids on the tetrammine, or in other ways.[1310-15]

Cis-trans isomerism among these compounds is to be expected, and various cases of isomerism have been reported. Of the simplest diammine $[Pd(NH_3)_2Cl_2]$ no less than four forms have been described.[1328-9,1332,1335,1347] One of these is the metameric dimer $[Pd(NH_3)_4] \cdot [PdCl_4]$; the first and third differ in chemical properties and are probably the *cis* and *trans*

[1359] F. P. Dwyer, *J.A.C.S.* 1941, **63**, 78.

forms, and the last, being identical in solution with the *trans* form, is probably a polymorphic modification of it.

As a rule, however, the diammines are only known in one form; the configuration of this has not been determined, but it probably[1338] is the *trans* form, except where the two amine groups are those of a diamine like *en*.

The transition from *cis* to *trans* or vice versa occurs with these palladium complexes with great ease, much more readily than with their platinum analogues. Thus Mann and his colleagues[1347] find that the diammine form I, which is probably *trans*, readily reacts with potassium oxalate to give the oxalato-compound

$$\text{H}_3\text{N} \diagdown \text{Pd} \diagup \text{O--C=O}$$
$$\text{H}_3\text{N} \diagup \qquad \diagdown \text{O--C=O}$$

which must be *cis*, while with potassium nitrite it gives the nitro-compound $\text{Pd}(\text{NH}_3)_2(\text{NO}_2)_2$ which is shown by X-ray analysis to be *trans*. Incidentally the X-ray analysis shows all the compounds examined to be planar.

The chlorine atoms in these diammines can be replaced by various other radicals both monovalent and divalent (ato). The bromides are very similar to the chlorides, and so are the iodides so far as they are known; no fluorides have been prepared.

Similar hydrazine complexes, such as $[\text{PdCl}_2(\text{N}_2\text{H}_4)_2]$ (orange crystals), have been made.[1360]

The amines can be replaced by tertiary phosphines and arsines. This group of compounds[1308] has been investigated in detail by Mann and his colleagues.[1346-7,1349,1354] They are of the types

$$(\text{R}_3\text{P})_2\text{PdCl}_2 \text{ and } (\text{R}_3\text{As})_2\text{PdCl}_2,$$

and are made by heating the phosphine or arsine with ammonium palladochloride $(\text{NH}_4)_2[\text{PdCl}_4]$ in water. In every case only one form is known, which appears to be the *trans*; this conclusion is supported by the low dipole moments; for example that of $(\text{Et}_3\text{P})_2\text{PdCl}_2$ is 1·05 D. The compounds are yellow or orange, have low melting-points, and are readily soluble in alcohol or benzene. Their most peculiar property is the parachor. If the value of this for palladium is calculated with the usual allowance for the alkyl groups, it is found[1346] to fall rapidly as these get larger:

Values of the Parachor of Palladium

	$(\text{R}_2\text{S})_2\text{PdCl}_2$		$(\text{R}_3\text{P})_2\text{PdCl}_2$		$(\text{R}_3\text{As})_2\text{PdCl}_2$	
	M. pt.	$[\text{P}]_{\text{Pd}}$	*M. pt.*	$[\text{P}]_{\text{Pd}}$	*M. pt.*	$[\text{P}]_{\text{Pd}}$
R = CH$_3$ . . .	130°	36	..	..	235°	..
C$_2$H$_5$ . . .	81°	27	139°	22	116°	12
n-Propyl . .	59°	16	96°	3	55°	−5
n-Butyl . .	32°	4	66°	−12	54°	−14
iso-butyl . .	97°	12	..	..	..	..
n-Amyl . .	41°	−7	47°	−14	10°	−29

[1360] V. I. Goremikin, *C.R. Acad. U.R.S.S.* 1941, **33**, 227.

A similar fall in the parachor for the metallic atom with an increase in the alkyl was found[1346] in the mercury mercaptides $Hg(S \cdot Alk)_2$ and in many chelate β-diketone derivatives of beryllium and aluminium.

Complex *cyanides* of the type $M_2[Pt(CN)_4]$ are known[1361] and are stable. The X-ray structure of the salt $Ba[Pd(CN)_4], 4 H_2O$ shows[1362] that it has a planar square anion, and that all the water is attached to the cation.

Similar *thiocyanates* have been made,[1309,1361] such as the ruby-red $K_2[Pd(CNS)_4]$.

Nitrile Compounds. When palladous chloride is heated in benzonitrile, it forms the orange-yellow solid $(C_6H_5 \cdot CN)_2PdCl_2$.[1353] This is remarkable for replacing when treated with ethylene the two nitrile molecules by one ethylene, giving the dimeric $[(C_2H_4)PdCl_2]_2$.

The *nitro-complexes* (sometimes wrongly called nitrito-) such as $K_2[Pd(NO_2)_4]$, a yellow powder,[1361] are of the same type.

Glycine Derivatives

These contain the chelate ring

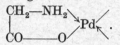

The non-ionized compound $Pd(Gl)_2[NH_2CH_2COOH = GlH]$ was shown[1340] to occur in *cis* and *trans* forms, one yellow prisms forming a trihydrate, the other pale yellow plates; they are interconvertible on heating with water, which the corresponding platinum compounds are not.

Compound of Ethylenediamine-bis-acetylacetone

This substance (ecH$_2$) has the formula

$$
\begin{array}{ccc}
& CH_3 & CH_3 \\
& | & | \\
CH_2-N{=}C-CH{=}C-OH \\
| \\
CH_2-N{=}C-CH{=}C-OH \\
& | & | \\
& CH_3 & CH_3
\end{array}
$$

It acts as a quadridentate group like two glycine molecules, and forms yellow needles of Pd(ec). (Morgan.[1327])

Salicylaldoxime compounds have been made.[1343] The corresponding nickel and platinum compounds are known in two isomeric forms, but the palladium compound only in one, which is shown by X-ray analysis to be the *trans*.

The benzoin-oxime compound has the dichelate structure with the ring

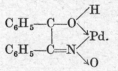

[1361] R. B. Janes, *J.A.C.S.* 1935, **57**, 471.
[1362] H. Brasseur and A. de Rassenfosse, *Soc. Franc. Min.* 1938, **61**, 129.

The nickel palladium and platinum compounds all occur in two forms; the nickel compounds, unlike the glyoximes, are paramagnetic, which has not been explained.[1344]

Thiosemicarbazide Complexes[1342]

Thiosemicarbazide (thH) has the tautomeric formulae

(I)   (II)

and can form chelate rings, either by direct addition or by replacement of the S—H hydrogen. It reacts with potassium palladochloride in solution to give a brown precipitate of the composition $Pd(thH)Cl_2$, which is no doubt the salt $[Pd(thH)_2] \cdot [PdCl_4]$, since it can be converted into the slightly soluble chloride $[Pd(thH)_2]Cl_2$ and the almost insoluble sulphate $[Pd(thH)_2]SO_4$; the cation must contain the two chelate groups

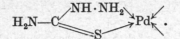

If the solution is made alkaline two equivalents of acid are removed, and a green precipitate is formed of a non-electrolyte, in which evidently the palladium has replaced two hydrogen atoms of the molecules of the thio-compound, no doubt in its sulphydryl form:

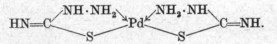

When it is warmed, this substance is converted into a brown crystalline isomer. The two forms are too insoluble for their molecular weights to be determined, but they are almost certainly the *cis* and *trans* forms.

Oxygen Complexes

These include a salicylato-compound and an acetylacetonate. Salicylic acid gives rise to a complex acid[1317]:

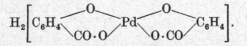

The acetylacetonate $Pd(C_5H_7O_2)_2$ forms yellow crystals; it is mono-meric in benzene by the freezing-point, and it is isomorphous with the corresponding cupric compound.[1316]

Sulphur Complexes

The amine groups in the palladous diammine derivatives can be replaced by organic sulphur compounds, and especially by thioethers. The first work on these compounds was that of Tschugaev.[1322-4] The sulphur is less firmly attached to the palladium than nitrogen, and no isomers of these sulphides are known. The compounds are monomeric in chloroform solution by the boiling-point, and in benzene by the freezing-point.[1313] The dimethyl compound $(Me_2S)_2PdCl_2$ has been shown by a detailed crystallographic examination[1339] to be completely isomorphous with the α-form of the corresponding platinum compound, which is known to have a planar *trans* structure, and so no doubt the palladous thioether compounds like the diammines have the *trans* configuration.

They are made (like the ammines) by the action of the sulphide on the palladochloride in water. The chlorides, bromides, and iodides are known.[1323] The products, which are all of the type $(R_2S)_2PdX_2$, are soluble in chloroform and benzene, and even in ligroin. As we have seen, their melting-points are low, and their parachors show an unexplained diminution as the size of the alkyl group increases.

The corresponding chelate compounds have been made from the disulphide $EtS \cdot CH_2 \cdot CH_2 \cdot SEt$ ('es') and are very similar,[1334] but their melting-points are higher and their solubilities less.[1338] They are obviously *cis*-compounds, and their properties are in agreement with this.

The complexes formed by aryl-alkyl sulphides[1363] can be used to identify the sulphides; those with palladous chloride nearly always are of the type $(C_6H_5 \cdot S \cdot R)_2PdCl_2$, but when the alkyl group R is tertiary butyl or tertiary amyl this type loses a molecule of the thioether to give the red compound, $(C_6H_5 \cdot S \cdot R)PdCl_2$, no doubt in the dimeric form.

Selenium Complexes

They are made[1320-1] in the same way as the sulphur compounds, and are very like them; they are all of the type $(R_2Se)_2PdX_2$, and the melting-points of the chlorides are: CH_3 127°; Et 45°; Bu 79°; C_6H_5 181°. The chlorides (yellow or orange), the bromides (dark orange), and the iodides (nearly black) are known; they are soluble in chloroform and in benzene, and monomeric in the latter by the freezing-points. They are only known in one series.

Fritzmann also prepared the chelate derivatives of

$$Et \cdot Se \cdot CH_2 \cdot CH_2 \cdot CH_2 \cdot Se \cdot Et.$$

Complex Palladous Halides

These salts, which have the general formula $M_2[Pd(hal)_4]$, are known with chlorine, bromine, and iodine, but not with fluorine.[1310-15,1318] The chlorides are yellow or brown, and are isomorphous with the platinous compounds; the bromides are brown, and reasonably stable; the iodides are greenish-black.

The chlorides are the first compounds in which it was shown that the 4-covalent palladous atom can be planar (Dickinson[1319]): see further, references [1333,1351]. The Pd—Cl distance is 2·29 A.

[1363] V. N. Ipatiev and B. S. Friedman, *J.A.C.S.* 1939, **61**, 684.

The dissociation constant of the chloro-palladite ion $[PdCl_4]^{--}$ has been found[1364] by E.M.F. measurements to be at 25° about 6×10^{-14}.

Complexes of the type $(PdAmR_2)_2$

These peculiar compounds are proved by the molecular weights in solution to be dimeric. The co-ordinated molecule Am here is not an amine, but can be a tertiary phosphine or arsine, or another molecule such as carbon monoxide or even ethylene. The phosphine and arsine compounds (Mann[1346,1349,1354-5]) can be made from the di-phosphine or diarsine compounds $(R_3P)_2PdCl_2$ and $(R_3As)_2PdCl_2$ by boiling them with alcohol, when one molecule of phosphine or arsine is removed. With the arsines the same change can be effected by distillation:

$$(R_3As)_2PdCl_2 \longrightarrow R_3As + (R_3AsPdCl_2)_2.$$

The (dimeric) product is always crystallographically homogeneous, and never occurs in two isomeric forms; the corresponding phosphorus and arsenic compounds are always isomorphous.

Compounds in which the chlorine of these substances is replaced by iodine, NO_2, or CNS can be made.[1346]

The dimerization evidently secures by co-ordination the four-fold covalency of the palladous atom; this can take place in three ways, as was originally suggested for a group of similar platinum compounds by Werner:

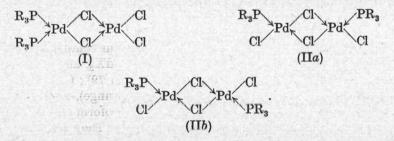

(I)   (IIa)

(IIb)

The most marked difference is between I and the two forms of II, since I has both the phosphine or arsine groups on the same palladium atom. The behaviour of these compounds is exactly like that of the monoalkyl auric halides $(Alk \cdot Au(hal)_2)_2$ (I. 186), except that the latter are not tautomeric in solution (as the palladium compounds are) but seem to be wholly of type I.

Two of the solid compounds, the chloride and bromide $(CH_3)_3AsPdX_2$ have been shown by X-ray analysis[1354-5] to be of the type IIb. The rest may probably be of the same type in the solid state, but in solution they all behave tautomerically, the reactions being sometimes those of I and sometimes of II; the dipole moments support this, that of $(R_3P \cdot PdCl_2)_2$ being 2·34,[1365] whereas that of $(Et \cdot AuBr_2)_2$ is 5·5 D.

[1364] D. H. Templeton, G. W. Watt, and C. S. Garner, ib. 1943, **65**, 1608.
[1365] J. Chatt and F. G. Mann, *J.C.S.* 1939, 1622.

Reactions of Type I. (Two P or As on one Pd)

1. They are formed directly from the diphosphine or arsine derivatives and the palladochloride, i.e. by the direct addition of $PdCl_2$ to a molecule already having two of these groups on the Pd.

2. α,α'-dipyridyl converts the compound into $(R_3P)_2PdCl_2+(dipy)PdCl_2$ (the arsine does the same).

3. The phosphine compound with potassium oxalate gives

$$(R_3P)_2PdCl_2PdOx$$

(the arsine gives no reaction here).

4. The phosphine compound with potassium nitrite gives a tetranitro-product whose unsymmetrical structure is shown by its further reactions with oxalic acid and with dipyridyl, as follows:

KNO_2 gives $(R_3P)_2Pd(NO_2)_2Pd(NO_2)_2$: with oxalic acid this gives $(R_3P)_2Pd(NO_2)_2PdOx$, and with dipyridyl

$$(R_3P)_2Pd(NO_2)_2 + (dipy)Pd(NO_2)_2.$$

5. With the arsine compound potassium nitrite gives a very similar reaction, the products being $(R_3As)_2Pd(NO_2)_2$ and $K_2[Pd(NO_2)_4]$.

6. With ammonia the arsine compound gives $[(R_3As)_2Pd(NH_3)_2]Cl_2$ and $(R_3As)_2PdCl_2$. The phosphine reacts with ammonia after formula II, as we shall see.

All these reactions give products which have two arsines or phosphines on one palladium, and therefore are derived from formula I.

Reactions of Type II. (1 P or As on each Pd atom)

1. The second method of preparation described above, the distillation of the arsine compound $(R_3As)_2PdCl_2$, which we should expect to begin with the loss of one arsine.

2. The phosphine compound when treated with aniline, p-toluidine, or pyridine forms two molecules of the type

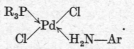

The arsine compound does the same, and so does the tetranitro-compound, with the NO_2 bridge.

3. Unlike the arsine, the phosphine reacts with ammonia to give either $[R_3P \cdot Pd(NH_3)_3]Cl_2$ or $R_3P \cdot Pd(NH_3)Cl_2$—in either case a compound with one phosphorus on each palladium.

The reaction of ethylene diamine is ambiguous. With the phosphine compound it gives in alcoholic solution $[R_3P \cdot Pd(en)Cl]Cl$ (a derivative of formula II) and in benzene a mixture of $[Pd\ en_2]Cl_2$ and $(R_3P)_2PdCl_2$, a derivative of I. The arsine compounds always react with ethylene diamine in the second way.

The evidence for the tautomeric behaviour of these compounds is very convincing, and it shows how readily the groups attached to the palladium can be interchanged.

The oxalato-compound $(Bu_3P)_2PdCl_2Pd(C_2O_4)$ would naturally be written

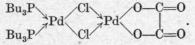

This, however, would involve a dipole moment of the order of 12 D, and the observed value is only 3·55.[1349] It therefore seems not impossible that it may be the oxalato-group that is forming the bridge, and not the chlorine atoms. This would be compatible with three isomeric structures, corresponding to the three tetrachlorides above:

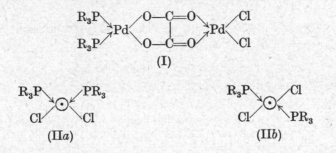

($\odot$ standing for the middle bridged ring).

The oxalato-group in this molecule would be symmetrical by resonance, so that the observed moment of 3·55 is not improbable for a tautomeric mixture of the 3.

Of the 'pure' double oxalates $M_2[Pd(C_2O_4)_2]$ a sodium salt with 2 and a potassium salt with 3 H_2O have been prepared.[1325]

As we have seen, a variety of atoms and groups can serve as bridges in these compounds. In the chlorobromide $(R_3P)_2Pd_2Cl_2Br_2$ an X-ray examination[1354] showed that the two atoms of the bridge are the same (not one chlorine and one bromine), and the reactions of the compounds indicate that they are most probably bromine. Among other groups which can act as bridges we have seen that there are NO_2, CNS (no doubt through the sulphur) and probably the oxalato-group. Another group is thio-alkyl (Alk. S—), the mercaptan radical. Chatt and Mann[1352] have shown that ethyl mercaptan acts on $(Bu_3P \cdot PdCl_2)_2$ to replace first one and then the other of the bridge chlorines by the Et·S— radical; this is proved by the fact that dipyridyl and *p*-toluidine, which will replace bridge chlorines, have no action on the product. These thio-compounds are as ready to react and interchange their groups as the other palladium compounds; the monothiol compound, having the bridge which is bright yellow, when it is dissolved in benzene is partly converted into the dithiol with the bridge

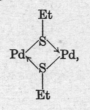

and the tetrachloro-compound, which is red; this is shown by the facts that the yellow colour turns to reddish, and the resulting solution reacts with dipyridyl, which only a bridge-chlorine will do.

It is now clear that various other compounds of divalent palladium, and still more of platinum, of the type $A \cdot PdX_2$ polymerize in the same way; among the palladous compounds are the carbonyl $CO \cdot PdCl_2$ (p. 1577): the phosphorus trichloride compound $(PCl_3)PdCl_2$, and the ester derived from it $(P(OEt)_3)PdCl_2$.[1366]

These compounds have not been proved to be dimeric, but there can be little doubt that they are so.

Possible 6-covalent Palladous Complexes

The number of these compounds is certainly very small, and in none of them is the 6-covalency established. The most important examples are:

1. Mann[1367-8] has described an apparently 6-covalent palladous compound of 1,2,3-triamino-propane ('trp'), $[Pd(trp)_2]I_2$. It is, however, possible that in this molecule only two of the three nitrogen atoms are acting as donors, which would reduce the covalency to 4.

2. The action[1332] of hydrochloric acid and hydrogen peroxide on $(NH_4)_2PdCl_4$ gives a black compound of the composition $(NH_3)_2PdCl_3$, which is no doubt a Pd^{ii}—Pd^{iv} compound of the structure whose dark

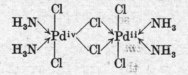

colour is due to the resonance and the accompanying shift of the electronic charge. The hydroxide $(NH_3)_2PdCl_2OH$[1369] is also black.

With these compounds it might be maintained that in either constituent form the 6 covalencies are only present on the tetravalent palladium atom, and the other two NH_3 groups are not really attached (like one of the fluorine atoms in the anion F_2H); if this is not regarded as satisfactory, it is at any rate obvious that the instability of the 6-covalency of divalent palladium is helped out by the resonance energy.

[1366] E. Fink, *C.R.* 1892, **115**, 176; 1898, **126**, 646.
[1367] *J.C.S.* 1928, 892. [1368] Ib. 1929, 656.
[1369] L. Tschugaev and J. Tscherniak, *Z. anorg. Chem.* 1929, **182**, 159.

Another apparently 6-covalent complex is the addition product formed by the diazo-amino-complex (p. 1563) with another molecule of the diazo-amino-compound; this is presumably tri-chelate.

In any case it is clear that the palladous atom practically always has a covalency of 4, and that it rarely, if ever, either falls below or exceeds it.

TRIVALENT PALLADIUM

THERE can be little doubt that palladium is able to assume the trivalent state, but this condition is usually very unstable, and the compounds are confined to the oxide, the fluoride, and a few unstable complex chlorides. It is probable that the compounds are all really complex, and they all appear to be decomposed by water at the ordinary temperature.

Palladium Sesquioxide, Pd_2O_3

Palladium sesquioxide,[1370] like the dioxide, is endothermic and decomposes at the ordinary temperature. It can be made (along with the dioxide) in the hydrated form Pd_2O_3 aq. by the cautious oxidation of a solution of palladous nitrate either anodically at $-8°$, or with ozone. This is an unstable chocolate-brown powder, going almost wholly into the monoxide PdO in 4 days in the cold, or more slowly in a desiccator. If it is heated the hydrate loses water, and then before this loss is complete it changes suddenly, with incandescence or explosion, into the monoxide. It is almost insoluble in nitric or sulphuric acid, but it readily dissolves in hydrochloric with evolution of chlorine, except at very low temperatures where it gives an unstable brown solution, which must contain trichloride or some complex derived from it.

The sulphide Pd_2S_3 does not seem to exist.[1374]

Palladium Trifluoride, PdF_3

It is very remarkable that this is the normal product of the action of fluorine on palladium or palladous chloride, and is more stable than the only other fluoride, the difluoride PdF_2. The trifluoride is made[1371] by the action of fluorine on palladium at $500°$ in a fluorite tube, or more easily on palladous chloride at $200–250°$, when a quartz tube can be used.

It is a black crystalline powder. It is isomorphous with the trifluorides of iron, cobalt, and rhodium,[1373] all of them being trigonal-rhombohedric[1372];

[1370] L. Wöhler and F. Martin, ib. 1908, **57**, 398.
[1371] O. Ruff and E. Ascher, ib., 1929, **183**, 206.
[1372] F. Ebert, ib. 1931, **196**, 395.
[1373] J. A. A. Ketelaar, *Nature*, 1931, **128**, 303.
[1374] W. Biltz and J. Laar, *Z. anorg. Chem.* 1936, **228**, 257.

the Pd—F distance is 2·06 A, and thus rather less than in the difluoride, where it is 2·15 A (theory 2·05).

Palladium trifluoride is very hygroscopic, and decomposes in the moist state, but can be kept in a desiccator. It is very reactive; it is very easily reduced, the products being the difluoride and then metallic palladium; with hydrochloric acid it evolves chlorine, and with water it gives off oxygen, leaving the hydrated monoxide $PdO, aq.$, or $Pd(OH)_2$. When heated in air it is converted into the monoxide and palladium. Hydrogen reduces it to palladium in the cold, with incandescence.

The black colour might suggest that the compound contains not trivalent palladium but a mixture of divalent and tetravalent; this, however, is improbable in view of the behaviour of the complex halides (see below), and a strong colour is found in other trihalides of Group VIII in which the trivalency is beyond doubt, for example, in FeF_3, green; CoF_3, brown; RhF_3, red.

COMPLEXES OF TRIVALENT PALLADIUM

THE solution of palladium sesquioxide in cold hydrochloric acid, which must contain trivalent palladium in some complex form, readily breaks up on addition of potassium chloride into the di- and tetravalent complex salts K_2PdCl_4 and K_2PdCl_6. At low temperatures, however, it is possible by adding to the solution rubidium or caesium chloride to obtain the trivalent complexes $Rb_2[PdCl_5]$ and $Cs_2[PdCl_5]$.[1370] The rubidium salt is grey-green and the caesium salt is dark green, whereas the divalent $Cs_2[PdCl_4]$ is flesh-coloured, and the tetravalent $Cs_2[PdCl_6]$ is orange. These trivalent salts can also be made by oxidizing palladous chloride with chlorine, and adding the alkaline chloride. On heating they evolve chlorine and are converted into the palladous salts $M_2[PdCl_4]$. There seems to be no doubt that these salts really contain trivalent palladium: but it is curious that they have an odd covalency, which might be due to a polymerization to a Pd^{ii}—Pd^{iv} structure such as

$$M_4\left[Cl_4Pd\underset{Cl}{\overset{Cl}{<}}{>}PdCl_4\right],$$

in which the palladium atoms would have an even covalency of 6.

A trivalent palladium solution can also be made by boiling the purple-red solution of palladium tetrachloride in water, when it turns brown from its reduction to the trivalent state; further boiling turns it yellow from the formation of the divalent palladium.

TETRAVALENT PALLADIUM

THIS state of palladium, though more stable than the trivalent, has but small stability, in marked contrast to platinum. As with trivalent palladium, the compounds are probably all complex; they are almost confined to the oxide, sulphide, complex sulphides, and complex halides. No fluorine compounds of tetravalent palladium, simple or complex, are known.

Palladium Dioxide, PdO_2

Like the sesquioxide, this can only be made in the wet way, and is only known in the hydrated form. It is formed as a dark red precipitate by treating the palladichloride M_2PdCl_6 with alkali. At 200° it loses oxygen and is converted into the monoxide PdO. It is a strong oxidizing agent, and slowly loses oxygen at the ordinary temperature.

Palladium Disulphide, PdS_2[1381]

This can be made by heating palladous chloride with excess of sulphur to 400–500° and extracting the product with carbon disulphide; by the action of acid on the complex sulphide Na_2PdS_3; or by heating the palladi-halide K_2PdCl_6 or Rb_2PdBr_6 with sulphur to 200–300°.

Palladium disulphide is a blackish-grey crystalline solid, easily soluble in aqua regia but in no other mineral acid. Its crystal structure seems to be unknown.

Tensimetric experiments[1381] showed it to be a stable compound, formed from the monosulphide and sulphur with the evolution of 1·5 to 2·0 k.cal.

Palladium Diselenide, $PdSe_2$

The corresponding diselenide, and also the *ditelluride* are known[1380]; the former is olive-grey, and is soluble in concentrated nitric acid or in aqua regia: the telluride form silver crystals, which are soluble in dilute nitric acid. The selenium compounds of palladium correspond exactly to those of sulphur: they are Pd_4Se, PdSe, and $PdSe_2$. With platinum the mono- and disulphides are much more stable than with palladium, and no sulphide of platinum lower than the monosulphide PtS is known.

Complex Sulphides of Tetravalent Palladium

Sodium thiopalladate Na_2PdS_3 (Schneider, 1870)[1375] is made by fusing the monosulphide PdS with sodium carbonate and sulphur: it forms reddish-brown needles—decomposed by water with the precipitation of the disulphide PdS_2.

A polysulphide which may contain divalent or tetravalent palladium is $(NH_4)_2PdS_{11}$, 1/2 H_2O, made by treating a palladochloride solution with ammonium pentasulphide.[1377] It is purified by washing with ether and carbon disulphide, but cannot be recrystallized.

Complex Halides of Tetravalent Palladium

No binary palladic tetrahalides are known, but there is a series of complex derivatives containing chlorine and bromine, but so far as is known neither fluorine nor iodine.

[1375] R. Schneider, *Pogg. Ann.* 1870, **141**, 526.
[1376] A. Rosenheim and T. A. Maas, *Z. anorg. Chem.* 1898, **18**, 331.
[1377] K. A. Hofmann and F. Höchtlen, *Ber.* 1904, **37**, 245.
[1378] P. Scherrer and P. Stoll, *Z. anorg. Chem.* 1922, **121**, 319.
[1379] H. B. Wellman, *J.A.C.S.* 1930, **52**, 985.
[1380] L. Wöhler, K. Ewald, and H. G. Krall, *Ber.* 1933, **66**, 1638.
[1381] W. Biltz and J. Laar, *Z. anorg. Chem.* 1936, **228**, 257.

In nearly all of these the palladium is in the anion, the type being $M_2Pd(hal)_6$, but a few diammines of the type of $Pd[py_2Cl_2]Cl_2$ have been made.[1376]   If a diammine of divalent palladium such as $Pd py_2Cl_2$ is suspended in chloroform and treated with chlorine, the tetravalent salt $[Pd py_2Cl_2]Cl_2$ is precipitated as a deep orange crystalline powder. This loses chlorine rapidly in moist air, and liberates iodine from potassium iodide.   If it is boiled with potassium hydroxide and the solution then neutralized with hydrochloric acid it is converted into the palladi-chloride K_2PdCl_6, so that it obviously is a genuine tetravalent palladium compound.

The corresponding bromides can also be made.

Halopalladates or Palladihalides, $M_2[Pd(hal)_6]$

These are the least unstable of the tetravalent palladium compounds. They are formed by chlorine and bromine with almost equal ease; they are all of the 6-covalent type $M_2[Pd(hal)_6]$.

Hexachlorides

They can be made by the action of aqua regia on metallic palladium, or by saturating a solution of palladous chloride with chlorine.   The potassium salt K_2PdCl_6 forms red octahedra which dissolve in dilute hydrochloric acid but not in a concentrated solution of an alkaline chloride.   The rubidium and caesium salts are almost insoluble in cold water, evolve chlorine when boiled with water, and are rapidly decomposed by concentrated ammonia solution with evolution of nitrogen.   The caesium salt is the stablest of the alkaline salts.[1384] The ammonium salt $(NH_4)_2PdCl_6$, also red crystals, can be made[1376] by the continued action of chlorine on the aqueous solution of the palladous diammine $[Pd(NH_3)_2Cl_2]°$.

The salts are easily decomposed.   Potassium palladichloride K_2PdCl_6 loses chlorine at all temperatures above $175°$,[1382] being converted into the palladous compound K_2PdCl_4.   The kinetics of the reaction have been examined by Wellman,[1379] who determined the equilibrium ratio

$$[PdCl_6'']/[PdCl_4''],$$

and found satisfactory values of the constant, with no indication of the production of a neutral hexachloride $PdCl_6$ or its complexes. He found the solubility product of $[K]_2[PdCl_6]$ to be 6×10^{-6} at $25°$.

Hexabromides

The corresponding hexabromides M_2PdBr_6 have also been prepared,[1383] most readily by the action of bromine vapour on a saturated solution of the palladobromide M_2PdBr_4.   They crystallize very well and are stable in air; like the chlorine compounds they are slightly soluble in cold water and

[1382] F. Puche, *C.R.* 1935, **200**, 1206.
[1383] A. Gutbier and A. Krell, *Ber.* 1905, **38**, 2385.
[1384] F. Puche, *C.R.* 1939, **208**, 656.

decomposed by hot, giving off bromine, and react violently with concentrated ammonia with evolution of nitrogen and formation of the palladous salt M_2PdBr_4. The potassium, rubidium, caesium, and ammonium salts are all black.

The rubidium salt is of interest because it was used[1378] (along with $Ni(NH_3)_6Cl_2$ and K_2PtCl_6) to prove by X-ray analysis the truth of Werner's octahedral theory of the MX_6 ion: it was chosen because the atomic numbers of the elements are close together (Rb 37; Pd 46; Br 35).

CARBONYL COMPOUNDS

THE only known carbonyl compound of palladium seems to be the halide $Pd(CO)Cl_2$. Dry palladous chloride does not react with dry carbon monoxide on heating, though the chlorides of other platinum metals (Ru, Os, Rh, Pt) do so, and these metals can thus be removed from the palladium salt at 250°.[1385] But if carbon monoxide is passed through a suspension of palladous chloride in absolute alcohol at 0°, or if carbon monoxide saturated with methyl alcohol is passed at the ordinary temperature over the dry chloride, $Pd(CO)Cl_2$ is formed as a pale yellow solid, stable when dry but decomposed at once by water.[1386] The molecular weight is unknown; it may well be dimeric like $(PdAmCl_2)_2$ (p. 1569), with the structure

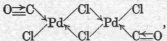

though as the E.A.N. of the metal in $Pd(CO)Cl_2$ is 52, we should expect it to be trimeric. This compound is peculiar among the simple carbonyl halides of the platinum metals in having only one CO to one metallic atom; the others (with Ru, Ir, and Pt) are of the type $M(CO)_2Cl_2$.

The transient formation by palladium of other carbonyl compounds is indicated by its peculiar power of causing the oxidation of carbon monoxide by water[1389,1386-7] or even its reduction by hydrogen.[1388]

NITROSYL COMPOUNDS

A NITROSYL halide $Pd(NO)_2Cl_2$ is formed[1390] in exactly the same way as the carbonyl, by passing nitric oxide saturated with methyl alcohol vapour over cold palladous chloride; the brownish-black product is readily decomposed by water with evolution of gas and the formation of a black precipitate. A similar compound $Pd(NO)_2SO_4$ is formed by the sulphate.

If these are covalent compounds the palladium has an E.A.N. of $46+2+6 = 54$, and they should be monomeric, in which case we should expect them to be volatile; the valency of the palladium would be zero.

[1385] W. Manchot, *Ber.* 1925, **58**, 2518.
[1386] W. Manchot and J. König, ib. 1926, **59**, 883.
[1387] W. Traube and W. Lange, ib. 1925, **58**, 2773.
[1388] H. S. Taylor and P. V. McKinney, *J.A.C.S.* 1931, **53**, 3604.
[1389] H. Wieland, *Ber.* 1912, **45**, 679.
[1390] W. Manchot and A. Waldmüller, ib. 1926, **59**, 2363.

PLATINUM

PLATINUM, the best known and the most abundant element of the family in the platinum ores, resembles palladium in its properties very closely, as we have seen. In nearly all its compounds it is either divalent or tetravalent (see above, p 1550), the tetravalent compounds being much more stable than those of palladium. In both these states it forms complexes with great readiness and in great variety, and these are much more stable, especially the tetravalent, than the corresponding palladium complexes.

Metallic Platinum

Platinum is a ductile and not very hard metal, melting at $1,773 \cdot 5 \pm 1°$.[1391] Like palladium it is attacked more readily by acids than the other platinum metals, but less by oxygen. The behaviour of the metal in presence of oxygen is in general that of a noble (i.e. non-oxidizable) metal: platinum can be precipitated from a solution of chloroplatinic acid in 6-normal hydrochloric acid at 25° by hydrogen under 30 atmospheres pressure[1392]; platinum vessels can of course be ignited in air without damage. But it is able to adsorb oxygen on the surface, and to hold it with a firmness which suggests chemical combination. Thus platinum, and especially platinum black, when heated in oxygen absorbs it apparently chemically, although the maximum amount absorbed does not exceed 2·5 per cent. (PtO contains 7·6 per cent. oxygen).[1393] So, too, in a discharge tube pure oxygen is readily absorbed by white-hot platinum until a hard vacuum remains[1394]: this method can be used to remove traces of oxygen from other gases.

Under ordinary conditions the metal is scarcely attacked by oxidizing agents. It is not acted on by sodium hydroxide below 400°.[1395] It is, however, soluble to some extent in potassium cyanide, even in the absence of air, when hydrogen is evolved[1396]; this is a sign of the strength of the link between platinum and a CN group. It is also perceptibly dissolved (platinum foil up to 0·04 mg. per square metre per hour) by concentrated sulphuric acid at its boiling-point.[1397]

Platinum can be obtained in a great variety of forms, ranging in their dispersity from the massive metal to a colloidal solution. Spongy platinum, made by heating ammonium chloroplatinate, has a considerable surface; platinum black, which can be made by warming a solution of platinous chloride in potassium hydroxide with alcohol, is a black powder with a very large surface and a high absorptive power for gases. What seems to be another form of this is the so-called explosive platinum, made (like explosive iridium or rhodium) by fusing platinum with zinc and

---

[1391] W. F. Roeser, F. R. Caldwell, and H. T. Wensel, *Bur. Stand. J. Res.* 1931, **6**, 1119.

[1392] V. G. Tronev, *Bull. Acad. Sci. U.R.S.S.* 1937, 333.

[1393] L. Wöhler, *Ber.* 1903, **36**, 3475.

[1394] E. Goldstein, ib. 1904, **37**, 4147.

[1395] M. le Blanc and L. Bergmann, ib. 1909. **42**, 4728.

[1396] F. Glaser, *Z. Elektrochem.* 1903, **9**, 11.

[1397] M. Delépine, *C.R.* 1905, **141**, 1013.

extracting the alloy with hydrochloric acid; this material, when heated in the air, will deflagrate or even explode, owing probably to the occluded hydrogen which it contains.[1398]

Colloidal platinum can be made by reducing platinic chloride with hydrazine in presence of a protective colloid such as sodium lysalbate,* or by Bredig's method of passing an electric arc between platinum poles under pure water. Its catalytic power is very great; Bredig found that the rate of decomposition of hydrogen peroxide was perceptibly increased when the solution contained 0·03 mg. of platinum per litre.

Platinum does not readily amalgamate with mercury, but Moissan[1399] describes an amalgam which has a peculiar power of emulsifying with water, forming a butter-like mass when shaken with it for 15 seconds; according to Lebeau[1400] this behaviour is peculiar to platinum, and is perceptible with as little as 0·038 per cent. It seems possible that these amalgams contain suspended particles of solid platinum, which hinder the separation of the two phases.

Platinum and Hydrogen

Platinum has a remarkable power, though far less than palladium, of absorbing hydrogen. To some extent the hydrogen enters into the metal: a platinum wire 0·3 mm. thick will absorb 0·15 volume of hydrogen at 409°, and 2·02 volumes (0·084 mg. per 100 g.) at 1,342°.[1401] But the absorption is mainly superficial, and depends on the state of division of the metal; with platinum black it may reach 160 volumes.[1402] Langmuir has shown[1403] that at low temperatures platinum will only absorb gases if it has been 'activated' by heating it to 300° in hydrogen and oxygen at low pressures; it then absorbs oxygen, hydrogen, or carbon monoxide up to a monomolecular layer.

Owing to these facts hydrogen has a power of passing through heated platinum (as it does through palladium) which no other gas has. The rate increases greatly with temperature up to a white heat, and at any given temperature is proportional[1404] to the square root of the pressure of the hydrogen, as it should be if it is the dissociated atoms that have to pass through. See further, references [1405-7].

Platinum black and colloidal platinum have been much used of recent years as carriers of hydrogen in organic reductions. Thus Willstätter and

---

* This is the soluble salt obtained by heating albumen with sodium hydroxide.

[1398] E. Cohen and T. Strengers, *Z. physikal. Chem.* 1908, **61**, 698.

[1399] H. Moissan, *C.R.* 1907, **144**, 593.

[1400] P. Lebeau, ib. 1907, **144**, 843.

[1401] A. Sieverts and E. Jurisch, *Ber.* 1912, **45**, 221.

[1402] A. Gutbier and O. Maisch, ib. 1919, **52**, 1368.

[1403] I. Langmuir, *J.A.C.S.* 1918, **40**, 1361.

[1404] O. W. Richardson, J. Nicol, and T. Parnell, *Phil. Mag.* 1904, [6] **8**, 1.

[1405] V. I. Goermikin, *Bull. Acad. Sci. U.R.S.S.* 1943, 401.

[1406] Id., ib. 1944, 185.   [1407] Id., ib. 105.

his co-workers have found that unsaturated compounds like oleic acid, geraniol, or cholesterol can be reduced by passing hydrogen into their solutions in presence of platinum black[1408-9]; the reaction often fails with pure platinum black, but occurs readily if the material has been exposed to oxygen[1410]; the activity ceases after a time and can be restored by reoxidation. Colloidal platinum is even more effective, being about as active as an equiatomic quantity of colloidal palladium.[1411] Roger Adams and his co-workers[1412-18] find an oxide of the composition PtO_2, H_2O, made from platinichloric acid by fusion with potassium nitrate, to be even more effective.

MONOVALENT PLATINUM

ONLY one compound of monovalent platinum has been isolated, and even this one not in the pure state. If platinum tetrachloride is heated[1419] under 1 atm. pressure of chlorine, it is converted successively into $PtCl_3$ (blackish-green) and platinous chloride $PtCl_2$, which is brownish-green. At a slightly higher temperature this last loses more chlorine and passes into a mixture of metallic platinum and a new yellow-green substance which is supposed to be the monochloride $PtCl$; it could not be got in a pure state, but its composition approximately agreed with this. Its stability range is only about 581–583° under a pressure of chlorine slightly less than an atmosphere. Iridium forms a monochloride in the same way (above, p. 1531), and also a monobromide and a monoiodide to which there are no platinum analogues.[1420]

Manchot has also shown[1421] that platinum can be obtained in solution in an apparently monovalent state, in the same way as palladium. If a solution of potassium platinocyanide $K_2Pt(CN)_4$ is reduced with sodium amalgam or any other strong reducing agent, the solution remains colourless but acquires strong reducing properties. It will reduce a mercurous or a cadmium solution to the metal: it evolves hydrogen vigorously on addition of hydrochloric acid: the platinocyanide has none of these reducing properties. A platinochloride does not do this, but is reduced to the metal. It is suggested that the reducing salt formed must be the cyanide $K_2[Pt(CN)_3]$, as with nickel; it is of course possible that it may be the not otherwise known $K_4[Pt(CN)_4]$.

[1408] R. Willstätter and E. W. Mayer, *Ber.* 1908, **41**, 1475.
[1409] Id., ib. 2199.   [1410] R. Willstätter and D. Jaquet, ib. 1918, **51**, 767.
[1411] C. Paal and A. Schwarz, ib. 1915, **48**, 994.
[1412] W. H. Carothers and R. Adams, *J.A.C.S.* 1923, **45**, 1071.
[1413] R. Adams and R. L. Shriner, ib. 2171.
[1414] W. E. Kaufmann and R. Adams, ib. 3029.
[1415] W. H. Carothers and R. Adams, ib. 1924, **46**, 1675.
[1416] Id., ib. 1925, **47**, 1047.
[1417] J. S. Pierce and R. Adams, ib. 1098.
[1418] J. W. Kern, R. L. Shriner, and R. Adams, ib. 1147.
[1419] L. Wöhler and S. Streicher, *Ber.* 1913, **46**, 1591.
[1420] L. Wöhler and F. Müller, *Z. anorg. Chem.* 1925, **149**, 377.
[1421] W. Manchot and G. Lehmann, *Ber.* 1930, **63**, 2775.

DIVALENT PLATINUM

THIS is one of the two main valencies of platinum, being only slightly if at all less stable than that of 4. None of the compounds dissociate to form the simple platinous ion Pt^{++}; nearly all are by their formulae necessarily complex, and the relatively few that are not, such as the binary compounds, are probably in fact auto-complex. We may take these apparently simple compounds first: they include an oxide, hydroxide, and sulphide, and three or perhaps four dihalides.

Platinous Oxide, PtO

Platinous oxide is a grey powder, which can be made by heating the hydrate $Pt(OH)_2$ or PtO, H_2O; but the water cannot all be removed without the loss of some oxygen as well.[1422] The stability limits of the oxides of platinum, and their dissociation tensions, are not easy to determine[1423] because the equilibrium is only slowly established, and also there is a wide range of solid solutions among the oxides. Platinous oxide can be made directly by the action of oxygen under 8 atm. pressure on the metal at 420–440°.[1425]

The hydroxide $Pt(OH)_2$ can be made by the action of hot potassium hydroxide solution on platinous chloride or potassium chloroplatinite or better[1424] by reducing the chloroplatinate with sulphur dioxide, and adding potassium hydroxide solution. It is a black powder which is easily oxidized by air, and so must be prepared in an inert atmosphere; it is reduced by hydrogen peroxide to the metal, and oxidized by ozone or potassium permanganate to the dioxide; it behaves as a weak base. It is obviously an unstable substance; hot alkalies or hydrochloric acid convert it partly into the platinic compound and metallic platinum.

Platinous Sulphide, PtS

This substance can be made from the elements or by fusing platinous chloride with sodium carbonate and sulphur. The dissociation tensions of sulphur in the system platinum-sulphur indicate[1426] that no compounds are there formed except the mono- and disulphides PtS and PtS_2.

Platinum monosulphide is a green powder, which can be converted into metallic platinum by heating in air or hydrogen.

The crystal structure shows that each platinum atom has 4 planar bonds, and each sulphur 4 tetrahedral bonds.[1427]

Platinous Fluoride, PtF_2

This is said to occur as a greenish-yellow solid which can be made from its elements, but it is not mentioned by Ruff.

[1422] L. Wöhler, *Z. anorg. Chem.* 1904, **40**, 423.
[1423] L. Wöhler and W. Frey, *Z. Elektrochem.* 1909, **15**, 129.
[1424] L. Wöhler and F. Martin, ib. 791.
[1425] P. Laffitte and P. Grandadam, *C.R.* 1935, **200**, 456.
[1426] W. Biltz and R. Juza, *Z. anorg. Chem.* 1930, **190**, 161.
[1427] Wells, *S.I.C.* 391–2.

Platinous Chloride, PtCl₂

This can be made by heating platinum in chlorine to 500°, or by the thermal decomposition of the tetrachloride. It is stable under a pressure of 1 atm. of chlorine at all temperatures from 435° to 581°[1428] (compare PtCl 581–583°). It is a brownish-green solid, insoluble in water, but dissolving in hydrochloric acid to form the platinochloride H_2PtCl_4, with, however, some decomposition to metallic platinum and the acid H_2PtCl_6. It forms many complexes.

Platinous Bromide, PtBr₂

This can be made by heating hydrogen platino- or platinibromide, which decomposes much more slowly than the chloride.[1429] It can also be got from the tetra- or the tribromide by loss of bromine at 410°, but with difficulty; it seems to have a stability range of not more than 5°. In water, hydrobromic acid, or alcohol, platinic bromide $PtBr_4$ dissolves very easily, the tribromide slowly, and platinous not at all. The dibromide has a brown colour.

Platinous Iodide, PtI₂

This is very like the bromide. It can be made by treating platinous chloride with potassium iodide, or the chloroplatinate with potassium iodide and iodine. The changes in the system platinum-iodine[1429] take the same course as with bromine, but are even slower; the system must be kept at constant temperature for days before equilibrium is reached. Platinic iodide PtI_4 loses iodine even in contact with saturated iodine vapour at 350°, and forms the tri-iodide. If at this temperature the pressure is lowered to 3 atm., the composition of the solid falls in 3 days to PtI_2, which, however, is difficult to get pure, as it forms a solid solution with the tri-iodide PtI_3.

Platinous iodide is a black powder like lamp-black, which is insoluble in water, alcohol, ether, and ethyl acetate.

Platinous Cyanide, Pt(CN)₂

A pale yellow precipitate of this composition, but of unknown structure, is got by adding mercuric cyanide to a solution of a chloroplatinate. It is insoluble in acids and alkalies.

Platinum Blue, Pt(NH·CO·CH₃)₂

If the yellow compound $PtCl_2(CH_3 \cdot CN)_2$ is treated with silver nitrate solution, silver chloride is immediately precipitated, and the compound goes into solution with the development of a vivid blue colour.[1430] This was shown[1431] to be due to the acetamide derivative $Pt(NH \cdot CO \cdot CH_3)_2$.

[1428] L. Wöhler and S. Streicher, *Ber.* 1913, **46**, 1591.
[1429] L. Wöhler and F. Müller, *Z. anorg. Chem.* 1925, **149**, 377.
[1430] K. A. Hofmann and G. Bugge, *Ber.* 1907, **40**, 1777.
[1431] Id., ib. 1908, **41**, 312.

This is most conveniently made by treating the acetonitrile compound $PtCl_2(CH_3 \cdot CN)_2$ with silver sulphate, adding methyl alcohol, and precipitating with ether. It forms deep blue crystals with a green reflex, of the composition $Pt(NH \cdot CO \cdot CH_3)_2 \, H_2O$. The molecular weight was found cryoscopically in water to be 334 (calculated for the monomeric form 329). The solution is stable to dilute sulphuric acid, acetic acid, sodium chloride sulphate, and carbonate, so that the blue substance is not colloidal. On standing with concentrated hydrochloric acid and potassium chloride it is converted into the chloroplatinite, showing that the platinum is divalent. It is evidently formed through the reaction

$$Pt \leftarrow N \equiv C \cdot CH_3 \longrightarrow Pt - NH - CO \cdot CH_3.$$

COMPLEXES OF DIVALENT PLATINUM

DIVALENT platinum has almost as strong a tendency to form complexes as any other element. The range of its complexes is very wide, and many of them are of remarkable stability. The tendency to co-ordination is as usual highly selective, the strongest links of divalent platinum being to nitrogen, sulphur, the halogens, and under special conditions carbon, while the link to oxygen is very weak. Complexes co-ordinated through nitrogen are formed by amines, hydrazine, hydroxylamine, nitriles, and NO_2 groups: complex halides are formed by all the halogens except fluorine, and sulphur compounds by the alkyl and aryl thio-ethers. Doubly linked carbon, especially, but not only, when doubly linked to another carbon, has a peculiarly strong affinity for platinum.

The covalency of platinum in its divalent complexes is almost invariably 4, even in some compounds where it seems to be 3; but in a few complexes it seems certain that the platinous atom has a covalency of 6, though not much is known of these.

The complexes cover the whole range from the tetrammines such as $[Pt(NH_3)_4]X_2$ to the tetra-acido-compounds such as $M_2[PtCl_4]$ or $M_2[Pt(CN)_4]$, all the intermediate types such as $[Pt(NH_3)_2Cl_2]$ being known.

Many of the complexes occur in apparently isomeric forms; Werner's view[1432] that the isomerism is due to the four atoms attached to a divalent platinum atom being in the same plane with it and at the points of a square, has finally, after much controversy, been established.

We may consider the small group of 6-covalent complexes first, and then proceed to the 4-covalent, which include the great majority.

6-Covalent Platinous Complexes

These are of four, all rather unusual kinds. The first two are all nitrile or isonitrile compounds,* and were discovered by Tschugaev and his

---

* The structure of the co-ordination compounds of divalent platinum with nitriles and isonitriles is discussed in more detail later, among the 4-covalent compounds (p. 1589).

[1432] A. Werner, *Z. anorg. Chem.* 1893, **3**, 351.

colleagues. They showed[1433] that the acetonitrile compound of platinous chloride, $Pt(CH_3 \cdot CN)_2Cl_2$ when treated with aqueous or liquid ammonia takes this up, and forms the *cis* and *trans* isomers of the compound $[Pt(CH_3 \cdot CN)_2(NH_3)_4]Cl_2$, colourless and very soluble substances, in which the ammonia is so firmly attached that it cannot be titrated with mineral acids, and can only be removed by boiling with concentrated hydrochloric acid, when the 4-covalent compound $[Pt(NH_3)_2Cl_2]°$ is left. There can be no doubt that in these compounds the platinum has a covalency of 6.

The second class[1434-5] are hydrazine derivatives of the phenyl isocyanide compound. The first series of these that were obtained were of the type

$$\left[(C_6H_5 \cdot NC)_4Pt \underset{NH-NH_2}{\overset{NH_2-NH}{\diagup\diagdown}} Pt(CN\Phi)_4 \right] X_2.$$

The chloride $[B]Cl_2$, $8\,H_2O$, which was the first made, is a red salt which was shown by the freezing-point and the conductivity to have in water the molecular weight to be expected of a tri-ionic salt. The colours of these salts suggest that they are dimorphic.[1435] The chloride is red, but turns green on heating, and recovers its red colour on cooling; the iodide $(4\,H_2O)$ is green; the perchlorate $(2\,H_2O)$ red; the azide $[B](N_3)_2$, $2\,H_2O$ red. The salts of the corresponding complex of ethyl isocyanide were also made (nitrate red; perchlorate yellow; iodide yellow; chloroplatinate red). All these compounds when treated with concentrated hydrochloric acid lose half their isonitrile, and give 4-covalent salts of the type of

$$\left[(R \cdot NC)_2Pt \underset{NH-NH_2}{\overset{NH_2-NH}{\diagup\diagdown}} Pt(R \cdot NC)_2 \right] X_2,\ 2\,HCl$$

(the 2 HCl are probably attached to the NH). Another group of compounds which probably but not certainly are 6-covalent are the triamino-propane derivatives of divalent platinum,[1436] such as the iodide, which may be written

$$\left[\begin{array}{cc} CH_2 \cdot NH_2 & NH_2 \cdot CH_2 \\ | & | \\ CH \cdot NH_2 \rightarrow Pt \leftarrow NH_2 \cdot CH \\ | & | \\ CH_2 \cdot NH_2 & NH_2 \cdot CH_2 \end{array} \right] I_2.$$

It is not proved, although it is probable, that all three amine groups of each molecule are attached to the platinum.

The last series of 6-covalent platinous complexes is of quite a different kind, consisting of some of the chelate oxygen-co-ordinated diketone derivatives. Werner[1437] found that acetylacetone (HA) acts on a chloro-

[1433] L. Tschugaev and W. Lebedinski, *C.R.* 1915, **161**, 563.

[1434] L. Tschugaev, M. Skanavy-Grigorieva, and A. Posniak, *Z. anorg. Chem.* 1925, **148**, 37.

[1435] Id., *Ann. Inst. Platine*, 1926, **4**, 299.

[1436] F. G. Mann, *J.C.S.* 1928, 890.

[1437] A. Werner, *Ber.* 1901, **34**, 2584.

platinite in presence of alkali to give (amongst other products in which the platinum is 4-covalent) a salt $K[PtClA_2]$ and a very soluble salt from which the sodium derivative $Na_2[PtCl_2A_2]$, 5 H_2O can be isolated: this is a yellow salt stable enough to be recrystallized from water. In this last salt the covalency of the platinum must be 6; the enolic form of acetylacetone is so weak an acid, and the affinity of the platinous atom for oxygen is so small, that an acetylacetone derivative could only acquire the stability which this compound is shown to have if it were chelate. In the other salt $M[PtA_2Cl]$ the covalency of the platinum must be 5; no other 5-covalent platinous salt is known.

4-Covalent Platinous Complexes

All the remaining platinous complexes are 4-covalent; they may be roughly classified according to the atoms (C, N, O, etc.) attached to the platinum.

Complexes with Ethylene Derivatives

All co-ordination tendencies are specific: just as the central atom of stannic chloride will attach itself to the oxygen of a ketone or aldehyde group, but not to that of an ether, nor to a double carbon link; just as the aluminium in aluminium bromide attacks first the carbonyl and then the ether oxygen, but does not touch the C=C link: so a divalent platinum atom, with little or no tendency to join itself to the oxygen atom either in an aldehyde or ketone, or in an ether, is very ready to co-ordinate with a doubly or triply linked carbon atom, whether the multiple link attaches the carbon to a different atom as in an isocyanide or in carbon monoxide, or to another carbon atom in ethylene and its derivatives.[1443]

A compound of platinous chloride with mesityl oxide was obtained by Zeise in 1840, and shown in 1900[1438] to have the composition $PtCl_2,C_6H_{10}O$, and to be monomeric by the freezing-point. Other compounds with unsaturated organic substances were also prepared.[1439]

Platinum has a strong tendency to combine with ethylene, as it has with carbon monoxide (see later, p. 1627). Metallic platinum in a finely divided state as platinum black, or still better as the hydrosol, will absorb up to 0·88 of a molecule of ethylene to 1 atom of platinum (palladium absorbs even more, but iridium and osmium none at all).[1440] The phenomenon is complicated by some kind of polymerization taking place on the surface of the metal. The power which platinum, especially in the form of the sol, has of catalysing the reduction of ethylene by hydrogen is no doubt connected with this.[1441]

The formation of a co-ordinate link with a C=C group is in general very unusual, and it is important to be sure that it is the C=C which

[1438] W. Prandtl and K. A. Hofmann, ib. 1900, **33**, 2981.
[1439] K. A. Hofmann and J. v. Narbutt, ib. 1908, **41**, 1625.
[1440] C. Paal and A. Schwarz, ib. 1915, **48**, 1195.   [1441] Id., ib. 1202.
[1442] E. Biilmann and A. Hoff, *Rec. Trav.* 1916, **36**, 306.
[1443] P. Pfeiffer and H. Hoyer, *Z. anorg. Chem.* 1933, **211**, 241.

actually forms the link. A large number of addition compounds of unsaturated alcohols, acids, and esters have been prepared by Biilmann[1442]; in order to make certain that in these compounds the linkage of the platinum is to the C=C and not to the oxygen, Pfeiffer compared each of Biilmann's organic components with the corresponding saturated alcohol, aldehyde, etc., and showed that in every case the latter refused to react. The co-ordination was shown by the red-brown colour of the platino-chloride solution turning to yellow, and the complex ion produced could then be isolated as the salt of such cations as $[Pt(NH_3)_4]''$ or $[Co(en)_2Cl_2]'$. The salt always had the composition $M[PtCl_3Un]$, where Un stands for one molecule of the unsaturated addendum: for example, with allyl alcohol the salt produced was $K[PtCl_3(CH_2 \cdot CH \cdot CH_2OH)]$. Salts of this type were obtained with allyl alcohol, allyl acetate, crotyl alcohol, crotyl acetate, and crotonic aldehyde, but not with propyl alcohol, propyl acetate, butyl alcohol, butyl acetate, or butyraldehyde. These results show very clearly that divalent platinum attaches itself very readily to C=C, but not to

$$-\overset{|}{\underset{|}{C}}-O- \text{ or } >C=O.$$

Most of the unsaturated molecules used for these addition products have been ethylene and its homologues; the products are all either of the salt type given above, or of the non-ionized type $[Pt(hal)_2Un_2]°$. The ethylene compound has already been mentioned. The corresponding propylene and amylene salts have been made, and an ethylene compound of the bromide, $K[PtBr_3(C_2H_4)]$. Recently Anderson[1444] has extracted 'Zeise's salt' $K[PtCl_3(C_2H_4)]$ or its basis $[PtCl_2(C_2H_4)]°$ with ether, and obtained a substance of the composition $PtCl_2 \cdot C_2H_4$. It forms orange crystals, fairly soluble in chloroform, slightly in benzene. The molecular weight found by the Berger-Rast method was dimeric. Excess of pyridine converts it into $PtCl_2py_2$, showing that the platinum is still divalent. It decomposes at 125–130°. Unlike its carbonyl analogue the compound will not take up any more ethylene. The slightly soluble quinoline salt (Quin. H) $[PtCl_3C_2H_4]$ can be recrystallized from hot water; excess of quinoline converts it into the non-ionized compound $[PtCl_2(quin)C_2H_4]°$.

If $[PtCl_2C_2H_4]$ is treated with hydrobromic acid and quinoline, it gives the bromide (Quin. H) $[PtBr_3C_2H_4]$, which is less stable than the chloride, and is decomposed by hot water. The stability of the complex $K[PtX_3C_2H_4]$ appears to decrease in the order $Cl > Br > NO_2 > CNS > CN$.

With the amino-ethylene compounds $[PtX_2Am(C_2H_4)]°$ Gelman[1447] has shown that the stability increases in the order

$$Am = S=C(NH_2)_2 < NH_3 < py < quin$$

and $$X = CN < CNS < NO_2 < I < Br < Cl:$$

[1444] J. S. Anderson, *J.C.S.* 1934, 971.   [1445] Id., ib. 1936, 1042.
[1446] M. S. Kharasch and T. A. Ashford, *J.A.C.S.* 1936, **58**, 1733.
[1447] A. Gelman, *Sci. Rep. Leningrad Univ.* 1936, **2**, 5.

the last series compares curiously with that given above, but it is obvious that in Gelman's neutral compounds, which must be dimeric, the X is performing a double function; it has to hold the two halves together, as in

Gelman[1448] has shown that K_2PtCl_4 combines with $R \cdot CH=CH_2$, where R = methyl, ethyl, or phenyl, to give $K[PtCl_3(R \cdot CH=CH_2)]$ which ammonia or pyridine (= B) convert into $[PtCl_2B(R \cdot CH=CH_2)]°$; if R is phenyl they also get $[(PtCl_2(\Phi \cdot CH=CH_2))]_2$. The *cis* and *trans* forms of $[PtBr_2B(CH_2=CH_2)]°$ (B = NH_3 or py) are produced by the action of ethylene on the salt $NH_4[PtBr_3B]$. The complex $K[PtCl_3(C_2H_4)]$ with aqueous sodium nitrite gives $K[PtCl(NO_2)_2(C_2H_4)]$.[1449] Butadiene C_4H_6 can co-ordinate strongly with either one or both of its double links,[1450] giving, for example, $(NH_4)_2[C_4H_6(PtCl_3)_2]$, and $[C_4H_6(PtCl_2NH_3)_2]°$, as well as $[PtCl_2py(C_4H_6)]°$ and $[PtCl_2NH_3(C_4H_6)]°$.

Further compounds can be made[1446] by boiling the hydrocarbon in benzene solution with platinic chloride $PtCl_4$, when the platinum is reduced to the divalent state, and the compound $PtCl_2Un$ is formed: for example, with dimethylethylene the compound $[(CH_3)_2C=CH_2 \cdot PtCl_2]°$, which was shown cryoscopically to be dimeric in benzene. The factors determining the stability of the complex salt have been studied by Anderson.[1445] The ease of formation depends not only on the position of equilibrium in the addition reaction, but also on the solubility of the salt produced; this difficulty can be largely overcome by making the salts of the cations $[Pt(NH_3)_4]''$ or $[Co(en)_2Cl_2]'$, which are relatively insoluble. In general, substitution in the ethylene greatly lowers the stability of the complex, as well as increasing the solubility of its salts. Direct addition of the alkylene to platinous chloride, or to the chloroplatinite, is only possible for ethylene and for styrene $\Phi \cdot CH=CH \cdot \Phi$. We can often replace ethylene in $PtCl_2C_2H_4$ or in $K[PtCl_3C_2H_4]$ directly by other unsaturated hydro-carbons, whose volatility largely determines the reaction. It is to be noticed that ethylene is not expelled even by carbon monoxide, so that the $Pt—C_2H_4$ link must be stronger than $Pt—CO$. The only hydrocarbons nearly as strong as ethylene were found to be styrene and amylene. The order of co-ordinating tendency (beginning with the strongest) was found to be ethylene > styrene > amylene > indene (C_9H_8) > cyclohexene > $\Phi_2C=CH_2$ and $\Phi(CH_3)C=CH_2$.

The *structures* of these C=C complexes are made clear up to a certain point by their resemblance to the carbonyls (below, p. 1627), which is remarkably close.[1444] We have three series of compounds $[PtX_2R]°$, $[PtX_2AmR]°$, and $M[PtX_3R]$, in which R may be either CO or $R_2C=CR_2$.

[1448] A. Gelman, *Ann. Sect. Platine*, 1939, No. **12**, 21.
[1449] Id., ib. No. **16**, 29.
[1450] A. Gelman and Z. P. Maximova, *C.R. Acad. Sci. U.R.S.S.* 1939, **24**, 748.

We have the salt $K[PtCl_3CO]$, H_2O corresponding to $K[PtCl_3(C_2H_4)]$, H_2O; both of these are decomposed by potassium cyanide to form the platino-cyanide $K_2Pt(CN)_4$, with quantitative liberation of the ethylene or the carbon monoxide. On heating with water to 100° both these salts decompose in almost exactly the same way:

$$K[PtCl_3CO] + H_2O = KCl + 2\,HCl + Pt + CO_2:$$
$$K[PtCl_3C_2H_4] + H_2O = KCl + 2\,HCl + Pt + CH_3 \cdot CHO.$$

In the carbonyls we know that the linking is $Pt \leftarrow C \equiv O$. It is therefore evident that in the alkylene compounds the $C = C$ group acts as a donor and fills one co-ordination place: the interpretation of addition compounds of unsaturated hydrocarbons is so difficult that it is satisfactory to get at least these points settled. We must therefore have a $Pt \leftarrow C$ link. Hence in the ethylene compound the carbon attached to the platinum must share two electrons with it, and 4 with the 2 hydrogen atoms: this leaves only 2 for the other carbon, so the $C - C$ link must be single, and the more remote carbon can only have a sextet of electrons, the structure of the group being (according to which symbols we prefer)

$$\begin{array}{cccc} & Pt \leftarrow CR_2 \leftarrow CR_2 & or & \bar{Pt} - CR_2 - \overset{+}{C}R_2. \\ \text{val. els.} & \quad 8 \qquad 6 & & \quad 8 \qquad 6 \end{array}$$

Complex Cyanides

The complex cyanides are all of the type $M_2[Pt(CN)_4]$. They are exceptionally stable, and are readily formed. Thus metallic platinum will dissolve in a solution of potassium cyanide or barium cyanide under the influence of an alternating current.[1451] In the same way other co-ordination compounds of platinum, for example the carbon monoxide and ethylene complexes, are converted by potassium cyanide into the platino-cyanides with separation of the co-ordinating groups. Potassium platino-cyanide $K_2Pt(CN)_4$ is conveniently made by fusing potassium ferrocyanide $K_4Fe(CN)_6$ with platinum, or by dissolving platinous chloride in potassium cyanide solution.

The free acid is relatively stable. If a concentrated solution of it is extracted with ether and the ethereal solution evaporated, red prisms of the acid, $H_2Pt(CN)_4$, $5\,H_2O$ separate, which are deliquescent, and decompose on heating above 140°.

Among the numerous platinocyanides are the following. Li, $4\,H_2O$, grass-green, goes over sulphuric acid at 25° to the canary-yellow anhydrous salt.[1458] Na, $3\,H_2O$.[1453-4] K, 12 and $3\,H_2O$, pleochroic, very soluble.

[1451] A. Brochet and J. Petit, *C.R.* 1904, **138**, 1095.
[1452] J. Milbauer, *Z. anorg. Chem.* 1907, **53**, 135.
[1453] H. Baumhauer, *Z. Krist.* 1907, **43**, 356.
[1454] Id., ib. 1911, **49**, 113.   [1455] J. Beuel, *Z. Wiss. Phot.* 1913, **11**, 150.
[1456] P. Tschirwinski, *Z. Krist.* 1913, **52**, 44.
[1457] N. Orlov, *Chem. Ztg.* 1913, **36**, 1407.
[1458] F. E. E. Germann and O. B. Muench, *J. Phys. Chem.* 1929, **33**, 415.

Rb, 3 H_2O[1454] (hydration very remarkable). $N(CH_3)_4$, anhydrous, very soluble in water.[1452] Ag, anhydrous, insoluble.[1452] Mg, 7 H_2O.[1453] Ca, 5 H_2O, dimorphic, stable form yellow, unstable red. Sr, 5 H_2O, dimorphic. Ba, 4 H_2O, dichroic, green and yellow; fluorescent, and used as a screen for making X-rays visible. $Sc_2[Pt(CN)_4]_3$, 21 (red) and 18 (yellow) H_2O.[1457] The lanthanum[1456] and yttrium[1454] salts are similar.

The colours, the dimorphism, and the fluorescence of the salts are remarkable. Beuel[1455] examined the fluorescence under cathode rays of twelve different platinocyanides, hydrated and anhydrous, and of very different colours; the positions of nearly all the bands were the same with all, but some had a single additional band of their own.

The platinocyanides can be converted by treatment with chlorine into the platinic compounds $M_2[Pt(CN)_4Cl_2]$, but these are much less stable; they are strong oxidizing agents, and readily revert to the platinocyanides.

Nitrile Complexes

These are fairly numerous, but much less stable than the isonitrile complexes. Platinous chloride combines with acetonitrile very slowly in the cold to form a yellow compound $PtCl_2(CH_3 \cdot CN)_2$.[1459] The mother liquor contains the acid $H[PtCl_3(CH_3 \cdot CN)]$, which can be precipitated as its $[Pt(NH_3)_4]$ salt.[1463] This formation of a trichloro-salt of the type of Cleve's salts $M[PtCl_3(NH_3)]$ is very unusual, though it occurs with the carbonyl and ethylene complexes. The benzonitrile compound $PtCl_2(\Phi \cdot CN)_2$ is formed[1460] by heating its components to 60–70° for many days. It is a yellow crystalline substance, which can be recrystallized from acetone. It appears to be dimorphic. Its solution is rather unstable; concentrated sulphuric acid converts it with loss of hydrochloric acid into a sulphate, presumably of the formula $PtSO_4(C_6H_5 \cdot CN)_2$. The bromide is similar, and is also yellow and dimorphic. The iodide was too unstable to be purified. These compounds must contain the group $Pt\leftarrow N\equiv C\!-\!R$.

Isonitrile Complexes

These are made much more easily than the nitrile compounds; they are practically all of two types, $PtX_2(RNC)_2$ and $[Pt(RNC)_4]X_2$. The first of these is remarkable for occurring in two strikingly different modifications.

Platinous chloride dissolves in an ethereal solution of phenyl isonitrile with the immediate precipitation of a purple compound $PtCl_2(\Phi NC)_2$. This can also be made from the isonitrile with aqueous potassium chloroplatinite. This is a blue-violet apparently amorphous powder, quite insoluble in all ordinary solvents, and so of unknown molecular weight and constitution. If it is boiled for 4 to 6 hours with chloroform it goes slowly into

[1459] K. A. Hofmann and G. Bugge, *Ber.* 1907, **40**, 1772.
[1460] L. Ramberg, ib. 2578.
[1461] L. Tschugaev and P. Teearu, ib. 1914, **47**, 568.   [1462] Id., ib. 2643.
[1463] L. Tschugaev and W. Lebedinski, *C.R.* 1916, **162**, 43.

solution as it is converted into the β-isomer, which crystallizes out on cooling in large colourless crystals, melting at 257–258°; from the boiling-point in chloroform it is found to be monomeric. It is insoluble in water, very slightly soluble in alcohol, rather more so in benzene and acetone; the best solvent is chloroform, sol^y 0·80/20°.

The bromides are made similarly, and behave in just the same way: α-, brownish-violet, apparently amorphous, insoluble; β-, colourless, m. pt. 245°. The iodide $PtI_2(\Phi \cdot NC)_2$ has only been made in one (β-) form, which is yellow. The nitro-salt $M_2Pt(NO_2)_4$ gives a nitro-compound

$$Pt(NO_2)_2(\Phi \cdot NC)_2,$$

also only known in the soluble β-form, which is red, but will crystallize with one molecule of acetone, and is then yellow.

The tetra-isonitrile derivatives $[Pt(RNC)_4]X_2$ can be made[1461] by the action of excess of isonitrile RNC (R= phenyl, CH_3, $(CH_3)_3C$) on the chloroplatinite, when a red salt $[Pt(RNC)_4] \cdot [PtCl_4]$ is produced, along with the di-isonitrile compound $PtCl_2(RNC)_2$, which can also be made by heating the red salt. The tertiary butyl compound $[Pt(C_4H_9NC)_4] \cdot [PtCl_4]$ has a very peculiar reaction[1462]; if it is treated with excess of the isonitrile, a yellow crystalline compound is slowly precipitated, which is

$$[Pt(C_4H_9NC)_2(CN)_2]° :$$

the tertiary butyl group is apparently split off. The reaction is very peculiar and is due to the ease with which tertiary compounds $Me_3C \cdot X$— even isocyanides—can be hydrolysed. The reaction must go thus:

$$[Pt(Me_3C \cdot NC)_4]Cl_2 + 2\ H_2O = [Pt(Me_3C \cdot NC)_2(CN)_2]° + 2\ Me_3C \cdot OH + 2\ HCl.$$

The formula is certain; the substance can be made from tertiary butyl isonitrile and platinous cyanide; it is a non-conductor of electricity.

The remarkable series of 6-covalent platinous compounds formed with an isocyanide and hydrazine, of the type

$$\left[(RNC)_4Pt \underset{NH-NH_2}{\overset{NH_2-NH}{\diagdown\diagup}} Pt(CNR)_4 \right] X_2$$

have already been described (p. 1584).

It is clear that the complexes of the isonitriles are far more stable than those of the nitriles, and resemble the stable cyanides $M_2[Pt(CN)_4]$ very closely. On general grounds we should have expected the Pt—N link to be stronger than the Pt—C; but the former must occur in the nitrile complexes, and the latter certainly in the isonitrile complexes, and almost certainly (see V. 671) in the complex cyanides. Evidently the Pt—C link is much strengthened by the triple linking of the carbon in these compounds, exactly as it is by the double linking in the C=C compounds we have just been considering.

Complex Thiocyanates

These occur in two types, as the salts $M_2[Pt(CNS)_4]$ and the neutral diammines such as $[Pt(NH_3)_2(CNS)_2]°$. The salts can be made from a thiocyanate and platinous chloride; the free acid is unstable; the salt $K_2[Pt(CNS)_4]$ forms carmine-red crystals (like the ferric salt), whose colour is visible in solution at a dilution of 1/10,000. The ammonium salt is similar.

The diammine $[Pt(NH_3)_2(CNS)_2]°$ has been obtained[1464] in two isomeric forms. The first was got by the action of the calculated quantity of ammonia on the salt $K_2[Pt(CNS)_4]$: it formed small yellow crystals; we may assume that as in other similar reactions it is the *cis* form that is here produced. The second form was got from the *trans* form of $[Pt(NH_3)_2Cl_2]$ (the chloride of Reiset's second base) with potassium thiocyanate. It forms large yellow crystals, less soluble than the α- but more stable to heat. The molecular conductivity of these two forms in water is negligible; the molecular weights by the boiling-points in acetone are *cis* 322; *trans* 314 (theory 345).

Ammines

Many of these have long been known, and were discovered at a time when their structure was not understood, and so have come to be called by the names of their discoverers; among the more important examples are the following:

Cleve's salts	$[Pt(NH_3)_3R]X$.
Magnus's green salt	$[Pt(NH_3)_4]\cdot[PtCl_4]$.
Peyrone's chloride	$[Pt(NH_3)_2Cl_2]°$ *cis*.
Reiset's first chloride	$[Pt(NH_3)_4]Cl_2$.
Reiset's second chloride	$[Pt(NH_3)_2Cl_2]°$ *trans*.
Zeise's salt	$K[PtCl_3(C_2H_4)], H_2O$.

The first of the ammines to be discovered was Magnus's green salt (above) by Magnus in 1828.

We may divide the ammines according to the number of amine groups they contain, and begin with the tetrammines $[PtAm_4]X_2$.

Tetrammines

The simple tetrammine $[Pt(NH_3)_4]X_2$, made from ammonia and platinous chloride, was the first ammine to be prepared (Magnus, 1828); a large number of its salts are known.*[1468] The ammonia can be replaced

---

* For the rate of interchange of heavy hydrogen between $[Pt(NH_3)_4]Cl_2$ and water see Anderson *et al.* reference [1658] (p. 1626).

[1464] A. A. Grünberg, *Z. anorg. Chem.* 1926, **157**, 299.
[1465] L. Tschugaev and W. Sokolov, *Ber.* 1909, **42**, 55.
[1466] L. Tschugaev and M. Grigoriev, ib. 1914, **47**, 2446.
[1467] L. Tschugaev, *J. Russ. Phys. Chem. Soc.* 1920, **51**, 193.
[1468] L. Tschugaev and N. K. Pschenicyn, ib. 1920, **52**, 47.

by many other amines, such as methyl-[1476] and ethylamine[1473,1475] (these primary amines seem to be almost as firmly linked to the platinum as ammonia, which is not usual), by pyridine and quinoline,[1471] as well as by a whole series of diamines such as ethylene diamine,[1465,1469-70,1472] propylene diamine,[1465] methyl-propylene diamine,[1469] isobutylene diamine,[1473] and dipyridyl.[1474] The less stable derivatives of hydrazine and hydroxylamine are discussed later.

The ordinary chelate diammines show their usual stability, but only when the NH_2 groups are not too far apart. Drew and Tress[1472] have prepared both the diammine $[Pt(en)Cl_2]^\circ$ and the tetrammine $[Pt(en)_2]Cl_2$ compounds from the diamines $NH_2(CH_2)_nNH_2$, where $n = 2$, 3, 4, and 5. With ethylene and propylene diamines ($n = 2$ and 3, giving 5 and 6-rings respectively) they get compounds of the usual type, like ordinary ammines: but with $n = 4$ or 5 the reaction is quite different, giving ill-defined insoluble products. It is clear that with these longer chains the chance of the ring closing is small, and the two NH_2 groups usually become attached to different platinum atoms.

Reihlen and Hühn[1470,1477-8] claim to have resolved salts of the $[Pt(en)_2]''$ type, with unsymmetrical *en* groups, showing that the platinum is tetrahedral; but they have not made out their claim. Mann[1469] failed to resolve a compound of this type, made from $NH_2 \cdot CH_2 \cdot CH(CH_3) \cdot CH_2 \cdot NH_2$. The definite proof of the planar structure of 4-covalent divalent platinum from the chemical side was given by Mills and Quibell.[1479] They pointed out that it is difficult to prove that isomerism which is supposed to be 'geometrical' (i.e. *cis-trans*) is really due to this cause [and not, for example, to dimorphism or polymerization], while there is no such difficulty about mirror-image isomerism. They therefore devised and synthesized an ingenious structure in which a planar arrangement of the valencies of the platinum (the arrangement which in ordinary molecules would lead to *cis-trans* isomerism) would cause optical activity, while a tetrahedral would not. They condensed the 1,1-dimethylethylene diamino-platinous chloride of Drew and Head[1473] with 1,2-diphenylethylene diamine, and so got a salt of which the divalent cation is

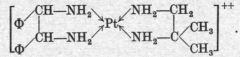

[1469] F. G. Mann, *J.C.S.* 1928, 1261.

[1470] H. Reihlen and W. Hühn, *Ann.* 1931, **489**, 42.

[1471] E. G. Cox, H. Saenger, and W. Wardlaw, *J.C.S.* 1932, 2216.

[1472] H. D. K. Drew and H. J. Tress, ib. 1933, 1335.

[1473] H. D. K. Drew and F. S. H. Head, ib. 1934, 221.

[1474] G. T. Morgan and F. H. Burstall, ib. 965.

[1475] H. Reihlen and E. Flohr, *Ber.* 1934, **67**, 2010.

[1476] H. D. K. Drew and H. J. Tress, *J.C.S.* 1935, 1212.

[1477] H. Reihlen and W. Hühn, *Ann.* 1935, **519**, 80.

[1478] H. Reihlen, G. Seipel, and W. E. Weinbrenner, ib. **520**, 256.

[1479] W. H. Mills and T. H. H. Quibell, *J.C.S.* 1935, 839.

It is easy to see that if the links of the platinum are planar, so that the two chelate rings lie in the same plane, the structure will be asymmetric and should be capable of resolution, while if they are arranged tetrahedrally, the structure will be symmetrical.

The salt was resolved by means of diacetyltartaric acid, and from the extreme fraction an iodide of [M]—68° in alcohol and a chloride of [M]—48·5° in water were obtained. Every conceivable objection to the conclusion of the planar structure of the platinum was ruled out. The product was shown to behave as a tri-ionic salt, giving the same molecular depression of freezing-point in water as barium chloride. The chloride and iodide crystallize with water of crystallization, but this water cannot be essential to the asymmetry, since the chloride can be dehydrated without losing its activity. To show that the activity is not due to the presence (or the production) of the active form of the stilbene-diamine, this diamine was recovered from the active salt and shown to be inactive.

This work proves beyond doubt the planar arrangement of the four covalencies of the platinum atom in these compounds. It does not necessarily imply that the covalencies of a platinous atom are always so arranged. It is still uncertain whether the same atom with the same valency and the same covalency can have more than one stereochemical configuration. But until we have direct evidence of the occurrence of a tetrahedral arrangement for the platinous atom we must assume that it is always planar. See above, under palladium, p. 1563.

The tetrammines derived from hydrazine are difficult to make, since the hydrazine usually reduces the divalent platinum to the metal. But by avoiding water as far as possible, and acting directly on the diammine $[Pt(NH_3)_2Cl_2]°$ with hydrazine hydrate, Tschugaev[1466] was able to prepare both the mixed derivative $[Pt(NH_3)_2(N_2H_4)_2]X_2$ (in the *cis* and *trans* forms), and also the pure compound $[Pt(N_2H_4)_4]X_2$. These compounds are definitely less stable than the ammonia derivatives,[1467] since an aqueous solution of $[Pt(NH_3)_2(N_2H_4)_2]Cl_2$ decomposes in 15 minutes in the cold. The terminal NH_2 of the hydrazine group can still act as a base (the other NH_2 has already become pentavalent in the co-ordination), and this salt can take up two molecules of hydrogen chloride to form the acid salt

$$[Pt(NH_3)_2(NH_2 \cdot NH_3)_2]Cl_4.$$

A curious N-chelate platinous derivative is the phthalocyanine compound $C_{32}H_{16}N_8Pt$. The crystal structure of this has been fully analysed[1480]; in spite of the excessive size of the platinum atom as compared with the rest, the positions of all the atoms except the hydrogen have been determined to 0·05 A; the structure is just like that of the other phthalocyanines.

Triammines, [PtAm₃R]X

Compounds of this type are known as Cleve's salts. They can be made by addition of ammonia to the diammine or by its removal from the

[1480] J. M. Robertson and I. Woodward, ib. 1940, 36.

tetrammine, but in either case the yields are small as it is difficult to stop the reaction at the right place. Tschugaev does this by two indirect methods. The first[1481] is to treat the diammine $Pt(NH_3)_2Cl_2$ with potassium cyanate and boil. From the resulting liquid potassium platino-chloride precipitates a mixture of the platinochlorides of the triammine and the tetrammine, and the former can be separated owing to its greater solubility. The reaction seems to consist in the formation of the iso-cyanato-compound and its subsequent hydrolysis:

$$Pt—Cl \longrightarrow Pt—N{=}C{=}O \longrightarrow Pt—NH—CO—OH$$
$$\longrightarrow Pt{\leftarrow}NH_2—CO \cdot OH \longrightarrow Pt{\leftarrow}NH_3 + CO_2.$$

A second method is to oxidize[1482] the diammino-dihydroxylamino-salt $[Pt(NH_3)_2(NH_2OH)_2]X_2$ with air. The hydroxylamine is oxidized away, and the residue rearranges itself to form $[Pt(NH_3)_3(OH_2)] \cdot [PtCl_4]$. A third less indirect method[1483] is from the monohydroxylamino-triammine by treatment with hydrochloric acid, when the less firmly attached NH_2OH group is replaced by chlorine:

$$[Pt(NH_3)_3(NH_2OH)]X_2 \longrightarrow [Pt(NH_3)_3Cl]Cl.$$

Diammines, $[PtAm_2R_2]°$

Werner in 1893[1484] found that compounds of this type occurred in two modifications, and suggested that the group was planar, and the isomerism *cis-trans*. Reihlen[1488] found that one of the chlorides $[Pt(NH_3)_2Cl_2]$ was dimeric in liquid ammonia, and claimed that this dimerization was the cause of the isomerism.

Hantzsch, however, showed[1489] that the isomeric pyridine compounds $[Pt(py)_2Cl_2]°$ are both monomeric in phenol. Grünberg[1490] found the same for the two thiocyanates $[Pt(NH_3)_2(CNS)_2]$ in acetone, and he further showed[1491] that if Werner's *cis* form of $[Pt(NH_3)_2Cl_2]$ (Peyrone's salt) is treated with silver nitrate and then with oxalic acid, it gives the slightly soluble non-electrolyte

$$\left[(H_3N)_2Pt{<}^{O—C{=}O}_{O—C{=}O}\right]°,$$

[1481] L. A. Tschugaev, *J.C.S.* 1915, **107**, 1247.
[1482] L. A. Tschugaev and I. Tscherniaev, *C.R.* 1915, **161**, 792.
[1483] Id., *J.C.S.* 1918, **113**, 884.
[1484] A. Werner, *Z. anorg. Chem.* 1893, **3**, 310.
[1485] I. Ostromisslensky and A. Bergmann, *Ber.* 1910, **43**, 2768.
[1486] L. Ramberg, *Z. anorg. Chem.* 1913, **83**, 33.
[1487] L. A. Tschugaev and S. Krassikoff, ib. 1923, **131**, 299.
[1488] H. Reihlen and K. N. Nestle, *Ann.* 1926, **447**, 211.
[1489] A. Hantzsch, *Ber.* 1926, **59**, 2761.
[1490] A. A. Grünberg, *Ann. Inst. Platine*, 1928, **6**, 122.
[1491] Id., *Helv. Chim. Acta*, 1931, **14**, 455.

while the isomeric *trans* (Reisert's) compound under the same conditions gives the complex acid

$$\text{HO·CO·CO·O} \diagdown \underset{\diagup\ \ \ \diagdown}{\text{Pt}} \diagup \text{NH}_3$$
$$\text{H}_3\text{N} \diagup \ \ \ \diagdown \text{O·CO·CO·OH}$$

with a dissociation constant of 6.3×10^{-4}. See further, reference [1485]. The evidence for the planar structure of the 4-covalent platinous atom in Dickinson's platinocyanides $M_2[Pt(CN)_4]$ and in Mills and Quibell's tetrammines, gave conclusive support to Werner's view.

Compounds of the type $[PtAm_2R_2]^\circ$ can be prepared with a variety of amines and a variety of acidic groups. The acid radical R may be chlorine, bromine,[1487] iodine,[1486-7] NO_2,[1486] CNS,[1490] SO_3H,[1487] or OH[1497]; the amines may be ammonia, an arylamine,[1486] pyridine,[1486] or a substituted (chloro- or amino-) pyridine,[1499] or quinoline.[1493]

Tschugaev[1487] finds that the reaction

$$[Pt(NH_3)_4]X_2 \longrightarrow [Pt(NH_3)_2X_2]^\circ + 2\,NH_3$$

takes place readily on heating. When X is a halogen, this goes more easily in the order $Cl < Br < I$; it also occurs with NO_2. A similar change that has long been known is that of Magnus's green salt on heating, $[Pt(NH_3)_4] \cdot [PtCl_4]$ going to $2[Pt(NH_3)_2Cl_2]^\circ$.[1468] The platinochlorides of the ammines of other metals, for example $[AgNH_3]X$, undergo this change much more easily.[1500]

The supposed third form of $[Pt(NH_3)_2Cl_2]$[1492] has been shown to be a mixture or solid solution of the other two.[1494-5]

The *cis* and *trans* forms differ in the basicity of the hydroxides

$$[Pt(NH_3)_2(OH)_2];$$

potentiometric titration with glass electrodes[1496,1498] shows that the classical dissociation constants are

	K_1	K_2
Cis . . .	0.16×10^{-7}	*ca.* zero
Trans . . .	0.63×10^{-7}	0.125×10^{-10}

the *cis* compound being a weaker base than the *trans*.

Compounds of the type $[Pt(NH_3)_2X_2]^\circ$ react with water, the halides and nitrites slowly and imperfectly, the nitrates and sulphates completely, to

[1492] H. D. K. Drew, F. W. Pinkard, W. Wardlaw, and E. G. Cox, *J.C.S.* 1932, 988.
[1493] E. G. Cox, H. Saenger, and W. Wardlaw, ib. 2216.
[1494] F. Rosenblatt and A. Schleede, *Naturwiss.* 1933, **21**, 178.
[1495] Id., *Ber.* 1933, **66**, 472.
[1496] A. A. Grünberg and D. Rjabtschikov, *Acta Phys.-Chem. U.R.S.S.* 1935, **3**, 555.
[1497] H. J. S. King, *J.C.S.* 1938, 1338.
[1498] D. I. Rjabtschikov, *Ann. Sect. Platine*, 1938, **15**, 35.
[1499] A. M. Rubinstein, *C.R. Acad. Sci. U.R.S.S.* 1938, **20**, 575.
[1500] L. A. Tschugaev and N. K. Pschenicyn, *J. Russ. Phys.-Chem. Soc.* 1920, **52**, 47.

give colourless very soluble aquo-complexes $[Pt(NH_3)_2(H_2O)_2]X_2$.[1501] These last are dibasic acids, as one or both of the H_2O groups can go to $OH+H$ (as in $[Pt(NH_3)_2(H_2O)OH]Cl+HCl$ or $[Pt(NH_3)_2(OH)_2]+2\ HCl$). The dissociation constants of *cis* and *trans* $[Pt(NH_3)_2(H_2O)_2]^{++}$ have been found[1501-2] to be

	K_1	K_2
Cis . . .	$2 \cdot 76 \times 10^{-6}$	$4 \cdot 79 \times 10^{-8}$
Trans . . .	$4 \cdot 79 \times 10^{-5}$	$4 \cdot 17 \times 10^{-8}$

Platinous Monammine, $Pt(NH_3)Cl_2$

This was obtained by Klason[1503] by evaporating an aqueous solution of ammonium platinochloride. Though its molecular weight has not been determined, there can be little doubt that this, like other apparently tricovalent platinous compounds, is really dimeric, with a structure such as

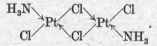

Hydroxylamine Derivatives

In the platinous ammines hydroxylamine can take the place of ammonia. Thus[1504] if chloroplatinic acid H_2PtCl_6 is treated with hydroxylamine hydrate, the platinum is reduced to the divalent state, and the tetra-salts $[Pt(NH_2OH)_4]X_2$ are formed; they are colourless and fairly soluble. All the intermediate compounds $[Pt(NH_2OH)_n(NH_3)_{4-n}]X_2$ can be made; the chlorides are all colourless.[1505] The base of the tetra-derivative

$$[Pt(NH_2OH)_4](OH)_2$$

is remarkable. While the corresponding ammonia complex $[Pt(NH_3)_4](OH)_2$ is a strong base and very soluble in water, the hydroxylamine base[1506] is only weakly basic, and almost insoluble in water, behaving like magnesia. Werner suggests that it is the 6-covalent compound $[Pt(NH_2OH)_4(OH)_2]°$.

Hydroxylamine is more easily removed from the platinum than ammonia, and the salt $[Pt(NH_3)_3(NH_2OH)]Cl_2$ is converted by hydrochloric acid into the triammine $[Pt(NH_3)_3Cl]Cl$ (Cleve's salt).

Amino-acid Derivatives

These are chelate compounds, with the platinum linked to nitrogen and oxygen. The platinochloride gives with an equivalent of glycine the salt

$$K\left[Cl_2Pt\underset{O \cdot CO}{\overset{NH_2}{\diagdown\diagup}}CH_2\right],$$

1501 K. A. Jensen, *Z. anorg. Chem.* 1939, **242**, 87.
1502 A. A. Grünberg and D. I. Rjabschikov, *C.R. Acad. Sci. U.R.S.S.* 1935, **4**, 259.
1503 P. Klason, *J. prakt. Chem.* 1902, [2] **67**, 1.
1504 R. Uhlenhuth, *Ann.* 1900, **311**, 120.
1505 L. A. Tschugaev and I. I. Tscherniaev, *C.R.* 1915, **161**, 637.
1506 Id., *J.C.S.* 1918, **113**, 884.

while with excess of glycine the dichelate non-salt

$$\left[CH_2 \overset{CO \cdot O}{\underset{NH_2}{\diagup}} Pt \overset{O \cdot CO}{\underset{NH_2}{\diagup}} CH_2 \right]$$

is produced.[1507] This last compound has been shown[1508] to occur in two forms, *cis* and *trans*. Other amino-acids such as alanine[1509] can take the place of glycine.

Glyoxime Compounds[1510]

Glyoximes

$$\underset{NOH \quad NOH}{R-\overset{|}{C}----\overset{|}{C}-R} \quad (= DH)$$

give a series of chelate derivatives of platinum, as of other transitional elements. The compounds of the type of PtD_2 (non-ionized, dichelate) are stable, and volatilize undecomposed in a vacuum. They can add on two atoms of bromine, the platinum becoming tetravalent. The methyl-ethyl compound (a violet sublimate) and the methyl-propyl, methyl-butyl, and diphenyl compounds were made.

Nitro-complexes

Platinous complexes containing NO_2 groups are numerous and stable.

Of the two possible structures $Pt-N\overset{O}{\underset{O}{\diagup}}$ and $Pt-O-N{=}O$, it is obvious

that the former must be the true one for these stable complexes since the affinity of divalent platinum for nitrogen is strong, and for oxygen weak.

Of the nitroplatinites $M_2Pt(NO_2)_4$ (Lang, 1861; Nilson, 1876)[1511-12] the potassium salt, $K_2Pt(NO_2)_4$ 2 and 0 H_2O, can be made by treating potassium chloroplatinate K_2PtCl_6 with potassium nitrite, which reduces the platinum to the divalent state. Sol^y 3·7/15°. The silver salt is yellow: the free acid decomposes on evaporation of its solution.

The nitro-groups are very firmly attached to the platinum. The aqueous solution gives no precipitate with alkaline hydroxide or even sulphide. The nitro-group must be more firmly bound to the platinum than a chlorine atom, for if the compound $K_2[PtCl_3NO_2]$ is treated with ammonia it is converted successively into

$$[Pt(NH_3)_2ClNO_2]° \quad \text{and} \quad [Pt(NH_3)_3NO_2]Cl,$$

the nitro-group not being disturbed until all the three chlorines have been removed.[1516] It is, however, possible to turn out the NO_2 groups by

[1507] H. Ley and K. Ficken, *Ber.* 1912, **45**, 377.

[1508] A. A. Grünberg and B. W. Ptizyn, *J. prakt. Chem.* 1933, [ii] **136**, 143.

[1509] A. A. Grünberg and L. M. Volschtein, *Bull. Acad. Sci. U.R.S.S.* 1937, 885.

[1510] L. Tschugaev, *Z. anorg. Chem.* 1905, **46**, 144.

[1511] L. F. Nilson, *Ber.* 1876, **9**, 1722.　　　　[1512] Id., ib. 1877, **10**, 934.

[1513] K. A. Hofmann and K. Buchner, ib. 1909, **42**, 3392.

[1514] L. A. Tschugaev and S. S. Kiltinovic, *J.C.S.* 1916, **109**, 1286.

[1515] L. A. Tschugaev and N. A. Vladimiroff, *J. Russ. Phys.-Chem. Soc.* 1920, **52**, 135.

[1516] I. I. Tscherniaev, *Ann. Inst. Platine*, 1928, **6**, 23.

oxalato-groups (with their chelate stability) and by amines. Potassium nitroplatinite $K_2Pt(NO_2)_4$ gives with oxalic acid the oxalato-salt

$$K_2[Pt(NO_2)_2Ox].^{1514}$$

Concentrated ammonia replaces two of the NO_2 groups by NH_3, to give

$$[Pt(NH_3)_2(NO_2)_2]^\circ;$$

the *cis* compound is first produced, and this can be converted into the *trans*, which reacts with more ammonia to replace a third NO_2, giving the salt $[Pt(NH_3)_3NO_2]NO_2.^{1514}$ The molecular conductivities at 25° and a dilution of $V = 1,000$ are:[1515]

$[Pt(NH_3)_4](NO_2)_2$	$[Pt(NH_3)_3NO_2]NO_2$	$[Pt(NH_3)_2(NO_2)_2]^\circ cis$
276·5	96·5	0·95

$[Pt(NH_3)_2(NO_2)_2]^\circ$ *trans*	$K_2[Pt(NO_2)_4]$
2·42	302·4

The reaction of the primary aromatic amines with the platinonitrites is peculiar. One NO_2 group is replaced by an amine, and the expelled NO_2 converts more of the amine into a diazoamino-compound[1513]; thus $K_2[Pt(NO_2)_4]$ with toluidine gives a mixture of diazoamino-toluene and colourless crystals of the salt $(C_7H_7NH_3)[Pt(C_7H_7NH_2)(NO_2)_3]$.

Phosphorus Complexes

Divalent platinum forms addition compounds with trivalent phosphorus in the forms of the trialkyls, the trihalides, the trihydroxide (phosphorous acid), and the tri-alkyloxy-derivatives $P(OAlk)_3$.

Cahours and Gal (1870) showed that triethyl phosphine will combine with platinous chloride to form an unstable compound of the composition $PtCl_2(PEt_3)_2$, which changes over into a stable isomer: this is presumably the unstable *cis* form going over to the stable *trans*

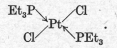

This substance takes up two molecules of ammonia[1517] to give a product that is soluble in water, and no doubt is the substituted tetrammine salt $[Pt(PEt_3)_2(NH_3)_2]Cl_2$.

The phosphorus trihalides can co-ordinate with divalent platinum in the same way. If platinum sponge is heated with phosphorus pentachloride the latter is reduced and the platinum chlorinated, and the products combine to give a complex of the composition $Cl_3P\cdot PtCl_2$. In the same way, by using phosphorus pentafluoride, Moissan was able to make the corresponding fluorine compound $F_3P\cdot PtF_2$, the nearest approach to a complex fluoride of divalent platinum that is known.[1519] Either one or two mole-

[1517] P. Klason and J. Wanselin, *J. prakt. Chem.* 1902, [2] **67**, 41.
[1518] A. Rosenheim and W. Löwenstamm, *Z. anorg. Chem.* 1903, **37**, 394.
[1519] A. A. Grünberg and A. D. Troitskaja, *Bull. Acad. Sci. U.R.S.S.* 1944, 178.

cules of phosphorus trichloride can also be added directly, to form either the above-mentioned $Cl_3P \cdot PtCl_2$ or $(Cl_3P)_2PtCl_2$. These compounds, which are crystalline substances soluble in organic solvents, react with hydroxylic compounds like phosphorus trichloride itself, the chlorine being replaced without removing the phosphorus from the platinum. Thus $Cl_3P \cdot PtCl_2$ dissolves in water, and on evaporation $(HO)_3P \cdot PtCl_2$ separates out; the other compound $(Cl_3P)_2PtCl_2$ behaves with water in the same way, giving $(P(OH)_3)_2PtCl_2$. Similarly with alcohol the chlorine on the phosphorus is replaced by ethyoxyl, and the compounds are converted into the esters $P(OEt)_3PtCl_2$ and $(P(OEt)_3)_2PtCl_2$.[1518]

The boiling-points of these substances in benzene showed that while the second (di-phosphorus) compound is monomeric, the first is dimeric, having no doubt the structure

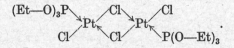

This compound takes up a molecule of aniline or pyridine,[1520] giving a complex of the type

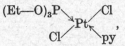

which occurs in *cis* and *trans* modifications. It will also take up two molecules of ammonia to give $Pt(P(OEt)_3)(NH_3)_2Cl_2$. Only half the chlorine in this reacts with silver nitrate,[1521] and the compound has the conductivity of a binary electrolyte, so that it must be $[(EtO)_3P \cdot Pt(NH_3)_2Cl]Cl$.

Phosphorus tribromide forms similar compounds.

Arsine Complexes[1522]

Mixed aryl-alkyl arsines will react in the same way as phosphines with chloroplatinic acid, reducing the platinum to the divalent state, and forming compounds which are non-ionized and of the diammine type $(R_3As)_2PtCl_2$. Examples (with their melting-points) are

$(\Phi_2MeAs)_2PtCl_2$ (214°); $(\Phi_2MeAs)_2PtBr_2$ (167°); $(\Phi Me_2As)_2PtCl_2$ (193°).

β-Diketone Derivatives

The platinous derivatives of acetylacetone (= HA) are, like the oxalato-salts, chelate compounds with the platinum attached to two oxygen atoms in each ring; some of them have already been described among the 6-covalent compounds. The group was examined by Werner,[1523] who showed

[1520] A. Rosenheim and W. Levy, *Z. anorg. Chem.* 1905, **43**, 34.
[1521] C. H. Herty and R. O. E. Davis, *J.A.C.S.* 1908, **30**, 1084.
[1522] G. J. Burrows and R. H. Parker, *J. Proc. Roy. Soc. N.S. Wales*, 1934, **68**, 39.
[1523] A. Werner, *Ber.* 1901, **34**, 2584.

that acetylacetone has no action on potassium chloroplatinite K_2PtCl_4 alone, but that in presence of alkali it reacts with it to form four different products: (1) $K[PtCl_2A]$, monochelate, 4-covalent; (2) $K[PtClA_2]$, dichelate and apparently 5-covalent; (3) a compound which was isolated as the sodium salt $Na_2[PtCl_2A_2]$, dichelate and 6-covalent; and finally (4) the simple PtA_2, dichelate and 4-covalent.

The potassium salt (1) is orange-yellow, fairly soluble in water, and insoluble in organic solvents. The potassium salt (2) is pale yellow, and easily soluble in water. From its solution hydrochloric acid precipitates the free acid $H[PtClA_2]$, a yellow amorphous mass, soluble in alkalies but not in water, soluble also in benzene and chloroform, but not in ether. The sodium salt of this acid is remarkable for dissolving in chloroform, from which it crystallizes as $Na[PtClA_2]$, $CHCl_3$, 2 H_2O. The rubidium salt is anhydrous, and easily soluble in water. The sodium salt of type (3), $Na_2[PtCl_2A_2]$ 5 aq. is yellow, and can be recrystallized from water. The non-ionized compound (4), PtA_2, forms yellow crystals which are soluble in benzene, and in this solvent it is shown by the boiling-points to be monomeric.

Oxalato-compounds

In spite of the relatively small affinity of the platinous atom for an oxygen, the chelate oxalato-complexes are quite stable.

As we have seen,[1524] potassium nitroplatinite $K_2Pt(NO_2)_4$ reacts with oxalic acid; it turns yellow and evolves nitrous fumes, with the production of the yellow salt $K_2[Pt(NO_2)_2Ox]$, H_2O. This salt loses its water at 100°, and at 240° decomposes violently to give platinum, carbon dioxide, and potassium nitrite. Other salts are known: Na, H_2O, dark yellow, sol^y 25/cold, 100/100°[1529]; Ba, 5 H_2O, yellow, and a mixed salt

$$BaK_2[Pt(NO_2)_2Ox]_2,^{1528}$$

which is yellow-brown.

Excess of oxalic acid converts these salts into the dioxalates

$$M_2[PtOx_2],\ aq.^{1526}$$

These are stable salts, and their solutions can be evaporated down without decomposition.[1524] These di-oxalates can also be made easily and reversibly from the platinochlorides by treatment with potassium oxalate[1525]:

$$[PtCl_4]^{--} \underset{HCl}{\overset{K_2Ox}{\rightleftharpoons}} [PtOx_2]^{--}.$$

In the same way the dioxalate can be converted by excess of potassium nitrite into the nitro-platinites. Various dioxalato-salts are known: K, 2 H_2O, copper red, fairly soluble in hot water; Na, 4 H_2O, dimorphic, yellow and red; Ca, 8 H_2O, yellow, 5 H_2O red. These salts are oxidized

[1524] M. Vèzes, *C.R.* 1897, **125**, 525.
[1525] Id., *Bull. Soc.* 1898, [3] **19**, 875.   [1526] Id., ib. 1899, [3] **21**, 143.
[1527] A. Werner and E. Grebe, *Z. anorg. Chem.* 1899, **21**, 377.
[1528] M. Vèzes, *Bull. Soc.* 1901, [3] **25**, 157.   [1529] Id., ib. 1903, [3] **29**, 83.

by chlorine, but without the oxalato-groups being affected: they are converted into the tetravalent platinum salts $M_2[PtOx_2Cl_2]$.[1527]

Cacodyl Oxide Complexes

These peculiar complexes seem to be the only ones in which divalent platinum is co-ordinated with non-chelate oxygen atoms. They were prepared by Jensen.[1530] Cacodyl oxide $(CH_3)_2As$—O—$As(CH_3)_2$ ($= Kd_2O$) acts on potassium chloroplatinite to give large colourless crystals of the composition $PtCl_2, Kd_2O, H_2O$, which lose their water at 150° and are converted into the yellow substance $PtCl_2, Kd_2O$. The corresponding bromides and iodides were made; they are all yellow in the hydrated form, but the anhydrous iodide is dark red. As the iodides are the most soluble of the halides in organic solvents, they were further examined. The hydrate PtI_2, Kd_2O, H_2O was shown by the freezing-points to be monomeric in bromoform, and it has a dipole moment in benzene solution of 8·5 D. The red anhydrous compound PtI_2, Kd_2O is dimeric by the freezing-points in bromoform, and its dipole moment in benzene is $1·8 \pm 0·5$ D (it is relatively insoluble). These results make it clear that while the hydrate is probably the *cis* compound

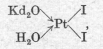

(but possibly the *trans*), the anhydrous compound, like so many of these apparently 3-covalent complexes, really has the symmetrical structure

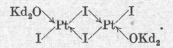

Platinous Sulphur Complexes

Divalent platinum forms complexes with sulphur, especially with the sulphur atom of a thioether, almost as readily as with the nitrogen atom of an amine.[1531,1534] The compounds are mostly of two kinds, $[PtX_2(SR_2)_2]°$ and $[Pt(SR_2)_4]X_2$. In place of the simple sulphides disulphides (dithioglycol ethers) can be used, giving cyclic complexes.

Dialkyl sulphides like dimethyl sulphide react with platinous chloride to give three different compounds of the same composition $PtCl_2, (R_2S)_2$. The first two (α and β) are fairly similar in properties, and though there has been some doubt about their structures, it has now been proved that they are the *cis* and *trans* forms of the monomeric $[PtCl_2(R_2S)_2]°$. The third

[1530] K. A. Jensen and E. Frederiksen, *Z. anorg. Chem.* 1936, **230**, 34.
[1531] K. A. Hofmann and F. Höchtlen, *Ber.* 1903, **36**, 3090.
[1532] L. A. Tschugaev and W. Subbotin, ib. 1910, **43**, 1200.
[1533] L. A. Tschugaev and D. Fraenkel, *C.R.* 1912, **154**, 33.
[1534] L. A. Tschugaev and W. G. Chlopin, *Z. anorg. Chem.* 1913, **82**, 401.

(γ) form is entirely different, and has been shown[1532] to have the structure $[Pt(Me_2S)_4]\cdot[PtCl_4]$, since on treatment with the tetrammine salt

$$[Pt(NH_3)_4]X_2$$

it gives a precipitate of Magnus's salt $[Pt(NH_3)_4]\cdot[PtCl_4]$. Similarly with diethyl or dipropyl dithioglycol $R\cdot S\cdot CH_2\cdot CH_2\cdot S\cdot R$ ($= S_2n$) two isomers are formed instead of three, one of them being the *cis* form of $[PtCl_2(S_2n)]^\circ$, the *trans* form of which is obviously impossible, and the other (γ) the salt $[Pt(S_2n)_2]\cdot[PtCl_4]$, as was proved in the same way as before. Further investigation showed[1533] that the corresponding bromides can also be made, and that the stability of the dimeric (γ) form becomes less when (I) a monosulphide replaces a disulphide (i.e. the cation is more stable when it is chelate) and (II) when bromide replaces chlorine (i.e. when the anion is $PtBr_4$ instead of $PtCl_4$); iodides are not formed at all. The sulphine compounds (as they may be called) can also be made from the nitroplatinites $K_2Pt(NO_2)_4$, but in this case the γ-form is only produced by a disulphide; monosulphides replace 2 NO_2 groups but not 4, giving only $[Pt(NO_2)_2(SR_2)_2]^\circ$.

The relations of the α- and β-forms of disulphine compounds such as $PtCl_2(R_2S)_2$ are unusual and have led to much discussion. The balance of the evidence clearly shows that the β-form is the *cis* and the α- the *trans* form of $[PtCl_2(R_2S)_2]^\circ$. They are monomeric in solution, and readily inter-convertible[1536-9]; the X-ray investigation of the α showed it to be the *trans*.[1537] The dipole moments of the α-forms (for R = ethyl, propyl, and butyl, and for $[PtCl_2(Et_2Se)_2]^\circ$) are from 2·35 to 2·41 D, while those of the β-forms of the same compounds are from 9·0 to 9·5 D.[1538-9] Further support is given by their reactions with ethylene diamine,[1537] when the β-form readily gives the salt $[Pt(en)Me_2S)_2]\cdot[PtCl_4]$, while the α reacts more slowly, and forms $[Pt(en)_2]\cdot[PtCl_4]$, with elimination of dimethyl sulphide.

The peculiar point is the difference between the behaviour of the two chlorides with water.[1535] The α-solution is almost non-conducting, while that of the β- indicates some 67 per cent. ionization at $V = 1,000$. They also differ chemically. With silver oxide the α-form reacts very slowly, splitting off the thioether and precipitating platinous oxide PtO, while the β- reacts readily, giving a base, apparently $Pt(R_2S)_2(OH)_2$, which re-forms the β-chloride with hydrochloric acid. These differences are remarkable, but the behaviour of the corresponding sulphates in water, and of the chlorides themselves in methyl alcohol, show similar but much smaller differences in the rate of hydrolysis of the two forms[1537,1539] with a fair agreement in the ultimate equilibrium value of the conductivity. This suggests that the differences are in general less violent than had been thought, and are compatible with their being *cis-trans* isomers, as all the

[1535] F. G. Angell, H. D. K. Drew, and W. Wardlaw, *J.C.S.* 1930, 349.
[1536] H. D. K. Drew, G. H. Preston, W. Wardlaw, and G. H. Wyatt, ib. 1933, 1294.
[1537] E. G. Cox, H. Saenger, and W. Wardlaw, ib. 1934, 182.
[1538] K. A. Jensen, *Z. anorg. Chem.* 1935, **225**, 97.   [1539] Id., ib. 115.

other evidence indicates. Certainly all attempts[1535] to provide a reasonably probable alternative structure (polymerized or not) for the β-compounds have failed.

There is also[1539] a series of thioether derivatives in which the platinum is attached only to one sulphur, as in [Pt(R₂S)Cl₂], which correspond to the apparently 3-covalent monammines already discussed. If the β-form of [Pt(R₂S)₂Cl₂] is treated with chloroplatinite we get the reaction

$$Pt(R_2S)_2Cl_2 + K_2PtCl_4 = 2\ PtCl_2(R_2S) + 2\ KCl.$$

The methyl and ethyl compounds of this type are quite insoluble in water. The boiling-point of the chloroform solution of the propyl derivative showed it to be dimeric. The ethyl compound reacts[1540] with ethyl mercaptan replacing one chlorine atom in the molecule and giving

$$PtCl(S\cdot Et)(SEt_2).$$

Jensen found that this compound also is dimeric (by the freezing-point in benzene) and that its dipole moment in benzene is 2·27.[1539] The Pt(R₂S)Cl₂ compounds can be shown not to have the formula [Pt(R₂S)₂]·[PtCl₄] (even if this were on other grounds possible) since they do not form Magnus's salt with the tetrammine [Pt(NH₃)₄]Cl₂. They are obviously non-ionized compounds, with the same kind of polymerized structure as we have seen before. They can be *cis* or *trans*. Their chemical behaviour is ambiguous, and it is quite possible that they are tautomeric, like the corresponding or at least similar palladium compounds (p. 1568).

The possible formulae are

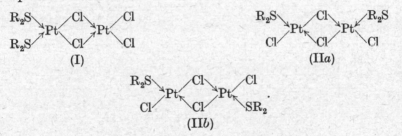

(I)   (IIa)

(IIb)

Platinous Selenium Compounds

These resemble the sulphur compounds very closely, and obviously have the same structural relations. Fritzmann[1541-2] has prepared a series of compounds of the type PtCl₂(R₂Se)₂, in which R = Me, Et, Pr, isoamyl, phenyl, and 2 R = Et·Se·CH₂·CH₂·CH₂·Se·Et. They occur in the same three forms (α, β, γ) as the sulphur complexes. In the cold the α-form is usually produced, but it goes over on warming to 70° or so to the β-. As examples we may take the methyl compound PtCl₂(Me₂Se)₂; the α-form, which is orange-red, has the sol^y 10·5/25° in chloroform, and 1·3/25° in

1540 P. Klason, *Ber.* 1895, **28**, 1499.
1541 E. Fritzmann, *Z. anorg. Chem.* 1911, **73**, 239.
1542 E. Fritzmann and V. V. Krinitzki, *J. Appl. Chem. Russ.* 1938, **11**, 1610.

toluene. The β-form is almost insoluble. At low temperatures the γ-form [Pt(Me$_2$Se)$_4$]·[PtCl$_4$] is produced. Of the other compounds examined the di-ethyl selenide gave the α- and β-forms: dipropyl, only α; amyl α and β; phenyl α and β. The diselenide Et·Se·CH$_2$·CH$_2$·CH$_2$·Se·Et gave the α and γ forms, which for a diselenide are of course the only modifications that are possible.

The α- and β-forms of the compound PtCl$_2$(Et$_2$Se)$_2$ agree with their sulphur analogues in being monomeric, and in the magnitude of their dipole moments.

Platinous Tellurium Complexes

These again are similar, but less stable. The compound PtCl$_2$(TeBz$_2$)$_2$ can be made[1543-4] by treating the chloroplatinite with a solution of dibenzyl telluride Te(CH$_2$·C$_6$H$_5$)$_2$. It forms orange crystals, easily soluble in chloroform, less so in alcohol, and insoluble in ether. The solid is stable, but the solution soon decomposes to give platinum, tellurium, and dibenzyl.

Owing no doubt to this instability, no isomers have been observed.

Chelate Sulphur—Oxygen Complexes

Compounds of this kind can be made, for example, from ethyl thio-glycollic acid Et·S·CH$_2$·CO·OH.[1545] The potassium salt of this acid reacts with a chloroplatinite to give a dichelate compound Pt(OCO·CH$_2$·S·Et)$_2$ (α-form), almost colourless, m. pt. 189–190°, forming with water a sesqui-hydrate, sol^y 1·49/25°. The *cis-trans* isomerism could be detected only by exposing the aqueous solution of this α-form to sunlight or the light of a Uviol lamp, when the colour darkens, and a canary-yellow isomer of m. pt. 204–205° separates, with a sol^y only 0·057/25°.

The freezing-points of the (necessarily very dilute) solutions showed that the α-form is some 50 per cent. associated in acetic acid and some 10 per cent. in water; the β-('photo') form was not found to be perceptibly associated. On heating with water, the β-form reverts to the α. These compounds are obviously dichelate, and it is to be presumed that they are the *cis* and *trans* modifications.

For further work on these complexes see references [1546-8].

Sulphito-complexes

A series of double sulphites of the type M$_6$[Pt(SO$_3$)$_4$] (so that it would seem that the SO$_3$ groups occupy only one co-ordinate place apiece) have been made[1549] from the chloroplatinate M$_2$PtCl$_6$ by treatment with sulphur dioxide or an acid sulphite; they are colourless.

[1543] E. Fritzmann, *J. Russ. Phys. Chem. Soc.* 1915, **47**, 588.
[1544] Id., *Z. anorg. Chem.* 1924, **133**, 131.
[1545] L. Ramberg, *Ber.* 1910, **43**, 580.   [1546] Id., ib. 1913, **46**, 2353.
[1547] I. Lifschitz and W. Froentjes, *Z. anorg. Chem.* 1939, **241**, 134.
[1548] L. Ramberg, *Ber.* 1913, **46**, 1696.
[1549] P. Bergsöe, *Z. anorg. Chem.* 1898, **19**, 318.

Thiosulphato-complexes such as $K_2[Pt(S_2O_3)_2]$, $[Pt(NH_3)_2S_2O_3(H_2O)]°$, and $[Pt(NH_3)_2S_2O_3]°$ have been described.[1550]

Complex Platinous Halides

Divalent platinum forms complex halides of the type $M_2Pt(hal)_4$ with chlorine, bromine, and probably iodine. The chlorides (platinochlorides or chloroplatinites), which are the best known, can be made by dissolving platinous chloride in a solution of an alkaline chloride, or by reducing the platinichloride M_2PtCl_6 solution with sulphur dioxide, an alkaline oxalate, or cuprous chloride. Platinous chloride dissolves in hydrochloric acid to give what is undoubtedly a solution of the free acid H_2PtCl_4, and if this solution is allowed to evaporate an amorphous mass remains behind which appears to have the composition H_2PtCl_4, H_2O.[1551] Numerous salts of this acid are known. The potassium salt is isomorphous with potassium platinocyanide and pallodocyanide $K_2[Pt(CN)_4]$, $K_2[Pd(CN)_4]$, and so presumably the anion has a planar structure.

Potassium bromoplatinite is similar to the chloro-salt. It forms brownish-red needles.

The iodide $M_2[PtI_4]$ is presumably formed when platinic chloride is treated with potassium iodide; the platinum is reduced quantitatively to the divalent state with the separation of elementary iodine, and the platinous iodide formed remains in solution, no doubt as the salt K_2PtI_4.

TRIVALENT PLATINUM

A CONSIDERABLE number of compounds have been made which appear from their composition to contain trivalent platinum. Practically none of them are soluble without decomposition except as salts, and in no case has the molecular weight been measured. This leaves the question open whether the molecule is monomeric with a single trivalent platinum atom or dimeric with one platinum divalent and the other tetravalent. For example, the trichloride might be written as

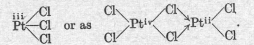

This question is more conveniently discussed after we have dealt with the individual compounds.

These can be divided as usual into the apparently simple and the complex. The former consist of a hydrated sesquioxide, three trihalides, and a tricyanide. The latter include both cations and anions, the chief types being $[PtAm_4X]X_2$, $[PtAm_2X_3]°$, and $M_2[PtX_5]$, X being a halogen or a CN group.

[1550] D. I. Rjabschikov, *C.R. Acad. Sci. U.R.S.S.* 1940, **28**, 231, 236; **27**, 349, 690; 1943, **40**, 229; **41**, 208.

[1551] L. F. Nilson, *J. prakt. Chem.* 1877, [2] **15**, 260.

Platinum Sesquioxide, Pt_2O_3, aq.

Wöhler and Frey[1555] measured the dissociation tension of the oxides of platinum; the work was difficult on account of the slowness with which equilibrium was attained, and the prevalence of solid solutions, but it was found that the dissociation tensions of the monoxide PtO and the sesquioxide Pt_2O_3 are both higher than that of the dioxide PtO_2 at the same temperatures (the range examined was about 400–500° C.), so that the dioxide on heating must go straight to the metal and oxygen. As the hydrated sesquioxide cannot be dehydrated without loss of oxygen, Pt_2O_3 itself has never been prepared, and there is no evidence that it can exist, except as a solid solution in excess of the dioxide.

The hydrated sesquioxide seems to be formed by the action of alkali on the complex sulphate of trivalent platinum (see below), and perhaps[1553] by heating platinum with sodium peroxide and extracting the product with water. It can be made[1556] from the trichloride: if this is treated with potassium hydroxide a dark brown precipitate of Pt_2O_3 aq. is formed, which is very different from the pale yellow PtO_2, aq., or the black PtO, aq. When dried, this precipitate has the composition Pt_2O_3, x aq. The hydrated monoxide PtO, aq. is, as we have seen, to some extent oxidized by oxygen at 100°, but not up to the composition Pt_2O_3.

The hydrated sesquioxide, unlike the hydrated monoxide, is not oxidized by air. In behaviour it is intermediate between PtO, aq. and PtO_2, aq.: it dissolves slowly in concentrated potassium hydroxide (in which the dioxide dissolves easily, and the monoxide not at all), but twice normal sulphuric acid or nitric acid have no action on it in the cold.

Platinum Antimonide, PtSb

This compound, which may be supposed to contain trivalent platinum, has been made by fusing the components together, and shown to have a nickel arsenide lattice.[1562]

Platinum Trichloride, $PtCl_3$

Wöhler and Streicher[1560] showed from the dissociation tensions of the chlorides of platinum that the trichloride is in equilibrium with one atmosphere of chlorine at 370° (it takes up chlorine at 364° but loses it at 374°). From their isothermals the heat of formation of the various chlorides from the metal or the solid chloride and gaseous chlorine are

[1552] S. M. Jörgensen, *J. prakt. Chem.* 1886, **33**, 489.

[1553] W. L. Dudley, *Am. Chem. J.* 1902, **28**, 59.

[1554] M. Blondel, *Ann. Chim. Phys.* 1905, [8] **6**, 81.

[1555] L. Wöhler and W. Frey, *Z. Elektrochem.* 1909, **15**, 129.

[1556] L. Wöhler and F. Martin, *Ber.* 1909, **42**, 3958.

[1557] Id., ib. 4100.   [1558] M. Delépine, *C.R.* 1910, **150**, 104.

[1559] L. A. Levy, *J.C.S.* 1912, **101**, 1081.

[1560] L. Wöhler and S. Streicher, *Ber.* 1913, **46**, 1591.

[1561] L. Wöhler and F. Müller, *Z. anorg. Chem.* 1925, **149**, 377.

[1562] L. Thomassen, *Z. physikal. Chem.* 1929, B **4**, 277.

worked out by the approximate methods of Nernst's heat theorem as follows:

$$Pt + \tfrac{1}{2} Cl_2 = PtCl + 16\cdot11 \text{ k.cals}$$
$$PtCl + \tfrac{1}{2} Cl_2 = PtCl_2 + 16\cdot09 \text{ k.cals}$$
$$PtCl_2 + \tfrac{1}{2} Cl_2 = PtCl_3 + 13\cdot1 \text{ k.cals}$$
$$PtCl_3 + \tfrac{1}{2} Cl_2 = PtCl_4 + 11\cdot78 \text{ k.cals}$$

The nearness of the first two figures makes it very doubtful whether the monochloride PtCl is a definite compound.

The trichloride can be made[1556] from the dichloride or the tetrachloride by heating in chlorine to a suitable temperature. It is a very dark green almost black powder, very different in appearance from the red-brown tetrachloride or the yellow dichloride. It is intermediate in properties between the other two chlorides: while $PtCl_4$ is excessively soluble in water, and $PtCl_2$ quite insoluble, not being even wetted by it, $PtCl_3$ dissolves slowly in cold and quickly in hot water to give a brown solution, which probably contains a mixture of the two oxychlorides $H_2Pt^{ii}Cl_2O$ and $H_2Pt^{iv}Cl_4O$: the trivalent platinum cannot be recovered from it. It is practically insoluble in cold concentrated hydrochloric acid, but on warming goes into solution, forming a mixture of the chloroacids of divalent and tetravalent platinum, H_2PtCl_4 and H_2PtCl_6.

Platinum Tribromide, $PtBr_3$[1561]

This is very like the chloride. If $PtBr_4$ is heated in bromine vapour at 1 atm. it is stable up to 320°, but at 335° it loses bromine and gives a solid solution of about the composition 2 $PtBr_3$, $PtBr_4$, the composition remaining constant at this temperature. At any temperature from 368° to 405° the composition remains constant at $PtBr_3$, and on cooling, still in bromine vapour at 1 atm. pressure, no bromine is taken up below 340°.

Platinum tribromide is a greenish-black substance, with properties very like those of the trichloride.

Platinum Tri-iodide, PtI_3

This is again similar[1561]; it is stable in 1 atm. of iodine vapour between 242° and 264°, but its reactions are so slow that the exact point is difficult to determine. In a sealed tube in saturated iodine vapour it is readily formed at 350°. It is a black graphite-like substance, which is insoluble in water, alcohol, ether, and ethyl acetate.

Platinum Tricyanide, $Pt(CN)_3$

This is a yellow powder, formed[1559] by heating the complex acid $H[Pt(CN)_4]$ to 120°; it is insoluble in water, but soluble in boiling potassium cyanide solution.

COMPLEXES OF TRIVALENT PLATINUM

THESE are of two kinds: (1) complexes of the ammine type, with the platinum either neutral or in the cation, and (2) complex cyanides, sulphates, or chlorides, in which it is in the anion.

Complex Trivalent Cyanides

Levy[1559] found that if $K_2Pt(CN)_4$ is treated with chlorine or oxidized with manganese dioxide or lead dioxide in acid solution, products are formed which seem to be intermediate between [or perhaps mixtures of] di- and tetravalent platinum and could not be got in the pure state. If, however, the oxidation was effected by hydrogen peroxide in presence of sulphuric acid, the $Pt(CN)_4^{--}$ ion was converted into $Pt(CN)_4^-$, or its salt $M[Pt(CN)_4]$. The salts so formed are bronze or copper coloured, and most of them dissolve readily in water to give colourless solutions.

When a solution of the free acid $H_2Pt(CN)_4$ is oxidized with hydrogen peroxide and evaporated, a green mass of the composition $H \cdot Pt(CN)_4, 2 H_2O$ is left, which is easily soluble in water, and decomposes at 120°, leaving a light yellow residue of the tricyanide $Pt(CN)_3$.

Complex Sulphates

If platinic sulphate $Pt(SO_4)_2$ is carefully reduced with oxalic acid, the acid $H[Pt^{iii}(SO_4)_2]$, 8, 5, and 1 H_2O is produced, from which various salts (Na, 4 H_2O, orange; K, H_2O, yellow) can be obtained.[1554] See further, reference [1558].

Ammines

Most of these contain as the amine either ethylamine ($=$ ae) or propylamine ($=$ pe), but this is probably merely a question of solubility.

If[1566] the hydrochloric acid solution of the colourless tetrammine salt $[Pt''ae_4]Cl_2, 2 H_2O$ is evaporated in air or oxidized with hydrogen peroxide, a brilliant red salt is formed which is slightly soluble in water, and insoluble in dilute hydrochloric acid. The salt has taken up covalently one atom of chlorine, giving a compound of the composition $[Ptae_4Cl]Cl_2, 2 H_2O$, where the platinum appears to be trivalent. The water is easily removed, the colour then changing from red to yellow. Further action of hydrochloric acid removes two molecules of the amine, leaving the insoluble non-ionized compound $[Ptae_2Cl_3]°$.

Drew and Tress[1567] confirmed these conclusions, and showed that the bromide has the composition $[Ptae_4Br]Br_2, H_2O$; this hydrate is green, but in the anhydrous state the salt is red; changes of temperature can, however, make both states assume both colours: the dimorphism here, and

[1563] L. Tschugaev and J. Tscherniaev, *Z. anorg. Chem.* 1929, **182**, 159.

[1564] H. D. K. Drew, F. W. Pinkard, W. Wardlaw, and E. G. Cox, *J.C.S.* 1932, 1013.

[1565] H. D. K. Drew and F. S. H. Head, ib. 1934, 221.

[1566] H. Reihlen and E. Flohr, *Ber.* 1934, **67**, 2010.

[1567] H. D. K. Drew and H. J. Tress, *J.C.S.* 1935, 1244.

no doubt in the chloride also, does not depend on the water. They also showed that the ethylamine could be replaced by propylamine.

The red salt [Ptae$_4$Cl]Cl$_2$ gives in hot water a pale yellow solution, which behaves as if it were a mixture of the colourless [Pt″ae$_4$]Cl$_2$ and the pale yellow [Pt^{iv}ae$_4$Cl$_2$]Cl$_2$; if solutions of these last two salts are mixed, the red salt separates at once. If the solution of the red salt is treated with sodium platinichloride Na$_2$PtCl$_6$ there is an immediate precipitation of a mixture of the two salts [Ptae$_4$]·[PtCl$_6$] and [Ptae$_4$Cl$_2$]·[PtCl$_6$].

Other salts of this kind, but with more usual amines, such as ammonia and pyridine, have also been made.[1552,1563-5] For example,[1563] Pt *en*Cl$_2$ when treated with ammonium persulphate gives the red compound Pt *en*Cl$_3$. If Pt *en*Cl$_2$ and Pt *en*Cl$_4$ are ground together, a red compound Pt *en*Cl$_3$ is formed. In the same way if α-Pt(NH$_3$)aeCl$_2$ and Pt(NH$_3$)aeCl$_4$ are heated together, a red substance is produced.[1565]

All these trivalent platinum compounds are insoluble in water, and so their molecular weights are unknown. Also it is to be noticed that they are only formed by compounds of the *cis* series: *trans* Pt(NH$_3$)$_2$Cl$_2$ does not react with ammonium persulphate in acid or neutral solution, and in alkaline solution it is converted into the sulphate of the platinic compound.

Complex Chlorides

A saturated solution of the (not very soluble) cæsium platinochloride Cs$_2$PtCl$_4$ if treated with chlorine water at 0° gives a dark green crystalline precipitate of Cs$_2$PtCl$_5$, which more chlorine converts into pale yellow Cs$_2$PtCl$_6$; the pentachloro-salt can also be made by adding cæsium chloride to a solution either of the hydrated sesquioxide in cold hydrochloric acid, or of platinum trichloride in water.[1563]

The free acid H$_2$PtCl$_5$ cannot be isolated, but it must be present in these solutions when they are first formed, since they then give the green precipitate with cæsium chloride, though after they have stood for a short time only the pink salt Cs$_2$PtCl$_4$ is precipitated.

Caesium pentachloroplatinate (we have no proper nomenclature for these compounds) is best distinguished by its dark green colour, as compared with the pink of Cs$_2$PtCl$_4$ and the pale yellow of Cs$_2$PtCl$_6$. Its chief property is its strong tendency to change over into a mixture of the other two (platinous and platinic) chlorides; the moist crystals can be seen changing in this way under the microscope; they do so rapidly in sunlight, so that the salt must be prepared in the dark. They change also on heating.

Conditions of Stability of Trivalent Platinum Compounds

Wöhler and Martin[1557] discuss the conditions of stability of these compounds. The dissociation tensions of oxygen show that the anhydrous sesquioxide must always decompose spontaneously. But the hydrated oxide Pt$_2$O$_3$, aq., is stable, and even at the boiling-point of water does not take up any oxygen from oxygen gas. The dissociation tension of chlorine reaches 1 atm. for the tetrachloride at 275°, for the trichloride at 370°, and for the dichloride at over 400°, so that the trichloride has a definite range of stability in contact with chlorine. The aqueous solutions of the three chlorides may be assumed to contain the acids H_2PtCl_nO, where $n = 2$, 3, and 4; the acid H_2PtCl_2O can be got in solution by reducing H_2PtCl_4O. The trivalent H_2PtCl_3O is stable with respect to the other two H_2PtCl_2O and H_2PtCl_4O; the mixed solution of these last two gives with caesium chloride the characteristic green precipitate of Cs_2PtCl_5.

On the other hand, when the oxychlorides are replaced by the pure complex chlorides the stability relations are reversed. The trivalent penta-chloro-salt M_2PtCl_5 is unstable with respect to the platinous and platinic compounds, and so the solutions of the hydrated sesquioxide or of the trichloride in hydrochloric acid have only a transient content of trivalent platinum. The complex salts show the same relations.

Changes like these are common in the relative stabilities of the different valencies of the noble metals, where the primary valencies have low energy values (this is what is meant by 'noble' elements), and accordingly their differences are also small.

As the molecular weights of these trivalent platinum compounds are all unknown, it is possible that the formulae should be doubled, and that the molecule contains not a trivalent platinum atom but a divalent and a tetravalent. With the binary compounds like the sesquioxide and the trihalides, this could only be settled by X-ray data, which are not available. But with the complexes we have some evidence. These, so far as they are known, belong to four types, which, written as monomeric, are $[PtAm_4Cl]X_2$, $[PtAm_4(OH)]X_2$, $[PtAm_2Cl_3]°$, and M_2PtCl_5. Thus in every case the platinum appears to be 5-covalent. Now the covalency of platinum in all its numerous divalent and tetravalent complexes is uniformly 4 or 6, and where it seems to be 3 this is proved to be converted into 4 by dimerization. This strongly suggests that in these trivalent complexes the covalency of 5 is relieved by dimerization, becoming 6, with one divalent and one tetravalent platinum atom, allowing of a resonance between the forms: thus

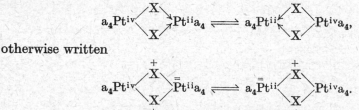

otherwise written

This polymerization would only be possible if the X atoms or groups were of a kind that could co-ordinate as a donor; but in all these trivalent platinum complexes that is so, there being always one halogen atom or hydroxyl group at least on each platinum. (Where X is a cyanide group such dimerization is stereochemically impossible: see I. 183.) Such a dimeric structure would very easily break up into its constituent platinous and platinic compounds, and would very easily be formed from them; the resonance would be a source of stability: and finally, this kind of resonance, involving the shift of an electric charge as we go from one structure to the other, is precisely a condition (the 'meri-quinoid' state) leading to intense colour, which these complexes exhibit.

Whether platinum atoms in this state, where there is a resonance between $Pt^{ii} \cdots Pt^{iv}$ and $Pt^{iv} \cdots Pt^{ii}$, are correctly described as trivalent, is mainly a matter of language.

TETRAVALENT PLATINUM

UNLIKE palladium, platinum is practically as stable in the tetravalent as in the divalent state (see summary, p. 1551).

Alkyl-platinum Compounds

Platinum is the only metal of the group which has so far been found to form alkyl compounds (as is practically its neighbour gold in I. B). These were first made in 1909 by Pope and Peachy[1568] by the action of the Grignard reagent on platinic chloride. The product of this reaction is treated with water and extracted with benzene, from which on evaporation yellow crystals of $(CH_3)_3PtI$ separate out.

Quite recently[1571] Gilman has obtained the pure platinum alkyls themselves. Tetramethyl platinum $(CH_3)_4Pt$ was made in 46 per cent. yield by treating the trimethyl iodide with sodium methyl $NaCH_3$; it is a solid which decomposes at high temperatures without melting, and is easily soluble in cold benzene, acetone, ether, and petroleum ether.

The hexamethyl compound $(CH_3)_3Pt—Pt(CH_3)_3$ was prepared in a 60 per cent. yield by the action of powdered metallic potassium on a solution of trimethyl platinum iodide in benzene. It is very soluble in benzene, acetone, or ether; it is monomeric by the freezing-point in benzene. It will take up iodine to give trimethyl platinum iodide, which is good evidence of its structure.

These alkyl platinum compounds are among the very few metallic alkyls which are not attacked by air or water, almost the only others being those of mercury and the dialkyl derivatives of thallium.

The crystal structures of these remarkable substances have recently been examined with unexpected results (see below).

Trimethyl platinic iodide $(CH_3)_3PtI$ forms orange crystals (a white form also appears to exist[1572]); it is 4 to 5 times associated in benzene both by the freezing-point and by the boiling-point.[1572] It is readily soluble in benzene and chloroform, slightly in alcohol and acetone, but insoluble in water.

[1568] W. J. Pope and S. J. Peachey, *J.C.S.* 1909, **95**, 571.
[1569] R. C. Menzies, ib. 1928, 565.
[1570] R. C. Menzies and E. R. Wiltshire, ib. 1933, 21.
[1571] H. Gilman and M. Lichtenwalter, *J.A.C.S.* 1938, **60**, 3085.
[1572] R. C. Menzies and H. Overton, *J.C.S.* 1933, 1290.

It is not attacked in the cold by concentrated acids or alkalies. On heating it decomposes without melting at about 250°.

In benzene solution it will take up ammonia, giving a diammine, $(CH_3)_3Pt(NH_3)_2I$, which is colourless, soluble in benzene, and insoluble in water (and hence obviously not a salt). The base $(CH_3)_3PtOH$ is made by treating the iodide with moist silver oxide: it forms colourless plates, insoluble in water, readily soluble in ether, alcohol, acetone, ethyl acetate, chloroform, and benzene, separating from the last three solvents with solvent of crystallization; it is not attacked by mineral acids in the cold, but is dissolved by hot nitric acid.

Other trimethyl platinum derivatives prepared were the chloride Me_3PtCl, got by the action of potassium chloride on the nitrate or sulphate: it is insoluble in water, fairly soluble in benzene or chloroform, but less so than the iodide; a nitrate, very soluble in water; a sulphate, $(Me_3Pt)_2SO_4, 2 H_2O$, easily soluble in water but practically insoluble in benzene or chloroform; and a cyanide, probably Me_3PtCN, white and insoluble in water. It may be assumed that those that are more soluble in organic solvents than in water are covalent, and the others ionized. See further, Lile and Menzies.[1574]

Menzies[1569-70] has investigated the compounds formed by trimethyl platinum with β-diketones and the like. Trimethyl platinum iodide reacts in benzene with thallous acetylacetone ($TlC_5H_7O_2 = TlA$) to give thallous iodide, and the compound Me_3PtA, presumably

as colourless crystals, which decompose without melting at 200°, but can sublime to some extent unchanged. It is easily soluble in organic solvents including hexane; the association factor in 3 per cent. benzene solution is 1·70. Other β-diketones behave in the same way; with dipropionyl methane the association factor is only 1·13.[1570]

The crystal structures of both tetramethyl platinum and trimethyl platinic chloride have[1573] recently been examined with very surprising results. The structures of the two are almost identical; both are tetrameric, the molecule forming a cube with four platinum atoms at alternate corners; the Pt . . . Pt distance is 3·73 A in Me_3PtCl, and 3·44 in Me_4Pt. In Me_3PtCl the other four corners of the cube are occupied by chlorines, the angle Pt—Cl—Pt being 99°. The Pt has an octahedral arrangement of six groups:

$$\begin{array}{c} CH_3 \\ CH_3 \\ CH_3 \end{array} \!\!\! \searrow Pt \!\!\! \swarrow \begin{array}{c} Cl \\ Cl. \\ Cl \end{array}$$

[1573] R. E. Rundle and J. H. Sturdivant, *J.A.C.S.* 1947, **69**, 1561.
[1574] W. J. Lile and R. C. Menzies, *Nature*, 1948, **162**, 298.

In Me₄Pt the structure is the same, except that the 4 Cl atoms are replaced by 4 carbon atoms or CH_3 groups. The structure of the chloride is not unusual, chlorine often acting as a donor. But it is very remarkable that a methyl group should do so. These methyl groups must in some way produce three links, possibly by resonance with C[H] groups.

Platinum Silicide, PtSi

This can be obtained in an apparently amorphous state by fusing the elements together at a red heat, or in a crystalline form by dissolving them in silver in an electric furnace, and treating the resulting mass alternately with dilute sodium hydroxide and nitric acid.[1575-6] The properties of the system platinum-silicon[1577] show that two compounds PtSi and Pt_2Si are formed. Pt_2Si melts at 1,100°; it is unaffected by nitric acid, hydrochloric, sulphuric, or hydrofluoric; it is soluble in aqua regia and in fused alkali.

Platinum Dioxide, PtO_2 and PtO_2, aq.

Platinum dioxide is a black powder, which can be made by heating the hydrated form, although the last traces of water cannot be removed without some loss of oxygen.[1579] It has a lower dissociation pressure than either the monoxide or the sesquioxide[1581] (1 atm. at 400°),[1584] and hence it must decompose directly to the metal and oxygen.

If platinum[1579] tetrachloride is boiled with excess of sodium hydroxide and acetic acid added, the precipitate that is formed is white, and on boiling turns yellow, having then the composition PtO_2, 3 H_2O. In this form it dissolves readily in alkalies, giving salts of the composition $M_2[Pt(OH)_6]$, which are isomorphous with the stannates $M_2[Sn(OH)_6]$: the hydroxide $Pt(OH)_4$ is thus definitely amphoteric. These salts are, properly speaking, complex, since the covalency of the platinum atom in them is greater than its valency, and they form the last stage in the replacement of the chlorine atoms of the chloroplatinate by hydroxyl. This pale yellow trihydrate PtO_2, 3 H_2O loses one molecule of water over sulphuric acid, giving the brown dihydrate, and this at 100° loses a second molecule to form the monohydrate PtO_2, H_2O, which is nearly black[1579-81]; the last molecule cannot be completely removed without some decomposition of the dioxide. The di- and trihydrated forms dissolve with difficulty in sulphuric or nitric acid, but easily in hydrochloric acid or in sodium hydroxide. The monohydrate is insoluble in hydrochloric acid and even aqua regia.

[1575] P. Lebeau and A. Novitzky, *C.R.* 1907, **145**, 241.
[1576] E. Vigouroux, ib. 376.
[1577] N. M. Voronov, *Ann. Sect. Platine*, 1936, **13**, 145.
[1578] C. Roessler, *Z. anorg. Chem.* 1897, **15**, 405.
[1579] L. Wöhler, ib. 1904, **40**, 423.
[1580] M. Blondel, *Ann. Chim. Phys.* 1905, [8] **6**, 81.
[1581] L. Wöhler and W. Frey, *Z. Elektrochem.* 1909, **15**, 129.
[1582] L. Moser and K. Atynski, *Mon.* 1925, **45**, 235.
[1583] W. Biltz and R. Juza, *Z. anorg. Chem.* 1930, **190**, 161.
[1584] P. Laffitte and P. Grandadam, *C.R.* 1935, **200**, 456.

Platinic Sulphide, PtS_2

Platinum and sulphur react rather slowly at 650° to give the disulphide PtS_2, the only compound of platinum and sulphur except the monosulphide PtS.[1583] It can also be made by the action of sulphur on ammonium platinichloride at a dark red heat. When prepared in the dry way it is a steel-grey powder, which is quite stable in air; it has a dissociation tension of 300 mm. at 690°. The crystals, like those of $PtSe_2$ and $PtTe_2$, have a cadmium iodide lattice.[1585] When it is made in the wet way, by the action of hydrogen sulphide on a solution of a platinichloride, it separates in a colloidal form or as a black precipitate, which is readily oxidized by air, and must be filtered and dried in an atmosphere of hydrogen sulphide.

Platinum Diselenide, $PtSe_2$[1582]

This is said to be formed from the elements, or by heating the triselenide $PtSe_3$ (p. 1626), as a black unstable substance, which dissolves in alkaline selenides to form complex salts.

Platinum Ditelluride, $PtTe_2$[1578]

This is made by fusing the elements together and removing the excess of tellurium by boiling with caustic potash solution or extracting with cold dilute nitric acid. It forms grey octahedra which are not attacked by concentrated nitric acid or potassium hydroxide.

PLATINUM TETRAHALIDES

Platinum Tetrafluoride, PtF_4

This was prepared by Moissan[1592] by passing fluorine over red-hot platinum. Attempts[1594] to prepare it by the action of hydrogen fluoride or potassium acid fluoride on platinic chloride were not successful. It forms yellow or red crystals which are hydrolysed violently by water.

Platinum Tetrachloride, $PtCl_4$

This can be made by heating platinum with chlorine or a source of chlorine.[1595] It is difficult to prepare the anhydrous compound except with a slight defect of chlorine: this is best avoided by heating platinum with arsenic trichloride and selenium tetrachloride in a sealed tube.[1593] It is commonly made by heating the acid H_2PtCl_6 to 300°.

[1585] L. Thomassen, *Z. physikal. Chem.* 1929, B **2**, 364.
[1586] V. Meyer and H. Züblin, *Ber.* 1880, **13**, 404.
[1587] W. Halberstadt, ib. 1884, **17**, 2962.
[1588] A. Miolati, *Z. anorg. Chem.* 1899, **22**, 445.
[1589] F. Kohlrausch, *Z. physikal. Chem.* 1900, **33**, 257.
[1590] A. Miolati and I. Bellucci, *Atti R.* 1900, [5] **9**, ii. 140.
[1591] I. Bellucci, ib. 1902, [5] **11**, i. 8.
[1592] H. Moissan, *Fluor*, 1910, p. 213.
[1593] A. Gutbier and F. Heinrich, *Z. anorg. Chem.* 1913, **81**, 378.
[1594] O. Ruff, *Ber.* 1913, **46**, 920.
[1595] L. Wöhler and S. Streicher, ib. 1591.

Platinum tetrachloride forms reddish-brown crystals which are easily soluble in water and acetone. It crystallizes from water as a variety of hydrates, usually with 5 H_2O, but a heptahydrate has been described, and tetra- and monohydrates can be made. These hydrates, or some of them, are clearly complex oxyhalide acids, of which $H_2PtCl_4(OH)_2$[1589] is the best marked (Hittorf and Salkowsky 1899). This is one of the series of compounds joining H_2PtCl_6 to $H_2Pt(OH)_6$; its formation in aqueous solution is shown by the titration, by the conductivity, and by the formation of salts, though most of these are too soluble to be isolated.[1587-8] (See later, p. 1623, under the complex halide acids.)

Platinum Tetrabromide, $PtBr_4$

This is made by dissolving platinum in hydrobromic acid solution containing free bromine, evaporating, and drying at 180°.[1586] It is a brownish-black powder, which is only slightly soluble in water, but easily in alcohol and ether.[1586-7] It is less stable than the chloride, and in its preparation must not be heated too long, as at 180° it begins to decompose into platinous bromide and bromine. The aqueous solution contains the complex acid $H_2PtBr_4(OH)_2$ from which salts can be prepared.[1590]

Platinum Tetraiodide, PtI_4

Platinum differs from palladium in giving a tetraiodide, a sign of the greater resistance of tetravalent platinum to reduction. It is a brown-black substance which can be made by treating concentrated chloroplatinic acid solution with hot solution of potassium iodide (Topsoe, 1889). It behaves like the tetrachloride and the tetrabromide. It dissolves in alcohol to give a solution which decomposes in light, and which mainly consists of the complex acid $H_2PtI_4(OH)_2$, from which the silver, thallous, and mercuric salts have been obtained.[1591]

COMPLEX COMPOUNDS OF TETRAVALENT PLATINUM

TETRAVALENT platinum forms almost as many kinds of complexes as divalent. They include cations, neutral molecules, and anions; the co-ordination number is in practically if not absolutely every case 6. The general preferences in the co-ordination are much the same as for the divalent element; the link to nitrogen is very strong; the link to oxygen, as in the platinous series, is very weak except in certain chelate compounds, and in the hydroxo-ammines, like $[PtAm_5OH]X_3$, where it can be remarkably strong. The link to sulphur, though stronger than that to oxygen, is weaker in the platinic than in the platinous series. In general the stability of the platinic state in the complexes is as great as that of the platinous, in the sense that the reduction to the divalent state requires a vigorous reagent. The platinic complexes include as many forms of ammines as the platinous, but not so many kinds of acid radicals; the halides and hydroxy-compounds are as stable as with divalent platinum, but the complexes with other negative groups, especially the nitro- and cyano-groups, are unstable and few.

Complex Cyanides

Various attempts by Mendeleeff and others to make complex cyanides of tetravalent platinum have so far failed,[1596-8] though it is probable (p. 1608) that trivalent cyanide complexes exist.

On the other hand, Miolati and Bellucci[1599] have been able to prepare an undoubted complex cyanide of tetravalent platinum, though not a pure cyanide. They found that by treating silver platinocyanide $Ag_2Pt(CN)_4$ with halogen they could oxidize it to the tetracyano-dihalides

$$Ag_2[Pt(CN)_4Cl_2]$$

and the corresponding dibromo- and di-iodo-cyanides, all of which are stable to water.

Thiocyanate Complexes

These are of the type $M_2[Pt(CNS)_6]$; they were discovered by Buckton in 1854.[1600] An X-ray examination of the ammonium, potassium, and rubidium salts[1601] seems to show that the CNS groups are attached to the platinum atom through the sulphur, although this is not certain.

Similar selenium compounds $M_2[Pt(SeCN)_6]$ have also been made.[1602]

Platinic Ammines

Platinic ammines are known of every type from $[PtAm_6]X_4$ to $M[PtAmX_5]$ and $M_2[PtX_6]$. Werner has pointed out that the molecular conductivities of these compounds (at 25° and $V = 1,000$), being roughly proportional to the number of ions into which the molecule breaks up (more nearly to the sum of their valencies), show how the ionic type changes along the series:

$[Pt(NH_3)_6]Cl_4$	522·9
$[Pt(NH_3)_5Cl]Cl_3$	404
$[Pt(NH_3)_4Cl_2]Cl_2$	228
$[Pt(NH_3)_3Cl_3]Cl$	96·8
$[Pt(NH_3)_2Cl_4]°$	*ca.* 0
$K[Pt(NH_3)Cl_5]$	108·5
$K_2[PtCl_6]$	256

A great variety of monamines and diamines can take the place of ammonia in these complexes, as can also hydrazine[1619] and hydroxylamine.[1620-1]

[1596] L. A. Levy, *J.C.S.* 1912, **101**, 1081.
[1597] J. E. Reynolds, *Proc. Roy. Soc.* 1909, **82**, 380.
[1598] H. Terrey, ib. 1930, **128**, 359.
[1599] A. Miolati and L. Bellucci, *Gaz.* 1901, **30**, ii. 588.
[1600] G. B. Buckton, *Ann.* 1854, **92**, 284.
[1601] S. B. Hendricks and H. E. Merwin, *Am. J. Sci.* 1928, [5] **15**, 487.
[1602] G. Spacu and V. Armeanu, *Bul. Soc. Stiinte Cluj*, 1934, **7**, 610.

The extensive group of ammines of tetravalent platinum is most conveniently divided according to the number of nitrogen atoms attached to the platinum, beginning with the hexammines.

Hexammines

The simplest of these, $[Pt(NH_3)_6]Cl_4$, can be made (Drechsel and Gerdes, 1879) in very bad yield by the electrolysis of ammonium carbonate solution with platinum electrodes and an alternating current, or much better (Tschugaev[1610]) by the action of liquid ammonia on ammonium platinichloride $(NH_4)_2[PtCl_6]$; it has $2 H_2O$. It forms a crystalline hydroxide $[Pt(NH_3)_6](OH)_4$, which is said to be almost insoluble in water.

The corresponding ethylene diamine compounds [Pt en_3]X_4 were made by Werner,[1607] who resolved them into their optical antimers, as did Smirnov[1609] with the propylene diamine compounds

$$H_2N \cdot \overset{*}{C}H(CH_3)CH_2 \cdot NH_2 \ (= \ pn):$$

the asymmetric carbon atoms ($\overset{*}{C}$) in the diamine each contribute 96° to the polarization [M], while the rest of the molecule contributes 747°.

The poly-ammines of tetravalent platinum show a tendency for one of the NH_3 groups to go over into NH_2, the change Pt←NH_3 to Pt—NH_2 corresponding exactly to that of Pt←OH_2 to Pt—OH. This makes them somewhat basic, since the nitrogen in Pt—NH_2 is trivalent and hence can act as a base. A series of platinic ammines were shown[1615] all to be more basic than pyridine, and the strongest, $[Pt(en)NH_2(NO_2)Cl]°$, was as strong as ammonia; the basicity is greater the smaller the positive charge on the complex.

Pentammines

These were first made by Tschugaev in 1915,[1605-6,1610] by the action of ammonia, either as the liquid or in concentrated aqueous solution, on the diammine $[Pt(NH_3)_2Cl_4]°$ (either the *cis* or the *trans* form), or more con-

[1603] H. Grossmann and B. Schück, *Ber.* 1906, **39**, 1900.
[1604] A. Werner, ib. 1907, **40**, 4093.
[1605] L. Tschugaev and N. Vladimirov, *C.R.* 1915, **160**, 840.
[1606] L. Tschugaev and I. Tscherniaev, ib. **161**, 637.
[1607] A. Werner, *Naturf. Ges. Zürich*, 1917, **62**, 553.
[1608] D. Strömholm, *Z. anorg. Chem.* 1919, **108**, 184.
[1609] A. P. Smirnov, *Helv. Chim. Acta*, 1920, **3**, 177.
[1610] L. Tschugaev, *Z. anorg. Chem.* 1924, **137**, 1.   [1611] Id., ib. 401.
[1612] L. Tschugaev and W. Chlopin, ib. 1926, **151**, 253.
[1613] F. G. Mann, *J.C.S.* 1927, 1224.
[1614] I. I. Tscherniaev, *Ann. Inst. Platine*, 1928, **6**, 40.
[1615] A. A. Grünberg and G. P. Faermann, *Z. anorg. Chem.* 1930, **193**, 193.
[1616] I. I. Tscherniaev, *Ann. Inst. Platine*, 1931, **8**, 37.
[1617] F. G. Mann, *J.C.S.* 1934, 466.
[1618] A. M. Rubinschtein, *Ann. Sect. Platine*, 1936, **13**, 21.
[1619] V. I. Goremikin and K. A. Gladischevskaja, *Bull. Acad. Sci. U.R.S.S.* 1943, 338.
[1620] Id., ib. 401.   [1621] V. I. Goremikin, ib. 1944, 105.

veniently on ammonium platinichloride $(NH_4)_2[PtCl_6]$, but only if there is present either ammonium carbonate or a soluble phosphate, such as sodium hydrogen phosphate Na_2HPO_4; the carbonate and phosphate ions form very insoluble salts with the pentammines, and so remove them from the sphere of the reaction. When once they are isolated, the pentammines show remarkable stability. From the carbonate $[Pt(NH_3)_5Cl]_2(CO_3)_3$ so formed the other salts can be made.

A series of salts of the chloropentammines $[Pt(NH_3)_5Cl]X_3$ ($= [B]X_3$) are known. The chloride $[B]Cl_3$ has only three-quarters of its chlorine precipitated by silver nitrate: the nitrate $[B](NO_3)_3$ gives no precipitate with silver nitrate even when hot. The chloride $[B]Cl_3$ is easily soluble in water; sol^y 17·4/0°; it is precipitated by the addition of hydrochloric acid. In the dry state it slowly loses ammonia, being converted mainly into the very insoluble tetrammine $[Pt(NH_3)_4Cl_2]Cl_2$ and the amino-compound $[Pt(NH_3)_4NH_2Cl]Cl_2$.

The bromide $[Pt(NH_3)_5Cl]Br_3$ is similar. The nitrate $[B](NO_3)_3$, sol^y 0·99/0°, 2·16/21° is stable. The trivalency of this cation is proved by the conductivity (given above), and also by its effect on the coagulation of arsenic trisulphide sol.[1605]

When these chloropentammine salts are warmed with excess of potassium iodide, a graphite-like precipitate of the iodo-tetrammine iodide $[Pt(NH_3)_4I_2]I_2$ is formed.

The bromopentammines $[Pt(NH_3)_5Br]X_3$ are similar in preparation and properties. The hydroxopentammines $[PtAm_5OH]X_3$[1610,1612] were first made[1606] by oxidizing the *cis* form of $[Pt(NH_3)_2Cl_4]°$ with ozone in presence of ammonia and (as before) of ammonium carbonate. An easier method is to heat the chloropentammine salt with 2–3 per cent. sodium hydroxide solution nearly to 100°; this converts it into the base $[Pt(NH_3)_5OH](OH)_3$, which with excess of hydrochloric acid gives the chloride of the hydroxo-pentammine $[Pt(NH_3)_5OH]Cl_3, H_2O$; the water is slowly lost at 110°. This compound is exceptionally stable; it only decomposes at high temperatures.

It is remarkable that all attempts to replace the chlorine in the cation of the chloropentammine by anything but bromine or hydroxyl have failed. The hydroxo-compound seems to be in every way exceptionally stable. If the chloro-compound $[Pt(NH_3)_5Cl]X_3$ is treated with potassium cyanide, which, as we have seen, is very effective in the platinous series in expelling other groups from a complex, the chlorine is indeed removed, but it is replaced by hydroxyl and not by a cyanide group. In the same way excess of ammonia transforms the chloropentammine into the hydroxo-compound and not into the hexammine.

In solubility these pentammine salts (and to some extent the hexammine salts also) are like the salts of barium and lead; thus the sulphate, chromate, and oxalate are all insoluble, the chloropentammine salts rather more than those of barium and lead, the hexammine salts rather less. The sol^{ies} at 0° are: $[Pt(NH_3)_5Cl]Cl_3$ 17·4; $[Pt(NH_3)_5OH]Cl_3$ 2·82; $[Pt(NH_3)_6]Cl_4$ 2·91.

All three series, hexammine, and chloro- and hydroxopentammine, are reduced by zinc and dilute acid to the platinous complex $[Pt(NH_3)_4]X_2$.

Tetrammines, $[PtAm_4R_2]X_2$

These salts can often be made from the platinous tetrammines by oxidation with halogens or other oxidizing agents: for example,[1604]

$$[Pt(NH_3)_4]X_2 + Br_2 = [Pt(NH_3)_4Br_2]X_2.$$

Also the chloropentammine chloride, as we have seen,[1610] loses ammonia to give the tetrammine $[Pt(NH_3)_4Cl_2]Cl_2$, a very insoluble salt. Further, a diammine or a hexa-acido-complex will sometimes exchange its acidic groups for a chelate diamine.[1603] Thus the complex thiocyanate

$$K_2[Pt(CNS)_6]$$

reacts with ethylene diamine to give a salt $[Pt\ en_2(CNS)_2](CNS)_2$, which is remarkable for being insoluble in water and even in strong acids, and only dissolving after long boiling with aqua regia.

The tetrammine structure seems to admit of a greater variety of acidic groups than the pentammine; thus in addition to chlorine, bromine, and hydroxyl we can have the thiocyanate, the nitro-group (by the direct oxidation of the platinous $[Pt(NH_3)_4]X_2$ with nitrogen peroxide), and SO_3: if the dichlorotetrammine $[Pt(NH_3)_4Cl_2](NO_3)_2$ is treated with sulphur dioxide the salt $[Pt(NH_3)_4SO_3]SO_3, 2\ H_2O$ is formed.[1608] This on boiling with water undergoes internal oxidation and reduction, and is converted into the platinous sulphate $[Pt(NH_3)_4]SO_4$.

The di-hydroxo-compounds,[1604] which can be made by hydrolysing the dibromo-compounds by means of sulphuric acid

$$[Pt(NH_3)_4Br_2]X_2 \longrightarrow [Pt(NH_3)_4(OH)_2]X_2$$

are peculiar in several ways. The sulphate $[Pt(NH_3)_4(OH)_2]SO_4$ is known both in the anhydrous state and as a tetrahydrate; both forms will recrystallize from the same solution, and the anhydrous seems to be more stable, but the hydrate shows remarkable metastability, as is common with sulphates.

Again, in these compounds the hydroxo-groups should be readily converted into H_2O on treatment with hydrochloric acid

$$[Pt(NH_3)_4(OH)_2]Cl_2 + 2\ HCl = [Pt(NH_3)_4(OH_2)_2]Cl_4.$$

But this does not happen. The intermediate aquo-hydroxo-tetrammine $[Pt(NH_3)_4(OH)(OH_2)]Cl_3$ can be made but it is hydrolysed back again even by atmospheric moisture.

The 'amino-salts' are formed by the reaction:

$$[Pt(NH_3)_5Cl]X_3 \longrightarrow [Pt(NH_3)_4NH_2Cl]X_2 + HX,$$

from the pentammine salt whenever its solution contains enough hydroxyl and X ions[1611]: thus the nitrate $[Pt(NH_3)_5Cl](NO_3)_3$ when treated with hot ammonia solution gives $[Pt(NH_3)_4NH_2Cl](NO_3)_2$. These salts, unlike the chloropentammines, are yellow. In solution they have a marked alkaline reaction, and can be titrated (see above, p. 1617) as monacid bases with methyl orange. The chlorine in the cation is not affected by acids, but alkalies, even ammonia, at once replace it by hydroxyl.

Tscherniaev[1614] has resolved the tetrammine salt $[Pt\ en(NH_3)_2Cl_2]X_2$ into its optical antimers. He finds that in these and similar compounds the sign of the rotation is reversed when an NH_3 group is converted into an NH_2.

Triammines, $[PtAm_3R_3]X$

Relatively few of these compounds are known; they can be made in the usual ways, for example, by the oxidation of a platinous triammine:

$$[Pt''(NH_3)_3NO_3]NO_3 \xrightarrow{Cl_2} [Pt^{iv}(NH_3)_3Cl_3]Cl.$$

Tscherniaev[1614,1616] has resolved into their optical antimers the salts $[Pt\ en(Am)Cl_2(NO_2)]X$, where $Am = NH_3$, ethylamine, and pyridine: and $[Pt\ en(Am)Cl(NO_2)_2]X$, where $Am =$ ethylamine and pyridine.

Diammines, $[PtAm_2R_4]°$

These non-ionized compounds can be made by oxidation of the platinous diammines (when of course the *cis-trans* isomerism is preserved), or by exchange from other platinic diammines.[1622] In particular, the replacement of hydroxyl by other groups seems to be much easier here than in the pentammines, for example in the reaction

$$[Pt(NH_3)_2(OH)_2(NO_3)_2]° \xrightarrow{HNO_3} [Pt(NH_3)_2(NO_3)_4]°.$$

They can also be made by boiling the chloroplatinate M_2PtCl_6 with amines. A great variety of bases have been introduced in this way,[1618] pyridine, pyrazol, isoxazol, etc. Mann[1613] prepared a compound of the $[Pt\ enCl_4]°$ type with α, β, γ-triaminopropane. The formula shows that the triamine only fills two co-ordination places, so that only two of its NH_2 groups are attached to the platinum. Hence there are two possible structures, according as it is the α- or the β-NH_2 that is free:

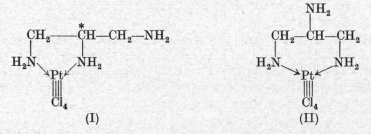

(I)   (II)

[1622] For the crystal structure of *trans*-Pt $(NH_3)_2Cl_4$ see N. V. Belov, G. B. Bokii, and L. A. Popova, *Bull. Acad. Sci. U.S.S.R.* 1947, 249.

It is possible to show which ring is formed, since the 5-ring of I, but not the 6-ring, has an asymmetric carbon atom (marked C*). Mann was able to resolve his product, showing that the structure is I. This is to be expected, since though the fully reduced 6-ring is as strainless as the 5, it is likely to be formed less rapidly (see IV. 499). The corresponding derivative of the triamine β, β-diaminodiethylamine $H_2N \cdot CH_2 \cdot CH_2 \cdot NH \cdot CH_2 \cdot CH_2 \cdot NH_2$, which should have an asymmetric nitrogen atom, could not be resolved.[1617]

Monammines, $M[PtAmR_5]$

These can be made by the oxidation of platinous monammines, or by the action of amines on a chloroplatinate, if it is not carried too far: for example, by heating the salt of the amine:

$$(pyH)_2[PtCl_6] \longrightarrow (pyH)[Pt\,pyCl_5] + HCl.$$

Nitro-dihalide Complexes

The nitro-compounds of tetravalent platinum are few.[1616] It has been found possible[1623-4] to prepare two isomeric forms of the non-ionized $[Pt\,en(NO_2)_2Cl_2]°$; it is remarkable that when they are treated with ammonia it is the chlorine and not the NO_2 that is displaced, giving $[Pt\,en(NH_3)(NO_2)_2Cl]Cl$.

The pure tetranitro-dibromo-complex $Ag_2[PtBr_2(NO_2)_4]$, can be made[1599] by the action of bromine on the platinonitrite, $Ag_2[Pt(NO_2)_4]$; it is a very unstable substance.

Hydroxy-halide Salts

The halogen atoms in a hexahalide can all be replaced successively by hydroxyl, and we can get any member of the series $M_2[PtCl_{6-n}(OH)_n]$ from M_2PtCl_6 to $M_2[Pt(OH)_6]$, except the trihalide $M_2[PtCl_3(OH)_3]$, which does not seem to have been prepared.

Tetrahydroxo-dihalides

The acid of this series can be made from the tetrachloro-silver salt just as that is made from the hexachloro-salt, by boiling in water:

$$Ag_2[PtCl_4(OH)_2] \longrightarrow H_2[PtCl_2(OH)_4] + 2\,AgCl.$$

Platinates, $M_2[Pt(OH)_6]$

This is the last product of the replacement of chlorine in the chloroplatinates by hydroxyl. The free acid is presumably contained (no doubt in a polymerized form) in the hydrate $PtO_2, 4\,H_2O$ discovered by Frémy in 1851: this may be written $H_2[Pt(OH)_6]$. It can be made[1625] by heating a solution of chloroplatinic acid H_2PtCl_6 to boiling with sodium hydroxide, and then precipitating with acetic acid. It is a pale yellow insoluble powder, which loses two of its water molecules at 100°, and the other two

[1623] I. I. Tscherniaev and A. N. Fedorova, *Ann. Inst. Platine*, 1929, **7**, 73.
[1624] I. I. Tscherniaev and F. M. Klatschkin, ib. 84.
[1625] I. Bellucci, *Atti R.* 103, [5] **12**, ii. 635.

at a higher temperature. When freshly made it is easily soluble in alkalies, giving a series of salts of the composition $M_2[Pt(OH)_6]$, which are soluble in water but insoluble in alcohol. They do not lose any water at 110°, but at a much higher temperature they give it off with decomposition. The sodium, potassium, silver, and thallous salts have been made, and they all behave in this way.[1625-7] They are as stable as the chloroplatinates. The potassium salt has been shown to be isomorphous with the stannate $K_2[Sn(OH)_6]$.[1628] This fact, together with the remarkable firmness with which the water is retained by the salt, is strong evidence of the correctness of the hexahydroxo-structure.

Oxalato-compounds

The oxalato platinic compounds are very few compared with the platinous, but Werner was able[1629] by the action of chlorine on the platino-oxalate Na_2PtOx_2 to make the mixed platinic complex $Na_2[PtCl_2Ox_2]$. It forms large yellow crystals, which are easily soluble in water. The potassium salt (H_2O) is similar; the caesium salt, which very unexpectedly has $6 H_2O$, is dark yellow.

Sulphur Complexes of Tetravalent Platinum

Sulphur seems to have less affinity for tetravalent than for divalent platinum, and various attempts to make thioether complexes like those of divalent platinum have failed, though some compounds of this type have been described (Ephraim). There is, however, one polysulphide which almost certainly contains tetravalent platinum. This is the compound $(NH_4)_2[PtS_{15}], 2 H_2O$ which is made[1630] by the action of ammonium polysulphide on chloroplatinic acid. A precipitate is formed which after washing with carbon disulphide and drying over sulphuric acid has the above composition; it forms red crystals which are stable when dry, and give a yellow-red solution in alcohol. In the absence of X-ray data we can only speculate on its structure; but if we agree that ammonium persulphide largely consists of the compound $(NH_4)_2[S_5]$, we can write this platinum compound $(NH_4)_2[Pt^{iv}(S_5)_3], 2 H_2O$. The covalency of course is not known so long as we are ignorant of the structure of the S_5 group. Palladium, as we have seen (p. 1575), gives a compound of similar but not identical composition, $(NH_4)_2PdS_{11}, 1/2 H_2O$.

Complex Platinic Halides
Hexafluoro-salts, M_2PtF_6

Schlesinger and Tapley[1649] prepared K_2PtF_6 by heating platinum black with the compound $3 KF,HF,PbF_4$; there is no other reference to these salts.

   [1626] M. Blondel, *Ann. Chim. Phys.* 1905, [8] **6**, 81.

   [1627] H. I. Schlesinger and R. E. Palmateer, *J.A.C.S.* 1930, **52**, 4316.

   [1628] A. Hantzsch, *Z. physikal. Chem.* 1910, **72**, 362.

   [1629] A. Werner and E. Grebe, *Z. anorg. Chem.* 1899, **21**, 377.

   [1630] K. A. Hofmann and F. Höchtlen, *Ber.* 1903, **36**, 3090.

Hexachloro-salts, M_2PtCl_6

These salts, the platinichlorides or chloroplatinates, are the best known of the hexahalides, especially on account of their use for the characterization of amines, owing to the insolubility of many of the amine salts, and the ease with which their platinum content can be determined.

The free acid is usually made directly by dissolving platinum in aqua regia, either by heat, or by making it the anode in the electrolysis of hydrochloric acid,[1636] or by the addition of hydrogen peroxide.[1646] On evaporation the free acid separates in brownish-red deliquescent crystals of H_2PtCl_6, $6 H_2O$, easily soluble in water, alcohol, or ether. A large number of its salts are known. Of the alkaline salts there are Li, $6 H_2O$, very soluble: Na, $6 H_2O$, red, very soluble: the other alkaline salts are anhydrous, and their sol[ies] at 20° are K $1{\cdot}12$; Rb $0{\cdot}141$; Cs $0{\cdot}070$. A nitrosyl salt $(NO)_2[PtCl_6]$ can be got by recrystallizing platinic chloride from aqua regia: it forms orange crystals, which evolve nitric oxide with water.

A large number of amine salts have been made for the characterization of amines. Many of the quaternary ammonium salts have been examined crystallographically by Ries.[1640] The tetramethyl ammonium salt $[(CH_3)_4N]_2[PtCl_6]$ has been shown[1650] to have the groups arranged tetrahedrally round the nitrogen, and octahedrally round the platinum.

The intensity of the colour of aqueous solutions of these salts is independent of the dilution (Beer's law) and practically of the solvent, as we should expect where the coloured ion is covalently saturated and not capable of further co-ordination.[1628,1637]

These salts have a tendency to hydrolyse in solution, which is much increased by light, especially by violet light.[1640,1647]

Hexabromo-salts, $M_2[PtBr_6]$

The acid of this series can be made by dissolving platinum in a mixture of hydrobromic acid and bromine,[1634] or of hydrobromic and nitric acids:

[1631] A. Miolati and I. Bellucci, *Atti R.* 1900, [5] **9**, ii. 51.
[1632] Id., ib. ii. 97. [1633] I. Bellucci, ib., 1902, [5] **11**, i. 8.
[1634] E. Biilmann and A. C. Anderson, *Ber.* 1903, **36**, 1365.
[1635] A. Miolati, *Z. anorg. Chem.* 1903, **33**, 251.
[1636] H. C. P. Weber, *J.A.C.S.* 1908, **30**, 29.
[1637] A. Hantzsch, *Ber.* 1908, **41**, 1216.
[1638] A. Gutbier and F. Bauriedel, ib. **4243**.
[1639] J. Jacobsen, *C.R.* 1909, **149**, 574.
[1640] A. Ries, *Z. Krist.* 1911, **49**, 513. [1641] M. Boll, *C.R.* 1913, **156**, 138.
[1642] R. L. Datta, *J.C.S.* 1913, **103**, 426. [1643] Id., *J.A.C.S.* 1913, **35**, 1185.
[1644] R. L. Datta and T. Ghosh, ib. 1914, **36**, 1017.
[1645] A. Gutbier, F. Krauss, and L. v. Müller, *Sitzb. Phys.-Med. Sozi. Erlangen,* 1914, **45**, 25.
[1646] P. Rudnick and J. D. Cooke, *J.A.C.S.* 1917, **39**, 633.
[1647] E. H. Archibald, *J.C.S.* 1920, **117**, 1104.
[1648] E. H. Archibald and W. A. Gale, ib. 1922, **121**, 2849.
[1649] H. I. Schlesinger and M. W. Tapley, *J.A.C.S.* 1924, **46**, 276.
[1650] M. L. Huggins, *Phys. Rev.* 1926, [ii] **27**, 638.

or by the action of hydrobromic acid on platinic chloride[1638,1645] It has the composition $H_2PtBr_6, 9 H_2O$, and forms dark red very soluble prisms. The salts are usually red or brown, and their aqueous solutions are red when concentrated and yellow when dilute. The alkaline salts crystallize in octahedra: their solubility decreases as the atomic weight of the alkali metal goes up (strong acid salts).[1645] The salts of organic bases, both aliphatic and aromatic, are as characteristic as the chloroplatinates.[1628,1637,1640-1] They are fairly stable in water, and can be recrystallized from it if the temperature does not rise too high, but the solutions hydrolyse on heating, especially in light,[1648] and it is usually better to recrystallize the salts from dilute hydrobromic acid.

If the solution is heated with an oxalate the salt is reduced, with evolution of carbon dioxide, to the platinous salt M_2PtBr_4.[1634]

The platinic hexahalides readily exchange halogens with the simple ions of another halogen; for example:

$$[PtBr_6]^{--} + 6\,Cl^- \rightleftharpoons [PtCl_6]^{--} + 6\,Br^-.$$

The reaction certainly takes place in stages; in fact a mixed salt

$$K_2[PtCl_4Br_2]$$

has been prepared[1651] by the action of bromine on an aqueous solution of the platinochloride K_2PtCl_4. The equilibrium in this reaction has been measured by Schlesinger by means of the colour.[1627] He finds that in order that the conversion of the $PtBr_6$ ion to $PtCl_6$ should go to 99 per cent. the ratio Cl/Br in the solution must be greater than 660; for a 99 per cent. conversion of PtI_6 to $PtBr_6$ the ratio Br/I must be at least 25,000; from which we can calculate that for a 99 per cent. conversion of PtI_6 to $PtCl_6$, the ratio Cl/I must be greater than 16 million.

Hexaiodo-salts, M_2PtI_6

These were discovered by Lassaigne in 1833; they can be made from the platinichloride and potassium iodide. The free acid $H_2PtI_6, 9 H_2O$ is brown, and very unstable; it readily decomposes into water, hydrogen iodide, iodine, and platinous iodide.

The salts are all chocolate or black; the rubidium salt is less soluble than the potassium, and the caesium less still.[1642] A large number of salts of organic bases have been made,[1642-4] which are similar to the bromides and chlorides; among the methyl-substituted ammonium salts the solubility diminishes as the number of methyl groups increases.

Pentahalides, $M_2[Pt(hal)_5OH]$

Salts of this type were obtained[1631-2] by fusing chloroplatinic acid H_2PtCl_6 with potassium hydroxide under diminished pressure. The lithium and sodium salts were too soluble to be isolated, but a barium salt $Ba[PtCl_5OH], 4 H_2O$, a silver salt (yellow), and a thallous salt (pink) have been prepared. These last two are both anhydrous.

[1651] R. Klement, *Z. anorg. Chem.* 1927, **164**, 195.

Tetrahalides, $M_2[PtCl_4(OH)_2]$

This seems to be the stablest type. Platinic chloride dissolves readily in water, and crystallizes out as a hydrate, which undoubtedly should be written as the free acid $H_2[PtCl_4(OH)_2]$, aq.[1635] The acid can also be made by boiling an aqueous solution of the silver salt $Ag_2[PtCl_6]$, which changes into $H_2[PtCl_4(OH)_2]+2$ AgCl. From the solution a silver salt

$$Ag_2[PtCl_4(OH)_2]$$

can be obtained.[1639] The salts of this acid can also be made by oxidizing the platinochloride M_2PtCl_4 with hydrogen peroxide or hydrogen persulphide H_2S_2.[1652-3]

The corresponding silver, thallous, lead, and mercuric *bromides*

$$M_2[PtBr_4(OH)_2]$$

can be made[1631] by adding the required base to a solution of platinum tetrabromide in water.

The *tetraiodides* $M_2[PtI_4(OH)_2]$ of silver, thallium, and mercury were made from PtI_4 in alcohol.[1633]

HEXAVALENT PLATINUM

A small number of platinum compounds have been described—an oxide, selenide, phosphide, and arsenide—in which the element appears to be hexavalent. While there is no theoretical reason against the occurrence of hexavalent platinum (hexavalent palladium is unknown, but the higher valencies are always more stable with the heavier elements), it is unfortunate that all these compounds are with polyvalent elements, which therefore might form links of the peroxide type —O—O—, involving a lower valency for the platinum than the formula suggests; also the X-ray structure has only been determined for the arsenide, where its results do not decide the valencies. In the trioxide, however, which is by far the best known of these compounds, the existence of hexavalent platinum seems almost certain.

Platinum Diphosphide, PtP_2

This compound, in which the platinum is *prima facie* hexavalent, is readily formed by heating the elements together, or by burning platinum in phosphorus vapour. It forms a bright metallic mass, not attacked by hydrochloric acid, but readily dissolved by ammonia.

Platinum Diarsenide, $PtAs_2$[1654]

This compound is probably the cause of the poisoning by arsenic of platinum as a catalyst in the production of sulphur trioxide. It cannot be made by the action of arsine AsH_3 on chloroplatinic acid, or by the fusion of platinum with arsenic in the presence of sodium carbonate. The only way in which the diarsenide (the sole established compound of these two

[1652] A. A. Grünberg and P. M. Filinov, *C.R. Acad. Sci. U.R.S.S.* 1937, **17**, 23.
[1653] Id., *Bull. Acad. Sci. U.R.S.S.* 1937, 907.
[1654] L. Wöhler, *Z. anorg. Chem.* 1930, **186**, 324.

elements) can be made is by the fusion of the elements in a sealed tube. So much heat is evolved that the mixture explodes at 270° unless excess of arsenic is used; the excess after reaction is sublimed off in carbon dioxide at 500–600°.

Platinum diarsenide is a dull grey solid; it is scarcely attacked by hot concentrated nitric acid, and only slowly by aqua regia; hot concentrated sulphuric acid removes the arsenic, leaving the platinum.

The X-ray powder diagram of the substance made in this way shows[1655] that it has the pyrites structure.

Platinum Trioxide, PtO_3

If a solution of platinic hydroxide $Pt(OH)_4$ in twice normal potassium hydroxide is electrolysed at 0°, there separates in the anodic compartment a grey-green solid of the composition $3 PtO_3, K_2O$[1656]; whether the alkali is adsorbed or combined is uncertain. If this is washed with dilute acetic acid, all the alkali is removed and a brownish-red product remains, of the composition of PtO_3 with a slight (about 10 per cent.) defect of oxygen. This is because the trioxide PtO_3 is extremely unstable; its suspension in water continuously evolves oxygen. The only dilute acid that affects it is hydrochloric, which at once gives off chlorine. The oxide also oxidizes sulphur dioxide, but not organic substances like alcohol. It is remarkable that hydrogen peroxide does not reduce it with evolution of oxygen nor indeed affect it in any way. This seems to show that it does not contain a peroxide link; in fact its whole behaviour is that of a high-valency oxide like MnO_2 or PbO_2, and it would seem as if it should be written $O{=}Pt{\diagup}^O_{\diagdown O}$.

The potentials of the various oxides of platinum have been measured against the mercurous sulphate electrode by Grube[1657] with the results:

PtO	$PtO_2, 2 H_2O$	$PtO_2, 4 H_2O$	PtO_3
0·9	1·04	1·06	1·5 volt.

By measurements of the dissociation pressures of oxygen at 1,200° Schneider and Esch[1658] have got signs of the formation of PtO_3 above 275 mm. and of PtO_4 above 850 mm.

Platinum Triselenide, $PtSe_3$

Though no trisulphide of platinum seems to have been made, Minozzi[1659] has prepared a triselenide by reducing a mixture of chloroplatinic acid and selenium dioxide in alkaline solution with formaldehyde. It forms a black precipitate of the composition $PtSe_3$, insoluble in carbon disulphide (so that it contains no free selenium), slowly soluble in aqua regia, but scarcely reacting with concentrated nitric or sulphuric acid. It is an unstable

[1655] L. Thomassen, *Z. physikal. Chem.* 1929, B **4**, 278.

[1656] L. Wöhler and F. Martin, *Ber.* 1909, **42**, 3326.

[1657] G. Grube, *Z. Elektrochem.* 1910, **16**, 621.

[1658] A. Schneider and U. Esch, ib. 1943, **49**, 55.

[1559] A. Minozzi, *Atti R.* 1909, [5] **18**, ii. 150.

substance, which slowly loses selenium at 140°, but if heated to a dull red heat in a current of carbon dioxide is reduced to the diselenide $PtSe_2$.

CARBONYL COMPLEXES OF PLATINUM

Platinum, like other metals of the group, can combine with carbon monoxide, even (like palladium) in the metallic state, though it is not possible even with platinum black to turn the whole of the metal into the carbonyl compound; it is, however, clear that the carbon monoxide forms a compound, since it cannot be driven out by other gases, and its absorption is not prevented by previously treating the platinum with hydrogen. On heating, the carbon monoxide is suddenly liberated at 250°.[1660] In the combined state platinum takes up carbon monoxide even more readily; platinous chloride begins to absorb it at 120°[1661]; a series of carbonyl compounds have been prepared, in all of which the platinum is divalent.

Schützenberger in 1868–70[1662] showed that if carbon monoxide and chlorine are passed in succession or together over platinum sponge at 250° a fusible crystalline sublimate is formed, containing the three volatile compounds $PtCl_2CO$: $PtCl_2(CO)_2$: $2PtCl_2, 3\,CO$: these can be separated by recrystallization from carbon tetrachloride, have different melting-points (194°, 142°, and 130° respectively), and are interconvertible. A non-volatile residue of uncertain nature was also formed.[1663]

These results have been confirmed[1661,1663] especially by Mylius and Foerster.[1664] They showed that of these compounds the simplest, $PtCl_2CO$ (the others seem much less stable, and in their reactions lose carbon monoxide and revert to the mono-carbonyl), behaves very like platinous chloride itself; it dissolves in hydrochloric acid to form a yellow solution from which the complex salts $M[PtCl_3CO]$ can be obtained, and which is evidently a solution of the free complex acid.

The carbonyls are decomposed by water in a complicated way.[1664]

The other carbonyl compounds of platinous chloride also dissolve in hydrochloric acid, but only with the elimination of all their excess of carbon monoxide, giving a solution of the mono-carbonyl $PtCl_2CO$.

The chlorine atoms in the monocarbonyl can be replaced by other groups, bromine, iodine, CNS, and sulphur. An orange-red bromide $PtBr_2CO$, m. pt. 181–2°, and a red iodide, decomposing at 140–150°, are similar to the chloride in preparation and properties; they also can form complexes $M[PtX_3CO]$. Of the three halides the chloride is the least fusible and the most stable to heat; the iodide is more fusible, less stable to heat, and less easily hydrolysed. In every respect the bromide is intermediate between the other two.

[1660] E. Harbeck and G. Lunge, *Z. anorg. Chem.* 1897, **16**, 50.
[1661] W. Manchot, *Ber.* 1925, **58**, 2518.
[1662] P. Schützenberger, *Ann. Chim. Phys.* 1868, [4] **15**, 100; ib., 1870, [4] **21**, 350; *C.R.* 1870, **70**, 1134, 1287; *Bull. Soc.* 1870, [2] **14**, 97.
[1663] W. Pullinger, *Ber.* 1891, **24**, 2291.
[1664] F. Mylius and F. Foerster, ib. 2426.

The corresponding thiocyanate can be got in the form of the complex salt K[Pt(CNS)$_3$CO], formed from potassium thiocyanate and the chloride: it is easily soluble in alcohol, and decomposed by water.

The sulphide PtSCO is formed as a blackish-brown precipitate when a solution of PtCl$_2$CO in hydrochloric acid (or of H[PtCl$_3$CO]) is treated with hydrogen sulphide; it is insoluble, but is oxidized by nitric acid or aqua regia.

A remarkable reaction of all these carbonyl compounds of divalent platinum is that with potassium cyanide they form K$_2$Pt(CN)$_4$, with quantitative evolution of carbon monoxide. It is probable that in this reaction the cyanide Pt(CN)$_2$CO is an intermediate product, but it decomposes before it can be isolated.

Complex Carbonyl Salts

Mylius and Foerster[1664] have shown that PtCl$_2$CO will combine with a variety of chlorides such as HCl, KCl, NH$_4$Cl, ZnCl$_2$ to give complex salts which are often too soluble to be isolated, but whenever they can be analysed are of the type M[PtCl$_3$CO]: this is the unusual triacido-type of Cleve's salt; it is common to find that one and only one CO will enter a complex, and in that case the triacido-form is the necessary result of the tetracovalency: what is less common in a carbonyl compound is that the E.A.N. of the platinum is only 84. A series of salts of organic bases (BH)[PtCl$_3$CO], which are less soluble, have been prepared. The amyl-amine salt is golden yellow; it is decomposed by water but can be recrystallized from hydrochloric acid; it is very easily soluble in ethyl acetate, less in ether, benzene, or chloroform, from the last of which solvents it can be recrystallized; it melts at 184°. The anilinium and pyridinium salts are similar, but less soluble; the quinolinium salt (m. pt. 166°) is still less soluble, but more stable.

If these salts are treated with organic bases,[1665] one of the three chlorine atoms is replaced, giving, for example, [PtCl$_2$(CO)py]° (m. pt. 127° with decomposition), and [PtCl$_2$(CO)NH$_3$]°, which decomposes at 180°.

All these salts have the characteristic reaction with potassium cyanide of forming the platinocyanide with quantitative evolution of carbon monoxide, which can be estimated in this way.

NITROSYL COMPOUNDS OF PLATINUM

It is stated[1666] that if a saturated solution of ammonium or potassium chloroplatinite is kept in an atmosphere of nitric oxide, the salt M[PtCl$_3$NO] is formed in solution, and when this is treated with [Pt(NH$_3$)$_4$]Cl$_2$ the salt [Pt(NH$_3$)$_4$]·[PtCl$_3$NO]$_2$ is formed. The original M[PtCl$_3$NO] gives with pyridine the *trans* form of [PtCl$_2$(NO)py]°; the *cis* was not obtained.

The platinum in these compounds would have these values of the valency and the E.A.N.: M[PtCl$_3$NO] 1, 85; [PtCl$_2$(NO)py] 1, 85.

[1665] A. Gelman and M. Bauman, *C.R. Acad. Sci. U.R.S.S.* 1938, **18**, 645.
[1666] A. Gelman and Z. P. Maximova, ib. 1939, **24**, 748.

AUTHOR INDEX TO VOLUMES I AND II

Donath, K., 244.
Donau, J., 1554.
Dondonov, J., 763.
Donnan, F. G., 149, 1391.
Donohue, J.,125,145,489,689, 710,790,877,888,893,1040.
Donzelot, P., 955.
Doolan, J. J., 952, 980.
Dorfman, M., 378, 539, 541.
Dorfmann, M. E., 610.
Dorner, O., 152.
Dorris, T. B., 393.
Dorsch, K. E., 16.
Dostal, H., 507.
Doty, P. M., 502, 1140.
Dougherty, G., 437.
Douglas, A. E., 380.
Douglas, T. B., 925.
Downing, D. C., 507.
Downing, J. R., 30.
Dragulescu, C., 322.
Drake, G. W., 669.
Dreher, E., 308, 312.
Dresdner, R. D., 1104.
Dresel, E., 924.
Drew, H. D. K., 164, 168, 434, 474, 561, 569, 570, 608, 613, 823, 967, 992, 1471, 1562, 1592, 1595, 1602, 1608.
Dreyer, H., 469.
Drikos, G., 43.
Driscoll, J. O'L., 240, 1436.
Drossbach, O., 979.
Druce, J. G. F., 581, 616, 1284, 1303, 1312.
Drucker, K., 272, 1012.
Drushinin, I. G., 1005, 1185.
Duane, A. J., 428.
Duane, W., 1191.
Dubnikoff, M., 945.
Dubnikov, L. M., 752.
Dubois, P., 1267.
Dubsky, J. V., 164, 1017.
Dudek, H., 772.
Dudley, W. L., 1606.
Düllberg, P., 810.
Duennebier, F. C., 670.
Düsing, J., 1314, 1460, 1463, 1487.
Düsing, W., 634.
Dufet, H., 1481, 1486.
Duff, J. C., 1410, 1412.
Duffield, R. B., 172.
Dufford, R. T., 231.
Duffour, A., 1536.
Duflos, A., 1405.
Dufour, —, 1281.
Duhm, B., 1016.
Duke, F. R., 1280.
Dukelski, M., 384.
Dullenkamp, W., 638.
Dullenkopf, W., 89.
Dunbrook, R. F., 993.
Duncan, A. B. F., 467, 1451.
Duncan, D. R., 1154, 1191, 1192, 1194, 1196.

Dunderman, F. V., 406.
Dundon, C. V., 1026.
Dundon, M. L., 257.
Dunitz, J. D., 526.
Dunker, M. F. W., 304.
Dunn, C. L., 175.
Dunn, R. E., 392.
Dunn, R. T., 431.
Dunnicliff, H. B., 258.
Dunning, J. R., 491.
Dunstan, W. R., 679.
Dunton, F. G., 823.
Duparc, L., 1002.
Duperier, A., 1518.
Dupire, A., 785.
Duppa, B. F., 304, 404.
Duppa, D. F., 369.
Duprat, P., 1336.
Dupre, A., 478.
Durand, J. F., 199, 200, 264, 413.
Durland, J. R., 862.
Durnow, A., 920.
Durrans, T. H., 935.
Durrant, R. G., 157, 1418.
Dutoit, P., 136.
Dutoit, W., 253.
Dutt, N. K., 475.
Dutton, F. B., 751.
Dutton, G. R., 745.
Duval, C., 1395, 1436.
Dwyer, F. P., 1465, 1498, 1516, 1525, 1532, 1562, 1564.
Dyke-Cruser, F., 1015.
Dyson, G. M., 929, 930.

Eastes, J. W., 1429.
Eatough, H., 563.
Ebeneder, F., 49.
Eberhartinger, R., 307.
Eberius, E., 624.
Ebers, E. S., 540.
Ebert, F., 119, 152, 293, 322, 1049, 1148, 1156, 1394, 1559, 1573.
Ebert, M. S., 175.
Ebert, W., 993.
Eberz, W. F., 130.
Ebler, E., 279.
Eckerson, B. A., 961.
Eckstein, H., 1545.
Edeleanu, A., 1133.
Edelhäuser, O., 1496.
Edgar, G., 818, 824.
Edgar, J. L., 860.
Edgell, W. F., 503.
Edlund, K. R., 1175.
Eduardoff, F., 564.
Edwards, G. H., 824.
Edwards, O. K., 961, 962.
Edwards, R. T., 1163.
Edwards, W. A. M., 7.
Egan, C. J., 501, 521.
Egartner, L., 887, 959.
Egerton, A. C. G., 868, 873.
Eggeling, H., 146.

Eggert, J., 113.
Egidius, T. F., 295.
Ehmann, E. A., 1422.
Ehret, W. F., 257, 424.
Ehrhard, W., 304.
Ehrhardt, E. F., 172.
Ehrhardt, O., 1500.
Ehrhorn, H., 1460, 1480, 1497.
Ehrlich, P., 617, 635, 762, 765, 1103, 1533, 1542.
Ehrmann, K., 945.
Eichelberger, L., 146.
Eicholz, W., 700.
Eidinoff, M. L., 57, 58, 171.
Eijkmann, J. K., 621.
Einicke, E., 459, 460.
Einstein, A., 688, 1087.
Eisner, A., 981.
Eisner, F., 634, 640, 1033, 1034, 1035, 1036, 1037.
Eissner, E. W., 1001, 1002.
Eitel, W., 254.
Ekeley, J. B., 474.
Ekholm, W. C., 256.
v. Elbe, G., 858, 859.
Elchardus, E., 231.
Eldau, K. H., 1080.
Elias, A., 191.
Elias, P. G., 877.
Elkins, M., 1403.
Elliott, G. A., 1186.
Elliott, J. R., 567.
Elliott, K. A. C., 500.
Elliott, N., 147, 190, 417, 424, 803, 1339, 1378.
Ellis, C. B., 444.
Ellis, L., 762.
Elöd, E., 622.
Elsey, H. M., 1118.
Elstner, G., 895, 907, 1006.
Elten, M., 276.
Emanuel, N., 880.
Emanuel, N. M., 880, 895.
Eméleus, H. J., 52, 553, 554, 564, 768, 960, 1099, 1257.
Eméleus, K. G., 17.
Emert, O., 1333.
Emmanuel-Zavizziano, H., 853.
Emmert, B., 86, 164, 1287, 1346, 1362, 1363.
Emmett, P. H., 1376.
v. Ende, C. L., 625.
Endredy, E., 1004.
Endres, R., 1218.
Engel, L., 712.
Engel, R., 162.
Engelmann, H., 1178.
Engeroff, F., 990.
Engle, H. R., 466.
English, J., 1026.
Englund, B., 766.
Enk, E., 1372, 1483.
Enklaar, C. J., 669.
Ennos, F. R., 1334.
Ensslin, F., 469.

Koton, M. M., 311, 592.
Kotov, S., 91.
Kotscheschkov, A. A., 303.
Kotscheschkov, K. A., 267, 578, 581, 583, 584, 592.
Kovalevski, W. V., 645.
Kovitz, J., 642.
Kowaski, I., 1356.
Kracek, F. C., 382, 662, 950.
Krafft, F., 962, 963, 965, 974, 987.
Krall, H. G., 1461, 1490, 1517, 1543, 1547, 1559, 1575.
Kramer, E. N., 972.
Kramer, J., 605.
Krapelka, J. H., 1273, 1285.
Krascheninnikova, V. M., 1294.
Krasny-Ergen, W., 1081.
Krassikov, S. E., 1537, 1594.
Kratky, O., 1352.
Kratzsch, G., 1232.
Kraus, C. A., 86, 88, 90, 91, 381, 399, 401, 404, 409, 461, 472, 554, 563, 569, 570, 571, 575, 578, 579, 580, 585, 587, 619, 950, 953, 1228, 1234.
Kraus, F., 427, 1368.
Kraus, O., 1043.
Kraus, P. B., 1234.
Kraus, R., 1009.
Krause, A., 1328, 1353.
Krause, E., xi, 70, 74, 114, 200, 224, 225, 265, 267, 298, 305, 311, 369, 370, 371, 373, 376, 392, 400, 404, 414, 415, 429, 430, 432, 463, 464, 465, 559, 568, 576, 577, 578, 582, 583, 586, 587, 588, 589, 590, 592, 593, 596, 597, 619, 620, 623, 624, 730, 747, 881, 968, 969.
Krause, O., 1045.
Krauskopf, C., 792.
Krauskopf, K. B., 524.
Krauss, A., 1364.
Krauss, F., 207, 1013, 1461, 1463, 1466, 1467, 1474, 1476, 1479, 1491, 1493, 1495, 1496, 1500, 1509, 1517, 1519, 1520, 1531, 1533, 1542, 1544, 1562, 1623.
Krauss, G., 1004.
Kraut, F., 1015.
Kraut, H., 419, 602.
Krebs, A., 1260.
Krefft, O. T., 1148.
Krell, A., 1561, 1576.
Kremann, R., 170.
Kremers, H. C., 449.
Kremers, H. E., 447.
Krepelka, J. H., 1273, 1283.
Kretschmer, C., 27.
Kretzschmar, H., 1220, 1227.
Kreuzer, J., 1105.

Krieble, R. H., 567.
Krieble, V. K., 670.
Krige, G. J. R., 9, 1139.
Krings, W., 617, 626.
Krinitzki, V. V., 1603.
Krishnamurti, P., 299.
Krishnan, K. S., 494.
Krishnaswami, K. R., 844.
Kritschevsky, J., 1178.
Kröger, C., 234, 734.
Kroeger, J. W., 385.
Kroepelin, H., 17.
Krokmaiski, E., 1172.
Kroll, W., 1000.
Krome, H., 709.
Kronberg, M. L., 710.
Kronenberg, P., 1072.
Kroning, E., 867.
Kronrad, J., 718.
Kroupa, E., 553.
Krsnjavi, B., 168.
v. Krueger, G., 749, 753, 756.
Krüger, H., 683.
Krüss, G., 178, 207, 218, 638, 814.
Krug, H., 1156.
Kruger, E., 1132.
Kruis, A. I., 43, 44, 878, 952.
Krumbhaar, W., 1325.
Krumholz, P., 1039, 1371.
Krustinsons, J., 255, 320, 600, 1435, 1560.
Krutter, H., 599.
Kruyer, S., 677.
Krynski, J., 303.
Ksanda, C. J., 150, 942.
Kubaschewski, O., 841.
Kubelka, P., 615.
Kubis, J., 1273.
Kuck, J. A., 373.
Küchlin, A. T., 388.
Kühl, H., 744.
Kühling, O., 246.
Kükenthal, H., 1466.
Külkens, H., 735.
Kürti, N., 1334.
Küspert, F., 1434.
Kuessner, H., 1287.
Kuhbier, F., 1363.
Kuhn, C. S., 1133.
Kuhn, H., 110, 288, 1169.
Kuhn, R., 168, 268, 1176, 1346.
Kuhn, W., 268, 500.
Kuhnel, M., 702.
Kulka, M., 1258.
Kullgren, C. F., 272.
Kumler, W., 924.
v. Kummer, U., 1338.
Kunin, R., 1079, 1082.
Kunschert, F., 133, 282.
Kunst, R., 1049.
Kunz, H., 234, 1103.
Kupfer, O., 713.
Kurakin, A. N., 1217.
Kurbatov, J. D., 445.
Kurnakov, N. S., 1351.

Kurowski, E., 206, 214, 242, 260, 283, 330, 487, 636, 642.
Kurtenacker, A., 159, 171, 892, 943, 1349, 1432, 1448.
Kurtz, R. A., 394.
Kurz, T., 943.
Kurzen, F., 342, 348.
Kusch, P., 66.
Kusmin, L. L., 733.
Kuss, E., 344, 362, 364, 394, 395, 1333.
Kustenmacher, H., 168.
Kutsch, W. A., 1007.
Kutscheroff, M., 160, 315.
Kwasnik, W., 703, 1301, 1308.
Kynch, G. J., 493, 505, 510.

Laar, J., 1533, 1542, 1559, 1573, 1575.
Laass, F., 1148.
Labhardt, H., 905.
Laby, T. H., xv.
La Chapelle, T. A., 1093.
Lacher, J. R., 44, 501, 502, 504, 1126, 1556.
Lachman, A., 715, 1144.
Lacoin, M., 64.
Lacombe, H., 198, 213.
Lacoss, D. A., 739.
Ladd, E. C., 1119, 1122, 1181.
Ladenburg, A., 312, 564, 567, 580, 585, 611.
Laffitte, P., 234, 249, 1581, 1613.
Lagally, H., 1372, 1528, 1548, 1549.
Lageman, R. T., 1437.
Lainé, P., 1334.
Laird, F. W., 1451.
La Lande, W. A., 1299.
Lahiri, T. K., 968.
Lamb, A. B., 505, 1237, 1349, 1356, 1401, 1523.
Lamb, S. A., 889.
Lambert, B., 257, 1555.
Lambert, J. D., 495.
LaMer, V. K., 47, 53, 388, 715.
Lamy, —, 484.
Land, A. H., 909.
Landau, L., 7.
Lander, K. H., 434.
Landesen, G. L., 1284, 1562.
Landmann, B., 962, 973.
Landolph, F., 406.
Landolt, H., 762, 774.
Landolt-Börnstein, 95, 236, 257.
Landquist, J. K., 168, 561, 570.
Lane, K. W., 168, 1387.
Lane, T. J., 406.
Lanford, O. E., 626, 821.
Lang, J., 281.
Lang, W., 292, 295.
Lange, E., 44, 45, 46.

Macleod, D. B., 31.
McLoughlin, C. S., 925.
McMahon, F. A., 957.
McMillan, E., 38, 889.
McMillan, E. M., 1090.
McMorris, J., 667, 1152, 1154.
McMurray, H. L., 419.
McNeight, S. A., 669.
McRae, J., 1246.
McReynolds, J. P., 900, 1084.
McVey, W. H., 1095.
Macwalter, R. J., 1390.
McWaters, L. S., 437.
Macwood, G. E., 5.
Macy, R., 1234.
Maddison, R. E. W., 1215.
Maddock, A. G., 554, 1087.
Madson, W. H., 792.
Mählmann, K., 1562.
Maeser, S., 952.
Maffei, A., 420.
Magat, M., 754.
Magaziner, E., 889.
Magee, M. Z., 1446.
Magnus, —, 1591.
Magnusson, F. F., 1288.
Magnusson, L. B., 1093.
Maheshwari, J. C., 1282.
Mai, A., 1058.
Mai, H., 1046.
Mai, J., 749.
Maiborn, A., 284.
Maier, C. G., 1331.
Maier-Hüser, H., 411.
Mailänder, R., 411.
Main Smith, J. D., 1407, 1562.
Maisch, K., 1496.
Maisch, O., 1479, 1514, 1515, 1579.
Maitland, W., 470.
Majert, H., 372.
Major, R. T., 680.
Majorana, E., 8.
Makarov, S. Z., 1005.
Makarova, L. G., 268.
Makolkin, I. A., 857.
Makseva, Z., 429.
Malatesta, L., 578, 1422, 1446.
Malhotra, K. L., 258.
Mallen, C. E., 137.
Malquori, G., 436, 1055, 1357.
Maltby, J. G., 567.
Maltzev, V. A., 1166.
Maly, R., 284.
Manchot, W., 113, 130, 131, 132, 253, 305, 306, 316, 685, 832, 972, 1009, 1288, 1314, 1343, 1349, 1360, 1372, 1373, 1374, 1398, 1452, 1459, 1460, 1461, 1463, 1482, 1483, 1484, 1485, 1487, 1509, 1529, 1549, 1557, 1577, 1580, 1627.
Manchot, W. J., 1459, 1482, 1484.

Mandrik, G. F., 971.
Mandal, H., 1017.
Manley, J. J., 9.
Mann, F. G., 139, 140, 189, 280, 329, 732, 884, 1400, 1474, 1522, 1526, 1562, 1569, 1572, 1584, 1592, 1617.
Manov, G. G., 127, 383.
Mantel, E., 217.
Mantell, C. L., 427.
Manulkin, Z., 561.
Manz, H., 806.
Marble, J. P., 553.
Marburg, E. C., 296, 308, 317, 327.
Marc, R., 949.
Marchand, B., 1500.
Marchi, L. E., 1056, 1084.
Marckwald, W., 706, 996.
Marcus, E., 68.
Marden, J. W., 633.
Marek, J., 1277.
Marin, R., 1373, 1376, 1422, 1425.
Marino, L., 832, 1535.
Marinsky, J. A., 445.
Maritz, A., 903.
Mark, H., 269, 343, 493, 507, 534, 535, 647, 1333.
Marker, R., 312.
Markert, E., 1002.
Markgraf, H., 1449.
Markovitsch, V. G., 224.
Markowicz, E., 824.
Markownikoff., W. B., 1175, 1177.
Markstein, G., 616.
Marlies, C. A., 715.
Maron, S. H., 420, 697.
Maroney, W., 45, 506.
Marple, K. E., 416.
Marquardt, A., 781, 966.
Marriott, J. A., 30.
Marriott, J. V. R., 1145.
Marsden, H., 564.
Marsden, R. J. B., 499.
Marsh, A. E. L., 1201, 1207, 1230.
Marsh, J. K., 444, 449, 451, 456, 457, 1227.
Marshall, A. L., 16, 1427.
Marshall, H., 472.
Martin, A. E., 27, 491, 864.
Martin, D. R., 409, 411.
Martin, F., 1351, 1436, 1573, 1581, 1606, 1626.
Martin, G., 565, 566, 567, 610.
Martin, H., 1080.
Martin, J., 1039.
Martin, J. H., 1194, 1197.
Martin, L. F., 437.
Martin, La V. L., 402.
Martin, W., 259, 806.
Martin, W. F., 567.
Martin, W. J., 26, 839.
Martinelli, M., 1251.

Martinet, J., 307.
Martini, H., 342, 354.
Martinsen, 638.
Martius, A., 1491, 1532, 1535.
Marvel, C. S., 31, 32, 70, 231, 305, 534, 535, 672, 732, 763, 899.
Marzano, C., 764.
Masaki, K., 1434, 1439.
Mascarelli, L., 1251, 1254, 1257.
Mason, C. W., 552.
Mason, R. I., 612.
Massanez, C., 338.
Massey, H. S. W., 21, 858.
Massie, S. P., 563.
Massini, P., 746.
Masson, I., 1143, 1245, 1252, 1256.
Masson, O., 169, 1192.
Mastin, T. W., 535.
Matei, I., 741.
Matejka, K., 943.
Mathers, F. C., 471, 616, 1101.
Mathes, W., 535.
Matheson, G. L., 868.
Matheson, H., 856.
Mathews, J. A., 113.
Mathies, M., 264.
Mathieson, A. McL., 887.
Mathing, W., 338, 342, 343, 405.
Matignon, C., 203, 205, 634, 638, 639.
Matissen, S., 1406.
Mattack, G., 868.
Mattauch, J., 37, 63, 64, 491, 553.
Matthews, F. E., 1182.
Matthews, J. M., 613.
Matthies, M., 761.
Mattox, W. J., 130.
Matuschek, J., 255.
Mau, W., 1006.
Maunsell, P. W., 407.
Maurer, R. J., 289.
Maurer, W., 1289.
Mavity, J. M., 414.
Mawrow, F., 1049.
Maxey, F. S., 745.
Maximova, Z. P., 1587, 1628.
Maxwell, L. R., 398, 689, 691, 727, 737, 759, 784, 855, 878, 948, 952, 995.
May, K., 92.
Maycock, R. L., 1103.
Mayer, E. W., 1580.
Mayer, J. E., 1140.
Mayer, K., 889.
Mayer, M. G., 723, 1072.
Maynard, J. L., 310.
Mayo, F. R., 1178, 1179, 1180, 1562.
Mayr, A., 1549.
Mazalev, L. J., 382.
Mazzucchelli, A., 636.
Mead, A., 1014, 1021, 1409.

Mead, D. J., 566.
Meadows, G. W., 394.
Meals, R. N., 71, 246, 309, 567.
Mears, W. H., 507, 857.
Mecke, R., 24, 27, 251, 658, 864.
Medlin, W. V., 1256.
Medox, G. V., 567.
Medox, H., 763.
Meek, C. A., 17.
Meer, N., 531, 1124.
Meerman, P. G., 738.
Meerum-Terwogt, P. C. E., 1154.
Meerwein, H., 372, 373, 386, 387, 392, 393, 405, 411, 421, 422, 431, 614, 748, 867.
Mees, G., 289.
Megaw, H. D., 24, 45.
Megerle, W., 1441.
Meggers, W. F., xxvi, 1092.
Megson, N. J. L., 153, 1348.
Mehl, E., 949.
Mehler, L., 1496.
Mehltretter, C. L., 972.
Meibohm, E. B., 365.
Meidinger, W., 1182.
Meier, H. A., 1411, 1437.
Meier, J. W., 535.
Meier-Mohar, T., 1397.
Meinel, K., 1222.
Meininger, H., 464, 580.
Meisel, K., 441, 448, 1300, 1460, 1491, 1517, 1533, 1542.
Meisenheimer, J., 228, 229, 231, 500, 1020.
Meissner, W., 1293.
Meister, M., 393.
Meister, R., 862.
Meitner, L., 632, 851, 1087.
Melamed, M., 373.
Meldrum, F. R., 707.
Meldrum, W. B., 1005.
Melikov, P., 814, 817, 843, 871, 1157.
Mellor, D. P., 1385, 1386, 1406, 1430, 1446, 1454, 1562.
Mellor, J. W., 1214.
Melnikov, N. N., 466, 971.
Meloche, V. W., 972, 1050.
Melville, H.W., 40, 51, 52, 727.
Melzer, W., 566, 611.
Mendeleeff, D. I., xvi, 1316.
Mendelssohn, K., 5, 6.
Mengdehl, H., 1367.
Menke, J. B., 993.
Menschutkin, B. N., 281, 429, 798, 1188.
Menzel, D. H., 33.
Menzel, H., 382, 383, 384, 745.
Menzel, W., 426, 432, 701, 704, 705, 1118, 1135, 1137, 1148, 1156, 1158, 1301.

Menzies, A. W. C., 50, 739.
Menzies, R. C., 309, 465, 474, 475, 484, 487, 1611, 1612.
Merck, F., 494.
Mericola, F. C., 930.
Merrigold, B. S., 1082.
Merritt, H. B., 1046.
Merry, E., 1360.
Mertes, A. T., 819.
Merton, T. R., 1268.
Merwein, H., 215.
Merwin, H. E., 382, 942, 1351, 1358, 1616.
Merz, A. R., 701.
Mesech, H., 899.
Messerknecht, C., 199, 205, 208.
Messerly, G. H., 561.
Messinger, C., 790.
Mettler, V., 282.
Metz, L., 1461, 1475, 1493.
Metzger, H., 979.
Metzler, A., 722, 1235.
Metzner, R., 981, 991, 994.
Meulen, H. ter, 1002.
Meulenhoff, J., 409.
Meunier, A. C., 1133, 1190.
Meusser, A., 155, 277, 1383, 1438.
Meuwsen, A., 892, 894, 905, 912, 921.
Meyer, A., 307.
Meyer, A. W., 88.
Meyer, C., 272, 273.
Meyer, F., 137, 431, 650, 728, 755, 903, 1101.
Meyer, G., 545, 581, 762.
Meyer, H., 810.
Meyer, J., 146, 158, 166, 217, 732, 733, 807, 812, 824, 832, 907, 933, 970, 972, 975, 976, 977, 978, 983, 988, 990, 1046, 1235, 1250, 1271, 1272, 1275, 1276, 1277, 1284, 1340, 1390, 1392, 1397, 1518, 1525, 1526.
Meyer, K., 1266.
Meyer, K. E., 499.
Meyer, K. H., 172, 282, 669, 723, 735, 878, 949, 1221, 1222.
Meyer, Lothar, xvi, 495, 1317.
Meyer, P., 1520.
Meyer, R., 717.
Meyer, R. E., 471, 475.
Meyer, R. J., 410, 452, 470, 472, 474, 476, 638, 1009, 1084, 1275, 1436.
Meyer, T., 1010.
Meyer, V., 120, 122, 272, 273, 621, 710, 732, 1181, 1245, 1250, 1254, 1255, 1331, 1614.
Meyer, W., 1461, 1479.
Meyering, J., 416, 424.
Meyers, C. H., 521.
Miau, T. B., 1131.

Michael, A., 68, 1053, 1178, 1207, 1212, 1216.
Michaelis, A., 303, 305, 312, 369, 370, 733, 767, 768, 770, 925.
Michaelis, C. A., 962, 973.
Michaelis, C. A. A., 772, 992.
Michaelis, C. A. U., 966.
Michaelis, L., 722, 723.
Michalek, J. C., 661.
Michel, A., 1427.
Michel, J., 1059.
Micklethwait, F. M. G., 774, 775.
Mickwitz, A., 1284.
Middleberg, W., 127, 136.
Middleton, E. B., 314, 1228.
Midgley, T., 588, 595, 1118.
Mieg, W., 768.
Miekley, H. S., 901.
Mieleitner, K., 202, 208.
Mijs, J. A., 409.
Miko, G., 244.
Miklauz, R., 84.
Miklukhin, G. P., 857.
Milas, N. A., 872.
Milbauer, J., 1021, 1077, 1588.
Miles, C. B., 1133.
Miles, F. D., 1339, 1463.
Miles, F. T., 50.
Miles, J. B., 546.
Millar, J. H., 191.
Millar, J. J., 1005.
Millen, D. J., 690.
Miller, C. C., 736.
Miller, D. R., 1162.
Miller, E. H., 1015.
Miller, F. W., 1234.
Miller, H. K., 436.
Miller, S. A., 307.
Miller, W. D., 1117.
Miller, W. H., 387.
Miller, W. S., 890.
Miller, W. T., 1118, 1122.
Milligan, J. C., 288.
Milligan, W. O., 151, 256, 441, 466, 635, 1284, 1339.
Millmann, S., 427, 1016, 1361.
Millon, E., 1205, 1210, 1244.
Millott, J. O'N., 973, 983.
Mills, G. A., 857.
Mills, J. E., 342.
Mills, W. H., 213, 500, 511, 765, 801, 1563, 1592.
Milsted, J., 532.
Miltschitzky, G., 1119.
Milward, J. L., 1425.
Minder, W., 1260.
Minkoff, G. J., 690, 868.
Minozzi, A., 1626.
Miolati, A., 1017, 1535, 1614, 1616, 1623.
Mirbach, P., 217.
Misciattelli, P., 1076.
Misener, A. D., 5, 6.
Mitchell, A. D., 740.

Mitchell, J. A., 1189.
Mitchell, J. E. H., 754.
Mitchell, J. W., 272.
Mittag, E., 929.
Mittasch, A., 1326, 1333.
Mocke, R., 864.
Möbius, E., 1377.
Möldner, H., 269.
Möller, H., 132.
Moeller, T., 447, 467, 475.
Möllgaard, H., 146.
Moelwyn-Hughes, E. A., 40, 1189, 1202, 1204, 1216.
Moerman, N. F., 523, 679, 888, 901.
Moers, K., 66, 836, 844, 1293.
Moeser, L., 810, 1368.
Moessen, G. W., 665.
Moesveld, A. L. T., 273, 276, 760.
Moffitt, W. G., 958.
Mohler, F. L., 340.
Mohr, S., 1337.
Mohrhenn, H. G. G., 527.
Mohry, F., 705, 1118.
Moissan, H., 70, 124, 246, 390, 396, 633, 638, 702, 807, 847, 930, 943, 1015, 1100, 1117, 1158, 1275, 1459, 1579, 1614.
Mojert, D., 1037, 1041.
Moldarski, B., 621.
Moldenhauer, H., 975, 983.
Moldenhauer, W., 707.
Moles, E., 424, 978, 1004, 1199, 1211.
Mollett, P., 26, 27.
Monacelli, W. J., 394.
Mond, L., 1066, 1369, 1422, 1426, 1451.
Mond, R. L., 1373, 1424.
Money, R. W., 1435.
Mong, W. L., 1118.
Monroe, C. J., 426.
Monroe, E., 764.
Montgomery, C. W., 895.
Montignie, E., 750, 803, 982, 984.
Moon, P. B., xv.
Mooney, R. C. L., 764, 938, 1192, 1200, 1256, 1289.
Moore, F. W., 70, 596.
Moore, G. E., 1001, 1070.
Moore, R. L., 451.
Moore, R. W., 554.
Moore, T. S., 23, 172, 659.
Moore, W. J., 620, 1558.
Moraht, H., 207, 218, 1494.
Moran, W. G., 289.
Morawietz, W., 382, 617, 1237.
Morehouse, C. K., 652.
Morel, J., 981.
Morell, J. C., 296, 331.
Morette, A., 809, 818, 824, 832, 1055.
Morey, G. W., 382.

Morgan, G. T., 143, 146, 164, 174, 177, 214, 260, 283, 284, 292, 330, 406, 407, 434, 474, 487, 569, 608, 613, 642, 773, 774, 775, 777, 822, 884, 956, 958, 959, 965, 968, 969, 992, 1305, 1407, 1441, 1464, 1469, 1474, 1487, 1562, 1592.
Morgan, H. H., 135.
Morgan, J. L. R., 751.
Morgan, L. O., 1095.
Morgan, P. S., 130.
Morgan, W. H., 666.
Morguleff, N., 668.
Morikawa, K., 51, 52.
Morison, D. M., 866.
Morita, N., 33, 857.
Morley, A. M., 1040.
Morley, J. F., 970.
Morningstar, O., 599.
Morrell, W. E., 24, 1105.
Morris, B. S., 1386.
Morris, H., 586, 598.
Morris, J. C., 1161, 1213.
Morris, W. C., 608, 1200.
Morrison, J., 1214.
Morse, H. N., 1267.
Mortensen, R. A., 780.
Morton, D. S., 600.
Morton, R. A., 1150, 1152, 1157.
Moseley, H. G.-J., 646.
Moser, F., 1440.
Moser, H., 1265.
Moser, L., 729, 1039, 1368, 1439, 1559, 1613.
Mosimann, P., 799, 1440.
Mosley, V. M., 398, 689, 691, 727, 759, 878, 948, 952.
Moss, C. C., 444.
Moss, H. W., 260, 283, 292, 330, 487, 822.
Mosses, A. N., 891.
Mostowitsch, W., 257.
Mott, F., 929.
Mott, N. F., 123, 412.
Motta, E. E., 1289.
Motzkus, E., 929.
Moulds, L. de V., 970.
Moureu, H., 733, 734, 735, 754.
Mousseron, M., 1219.
Moy, J. A. E., 26.
Mrozowski, S., 288.
Mühlbauer, F., 177, 1027, 1066, 1370, 1422.
Müller, A., 497, 498, 974.
Müller, E., 72, 151, 532, 537, 722, 756, 933, 952, 953, 1216, 1227, 1349, 1398, 1435, 1459, 1475, 1490, 1499, 1560.
Müller, E. L., 1074.
Müller, F., 506, 717, 1554, 1580, 1582, 1606.
Müller, F. H., 45.

Müller, G. J., 44, 901.
Müller, H., 1079, 1080, 1145, 1329.
Müller, J., 746, 762.
Müller, J. A., 1343.
Müller, J. H., 569, 600, 601, 602, 615, 1299.
v. Müller, L., 1623.
Müller, M., 799, 1526.
Mueller, M. B., 535.
Müller, R., 205, 256, 306.
Müller, W., 959, 960, 1154, 1340, 1515.
Müller-Goldegg, G., 447.
Müller-Redloff, I., 537.
Müller-Skjold, F., 717.
Muench, O. B., 1588.
Münzberg, F. K., 55.
Muir, M. M. P., 1210.
Mulder, D., 725.
Mulliken, R. S., 340, 505, 522, 656.
Mumbrauer, R., 997.
Munch, R. H., 293.
Murooka, T., 1135.
Murphey, B. F., 553, 856.
Murphy, A., 1053.
Murphy, G. M., 33, 34, 1103.
Murray, A. G., 567.
Murray, A. R., 506.
Murray, J. W., 1451.
Murray, L. A., 93.
Murray, M. J., 131, 498, 1188.
Murray, W. M., 1355.
Murray-Rust, D. M., 675, 696, 1234.
Murty, G. V. L. N., 28.
Muthmann, W., 447, 806, 835, 894, 990, 1029, 1030, 1045, 1058.
Muus, J., 744.
Myddleton, W. W., 316.
Mydo, B., 230.
Myers, W. R., 1266.
Myiamoto, G., 1289.
Mylius, A., 1421.
Mylius, F., 238, 276, 984, 1627.
Mytyzek, R., 269, 467.

Nachod, F. C., 49.
Nachod, H., 1084.
Näsänen, R., 1283.
Naess, G. B., 1017.
Nagel, P., 796.
Nagel, W., 1045, 1058.
Nagelschmidt, J. G., 1359.
Nagorskaja, N. D., 218.
Nahinsky, P., 1335.
Nakamura, H., 151.
Nann, H., 1460.
v. Náráy-Szábo, S., 147, 436, 1226, 1229.
v. Narbutt, J., 1585.
Nasini, A. G., 598.
Nast, R., 1373.
Natanson, G. L., 1326.

Nathan, W. S., 527.
Natta, G., 269, 965, 1376.
Naudé, S. M., 657.
Naumann, A., 162, 255, 273, 281, 328, 622, 810.
Naumann, R., 673.
Nazmi, F., 501.
Neal, A. M., 579, 580.
Neal, J. L., 973.
Nef, J. U., 69, 1190.
Negiski, G. R., 610.
Neiman, I., 1013.
Nekrassov, B. V., 1336, 1358.
Nelson, E. B., 1437.
Nelson, J. F., 268, 312, 313.
Nelson, R. A., 738.
Nelson, W. K., 563.
de Nemitz, S., 863.
Nenitzescu, C. D., 437.
Neogi, P., 475.
Nerdel, F., 111.
Nerlich, R., 1275, 1276.
Nernst, C., 1048, 1053.
Nernst, W., 66, 1160, 1161, 1384.
Nesmejanov, A. N., 267, 268, 303, 304, 305, 308, 332, 578, 581, 584.
Nespital, W., 422, 426, 429, 430, 432, 433, 435, 1145.
Nestle, K. N., 1594.
Nettleton, H. R., 1433.
Neu, R., 1247.
Neuber, A., 268, 1002.
Neuberger, M. C., 62, 1141.
Neugebauer, J., 1229.
Neugebauer, Th., 1161.
Neuman, E. W., 91.
Neuman, I. A., 208.
Neumann, B., 203, 234, 634.
Neumann, E., 207, 217.
Neumann, F., 650.
Neumann, G., 1022.
Neumann, K., 876, 948.
Neumann, W., 692, 701.
Neumayer, S., 467.
Neunhöffer, O., 111, 1554.
Neusser, E., 803, 1297.
Nevill, H. A. D., 332.
Neville, A., 958.
Nevin, T. E., 1266.
New, R. G. A., 546, 547, 672.
Newbury, E., 295.
Newitt, D. M., 266, 267, 371.
Newkirk, A. E., 337, 338, 615.
Newling, W. B. S., 527.
Newman, A. C. C., 970.
Newman, M. S., 1121, 1127.
Nicholls, F. H., 1048, 1049.
Nichols, A. R., 1284.
Nichols, M. S., 1102.
Nichols, P. M., 1280.
Nichols, W. A., 858.
Nicholson, P. J., 950.
Nicklas, A., 354.
Nicol, J., 1579.

Niederländer, K., 836, 844, 847.
Nielsen, H. H., 952.
Nielsen, J. P., 952.
Nielsen, J. R., 675.
Niemann, H., 260, 1435.
Niemann, W., 1474.
Nier, A. O., 63, 491, 553, 876, 1139.
Nies, N. P., 1157.
Nieuwkamp, W., 599.
Nieuwland, J. A., 303, 315, 385, 393, 403, 406, 566.
Niggli, P., 117.
Nightingale, D., 1356.
Nijveld, W. J., 901.
Nikitin, B. A., 9, 10.
Nikolaev, A. V., 384.
Nikolow, M., 1049.
Nilson, L. F., 198, 203, 477, 478, 480, 481, 638, 1331, 1597, 1605.
Nishida, D., 535.
Nishizawa, K., 248.
Nissenmann, L., 636.
Nitka, H., 1265.
Nitsche, R., 369, 370, 392.
Nitta, I., 44.
Nixon, I. G., 511.
Nobbe, P., 371, 373, 400.
Noddack, I., xi, 129, 552, 1262, 1289, 1291, 1293, 1295, 1297, 1299, 1301, 1302, 1303, 1306, 1307, 1310.
Noddack, W., xi, 129, 454, 552, 1262, 1289, 1291, 1293, 1295, 1297, 1299, 1301, 1302, 1303, 1306, 1307, 1310.
Nörring, O., 554.
Noller, C. R., 265, 745.
Nordenskjöld, I., 1036, 1047.
Nordsiek, H. H., xxi, 671, 1056.
Norris, J. F., 990, 1176.
Norrish, R. G. W., 494, 1175.
Norton, H. M., 601.
Norton, J. A., 1178.
Novak, J., 223.
Novakovski, R., 952, 953.
Novitzky, A., 1613.
Novoselova, A. V., 207, 218.
Nowacki, W., 441, 454.
Nowotny, H., 616, 1002, 1352.
Noyes, A. A., 170, 175, 256, 260, 626, 1194, 1392.
Noyes, W. A., 706, 1240.
Nozaki, K., 506, 874, 1177.
Nuka, P., 271.
Nuñez, F. P., 816.
Nutting, G. C., 444.
Nutting, H. S., 571.
Nyholm, R. S., 1465, 1493, 1516, 1525, 1532.
Nylen, P., 742, 743, 746, 765.

Oakdale, U. O., 779, 782.
Oberholzer, V., 1037, 1050.
Oblad, A. G., 426.
O'Brien, S. J., 1166.
Occleshaw, V. J., 676.
Ochs, K., 537.
Ochs, R., 68.
O'Daniel, H., 218.
Oddie, G. T., 427.
Oddo, G., 404, 913, 1152.
Odling, W., 1217.
O'Donnell, G., 246.
Oesper, P. F., 583, 592, 721.
Oesterheld, G., 198.
Offenbacher, M., 723.
Oftedal, I., 1490.
Ogata, K., 1139.
Ogawa, E., 1500.
Ogburn, S. C., 528, 1560.
Ogden, G., 40.
Ogg, A., 289.
Ogg, R., 506.
Ogg, R. A., 531, 691, 1174, 1177.
Ogier, J., 936, 1212.
O'Gorman, J. M., 525, 1185.
Ohl, H., 1007.
Ohnmais, K., 814.
Okuda, S., 1139.
Oldenberg, O., 865, 866.
Oldham, J. W. H., 1244.
O'Leary, L. A., 405.
Oliphant, M. L., 19, 37, 38, 61.
Oliphant, M. L. E., 2, 19, 57.
Olivari, F., 989.
Olivier, S. C. T., 1189.
Ollard, E. F., 1000.
Olsen, E., 972.
Olsen, F. V., 282.
Olsen, J. C., 638, 658, 1267.
Olson, A. R., 45, 506, 708, 1167.
Olson, L. E., 1153.
Olsson, E., 878.
Olsson, F., 1078.
Olsson, O., 1051, 1052, 1056, 1060.
Olsson-Collenberg, O., 1060.
O'Neal, R. D., 57.
Oneto, J. F., 763.
Onnes, K., 4.
van Oordt, G., 213.
Oppenheim, K., 281, 329.
Oriani, R. A., 1103.
Orlov, N., 1588.
Orndorff, W. K., 569, 572.
Orndorff, W. R., 602, 609, 618.
Orth, P., 540.
Ortner, G., 467, 477, 480.
Ortner, K., 972.
Orton, K. J. P., 707, 1223.
Osaka, Y., 254.
Osawa, A., 1326.
Osborne, D. W., 502, 880, 881, 1122.

Osborne, N. S., 503, 864.
Ostromisslensky, I., 1594.
Ostroumov, E. A., 634.
Ostwald, E., 520.
Ostwald, W., 810, 1001, 1227.
Oswald, M., 255.
Oswalt, R. L., 1351.
Ott, E., 320, 1431, 1450.
Ott, F., 835.
Ott, H., 418, 493.
Ottenstein, B., 1544.
Otto, R., 308, 312, 937.
Otto, W. H., 859.
Ourisson, J., 1214.
Ouvrard, L., 84.
Overstreet, R., 1160.
Overton, H., 309, 1611.
Owen, B. B., 383, 1026.
Owen, E. A., 1556.
Oxford, A. E., 515.
Oza, T. M., 1211.
Ozegowski, W., 532.

Paal, C., 957, 1054, 1058, 1580, 1585.
Pace, E. L., 1128.
Pacevitz, H. A., 69.
Paciello, A., 159.
Packer, J., 170, 253, 1196.
Padelt, E., 1205.
Paetow, U., 767, 768.
Pätsch, R., 1010.
Pagel, H. A., 452, 745.
Pahl, M., 62, 444.
Pahlke, H., 1105.
Pajeau, R., 204.
Palacios, J., 452.
Palin, D. E., 697.
Palmaer, W., 1535.
Palmateer, R. E., 1622.
Palme, H., 938.
Palmer, A., 762.
Palmer, C. S., 771.
Palmer, K. J., 417, 424, 668, 701, 930, 945.
Pampanini, G., 1381.
Panagiotakos, P. C., 872.
Paneth, F. A., 1, 11, 20, 22, 64, 264, 445, 530, 554, 761, 778, 860, 996, 1261, 1557.
Pankow, G. W., 735.
Pannwitz, W., 386.
Pantanelli, E., 636.
Paoletti, M., 1387.
Papaconstantinou, B., 1514.
Pape, C., 564.
Pape, H., 1017.
Pape, W., 253.
Papish, J., 64, 552, 604.
Paris, R., 739.
Parisi, E., 818.
Park, J. D., 1126.
Parker, B., 465.
Parker, C. A., 771.
Parker, H. C., 1228.
Parker, H. M., 1330.
Parker, R. H., 1599.

Parker, T. W., 974, 983.
Parker, W. H., 1059.
Parkes, G. D., 1199.
Parkes, G. S., 610.
Parks, G. S., 503, 507.
Parks, W. G., 289.
Parmenter, E. F., 91.
Parnell, T., 1579.
Parravano, N., 602, 603, 1055.
Parsons, C. A., 492.
Parsons, C. L., 205, 206, 207, 210, 212.
Parsons, J. B., 469.
Partington, J. R., 669, 672, 676, 696, 715, 736, 900, 905, 943, 952, 980, 1203, 1210, 1237.
Parton, H. N., 272.
Partridge, E. P., 745.
Partridge, H. M., 447.
Parts, A., 1211.
Parve, E. P. S., 738.
Pascal, P., 785, 985.
Passarge, W., 1025.
Passerini, L., 824, 984.
Passino, H. J., 1132.
Pastor, J., 1441.
Pastorello, S., 1542.
Patat, F., 717, 859.
Patein, G., 284, 403.
Patelski, R. A., 770.
Patent, D. R., 303, 307.
Pathuis, J. C., 901.
Patnode, W. I., 461, 566, 572.
Patnowski, J., 1152.
Patry, M., 984, 985, 1500.
Patterson, E. S., 1194.
Patterson, H. S., 1118.
Patterson, R. F., 503.
Pattock, K., 138.
Pauling, L., xi, xv, xvi, xvii, xviii, xxi, xxii, 8, 15, 24, 25, 26, 29, 66, 67, 122, 147, 163, 190, 201, 202, 214, 336, 340, 341, 368, 384, 412, 454, 461, 498, 505, 509, 510, 512, 522, 524, 525, 536, 543, 547, 554, 601, 606, 620, 645, 661, 662, 668, 674, 683, 684, 704, 716, 717, 748, 751, 752, 788, 858, 863, 865, 879, 881, 914, 984, 1041, 1055, 1061, 1070, 1098, 1128, 1330, 1369, 1379, 1433, 1443, 1558.
Paulus, R., 234, 419.
Pawletta, A., 812, 972.
Payne, D. S., 564.
Peachey, S. J., 582, 891, 1611.
Peak, D. A., 422, 434.
Pearce, D. W., 454.
Pearce, J. N., 1197.
Pearlson, W. H., 567, 1133.
Pearse, P. L., 731.
Pearson, J. H., 1117.
Pearson, R., 230.

Pearson, T. G., 531, 532, 890, 957, 965, 979.
Pease, R. N., 40, 1161.
Pechard, E., 643.
v. Pechmann, H., 713.
Pechukas, A., 245.
Peck, R. E., 504.
Pedrina, S., 989.
Peel, J. B., 306, 957, 979.
Peeling, E. R. A., 690.
Pegram, G. B., 34.
Peierls, R. E., xv.
Peiser, H. S., 280.
Pelabon, H., 320.
Pelissier, G. E., 552.
Pelletier, B., 1194.
Pellini, G., 967, 984, 989.
Pelz, W., 1554.
Penfield, S. L., 470, 604, 1196, 1199.
Penney, W. G., xxx, 493, 494, 505, 509, 510, 531, 656, 689, 709, 870.
Penz, H., 765.
Peppard, D. F., 601.
Percival, E. G. V., 1389, 1418.
Percy, R., 1268.
Perdok, W. G., 1437.
Perdreau, H., 767.
Perey, M., 64.
Perkin, F. M., 1405.
Perkins, T. R., 202, 270.
Perlmann, I., 1087, 1096.
Perlmann, M. L., 1091, 1143.
Perlow, G. J., 57.
Perman, E. P., 1350.
Pernot, M., 333.
Perret, A., 679.
Perreu, J., 1285.
Perrier, C., 1289.
Perrin, M. W., 507.
Perrot, R., 679.
Perrottet, E., 863.
Perry, J. H., 667, 668.
Perutz, M. F., 189.
Peshkov, V., 7.
Petch, N. J., 1324.
Peter, A., 1431, 1450.
Peter, W., 1254, 1259.
Peters, A. T., 732.
Peters, C., 552, 1268.
Peters, K., 20, 66, 1557.
Peters, R., 1354, 1366, 1384.
Peters, W., 328, 1440, 1472.
Petersen, A., 1398.
Petersen, E., 178, 824, 832.
Petersen, J., 275.
Petersen, M., 624.
Peterson, J. M., 228, 266.
Petit, J., 1588.
Petrich, W., 1411.
Petrov, I., 592.
Petscherskaja, K. A., 1428.
Petschner, E., 278, 429.
Pettersson, O., 198, 203, 477, 478, 480, 481, 1331.
Petzchner, E., 70.

Smith, A. J., 726.
Smith, D. P., 1555, 1556.
Smith, E. A., 503, 507, 527, 1175.
Smith, E. C. W., 17.
Smith, E. F., 835, 843, 1035, 1037, 1050, 1063.
Smith, E. R., 35, 856.
Smith, F., 1116.
Smith, F. B., 70.
Smith, F. D., 770, 771, 779, 782.
Smith, G. B. L., 972.
Smith, G. F., 101, 241, 258, 452, 1216, 1232, 1233, 1239.
Smith, G. M., 764.
Smith, G. W., 745.
Smith, H. A., 506, 1175.
Smith, J. C., 515, 1178.
Smith, J. W., 931.
Smith, L. G., 57.
Smith, L. I., 312.
Smith, M. A., 1451.
Smith, N. O., 901, 1012.
Smith, P. T., 2.
Smith, R. E., 524.
Smith, S. R., 856.
Smith, W. R., 506.
Smith, W. T., 1233, 1297.
Smits, A., 44, 416, 424, 661, 662, 726, 738, 784, 901.
Smyth, C. P., 415, 583, 592, 668, 669, 691, 721, 879, 886, 987, 1072, 1103.
Smyth, G. P., 662.
Smyth, H. D., 2, 1070.
Smythe, W. R., 61, 63.
Snell, A. H., 1140.
Snethlage, H. C. S., 1003.
Snyder, H. A., 369.
Snyder, H. R., 373, 398.
Snyder, P. E., 1032.
Sobatzki, R. J., 308.
Sobodka, H., 857.
Soddy, F., 851.
v. Soden, H., 733.
Sodomann, H., 91, 953.
Söderbäck, E., 675, 1350.
Söffge, K. H., 1530.
Sönke, H., 372, 373.
Sörensen, J. U., 675.
Sokolev, N. N., 1045.
Sokolov, W., 1591.
Solberg, A., 1269.
Soldate, A. M., 365.
Soloduschenkov, S. N., 1213, 1217.
Solomon, A. K., 491, 509, 1140.
Someya, K., 1050.
Somieski, C., 562.
Sommer, F., 283.
Sommer, L. H., 560, 564, 565.
Sommerfeld, A., xvii, 109, 110, 287.
Sommers, H. S., 3.

Sonder, R. A., 1426.
Sonnekalb, F., 473, 1370.
Soper, F. G., 451, 896, 1214, 1216, 1239.
Sorenson, B. E., 937.
Sorge, O., 643.
Soroos, H., 303, 503, 588, 589, 595, 707.
Soschestvenskaja, E. M., 561.
Soubarev-Chatelain, Z., 1039.
Souchay, A., 282.
Southard, J. C., 257, 382, 738.
Southwood, W. W., 612.
Sowa, F. J., 385, 393, 566.
Spacu, G., 164, 322, 604, 1340, 1361, 1616.
Spacu, P., 164.
Späth, E., 238, 275, 1020, 1275.
Späth, W., 950.
Spahr, R. T., 303.
Spanagel, E. W., 499.
Spangenberg, A. L., 860.
Spedding, F. H., 444.
Spencer, H. M., 824.
Spencer, J. F., 269, 427, 451, 472, 475.
Sperl, H., 282, 644.
Spessard, D. R., 567.
Speyer, E., 1369.
Spicin, V. = Spitzin, V., 635, 645.
Spiess, K. F., 419.
Spinks, J. W., 1206.
Spiro, L., 167.
Spitalsky, E., 1007.
Spittle, H. M., 1050, 1057.
Spitzer, R., 498, 607.
Spitzin, V. = Spicin, V., 635, 645.
Spivey, E., 1349.
Sponer, H., 93, 656.
Spong, A. H., 945.
Spoor, N. L., 1399, 1563.
Spormann, W., 1235.
Sprauer, J. W., 1133.
Sprenger, G., 692, 702.
Spring, W., 621.
Springall, H. D., 494, 512, 513, 668.
Sprowls, W. R., 56, 313.
Spruck, W., 1441.
Spulnik, J. B., 710.
Spurr, R. A., 683, 861, 993.
Squire, C. F., 1282.
Ssusi, A. K., 230.
Stacanova, M. S., 1428.
Stacey, G. J., 749.
Stack, G. G., 386.
v. Stackelberg, M., 234, 246, 414, 419.
Stadler, W., 161.
Stadnikov, G. L., 637.
Stähler, A., 638, 640, 650, 651, 824, 835.
Stäuber, K., 701.

Stahn, R., 1025.
Stair, J., 860.
Stallmann, H., 1509, 1510.
Stamm, H., 912, 942, 943, 945, 1228, 1229.
Staneslow, B. J., 615.
Stanford, S. C., 28, 30.
Stanger, G. B., 1342.
Stanger, H., 873, 1287.
Stang-Lund, F., 86.
Stapler, A., 229.
Stark, W., 106.
Starkey, E. B., 114, 304.
Starkweather, H. W., 1450.
Staronka, W., 742.
Stateczny, V., 976, 978, 1046.
Statham, F. S., 927.
Stathis, C., 1294.
Stathis, E. C., 873.
Staub, H., 3.
Staub, L., 704.
Staudenmaier, L., 983.
Staudinger, H., 507, 713, 732, 733.
Staufenbiel, E., 270.
Stauff, J., 1181.
Staveley, L. A. K., 26.
Steacie, E. W. R., 51, 112.
Stecher, O., 415, 416, 461.
Steel, C., 231.
Steele, A. R., 568.
Steele, B. D., 169, 342, 1388, 1437.
Steffens, C. C., 943.
Stehlik, B., 980.
Steil, O., 672.
Stein, C. P., 1149.
Stein, G., 749.
Stein, N. O., 952.
Stein, R. S., 1146.
Stein, W., 900, 1243, 1560.
Steinberg, H., 1047, 1056.
Steiner, B., 787.
Steiner, O., 965, 987.
Steiner, W., 17, 863, 1142.
Steinhäuser, S., 145.
Steinkopf, W., 136, 306, 308, 313, 702, 762, 764, 765, 768, 769, 772, 881, 934.
Steinman, R., 734.
Steinmetz, H., 202, 206, 208, 214, 472, 475, 675.
Steinrath, H., 1017.
v. Steinwehr, H., 759.
Stelling, O., 202, 743.
Stempel, B., 199.
Stephens, W. E., xv, 3.
Stephenson, C. C., 662, 728, 897.
Sterba-Böhm, J. P., 441.
Sterba-Böhm, J. S., 441.
Stern, O., 105.
Stern, S., 1210, 1244.
Stettbacher, A., 113.
Stevens, P. G., 423.
Stevens, T. S., 399.
Stevenson, D. F., 897.

Vol. II, pp. 855–1628.

SUBJECT INDEX TO VOLUMES I AND II

(Vol. I, pp. i–xxxii, 1–853; Vol. II, pp. 855–1628)

With the later transitional elements the compounds have been grouped under the several valencies of the elements, and these have been arranged in numerical and not in alphabetical order

Phosphoryl, thio: chloride, fluoride, halides, 752.

Plaster of Paris, 256.

Platinum and hydrogen, 1579.

Platinum blue Pt(NH·CO·CH₃)₂, 1582.

Platinum metal, 1578; valencies, 1550.

Platinum metals, general, 1454.

Platinum, monovalent: chloride PtCl, 1580; in solution, 1580.

Platinum divalent (platinous), 1581.

　Platinous acetylacetonate complex salts, 1599.

　Platinous amino-acid derivatives, 1596.

　Platinous ammines: *see under* Diammines, Triammines, Tetrammines.

　Platinous arsine complexes, 1599.

　Platinous bromide $PtBr_2$, 1582; complexes $M_2[PtBr_4]$, 1605.

　Platinous cacodyl oxide complexes, 1601.

　Platinous chloride, 1582; complexes, 1605.

　Platinous complexes, 1583.

　Platinous complexes, 6-covalent, 1583; triamine derivatives, 1584; 4-covalent, 1585; C=C co-ordination complexes, 1585–6; structures, 1586.

　Platinous cyanide, 1582; complexes $M_2[Pt(CN)_4]$, 1588.

　Platinous diammines $[PtAm_2R_2]°$, 1594; planar structure, *cis-trans* isomerism: *cis-trans* differences, 1594–5.

　Platinous fluoride PtF_2, 1581.

　Platinous glyoxime complexes, 1597.

　Platinous halide complexes, 1605.

　Platinous hydroxylamine derivatives, 1596.

　Platinous iodide, 1582; complexes, 1605.

　Platinous nitro-ammine complexes, 1598.

　Platinous nitro-complexes $M_2[Pt(NO_2)_4]$, 1597.

　Platinous oxalato-complexes, 1600.

　Platinous oxide, hydroxide, 1581.

　Platinous phosphorus complexes, 1598.

　Platinous selenium complexes, 1602.

　Platinous sulphide PtS, 1581.

　Platinous sulphito-complexes, 1604.

　Platinous sulphur complexes, as $[PtX_2(SR_2)_2]$, 1601; structures, 1602; chelate sulphur-oxygen complexes, 1604.

　Platinous tellurium complexes, 1603.

　Platinous tetrammines $[PtAm_4]X$: chelate tetrammines: evidence of planar structure, 1592; hydrazine derivatives, 1593.

　Platinous triammines $[PtAm_3R]X$, 1593.

Platinum, trivalent, 1605.

　Platinum‴ ammines, 1608.

　Platinum antimonide PtSb, 1606.

　Platinum‴ complexes, conditions of stability, 1609.

　Platinum sesquioxide Pt_2O_3, 1606.

　Platinum sulphates, complex, 1609.

　Platinum tribromide, 1607.

　Platinum trichloride, 1606; complexes, 1609.

　Platinum tricyanide, 1607; complexes, 1608.

　Platinum tri-iodide, 1607.

Platinum, tetravalent (platinic), 1611.

　Platinic alkyl compounds, 1611; structures, 1612.

　Platinic ammines, 1616.

　Platinic complexes, 1615.

　Platinic cyanide complexes, 1616.

　Platinic dioxide PtO_2, PtO_2, aq., 1613.

　Platinic hexabromides $M_2[PtBr_6]$, 1623.

　Platinic hexachlorides, 1623.

　Platinic hexafluorides, 1622.

　Platinic hexa-iodides, 1624.

　Platinic hexamethyl $Me_3Pt–PtMe_3$, 1611.

　Platinic hexammines, 1617.

　Platinic monammines, 1621.

　Platinic nitro-halide ammines, 1621.

　Platinic oxalato-complexes, 1622.

　Platinic pentahalides $M_2[PtX_5OH]$, 1624.

　Platinic pentammines, 1617.

　Platinic salts (platinates) $M_2[Pt(OH)_6]$, 1621.

　Platinic selenide $PtSe_2$, 1614.

　Platinic silicide PtSi, 1613.

　Platinic sulphide PtS_2, 1614; complexes $M_2[PtS_{15}]$, 1622.

　Platinic telluride $PtTe_2$, 1614.

　Platinic tetrabromide $PtBr_4$, 1615.

　Platinic tetrachloride, 1614.

　Platinic tetrafluoride, 1614.

　Platinic tetrahalides $M_2[PtX_4(OH)_2]$, 1625.

　Platinic tetrahydroxo-dihalides, 1621.

　Platinic tetra-iodide, 1615.

　Platinic tetramethyl $PtMe_4$, 1611.

　Platinic tetrammines $[PtAm_4R_2]X_2$, 1619.

　Platinic thiocyanate complexes, 1616.

　Platinic triammines, 1620.

　Platinic trimethyl iodide Me_3PtI, 1611; acetylacetonates Me_3PtA, ammines, base, 1612.

Platinum, hexavalent, 1625.

　Diarsenide $PtAs_2$, diphosphide Pt P_2, 1625.

　Trioxide PtO_3, triselenide $PtSe_3$, 1626.

Platinum carbonyl derivatives, 1627; carbonyl halides, 1627; sulphides, &c., 1628; complex salts, as $M[PtCl_3CO]$, 1628.

Platinum nitrosyl compounds $M[PtCl_3NO]$, 1628; complexes, as $[PtCl_3(NO)py]$, 1628.

Plumbane, diethyl-, nitrate $Et_2Pb(NO_3)_2$, 590.

Plumbane, diphenyl difluoride, 594.

Plumbane, diphenyl-nitrate, 591.

Plumbane, plumbic, plumbous, *see also under* Lead.

Plumbane PbH_4, 553.

Plumbane, tetramethyl, 588.

Plumbane triaryl-sodium $Φ_3Pb·Na$, 590.

Plumbane triethyl monol $Et_3Pb·OH$, 590.

Plumbane, triphenyl bromide, 593; chloride, fluoride, iodide, 593.

Plumbane triphenyl monol $Φ_3Pb·OH$, 590.

Plumbanes, alkyl and aryl, 587, 589.

Plumbanes, alkyl and aryl halides, 592; preparation, 592; dipole moments, 592.

Plumbanes, alkyl and aryl fluorides, 591.

Plumbanes, alkyl-trihalide, 594; dialkyl dihalides, 593, 594.

PRINTED IN
GREAT BRITAIN
AT THE
UNIVERSITY PRESS
OXFORD
BY
CHARLES BATEY
PRINTER
TO THE
UNIVERSITY